APPLET CORRELATION

Applet	Concept Illustrated	Description	Applet Activity
Sample from a population	Assesses how well a sample represents the population and the role that sample size plays in the process.	Produces random sample from population from specified sample size and population distribution shape. Reports mean, median, and standard deviation; applet creates plot of sample.	**4.4**, 196; **4.6**, 216; **4.7**, 235
Sampling distributions	Compares means and standard deviations of distributions; assesses effect of sample size; illustrates undbiasedness.	Simulates repeatedly choosing samples of a fixed size n from a population with specified sample size, number of samples, and shape of population distribution. Applet reports means, medians, and standard deviations; creates plots for both.	**4.9**, 251; **4.10**, 251
Random numbers	Uses a random number generator to determine the experimental units to be included in a sample.	Generates random numbers from a range of integers specified by the user.	**1.1**, 22; **1.2**, 22; **3.6**, 164; **4.1**, 183; **4.8**, 245

Long-run probability demonstrations illustrate the concept that theoretical probabilities are long-run experimental probabilities.

Applet	Concept Illustrated	Description	Applet Activity
Simulating probability of rolling a 6	Investigates relationship between theoretical and experimental probabilities of rolling 6 as number of die rolls increases.	Reports and creates frequency histogram for each outcome of each simulated roll of a fair die. Students specify number of rolls; applet calculates and plots proportion of 6s.	**3.1**, 128; **3.3**, 138; **3.4**, 138; **3.5**, 152
Simulating probability of rolling a 3 or 4	Investigates relationship between theoretical and experimental probabilities of rolling 3 or 4 as number of die rolls increases.	Reports outcome of each simulated roll of a fair die; creates frequency histogram for outcomes. Students specify number of rolls; applet calculates and plots proportion of 3s and 4s.	**3.3**, 138; **3.4**, 138
Simulating the probability of heads: fair coin	Investigates relationship between theoretical and experimental probabilities of getting heads as number of fair coin flips increases.	Reports outcome of each fair coin flip and creates a bar graph for outcomes. Students specify number of flips; applet calculates and plots proportion of heads.	**3.2**, 128; **4.2**, 183
Simulating probability of heads: unfair coin $(P(H) = .2)$	Investigates relationship between theoretical and experimental probabilities of getting heads as number of unfair coin flips increases.	Reports outcome of each flip for a coin where heads is less likely to occur than tails and creates a bar graph for outcomes. Students specify number of flips; applet calculates and plots the proportion of heads.	**4.3**, 196
Simulating probability of heads: unfair coin $(P(H) = .8)$	Investigates relationship between theoretical and experimental probabilities of getting heads as number of unfair coin flips increases.	Reports outcome of each flip for a coin where heads is more likely to occur than tails and creates a bar graph for outcomes. Students specify number of flips; applet calculates and plots the proportion of heads.	**4.3**, 196
Simulating the stock market	Theoretical probabilities are long run experimental probabilities.	Simulates stock market fluctuation. Students specify number of days; applet reports whether stock market goes up or down daily and creates a bar graph for outcomes. Calculates and plots proportion of simulated days stock market goes up.	**4.5**, 196
Mean versus median	Investigates how skewedness and outliers affect measures of central tendency.	Students visualize relationship between mean and median by adding and deleting data points; applet automatically updates mean and median.	**2.1**, 61; **2.2**, 61; **2.3**, 61

(Continued)

Applet	Concept Illustrated	Description	Applet Activity
Standard deviation	Investigates how distribution shape and spread affect standard deviation.	Students visualize relationship between mean and standard deviation by adding and deleting data points; applet updates mean and standard deviation.	**2.4**, 68; **2.5**, 68; **2.6**, 69; **2.7**, 81
Confidence intervals for a proportion	Not all confidence intervals contain the population proportion. Investigates the meaning of 95% and 99% confidence.	Simulates selecting 100 random samples from the population and finds the 95% and 99% confidence intervals for each. Students specify population proportion and sample size; applet plots confidence intervals and reports number and proportion containing true proportion.	**5.5**, 294; **5.6**, 295
Confidence intervals for a mean (the impact of confidence level)	Not all confidence intervals contain the population mean. Investigates the meaning of 95% and 99% confidence.	Simulates selecting 100 random samples from population; finds 95% and 99% confidence intervals for each. Students specify sample size, distribution shape, and population mean and standard deviation; applet plots confidence intervals and reports number and proportion containing true mean.	**5.1**, 277; **5.2**, 277
Confidence intervals for a mean (not knowing standard deviation)	Confidence intervals obtained using the sample standard deviation are different from those obtained using the population standard deviation. Investigates effect of not knowing the population standard deviation.	Simulates selecting 100 random samples from the population and finds the 95% z-interval and 95% t-interval for each. Students specify sample size, distribution shape, and population mean and standard deviation; applet plots confidence intervals and reports number and proportion containing true mean.	**5.3**, 287; **5.4**, 287
Hypothesis tests for a proportion	Not all tests of hypotheses lead correctly to either rejecting or failing to reject the null hypothesis. Investigates the relationship between the level of confidence and the probabilities of making Type I and Type II errors.	Simulates selecting 100 random samples from population; calculates and plots z-statistic and P-value for each. Students specify population proportion, sample size, and null and alternative hypotheses; applet reports number and proportion of times null hypothesis is rejected at 0.05 and 0.01 levels.	**6.5**, 354; **6.6**, 354
Hypothesis tests for a mean	Not all tests of hypotheses lead correctly to either rejecting or failing to reject the null hypothesis. Investigates the relationship between the level of confidence and the probabilities of making Type I and Type II errors.	Simulates selecting 100 random samples from population; calculates and plots t statistic and P-value for each. Students specify population distribution shape, mean, and standard deviation; sample size, and null and alternative hypotheses; applet reports number and proportion of times null hypothesis is rejected at both 0.05 and 0.01 levels.	**6.1**, 329; **6.2**, 334; **6.3**, 334; **6.4**, 334
Correlation by eye	Correlation coefficient measures strength of linear relationship between two variables. Teaches user how to assess strength of a linear relationship from a scattergram.	Computes correlation coefficient r for a set of bivariate data plotted on a scattergram. Students add or delete points and guess value of r; applet compares guess to calculated value.	**10.2**, 597
Regression by eye	The least squares regression line has a smaller SSE than any other line that might approximate a set of bivariate data. Teaches students how to approximate the location of a regression line on a scattergram.	Computes least squares regression line for a set of bivariate data plotted on a scattergram. Students add or delete points and guess location of regression line by manipulating a line provided on the scattergram; applet plots least squares line and displays the equations and the SSEs for both lines.	**10.1**, 572

James T. McClave • P. George Benson • Terry Sincich

Statistics for Business and Economics

Custom Edition for DePaul University

Taken from:
Statistics for Business and Economics, Eleventh Edition
by James T. McClave, P. George Benson, and Terry Sincich

Cover Art: Chicago 53, Chicago 74, Chicago 50 by Patrick Linehan

Taken from:
Statistics for Business and Economics, Eleventh Edition
by James T. McClave, P. George Benson, and Terry Sincich
Copyright © 2011, 2008, 2005 Pearson Education, Inc.
Boston, Massachusetts 02116

This special edition published in cooperation with Pearson Learning Solutions.

Pearson Learning Solutions, 501 Boylston Street, Suite 900, Boston, MA 02116
A Pearson Education Company
www.pearsoned.com

Printed in the United States of America

4 5 6 7 8 9 10 V0UD 18 17 16 15 14

000200010270757842

CXS

ISBN 10: 1-256-51713-5
ISBN 13: 978-1-256-51713-9

DEPAUL

You are enrolled in MAT 137 – Business Statistics.

This course covers basic concepts of statistics and applications; data analysis with the use of Excel; theoretical distributions; sampling distributions; problems of estimation; hypothesis testing; problems of sampling; linear regression and correlation.

The Department of Mathematical Sciences has worked with Pearson Learning Solutions to produce this book exclusively for students enrolled in MATH 137. It is composed of chapters from *Statistics for Business and Economics*, 11/e by McClave, Benson, and Sincich. In doing so, we have removed parts of the book that are not used in the course. Thus providing you with just the book you need at a reduced price.

Contents

*Indicates an optional chapter.

Chapter 4   Random Variables and Probability Distributions   173

Chapter 5   Inferences Based on a Single Sample: Estimation with Confidence Intervals   269

Chapter 6   Inferences Based on a Single Sample: Tests of Hypotheses   319

Chapter 7   Simple Linear Regression   380

Appendices

Preface

Incorporating extensive feedback from reviewers, we refined the eleventh edition of *Statistics for Business and Economics* to build on its reputation as the textbook for professors seeking a balanced and comprehensive approach. As in earlier editions, this revision contains an abundance of real-world business applications and many new and updated exercises. We focus on the data collection and analysis techniques students will need to evaluate reports of statistical studies and make informed business decisions. We emphasize inference, and we assume a mathematical background of basic algebra. Because it is so important, we continue to stress the development of statistical thinking, the assessment of credibility, and the value of inferences made from data, both by those who consume and those who produce them.

The text incorporates the following strategies, developed from the American Statistical Association (ASA)-sponsored conferences on *Making Statistics More Effective in Schools of Business* (MSMESB) and ASA's *Guidelines for Assessment and Instruction in Statistics Education* (GAISE).

1. Emphasize statistical literacy and develop statistical thinking
2. Use real data in applications
3. Use technology for developing conceptual understanding and analyzing data
4. Foster active learning in the classroom
5. Stress conceptual understanding rather than mere knowledge of procedures
6. Emphasize intuitive concepts of probability

New to This Edition

In this eleventh edition, we've made changes to strengthen our real-world focus, make use of the latest technology, and improve readability.

- **Updated exercises.** Thirty percent of the book's exercises have been updated. The text contains more than 1,200 exercises, and many are based on contemporary business-related studies and use real data. Most exercises foster and promote critical thinking skills. We also provide a few simpler exercises with smaller data sets in the first few exercises in the "Applying the Concepts—Basic" sections.

- **New Statistics in Action and Making Business Decisions cases.** Five of the 14 Statistics in Action cases are new, each based on real data from a recent business study. We've also added a new Making Business Decisions case after Chapter 12 (these were titled Real-World Case in previous editions).

- **Emphasis on ethics.** Where appropriate, Ethics in Statistics discussions have been added in every chapter to emphasize the importance of ethical behavior when collecting, interpreting, and reporting on data with statistics. These boxes provide the student with reminders of how to apply sound statistical methodology and to recognize when unethical statistics are clearly employed in a study.

- **Updated examples.** Twenty percent of the book's examples have been updated with the most current business-related data to be more timely and relevant.

- **Updated technology.** The Using Technology sections at the end of each chapter have been streamlined into easy-to-use steps. All output from statistical software (Excel®/DDXL, SPSS/PASW®, and Minitab®, plus the TI-84 graphing calculator) and corresponding instructions have been revised to reflect the latest versions of the technology.

- **Additional probability coverage.** Hypergeometric and exponential probability distributions are now introduced in Chapter 4 to give instructors added flexibility when covering probability.
- **Redesigned end-of-chapter summaries.** End-of-chapter notes have been redesigned for improved readability and reference. Important points are reinforced through flowcharts (which aid in selecting the appropriate statistical method), and Key Terms, Key Symbols or Formulas, and Key Ideas reinforce the chapter's concepts in a linear, easy-to-read way.
- **Updated data sets.** All data sets have been updated to include data from the year 2000 and later (with the exception of a few cases where the study is considered a "classic").

Content-Specific Changes to This Edition

- **Chapter 4 (Random Variables and Probability Distributions).** At the request of reviewers, we've added back material on two probability distributions—the hypergeometric and the exponential distributions. For pedagogical purposes, we've organized the chapter into three parts: "Discrete Random Variables" (the binomial, Poisson, and hypergeometric distributions), "Continuous Random Variables" (the normal, uniform, and exponential distributions), and "Random Variables Based on Sampling Distributions."
- **Chapter 5 (Confidence Intervals).** The methodology for finding a confidence interval for a population mean is developed based on using either a normal (z) statistic (Section 5.2) or a Student's t-statistic (Section 5.3). This change allows instructors to emphasize the theory behind confidence intervals while providing the flexibility of focusing on whether the sample is large or small.
- **Chapter 6 (Tests of Hypotheses).** We've added a new section emphasizing the formulation of the null and alternative hypotheses (Section 6.2).
- **Chapter 10 (Simple Linear Regression).** To streamline the chapter, we've combined and refined several sections from the previous edition. We now include the section on estimating σ^2 in Section 10.3 ("Model Assumptions") and combine the sections on the coefficients of correlation and determination into a single section (Section 10.5).
- **Chapter 11 (Multiple Regression and Model Building).** For pedagogical purposes, the chapter is now divided into three parts: "First-Order Models with Quantitative Independent Variables," "Model Building in Multiple Regression," and "Multiple Regression Diagnostics."

Traditional Strengths and Features

We have maintained or strengthened the pedagogical features that make *Statistics for Business and Economics* unique among introductory business statistics texts. These features assist the student in achieving an overview of statistics and an understanding of its relevance in both the business world and everyday life.

- **Use of examples as a teaching device.** Almost all new ideas are introduced and illustrated by data-based applications and examples. We believe that students understand definitions, generalizations, and theoretical concepts better *after* seeing an application. All examples have three components: (1) Problem, (2) Solution, and (3) Look Back. This step-by-step process provides students with a defined structure to approach problems, and it enhances their problem-solving skills. The Look Back feature often gives helpful hints to solving the problem and/or provides a further reflection or insight into the concept or procedure that is covered. At least 20 percent of the Examples have been updated.
- **Now Work exercises.** Now Work exercise suggestions follow most examples. The Now Work exercise (marked with the NW icon [NW] in the exercise sets) is similar in style and concept to the text example. This provides students with an opportunity to immediately test and confirm their understanding.

- **Statistics in Action.** Each chapter begins with a business case based on an actual contemporary, controversial, or high-profile issue. We present relevant research questions and data from the study and demonstrate the proper analysis in short Statistics in Action Revisited boxes throughout the chapter. These motivate students to critically evaluate the findings and think through the statistical issues involved.

- **Hands-on activity features.** In each chapter, we provide students with several opportunities to participate in hands-on classroom activities, ranging from data collection to formal statistical analysis. Students can perform these activities individually or as a class.

- **Applet exercises.** The text is accompanied by a CD containing applets (short JAVA computer programs). These point-and-click applets allow students to easily run simulations that visually demonstrate some of the more difficult statistical concepts (such as sampling distributions and confidence intervals). Each chapter contains several optional applet exercises in the exercise sets. They are denoted with the following icon:

- **Making Business Decisions cases.** Seven extensive business problem-solving cases, with real data and assignments for the student, cover two or three chapters. Each case serves as a capstone and review of the material that precedes it and requires the student to apply the methods presented in these chapters.

- **Real data–based exercises.** The text includes more than 1,200 exercises based on a wide variety of business applications. Nearly all of the applied exercises use current, real data extracted from newspapers, magazines, current business journals, and the Internet. Some students have difficulty learning the mechanics of statistical techniques when all problems are couched in terms of realistic applications. For this reason, most exercise sections are divided into at least four parts:

    Learning the Mechanics. Designed as straightforward applications of new concepts, these exercises test students' ability to comprehend a mathematical concept or a definition.

    Applying the Concepts—Basic. Based on applications taken from a wide variety of journals, newspapers, and other sources, these short exercises with smaller data sets help students begin developing the skills necessary to diagnose and analyze real-world problems.

    Applying the Concepts—Intermediate. Based on more detailed real-world applications, these exercises require students to apply their knowledge of the technique presented in the section.

    Applying the Concepts—Advanced. These more difficult real-data exercises require students to use their growing knowledge and developing critical thinking skills.

    Critical Thinking Challenges. These appear at the end of the "Supplementary Exercises" section and present students with one or two challenging real-life problems.

- **Exploring data with statistical software and the graphing calculator.** We demonstrate each statistical analysis method presented using output from three leading statistical software packages: Excel (with DDXL—an Excel add-in included on the companion CD), SPSS (PASW), and Minitab. These outputs appear throughout the text in examples and exercises, exposing students to the output they will encounter in today's high-tech business world. In addition, we provide output and keystroke instructions for the TI-83/TI-84 Graphing Calculator in the Using Technology section at the end of each chapter.

- **Using Technology tutorials.** At the end of each chapter we've included statistical software tutorials with instructions and screen shots for Minitab, SPSS (PASW), Excel (using the DDXL add-in), and the TI-83/TI-84 Graphing Calculator. These step-by-step tutorials, which have been streamlined for this edition, are easily located and show students how to best use statistical software.

- **Profiles of statisticians in history (Biography).**   Brief descriptions of famous statisticians and their achievements are presented in side boxes with our hope that students will develop an appreciation of the statistician's efforts and the discipline of statistics as a whole.
- **Companion CD–ROM.**   New copies of the text are accompanied by a CD that contains data set files for all of the text examples, exercises, Statistics in Action, and Making Business Decisions cases marked with a 🔵. Data sets are formatted for Excel, Minitab 14, Minitab 15, JMP, and SPSS (PASW), and are available as .txt files. The CD also contains DDXL (an Excel add-in), Chapters 13 and 14, and a set of applets that illustrate statistical concepts.

Flexibility in Coverage

We have designed the text to allow the instructor flexibility in coverage of topics. Here are suggestions for two topics, probability and regression:

- **Probability and counting rules.**   One of the most troublesome aspects of an introductory Business Statistics course is the study of probability. Probability poses a challenge for instructors because they must decide on the level of presentation, and students find it a difficult subject to comprehend. We believe one cause of these problems is the mixture of probability and counting rules that occurs in most introductory texts. Consequently, we have included the counting rules (with examples) in an appendix (Appendix A) rather than in the body of Chapter 3. Thus, the instructor can control the level of coverage.
- **Multiple regression and model building.**   This topic represents one of the most useful statistical tools for the solution of applied problems. Although an entire text could be devoted to regression modeling, we present coverage that is understandable, usable, and much more comprehensive than the presentations in other introductory Business Statistics texts. We devote two full chapters to discussing the major types of inferences that can be derived from a regression analysis, showing how these results appear in the output from statistical software, and, most importantly, selecting multiple regression models to be used in an analysis. Thus, the instructor has the choice of a one-chapter coverage of simple linear regression (Chapter 10), a two-chapter treatment of simple and multiple regression (excluding the sections on model building in Chapter 11), or complete coverage of regression analysis, including model building and regression diagnostics. This extensive coverage of such useful statistical tools provides added evidence to the student of the relevance of statistics to real-world problems.
- **Footnotes.**   Although the text is designed for students with a noncalculus background, footnotes explain the role of calculus in various derivations. Footnotes are also used to inform the student about some of the theory underlying certain methods of analysis. These footnotes allow additional flexibility in the mathematical and theoretical level at which the material is presented.

Supplements

For the Student

Student's Solutions Manual, by Nancy Boudreau (Bowling Green State University), provides detailed, worked-out solutions to all odd-numbered text exercises. (ISBN-10: 0-321-64175-2; ISBN-13: 978-0-321-64175-5)

Excel Technology Manual, by Mark Dummeldinger (University of South Florida), provides tutorial instruction and worked-out text examples for Excel. (ISBN-10: 0-321-64180-9; ISBN-13: 978-0-321-64180-9)

Business Insight Videos. This series of videos, each about a well-known business and the challenges it faces, focuses on statistical concepts as they pertain to the real world. The videos can be downloaded to Video iPods® from within MyStatLab. Contact your Pearson representative for details.

Study Cards for Business Statistics Software. This series of study cards, available for Excel (0-321-64191-4), Minitab (0-321-64421-2), JMP (0-321-64423-9), SPSS/PASW (0-321-64422-0), R (0-321-64469-7), StatCrunch (0-321-62892-6), and TI-83/84 graphing calculators (0-321-57077-4) provides students with easy step-by-step guides to the most common business statistics software.

For the Instructor

Annotated Instructor's Edition contains answers to text exercises. Annotated marginal notes include Teaching Tips, suggested exercises to reinforce the statistical concepts discussed in the text, and short answers to the exercises within the exercise sets. (ISBN-10: 0-321-64176-0; ISBN-13: 978-0-321-64176-2)

Instructor's Solutions Manual, by Nancy Boudreau (Bowling Green State University), provides detailed, worked-out solutions to all of the book's exercises. Careful attention has been paid to ensure that all methods of solution and notation are consistent with those used in the core text. Available for download at www.pearsonhighered.com/irc.

TestGen® (www.pearsonhighered.com/testgen) enables instructors to build, edit, print, and administer tests using a computerized bank of questions developed to cover all the objectives of the text. TestGen is algorithmically based, allowing instructors to create multiple but equivalent versions of the same question or test with the click of a button. Instructors can also modify test bank questions or add new questions. Tests can be printed or administered online. The software and testbank are available for download from Pearson Education's online catalog (www.pearsonhighered.com/irc).

Technology Resources

A companion **CD-ROM** is bound in new copies of *Statistics for Business and Economics.* The CD holds a number of support materials, including:

- **Data sets** formatted for Minitab 14 and 15, SPSS (PASW), JMP, text, and Excel.
- **DDXL,** an Excel add-in, adds sound statistics and statistical graphics capabilities to Excel. Among other capabilities, DDXL adds box plots, histograms, statistical scatterplots, normal probability plots, and statistical inference procedures not available in Excel's "Data Analysis" pack.
- **Applets** (short JAVA computer programs). These point-and-click applets allow students to run simulations that visually demonstrate statistical concepts. (See page xv for a complete description.)
- **Chapters 13 and 14**

ActivStats® for Business Statistics (Mac and PC) by Data Description and Paul Velleman is an award-winning multimedia program that supports learning chapter-by-chapter with the book. It complements the book with videos of real-world stories, worked examples, animated expositions of all major statistics topics, and tools for performing simulations, visualizing inference, and learning to use statistics software. ActivStats includes 15 short video clips; 183 animated activities and teaching applets; 260 data sets; interactive graphs, simulations, and visualization tools; and much more. ActivStats (Mac and PC) is available in an all-in-one version for Data Desk, Excel, JMP, Minitab, and SPSS/PASW. (ISBN-10: 0-321-57719-1; ISBN-13: 978-0-321-57719-1)

MathXL® for Statistics Online Course (access code required) MathXL® for Statistics is a powerful online homework, tutorial, and assessment system that accompanies Pearson textbooks in statistics. With MathXL for Statistics, instructors can

- Create, edit, and assign online homework and tests using algorithmically generated exercises correlated at the objective level to the textbook.
- Create and assign their own online exercises and import TestGen tests for added flexibility.
- Maintain records of all student work, tracked in MathXL's online gradebook.

With MathXL for Statistics, students can:

- Take chapter tests in MathXL and receive personalized study plans based on their test results.

- Use the student plan to link directly to tutorial exercises for the objectives they need to study and retest.
- Students can also access supplemental animations and video clips directly from selected exercises.

MathXL for Statistics is available to qualified adopters. For more information, visit our website at www.mathxl.com, or contact your Pearson sales representative.

MyStatLab™ Online Course (access code required)—part of the MyMathLab® product family—is a text-specific, easily customizable online course that integrates interactive multimedia instruction with textbook content. MyStatLab gives you the tools you need to deliver all or a portion of your course online, whether your students are in a lab setting or working from home.

- **Interactive homework exercises,** correlated to your textbook at the objective level, are algorithmically generated for unlimited practice and mastery. Most exercises are free response and provide guided solutions, sample problems, and learning aids for extra help.
- **Personalized study plan,** generated when students complete a test or quiz, indicates which topics have been mastered and links to tutorial exercises for topics students have not mastered.
- **Multimedia learning aids,** such as video lectures, animations, and a complete multimedia textbook, help students independently improve their understanding and performance.
- **Statistics tools** MyStatLab includes built-in tools for statistics, including StatCrunch. Students also have access to statistics animations and applets that illustrate key ideas for the course. For those who use technology in their course, technology manual PDFs are included.
- **Assessment manager** lets you create online homework, quizzes, and tests that are automatically graded. Select just the right mix of questions from the MyStatLab exercise bank, instructor-created custom exercises, and/or TestGen test items.
- **Gradebook,** designed specifically for mathematics and statistics, automatically tracks students' results and gives you control over how to calculate final grades. You can also add offline (paper-and-pencil) grades to the gradebook.
- **MathXL Exercise Builder** allows you to create static and algorithmic exercises for your online assignments. You can use the library of sample exercises as an easy starting point.
- **Pearson Tutor Center** (www.pearsontutorservices.com) access is automatically included with

MyMathLab. The Tutor Center is staffed by qualified math instructors who provide textbook-specific tutoring for students via toll-free phone, fax, e-mail, and interactive Web sessions.

MyStatLab is powered by CourseCompass™, Pearson Education's online teaching and learning environment, and by MathXL®, our online homework, tutorial, and assessment system. MyStatLab is available to qualified adopters. For more information, visit our Web site at www.mystatlab.com or contact your Pearson sales representative.

PowerPoint lecture slides provide an outline to use in a lecture setting, presenting definitions, key concepts, and figures from the text. These slides are available within MyStatLab or at www.pearsonhighered.com/irc.

StatCrunch is an online statistical software website that allows users to perform complex analyses, share data sets, and generate compelling reports of their data. Developed by Webster West, Texas A&M University, StatCrunch already has more than ten thousand data sets available for students to analyze, covering almost any topic of interest. Interactive graphics are embedded to help users understand statistical concepts and are available for export to enrich reports with visual representations of data. Additional features include:

- A full range of numerical and graphical methods that allow users to analyze and gain insights from any data set.
- Flexible upload options that allow users to work with their .txt or Excel® files, both online and offline.
- Reporting options that help users create a wide variety of visually-appealing representations of their data.

StatCrunch is available to qualified adopters. For more information, visit our website at www.statcrunch.com, or contact your Pearson sales representative.

The Student Edition of Minitab is a condensed edition of the professional release of Minitab statistical software. It offers the full range of statistical methods and graphical capabilities, along with worksheets that can include up to 10,000 data points. Individual copies of the software can be bundled with the text. (ISBN-10: 0-321-11313-6; ISBN-13: 978-0-321-11313-9)

JMP Student Edition is an easy-to-use, streamlined version of JMP desktop statistical discovery software from SAS Institute, Inc., and is available for bundling with the text. (ISBN-10: 0-321-67212-7; ISBN-13: 978-0-321-67212-4)

SPSS (PASW), a statistical and data management software package, is also available for bundling with the text. (ISBN-10: 0-321-67537-1; ISBN-13: 978-0-321-67537-8)

Acknowledgments

This book reflects the efforts of a great many people over a number of years. First, we would like to thank the following professors, whose reviews and comments on this and prior editions have contributed to the eleventh edition:

Reviewers of the Eleventh Edition of *Statistics for Business and Economics*

Sukhwinder Bagi, *Bloomsburg University*
John Beyers, *University of Maryland–University College*
Leszek Gawarecki, *Kettering University*
Katarina Jegdic, *University of Houston–Downtown*
Kenneth Leong, *College of New Rochelle*
Mark R. Marino, *Niagara University/Erie Community College*
Richard N. McGrath, *Bowling Green State University*
Keith Ord, *Georgetown University*
Leonard Presby, *William Paterson University*
James Wright, *Chadron State College*

Reviewers of Previous Editions

CALIFORNIA Joyce Curley-Daly, Jim Daly, Robert K. Smidt, *California Polytechnic State University* • Jim Davis, *Golden Gate University* • Carol Eger, *Stanford University* • Paul W. Guy, *California State University, Chico* • Judd Hammack, P. Kasliwal, *California State University, Los Angeles* • Mabel T. King, *California State University, Fullerton* • James Lackritz, *California State University, San Diego* • Beth Rose, *University of Southern California* **COLORADO** Rick L. Edgeman, Charles F. Warnock, *Colorado State University* • Eric Huggins, *Fort Lewis College* • William J. Weida, *United States Air Force Academy* **CONNECTICUT** Alan E. Gelfand, Joseph Glaz, Timothy J. Killeen, *University of Connecticut* **DISTRICT OF COLUMBIA** Phil Cross, Jose Luis Guerrero-Cusumano, *Georgetown University* Gaminie Meepagala, *Howard University* **FLORIDA** John M. Charnes, *University of Miami* • C. Brad Davis, *Clearwater Christian College* • Fred Leysieffer, Pi-Erh Lin, Doug Zahn, *Florida State University* • P. V. Rao, *University of Florida* • Jeffrey W. Steagall, *University of North Florida* • Edna White, *Florida Atlantic University* **GEORGIA** Robert Elrod, *Georgia State University* **HAWAII** Steve Hora, *University of Hawaii, Hilo* **ILLINOIS** Edward Minieka, *University of Illinois at Chicago* • Don Robinson, *Illinois State University* • Chipei Tseng, *Northern Illinois University* • Pankaj Vaish, *Arthur Anderson & Company* **IOWA** Dileep Dhavale, *University of Northern Iowa* • William Duckworth II, William Q. Meeker, *Iowa State University* • Tim E. McDaniel, *Buena Vista University* **KANSAS** Paul I. Nelson, *Kansas State University* • Lawrence A. Sherr, *University of Kansas* **LOUISIANA** James Willis, *Louisiana State University* **MARYLAND** John F. Beyers, Michael Kulansky, *University of Maryland–University College* • Glenn J. Browne, Mary C. Christman, *University of Maryland* **MASSACHUSETTS** Warren M. Holt, *Southeastern Massachusetts University* **MICHIGAN** Atul Agarwal, Petros Ioannatos, *GMI Engineering and Management Institute* • Richard W. Andrews, Peter Lenk, Benjamin Lev, *University of Michigan* • Toni M. Somers, *Wayne State University* • William Welch, *Saginaw Valley State University* • T. J. Wharton, *Oakland University* **MINNESOTA** Gordon J. Alexander, Donald W. Bartlett, David M. Bergman, Atul Bhatia, Benny Lo, Karen Lundquist, Vijay Pisharody, Donald N. Steinnes, Robert W. Van Cleave, Steve Wickstrom, *University of Minnesota* • Daniel G. Brick, Leigh Lawton, *University of St. Thomas* • Susan Flach, *General Mills, Inc.* • David D. Krueger, Ruth K. Meyer, Jan Saraph, Gary Yoshimoto, *St. Cloud State University* • Paula M. Oas, *General Office Products* • Fike Zahroom, *Moorhead State University* **MISSISSIPPI** Eddie M. Lewis, *University of Southern Mississippi* • Alireza Tahai, *Mississippi State University* **MISSOURI** James Holstein, Lawrence D. Ries, *University of Missouri, Columbia* • Marius Janson, *University of Missouri, St. Louis* • Farroll Tim Wright, *University of Missouri* **NEW HAMPSHIRE** Ken Constantine, *University of New Hampshire* **NEW JERSEY** Lewis Coopersmith, *Rider University* • Cengiz Haksever, *Rider University* • Lei Lei, Xuan Li, Zina Taran, *Rutgers University* •

Philip Levine, *William Paterson University* **NEW MEXICO** S. Howard Kraye, *University of New Mexico* **NEW YORK** James Czachor, *Fordham-Lincoln Center, AT&T* • Bernard Dickman, *Hofstra University* • Joshua Fogel, *Brooklyn College of City University of New York* • Martin Labbe, *State University of New York, College at New Paltz* • G. E. Martin, *Clarkson University* • Thomas J. Pfaff, *Ithaca College* • Gary Simon, *New York University, Stern School of Business* • Rungrudee Suetorsak, *SUNY-Fredonia* **NORTH CAROLINA** Golam Azam, *North Carolina Agricultural & Technical University* • Edward Carlstein, Douglas A. Elvers, *University of North Carolina at Chapel Hill* • Barry P. Cuffe, *Wingate University* • Don Holbert, *East Carolina University* • J. Morgan Jones, *University of North Carolina* • Douglas S. Shafer, *University of North Carolina, Charlotte* **OHIO** William H. Beyer, *University of Akron* • Michael Broida, Tim Krehbiel, *Miami University of Ohio* • Chih-Hsu Cheng, Douglas A. Wolfe, *Ohio State University* • Ronald L. Coccari, *Cleveland State University* • Richard W. Culp, *Wright-Patterson AFB, Air Force Institute of Technology* **OKLAHOMA** Larry Claypool, Brenda Masters, Rebecca Moore, *Oklahoma State University* • Robert Curley, *University of Central Oklahoma* **PENNSYLVANIA** Mohammed Albohali, *Indiana University of Pennsylvania* • Carl Bedell, *Philadelphia College of Textiles and Science* • Douglas H. Frank, *Indiana University of Pennsylvania* • Ann Hussein, *Philadelphia University* • Behnam Nakhai, *Millersville University* • Rose Prave, *University of Scranton* • Farhad Saboori, *Albright College* • Kathryn Szabet, *LaSalle University* • Christopher J. Zappe, *Bucknell University* **SOUTH CAROLINA** Iris Fetta, Robert Ling, *Clemson University* • Kathleen M. Whitcomb, *University of South Carolina* **TENNESSEE** Francis J. Brewerton, *Middle Tennessee State University* **TEXAS** Larry M. Austin, *Texas Tech University* • Jim Branscome, Robert W. Brobst, Mark Eakin, Grace Esimai, Michael E. Hanna, Craig W. Slinkman, *University of Texas at Arlington* • Virgil F. Stone, *Texas A & M University* **VIRGINIA** Edward R. Clayton, *Virginia Polytechnic Institute and State University* **WASHINGTON** June Morita, Kim Tamura, *University of Washington* **WISCONSIN** Ross H. Johnson, *Madison College* **CANADA** Clarence Bayne, *Concordia University* • Edith Gombay, *University of Alberta* **TURKEY** Dilek Onkal, *Bilkent University, Ankara* **OTHER** Michael P. Wegmann, *Keller Graduate School of Management.*

Other Contributors

Special thanks are due to our supplements authors, Nancy Boudreau and Mark Dummeldinger, who have worked with us for many years. C. Brad Davis provided the excellent student activities and applet exercises, while accuracy checkers Jackie Miller and Ann Cannon helped ensure a highly accurate, clean text. Finally, the Pearson Education staff of Deirdre Lynch, Chere Bemelmans, Christina Lepre, Dana Jones, Alex Gay, Kathleen DeChavez, Jean Choe, Tracy Patruno, Raegan Heerema, Thomas Benfatti, and Elm Street Publishing Services' Amanda Zagnoli all helped greatly with various stages of the book and media.

Statistics
for Business and Economics

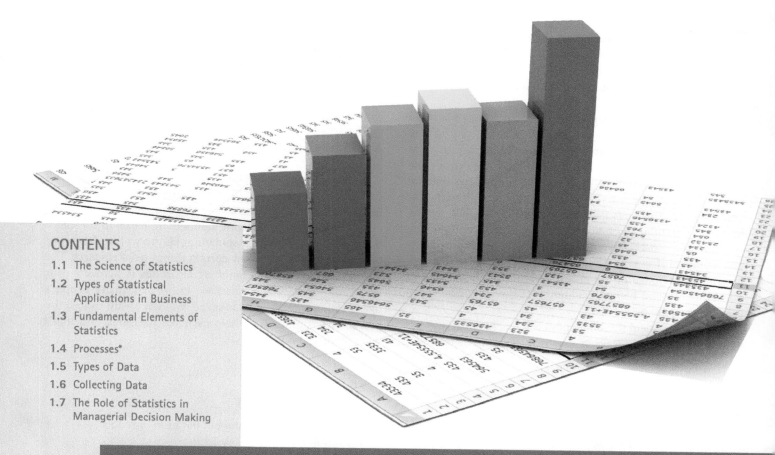

CONTENTS

1 Statistics, Data, and Statistical Thinking

Where We're Going

- Introduce the field of statistics.
- Demonstrate how statistics applies to business.
- Establish the link between statistics and data.
- Identify the different types of data and data-collection methods.
- Differentiate between population and sample data.
- Differentiate between descriptive and inferential statistics.

Statistics IN Action   A *20/20* View of Surveys: Fact or Fiction?

"Did you ever notice that, no matter where you stand on popular issues of the day, you can always find statistics or surveys to back up your point of view—whether to take vita-mins, whether daycare harms kids, or what foods can hurt you or save you? There is an endless flow of information to help you make decisions, but is this information accurate, unbiased? John Stossel decided to check that out, and you may be surprised to learn if the picture you're getting doesn't seem quite right, maybe it isn't."

Barbara Walters gave this introduction to a segment of the popular prime-time ABC television program *20/20*. The story was titled "Fact or Fiction?—Exposés of So-Called Surveys." One of the surveys investigated by ABC correspondent John Stossel compared the discipline problems experienced by teachers in the 1940s and those experienced today. The results: In the 1940s, teachers worried most about students talking in class, chewing gum, and running in the halls. Today, they worry most about being assaulted! This information was highly publicized in the print media—in daily newspapers, weekly magazines, Ann Landers's column, the *Congressional Quarterly,* and the   *(continued)*

Wall Street Journal, among others— and referenced in speeches by a variety of public figures, including former first lady Barbara Bush and former Education Secretary William Bennett.

"Hearing this made me yearn for the old days when life was so much simpler and gentler, but was life that simple then?" asks Stossel. "Wasn't there juvenile delinquency [in the 1940s]? Is the survey true?" With the help of a Yale School of Management professor, Stossel found the original source of the teacher survey—Texas oilman T. Colin Davis— and discovered it wasn't a survey at all! Davis had simply identified certain disciplinary problems encountered by teachers in a conservative newsletter—a list he admitted was not obtained from a statistical survey, but from Davis's personal knowledge of the problems in the 1940s. ("I was in school then") and his understanding of the problems today ("I read the papers").

Stossel's critical thinking about the teacher "survey" led to the discovery of research that is misleading at best and unethical at worst. Several more misleading (and possibly unethical) surveys, conducted by businesses or special interest groups with specific objectives in mind, were presented on the ABC program. These are listed below. A sixth study, published in the *New York Times,* is also discussed.

The *20/20* segment ended with an interview of Cynthia Crossen, author of *Tainted Truth,* an exposé of misleading and biased surveys. Crossen warns, "If everybody is misusing numbers and scaring us with numbers to get us to do something, however good [that something] is, we've lost the power of numbers. Now, we know certain things from research. For example, we know that smoking cigarettes is hard on your lungs and heart, and because we know that, many people's lives have been extended or saved. We don't want to lose the power of information to help us make decisions, and that's what I worry about."

Reported Information (Source)	Actual Study Information
1. Eating oat bran is a cheap and easy way to reduce your cholesterol. (Quaker Oats)	Diet must consist of nothing but oat bran to reduce your cholesterol count.
2. 150,000 women a year die from anorexia. (Feminist group)	Approximately 1,000 women a year die from problems that were likely caused by anorexia.
3. Domestic violence causes more birth defects than all medical issues combined. (March of Dimes)	No study—false report.
4. Only 29% of high school girls are happy with themselves, compared to 66% of elementary school girls. (American Association of University Women)	Of 3,000 high school girls, 29% responded "Always true" to the statement "I am happy the way I am." Most answered "Sort of true" and "Sometimes true."
5. One in four American children under age 12 is hungry or at risk of hunger. (Food Research and Action Center)	Based on responses to questions: "Do you ever cut the size of meals?" "Do you ever eat less than you feel you should?" "Did you ever rely on limited numbers of foods to feed your children because you were running out of money to buy food for a meal?"
6. There is a strong correlation between a CEO's golf handicap and the company's stock performance: The lower the CEO's handicap (i.e., the better the golfer), the better the stock performs. (*New York Times,* May 31, 1998)	Survey sent to CEOs of 300 largest U.S. companies; only 74 revealed their golf handicaps. Data for several top-ranking CEOs were excluded from the analysis.

In the following *Statistics in Action Revisited* sections, we discuss several key statistical concepts covered in this chapter that are relevant to misleading surveys like those exposed in the *20/20* program.

Statistics IN Action Revisited

- Identifying the population, sample, and inference (p. 10)
- Identifying the data-collection method and data type (p. 17)
- Critically assessing the ethics of a statistical study (p. 20)

1.1 The Science of Statistics

What does *statistics* mean to you? Does it bring to mind batting averages? Gallup polls, unemployment figures, or numerical distortions of facts (lying with statistics!)? Or is it simply a college requirement you have to complete? We hope to persuade you that statistics is a meaningful, useful science whose broad scope of applications to business, government, and the physical and social sciences is almost limitless. We also want to show that statistics can lie only when they are misapplied. Finally, we wish to demonstrate the key role statistics play in critical thinking—whether in the classroom, on the job, or in everyday life. Our objective is to leave you with the impression that the time you spend studying this subject will repay you in many ways.

The *Random House College Dictionary* defines *statistics* as "the science that deals with the collection, classification, analysis, and interpretation of information or data." Thus, a statistician isn't just someone who calculates batting averages at baseball games or tabulates the results of a Gallup poll. Professional statisticians are trained in *statistical science*—that is, they are trained in collecting numerical information in the form of **data,** evaluating it, and drawing conclusions from it. Furthermore, statisticians determine what information is relevant in a given problem and whether the conclusions drawn from a study are to be trusted.

> **Statistics** is the science of data. It involves collecting, classifying, summarizing, organizing, analyzing, and interpreting numerical information.

In the next section, you'll see several real-life examples of statistical applications in business and government that involve making decisions and drawing conclusions.

1.2 Types of Statistical Applications in Business

BIOGRAPHY

**FLORENCE NIGHTINGALE
(1820–1910)**

The Passionate Statistician

In Victorian England, the "Lady of the Lamp" had a mission to improve the squalid field hospital conditions of the British army during the Crimean War. Today, most historians consider Florence Nightingale to be the founder of the nursing profession. To convince members of the British Parliament of the need for supplying nursing and medical care to soldiers in the field, Nightingale compiled massive amounts of data from the army files. Through a remarkable series of graphs (which included the first "pie chart"), she demonstrated that most of the deaths in the war were due to illnesses contracted outside the battlefield or long after battle action from wounds that went untreated. Florence Nightingale's compassion and self-sacrificing nature, coupled with her ability to collect, arrange, and present large amounts of data, led some to call her the "Passionate Statistician." ∎

Statistics means "numerical descriptions" to most people. Monthly unemployment figures, the failure rate of startup companies, and the proportion of female executives in a particular industry all represent statistical descriptions of large sets of data collected on some phenomenon. Often the data are selected from some larger set of data whose characteristics we wish to estimate. We call this selection process *sampling*. For example, you might collect the ages of a sample of customers at a video store to estimate the average age of *all* customers of the store. Then you could use your estimate to target the store's advertisements to the appropriate age group. Notice that statistics involves two different processes: (1) describing sets of data and (2) drawing conclusions (making estimates, decisions, predictions, etc.) about the sets of data based on sampling. So, the applications of statistics can be divided into two broad areas: *descriptive statistics* and *inferential statistics*.

> **Descriptive statistics** utilizes numerical and graphical methods to look for patterns in a data set, to summarize the information revealed in a data set, and to present the information in a convenient form.

> **Inferential statistics** utilizes sample data to make estimates, decisions, predictions, or other generalizations about a larger set of data.

Although we'll discuss both descriptive and inferential statistics in the following chapters, the primary theme of the text is **inference.**

Let's begin by examining some business studies that illustrate applications of statistics.

Study 1   "U.S. Market Share for Credit Cards" (*Nilson Report,* May 2008)

The *Nilson Report* is the world's leading source of news and research on the consumer payment industry. The company tracked all credit card purchases in the United States during 2007. The amount of each purchase was recorded and classified according to type of card used (American Express, Discover, MasterCard, or VISA). The results are shown in Figure 1.1. From the graph, you can clearly see that nearly half of the purchases were made with a VISA card and more than 35% with a MasterCard. Because Figure 1.1 *describes* the type of card used in all credit card purchases in 2007, the graphic is an example of *descriptive statistics.*

Figure 1.1
U.S. credit card market shares
Source: www.carddata.com

Study 2   "The Executive Compensation Scoreboard" (*Forbes,* April 30, 2008)

How much are the top corporate executives in the United States being paid, and are they worth it? To answer these questions, *Forbes* magazine compiles the "Executive Compensation Scoreboard" each year based on a survey of executives at the 500 largest U.S. companies. To determine which executives are worth their pay, *Forbes* also records the performance of shareholders' stock for the CEO's company over the previous 6 years. Based on a comparison of the stock's performance and the CEO's annual salary, each CEO is given an "efficiency" rating—the lower the rating, the more the CEO is worth his/her pay. An analysis of the scoreboard data in 2008 is summarized in Table 1.1. The table reveals that CEOs in the business services industry have the lowest average* efficiency rating (40.67), thus, they are the best performers. The CEOs in the food markets industry are the worst performers, with the highest efficiency rating (167). Armed with this sample information, *Forbes* might *infer* that, from the shareholders' perspective, typical chief executives in food markets are overpaid relative to CEOs in business services. Thus, this study is an example of *inferential statistics.*

Study 3   "The Consumer Price Index" (*U.S. Department of Labor*)

A data set of interest to virtually all Americans is the set of prices charged for goods and services in the U.S. economy. The general upward movement in this set of prices is referred to as *inflation;* the general downward movement is referred to as *deflation.* In order to *estimate* the change in prices over time, the Bureau of Labor Statistics (BLS) of the U.S. Department of Labor developed the Consumer Price Index (CPI). Each month, the BLS collects price data about a specific collection of goods and services

Table 1.1	**Average Pay-for-Performance Efficiency Ratings of CEOs, by Industry**		
Industry	Average Efficiency Rating	Industry	Average Efficiency Rating
Aerospace and Defense	95.50	Hotels, Restaurants	100.00
Banking	97.08	Household Products	94.33
Business Services	40.67	Insurance	68.50
Capital Goods	88.44	Materials	69.62
Chemicals	127.00	Media	60.67
Conglomerates	97.00	Oil and Gas Operations	96.48
Construction	114.00	Retailing	83.00
Consumer Durables	108.33	Semiconductors	106.00
Diversified Financial	67.89	Software and Services	106.75
Drugs and Biotechnology	100.00	Technology Hardware	103.50
Food, Drink, and Tobacco	112.00	Telecommunications	95.67
Food Markets	167.00	Transportation	51.33
Health Care Equipment	102.71	Utilities	79.10

Source: Analysis of data in "Executive Compensation Scoreboard," *Forbes,* April 30, 2008.

*Although we will not formally define the term *average* until Chapter 2, *typical* or *middle* can be substituted here without confusion.

(called a *market basket*) from 85 urban areas around the country. Statistical procedures are used to compute the CPI from this sample price data and other information about consumers' spending habits. By comparing the level of the CPI at different points in time, it is possible to *estimate* (make an inference about) the rate of inflation over particular time intervals and to compare the purchasing power of a dollar at different points in time.

One major use of the CPI as an index of inflation is as an indicator of the success or failure of government economic policies. A second use of the CPI is to escalate income payments. Millions of workers have *escalator clauses* in their collective bargaining contracts; these clauses call for increases in wage rates based on increases in the CPI. In addition, the incomes of Social Security beneficiaries and retired military and federal civil service employees are tied to the CPI. It has been estimated that a 1% increase in the CPI can trigger an increase of over $1 billion in income payments. Thus, it can be said that the very livelihoods of millions of Americans depend on the behavior of a statistical estimator, the CPI.

Like Study 2, this study is an example of *inferential statistics*. Market basket price data from a sample of urban areas (used to compute the CPI) are used to make inferences about the rate of inflation and wage rate increases.

These studies provide three real-life examples of the uses of statistics in business, economics, and government. Notice that each involves an analysis of data, either for the purpose of describing the data set (Study 1) or for making inferences about a data set (Studies 2 and 3).

1.3 Fundamental Elements of Statistics

Statistical methods are particularly useful for studying, analyzing, and learning about *populations* of *experimental units*.

> An **experimental unit** is an object (e.g., person, thing, transaction, or event) upon which we collect data.

> A **population** is a set of units (usually people, objects, transactions, or events) that we are interested in studying.

For example, populations may include (1) *all* employed workers in the United States, (2) *all* registered voters in California, (3) *everyone* who has purchased a particular brand of cellular telephone, (4) *all* the cars produced last year by a particular assembly line, (5) the *entire* stock of spare parts at United Airlines' maintenance facility, (6) *all* sales made at the drive-through window of a McDonald's restaurant during a given year, and (7) the set of *all* accidents occurring on a particular stretch of interstate during a holiday period. Notice that the first three population examples (1–3) are sets (groups) of people, the next two (4–5) are sets of objects, the next (6) is a set of transactions, and the last (7) is a set of events. Also notice that *each set includes all the experimental units in the population* of interest.

In studying a population, we focus on one or more characteristics or properties of the experimental units in the population. We call such characteristics *variables*. For example, we may be interested in the variables age, gender, income, and/or the number of years of education of the people currently unemployed in the United States.

> A **variable** is a characteristic or property of an individual experimental unit.

The name *variable* is derived from the fact that any particular characteristic may vary among the experimental units in a population.

In studying a particular variable, it is helpful to be able to obtain a numerical representation for it. Often, however, numerical representations are not readily available, so the process of measurement plays an important supporting role in statistical studies. **Measurement** is the process we use to assign numbers to variables of individual population units. We might, for instance, measure the preference for a food product by asking a consumer to rate the product's taste on a scale from 1 to 10. Or we might measure workforce age by simply asking each worker, "How old are you?" In other cases, measurement involves the use of instruments such as stopwatches, scales, and calipers.

If the population we wish to study is small, it is possible to measure a variable for every unit in the population. For example, if you are measuring the starting salary for all University of Michigan MBA graduates last year, it is at least feasible to obtain every salary. When we measure a variable for every experimental unit of a population, the result is called a **census** of the population. Typically, however, the populations of interest in most applications are much larger, involving perhaps many thousands or even an infinite number of units. Examples of large populations include the 7 listed above, as well as all invoices produced in the last year by a *Fortune* 500 company, all potential buyers of a new fax machine, and all stockholders of a firm listed on the New York Stock Exchange. For such populations, conducting a census would be prohibitively time-consuming and/or costly. A reasonable alternative would be to select and study a *subset* (or portion) of the units in the population.

A **sample** is a subset of the units of a population.

For example, suppose a company is being audited for invoice errors. Instead of examining all 15,472 invoices produced by the company during a given year, an auditor may select and examine a sample of just 100 invoices (see Figure 1.2). If he is interested in the variable "invoice error status," he would record (measure) the status (error or no error) of each sampled invoice.

After the variable(s) of interest for every experimental unit in the sample (or population) is measured, the data are analyzed, either by descriptive or inferential statistical methods. The auditor, for example, may be interested only in *describing* the error rate in the sample of 100 invoices. More likely, however, he will want to use the information in the sample to make *inferences* about the population of all 15,472 invoices.

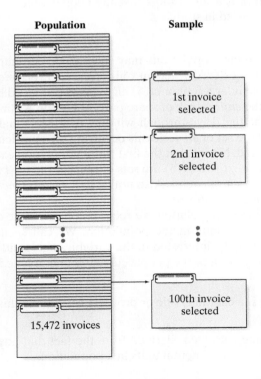

Figure 1.2
A sample of all company invoices

> A **statistical inference** is an estimate or prediction or some other generalization about a population based on information contained in a sample.

*That is, we use the information contained in the sample to learn about the larger population.** Thus, from the sample of 100 invoices, the auditor may estimate the total number of invoices containing errors in the population of 15,472 invoices. The auditor's inference about the quality of the firm's invoices can be used in deciding whether to modify the firm's billing operations.

Example 1.1 Key Elements of a Statistical Problem	**Problem** According to *Variety* (June 29, 2008), the average age of viewers of television programs broadcast on ABC is 50 years. Suppose a rival network (e.g., FOX) executive hypothesizes that the average age of FOX viewers is less than 50. To test her hypothesis, she samples 200 FOX viewers and determines the age of each. **a.** Describe the population. **b.** Describe the variable of interest. **c.** Describe the sample. **d.** Describe the inference. **Solution** **a.** The population is the set of units of interest to the TV executive, which is the set of all FOX viewers. **b.** The age (in years) of each viewer is the variable of interest. **c.** The sample must be a subset of the population. In this case, it is the 200 FOX viewers selected by the executive. **d.** The inference of interest involves the *generalization* of the information contained in the sample of 200 viewers to the population of all FOX viewers. In particular, the executive wants to *estimate* the average age of the viewers in order to determine whether it is less than 50 years. She might accomplish this by calculating the average age in the sample and using the sample average to estimate the population average. **Look Back** A key to diagnosing a statistical problem is to identify the data set collected (in this example, the ages of the 200 FOX TV viewers) as a population or sample.
Example 1.2 Key Elements of a Statistical Problem	**Problem** *Cola wars* is the popular term for the intense competition between Coca-Cola and Pepsi displayed in their marketing campaigns. Their campaigns have featured movie and television stars, rock videos, athletic endorsements, and claims of consumer preference based on taste tests. Suppose, as part of a Pepsi marketing campaign, 1,000 cola consumers are given a blind taste test (i.e., a taste test in which the two brand names are disguised). Each consumer is asked to state a preference for brand A or brand B.

*The terms *population* and *sample* are often used to refer to the sets of measurements themselves, as well as to the units on which the measurements are made. When a single variable of interest is being measured, this usage causes little confusion. But when the terminology is ambiguous, we'll refer to the measurements as *population data sets* and *sample data sets*, respectively.

a. Describe the population.

b. Describe the variable of interest.

c. Describe the sample.

d. Describe the inference.

Solution

a. Because we are interested in the responses of cola consumers in a taste test, a cola consumer is the experimental unit. Thus, the population of interest is the collection or set of all cola consumers.

b. The characteristic that Pepsi wants to measure is the consumer's cola preference as revealed under the conditions of a blind taste test, so cola preference is the variable of interest.

c. The sample is the 1,000 cola consumers selected from the population of all cola consumers.

d. The inference of interest is the *generalization* of the cola preferences of the 1,000 sampled consumers to the population of all cola consumers. In particular, the preferences of the consumers in the sample can be used to *estimate* the percentage of all cola consumers who prefer each brand.

Look Back In determining whether the inference is inferential or descriptive, we assess whether Pepsi is interested in the responses of only the 1,000 sampled customers (descriptive statistics) or in the responses for the entire population of consumers (inferential statistics).

Now Work Exercise 1.14b

The preceding definitions and examples identify four of the five elements of an inferential statistical problem: a population, one or more variables of interest in a sample, and an inference. But making the inference is only part of the story. We also need to know its **reliability**—that is, how good the inference is. The only way we can be certain that an inference about a population is correct is to include the entire population in our sample. However, because of *resource constraints* (e.g., insufficient time and/or money), we usually can't work with whole populations, so we base our inferences on just a portion of the population (a sample). Consequently, whenever possible, it is important to determine and report the reliability of each inference made. Reliability, then, is the fifth element of inferential statistical problems.

The measure of reliability that accompanies an inference separates the science of statistics from the art of fortune-telling. A palm reader, like a statistician, may examine a sample (your hand) and make inferences about the population (your life). However, unlike statistical inferences, the palm reader's inferences include no measure of reliability.

Suppose, like the TV executive in Example 1.1, we are interested in the *error of estimation* (i.e., the difference between the average age for the population of TV viewers and the average age of a sample of TV viewers). Using statistical methods, we can determine a *bound on the estimation error*. This bound is simply a number that our estimation error (the difference between the average age of the sample and the average age of the population) is not likely to exceed. We'll see in later chapters that this bound is a measure of the uncertainty of our inference. The reliability of statistical inferences is discussed throughout this text. For now, we simply want you to realize that an inference is incomplete without a measure of its reliability.

> A **measure of reliability** is a statement (usually quantified) about the degree of uncertainty associated with a statistical inference.

Let's conclude this section with a summary of the elements of both descriptive and inferential statistical problems and an example to illustrate a measure of reliability.

> **Four Elements of Descriptive Statistical Problems**
>
> 1. The population or sample of interest
> 2. One or more variables (characteristics of the population or sample units) that are to be investigated
> 3. Tables, graphs, or numerical summary tools
> 4. Identification of patterns in the data

> **Five Elements of Inferential Statistical Problems**
>
> 1. The population of interest
> 2. One or more variables (characteristics of the population units) that are to be investigated
> 3. The sample of population units
> 4. The inference about the population based on information contained in the sample
> 5. A measure of reliability for the inference

Example 1.3
Reliability of an Inference

Problem Refer to Example 1.2, in which the cola preferences of 1,000 consumers were indicated in a taste test. Describe how the reliability of an inference concerning the preferences of all cola consumers in the Pepsi bottler's marketing region could be measured.

Solution When the preferences of 1,000 consumers are used to estimate the preferences of all consumers in the region, the estimate will not exactly mirror the preferences of the population. For example, if the taste test shows that 56% of the 1,000 consumers chose Pepsi, it does not follow (nor is it likely) that exactly 56% of all cola drinkers in the region prefer Pepsi. Nevertheless, we can use sound statistical reasoning (which is presented later in the text) to ensure that our sampling procedure will generate estimates that are almost certainly within a specified limit of the true percentage of all consumers who prefer Pepsi. For example, such reasoning might assure us that the estimate of the preference for Pepsi from the sample is almost certainly within 5% of the actual population preference. The implication is that the actual preference for Pepsi is between 51% [i.e., $(56 - 5)\%$] and 61% [i.e., $(56 + 5)\%$]—that is, $(56 \pm 5)\%$. This interval represents a measure of reliability for the inference.

Look Back The interval 56 ± 5 is called a *confidence interval,* because we are "confident" that the true percentage of customers who prefer Pepsi in a taste test falls into the range $(51, 61)$. In Chapter 5, we learn how to assess the degree of confidence (e.g., 90% or 95% confidence) in the interval.

Statistics ɪɴ Action | Revisited | **Identifying the Population, Sample, and Inference**

Consider the study on the link between a CEO's golf handicap and the company's stock performance, reported in the *New York Times* (May 31, 1998). The newspaper gathered information on golf handicaps of corporate executives obtained from a *Golf Digest* survey sent to CEOs of the 300 largest U.S. companies. (A golf handicap is a numerical "index" that allows golfers to compare skills; the lower the handicap, the better the golfer.) For the 51 CEOs who reported their handicaps, the *New York Times* then determined each CEO's company stock market performance over a 3-year period (measured as a rate-of-return index, from a low value of 0 to a high value of 100). Thus, the experimental unit for the study is a corporate executive, and the two variables measured are golf handicap and stock performance index. Also, the data for the 51 CEOs represent a sample selected from the much larger population of all corporate executives in the United States. (These data are available in the **GOLFCEO** file.)

The *New York Times* discovered a "statistical correlation" (a method discussed in Chapter 10) between golf handicap and stock performance. Thus, the newspaper inferred that the better the CEO is at golf, the better the company's stock performance.

Data Set: GOLFCEO

1.4 Processes*

Sections 1.2 and 1.3 focused on the use of statistical methods to analyze and learn about populations, which are sets of *existing* units. Statistical methods are equally useful for analyzing and making inferences about *processes*.

> A **process** is a series of actions or operations that transforms inputs to outputs. A process produces or generates output over time.

The most obvious processes of interest to businesses are those of production or manufacturing. A manufacturing process uses a series of operations performed by people and machines to convert inputs, such as raw materials and parts, to finished products (the outputs). Examples include the process used to produce the paper on which these words are printed, automobile assembly lines, and oil refineries.

Figure 1.3 presents a general description of a process and its inputs and outputs. In the context of manufacturing, the process in the figure (i.e., the transformation process) could be a depiction of the overall production process or it could be a depiction of one of the many processes (sometimes called *subprocesses*) that exist within an overall production process. Thus, the output shown could be finished goods that will be shipped to an external customer or merely the output of one of the steps or subprocesses of the overall process. In the latter case, the output becomes input for the next subprocess. For example, Figure 1.3 could represent the overall automobile assembly process, with its output being fully assembled cars ready for shipment to dealers. Or, it could depict the windshield assembly subprocess, with its output of partially assembled cars with windshield ready for "shipment" to the next subprocess in the assembly line.

Besides physical products and services, businesses and other organizations generate streams of numerical data over time that are used to evaluate the performance of

Figure 1.3
Graphical depiction of
a manufacturing process

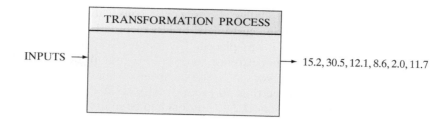

Figure 1.4
A black box process with numerical output

the organization. Examples include weekly sales figures, quarterly earnings, and yearly profits. The U.S. economy (a complex organization) can be thought of as generating streams of data that include the gross domestic product (GDP), stock prices, and the Consumer Price Index (see Section 1.2). Statisticians and other analysts conceptualize these data streams as being generated by processes. Typically, however, the series of operations or actions that cause particular data to be realized are either unknown or so complex (or both) that the processes are treated as *black boxes*.

> A process whose operations or actions are unknown or unspecified is called a **black box.**

Frequently, when a process is treated as a black box, its inputs are not specified either. The entire focus is on the output of the process. A black box process is illustrated in Figure 1.4.

In studying a process, we generally focus on one or more characteristics, or properties, of the output. For example, we may be interested in the weight or the length of the units produced or even the time it takes to produce each unit. As with characteristics of population units, we call these characteristics *variables*. In studying processes whose output is already in numerical form (i.e., a stream of numbers), the characteristic, or property, represented by the numbers (e.g., sales, GDP, or stock prices) is typically the variable of interest. If the output is not numeric, we use *measurement processes* to assign numerical values to variables.* For example, if in the automobile assembly process the weight of the fully assembled automobile is the variable of interest, a measurement process involving a large scale will be used to assign a numerical value to each automobile.

As with populations, we use sample data to analyze and make inferences (estimates, predictions, or other generalizations) about processes. But the concept of a sample is defined differently when dealing with processes. Recall that a population is a set of existing units and that a sample is a subset of those units. In the case of processes, however, the concept of a set of existing units is not relevant or appropriate. Processes generate or create their output *over time*—one unit after another. For example, a particular automobile assembly line produces a completed vehicle every four minutes. We define a sample from a process in the box.

> Any set of output (object or numbers) produced by a process is called a **sample.**

Thus, the next 10 cars turned out by the assembly line constitute a sample from the process, as do the next 100 cars or every fifth car produced today.

Example 1.4
**Key Elements
of a Process**

Problem A particular fast-food restaurant chain has 6,289 outlets with drive-through windows. To attract more customers to its drive-through services, the company is considering offering a 50% discount to customers who wait more than a specified number of minutes to receive their order. To help determine what the time limit should be, the company decided to estimate the average waiting time at a particular drive-through

*A process whose output is already in numerical form necessarily includes a measurement process as one of its subprocesses.

window in Dallas, Texas. For 7 consecutive days, the worker taking customers' orders recorded the time that every order was placed. The worker who handed the order to the customer recorded the time of delivery. In both cases, workers used synchronized digital clocks that reported the time to the nearest second. At the end of the 7-day period, 2,109 orders had been timed.

a. Describe the process of interest at the Dallas restaurant.

b. Describe the variable of interest.

c. Describe the sample.

d. Describe the inference of interest.

e. Describe how the reliability of the inference could be measured.

Solution

a. The process of interest is the drive-through window at a particular fast-food restaurant in Dallas, Texas. It is a process because it "produces," or "generates," meals over time—that is, it services customers over time.

b. The variable the company monitored is customer waiting time, the length of time a customer waits to receive a meal after placing an order. Because the study is focusing only on the output of the process (the time to produce the output) and not the internal operations of the process (the tasks required to produce a meal for a customer), the process is being treated as a black box.

c. The sampling plan was to monitor every order over a particular 7-day period. The sample is the 2,109 orders that were processed during the 7-day period.

d. The company's immediate interest is in learning about the drive-through window in Dallas. They plan to do this by using the waiting times from the sample to make a statistical inference about the drive-through process. In particular, they might use the average waiting time for the sample to estimate the average waiting time at the Dallas facility.

e. As for inferences about populations, measures of reliability can be developed for inferences about processes. The reliability of the estimate of the average waiting time for the Dallas restaurant could be measured by a bound on the error of estimation—that is, we might find that the average waiting time is 4.2 minutes, with a bound on the error of estimation of 0.5 minutes. The implication would be that we could be reasonably certain that the true average waiting time for the Dallas process is between 3.7 and 4.7 minutes.

Look Back Notice that there is also a population described in this example: the company's 6,289 existing outlets with drive-through facilities. In the final analysis, the company will use what it learns about the process in Dallas and, perhaps, similar studies at other locations to make an inference about the waiting times in its population of outlets.

Now Work Exercise 1.30

Note that output already generated by a process can be viewed as a population. Suppose a soft-drink canning process produced 2,000 twelve-packs yesterday, all of which were stored in a warehouse. If we were interested in learning something about those 2,000 twelve-packs—such as the percentage with defective cardboard packaging—we could treat the 2,000 twelve-packs as a population. We might draw a sample from the population in the warehouse, measure the variable of interest, and use the sample data to make a statistical inference about the 2,000 twelve-packs, as described in Sections 1.2 and 1.3.

In this optional section, we have presented a brief introduction to processes and the use of statistical methods to analyze and learn about processes. In Chapters 12 and 13 we present an in-depth treatment of these subjects.

1.5 Types of Data

You have learned that statistics is the science of data and that data are obtained by measuring the values of one or more variables on the units in the sample (or population). All data (and hence the variables we measure) can be classified as one of two general types: *quantitative* and *qualitative*.

Quantitative data are data that are measured on a naturally occurring numerical scale.* The following are examples of quantitative data:

1. The temperature (in degrees Celsius) at which each unit in a sample of 20 pieces of heat-resistant plastic begins to melt

2. The current unemployment rate (measured as a percentage) for each of the 50 states

3. The scores of a sample of 150 MBA applicants on the GMAT, a standardized business graduate school entrance exam administered nationwide

4. The number of female executives employed in each of a sample of 75 manufacturing companies

> **Quantitative data** are measurements that are recorded on a naturally occurring numerical scale.

In contrast, qualitative data cannot be measured on a natural numerical scale; they can only be classified into categories.† Examples of qualitative data are as follows:

1. The political party affiliation (Democrat, Republican, or Independent) in a sample of 50 CEOs

2. The defective status (defective or not) of each of 100 computer chips manufactured by Intel

3. The size of a car (subcompact, compact, midsize, or full-size) rented by each of a sample of 30 business travelers

4. A taste tester's ranking (best, worst, etc.) of four brands of barbecue sauce for a panel of 10 testers

Often, we assign arbitrary numerical values to qualitative data for ease of computer entry and analysis. But these assigned numerical values are simply codes: They cannot be meaningfully added, subtracted, multiplied, or divided. For example, we might code Democrat = 1, Republican = 2, and Independent = 3. Similarly, a taste tester might rank the barbecue sauces from 1 (best) to 4 (worst). These are simply arbitrarily selected numerical codes for the categories and have no utility beyond that.

> **Qualitative data** are measurements that cannot be measured on a natural numerical scale; they can only be classified into one of a group of categories.

Example 1.5
Types of Data

Problem Chemical and manufacturing plants sometimes discharge toxic-waste materials such as DDT into nearby rivers and streams. These toxins can adversely affect the plants and animals inhabiting the river and the riverbank. The U.S. Army Corps of Engineers conducted a study of fish in the Tennessee River (in Alabama) and its three tributary

---

*Quantitative data can be subclassified as either *interval* or *ratio*. For ratio data, the origin (i.e., the value 0) is a meaningful number. But the origin has no meaning with interval data. Consequently, we can add and subtract interval data, but we can't multiply and divide them. Of the four quantitative data sets listed, (1) and (3) are interval data, while (2) and (4) are ratio data.

†Qualitative data can be subclassified as either *nominal* or *ordinal*. The categories of an ordinal data set can be ranked or meaningfully ordered, but the categories of a nominal data set can't be ordered. Of the four qualitative data sets listed, (1) and (2) are nominal and (3) and (4) are ordinal.

creeks: Flint Creek, Limestone Creek, and Spring Creek. A total of 144 fish were captured, and the following variables were measured for each:

1. River/creek where each fish was captured
2. Species (channel catfish, largemouth bass, or smallmouth buffalo fish)
3. Length (centimeters)
4. Weight (grams)
5. DDT concentration (parts per million)

These data are saved in the **DDT** file. Classify each of the five variables measured as quantitative or qualitative.

Solution The variables length, weight, and DDT are quantitative because each is measured on a numerical scale: length in centimeters, weight in grams, and DDT in parts per million. In contrast, river/creek and species cannot be measured quantitatively: They can only be classified into categories (e.g., channel catfish, largemouth bass, and smallmouth buffalo fish for species). Consequently, data on river/creek and species are qualitative.

Look Back It is essential that you understand whether data are quantitative or qualitative in nature because the statistical method appropriate for describing, reporting, and analyzing the data depends on the data type (quantitative or qualitative).

Now Work Exercise 1.16

We demonstrate many useful methods for analyzing quantitative and qualitative data in the remaining chapters of the text. But first, we discuss some important ideas on data collection.

1.6 Collecting Data

Once you decide on the type of data—quantitative or qualitative—appropriate for the problem at hand, you'll need to collect the data. Generally, you can obtain the data in four different ways:

1. Data from a *published source*
2. Data from a *designed experiment*
3. Data from a *survey*
4. Data collected *observationally*

Sometimes, the data set of interest has already been collected for you and is available in a **published source,** such as a book, journal, newspaper, or Web site. For example, you may want to examine and summarize the unemployment rates (i.e., percentages of eligible workers who are unemployed) in the 50 states of the United States. You can find this data set (as well as numerous other data sets) at your library in the *Statistical Abstract of the United States,* published annually by the U.S. government. Similarly, someone who is interested in monthly mortgage applications for new home construction would find this data set in the *Survey of Current Business,* another government publication. Other examples of published data sources include the *Wall Street Journal* (financial data) and the *The Sporting News* (sports information).*

A second method of collecting data involves conducting a **designed experiment,** in which the researcher exerts strict control over the units (people, objects, or events) in the study. For example, a medical study investigated the potential of aspirin in preventing heart attacks. Volunteer physicians were divided into two groups—the *treatment* group and the *control* group. In the treatment group, each physician took one aspirin tablet a day

*With published data, we often make a distinction between the *primary source* and *secondary source*. If the publisher is the original collector of the data, the source is primary. Otherwise, the data are secondary source.

for 1 year, while each physician in the control group took an aspirin-free placebo (no drug) made to look like an aspirin tablet. The researchers, not the physicians under study, controlled who received the aspirin (the treatment) and who received the placebo. As you will learn in Chapter 10, a properly designed experiment allows you to extract more information from the data than is possible with an uncontrolled study.

Surveys are a third source of data. With a **survey,** the researcher samples a group of people, asks one or more questions, and records the responses. Probably the most familiar type of survey is the political polls conducted by any one of a number of organizations (e.g., Harris, Gallup, Roper, and CNN) and designed to predict the outcome of a political election. Another familiar survey is the Nielsen survey, which provides the major television networks with information on the most watched TV programs. Surveys can be conducted through the mail, with telephone interviews, or with in-person interviews. Although in-person interviews are more expensive than mail or telephone surveys, they may be necessary when complex information must be collected.

Finally, observational studies can be employed to collect data. In an **observational study,** the researcher observes the experimental units in their natural setting and records the variable(s) of interest. For example, a company psychologist might observe and record the level of "Type A" behavior of a sample of assembly line workers. Similarly, a finance researcher may observe and record the closing stock prices of companies that are acquired by other firms on the day prior to the buyout and compare them to the closing prices on the day the acquisition is announced. Unlike a designed experiment, an observational study is one in which the researcher makes no attempt to control any aspect of the experimental units.

Regardless of the data-collection method employed, it is likely that the data will be a sample from some population. And if we wish to apply inferential statistics, we must obtain a *representative sample*.

A **representative sample** exhibits characteristics typical of those possessed by the population of interest.

For example, consider a political poll conducted during a presidential election year. Assume the pollster wants to estimate the percentage of all 140,000,000 registered voters in the United States who favor the incumbent president. The pollster would be unwise to base the estimate on survey data collected for a sample of voters from the incumbent's own state. Such an estimate would almost certainly be *biased* high.

The most common way to satisfy the representative sample requirement is to select a random sample. A **random sample** ensures that every subset of fixed size in the population has the same chance of being included in the sample. If the pollster samples 1,500 of the 140,000,000 voters in the population so that every subset of 1,500 voters has an equal chance of being selected, he has devised a random sample. The procedure for selecting a random sample is discussed in Chapter 3. Here, however, let's look at two examples involving actual sampling studies.

A **random sample** of n experimental units is a sample selected from the population in such a way that every different sample of size n has an equal chance of selection.

Example 1.6

Method of Data Collection

Problem How do consumers feel about using the Internet for online shopping? To find out, a customer-experience software company commissioned a nationwide survey of 1,859 U.S. adults who had conducted at least one online transaction at a banking, shopping, travel, or insurance Web site in the past year. The findings, reported on *BusinessWeek.com* (January 5, 2006), revealed that 1,655 respondents, or 89%, experienced technical problems with an online transaction. Also, more than one-third of the consumers go to a competitor's Web site when a glitch in the online transaction occurs.

a. Identify the data-collection method.

b. Identify the target population.

c. Are the sample data representative of the population?

Solution

a. The data-collection method is a survey: 1,859 adults completed the questionnaire.

b. Presumably, the software company who commissioned the survey is interested in all consumers who have made at least one online transaction in the past year. Consequently, the target population is *all* consumers who use the Internet for online transactions.

c. Because the 1,859 respondents clearly make up a subset of the target population, they do form a sample. Whether or not the sample is representative is unclear because *BusinessWeek.com* provided no detailed information on how the 1,859 respondents were selected. If the respondents were obtained using, say, random-digit telephone dialing, then the sample is likely to be representative because it is a random sample. However, if the questionnaire was made available to anyone surfing the Internet, then the respondents are *self-selected* (i.e., each Internet user who saw the survey chose whether or not to respond to it). Such a survey often suffers from *nonresponse* bias. It is possible that many Internet users who chose not to respond (or who never saw the questionnaire) would have answered the questions differently, leading to a lower (or higher) sample percentage.

Look Back Any inferences based on survey samples that employ self-selection are suspect due to potential nonresponse bias.

Example 1.7

Data–Collection Method; Representative Data

Problem Marketers use wording such as "was $100, now $80" to indicate a price promotion. The promotion is typically compared to the retailer's previous price or to a competitor's price. A study in the *Journal of Consumer Research* investigated whether between-store comparisons result in greater perceptions of value by consumers than within-store comparisons. Suppose 50 consumers were randomly selected from all consumers in a designated market area to participate in the study. The researchers randomly assigned 25 consumers to read a within-store price promotion advertisement ("was $100, now $80") and 25 consumers to read a between-store price promotion ("$100 there, $80 here"). The consumers then gave their opinion on the value of the

---

Activity 1.1   *Keep the Change:* Collecting Data

Recently, Bank of America introduced a savings program called *Keep the Change*. Each time a customer enrolled in the program uses his or her debit card to make a purchase, the difference between the purchase total and the next higher dollar amount is transferred from the customer's checking account to a savings account. For example, if you were enrolled in the program and used your debit card to purchase a latte for $3.75, then $0.25 would be transferred from your checking to your savings account. For the first 90 days that a customer is enrolled in the program, Bank of America matches the amounts transferred up to $250. In this and subsequent activities, we will investigate the potential benefit to the customer and cost to the bank.

1. Simulate the program by keeping track of all purchases that you make during one week that could be made with a debit card, even if you use a different form of payment. For each purchase, record both the purchase total and the amount that would be transferred from checking to savings with the *Keep the Change* program.

2. You now have two sets of data: *Purchase Totals* and *Amounts Transferred*. Both sets contain quantitative data. For each data set, identify the corresponding naturally occurring numerical scale. Explain why each set has an obvious lower bound but only one set has a definite upper bound.

3. Find the total of the amounts transferred for the one-week period. Because 90 days is approximately 13 weeks, multiply the total by 13 to estimate how much the bank would have to match during the first 90 days. Form a third data set, *Bank Matching,* by collecting the 90-day estimates of all the students in your class. Identify the naturally occurring scale, including bounds, for this set of data.

Keep the data sets from this activity for use in other activities. We suggest you save the data using statistical software (e.g., Minitab) or a graphing calculator.

discount offer on a 10-point scale (where 1 = lowest value and 10 = highest value). The value opinions of the two groups of consumers were compared.

a. Identify the data-collection method.

b. Are the sample data representative of the target population?

Solution

a. Here, the experimental units are the consumers. Because the researchers controlled which price promotion ad—"within-store" or "between-store"—the experimental units (consumers) were assigned to, a designed experiment was used to collect the data.

b. The sample of 50 consumers was randomly selected from all consumers in the designated market area. If the target population is all consumers in this market, it is likely that the sample is representative. However, the researchers warn that the sample data should not be used to make inferences about consumer behavior in other, dissimilar markets.

Look Back By using randomization in a designed experiment, the researcher is attempting to eliminate different types of bias, including self-selection bias.

Now Work Exercise 1.15

Statistics IN Action | Revisited | Identifying the Data-Collection Method and Data Type

Refer to the *New York Times* study on the link between a CEO's golf handicap and the company's stock performance. Recall that the newspaper gathered information on golf handicaps of corporate executives obtained from a *Golf Digest* survey that was sent to 300 corporate executives. Thus, the data-collection method is a survey. In addition to golf handicap (a numerical "index" that allows golfers to compare skills), the *Times* measured the CEO's company stock market performance over a 3-year period on a scale of 0 to 100. Because both variables, golf handicap and stock performance, are numerical in nature, they are quantitative data.

Data Set: GOLFCEO

1.7 The Role of Statistics in Managerial Decision Making

According to H. G. Wells, author of such science-fiction classics as *The War of the Worlds* and *The Time Machine*, "*Statistical thinking* will one day be as necessary for efficient citizenship as the ability to read and write." Written more than a hundred years ago, Wells's prediction is proving true today.

BIOGRAPHY H. G. WELLS (1866–1946)
Writer and Novelist

English-born Herbert George Wells published his first novel, *The Time Machine,* in 1895 as a parody of the English class division and as a satirical warning that human progress is inevitable. Although most famous as a science-fiction novelist, Wells was a prolific writer as a journalist, sociologist, historian, and philosopher. Wells's prediction about statistical thinking (see above) is just one of a plethora of observations he made about life on this world. Here are a few more of H. G. Wells's more famous quotes:

"Advertising is legalized lying."

"Crude classification and false generalizations are the curse of organized life."

"The crisis of today is the joke of tomorrow."

"Fools make researchers and wise men exploit them."

"The only true measure of success is the ratio between what we might have done and what we might have been on the one hand, and the thing we have made and the things we have made of ourselves on the other." ∎

The growth in data collection associated with scientific phenomena, business operations, and government activities (quality control, statistical auditing, forecasting, etc.) has been remarkable in the past several decades. Every day the media present us with the published results of political, economic, and social surveys. In increasing government emphasis on drug and product testing, for example, we see vivid evidence of the need for *quantitative literacy,* i.e., the ability to evaluate data intelligently. Consequently, each of us has to develop a discerning sense—an ability to use rational thought to interpret and understand the meaning of data. Quantitative literacy can help you make intelligent decisions, inferences, and generalizations; that is, it helps you *think critically* using statistics.

> **Statistical thinking** involves applying rational thought and the science of statistics to critically assess data and inferences. Fundamental to the thought process is that variation exists in populations and process data.

To gain some insight into the role statistics plays in critical thinking, we present two examples of some misleading or faulty surveys.

Example 1.8
Biased Sample

Problem An article in the *New York Times* considered the question of whether motorcyclists should be required by law to wear helmets. In supporting his argument for no helmets, the editor of a magazine for Harley-Davidson bikers presented the results of one study that claimed "nine states without helmet laws had a lower fatality rate (3.05 deaths per 10,000 motorcycles) than those that mandated helmets (3.38)" and a survey that found "of 2,500 bikers at a rally, 98% of the respondents opposed such laws." Based on this information, do you think it is safer to ride a motorcycle without a helmet? What further statistical information would you like?

Solution You can use statistical thinking to help you critically evaluate the study. For example, before you can evaluate the validity of the 98% estimate, you would want to know how the data were collected. If a survey was, in fact, conducted, it's possible that the 2,500 bikers in the sample were not selected at random from the target population of all bikers, but rather were "self-selected." (Remember, they were all attending a rally—a rally likely for bikers who oppose the law.) If the respondents were likely to have strong opinions regarding the helmet law (e.g., strongly oppose the law), the resulting estimate is probably biased high. Also, if the biased sample was intentional, with the sole purpose to mislead the public, the researchers would be guilty of **unethical statistical practice.**

Ethics ɪɴ Statistics

Intentionally selecting a biased sample in order to produce misleading statistics is considered *unethical statistical practice.*

You would also want more information about the study comparing the motorcycle fatality rate of the nine states without a helmet law to those states that mandate helmets. Were the data obtained from a published source? Where all 50 states included in the study, or were only certain states selected? That is, are you seeing sample data or population data? Furthermore, do the helmet laws vary among states? If so, can you really compare the fatality rates?

Look Back Questions such as these led a group of mathematics and statistics teachers attending an American Statistical Association course to discover a scientific and statistically sound study on helmets. The study reported a dramatic *decline* in motorcycle crash deaths after California passed its helmet law.

Example 1.9
Manipulative or Ambiguous Survey Questions

Problem Recently, Howard Stern moved his controversial radio program from free, over-the-air (AM/FM) radio to Sirius satellite radio (now called Sirius XM). The move was perceived in the industry to boost satellite radio subscriptions. This led American Media Services, a developer of AM/FM radio properties, to solicit a January 2006 nationwide random-digit dialing phone survey of 1,008 people. The purpose of the survey was to determine how much interest Americans really have in buying satellite radio service. After providing some background on Howard Stern's controversial radio program, one of the questions asked, "How likely are you to purchase a subscription to satellite radio after Howard Stern's move to Sirius?" The result: 86% of the respondents stated that they aren't likely to buy satellite radio because of Stern's move. Consequently, American Media Services concluded that "the Howard Stern Factor is overrated" and that "few Americans expect to purchase satellite radio"—claims that made the headlines of news reports and Web blogs. Do you agree?

Solution First, we need to recognize that American Media Services has a vested interest in the outcome of the survey—the company makes its money from over-the-air broadcast radio stations. Second, although the phone survey was conducted using random-digit dialing, there is no information provided on the response rate. It's possible that non-respondents (people who were not home or refused to answer the survey questions) tend to be people who use cell phones more than their landline phone, and, consequently, are more likely to use the latest in electronic technology, including satellite radio. Finally, the survey question itself is ambiguous. Do the respondents have negative feelings about satellite radio, Howard Stern, or both? If not for Howard Stern's program, would the respondents be more likely to buy satellite radio? To the critical thinker, it's unclear what the results of the survey imply.

Look Back Examining the survey results from the perspective of satellite radio providers, 14% of the respondents indicated that they would be likely to purchase satellite radio. Projecting the 14% back to the population of all American adults, this figure represents about 50 million people; what is interpreted as "few Americans" by American Media Services could be music to the ears of satellite radio providers.

As in both the motorcycle helmet study and satellite radio study, many statistical studies are based on survey data. Most of the problems with these surveys result from the use of *nonrandom* samples. These samples are subject to potential errors, such as *selection bias*, *nonresponse bias* (recall Example 1.6), and *measurement error*. Researchers who are aware of these problems and continue to use the sample data to make inferences are practicing unethical statistics.

> **Selection bias** results when a subset of the experimental units in the population is excluded so that these units have no chance of being selected for the sample.

> **Nonresponse bias** results when the researchers conducting a survey or study are unable to obtain data on all experimental units selected for the sample.

> **Measurement error** refers to inaccuracies in the values of the data recorded. In surveys, the error may be due to ambiguous or leading questions and the interviewer's effect on the respondent.

Successful managers rely heavily on statistical thinking to help them make decisions. The role statistics can play in managerial decision making is displayed in the flow diagram in Figure 1.5. Every managerial decision-making problem begins with a real-world problem. This problem is then formulated in managerial terms and framed

Statistics ɪɴ Action Revisited   Critically Assessing the Ethics of a Statistical Study

The *New York Times* reported a strong link between a corporate executive's golf handicap and his/her company's stock performance. Thus, the newspaper inferred that the better the CEO is at golf, the better the company's stock performance will be. To critically assess this study, consider the following facts:

1. *Golf Digest* sent surveys to the CEOs at the 300 largest U.S. firms. Only 74 executives agreed to reveal their golf handicaps. Of these 74 CEOs, the *Times* collected data on stock performance for only 51 of the companies. (The other 23 CEOs were not in the stock performance database used by the newspaper.)

2. The *New York Times* researcher who performed the analysis of the data stated that "for all the different factors I've tested as possible links to predicting which CEOs are going to perform well or poorly, [golf handicap] is certainly one of the...strongest."

3. According to the *Times,* the researcher "scientifically sifted out a handful of CEOs because of their statistical extremes," in effect "removing seven CEOs from the final analysis because [their data] destroyed the trend lines."

These observations lead a critical thinker to doubt the validity of the inference made by the *New York Times* researcher. Consider first that the sample of CEOs analyzed was not randomly selected from all CEOs in the United States. In fact, they were self-selected—only those CEOs who chose to report their golf handicap were included in the study. (Not even all these "self-reporters" were included; some were eliminated because the newspaper did not have information on their company's stock performance in the database.) Thus, the potential for selection and/or nonresponse bias is extremely high.

Second, based on fact #2, it is likely that the researcher tested a multitude of factors and found only one (golf handicap) that had a link to stock performance. We will learn in subsequent chapters that when a plethora of irrelevant variables are tested statistically, by chance one or more of the variables will be found "statistically significant."

Finally, the researcher removed the data for seven CEOs based on their "statistical extremes." In the next chapter, we learn about statistical "outliers"—how to detect them and how to treat them when discovered. However, it can be shown (using the methods outlined in the text) that these seven data points are not outliers. If the data points are included in the analysis, the link between golf handicap and stock performance is found to be weak, at best.

🔘 *Data Set:* GOLFCEO

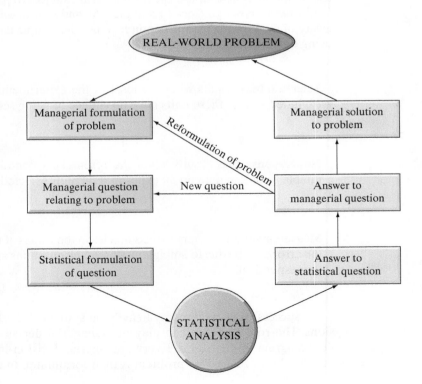

Figure 1.5
Flow diagram showing the role of statistics in managerial decision making *Source:* Chervany, N. L., Benson, G., and Iyer, R. K. (1980), "The Planning Stage in Statistical Reasoning," *The American Statistician.* © 1980 by the American Statistical Association. All rights reserved.

as a managerial question. The next sequence of steps (proceeding counterclockwise around the flow diagram) identifies the role that statistics can play in this process. The managerial question is translated into a statistical question, the sample data are collected and analyzed, and the statistical question is answered. The next step in the process is using the answer to the statistical question to reach an answer to the managerial question. The answer to the managerial question may suggest a reformulation of the original managerial problem, suggest a new managerial question, or lead to the solution of the managerial problem.

One of the most difficult steps in the decision-making process—one that requires a cooperative effort among managers and statisticians—is the translation of the managerial question into statistical terms (for example, into a question about a population). This statistical question must be formulated so that, when answered, it will provide the key to the answer to the managerial question. Thus, as in the game of chess, you must formulate the statistical question with the end result, the solution to the managerial question, in mind.

In the remaining chapters of the text, you'll become familiar with the tools essential for building a firm foundation in statistics and statistical thinking.

Activity 1.2 | Identifying Misleading Statistics

In the *Statistics in Action* feature at the beginning of this chapter, several examples of false or misleading statistics were discussed. Claims such as *One in four American children under age 12 is hungry or at risk of hunger* are often used to persuade the public or the government to donate or allocate more money to charitable groups that feed the poor. Researchers sometimes claim a relationship exists between two seemingly unrelated quantities such as a CEO's golf handicap and the company's stock performance; such relationships are often weak at best and of little practical importance. Read the *Statistics in Action* and *Statistics in Action Revisited* features in this chapter before completing this activity.

1. Look for an article in a newspaper or on the Internet in which a large proportion or percentage of a population is purported to be "at risk" of some calamity, as in the childhood hunger

example. Does the article cite a source or provide any information to support the proportion or percentage reported? Is the goal of the article to persuade some individual or group to take some action? If so, what action is being requested? Do you believe that the writer of the article may have some motive for exaggerating the problem? If so, give some possible motives.

2. Look for another article in which a relationship between two seemingly unrelated quantities is purported to exist, as in the CEO golf handicap and stock performance study. Select an article that contains some information on how the data were collected. Identify the target population and the data collection method. Based on what is presented in the article, do you believe that the data are representative of the population? Explain. Is the purported relationship of any practical interest? Explain.

CHAPTER NOTES

Key Terms

Note: Starred (*) terms are from the optional section in this chapter.

*Black box 11
Census 6
Data 3
Descriptive statistics 3
Designed experiment 14
Experimental unit 5
Inference 3
Inferential statistics 3
Measurement 6
Measurement error 19
Measure of reliability 9
Nonresponse bias 19
Observational study 15
Population 5
*Process 10

Published source 14
Qualitative data 13
Quantitative data 13
Quantitative literacy 18
Random sample 15
Reliability 8
Representative sample 15
Sample 6, 11
Selection bias 19
Statistical inference 7
Statistical thinking 18
Statistics 3
Survey 15
Unethical statistical practice 18
Variable 5

Key Ideas

Types of Statistical Applications

Descriptive
1. Identify **population** or **sample** (collection of **experimental units**)
2. Identify **variable(s)**
3. Collect **data**
4. **Describe** data

Inferential
1. Identify **population** (collection of *all* **experimental units**)
2. Identify **variable(s)**
3. Collect **sample** data (*subset* of population)
4. **Inference** about population based on sample
5. **Measure of reliability** for inference

Types of Data

1. **Quantitative** (numerical in nature)
2. **Qualitative** (categorical in nature)

Data-Collection Methods

1. **Observational**
2. **Published source**
3. **Survey**
4. **Designed experiment**

Problems with Nonrandom Samples

1. **Selection bias**
2. **Nonresponse bias**
3. **Measurement error**

Exercises 1.1–1.32

Note: Starred (*) exercises are from the optional section in this chapter.

Learning the Mechanics

1.1 What is statistics?

1.2 Explain the difference between descriptive and inferential statistics.

1.3 List and define the four elements of a descriptive statistics problem.

1.4 List and define the five elements of an inferential statistical analysis.

1.5 List the four major methods of collecting data and explain their differences.

1.6 Explain the difference between quantitative and qualitative data.

1.7 Explain how populations and variables differ.

1.8 Explain how populations and samples differ.

1.9 What is a representative sample? What is its value?

1.10 Why would a statistician consider an inference incomplete without an accompanying measure of its reliability?

*1.11 Explain the difference between a population and a process.

1.12 Define *statistical thinking*.

1.13 Suppose you're given a data set that classifies each sample unit into one of four categories: A, B, C, or D. You plan to create a computer database consisting of these data, and you decide to code the data as A = 1, B = 2, C = 3, and D = 4. Are the data consisting of the classifications A, B, C, and D qualitative or quantitative? After the data are input as 1, 2, 3, or 4, are they qualitative or quantitative? Explain your answers.

Applet Exercise 1.1

The *Random Numbers* applet generates a list of n random numbers from 1 to N, where n is the size of the sample and N is the size of the population. The list generated often contains repetitions of one or more numbers.

a. Using the applet *Random Numbers*, enter 1 for the minimum value, 10 for the maximum value, and 10 for the sample size. Then click on *Sample*. Look at the results and list any numbers that are repeated and the number of times each of these numbers occurs.

b. Repeat part **a**, changing the maximum value to 20 and keeping the size of the sample fixed at 10. If you still have repetitions, repeat the process, increasing the maximum value by 10 each time but keeping the size of the sample fixed. What is the smallest maximum value for which you had no repetitions?

c. Describe the relationship between the population size (maximum value) and the number of repetitions in the list of random numbers as the population size increases and the sample size remains the same. What can you conclude about using a random number generator to choose a relatively small sample from a large population?

Applet Exercise 1.2

The *Random Numbers* applet can be used to select a random sample from a population, but can it be used to simulate data? In parts **a** and **b**, you will use the applet to create data sets. Then you will explore whether those data sets are realistic.

a. In the activity *Keep the Change* on page 16, a data set called *Amounts Transferred* is described. Use the *Random Numbers* applet to simulate this data set by setting the minimum value equal to 0, the maximum value equal to 99, and the sample size equal to 30. Explain what the numbers in the list produced by the applet represent in the context of the activity. (You may need to read the activity.) Do the numbers produced by the applet seem reasonable? Explain.

b. Use the *Random Numbers* applet to simulate grades on a statistics test by setting the minimum value equal to 0, the maximum value equal to 100, and the sample size equal to 30. Explain what the numbers in the list produced by the applet represent in this context. Do the numbers produced by the applet seem reasonable? Explain.

c. Referring to parts **a** and **b**, why do the randomly generated data seem more reasonable in one situation than in the other? Comment on the usefulness of using a random number generator to produce data.

Applying the Concepts—Basic

1.14 **Credit card market shares.** Refer to the study of credit card purchases in the United States in Section 1.2 (Study 1, p. 4). Recall that the Nilson Report tracked all credit card purchases during 2007 and measured two variables: (1) the type of credit card used (VISA, MasterCard, American Express, or Discover), and (2) the amount (in dollars) of each purchase.

a. Identify the type (quantitative or qualitative) of each variable measured.

b. Does the data set collected represent a population or a sample? Explain.

1.15 **Opinion polls.** Pollsters regularly conduct opinion polls to determine the popularity rating of the current president. Suppose a poll is to be conducted tomorrow in which 2,000 individuals will be asked whether the president is doing a good or bad job. The 2,000 individuals will be selected by random-digit telephone dialing and asked the question over the phone.

a. What is the relevant population?

b. What is the variable of interest? Is it quantitative or qualitative?

c. What is the sample?

d. What is the inference of interest to the pollster?

e. What method of data collection is employed?

f. How likely is the sample to be representative?

1.16 **College application data.** Colleges and universities are requiring an increasing amount of information about applicants before making acceptance and financial aid decisions. Classify each of the following types of data required on a college application as quantitative or qualitative.

a. High school GPA

b. Honors, awards

c. Applicant's score on the SAT or ACT

d. Gender of applicant

e. Parents' income

f. Age of applicant

1.17 **Microsoft survey of Windows.** Windows Vista is a computer software product made by Microsoft Corporation. In designing Windows Vista, Microsoft telephoned thousands of users of an earlier version of Windows and asked them how the product could be improved. Assume customers were asked the following questions:

I. Are you the most frequent user of Windows in your household?

II. What is your age?

III. Are the tutorial instructions that accompany Windows helpful?

IV. When using a printer with Windows, do you most frequently use a laser printer or another type of printer?

V. If the speed of Windows could be changed, which one of the following would you prefer: slower, unchanged, or faster?

VI. How many people in your household have used Windows at least once?

Each of these questions defines a variable of interest to the company. Classify the data generated for each variable as quantitative or qualitative. Justify your classification.

1.18 **Going online for health information.** A *cyberchondriac* is defined as a person who regularly searches the Web for health care information. Each year a Harris Poll is conducted to determine the number of cyberchondriacs in the United States. In 2008, the Harris Poll surveyed 1,010 U.S. adults by telephone and asked the following questions:

1. Have you ever gone online to look for health care information?

2. How many times per month do you look for health care information online?

3. In the past year, have you ever discussed with your doctor the information you found online?

a. For each question, determine whether the type of data collected is quantitative or qualitative.

b. Do the data collected for the 1,010 adults represent a sample or a population? Explain.

1.19 **The executive compensation scoreboard.** Each year, *Forbes* publishes its Executive Compensation Scoreboard. (See Study #2, p. 4) For the 2008 scoreboard, data were collected for chief executive officers at the 500 largest U.S. companies and the following variables were measured for each CEO: (1) the industry type of the CEO's company

(e.g., banking, retailing, etc.), (2) the CEO's total compensation ($ millions) for the year, (3) the CEO's total compensation ($ millions) over the previous 5 years, (4) the number of company stock shares (millions) held, (5) the CEO's age (years), and (6) the CEO's efficiency rating. (Data are saved in the file **CEOPAY2008.**)

a. Are the data for the 500 CEOs in the 2008 Executive Compensation Scoreboard a population or sample? Explain.

b. Identify the type (quantitative or qualitative) of each variable measured.

1.20 **Annual survey of computer crimes.** The Computer Security Institute (CSI) conducts an annual survey of computer crime at United States businesses. CSI sends survey questionnaires to computer security personnel at all U.S. corporations and government agencies. In 2006, 616 organizations responded to the CSI survey. Fifty-two percent of the respondents admitted unauthorized use of computer systems at their firms during the year. (*Computer Security Issues & Trends*, Spring 2006)

a. Identify the population of interest to CSI.

b. Identify the data-collection method used by CSI. Are there any potential biases in the method used?

c. Describe the variable measured in the CSI survey. Is it quantitative or qualitative?

d. What inference can be made from the study result?

Applying the Concepts—Intermediate

1.21 **Satellite radio in cars.** A recent survey conducted for the National Association of Broadcasters investigated satellite radio subscriber service and usage. The June 2007 survey, conducted by Wilson Research Strategies, consisted of a random sample of 501 satellite radio subscribers. One of the questions of interest was, "Do you have a satellite radio receiver in your car?" The survey found that 396 subscribers did, in fact, have a satellite receiver in their car.

a. Identify the population of interest to the National Association of Broadcasters.

b. Based on the survey question, what is the variable of interest?

c. Does the variable produce quantitative or qualitative data?

d. Describe the sample of interest. Is it representative of the population?

e. What inference can be made from the survey results?

1.22 **New cancer screening method.** According to the American Lung Association, lung cancer accounts for 28% of all cancer deaths in the United States. A new type of screening for lung cancer, computed tomography (CT), has been developed. Medical researchers believe CT scans are more sensitive than regular X-rays in pinpointing small tumors. The H. Lee Moffitt Cancer Center at the University of South Florida is currently conducting a clinical trial of 50,000 smokers nationwide to compare the effectiveness of CT scans with X-rays for detecting lung cancer (*Todays' Tomorrows*, Fall 2002). Each participating smoker is randomly assigned to one of two screening methods, CT or chest X-ray, and his or her progress is tracked over time. The age at which the scanning method first detects a tumor is the variable of interest.

a. Identify the data-collection method used by the cancer researchers.

b. Identify the experimental units of the study.

c. Identify the type (quantitative or qualitative) of the variable measured.

d. Identify the population and sample.

e. What is the inference that will ultimately be drawn from the clinical trial?

1.23 **Inspection of highway bridges.** All highway bridges in the United States are inspected periodically for structural deficiency by the Federal Highway Administration (FHWA). Data from the FHWA inspections are compiled into the National Bridge Inventory (NBI). Several of the nearly 100 variables maintained by the NBI are listed below. Classify each variable as quantitative or qualitative.

a. Length of maximum span (feet)

b. Number of vehicle lanes

c. Toll bridge (yes or no)

d. Average daily traffic

e. Condition of deck (good, fair, or poor)

f. Bypass or detour length (miles)

g. Route type (interstate, U.S., state, county, or city)

1.24 **Structurally deficient highway bridges.** Refer to Exercise 1.23. The 2007 NBI data were analyzed and the results made available at the FHWA Web site (www.fhwa.dot.gov). Using the FHWA inspection ratings, each of the 599,766 highway bridges in the United States was categorized as structurally deficient, functionally obsolete, or safe. About 12% of the bridges were found to be structurally deficient, while 13.5% were functionally obsolete.

a. What is the variable of interest to the researchers?

b. Is the variable of part **a** quantitative or qualitative?

c. Is the data set analyzed a population or a sample? Explain.

d. How did the NBI obtain the data for the study?

∗1.25 **Monitoring product quality.** The Wallace Company of Houston is a distributor of pipes, valves, and fittings to the refining, chemical, and petrochemical industries. The company was a recent winner of the Malcolm Baldrige National Quality Award. One of the steps the company takes to monitor the quality of its distribution process is to send out a survey twice a year to a subset of its current customers, asking the customers to rate the speed of deliveries, the accuracy of invoices, and the quality of the packaging of the products they have received from Wallace.

a. Describe the process studied.

b. Describe the variables of interest.

c. Describe the sample.

d. Describe the inferences of interest.

e. What are some of the factors that are likely to affect the reliability of the inferences?

1.26 **Guilt in decision making.** The effect of guilt emotion on how a decision maker focuses on the problem was investigated in the *Journal of Behavioral Decision Making* (January 2007). A total of 171 volunteer students participated in the experiment, where each was randomly assigned to one of three emotional states (guilt, anger, or neutral) through a reading/writing task. Immediately after the task, the students were presented with a decision problem (e.g., whether or not to spend money on repairing a very old car). The researchers found that a higher proportion of students in the guilty-state group chose to repair the car than those in the neutral-state and anger-state groups.

a. Identify the population, sample, and variables measured for this study.

b. Identify the data-collection method used.

c. What inference was made by the researcher?

d. In later chapters you will learn that the reliability of an inference is related to the size of the sample used. In addition to sample size, what factors might affect the reliability of the inference drawn in this study?

1.27 **Accounting and Machiavellianism.** *Behavioral Research in Accounting* (January 2008) published a study of Machiavellian traits in accountants. *Machiavellian* describes negative character traits that include manipulation, cunning, duplicity, deception, and bad faith. A questionnaire was administered to a random sample of 700 accounting alumni of a large southwestern university; however, due to non-response and incomplete answers, only 198 questionnaires could be analyzed. Several variables were measured, including age, gender, level of education, income, job satisfaction score, and Machiavellian ("Mach") rating score. The research findings suggest that Machiavellian behavior is not required to achieve success in the accounting profession.

a. What is the population of interest to the researcher?

b. What type of data (quantitative or qualitative) is produced by each of the variables measured?

c. Identify the sample.

d. Identify the data-collection method used.

e. What inference was made by the researcher?

f. How might the nonresponses impact the inference?

1.28 **Success/failure of software reuse.** The PROMISE Software Engineering Repository, hosted by the University of Ottawa, is a collection of publicly available data sets to serve researchers in building prediction software models. A PROMISE data set on software reuse, saved in the **SWREUSE** file, provides information on the success or failure of reusing previously developed software for each in a sample of 24 new software development projects. (Data source: *IEEE Transactions on Software Engineering*, Vol. 28, 2002.) Of the 24 projects, 9 were judged failures and 15 were successfully implemented.

a. Identify the experimental units for this study.

b. Describe the population from which the sample is selected.

c. What is the variable of interest in the study? Is it quantitative or qualitative?

d. Use the sample information to make an inference about the population.

Applying the Concepts—Advanced

1.29 **Bank corporate mergers.** *Corporate merger* is a means through which one firm (the bidder) acquires control of the assets of another firm (the target). During the late 1990s, there was a frenzy of bank mergers in the United States, as the banking industry consolidated into more efficient and more competitive units.

a. Construct a brief questionnaire (two or three questions) that could be used to query a sample of bank presidents concerning their opinions of why the industry is consolidating and whether it will consolidate further.

b. Describe the population about which inferences could be made from the results of the survey.

c. Discuss the pros and cons of sending the questionnaire to all bank presidents versus a sample of 200.

*1.30 **Monitoring the production of soft drink cans.** The Wakefield plant of Coca-Cola and Schweppes Beverages Limited (CCSB) can produce 4,000 cans of soft drink per minute. The automated process consists of measuring and dispensing the raw ingredients into storage vessels to create the syrup, and then injecting the syrup, along with carbon dioxide, into the beverage cans. In order to monitor the subprocess that adds carbon dioxide to the cans, five filled cans are pulled off the line every 15 minutes, and the amount of carbon dioxide in each of these five cans is measured to determine whether the amounts are within prescribed limits.

a. Describe the process studied.

b. Describe the variable of interest.

c. Describe the sample.

d. Describe the inference of interest.

e. *Brix* is a unit for measuring sugar concentration. If a technician is assigned the task of estimating the average brix level of all 240,000 cans of beverage stored in a warehouse near Wakefield, will the technician be examining a process or a population? Explain.

1.31 **Current population survey.** The employment status (employed or unemployed) of each individual in the U.S. workforce is a set of data that is of interest to economists, businesspeople, and sociologists. To obtain information about the employment status of the workforce, the U.S. Bureau of the Census conducts what is known as the *Current Population Survey.* Each month interviewers visit about 59,000 of the 98 million households in the United States and question the occupants over 14 years of age about their employment status. Their responses enable the Bureau of the Census to *estimate* the percentage of people in the labor force who are unemployed (the *unemployment rate*).

a. Define the population of interest to the Census Bureau.

b. What variable is being measured? Is it quantitative or qualitative?

c. Is the problem of interest to the Census Bureau descriptive or inferential?

d. In order to monitor the rate of unemployment, it is essential to have a definition of *unemployed.* Different economists and even different countries define it in various ways. Develop your own definition of an "unemployed person." Your definition should answer such questions as: Are students on summer vacation unemployed? Are college professors who do not teach summer school unemployed? At what age are people considered to be eligible for the workforce? Are people who are out of work but not actively seeking a job unemployed?

Critical Thinking Challenge

1.32 *20/20* **survey exposé.** Refer to the "Statistics in Action" box of this chapter (p. 1). Recall that the popular prime-time ABC television program *20/20* presented several misleading (and possibly unethical) surveys in a segment titled "Facts or Fiction?—Exposés of So-Called Surveys." The information reported from four of these surveys are reproduced here (actual survey facts are provided in parentheses).

Quaker Oats study: Eating oat bran is a cheap and easy way to reduce your cholesterol count. (Fact: Diet must consist of nothing but oat bran to achieve a slightly lower cholesterol count.)

March of Dimes report: Domestic violence causes more birth defects than all medical issues combined. (Fact: No study—false report.)

American Association of University Women (AAUA) study: Only 29% of high school girls are happy with themselves, compared to 66% of elementary school girls. (Fact: Of 3,000 high school girls, 29% responded "Always true" to the statement "I am happy the way I am." Most answered "Sort of true" and "Sometimes true.")

Food Research and Action Center study: One in four American children under age 12 is hungry or at risk of hunger. (Fact: Based on responses to questions "Do you ever cut the size of meals?" and "Do you ever eat less than you feel you should?" and "Did you ever rely on limited numbers of foods to feed your children because you were running out of money to buy food for a meal?")

a. Refer to the Quaker Oats study relating oat bran to cholesterol levels. Discuss why it is unethical to report the results as stated.

b. Consider the false March of Dimes report on domestic violence and birth defects. Discuss the type of data required to investigate the impact of domestic violence on birth defects. What data-collection method would you recommend?

c. Refer to the AAUW study of self-esteem of high school girls. Explain why the results of the study are likely to be misleading. What data might be appropriate for assessing the self-esteem of high school girls?

d. Refer to the Food Research and Action Center study of hunger in America. Explain why the results of the study are likely to be misleading. What data would provide insight into the proportion of hungry American children?

References

Careers in Statistics, American Statistical Association, 2008 (www.amstat.org)

Cochran, W. G. *Sampling Techniques,* 3rd ed. New York: Wiley, 1977.

Deming, W. E. *Sample Design in Business Research.* New York: Wiley, 1963.

Ethical Guidelines for Statistical Practice, American Statistical Association, 1999. (www.amstat.org)

Hahn, G. J. and Doganaksoy, N. *The Role of Statistics in Business and Industry.* New York: Wiley, 2008.

Huff, D. *How to Lie with Statistics.* New York: Norton, 1982 (paperback 1993).

Hoerl, R. and Snee, R. *Statistical Thinking: Improving Business Performance.* Boston: Duxbury, 2002.

Kish, L. *Survey Sampling.* New York: Wiley, 1965 (paperback, 1995).

Peck, R., Casella, G., Cobb, G., Hoerl, R., Nolan, D., Starbuck, R., and Stern, H. *Statistics: A Guide to the Unknown,* 4th ed. Cengage Learning, 2005.

Scheaffer, R., Mendenhall, W., and Ott, R. L. *Elementary Survey Sampling,* 6th ed. Boston: Duxbury, 2005.

What Is a Survey? American Statistical Association (F. Scheuren, editor), 2nd ed., 2005 (www.amstat.org)

Using Technology

SPSS: Accessing and Listing Data

When you start an SPSS session, you will see a screen similar to Figure 1.S.1. The main portion of the screen is an empty spreadsheet, with columns representing variables and rows representing observations (or cases). The very top of the screen is the SPSS main menu bar, with buttons for the different functions and procedures available in SPSS. Once you have entered data into the spreadsheet, you can analyze the data by clicking the appropriate menu buttons.

Figure 1.S.1 Initial screen viewed by the SPSS user

Entering Data

Step 1 To create an SPSS data file, enter data directly into the spreadsheet. See Figure 1.S.2, which shows data entered on a variable called "Fill."

Figure 1.S.2 Data entered into the SPSS spreadsheet

Step 2 Name the variables (columns) by selecting the "Variable View" button at the bottom of the screen and typing in the name of each variable.

Accessing Data from a File

If the data are saved in an external data file, you can access the data using the options available in SPSS.

Step 1 Click the "File" button on the menu bar, and then click "Read Text Data," as shown in Figure 1.S.3. A dialog box similar to Figure 1.S.4 will appear.

Figure 1.S.3 SPSS options for reading data from an external file

Figure 1.S.4 Selecting the external data file in SPSS

Step 2 Specify the disk drive and folder that contains the data file, click on the data file, and then click "Open," as shown in Figure 1.S.4. The SPSS Text Import Wizard Opens.

Step 3 The Text Import Wizard is a series of six screen menus. Make the appropriate selections on the screen, and click "Next" to go to the next screen.

Step 4 When finished, click "Finish." The SPSS spreadsheet will reappear with the data from the external data file, as shown in Figure 1.S.5.

Figure 1.S.5 The SPSS spreadsheet with the imported data

Reminder: The variable (columns) can be named by selecting the "Variable View" button at the bottom of the spreadsheet screen and typing in the name of each variable.

To access a previously saved SPSS data file, click "File," then "Open," then select the SPSS file name.

Listing (Printing) Data

Step 1 Click on the "Analyze" button on the SPSS main menu bar, then click on "Reports," and then on "Report Summaries in Rows" (see Figure 1.S.6). The resulting menu, or dialog box, appears as in Figure 1.S.7.

Step 2 Enter the names of the variables you want to print in the "Data Columns" box (you can do this by simply clicking on the variables), check the "Display cases" box at the bottom left, and then click "OK." The printout will show up on your screen.

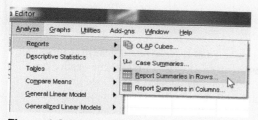

Figure 1.S.6 SPSS menu options for obtaining a data listing

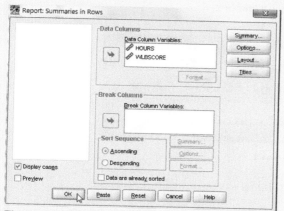

Figure 1.S.7 SPSS data report dialog box

Minitab: Accessing and Listing Data

When you start a Minitab session, you will see a screen similar to Figure 1.M.1. The bottom portion of the screen is an empty spreadsheet—called a Minitab worksheet—with columns representing variables and rows representing observations (or cases). The very top of the screen is the Minitab main menu bar, with buttons for the different functions and procedures available in Minitab. Once you have entered data into the spreadsheet, you can analyze the data by clicking the appropriate menu buttons. The results will appear in the Session window.

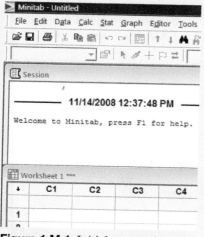

Figure 1.M.1 Initial screen viewed by the Minitab user

Entering Data

Create a Minitab data file by entering data directly into the worksheet. Figure 1.M.2 shows data entered for a variable called "FILL." Name the variables (columns) by typing in the name of each variable in the box below the column number.

Figure 1.M.2 Data entered into the Minitab worksheet

Accessing External Data from a File

Step 1 Click the "File" button on the menu bar, and then click "Open Worksheet" as shown in Figure 1.M.3. A dialog box similar to Figure 1.M.4 will appear.

Figure 1.M.3 Minitab options for reading data from an external file

Figure 1.M.4 Selecting the external data file in Minitab

Step 2 Specify the disk drive and folder that contains the external data file and the file type, and then click on the file name, as shown in Figure 1.M.4.

Step 3 If the data set contains qualitative data or data with special characters, click on the "Options" button as shown in Figure 1.M.4. The Options dialog box, shown in Figure 1.M.5, will appear.

Step 4 Specify the appropriate options for the data set, and then click "OK" to return to the "Open Worksheet" dialog box (Figure 1.M.4).

Figure 1.M.5 Selecting the Minitab data input options

Step 5 Click "Open" and the Minitab worksheet will appear with the data from the external data file, as shown in Figure 1.M.6.

Figure 1.M.6 Minitab worksheet with the imported data

Reminder: The variables (columns) can be named by typing in the name of each variable in the box under the column number.

To access a previously saved Minitab worksheet, click "File," then "Open Worksheet," then select the Minitab file.

Listing (Printing) Data

Step 1 Click on the "Data" button on the Minitab main menu bar, and then click on "Display Data." The resulting menu, or dialog box, appears as in Figure 1.M.7.

Figure 1.M.7 Minitab Display Data dialog box

Step 2 Enter the names of the variables you want to print in the "Columns, constants, and matrices to display" box (you can do this by simply double clicking on the variables), and then click "OK." The printout will show up on your Minitab session screen.

Excel: Accessing and Listing Data

When you open Excel, you will see a screen similar to Figure 1.E.1. The majority of the screen window is a spreadsheet—called an Excel workbook—with columns (labeled A, B, C, etc.) representing variables, and rows representing observations (or cases). The very top of the screen is the Excel main menu bar, with buttons for the different functions and procedures available in Excel. Once you have entered data into the spreadsheet, you can analyze the data by clicking the appropriate menu buttons. The results will appear in a new workbook.

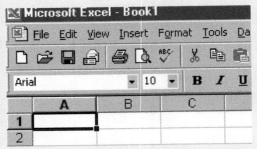

Figure 1.E.1 Initial screen viewed by Excel user

Entering Data

Enter data directly into the appropriate row and column of the spreadsheet. Figure 1.E.2 shows data entered in the first (A) column. Optionally, you can add names for the variables (columns) in the first row of the workbook.

Figure 1.E.2 Data entered into the Excel workbook

Accessing Data from a File

Step 1 Click the "File" button on the menu bar, and then click "Open," as shown in Figure 1.E.3. A dialog box similar to Figure 1.E.4 will appear.

Figure 1.E.3 Excel options for reading data from an external file

Figure 1.E.4 Selecting the external data file in Excel

Step 2 Specify the disk drive and folder that contains the external data file and the file type, then click on the file name and click on "Open," as shown in Figure 1.E.4. The Excel Text Import Wizard opens (Figure 1.E.5.)

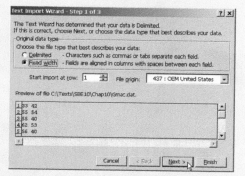

Figure 1.E.5 Excel Text Import Wizard, Screen 1

Step 3 Make the appropriate selections on the screen, and click "Next" to go to the next screen.

Step 4 When finished, click "Finish." The Excel workbook will reappear with the data from the external data file, as shown in Figure 1.E.6.

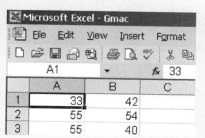

Figure 1.E.6 The Excel workbook with the imported data

Naming Variables

Step 1 Select "Insert" from the Excel main menu, and then select "Rows." A blank (empty) row will be added in the first row of the spreadsheet.

Step 2 Type the name of each variable in the first row under the appropriate column.

To access a previously created Excel workbook, click "File," then "Open," then select the Excel file.

Listing (Printing) Data

Step 1 Click on the "File" button on the Excel main menu bar.

Step 2 Click on "Print" (see Figure 1.E.7).

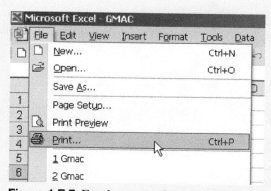

Figure 1.E.7 Excel menu options for obtaining a data listing

CONTENTS

2 Methods for Describing Sets of Data

Where We've Been

- Examined the difference between inferential and descriptive statistics
- Described the key elements of a statistical problem
- Learned about the two types of data—quantitative and qualitative
- Discussed the role of statistical thinking in managerial decision making

Where We're Going

- Describe data using graphs
- Describe data using numerical measures

Statistics IN Action   Factors That Influence a Doctor to Refuse Ethics Consultation

Ethical dilemmas commonly arise in the course of a physician's clinical practice. These dilemmas include (but are not limited to) end-of-life issues, treatment of patients without health insurance, providing nonbeneficial treatment at the patient's request, obtaining informed consent, maintaining patient autonomy, truth-telling and confidentiality, involvement of children in research, designing of clinical trials, and termination of subject participation in research protocols. Empirical studies have found that an ethical issue will arise in one of every five clinical encounters.

Over the past 10 years, ethics consultation has evolved as a means of assisting physicians who are confused about how to best approach an ethical dilemma. About 80% of general hospitals in the United States now provide ethics consultation services to staff physicians. When faced with a difficult ethical decision, the doctor may request advice from a panel of ethics experts, with assurances that all communications will be anonymous and confidential. However, not all physicians take advantage of this service; in fact, some doctors refuse to use ethics consultation.

(continued)

Medical researchers at University Community Hospital (UCH) in Tampa, Florida, undertook a study to determine the factors that might influence a physician's decision to request or to refuse ethics consultation.*

Survey questionnaires were distributed to all 746 physicians on staff at UCH; 118 of the questionnaires were returned, yielding a response rate of approximately 16%. The survey was designed to obtain data on the following variables for each physician:

1. *Level of previous ethics consultation use* **at UCH** ("used at least once" or "never used")
2. *Practitioner specialty* ("medical" or "surgical")
3. *Length of time in practice* (number of years)
4. *Amount of exposure to ethics in medical school* (number of hours)
5. *Would you ever consider using ethics consultation* **in the future** (yes or no)

The physicians were also asked to elicit opinions on the following statements about ethics consultants. (All responses were measured on a 5-point scale, where 1 = "strongly disagree," 2 = "somewhat disagree," 3 = "neither agree nor disagree," 4 = "somewhat disagree," or 5 = "strongly agree.")

6. *Ethics consultants have extensive training in ethics and ethics principles.*
7. *Ethics consultants participate in frequent ethics education.*

8. *Ethics consultants think they are "moral experts."*
9. *Ethics consultants cannot grasp the full picture from the "outside."*

The UCH medical researchers wanted to use the survey results to develop insight into why certain physicians use ethics consultation and others do not. The researchers hypothesized that more experienced doctors and physicians who specialize in surgery would be less likely to use ethics consultation. The data for the study are stored in the file named **ETHICS** in SPSS, Minitab, and Excel.

In the following *Statistics in Action Revisited* sections, we apply the graphical and numerical descriptive techniques of this chapter to the **ETHICS** data to answer some of the researchers' questions.

Statistics ɪɴ Action Revisited

- Interpreting pie charts (p. 37)
- Interpreting histograms (p. 47)
- Interpreting numerical descriptive measures (p. 74)
- Detecting outliers (p. 88)
- Interpreting scatterplots (p. 92)

Data Set: ETHICS

Suppose you wish to evaluate the managerial capabilities of a class of 400 MBA students based on their Graduate Management Aptitude Test (GMAT) scores. How would you describe these 400 measurements? Characteristics of the data set include the typical or most frequent GMAT score, the variability in the scores, the highest and lowest scores, the "shape" of the data, and whether or not the data set contains any unusual scores. Extracting this information by "eye-balling" the data isn't easy. The 400 scores may provide too many bits of information for our minds to comprehend. Clearly, we need some formal methods for summarizing and characterizing the information in such a data set. Methods for describing data sets are also essential for statistical inference. Most populations are large data sets. Consequently, we need methods for describing a sample data set that let us make descriptive statements (inferences) about the population from which the sample was drawn.

Two methods for describing data are presented in this chapter, one *graphical* and the other *numerical*. Both play an important role in statistics. Section 2.1 presents both graphical and numerical methods for describing qualitative data. Graphical methods for describing quantitative data are presented in Sections 2.2, 2.8, and 2.10 and optional Section 2.9; numerical descriptive methods for quantitative data are presented in Sections 2.3–2.7. We end this chapter with a section on the *misuse* of descriptive techniques.

*Orlowski, J. P., Hein, S., Meinke, R., Christenson, J., and Sincich, T. "Why Physicians Use or Do Not Use Ethics Consultation," *Journal of Medical Ethics,* Vol. 32, 2006.

2.1 Describing Qualitative Data

Recall the "Executive Compensation Scoreboard" tabulated annually by *Forbes* (see Study 2 in Section 1.2). In addition to salary information, *Forbes* collects and reports personal data on the CEOs, including level of education. Do most CEOs have advanced degrees, such as masters degrees or doctorates? To answer this question, Table 2.1 gives the highest college degree obtained (bachelors, MBA, masters, law, PhD, or none) for each of the 40 best-paid CEOs in 2008.

For this study, the variable of interest, highest college degree obtained, is qualitative in nature. Qualitative data are nonnumerical; thus, the value of a qualitative variable can be classified only into categories called *classes*. The possible degree types—bachelors, MBA, masters, law, PhD, or none—represent the classes for this qualitative variable. We can summarize such data numerically in two ways: (1) by computing the *class frequency*—the number of observations in the data set that fall into each class;

Table 2.1	Data on 40 Best-Paid Executives			
CEO	Company	Salary ($ millions)	Age	Degree
1 Lawrence J Ellison	Oracle	192.92	63	None
2 Frederic M Poses	Trane	127.1	66	Bachelors
3 Aubrey K McClendon	Chesapeake Energy	116.89	47	Bachelors
4 Angelo R Mozilo	Countrywide Financial	102.84	69	Bachelors
5 Howard D Schultz	Starbucks	98.6	54	Bachelors
6 Nabeel Gareeb	MEMC Electronic Mats	79.56	43	None
7 Daniel P Amos	Aflac	75.16	56	Bachelors
8 Lloyd C Blankfein	Goldman Sachs Group	73.72	53	Law
9 Richard D Fairbank	Capital One Financial	73.17	57	MBA
10 Bob R Simpson	XTO Energy	72.27	59	MBA
11 Richard S Fuld Jr	Lehman Bros Holdings	71.9	62	MBA
12 Steven Roth	Vornado Realty	71.85	66	MBA
13 Marijn E Dekkers	Thermo Fisher	69	50	PhD
14 Steven A Burd	Safeway	67.17	58	Masters
15 Gregg L Engles	Dean Foods	66.08	50	Law
16 Nicholas D Chabraja	General Dynamics	60.26	65	Law
17 Leslie H Wexner	Limited Brands	56.06	70	Bachelors
18 David C Novak	Yum Brands	54.91	55	Bachelors
19 John T Chambers	Cisco Systems	54.77	58	MBA
20 William R Berkley	WR Berkley	54.6	62	MBA
21 Ray R Irani	Occidental Petroleum	54.4	73	PhD
22 Bradbury H Anderson	Best Buy	49.26	58	Bachelors
23 John W Rowe	Exelon	47.68	63	Law
24 Robert W Lane	Deere & Co	47.19	58	MBA
25 John B Hess	Hess	46.78	54	MBA
26 David E I Pyott	Allergan	46.19	55	Masters
27 Sol J Barer	Celgene	46.07	61	PhD
28 Albert L Lord	SLM	45.99	62	Bachelors
29 John H Hammergren	McKesson	44.91	49	MBA
30 Miles D White	Abbott Laboratories	44.76	53	MBA
31 J Willard Marriott Jr	Marriott International	44.09	76	Bachelors
32 Howard Solomon	Forest Labs	40.89	80	Law
33 Michael D Watford	Ultra Petroleum	40.64	54	MBA
34 Brian L Roberts	Comcast	38.98	48	Bachelors
35 James L Dolan	Cablevision	38.81	53	Bachelors
36 Richard C Adkerson	Freeport Copper	38.66	61	MBA
37 Paul J Evanson	Allegheny Energy	37.29	66	Law
38 Robert J Stevens	Lockheed Martin	36.56	56	Masters
39 Matthew K Rose	Burlington Santa Fe	36.52	49	Bachelors
40 Hugh Grant	Monsanto	35.78	50	Bachelors

Source: Data on 40 Best-Paid Executives, *Forbes*, April 30, 2008. Reprinted by permission of Forbes.com. © 2009 Forbes LLC.

Data Set: FORBES40

or (2) by computing the *class relative frequency*—the proportion of the total number of observations falling into each class.

> A **class** is one of the categories into which qualitative data can be classified.

> The **class frequency** is the number of observations in the data set falling into a particular class.

> The **class relative frequency** is the class frequency divided by the total number of observations in the data set.

Examining Table 2.1, we observe that 2 of the 40 best-paid CEOs did not obtain a college degree, 14 obtained bachelors degrees, 12 MBAs, 3 masters degrees, 3 PhDs, and 6 law degrees. These numbers—2, 14, 12, 3, 3, and 6—represent the class frequencies for the six classes and are shown in the summary table, Figure 2.1, produced using SPSS.

> The **class percentage** is the class relative frequency multiplied by 100.

Figure 2.1 also gives the relative frequency of each of the five degree classes. We know that we calculate the relative frequency by dividing the class frequency by the total number of observations in the data set. Thus, the relative frequencies for the five degree types are

$$\text{Bachelors: } \frac{14}{40} = .35$$

$$\text{Law: } \frac{6}{40} = .15$$

$$\text{Masters: } \frac{3}{40} = .075$$

$$\text{MBA: } \frac{12}{40} = .30$$

$$\text{None: } \frac{2}{40} = .05$$

$$\text{PhD: } \frac{3}{40} = .075$$

These values, expressed as a percentage, are shown in the "Percent" column in the SPSS summary table, Figure 2.1. If we sum the relative frequencies for MBA,

DEGREE

		Frequency	Percent	Valid Percent	Cumulative Percent
Valid	Bachelors	14	35.0	35.0	35.0
	Law	6	15.0	15.0	50.0
	Masters	3	7.5	7.5	57.5
	MBA	12	30.0	30.0	87.5
	None	2	5.0	5.0	92.5
	PhD	3	7.5	7.5	100.0
	Total	40	100.0	100.0	

Figure 2.1

SPSS summary table for degrees of 40 CEOs

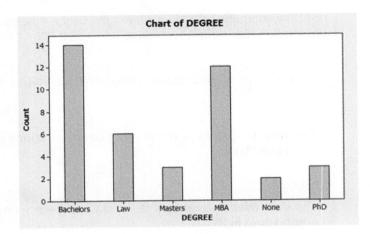

Figure 2.2

Minitab bar graph for
degrees of 40 CEOs

masters, law, and PhD, we obtain $.30 + .075 + .15 + .075 = .60$. Therefore, 60%
of the 40 best-paid CEOs obtained at least a masters degree (MBA, masters, law,
or PhD).

Although the summary table in Figure 2.1 adequately describes the data in Table 2.1,
we often want a graphical presentation as well. Figures 2.2 and 2.3 show two of the most
widely used graphical methods for describing qualitative data—**bar graphs** and **pie charts.**
Figure 2.2 is a bar graph for "highest degree obtained" produced with Minitab. Note that
the height of the rectangle, or "bar," over each class is equal to the class frequency.
(Optionally, the bar heights can be proportional to class relative frequencies.) In contrast,
Figure 2.3 (also created using Minitab) shows the relative frequencies (expressed as a percentage) of the six degree types in a *pie chart*. Note that the pie is a circle (spanning 360°),
and the size (angle) of the "pie slice" assigned to each class is proportional to the class relative frequency. For example, the slice assigned to the MBA degree is 30% of 360°, or
$(.30)(360°) = 108°$.

Before leaving the data set in Table 2.1, consider the bar graph shown in Figure 2.4,
produced using SPSS with annotations. Note that the bars for the CEO degree categories
are arranged in descending order of height from left to right across the horizontal axis—
that is, the tallest bar (bachelors) is positioned at the far left and the shortest bar is at the
far right. This rearrangement of the bars in a bar graph is called a Pareto diagram. One
goal of a Pareto diagram (named for the Italian economist, Vilfredo Pareto) is to make it
easy to locate the "most important" categories—those with the largest frequencies. For
the 40 best-paid CEOs in 2008, a bachelor's degree was the highest degree obtained by
the most CEOs (35%).

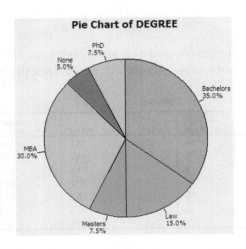

Figure 2.3

Minitab pie chart for
degrees of 40 CEOs

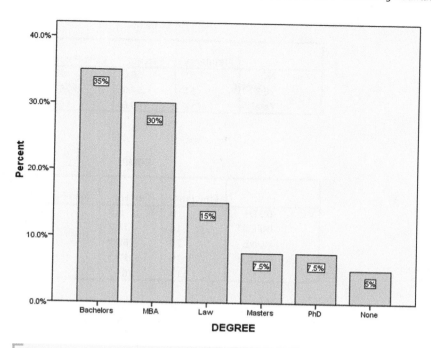

Figure 2.4

SPSS Pareto diagram for degrees of 40 CEOs

Summary of Graphical Descriptive Methods for Qualitative Data

Bar graph: The categories (classes) of the qualitative variable are represented by bars, where the height of each bar is either the class frequency, class relative frequency, or class percentage.

Pie chart: The categories (classes) of the qualitative variable are represented by slices of a pie (circle). The size of each slice is proportional to the class relative frequency.

Pareto diagram: A bar graph with the categories (classes) of the qualitative variable (i.e., the bars) arranged by height in descending order from left to right.

Let's look at a practical example that requires interpretation of the graphical results.

Example 2.1
Graphing and Summarizing Qualitative Data

Problem A group of cardiac physicians in southwest Florida have been studying a new drug designed to reduce blood loss in coronary artery bypass operations. Blood loss data for 114 coronary artery bypass patients (some who received a dosage of the drug and others who did not) are saved in the **BLOODLOSS** file. Although the drug shows promise in reducing blood loss, the physicians are concerned about possible side effects and complications. So their data set includes not only the qualitative variable, DRUG, which indicates whether or not the patient received the drug, but also the qualitative variable, COMP, which specifies the type (if any) of complication experienced by the patient. The four values of COMP recorded by the physicians are (1) redo surgery, (2) post-op infection, (3) both, or (4) none.

a. Figure 2.5, generated using SPSS, shows summary tables for the two qualitative variables, DRUG and COMP. Interpret the results.

b. Interpret the Minitab output shown in Figure 2.6 and the SPSS output shown in Figure 2.7.

Solution

a. The top table in Figure 2.5 is a summary frequency table for DRUG. Note that exactly half (57) of the 114 coronary artery bypass patients received the drug and half did not. The bottom table in Figure 2.5 is a summary frequency table for COMP. We see that about 69% of the 114 patients had no complications, leaving about 31% who experienced either a redo surgery, a post-op infection, or both.

DRUG

		Frequency	Percent	Valid Percent	Cumulative Percent
Valid	NO	57	50.0	50.0	50.0
	YES	57	50.0	50.0	100.0
	Total	114	100.0	100.0	

COMP

		Frequency	Percent	Valid Percent	Cumulative Percent
Valid	BOTH	6	5.3	5.3	5.3
	INFECT	15	13.2	13.2	18.4
	NONE	79	69.3	69.3	87.7
	REDO	14	12.3	12.3	100.0
	Total	114	100.0	100.0	

Figure 2.5

SPSS summary tables for
DRUG and COMP

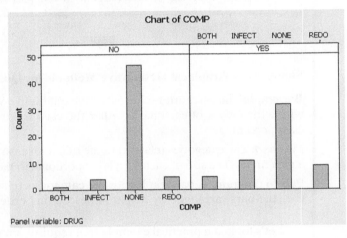

Figure 2.6

Minitab side-by-side bar graphs
for COMP, by value of DRUG

COMP

DRUG			Frequency	Percent	Valid Percent	Cumulative Percent
NO	Valid	BOTH	1	1.8	1.8	1.8
		INFECT	4	7.0	7.0	8.8
		NONE	47	82.5	82.5	91.2
		REDO	5	8.8	8.8	100.0
		Total	57	100.0	100.0	
YES	Valid	BOTH	5	8.8	8.8	8.8
		INFECT	11	19.3	19.3	28.1
		NONE	32	56.1	56.1	84.2
		REDO	9	15.8	15.8	100.0
		Total	57	100.0	100.0	

Figure 2.7

SPSS summary tables for
COMP by value of DRUG

b. Figure 2.6 is a Minitab side-by-side bar graph for the data. The four bars on the left represent the frequencies of COMP for the 57 patients who did not receive the drug; the four bars on the right represent the frequencies of COMP for the 57 patients who did receive a dosage of the drug. The graph clearly shows that patients who did not get the drug suffered fewer complications. The exact percentages are displayed in the SPSS summary tables of Figure 2.7. About 56% of the patients who got the drug had no complications, compared to about 83% for the patients who did not get the drug.

Look Back Although the drug may be effective in reducing blood loss, the results in Figures 2.6 and 2.7 also imply that patients on the drug may have a higher risk of complications. But before using this information to make a decision about the drug, the physicians will need to provide a measure of reliability for the inference—that is, the physicians will want to know whether the difference between the percentages of patients with complications observed in this sample of 114 patients is generalizable to the population of all coronary artery bypass patients.

Now Work Exercise 2.12

Statistics IN Action Revisited | Interpreting Pie Charts

In the survey of University Community Hospital physicians, the medical researchers measured three qualitative variables: *Level of previous ethics consultation use* ("never used" or "used"), *Practitioner specialty* ("medical" or "surgical"), and *Future use of ethics consultation* ("yes" or "no"). Pie charts and bar graphs can be used to summarize and describe the physicians' responses to these survey questions. Recall that the data are saved in the **ETHICS** file. These variables are named PREVUSE, SPEC, and FUTUREUSE in the data file. We created pie charts for these variables using both Minitab and Data Desk/XL, an Excel add-in (called DDXL).

Figure SIA2.1 is a pie chart for the PREVUSE variable. Clearly, a higher percentage of physicians (71.2%) has previously never used ethics consultation at the hospital than have (28.8%). The researchers want to know if this "previous use" pattern differs for the two practitioner specialties. Figure SIA2.2 shows side-by-side pie charts of the PREVUSE variable for each level of the SPEC variable. The left-side chart describes the pattern of previous use by medical specialists,

and the right-side chart describes the pattern of previous use by surgeons. Figure SIA2.2 shows that slightly fewer surgeons (27.9%) have used ethics consultation in the past than have medical practitioners (29.3%).

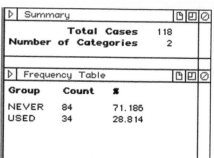

We produced a similar set of side-by-side pie charts to describe the qualitative variable FUTUREUSE in Figure SIA2.3. Apparently, the gap between surgeons and medical specialists has widened. These charts again show that fewer surgeons (76.7%) would consider using ethics consultation in the future than medical specialists (82.7%), but the difference in the percentages is greater than for previous use. The researchers' theory that surgical specialists at UCH are less likely to use ethics consultation than medical specialists is supported by the pie charts.

Data Set: ETHICS

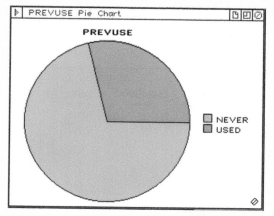

PREVUSE Pie Chart

PREVUSE

☐ NEVER
☐ USED

Summary
Total Cases 118
Number of Categories 2

Frequency Table

Group	Count	**%**
NEVER	84	71.186
USED	34	28.814

Figure SIA2.1

DDXL pie chart for previous use of ethics consultation

Figure SIA2.2
Minitab pie charts for previous use of ethics consultation—medical versus surgical specialty

Figure SIA2.3
Minitab pie charts for future use of ethics consultation—medical versus surgical specialty

Exercises 2.1–2.15

Learning the Mechanics

2.1 Complete the following table.

Grade on Business Statistics Exam	Frequency	Relative Frequency
A: 90–100	—	.08
B: 80–89	36	—
C: 65–79	90	—
D: 50–64	30	—
F: Below 50	28	—
Total	200	1.00

2.2 A qualitative variable with three classes (X, Y, and Z) is measured for each of 20 units randomly sampled from a target population. The data (observed class for each unit) are listed below.

Y X X Z X Y Y Y Y X X Z X
Y Y X Z Y Y Y X

a. Compute the frequency for each of the three classes.
b. Compute the relative frequency for each of the three classes.

c. Display the results, part **a**, in a frequency bar graph.
d. Display the results, part **b**, in a pie chart.

Applying the Concepts—Basic

2.3 **Industrial robots.** The Robotics Industries Association estimates that there are 184,000 industrial robots operating in North America. The graph on the next page shows the percentages of industrial robot units assigned to each of six task categories: (1) spot welding, (2) arc welding, (3) material removal, (4) material handling, (5) assembly, and (6) dispensing/coating.

a. What type of graph is used to describe the data?
b. Identify the variable measured for each of the 184,000 industrial robots.
c. Use the graph to identify the task that uses the highest percentage of industrial robots.
d. How many of the 184,000 industrial robots are used for spot welding?
e. What percentage of industrial robots are used for either spot welding or arc welding?

2.4 **Who is to blame for rising health-care costs?** Rising health-care costs are of major concern to Americans. A nationwide survey of 2,119 U.S. adults was conducted to elicit opinions on who is to blame for the rising costs (*The Harris Poll*, Oct. 28, 2008). The next table summarizes the responses to the

Graph for Exercise 2.3

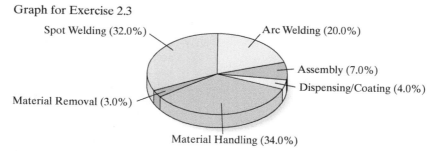

Spot Welding (32.0%)
Arc Welding (20.0%)
Assembly (7.0%)
Dispensing/Coating (4.0%)
Material Removal (3.0%)
Material Handling (34.0%)

question "When you think of the rising costs of health care, who do you think is most responsible?"

a. Compute the relative frequencies in each response category.

b. Construct a relative frequency bar graph for the data.

c. Convert the relative frequency bar graph into a Pareto diagram. Interpret the graph.

Most Responsible for Rising Health-care Costs	Number Responding
Insurance companies	869
Pharmaceutical companies	339
Government	338
Hospitals	127
Physicians	85
Other	128
Not at all sure	233
Total	2,119

2.5 PIN pad shipments. Personal identification number (PIN) pads are devices that connect to point-of-sale electronic cash registers for debit and credit card purchases. The PIN pad allows the customer card to be accessed and the PIN encrypted before it is sent to the transaction manager. *The Nilson Report* (Oct. 2008) listed the volume of PIN pad shipments by manufacturers worldwide in 2007. For the 12 manufacturers listed in the table, a total of 334,039 PIN pads were shipped in 2007. (The data are saved in the **PINPADS** file.)

Manufacturer	Number Shipped (units)
Bitel	13,500
CyberNet	16,200
Fujian Landi	119,000
Glintt (ParaRede)	5,990
Intelligent	4,562
KwangWoo	42,000
Omron	20,000
Pax Tech.	10,072
ProvencoCadmus	20,000
SZZT Electronics	67,300
Toshiba TEC	12,415
Urmet	3,000

Source: The Nilson Report, No. 912, October 2008 (p. 9).

a. One of the 334,039 PIN pads is selected and the manufacturer of the pad is determined. What type of data (quantitative or qualitative) is measured?

b. Construct a frequency bar chart for the data summarized in the table.

c. Convert the frequency bar chart, part **b,** into a Pareto diagram. Interpret the results.

2.6 Management system failures. The U.S. Chemical Safety and Hazard Investigation Board (CSB) is responsible for determining the root cause of industrial accidents. Since its creation in 1998, the CSB has identified 83 incidents that were caused by management system failures (*Process Safety Progress,* Dec. 2004). The accompanying table gives a breakdown of the root causes of these 83 incidents.

Management System Cause Category	Number of Incidents
Engineering & Design	27
Procedures & Practices	24
Management & Oversight	22
Training & Communication	10
Total	83

Source: Blair, A. S. "Management system failures identified in incidents investigated by the U.S. Chemical Safety and Hazard Investigation Board,"*Process Safety Progress,* Vol. 23, No. 4, Dec. 2004, pp. 232–236 (Table 1). Reprinted with permission of John Wiley & Sons, Inc.

a. Find the relative frequency of the number of incidents for each cause category.

b. Construct a Pareto diagram for the data.

c. From the Pareto diagram, identify the cause categories with the highest (and lowest) relative frequency of incidents.

2.7 Non-cash payments in the U.S. The "2007 Federal Reserve Payments Study," sponsored by the federal government, found that the number of non-cash payments in the United States reached 93.3 billion transactions during the year. (*CardTrak.com News,* Dec. 13, 2007.) The pie chart shown below describes the proportions of these non-cash transactions that were made with credit cards, debit cards, checks, electronic benefit transfer (EBT) cards for the Food Stamps program, and Automatic Clearing House (ACH) payments.

a. Describe the population of interest in the study.

b. Estimate the number of non-cash payments in 2007 that were made with credit cards.

c. What percentage of all non-cash payments in 2007 were made with either credit or debit cards?

d. Convert the pie chart into a Pareto diagram and interpret the figure.

Applying the Concepts—Intermediate

2.8 Products "Made in the USA." "Made in the USA" is a claim stated in many product advertisements or on product labels. Advertisers want consumers to believe that the product is manufactured with 100% U.S. labor and materials—which is often not the case. What does "Made in the USA" mean to the typical consumer? To answer this question, a group of marketing professors conducted an experiment at a shopping mall in Muncie, Indiana (*Journal of Global*

Graph for Exercise 2.7

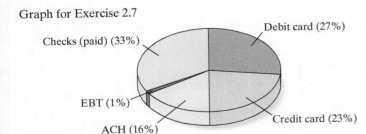

Checks (paid) (33%)
Debit card (27%)
EBT (1%)
ACH (16%)
Credit card (23%)

Business, Spring 2002). They asked every fourth adult entrant to the mall to participate in the study. A total of 106 shoppers agreed to answer the question, "'Made in the USA' means what percentage of U.S. labor and materials?" The responses of the 106 shoppers are summarized in the following table.

Response to "Made in the USA"	Number of Shoppers
100%	64
75 to 99%	20
50 to 74%	18
Less than 50%	4

Source: "'Made in the USA': Consumer Perceptions, Deception and Policy Alternatives," *Journal of Global Business,* Vol. 13, No. 24, Spring 2002 (Table 3).

a. What type of data-collection method was used?

b. What type of variable, quantitative or qualitative, is measured?

c. Present the data in the table in graphical form. Use the graph to make a statement about the percentage of consumers who believe "Made in the USA" means 100% U.S. labor and materials.

2.9 **Blogs for Fortune 500 firms.** Web site communication through blogs and forums is becoming a key marketing tool for companies. The *Journal of Relationship Marketing* (Vol. 7, 2008) investigated the prevalence of blogs and forums at Fortune 500 firms with both English and Chinese Web sites. Of the firms that provided blogs/forums as a marketing tool, the accompanying table gives a breakdown on the entity responsible for creating the blogs/forums. Use a graphical method to describe the data summarized in the table. Interpret the graph.

Blog/Forum	Percentage of Firms
Created by company	38.5
Created by employees	34.6
Created by third party	11.5
Creator not identified	15.4

Source: Mishra, K. & Li, C. "Relationship marketing in *Fortune* 500 U.S. and Chinese web sites," *Journal of Relationship Marketing,* Vol. 7, No. 1, 2008. Copyright © 2008 Routledge.

2.10 **The Executive Compensation Scoreboard.** Refer to the *Forbes* "Executive Compensation Scoreboard" for 2008, described in Chapter 1 (p. 4) and in Exercise 1.19 (p. 23). Recall that the industry type of the CEO's company (e.g., banking, retailing, etc.) was recorded for each of the 175 CEOs with the highest efficiency (pay-for-performance) ratings. (See Table 1.1, p. 4, for a list of the industries.) Access the

CEOPAYTOP175 file and use a graphical method to describe the frequency of occurrence of the industry types.

2.11 **Color and clarity of diamonds.** Diamonds are categorized according to the "four C's": carats, clarity, color, and cut. Each diamond stone that is sold on the open market is provided a certificate by an independent diamond assessor that lists these characteristics. Data for 308 diamonds were extracted from Singapore's *Business Times* and are saved in the **DIAMONDS** file (*Journal of Statistics Education,* Vol. 9, No. 1, 2001). Color is classified as D, E, F, G, H, or I, while clarity is classified as IF, VVS1, VVS2, VS1, or VS2. Use a graphical technique to summarize the color and clarity of the 308 diamond stones. What is the color and clarity that occurs most often? Least often?

2.12 **History of corporate acquisitions.** A corporate acquisition occurs when one corporation purchases all the stock shares of another, essentially taking over the other. The *Academy of Management Journal* (Aug. 2008) investigated the performance and timing of corporate acquisitions for a large sample of firms over the years 1980 to 2000. The accompanying data table (saved in the **ACQUISITIONS** file) gives the number of firms sampled and number that announced one or more acquisitions during the year for each year. Construct side-by-side bar charts to describe the firms with and without acquisitions in the years 1980 and 2000. Compare and contrast the bar charts.

Year	Number of Firms Sampled	Number with Acquisitions
1980	1,963	18
1981	2,044	115
1982	2,029	211
1983	2,187	273
1984	2,248	317
1985	2,238	182
1986	2,277	232
1987	2,344	258
1988	2,279	296
1989	2,231	350
1990	2,197	350
1991	2,261	370
1992	2,363	427
1993	2,582	532
1994	2,775	626
1995	2,890	652
1996	3,070	751
1997	3,099	799
1998	2,913	866
1999	2,799	750
2000	2,778	748
Total	51,567	9,123

Source: Iyer, D. N. & Miller, K. D. "Performance feedback, slack, and the timing of acquisitions," *Academy of Management Journal,* Vol. 51, No. 4, August 2008, pp. 808–822 (Table 1). Copyright 2008 by Academy of Management (NY). Reproduced with permission of Academy of Management (NY) in the format Textbook and electronic usage via Copyright Clearance Center.

Applying the Concepts—Advanced

2.13 **Advertising with reader-response cards.** "Reader-response cards" are used by marketers to advertise their product and obtain sales leads. These cards are placed in magazines and trade publications. Readers detach and mail in the cards to indicate their interest in the product, expecting literature or a phone call in return. How effective are these cards (called "bingo cards" in the industry) as a marketing tool? Performark, a Minneapolis business that helps companies close on sales leads, attempted to answer this question by responding to 17,000 card-advertisements placed by industrial marketers in a wide variety of trade publications over a 6-year period. Performark kept track of how long it took for each advertiser to respond. A summary of the response times, reported in *Inc.* magazine (July 1995), is given in the following table.

a. Describe the variable measured by Performark.

b. *Inc.* displayed the results in the form of a pie chart. Reconstruct the pie chart from the information given in the table.

c. How many of the 17,000 advertisers never responded to the sales lead?

d. Advertisers typically spend at least a million dollars on a reader-response card marketing campaign. Many industrial marketers feel these "bingo cards" are not worth their expense. Does the information in the pie chart, part **b,** support this contention? Explain why or why not. If not, what information can be gleaned from the pie chart to help potential "bingo card" campaigns?

Advertiser's Response Time	Percentage
Never responded	21
13–59 days	33
60–120 days	34
More than 120 days	12
Total	100

2.14 **Stewardship at MBA programs.** *Business Ethics* (Fall 2005) reported on a survey designed to rank master in business administration (MBA) programs worldwide on how well they prepare students for social and environmental stewardship. Each business school was ranked according to four criteria: *student exposure* (class time dedicated to social and environmental issues), *student opportunity* (courses with social and environmental content), *course content* (courses emphasize business as a force for positive social and environmental change), and *faculty research* (published articles that examine business in a social/environmental context). Each area was rated from 1 star (lowest rating) to 5 stars (highest rating). Overall, Stanford University received the top ranking, followed by ESADE (Spain), York University (Canada), Monterrey Technical Institute (Mexico), and the University of Notre Dame. A summary of the rankings (star ratings) for the top 30 MBA programs is shown in the table.

a. Illustrate the differences and similarities of the star-ranking distributions for the four different criteria.

b. Give a plausible reason why there were no 1-star ratings for the 30 MBA programs.

Criteria	5 Stars	4 Stars	3 Stars	2 Stars	1 Star	Total
Student Exposure	2	9	14	5	0	30
Student Opportunity	3	10	14	3	0	30
Course Content	3	9	17	1	0	30
Faculty Research	3	10	11	4	0	28

Source: Adapted from Stewardship at MBA programs – Biello, D. "MBA Programs for Social and Environmental Stewardship," *Business Ethics,* Fall 2005, p. 25. Used with permission of the Aspen Institute.

2.15 **Groundwater contamination in wells.** In New Hampshire, about half the counties mandate the use of reformulated gasoline. This has led to an increase in the contamination of groundwater with methyl *tert*-butyl ether (MTBE). *Environmental Science & Technology* (Jan. 2005) reported on the factors related to MTBE contamination in public and private New Hampshire wells. Data were collected for a sample of 223 wells. These data are saved in the **MTBE** file. Three of the variables are qualitative in nature: well class (public or private), aquifer (bedrock or unconsolidated), and detectible level of MTBE (below limit or detect). [Note: A detectible level of MTBE occurs if the MTBE value exceeds .2 micrograms per liter.] The data for 10 selected wells are shown in the accompanying table.

a. Use graphical methods to describe each of the three qualitative variables for all 223 wells.

b. Use side-by-side bar charts to compare the proportions of contaminated wells for private and public well classes.

c. Use side-by-side bar charts to compare the proportions of contaminated wells for bedrock and unconsolidated aquifers.

d. What inferences can be made from the bar charts, parts **a–c?**

Well Class	Aquifer	Detect MTBE
Private	Bedrock	Below Limit
Private	Bedrock	Below Limit
Public	Unconsolidated	Detect
Public	Unconsolidated	Below Limit
Public	Unconsolidated	Below Limit
Public	Unconsolidated	Below Limit
Public	Unconsolidated	Detect
Public	Unconsolidated	Below Limit
Public	Unconsolidated	Below Limit
Public	Bedrock	Detect
Public	Bedrock	Detect

Source: Ayotte, J. D., Argue, D. M., and McGarry, F. J. "Methyl *tert*-Butyl Ether Occurrence and Related Factors in Public and Private Wells in Southeast New Hampshire," *Environmental Science & Technology,* Vol. 39, No. 1, Jan. 2005, pp. 9–16. Copyright © 2005 American Chemical Society.

2.2 Graphical Methods for Describing Quantitative Data

Recall from Section 1.5 that quantitative data sets consist of data that are recorded on a meaningful numerical scale. For describing, summarizing, and detecting patterns in such data, we can use three graphical methods: **dot plots, stem-and-leaf displays,** and **histograms.** Because almost all statistical software packages can produce these graphs, we'll focus here on their interpretations rather than their construction.

For example, suppose a financial analyst is interested in the amount of resources spent by computer hardware and software companies on research and development

Table 2.2	Percentage of Revenues Spent on Research and Development						
Company	Percentage	Company	Percentage	Company	Percentage	Company	Percentage
1	13.5	14	9.5	27	8.2	39	6.5
2	8.4	15	8.1	28	6.9	40	7.5
3	10.5	16	13.5	29	7.2	41	7.1
4	9.0	17	9.9	30	8.2	42	13.2
5	9.2	18	6.9	31	9.6	43	7.7
6	9.7	19	7.5	32	7.2	44	5.9
7	6.6	20	11.1	33	8.8	45	5.2
8	10.6	21	8.2	34	11.3	46	5.6
9	10.1	22	8.0	35	8.5	47	11.7
10	7.1	23	7.7	36	9.4	48	6.0
11	8.0	24	7.4	37	10.5	49	7.8
12	7.9	25	6.5	38	6.9	50	6.5
13	6.8	26	9.5				

Data Set: R&D

(R&D). She samples 50 of these high-technology firms and calculates the amount each spent last year on R&D as a percentage of their total revenue. The results are given in Table 2.2. As numerical measurements made on the sample of 50 units (the firms), these percentages represent quantitative data. The analyst's initial objective is to summarize and describe these data in order to extract relevant information.

A visual inspection of the data indicates some obvious facts. For example, the smallest R&D percentage is 5.2% (company 45) and the largest is 13.5% (companies 1 and 16). But it is difficult to provide much additional information on the 50 R&D percentages without resorting to some method of summarizing the data. One such method is a dot plot.

Dot Plots

A **dot plot** for the 50 R&D percentages, produced using SPSS software, is shown in Figure 2.8. The horizontal axis of Figure 2.8 is a scale for the quantitative variable, percent. The numerical value of each measurement in the data set is located on the horizontal scale by a dot. When data values repeat, the dots are placed above one another, forming a pile at that particular numerical location. As you can see, this dot plot shows that almost all of the R&D percentages are between 6% and 12%, with most falling between 7% and 9%.

Stem–and–Leaf Display

We used Minitab to generate another graphical representation of these same data, a **stem-and-leaf display,** in Figure 2.9. In this display the *stem* is the portion of the measurement (percentage) to the left of the decimal point, while the remaining portion to the right of the decimal point is the *leaf.*

The stems for the data set are listed in the second column of Figure 2.9 from the smallest (5) to the largest (13). Then the leaf for each observation is recorded in the row of the display corresponding to the observation's stem.* For example, the leaf 5 of the first observation (13.5) in Table 2.2 is placed in the row corresponding to the stem 13. Similarly, the leaf 4 for the second observation (8.4) in Table 2.2 is recorded in the row corresponding

Figure 2.8
SPSS dot plot for 50 R&D percentages

*The first column of the Minitab stem-and-leaf display represents the cumulative number of measurements from the class interval to the nearest extreme class interval.

```
Stem-and-leaf of RDPct   N  = 50
Leaf Unit = 0.10


    3    5    269
   12    6    055568999
   23    7    11224557789
   (9)   8    001222458
   18    9    02455679
   10   10    1556
    6   11    137
    3   12
    3   13    255
```

Figure 2.9

Minitab stem-and-leaf display
for 50 R&D percentages

to the stem 8, while the leaf 5 for the third observation (10.5) is recorded in the row corresponding to the stem 10. (The leaves for these first three observations are shaded in Figure 2.9.) Typically, the leaves in each row are ordered as shown in Figure 2.9.

The stem-and-leaf display presents another compact picture of the data set. You can see at a glance that most of the sampled computer companies (37 of 50) spent between 6.0% and 9.9% of their revenues on R&D, and 11 of them spent between 7.0% and 7.9%. Relative to the rest of the sampled companies, three spent a high percentage of revenues on R&D—in excess of 13%.

The definitions of the stem and leaf can be modified to alter the graphical display. For example, suppose we had defined the stem as the tens digit for the R&D percentage data, rather than the ones and tens digits. With this definition, the stems and leaves corresponding to the measurements 13.5 and 8.4 would be as follows:

Stem	Leaf		Stem	Leaf
1	3		0	8

Note that the decimal portion of the numbers has been dropped. Generally, only one digit is displayed in the leaf.

If you look at the data, you'll see why we didn't define the stem this way. All the R&D measurements fall below 13.5, so all the leaves would fall into just two stem rows—1 and 0—in this display. The picture resulting from using only a few stems would not be nearly as informative as Figure 2.9.

Histograms

An **Excel/DDXL histogram** for these 50 R&D measurements is displayed in Figure 2.10. The horizontal axis for Figure 2.10, which gives the percentage amounts spent on R&D for each company, is divided into **class intervals** commencing with the interval (5.0−6.0) and proceeding in intervals of equal size to (13.0−14.0). The vertical axis gives the number (or *frequency*) of the 50 measurements that fall in each class interval. You can see that the class interval (7.0−8.0) (i.e., the class with the highest bar) contains the largest frequency of 11 R&D percentage measurements; the remaining class intervals tend to contain a smaller number of measurements as R&D percentage gets smaller or larger.

Histograms can be used to display either the *frequency* or *relative frequency* of the measurements falling into the class intervals. The class intervals, frequencies, and relative

---

BIOGRAPHY JOHN TUKEY (1915–2000)

The Picasso of Statistics

Like the legendary artist Pablo Picasso, who mastered and revolutionized a variety of art forms during his lifetime, John Tukey is recognized for his contributions to many subfields of statistics. Born in Massachusetts, Tukey was home-schooled, graduated with his bachelor's and master's degrees in chemistry from Brown University, and received his PhD in mathematics from Princeton University. While at Bell Telephone Laboratories in the 1960s and early 1970s, Tukey developed "exploratory data analysis," a set of graphical descriptive methods for summarizing and presenting huge amounts of data. Many of these tools, including the stem-and-leaf display and the box plot (see Section 2.8), are now standard features of modern statistical software packages. (In fact, it was Tukey himself who coined the term *software* for computer programs.) ∎

Figure 2.10
Excel/DDXL histogram
for 50 R&D percentages

frequencies for the 50 R&D measurements are shown in Table 2.3.* By summing the relative frequencies in the intervals (6.0−7.0), (7.0−8.0), (8.0−9.0), (9.0−10.0), and (10.0−11.0), we find that .18 + .22 + .18 + .16 + .08 = .82, or 82%, of the R&D measurements are between 6.0 and 11.0. Similarly, summing the relative frequencies in the last two intervals, (12.0−13.0) and (13.0−14.0), we find that 6% of the companies spent over 12.0% of their revenues on R&D. Many other summary statements can be made by further study of the histogram.

When interpreting a histogram (say, the histogram in Figure 2.10), consider two important facts. First, the proportion of the total area under the histogram that falls above a particular interval of the horizontal axis is equal to the relative frequency of measurements falling in the interval. For example, the relative frequency for the class interval 7.0−8.0 is .22. Consequently, the rectangle above the interval contains 22% of the total area under the histogram.

Second, you can imagine the appearance of the relative frequency histogram for a very large set of data (say, a population). As the number of measurements in a data set is increased, you can obtain a better description of the data by decreasing the width of the class intervals. When the class intervals become small enough, a relative frequency histogram will (for all practical purposes) appear as a smooth curve (see Figure 2.11). Some recommendations for selecting the number of intervals in a histogram for smaller data sets are given in the box below Figure 2.11.

While histograms provide good visual descriptions of data sets—particularly very large ones—they do not let us identify individual measurements. In contrast, each of the original measurements is visible to some extent in a dot plot and clearly visible in a stem-and-leaf display. The stem-and-leaf display arranges the data in ascending order, so it's easy to locate the individual measurements. For example, in Figure 2.9, we can easily see that three of the R&D measurements are equal to 8.2, but we can't see that

Table 2.3	Class Intervals, Frequencies, and Relative Frequencies for the 50 R&D Measurements		
Class	Class Interval	Class Frequency	Class Relative Frequency
1	5.0−6.0	3	3/50 = .06
2	6.0−7.0	9	9/50 = .18
3	7.0−8.0	11	11/50 = .22
4	8.0−9.0	9	9/50 = .18
5	9.0−10.0	8	8/50 = .16
6	10.0−11.0	4	4/50 = .08
7	11.0−12.0	3	3/50 = .06
8	12.0−13.0	0	0/50 = .00
9	13.0−14.0	3	3/50 = .06
Totals		50	1.00

*DDXL, like many statistical software packages, will classify an observation that falls on the borderline of a class interval into the next highest class interval. For example, the R&D measurement of 8.0, which falls on the border between the intervals (7.0−8.0) and (8.0−9.0), is classified into the (8.0−9.0) interval. The frequencies in Table 2.3 reflect this convention.

Figure 2.11

Effect of the size of a data set on the outline of a histogram

a. Small data set

b. Larger data set

c. Very large data set

fact by inspecting the histogram in Figure 2.10. However, stem-and-leaf displays can become unwieldy for very large data sets. A very large number of stems and leaves causes the vertical and horizontal dimensions of the display to become cumbersome, diminishing the usefulness of the visual display.

Determining the Number of Classes in a Histogram

Number of Observations in Data Set	Number of Classes
Less than 25	5–6
25–50	7–14
More than 50	15–20

Example 2.2

Graphs for a Quantitative Variable

Problem A manufacturer of industrial wheels suspects that profitable orders are being lost because of the long time the firm takes to develop price quotes for potential customers. To investigate this possibility, 50 requests for price quotes were randomly selected from the set of all quotes made last year, and the processing time was determined for each quote. The processing times are displayed in Table 2.4, and each quote

Table 2.4	**Price Quote Processing Time (Days)**				
Request Number	Processing Time	Lost?	Request Number	Processing Time	Lost?
1	2.36	No	26	3.34	No
2	5.73	No	27	6.00	No
3	6.60	No	28	5.92	No
4	10.05	Yes	29	7.28	Yes
5	5.13	No	30	1.25	No
6	1.88	No	31	4.01	No
7	2.52	No	32	7.59	No
8	2.00	No	33	13.42	Yes
9	4.69	No	34	3.24	No
10	1.91	No	35	3.37	No
11	6.75	Yes	36	14.06	Yes
12	3.92	No	37	5.10	No
13	3.46	No	38	6.44	No
14	2.64	No	39	7.76	No
15	3.63	No	40	4.40	No
16	3.44	No	41	5.48	No
17	9.49	Yes	42	7.51	No
18	4.90	No	43	6.18	No
19	7.45	No	44	8.22	Yes
20	20.23	Yes	45	4.37	No
21	3.91	No	46	2.93	No
22	1.70	No	47	9.95	Yes
23	16.29	Yes	48	4.46	No
24	5.52	No	49	14.32	Yes
25	1.44	No	50	9.01	No

Data Set: PRICEQUOTES

Figure 2.12

SPSS frequency histogram for price quote data

was classified according to whether the order was "lost" or not (i.e., whether or not the customer placed an order after receiving a price quote).

a. Use a statistical software package to create a frequency histogram for these data. Then shade the area under the histogram that corresponds to lost orders. Interpret the result.

b. Use a statistical software package to create a stem-and-leaf display for these data. Then shade each leaf of the display that corresponds to a lost order. Interpret the result.

Solution

a. We used SPSS to generate the frequency histogram in Figure 2.12. Note that 20 classes were formed by the SPSS program. The class intervals are (1.0–2.0), (2.0–3.0), ..., (20.0–21.0). This histogram clearly shows the clustering of the measurements in the lower end of the distribution (between approximately 1 and 8 days), and the relatively few measurements in the upper end of the distribution (greater than 12 days). The shading of the area of the frequency histogram corresponding to lost orders (green bars) clearly indicates that they lie in the upper tail of the distribution.

b. We used Minitab to generate the stem-and-leaf display in Figure 2.13. Note that the stem (the second column of the printout) consists of the number of whole days (digits to the left of the decimal). The leaf (the third column of the printout) is the tenths digit (first digit after the decimal) of each measurement. Thus, the leaf 2 in the stem 20 (the last row of the printout) represents the time of 20.23 days. Like the histogram, the stem-and-leaf display shows the shaded "lost" orders in the upper tail of the distribution.

```
Stem-and-leaf of TIME   N  = 50
Leaf Unit = 0.10

  5    1   24789
 10    2   03569
 18    3   23344699
 24    4   034469
 (6)   5   114579
 20    6   01467
 15    7   24557
 10    8   2
  9    9   049
  6   10   0
  5   11
  5   12
  5   13   4
  4   14   03
  2   15
  2   16   2
  1   17
  1   18
  1   19
  1   20   2
```

Figure 2.13

Minitab stem-and-leaf display for price quote data

Look Back As is usually the case for data sets that are not too large (say, fewer than 100 measurements), the stem-and-leaf display provides more detail than the histogram without being unwieldy. For instance, the stem-and-leaf display in Figure 2.13 clearly indicates that the lost orders are associated with high processing times (as does the histogram in Figure 2.12), and exactly which of the times correspond to lost orders. Histograms are most useful for displaying very large data sets, when the overall shape of the distribution of measurements is more important than the identification of individual measurements. Nevertheless, the message of both graphical displays is clear: Establishing processing time limits may well result in fewer lost orders.

Now Work Exercise 2.20

Most statistical software packages can be used to generate histograms, stem-and-leaf displays, and dot plots. All three are useful tools for graphically describing data sets. We recommend that you generate and compare the displays whenever you can. You'll find that histograms are generally more useful for very large data sets, while stem-and-leaf displays and dot plots provide useful detail for smaller data sets.

Summary of Graphical Descriptive Methods for Quantitative Data

Dot plot: The numerical value of each quantitative measurement in the data set is represented by a dot on a horizontal scale. When data values repeat, the dots are placed above one another vertically.

Stem-and-leaf display: The numerical value of the quantitative variable is partitioned into a "stem" and a "leaf." The possible stems are listed in order in a column. The leaf for each quantitative measurement in the data set is placed in the corresponding stem row. Leaves for observations with the same stem value are listed in increasing order horizontally.

Histogram: The possible numerical values of the quantitative variable are partitioned into class intervals, where each interval has the same width. These intervals form the scale of the horizontal axis. The frequency or relative frequency of observations in each class interval is determined. A vertical bar is placed over each class interval, with height equal to either the class frequency or class relative frequency.

Statistics ɪɴ Action | **Revisited** | **Interpreting Histograms**

One of the quantitative variables measured in the ethics consultation survey of physicians was *Length of time in practice* (i.e., years of experience). Recall that the medical researchers hypothesize that older, more experienced physicians will be less likely to use ethics consultation in the future. To check the believability of this claim, we accessed the **ETHICS** data file in Minitab and created two frequency histograms for years of experience—one for physicians who indicated they would use ethics consultation in the future, and one for physicians who would not use ethics consultation. These side-by-side histograms are displayed in Figure SIA2.4.

From the histograms, you can see there is some support for the researchers' assertion. The histogram for the physicians who indicated they would use ethics consultation (the histogram on the right in Figure SIA2.4) shows that

most of these physicians have been in practice between 10 and 20 years, while the histogram for nonusers (the histogram on the left in Figure SIA2.4) shows a tendency for these physicians to have more experience (over 20 years). However, the lack of data (only 21 observations) for the sample of physicians who would not use ethics consultation makes it difficult to reliably extend this inference to the population of physicians. In later chapters, we'll learn how to attach a measure of reliability to such an inference, even for small samples.

Data Set: ETHICS

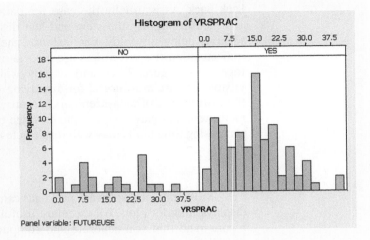

Figure SIA2.4
Minitab histograms for years of practice—ethics consultation users versus nonusers

Exercises 2.16–2.32

Learning the Mechanics

2.16 Graph the relative frequency histogram for the 500 measurements summarized in the accompanying relative frequency table.

Measurement Class	Relative Frequency
.5–2.5	.10
2.5–4.5	.15
4.5–6.5	.25
6.5–8.5	.20
8.5–10.5	.05
10.5–12.5	.10
12.5–14.5	.10
14.5–16.5	.05

2.17 Refer to Exercise 2.16. Calculate the number of the 500 measurements falling into each of the measurement classes. Then graph a frequency histogram for these data.

2.18 Consider the stem-and-leaf display shown here.

Stem	Leaf
5	1
4	457
3	00036
2	1134599
1	2248
0	012

a. How many observations were in the original data set?
b. In the bottom row of the stem-and-leaf display, identify the stem, the leaves, and the numbers in the original data set represented by this stem and its leaves.
c. Re-create all the numbers in the data set and construct a dot plot.

2.19 Minitab was used to generate the following histogram:

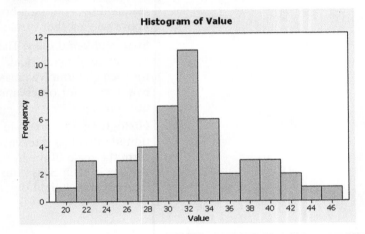

a. Is this a frequency histogram or a relative frequency histogram? Explain.
b. How many measurement classes were used in the construction of this histogram?
c. How many measurements are in the data set described by this histogram?

Applying the Concepts—Basic

2.20 **Computer security survey.** Refer to the 2006 CSI/FBI
[NW] Computer Crime and Security Survey, Exercise 1.20 (p. 23). One of the survey questions asked respondents to indicate the percentage of computer security functions that their company outsources. Consequently, the quantitative variable of interest is measured as a percentage for each of 609 respondents in the 2006 survey. The following histogram summarizes the data.

a. Which measurement class contains the highest proportion of respondents?
b. What proportion of the 609 respondents indicate that they outsource between 20% and 40% of computer security functions?

c. What proportion of the 609 respondents outsource at least 40% of computer security functions?

d. How many of the 609 respondents outsource less than 20% of computer security functions?

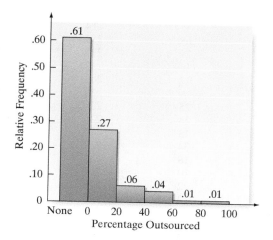

2.21 **USGA golfing handicaps.** The United States Golf Association (USGA) Handicap System is designed to allow golfers of differing abilities to enjoy fair competition. The handicap index is a measure of a player's potential scoring ability on an 18-hole golf course of standard difficulty. For example, on a par-72 course, a golfer with a handicap of 7 will typically have a score of 79 (seven strokes over par). Over 4.5 million golfers have an official USGA handicap index. The handicap indexes for both male and female golfers were obtained from the USGA and are summarized in the following two histograms.

a. What percentage of male USGA golfers have a handicap greater than 20?

b. What percentage of female USGA golfers have a handicap greater than 20?

2.22 **Sanitation inspection of cruise ships.** To minimize the potential for gastrointestinal disease outbreaks, all passenger cruise ships arriving at U.S. ports are subject to unannounced sanitation inspections. Ships are rated on a 100-point scale by the Centers for Disease Control and Prevention. A score of 86 or higher indicates that the ship is providing an accepted standard of sanitation. The latest (as of Dec. 2008) sanitation scores for 183 cruise ships are saved in the **SHIPSANIT** file. The first five and last five observations in the data set are listed in the accompanying table.

Ship Name	Sanitation Score
Adventure of the Seas	99
Albatross	94
Amsterdam	98
AIDAaura	99
Amadea	84
⋮	⋮
Westerdam	98
Wind Spirit	88
Wind Surf	95
Zaandam	99
Zuiderdam	96

Source: U.S. Department of Health and Human Services, Centers for Disease Control and Prevention/National Center for Environmental Health and Agency for Toxic Substances and Disease Registry. May 24, 2006.

a. Generate both a stem-and-leaf display and histogram of the data.

b. Use the graphs to estimate the proportion of ships that have an accepted sanitation standard. Which graph did you use?

c. Locate the inspection score of 72 (*Legacy*) on the graph. Which graph did you use?

2.23 **History of corporate acquisitions.** Refer to the *Academy of Management Journal* (Aug. 2008) study of corporate acquisitions from 1980 to 2000, Exercise 2.12 (p. 40). The data are saved in the **ACQUISITIONS** file.

a. Construct either a dot plot or a stem-and-leaf display for the annual number of firms with at least one acquisition.

b. On the graph, part **a**, highlight (or circle) the values for the years 1996–2000. Do you detect a pattern? If so, what conclusion can you draw from the data?

Applying the Concepts—Intermediate

2.24 **Most valuable NFL teams.** Each year *Forbes* reports on the value of all teams in the National Football League. Although England's soccer team, Manchester United, is the most valuable team in the world ($1.8 billion), the NFL now has 19 teams worth at least $1 billion. For 2008, *Forbes* reports that the Dallas Cowboys are the most valuable team in the NFL, worth $1.6 billion. The current values (in $ millions) of all 32 NFL teams, as well as the percentage changes in values from 2007 to 2008, debt-to-value ratios, annual revenues, and operating incomes are listed in the accompanying table. (The data are saved in the **NFLTEAMVALUES** file.)

a. Use a graph to describe the distribution of current values for the 32 NFL teams.

b. Use a graph to describe the distribution of the 1-year change in current value for the 32 NFL teams.

Rank	Team	Current Value ($ mil)	1-Yr Value Change (%)	Debt/Value (%)	Revenue ($ mil)	Operating Income ($ mil)
1	Dallas Cowboys	1,612	7	39	269	30.6
2	Washington Redskins	1,538	5	16	327	58.1
3	New England Patriots	1,324	10	21	282	39.2
4	New York Giants	1,178	21	55	214	41.2
5	New York Jets	1,170	21	68	213	25.9
6	Houston Texans	1,125	7	27	239	43.9
7	Philadelphia Eagles	1,116	6	16	237	33.5
8	Indianapolis Colts	1,076	18	4	203	16.1
9	Chicago Bears	1,064	8	9	226	33.7
10	Baltimore Ravens	1,062	10	25	226	23
11	Denver Broncos	1,061	7	14	226	18.8
12	Tampa Bay Buccaneers	1,053	9	13	224	39.3
13	Miami Dolphins	1,044	11	34	232	36.1
14	Carolina Panthers	1,040	9	18	221	22.3
15	Cleveland Browns	1,035	7	10	220	19.3
16	Green Bay Packers	1,023	10	2	218	21.9
17	Kansas City Chiefs	1,016	6	13	214	11.9
18	Pittsburgh Steelers	1,015	9	10	216	14.4
19	Seattle Seahawks	1,010	10	12	215	8.9
20	Tennessee Titans	994	8	13	216	24.5
21	Cincinnati Bengals	941	3	11	205	22
22	New Orleans Saints	937	10	13	213	21.5
23	St. Louis Rams	929	2	6	206	26.4
24	Detroit Lions	917	5	38	204	−3.1
25	Arizona Cardinals	914	3	16	203	19.7
26	San Diego Chargers	888	7	11	207	19
27	Buffalo Bills	885	8	11	206	12.4
28	Jacksonville Jaguars	876	8	13	204	27.6
29	Atlanta Falcons	872	10	31	203	30.9
30	San Francisco 49ers	865	8	12	201	4.1
31	Oakland Raiders	861	6	6	205	27
32	Minnesota Vikings	839	7	38	195	18.9

Source: "Most Valuable Teams," *Forbes,* September 11, 2008. Reprinted by permission of Forbes.com. © 2009 Forbes LLC.

c. Use a graph to describe the distribution of debt-to-value ratios for the 32 NFL teams.

d. Use a graph to describe the distribution of the annual revenues for the 32 NFL teams.

e. Use a graph to describe the distribution of operating incomes for the 32 NFL teams.

f. Compare and contrast the graphs, parts **a–e.**

2.25 Color and clarity of diamonds. Refer to the *Journal of Statistics Education* study of diamonds, Exercise 2.11 (p. 40). In addition to color and clarity, the independent certification group (GIA, HRD, or IGI) and the number of carats were recorded for each of 308 diamonds for sale on the open market. Recall that the data are saved in the **DIAMONDS** file.

a. Use a graphical method to describe the carat distribution of all 308 diamonds.

b. Use a graphical method to describe the carat distribution of diamonds certified by the GIA group.

c. Repeat part **b** for the HRD and IGI certification groups.

d. Compare the three carat distributions, parts **b** and **c.** Is there one particular certification group that appears to be assessing diamonds with higher carats than the others?

2.26 Items arriving and departing a work center. In a manufacturing plant, a *work center* is a specific production facility that consists of one or more people and/or machines and is treated as one unit for the purposes of capacity requirements planning and job scheduling. If jobs arrive at

Number of Items Arriving at Work Center per Hour											
155	115	156	150	159	163	172	143	159	166	148	175
151	161	138	148	129	135	140	152	139			

Number of Items Departing Work Center per Hour											
156	109	127	148	135	119	140	127	115	122	99	106
171	123	135	125	107	152	111	137	161			

a particular work center at a faster rate than they depart, the work center impedes the overall production process and is referred to as a *bottleneck*. The data in the table on the bottom of page 50 (saved in the **WORKCTR** file) were collected by an operations manager for use in investigating a potential bottleneck work center. Construct dot plots for the two sets of data. Do the dot plots suggest that the work center may be a bottleneck? Explain.

2.27 Environmental failures of Arkansas companies. Any corporation doing business in the United States must be aware of and obey both federal and state environmental regulations. Failure to do so may result in irreparable damage to the environment and costly financial penalties to guilty corporations. Of the 55 civil actions filed against corporations within the state of Arkansas by the U.S. Department of Justice on behalf of the Environmental Protection Agency, 38 resulted in financial penalties. These penalties along with the laws that were violated are listed in the table below and in the data saved in the **CLEANAIR** file. (*Note:* Some companies were involved in more than one civil action.)

a. Construct a stem-and-leaf display for all 38 penalties.

b. Circle the individual leaves that are associated with penalties imposed for violations of the Clean Air Act (CAA).

c. What does the pattern of circles in part **b** suggest about the severity of the penalties imposed for CAA violations relative to the other types of violations reported in the table? Explain.

2.28 Is honey a cough remedy? Coughing at night is a common symptom of an upper respiratory tract infection, yet there is no accepted therapeutic cure. Does a teaspoon of honey before bed really calm a child's cough? To test the folk remedy, pediatric researchers at Pennsylvania State University carried out a designed study conducted over two nights (*Archives of Pediatrics and Adolescent Medicine,* Dec. 2007). A sample of 105 children who were ill with an upper respiratory tract infection and their parents participated in the study. On the first

night, the parents rated their children's cough symptoms on a scale from 0 (no problems at all) to 6 (extremely severe) in five different areas. The total symptoms score (ranging from 0 to 30 points) was the variable of interest for the 105 patients. On the second night, the parents were instructed to give their

Honey Dosage:	12	11	15	11	10	13	10	4	15	16	9	14
	10	6	10	8	11	12	12	8	9	5	12	
	12	9	11	15	10	15	9	13	8	12	10	8
DM Dosage:	4	6	9	4	7	7	7	9	12	10	11	6	3
	4	9	12	7	6	8	12	12	4	12	10	15	9
	13	7	10	13	9	4	4						
No Dosage (Control):	5	8	6	1	0	8	12	8	7	7	1	6	7
	7	12	7	9	7	9	5	11	9	5	1	4	3
	6	8	8	6	7	10	9	4	8	7	3		

Source: Paul, I. M., et al. "Effect of honey, dextromethorphan, and no treatment on nocturnal cough and sleep quality for coughing children and their parents," *Archives of Pediatrics and Adolescent Medicine,* Vol. 161, No. 12, Dec. 2007 (data simulated).

Company Identification Number	Penalty	Law*	Company Identification Number	Penalty	Law*
01	$ 930,000	CERCLA	17	20,000	CWA
02	10,000	CWA	18	40,000	CWA
03	90,600	CAA	19	20,000	CWA
04	123,549	CWA	20	40,000	CWA
05	37,500	CWA	21	850,000	CWA
06	137,500	CWA	22	35,000	CWA
07	2,500	SDWA	23	4,000	CAA
08	1,000,000	CWA	24	25,000	CWA
09	25,000	CAA	25	40,000	CWA
09	25,000	CAA	26	30,000	CAA
10	25,000	CWA	27	15,000	CWA
10	25,000	RCRA	28	15,000	CAA
11	19,100	CAA	29	105,000	CAA
12	100,000	CWA	30	20,000	CWA
12	30,000	CWA	31	400,000	CWA
13	35,000	CAA	32	85,000	CWA
13	43,000	CWA	33	300,000	CWA/ RCRA/ CERCLA
14	190,000	CWA			
15	15,000	CWA			
16	90,000	RCRA	34	30,000	CWA

*CAA: Clean Air Act; CERCLA: Comprehensive Environmental Response, Compensation, and Liability Act; RCRA: Resource Conservation and Recovery Act; SDWA: Safe Drinking Water Act.

Source: Tabor, R. H. and Stanwick, S. D. "Arkansas: An environmental perspective," *Arkansas Business and Economic Review,* Vol. 28, No. 2, Summer 1995, pp. 22–32 (Table 4).

sick child a dosage of liquid "medicine" prior to bedtime. Unknown to the parents, some were given a dosage of dextromethorphan (DM)—an over-the-counter cough medicine—while others were given a similar dose of honey. Also, a third group of parents (the control group) gave their sick children no dosage at all. Again, the parents rated their children's cough symptoms, and the improvement in total cough symptoms score was determined for each child. The data (improvement scores) for the study (saved in the **HONEYCOUGH** file) are shown in the table on the previous page, followed by a Minitab dot plot of the data. Notice that the green dots represent the children who received a dose of honey, the red dots represent those who got the DM dosage, and the black dots represent the children in the control group. What conclusions can pediatric researchers draw from the graph? Do you agree with the statement (extracted from the article), "honey may be a preferable treatment for the cough and sleep difficulty associated with childhood upper respiratory tract infection"?

Applying the Concepts—Advanced

2.29 **State SAT scores.** Educators are constantly evaluating the efficacy of public schools in the education and training of American students. One quantitative assessment of change over time is the difference in scores on the SAT, which has been used for decades by colleges and universities as one criterion for admission. The file **SATSCORES** contains the average SAT scores for each of the 50 states and District of Columbia for the years 2000 and 2007. The first five observations and last two observations in the data set are shown in the table.

   a. Use graphs to display the two SAT score distributions. How have the distributions of state scores changed over time?

   b. As another method of comparing the 2000 and 2007 SAT scores, compute the *paired difference* by subtracting the 2000 score from the 2007 score for each state. Summarize these differences with a graph.

   c. Interpret the graph, part **b**. How do your conclusions compare to those of part **a**?

   d. Based on the graph, part **b**, what is the largest improvement in SAT score between 2000 and 2007? Identify the state associated with this improvement.

State	2000	2007
Alabama	1114	1119
Alaska	1034	1036
Arizona	1044	1044
Arkansas	1117	1144
California	1015	1015
⋮	⋮	⋮
Wisconsin	1181	1185
Wyoming	1090	1136

Source: "College-Bound Seniors 2008." Copyright © 2008 the College Board. www.collegeboard.com. Reproduced with permission.

2.30 **Time in bankruptcy.** Financially distressed firms can gain protection from their creditors while they restructure by filing for protection under U.S. Bankruptcy Codes. In a *prepackaged bankruptcy,* a firm negotiates a reorganization plan with its creditors prior to filing for bankruptcy. This can result in a much quicker exit from bankruptcy

than traditional bankruptcy filings. Brian Betker conducted a study of 49 prepackaged bankruptcies and reported the results in *Financial Management* (Spring 1995). The table below lists the time (in months) in bankruptcy for these 49 companies. The table also lists the results of a vote by each company's board of directors concerning their preferred reorganization plan. (*Note:* "Joint" = joint exchange offer with prepackaged bankruptcy solicitation; "Prepack" = prepackaged bankruptcy solicitation only;

Company	Prefiling Votes	Time in Bankruptcy (months)
AM International	None	3.9
Anglo Energy	Prepack	1.5
Arizona Biltmore*	Prepack	1.0
Astrex	None	10.1
Barry's Jewelers	None	4.1
Calton	Prepack	1.9
Cencor	Joint	1.4
Charter Medical*	Prepack	1.3
Cherokee*	Joint	1.2
Circle Express	Prepack	4.1
Cook Inlet Comm.	Prepack	1.1
Crystal Oil	None	3.0
Divi Hotels	None	3.2
Edgell Comm.*	Prepack	1.0
Endevco	Prepack	3.8
Gaylord Container	Joint	1.2
Great Amer. Comm.*	Prepack	1.0
Hadson	Prepack	1.5
In-Store Advertising	Prepack	1.0
JPS Textiles*	Prepack	1.4
Kendall*	Prepack	1.2
Kinder-Care	None	4.2
Kroy*	Prepack	3.0
Ladish*	Joint	1.5
LaSalle Energy*	Prepack	1.6
LIVE Entertainment	Joint	1.4
Mayflower Group*	Prepack	1.4
Memorex Telex*	Prepack	1.1
Munsingwear	None	2.9
Nat'l Environmental	Joint	5.2
Petrolane Gas	Prepack	1.2
Price Communications	None	2.4
Republic Health*	Joint	4.5
Resorts Int'l*	None	7.8
Restaurant Enterprises*	Prepack	1.5
Rymer Foods	Joint	2.1
SCI TV*	Prepack	2.1
Southland*	Joint	3.9
Specialty Equipment*	None	2.6
SPI Holdings*	Joint	1.4
Sprouse-Reitz	Prepack	1.4
Sunshine Metals	Joint	5.4
TIE/Communications	None	2.4
Trump Plaza	Prepack	1.7
Trump Taj Mahal	Prepack	1.4
Trump's Castle	Prepack	2.7
USG	Prepack	1.2
Vyquest	Prepack	4.1
West Point Acq.*	Prepack	2.9

*Leveraged buyout.

Source: Betker, B. L. "An empirical examination of prepackaged bankruptcy," *Financial Management,* Vol. 24, No. 1, Spring 1995, p. 6 (Table 2). Reprinted with permission of John Wiley & Sons, Inc.

"None" = no prefiling vote held.) (These data are saved in the **BANKRUPT** file.)

a. Construct a stem-and-leaf display for the length of time in bankruptcy for all 49 companies.

b. Summarize the information reflected in the stem-and-leaf display, part **a.** Make a general statement about the length of time in bankruptcy for firms using "prepacks."

c. Select a graphical technique that will permit a comparison of the time-in-bankruptcy distributions for the three types of "prepack" firms: those who held no prefiling vote; those who voted their preference for a joint solution; and those who voted their preference for a prepack.

d. The companies that were reorganized through a leveraged buyout are identified by an asterisk in the table. Identify these firms on the stem-and-leaf display, part **a,** by circling their bankruptcy times. Do you observe any pattern in the graph? Explain.

2.31 Phishing attacks to e-mail accounts. *Phishing* is the term used to describe an attempt to extract personal/financial information (e.g., PIN numbers, credit card information, bank account numbers) from unsuspecting people through fraudulent e-mail. An article in *Chance* (Summer 2007), demonstrates how statistics can help identify phishing attempts and make e-commerce safer. Data from an actual phishing attack against an organization were used to determine whether the attack may have been an "inside job" that originated within the company. The company set up a publicized e-mail account—called a "fraud box"—which enabled employees to notify them if they suspected an e-mail phishing attack. The interarrival times, i.e., the time differences (in seconds), for 267 fraud box e-mail notifications were recorded. *Chance* showed that if there is minimal or no collaboration or collusion from within the company, the interarrival times would have a frequency distribution similar to the one shown in the accompanying figure. The 267 interarrival times are saved in the **PHISHING** file. Construct a frequency histogram for the interarrival times. Give your opinion on whether the phishing attack against the organization was an "inside job."

2.32 Made-to-order delivery times. Production processes may be classified as *make-to-stock processes* or *make-to-order processes.* Make-to-stock processes are designed to produce a standardized product that can be sold to customers from the firm's inventory. Make-to-order processes are designed to produce products according to customer specifications (Schroeder, *Operations Management,* 2008). In general, performance of make-to-order processes is measured by delivery time—the time from receipt of an order until the product is delivered to the customer. The following data set (saved in the **DELTIMES** file) is a sample of delivery times (in days) for a particular make-to-order firm last year. The delivery times marked by an asterisk are associated with customers who subsequently placed additional orders with the firm.

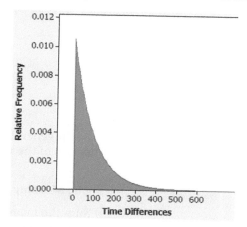

Concerned that they are losing potential repeat customers because of long delivery times, the management would like to establish a guideline for the maximum tolerable delivery time. Use a graphical method to help suggest a guideline. Explain your reasoning.

50*	64*	56*	43*	64*	82*	65*	49*	32*	63*	44*	71
54*	51*	102	49*	73*	50*	39*	86	33*	95	59*	51*
68											

2.3 Summation Notation

Now that we've examined some graphical techniques for summarizing and describing quantitative data sets, we turn to numerical methods for accomplishing this objective. Before giving the formulas for calculating numerical descriptive measures, let's look at some shorthand notation that will simplify our calculation instructions. Remember that such notation is used for one reason only—to avoid repeating the same verbal descriptions over and over. If you mentally substitute the verbal definition of a symbol each time you read it, you'll soon get used to it.

We denote the measurements of a quantitative data set as follows: $x_1, x_2, x_3, \ldots, x_n$, where x_1 is the first measurement in the data set, x_2 is the second measurement in the data set, x_3 is the third measurement in the data set, ..., and x_n is the nth (and last) measurement in the data set. Thus, if we have five measurements in a set of data, we will write x_1, x_2, x_3, x_4, x_5 to represent the measurements. If the actual numbers are 5, 3, 8, 5, and 4, we have $x_1 = 5$, $x_2 = 3$, $x_3 = 8$, $x_4 = 5$, and $x_5 = 4$.

Most of the formulas we use require a summation of numbers. For example, one sum we'll need to obtain is the sum of all the measurements in the data set, or $x_1 + x_2 + x_3 + \cdots + x_n$. To shorten the notation, we use the symbol Σ for the summation—that is, $x_1 + x_2 + x_3 + \cdots + x_n = \sum_{i=1}^{n} x_i$. Verbally translate $\sum_{i=1}^{n} x_i$ as follows: "The sum of the measurements, whose typical member is x_i, beginning with the member x_1 and ending with the member x_n."

Suppose, as in our earlier example, that $x_1 = 5$, $x_2 = 3$, $x_3 = 8$, $x_4 = 5$, and $x_5 = 4$.

Then the sum of the five measurements, denoted $\sum_{i=1}^{n} x_i$, is obtained as follows:

$$\sum_{i=1}^{5} x_i = x_1 + x_2 + x_3 + x_4 + x_5$$
$$= 5 + 3 + 8 + 5 + 4 = 25$$

Another important calculation requires that we square each measurement and then sum the squares. The notation for this sum is $\sum_{i=1}^{n} x_i^2$. For the preceding five measurements, we have

$$\sum_{i=1}^{5} x_i^2 = x_1^2 + x_2^2 + x_3^2 + x_4^2 + x_5^2$$
$$= 5^2 + 3^2 + 8^2 + 5^2 + 4^2$$
$$= 25 + 9 + 64 + 25 + 16 = 139$$

In general, the symbol following the summation sign represents the variable (or function of the variable) that is to be summed.

The Meaning of Summation Notation $\sum_{i=1}^{n} x_i$

Sum the measurements on the variable that appears to the right of the summation symbol, beginning with the 1st measurement and ending with the nth measurement.

Exercises 2.33–2.36

Learning the Mechanics

Note: In all exercises, Σ represents $\sum_{i=1}^{n}$.

2.33 A data set contains the observations 5, 1, 3, 2, 1. Find
 a. Σx
 b. Σx^2
 c. $\Sigma(x - 1)$
 d. $\Sigma(x - 1)^2$
 e. $(\Sigma x)^2$

2.34 Suppose a data set contains the observations 3, 8, 4, 5, 3, 4, 6. Find
 a. Σx
 b. Σx^2
 c. $\Sigma(x - 5)^2$

 d. $\Sigma(x - 2)^2$
 e. $(\Sigma x)^2$

2.35 Refer to Exercise 2.33. Find
 a. $\Sigma x^2 - \dfrac{(\Sigma x)^2}{5}$
 b. $\Sigma(x - 2)^2$
 c. $\Sigma x^2 - 10$

2.36 A data set contains the observations 6, 0, -2, -1, 3. Find
 a. Σx
 b. Σx^2
 c. $\Sigma x^2 - \dfrac{(\Sigma x)^2}{5}$

2.4 Numerical Measures of Central Tendency

When we speak of a data set, we refer to either a sample or a population. If statistical inference is our goal, we'll wish ultimately to use sample **numerical descriptive measures** to make inferences about the corresponding measures for the population.

As you'll see, a large number of numerical methods are available to describe quantitative data sets. Most of these methods measure one of two data characteristics:

1. The **central tendency** of the set of measurements—that is, the tendency of the data to cluster, or center, about certain numerical values (see Figure 2.14a).

2. The **variability** of the set of measurements—that is, the spread of the data (see Figure 2.14b).

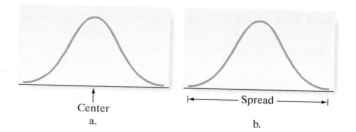

Figure 2.14
Numerical descriptive measures

In this section we concentrate on measures of central tendency. In the next section, we discuss measures of variability.

The most popular and best-understood measure of central tendency for quantitative data is the arithmetic mean (or simply the mean) of a data set.

> The **mean** of a set of quantitative data is the sum of the measurements divided by the number of measurements contained in the data set.

In everyday terms, the mean is the average value of the data set and is often used to represent a "typical" value. We denote the **mean of a sample** of measurements by $\bar{x}$ (read "x-bar") and represent the formula for its calculation as shown in the box below.

> **Formula for a Sample Mean**
>
> $$\bar{x} = \frac{\sum\limits_{i=1}^{n} x_i}{n}$$

Example 2.3

Calculating the Sample Mean

Problem Calculate the mean of the following five sample measurements: 5, 3, 8, 5, 6.

Solution Using the definition of sample mean and the summation notation, we find

$$\bar{x} = \frac{\sum\limits_{i=1}^{5} x_i}{5} = \frac{5 + 3 + 8 + 5 + 6}{5} = \frac{27}{5} = 5.4$$

Thus, the mean of this sample is 5.4.

Look Back There is no specific rule for rounding when calculating $\bar{x}$ because $\bar{x}$ is specifically defined to be the sum of all measurements divided by n—that is, it is a specific fraction. When $\bar{x}$ is used for descriptive purposes, it is often convenient to round the calculated value of $\bar{x}$ to the number of significant figures used for the original measurements. When $\bar{x}$ is to be used in other calculations, however, it may be necessary to retain more significant figures.

Now Work Exercise 2.38

Example 2.4

The Sample Mean on a Printout

Problem Calculate the sample mean for the R&D expenditure percentages of the 50 companies given in Table 2.2.

Solution The mean R&D percentage for the 50 companies is denoted

$$\bar{x} = \frac{\sum\limits_{i=1}^{50} x_i}{50}$$

We employed Excel to compute the mean. The Excel printout is shown in Figure 2.15. The sample mean, highlighted on the printout, is $\bar{x} = 8.492$.

	A	B
1	RDPct	
2		
3	Mean	8.492
4	Standard Error	0.2801
5	Median	8.05
6	Mode	6.9
7	Standard Deviation	1.980604
8	Sample Variance	3.922792
9	Kurtosis	0.419288
10	Skewness	0.854601
11	Range	8.3
12	Minimum	5.2
13	Maximum	13.5
14	Sum	424.6
15	Count	50
16		

Figure 2.15

Excel numerical descriptive measures for 50 R&D percentages

Look Back Given this information, you can visualize a distribution of R&D percentages centered in the vicinity $\bar{x} = 8.492$. An examination of the relative frequency histogram (Figure 2.10) confirms that $\bar{x}$ does, in fact, fall near the center of the distribution.

The sample mean $\bar{x}$ will play an important role in accomplishing our objective of making inferences about populations based on sample information. For this reason, we need to use a different symbol for the *mean of a population*—the mean of the set of measurements on every unit in the population. We use the Greek letter μ (mu) for the population mean.

Symbols for the Sample and Population Mean

In this text, we adopt a general policy of using Greek letters to represent population numerical descriptive measures and Roman letters to represent corresponding descriptive measures for the sample. The symbols for the mean are

$$\bar{x} = \text{Sample mean}$$
$$\mu = \text{Population mean}$$

We'll often use the sample mean $\bar{x}$ to estimate (make an inference about) the population mean, μ. For example, the percentages of revenues spent on R&D by the population consisting of *all* U.S. companies has a mean equal to some value, μ. Our sample of 50 companies yielded percentages with a mean of $\bar{x} = 8.492$. If, as is usually the case, we don't have access to the measurements for the entire population, we could use $\bar{x}$ as an estimator or approximator for μ. Then we'd need to know something about the reliability of our inference—that is, we'd need to know how accurately we might expect $\bar{x}$ to estimate μ. In Chapter 5, we'll find that this accuracy depends on two factors:

1. The *size of the sample*. The larger the sample, the more accurate the estimate will tend to be.

2. The *variability, or spread, of the data*. All other factors remaining constant, the more variable the data, the less accurate the estimate.

Another important measure of central tendency is the *median*.

The **median** of a quantitative data set is the middle number when the measurements are arranged in ascending (or descending) order.

The median is of most value in describing large data sets. If the data set is characterized by a relative frequency histogram (Figure 2.16), the median is the point on the *x*-axis such that half the area under the histogram lies above the median and half lies below. [*Note:* In Section 2.2 we observed that the relative frequency associated with a particular interval on the horizontal axis is proportional to the amount of area under the histogram that lies above the interval.] We denote the *median of a sample* by *m*.

Calculating a Sample Median, *m*

Arrange the *n* measurements from smallest to largest.

1. If *n* is odd, *m* is the middle number.

2. If *n* is even, *m* is the mean of the middle two numbers.

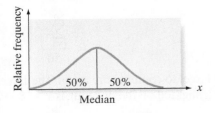

Figure 2.16

Location of the median

Example 2.5
Finding the Median

Problem Consider the following sample of $n = 7$ measurements: 5, 7, 4, 5, 20, 6, 2.

a. Calculate the median m of this sample.

b. Eliminate the last measurement (the 2) and calculate the median of the remaining $n = 6$ measurements.

Solution

a. The seven measurements in the sample are ranked in ascending order: 2, 4, 5, 5, 6, 7, 20. Because the number of measurements is odd, the median is the middle measurement. Thus, the median of this sample is $m = 5$ (the second 5 listed in the sequence).

b. After removing the 2 from the set of measurements, we rank the sample measurements in ascending order as follows: 4, 5, 5, 6, 7, 20. Now the number of measurements is even, so we average the middle two measurements. The median is $m = (5 + 6)/2 = 5.5$.

Look Back When the sample size n is even and the two middle numbers are different (as in part **b**), exactly half of the measurements will fall below the calculated median m. However, when n is odd (as in part **a**), the percentage of measurements that fall below m is approximately 50%. This approximation improves as n increases.

Now Work Exercise 2.37

In certain situations, the median may be a better measure of central tendency than the mean. In particular, the median is less sensitive than the mean to extremely large or small measurements. Note, for instance, that all but one of the measurements in part **a** of Example 2.5 center about $x = 5$. The single relatively large measurement, $x = 20$, does not affect the value of the median, 5, but it causes the mean, $\bar{x} = 7$, to lie to the right of most of the measurements.

As another example of data for which the central tendency is better described by the median than the mean, consider the salaries of professional athletes (e.g., National Basketball Association players). The presence of just a few athletes (e.g., LeBron James) with extremely high salaries will affect the mean more than the median. Thus, the median will provide a more accurate picture of the typical salary for the professional league. The mean could exceed the vast majority of the sample measurements (salaries), making it a misleading measure of central tendency.

Example 2.6
The Median on a Printout

Problem Calculate the median for the 50 R&D percentages given in Table 2.2. Compare the median to the mean found in Example 2.4.

Solution For this large data set, we again resort to a computer analysis. The median is highlighted on the Excel printout, Figure 2.15. You can see that the median is 8.05. This value implies that half of the 50 R&D percentages in the data set fall below 8.05 and half lie above 8.05.

Note that the mean (8.492) for these data is larger than the median. This fact indicates that the data are **skewed** to the right—that is, there are more extreme measurements in the right tail of the distribution than in the left tail (recall the histogram in Figure 2.10).

Look Back In general, extreme values (large or small) affect the mean more than the median because these values are used explicitly in the calculation of the mean. On the other hand, the median is not affected directly by extreme measurements because only the middle measurement (or two middle measurements) is explicitly used to calculate the median. Consequently, if measurements are pulled toward one end of the distribution (as with the R&D percentages), the mean will shift toward that tail more than the median.

A data set is said to be **skewed** if one tail of the distribution has more extreme observations than the other tail.

A comparison of the mean and the median gives us a general method for detecting skewness in data sets, as shown in the next box. With *rightward skewed* data, the right tail (high end) of the distribution has more extreme observations. These few, but large, measurements pull the mean away from the median toward the right; that is, rightward skewness indicates that the mean is greater than the median. Conversely, with *leftward skewed* data, the left tail (low end) of the distribution has more extreme observations. These few, but small, measurements also pull the mean away from the median but toward the left; consequently, leftward skewness implies that the mean is smaller than the median.

Detecting Skewness by Comparing the Mean and the Median

If the data set is skewed to the right, then the median is less than the mean.

Rightward skewness

If the data set is symmetric, the mean equals the median.

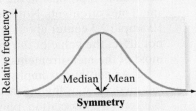

Symmetry

If the data set is skewed to the left, the mean is less than (to the left of) the median.

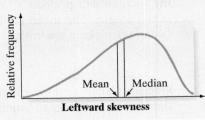

Leftward skewness

A third measure of central tendency is the *mode* of a set of measurements.

The **mode** is the measurement that occurs most frequently in the data set.

Example 2.7

Finding the Mode

Problem Each of 10 taste testers rated a new brand of barbecue sauce on a 10-point scale, where 1 = awful and 10 = excellent. Find the mode for the 10 ratings shown below.

$$8 \quad 7 \quad 9 \quad 6 \quad 8 \quad 10 \quad 9 \quad 9 \quad 5 \quad 7$$

Solution Because 9 occurs most often, the mode of the 10 taste-ratings is 9.

Look Back Note that the data are actually qualitative in nature (e.g., "awful," "excellent"). The mode is particularly useful for describing qualitative data. The modal category is simply the category (or class) that occurs most often.

Now Work Exercise 2.41

Because it emphasizes data concentration, the mode is used with quantitative data sets to locate the region in which much of the data are concentrated. A retailer of men's clothing would be interested in the modal neck size and sleeve length of potential customers. The modal income class of the laborers in the United States is of interest to the Labor Department.

For some quantitative data sets, the mode may not be very meaningful. For example, consider the percentages of revenues spent on R&D by 50 companies, Table 2.2. A reexamination of the data reveals that three of the measurements are repeated three times: 6.5%, 6.9%, and 8.2%. Thus, there are three modes in the sample, and none is particularly useful as a measure of central tendency.

A more meaningful measure can be obtained from a relative frequency histogram for quantitative data. The class interval containing the largest relative frequency is called the **modal class.** Several definitions exist for locating the position of the mode within a modal class, but the simplest is to define the mode as the midpoint of the modal class. For example, examine the relative frequency histogram for the price quote processing times in Figure 2.12. You can see that the modal class is the interval (3.0–4.0). The mode (the midpoint) is 3.5. This modal class (and the mode itself) identifies the area in which the data are most concentrated, and in that sense it is a measure of central tendency. However, for most applications involving quantitative data, the mean and median provide more descriptive information than the mode.

Example 2.8

Comparing the Mean, Median, and Mode of CEO Salaries

Problem Refer to *Forbes* magazine's "Executive Compensation Scoreboard," which lists the total annual pay for CEOs at the 500 largest U.S. firms. The data for the 2008 scoreboard, saved in the **CEOPAY2008** file, includes the quantitative variables total annual

Statistics

		PAY2008	AGE
N	Valid	497	500
	Missing	3	0
	Mean	12.87383	55.77
	Median	6.47000	56.00
	Mode	2.010ᵃ	53

a. Multiple modes exist. The smallest value is shown.

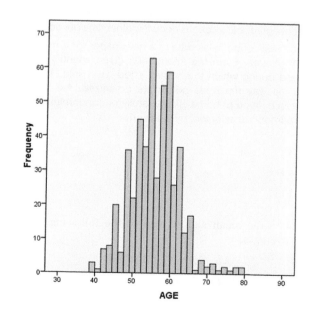

Figure 2.17

SPSS analysis of total 2008 pay and age for 500 CEOs

pay (in millions of dollars) and age. Find the mean, median, and mode for both of these variables. Which measure of central tendency is better for describing the distribution of total annual pay? Age?

Solution Measures of central tendency for the two variables were obtained using SPSS. The means, medians, and modes are displayed at the top of the SPSS printout, Figure 2.17.

For total annual pay, the mean, median, and mode are $12.87 million, $6.47 million, and $2.01 million, respectively. Note that the mean is much greater than the median, indicating that the data are highly skewed right. This rightward skewness (graphically shown on the histogram for total pay in Figure 2.17) is due to several exceptionally high CEO salaries in 2008. Consequently, we would probably want to use the median, $6.47 million, as the "typical" value for annual pay for CEOs at the 500 largest firms. The mode of $2.01 million is the total pay value that occurs most often in the data set, but it is not very descriptive of the "center" of the total annual pay distribution.

For age, the mean, median, and mode are 55.77, 56, and 53 years, respectively. All three values are nearly the same, which is typical of symmetric distributions. From the age histogram to the right in Figure 2.17, you can see that the age distribution is nearly symmetric. Consequently, any of the three measures of central tendency could be used to describe the "middle" of the age distribution.

Look Back The choice of which measure of central tendency to use will depend on the properties of the data set analyzed and on the application. Consequently, it is vital that you understand how the mean, median, and mode are computed.

Now Work Exercise 2.46a, b

Activity 2.1: *Real Estate Sales:* Measures of Central Tendency

In recent years, the price of real estate in America's major metropolitan areas has skyrocketed. Newspapers usually report recent real estate sales data in their Saturday editions, both hard copies and online. These data usually include the actual prices paid for homes by geographical location during a certain time period, usually a one-week period six to eight weeks earlier, and some summary statistics, which might include comparisons to real estate sales data in other geographical locations or during other time periods.

1. Locate the real estate sales data in a newspaper for a major metropolitan area. From the information given, identify the time period during which the homes listed were sold. Then describe the way the sales prices are organized. Are they categorized by type of home (single family or condominium), by neighborhood or address, by sales price, etc.?

2. What summary statistics and comparisons are provided with the sales data? Describe several groups of people who might be interested in this data and how each of the summary statistics and comparisons would be helpful to them. Why are the measures of central tendency listed more useful in the real estate market than other measures of central tendency?

3. Based on the lowest and highest sales prices represented in the data, create ten intervals of equal size and use these intervals to create a relative frequency histogram for the sales data. Describe the shape of the histogram and explain how the summary statistics provided with the data are illustrated in the histogram. Based on the histogram, describe the "typical" home price.

Exercises 2.37–2.55

Learning the Mechanics

2.37 Calculate the mean and median of the following grade
[NW] point averages:

$$3.2 \quad 2.5 \quad 2.1 \quad 3.7 \quad 2.8 \quad 2.0$$

2.38 Calculate the mean for samples where
[NW]
   a. $n = 10, \Sigma x = 85$
   b. $n = 16, \Sigma x = 400$

   c. $n = 45, \Sigma x = 35$
   d. $n = 18, \Sigma x = 242$

2.39 Explain how the relationship between the mean and median provides information about the symmetry or skewness of the data's distribution.

2.40 Explain the difference between the calculation of the median for an odd and an even number of measurements. Construct one data set consisting of five measurements and another consisting of six measurements for which the medians are equal.

2.41 Calculate the mode, mean, and median of the following data:

NW

18   10   15   13   17   15   12   15   18   16   11

2.42 Calculate the mean, median, and mode for each of the following samples:
  a. 7, − 2, 3, 3, 0, 4
  b. 2, 3, 5, 3, 2, 3, 4, 3, 5, 1, 2, 3, 4
  c. 51, 50, 47, 50, 48, 41, 59, 68, 45, 37

⊙ Applet Exercise 2.1

Use the applet entitled *Mean versus Median* to find the mean and median of each of the three data sets in Exercise 2.42. For each data set, set the lower limit to a number less than all of the data, set the upper limit to a number greater than all of the data, and then click on *Update*. Click on the approximate location of each data item on the number line. You can get rid of a point by dragging it to the trash can. To clear the graph between data sets, simply click on the trash can.

  a. Compare the means and medians generated by the applet to those you calculated by hand in Exercise 2.42. If there are differences, explain why the applet might give values slightly different from the hand calculations.
  b. Despite providing only approximate values of the mean and median of a data set, describe some advantages of using the applet to find these values.

2.43 Describe how the mean compares to the median for a distribution as follows:
  a. Skewed to the left
  b. Skewed to the right
  c. Symmetric

⊙ Applet Exercise 2.2

Use the applet *Mean versus Median* to illustrate your descriptions in Exercise 2.43. For each part **a, b,** and **c,** create a data set with ten items that has the given property. Using the applet, verify that the mean and median have the relationship you described in Exercise 2.43.

⊙ Applet Exercise 2.3

Use the applet *Mean versus Median* to study the effect that an extreme value has on the difference between the mean and median. Begin by setting appropriate limits and plotting the given data on the number line provided in the applet.

0   6   7   7   8   8   8   9   9   10

  a. Describe the shape of the distribution and record the value of the mean and median. Based on the shape of the distribution, do the mean and median have the relationship that you would expect?
  b. Replace the extreme value of 0 with 2, then 4, and then 6. Record the mean and median each time. Describe what is happening to the mean as 0 is replaced by higher numbers. What is happening to the median?

How is the difference between the mean and the median changing?
  c. Now replace 0 with 8. What values does the applet give you for the mean and the median? Explain why the mean and the median should be the same.

Applying the Concepts—Basic

2.44 **Spending by banks following acquisitions.** Recently there has been a flurry of mergers of major U.S. banks, including Wells Fargo's acquisition of Wachovia, JPMorgan Chase's buyout of Washington Mutual, and Bank of America's takeover of Merrill Lynch. *The Nilson Report* (Oct. 2008) ranked U.S. banks with recent acquisitions by the amount charged to credit and debit cards issued by the banks. The following table gives the total amount charged in 2007 for the top ranked banks. (The data are saved in the **BANKCHARGE** file.)

U.S. Bank/ Card Issuer	Amount Charged ($ billions)
Bank of America	462.20
JPMorgan Chase	458.84
American Express	445.32
Citigroup	240.58
Wells Fargo	192.68

Source: The Nilson Report, No. 912, October 2008 (p. 8).

  a. Find the mean amount charged for the top five banks and practically interpret this value.
  b. Find the median amount charged for the top five banks and practically interpret this value.

2.45 **U.S. wine export markets.** The data in the next table, compiled by the Center for International Trade Development (CITD), provide a listing of the top 30 U.S. export markets for sparkling wines in 2007. (These data are saved in the **WINEEXPORTS** file.) Descriptive statistics for the amount exported (thousands of dollars) and three-year percentage change for the 30 countries are shown in the Minitab printout below.
  a. Locate the mean amount exported on the printout and practically interpret its value.
  b. Locate the median amount exported on the printout and practically interpret its value.
  c. Locate the mean 3-year percentage change on the printout and practically interpret its value.
  d. Locate the median 3-year percentage change on the printout and practically interpret its value.

Descriptive Statistics: EXPORT, CHANGE

Variable	N	N*	Mean	StDev	Minimum	Q1	Median	Q3	Maximum	IQR
EXPORT	30	0	653	1113	70	105	231	523	4952	418
CHANGE	28	2	481	1098	−49	21	156	499	5750	478

Top 30 U.S. Sparkling Wine Export Markets, 2007

Country	Export ($ Thousands)	3-Year Change (%)
Canada	4952	71.9
Japan	3714	−16.9
Mexico	2104	143.2
Cayman Islands	1576	280.7
United Kingdom	1041	465.8
Netherlands	807	550.8
Germany	645	658.8
Korea	482	20.5
France	449	−48.7
Russia	351	5750
Jamaica	350	21.5
China	339	539.6
Taiwan	309	505.9
Colombia	272	159
Hong Kong	232	114.8
Aruba	229	−31.6
Australia	225	1223.5
Haiti	191	478.8
Switzerland	181	70.8
Trinidad & Tobago	175	1490.9
Costa Rica	170	NA
Panama	126	447.8
Slovenia	106	NA
Neth. Antilles	103	−41.8
Bahamas	92	−20.7
New Zealand	91	193.5
Honduras	74	51
Philippines	72	242.9
Greece	71	153.6
Belgium	70	−16.7

Source: "Best Export Markets for U.S. Wines, 2008," *Center for International Trade Development* (Table II. A-3). Used with permission of Center for International Trade Development. citd.org.

2.46 **Surface roughness of oil field pipe.** Oil field pipes are internally coated in order to prevent corrosion. Researchers at the University of Louisiana, Lafayette, investigated the influence that coating may have on the surface roughness of oil field pipes (*Anti-corrosion Methods and Materials,* Vol. 50, 2003). A scanning probe instrument was used to measure the surface roughness of each in a sample of 20 sections of coated interior pipe. The data (in micrometers) are provided in the table and saved in the **ROUGHPIPE** file.

1.72	2.50	2.16	2.13	1.06	2.24	2.31	2.03	1.09	1.40
2.57	2.64	1.26	2.05	1.19	2.13	1.27	1.51	2.41	1.95

Source: Farshad, F., and Pesacreta, T. "Coated pipe interior surface roughness as measured by three scanning probe instruments." *Anti-corrosion Methods and Materials,* Vol. 50, No. 1, 2003 (Table III). Copyright © 2003 MCB UP Ltd.

[NW] **a.** Find and interpret the mean of the sample.
[NW] **b.** Find and interpret the median of the sample.
c. Which measure of central tendency—the mean or the median—best describes the surface roughness of the sampled pipe sections? Explain.

2.47 **Is honey a cough remedy?** Refer to the *Archives of Pediatrics and Adolescent Medicine* (Dec. 2007) study of honey as a remedy for coughing, Exercise 2.28 (p. 51). Recall that the 105 ill children in the sample were randomly divided into three groups: those who received a dosage of an over-the-counter cough medicine (DM), those who received a dosage of honey (H), and those who received no dosage (control group). The coughing improvement scores (as determined by the children's parents) for the patients, reproduced in the accompanying table, are saved in the **HONEYCOUGH** file.
a. Find the median improvement score for the honey dosage group.
b. Find the median improvement score for the DM dosage group.
c. Find the median improvement score for the control group.
d. Based on the results, parts **a–c**, what conclusions can pediatric researchers draw? (We show how to support these conclusions with a measure of reliability in subsequent chapters.)

Honey Dosage:	12	11	15	11	10	13	10	4	15	16	9	14
	10	6	10	8	11	12	12	8	12	9	11	15
	10	15	9	13	8	12	10	8	9	5	12	

DM Dosage:	4	6	9	4	7	7	7	9	12	10	11	6	3	4
	9	12	7	6	8	12	12	4	12	13	7	10		
	13	9	4	4	10	15	9							

No Dosage (Control):	5	8	6	1	0	8	12	8	7	7	1	6	7	7	12
	7	9	7	9	5	11	9	5	6	8					
	8	6	7	10	9	4	8	7	3	1	4	3			

Source: Paul, I. M., et al. "Effect of honey, dextromethorphan, and no treatment on nocturnal cough and sleep quality for coughing children and their parents," *Archives of Pediatrics and Adolescent Medicine,* Vol. 161, No. 12, Dec. 2007 (data simulated).

Applying the Concepts—Intermediate

2.48 **Most powerful business women in America.** *Fortune* (Oct. 16, 2008) published a list of the 50 most powerful women in business in the United States. The data on age (in years) and title of each of these 50 women are stored in the **WPOWER50** file. The first five and last five observations of the data set are listed in the table on page 63.
a. Find the mean, median, and modal age of these 50 women.
b. What do the mean and median indicate about the skewness of the age distribution?
c. Construct a relative frequency histogram for the age data. What is the modal age class?

2.49 **Size of diamonds sold at retail.** Refer to Exercise 2.25 (p. 50) and the *Journal of Statistics Education* data on diamonds saved in the **DIAMONDS** file. Consider the quantitative variable, number of carats, recorded for each of the 308 diamonds for sale on the open market.
a. Find and interpret the mean of the data set.
b. Find and interpret the median of the data set.
c. Find and interpret the mode of the data set.
d. Which measure of central tendency best describes the 308 carat values? Explain.

Table for Exercise 2.48

Rank	Name	Age	Company	Title
1	Indra Nooyi	52	PepsiCo	CEO/Chairman
2	Irene Rosenfeld	55	Kraft Foods	CEO/Chairman
3	Pat Woertz	55	Archer Daniels Midland	CEO/Chairman
4	Anne Mulcahy	55	Xerox	CEO/Chairman
5	Angela Braley	47	Wellpoint	CEO/President
⋮		⋮	⋮	⋮
46	Lorrie Norrington	48	eBay	CEO
47	Terri Dial	58	Citigroup	CEO
48	Lynn Elsenhans	52	Sunoco	CEO/President
49	Cathie Black	64	Hearst Magazines	President
50	Marissa Mayer	33	Google	VP

Source: "50 most powerful women," *Fortune*, Oct. 16, 2008.

2.50 **Ranking driving performance of professional golfers.** A group of Northeastern University researchers developed a new method for ranking the total driving performance of golfers on the Professional Golf Association (PGA) tour. (*The Sport Journal*, Winter 2007.) The method requires knowing a golfer's average driving distance (yards) and driving accuracy (percent of drives that land in the fairway). The values of these two variables are used to compute a driving performance index. Data for the top 40 PGA golfers (as ranked by the new method) are saved in the **PGADRIVER** file. The first five and last five observations are listed in the accompanying table.

a. Find the mean, median, and mode for the 40 driving performance index values.

b. Interpret each of the measures of central tendency, part **a.**

c. Use the results, part **a,** to make a statement about the type of skewness in the distribution of driving performance indexes. Support your statement with a graph.

Rank	Player	Driving Distance (yards)	Driving Accuracy (%)	Driving Performance Index
1	Woods	316.1	54.6	3.58
2	Perry	304.7	63.4	3.48
3	Gutschewski	310.5	57.9	3.27
4	Wetterich	311.7	56.6	3.18
5	Hearn	295.2	68.5	2.82
⋮		⋮	⋮	⋮
36	Senden	291	66	1.31
37	Mickelson	300	58.7	1.30
38	Watney	298.9	59.4	1.26
39	Trahan	295.8	61.8	1.23
40	Pappas	309.4	50.6	1.17

Source: Wiseman, F., et al. "A New Method for Ranking Total Driving Performance on the PGA Tour," *The Sport Journal*, Vol. 10, No. 1, Winter 2007 (Table 2).

2.51 **Semester hours taken by CPA candidates.** In order to become a certified public accountant (CPA), you must pass the Uniform CPA Exam. Many states require a minimum of 150 semester hours of college education before a candidate can sit for the CPA exam. However, traditionally, colleges only require 128 semester hours for an undergraduate degree. A study of whether the "extra" 22 hours of college credit is warranted for CPA candidates was published in the *Journal of Accounting and Public Policy* (Spring 2002). For one aspect of the study, researchers sampled over 100,000 first-time candidates for the CPA exam and recorded the total semester hours of college credit for each candidate. The mean and median for the data set were 141.31 and 140 hours, respectively. Interpret these values. Make a statement about the type of skewness, if any, that exists in the distribution of total semester hours.

2.52 **Symmetric or skewed?** Would you expect the data sets described below to possess relative frequency distributions that are symmetric, skewed to the right, or skewed to the left? Explain.

a. The salaries of all persons employed by a large university

b. The grades on an easy test

c. The grades on a difficult test

d. The amounts of time students in your class studied last week

e. The ages of automobiles on a used-car lot

f. The amounts of time spent by students on a difficult examination (maximum time is 50 minutes)

Applying the Concepts—Advanced

2.53 **Time in bankruptcy.** Refer to the *Financial Management* (Spring 1995) study of prepackaged bankruptcy filings, Exercise 2.30 (p. 52). Recall that each of 49 firms that negotiated a reorganization plan with its creditors prior to filing for bankruptcy was classified in one of three categories: joint exchange offer with prepack, prepack solicitation only, and no prefiling vote held. Consider the quantitative variable length of time in bankruptcy (months) saved in the **BANKRUPT** file. Is it reasonable to use a single number (e.g., mean or median) to describe the center of the time-in-bankruptcy distributions? Or should three "centers" be calculated, one for each of the three categories of prepack firms? Explain.

2.54 **Active nuclear power plants.** The U.S. Energy Information Administration monitors all nuclear power plants operating in the United States. The table on the next page lists the number of active nuclear power plants operating in each of a sample of 20 states. (These data are saved in the **NUCLEAR** file.)

a. Find the mean, median, and mode of this data set.

b. Eliminate the largest value from the data set and repeat part **a.** What effect does dropping this measurement have on the measures of central tendency found in part **a?**

c. Arrange the 20 values in the table from lowest to highest. Next, eliminate the lowest two values and the highest two values from the data set and find the mean of the remaining data values. The result is called a *10% trimmed mean,* because it is calculated after removing the highest 10% and the lowest 10% of the data values. What advantages does a trimmed mean have over the regular arithmetic mean?

State	Number of Power Plants	State	Number of Power Plants
Alabama	5	New Hampshire	1
Arizona	3	New York	6
California	4	North Carolina	5
Florida	5	Ohio	3
Georgia	4	Pennsylvania	9
Illinois	11	South Carolina	7
Kansas	1	Tennessee	3
Louisiana	2	Texas	4
Massachusetts	1	Vermont	1
Mississippi	3	Wisconsin	3

Source: Statistical Abstract of the United States, 2005 (Table 906). U.S. Energy Information Administration, Electric Power Annual.

2.55   **Professional athletes' salaries.** The salaries of superstar professional athletes receive much attention in the media. The multimillion-dollar long-term contract is now commonplace among this elite group. Nevertheless, rarely does a season pass without negotiations between one or more of the players' associations and team owners for additional salary and fringe benefits for *all* players in their particular sports.

a. If a players' association wanted to support its argument for higher "average" salaries, which measure of central tendency do you think it should use? Why?

b. To refute the argument, which measure of central tendency should the owners apply to the players' salaries? Why?

2.5 Numerical Measures of Variability

Measures of central tendency provide only a partial description of a quantitative data set. The description is incomplete without a **measure of the variability,** or **spread,** of the data set. Knowledge of the data's variability along with its center can help us visualize the shape of a data set as well as its extreme values.

For example, suppose we are comparing the profit margin per construction job (as a percentage of the total bid price) for 100 construction jobs for each of two cost estimators working for a large construction company. The histograms for the two sets of 100 profit margin measurements are shown in Figure 2.18. If you examine the two histograms, you will notice that both data sets are symmetric with equal modes, medians, and means. However, cost estimator A (Figure 2.18a) has profit margins spread with almost equal relative frequency over the measurement classes, while cost estimator B (Figure 2.18b) has profit margins clustered about the center of the distribution. Thus, estimator B's profit margins are *less variable* than estimator A's. Consequently, you can see that we need a measure of variability as well as a measure of central tendency to describe a data set.

Perhaps the simplest measure of the variability of a quantitative data set is its *range*.

The **range** of a quantitative data set is equal to the largest measurement minus the smallest measurement.

Figure 2.18

Profit margin histograms for two cost estimators

a. Cost estimator A

b. Cost estimator B

Table 2.5	Two Hypothetical Data Sets	
	Sample 1	Sample 2
Measurements	$1, 2, 3, 4, 5$	$2, 3, 3, 3, 4$
Mean	$\bar{x} = \dfrac{1 + 2 + 3 + 4 + 5}{5} = \dfrac{15}{5} = 3$	$\bar{x} = \dfrac{2 + 3 + 3 + 3 + 4}{5} = \dfrac{15}{5} = 3$
Deviations of measurement values from $\bar{x}$	$(1 - 3), (2 - 3), (3 - 3), (4 - 3),$ $(5 - 3),$ or $-2, -1, 0, 1, 2$	$(2 - 3), (3 - 3), (3 - 3), (3 - 3),$ $(4 - 3),$ or $-1, 0, 0, 0, 1$

The range is easy to compute and easy to understand, but it is a rather insensitive measure of data variation when the data sets are large. This is because two data sets can have the same range and be vastly different with respect to data variation. This phenomenon is demonstrated in Figure 2.18. Although the ranges are equal and all central tendency measures are the same for these two symmetric data sets, there is an obvious difference between the two sets of measurements. The difference is that estimator B's profit margins tend to be more stable—that is, to pile up or to cluster about the center of the data set. In contrast, estimator A's profit margins are more spread out over the range, indicating a higher incidence of some high profit margins but also a greater risk of losses. Thus, even though the ranges are equal, the profit margin record of estimator A is more variable than that of estimator B, indicating a distinct difference in their cost-estimating characteristics.

Let's see if we can find a measure of data variation that is more sensitive than the range. Consider the two samples in Table 2.5: Each has five measurements. (We have ordered the numbers for convenience.)

Note that both samples have a mean of 3 and that we have also calculated the distance and direction, or *deviation*, between each measurement and the mean. What information do these deviations contain? If they tend to be large in magnitude, as in sample 1, the data are spread out, or highly variable, as shown in Figure 2.19a. If the deviations are mostly small, as in sample 2, the data are clustered around the mean, $\bar{x}$, and therefore do not exhibit much variability, as shown in Figure 2.19b. You can see that these deviations provide information about the variability of the sample measurements.

The next step is to condense the information in these deviations into a single numerical measure of variability. Averaging the deviations from $\bar{x}$ won't help because the negative and positive deviations cancel; that is, the sum of the deviations (and thus the average deviation) is always equal to zero.

Two methods come to mind for dealing with the fact that positive and negative deviations from the mean cancel. The first is to treat all the deviations as though they were positive, ignoring the sign of the negative deviations. We won't pursue this line of thought because the resulting measure of variability (the mean of the absolute values of the deviations) presents analytical difficulties beyond the scope of this text. A second method of eliminating the minus signs associated with the deviations is to square them. The quantity we can calculate from the squared deviations will provide a meaningful description of the variability of a data set and presents fewer analytical difficulties in inference making.

To use the squared deviations calculated from a data set, we first calculate the *sample variance*.

Figure 2.19
Dot plots for two data sets

The **sample variance** for a sample of n measurements is equal to the sum of the squared deviations from the mean divided by $(n - 1)$. In symbols, using s^2 to represent the sample variance,

$$s^2 = \frac{\sum_{i=1}^{n}(x_i - \bar{x})^2}{n - 1}$$

Note: A shortcut formula for calculating s^2 is

$$s^2 = \frac{\sum_{i=1}^{n} x_i^2 - \frac{\left(\sum_{i=1}^{n} x_i\right)^2}{n}}{n - 1}$$

Referring to the two samples in Table 2.5, you can calculate the variance for sample 1 as follows:

$$s^2 = \frac{(1 - 3)^2 + (2 - 3)^2 + (3 - 3)^2 + (4 - 3)^2 + (5 - 3)^2}{5 - 1}$$

$$= \frac{4 + 1 + 0 + 1 + 4}{4} = 2.5$$

The second step in finding a meaningful measure of data variability is to calculate the *standard deviation* of the data set.

The **sample standard deviation, s,** is defined as the positive square root of the sample variance, s^2. Thus, $s = \sqrt{s^2}$.

The population variance, denoted by the symbol σ^2 (sigma squared), is the average of the squared distances of the measurements on *all* units in the population from the mean, μ, and σ (sigma) is the square root of this quantity. Because we never really compute σ^2 or σ from the population (the object of sampling is to the avoid this costly procedure), we simply denote these two quantities by their respective symbols.

Symbols for Variance and Standard Deviation

s^2 = Sample variance

s = Sample standard deviation

σ^2 = Population variance

σ = Population standard deviation

Notice that, unlike the variance, the standard deviation is expressed in the original units of measurement. For example, if the original measurements are in dollars, the variance is expressed in the peculiar units "dollars squared," but the standard deviation is expressed in dollars.

You may wonder why we use the divisor $(n - 1)$ instead of n when calculating the sample variance. Wouldn't using n be more logical so that the sample variance would be the average squared deviation from the mean? The trouble is that using n tends to produce an underestimate of the population variance, σ^2, so we use $(n - 1)$ in the denominator to provide the appropriate correction for this tendency.* Because sample statistics such as s^2 are primarily used to estimate population parameters such as σ^2, $(n - 1)$ is preferred to n when defining the sample variance.

Example 2.9
Computing Measures of Variation

Problem Calculate the variance and standard deviation of the following sample: 2, 3, 3, 3, 4.

Solution If you calculate the values of s and s^2 using the formula in the box at the top of page 66, you first need to compute $\bar{x}$. From the table below, we see that $\Sigma x = 15$. Thus, $\bar{x} = \dfrac{\Sigma x}{n} = \dfrac{15}{5} = 3$. Now, for each measurement, find $(x - \bar{x})$ and $(x - \bar{x})^2$, as shown.

x	$(x - \bar{x})$	$(x - \bar{x})^2$
2	-1	1
3	0	0
3	0	0
3	0	0
4	1	1
$\Sigma x = 15$		$\Sigma(x - \bar{x})^2 = 2$

Then we use[†]

$$s^2 = \frac{\sum_{i=1}^{n}(x - \bar{x})^2}{n - 1} = \frac{2}{5 - 1} = \frac{2}{4} = .5$$

$$s = \sqrt{.5} = .71$$

Look Back As the sample size n increases, these calculations can become very tedious. As the next example shows, we can use the computer to find   and s.

Now Work Exercise 2.57

Example 2.10
Measures of Variation on the Computer

Problem Use the computer to find the sample variance s^2 and the sample standard deviation s for the 50 companies' percentages of revenues spent on R&D.

Solution The Excel printout describing the R&D percentage data is reproduced in Figure 2.20. The variance and standard deviation, highlighted on the printout, are $s^2 = 3.922792$ and $s = 1.980604$.

	A	B
1	RDPct	
2		
3	Mean	8.492
4	Standard Error	0.2801
5	Median	8.05
6	Mode	6.9
7	Standard Deviation	1.980604
8	Sample Variance	3.922792
9	Kurtosis	0.419288
10	Skewness	0.854601
11	Range	8.3
12	Minimum	5.2
13	Maximum	13.5
14	Sum	424.6
15	Count	50
16		

Figure 2.20

Reproduction of Excel numerical descriptive measures for 50 R&D percentages

You now know that the standard deviation measures the variability of a set of data. The larger the standard deviation, the more variable the data. The smaller the standard deviation, the less variable the data. But how can we practically interpret the standard deviation and use it to make inferences? This is the topic of Section 2.6

Appropriate here means that s^2 with the divisor $(n - 1)$ is an *unbiased estimator* of σ^2. We define and discuss *unbiasedness* of estimators in Chapter 4.

[†]When calculating s^2, how many decimal places should you carry? Although there are no rules for the rounding procedure, it's reasonable to retain twice as many decimal places in s^2 as you ultimately wish to have in s. If you wish to calculate s to the nearest hundredth (two decimal places), for example, you should calculate s^2 to the nearest ten-thousandth (four decimal places).

Activity 2.2:	*Keep the Change:* Measures of Central Tendency and Variability

In this activity, we continue our study of the Bank of America *Keep the Change* savings program by looking at the measures of central tendency and variability for the three data sets collected in Activity 1.1 (p. 16).

1. Before performing any calculations, explain why you would expect greater variability in the data set *Purchase Totals* than in *Amounts Transferred.* Then find the mean and median of each of these two data sets. Are the mean and median essentially the same for either of these sets? If so, which one? Can you offer an explanation for these results?

2. Make a histogram for each of the data sets *Amounts Transferred* and *Bank Matching.* Describe any properties of the data that are evident in the histograms. Explain why it is more likely that *Bank Matching* is skewed to the right than

Amounts Transferred. Based on your data and histogram, how concerned does Bank of America need to be about matching the maximum amount of $250 for its customers who are college students?

3. Form a fourth data set *Mean Amounts Transferred* by collecting the mean of the data set *Amounts Transferred* for each student in your class. Before performing any calculations, inspect the new data and describe any trends that you notice. Then find the mean and standard deviation of *Mean Amounts Transferred.* How close is the mean to $0.50? Without performing further calculations, determine whether the standard deviation of *Amounts Transferred* is less than or greater than the standard deviation of *Mean Amounts Transferred.* Explain.

Keep your results from this activity for use in other activities.

Exercises 2.56–2.70

Learning the Mechanics

2.56 Answer the following questions about variability of data sets:
   a. What is the primary disadvantage of using the range to compare the variability of data sets?
   b. Describe the sample variance using words rather than a formula. Do the same with the population variance.
   c. Can the variance of a data set ever be negative? Explain. Can the variance ever be smaller than the standard deviation? Explain.

2.57 Calculate the range, variance, and standard deviation for
[NW] the following samples:
   a. 4, 2, 1, 0, 1
   b. 1, 6, 2, 2, 3, 0, 3
   c. 8, −2, 1, 3, 5, 4, 4, 1, 3, 3
   d. 0.2, 0, 0, −1, 1, −2, 1, 0, −1, 1, −1, 0, −3, −2, −1, 0, 1

2.58 Calculate the variance and standard deviation for samples where
   a. $n = 10$, $\Sigma x^2 = 84$, $\Sigma x = 20$
   b. $n = 40$, $\Sigma x^2 = 380$, $\Sigma x = 100$
   c. $n = 20$, $\Sigma x^2 = 18$, $\Sigma x = 17$

⚫ Applet Exercise 2.4

Use the applet entitled *Standard Deviation* to find the standard deviation of each of the four data sets in Exercise 2.57. For each data set, set the lower limit to a number less than all of the data, set the upper limit to a number greater than all of the data, and then click on *Update.* Click on the approximate location of each data item on the number line. You can get rid of a point by dragging it to the trash can. To clear the graph between data sets, simply click on the trash can.
   a. Compare the standard deviations generated by the applet to those you calculated by hand in Exercise 2.57. If there are differences, explain why the applet might give values slightly different from the hand calculations.
   b. Despite providing a slightly different value of the standard deviation of a data set, describe some advantages of using the applet.

2.59 Compute $\bar{x}$, s^2, and s for each of the following data sets. If appropriate, specify the units in which your answer is expressed.

   a. 3, 1, 10, 10, 4
   b. 8 feet, 10 feet, 32 feet, 5 feet
   c. −1, −4, −3, 1, −4, −4
   d. $\frac{1}{5}$ ounce, $\frac{1}{5}$ ounce, $\frac{1}{5}$ ounce, $\frac{2}{5}$ ounce, $\frac{1}{5}$ ounce, $\frac{4}{5}$ ounce,

2.60 Calculate the range, variance, and standard deviation for the following samples:
   a. 39, 42, 40, 37, 41
   b. 100, 4, 7, 96, 80, 3, 1, 10, 2
   c. 100, 4, 7, 30, 80, 30, 42, 2

2.61 Using only integers between 0 and 10, construct two data sets with at least 10 observations each that have the same range but different means. Construct a dot plot for each of your data sets, and mark the mean of each data set on its dot diagram.

2.62 Using only integers between 0 and 10, construct two data sets with at least 10 observations each so that the two sets have the same mean but different variances. Construct dot plots for each of your data sets and mark the mean of each data set on its dot diagram.

2.63 Consider the following sample of five measurements: 2, 1, 1, 0, 3.
   a. Calculate the range, s^2, and s.
   b. Add 3 to each measurement and repeat part **a.**
   c. Subtract 4 from each measurement and repeat part **a.**
   d. Considering your answers to parts **a, b,** and **c,** what seems to be the effect on the variability of a data set by adding the same number to or subtracting the same number from each measurement?

⚫ Applet Exercise 2.5

Use the applet *Standard Deviation* to study the effect that multiplying or dividing each number in a data set by the same number has on the standard deviation. Begin by setting appropriate limits and plotting the given data on the number line provided in the applet.

0 1 1 1 2 2 3 4

a. Record the standard deviation. Then multiply each data item by 2, plot the new data items, and record the standard deviation. Repeat the process, first multiplying each of the original data items by 3 and then by 4. Describe what is happening to the standard deviation as the data items are multiplied by higher numbers. Divide each standard deviation by the standard deviation of the original data set. Do you see a pattern? Explain.

b. Divide each of the original data items by 2, plot the new data, and record the standard deviation. Repeat the process, first dividing each of the original data items by 3 and then by 4. Describe what is happening to the standard deviation as the data items are divided by higher numbers. Divide each standard deviation by the standard deviation of the original data set. Do you see a pattern? Explain.

c. Using your results from parts **a** and **b,** describe what happens to the standard deviation of a data set when each of the data items in the set is multiplied or divided by a fixed number n. Experiment by repeating parts **a** and **b** for other data sets if you need to.

Applet Exercise 2.6

Use the applet *Standard Deviation* to study the effect that an extreme value has on the standard deviation. Begin by setting appropriate limits and plotting the given data on the number line provided in the applet.

0 6 7 7 8 8 8 9 9 10

a. Record the standard deviation. Replace the extreme value of 0 with 2, then 4, and then 6. Record the standard deviation each time. Describe what is happening to the standard deviation as 0 is replaced by higher numbers.

b. How would the standard deviation of the data set compare to the original standard deviation if the 0 were replaced by 16? Explain.

Applying the Concepts—Basic

2.64 **Spending by banks following acquisitions.** Refer to *The Nilson Report* (Oct. 2008) study of the amount charged to credit and debit cards issued by U.S. banks with recent acquisitions, Exercise 2.44 (p. 61). The data for the five top-ranked banks, reproduced in the table, are saved in the **BANKCHARGE** file.

U.S. Bank/ Card Issuer	Amount Charged ($ billions)
Bank of America	462.20
JPMorgan Chase	458.84
American Express	445.32
Citigroup	240.58
Wells Fargo	192.68

Source: The Nilson Report, No. 912, October 2008 (p. 8).

a. Find the range of the data for the five top-ranked banks. Give the units of measurement for the range.

b. Find the variance of the data for the five top-ranked banks. If possible, give the units of measurement for the variance.

c. Find the standard deviation of the data for the five top-ranked banks. Give the units of measurement for the standard deviation.

2.65 **U.S. wine export markets.** Refer to the data on the top 30 U.S. export markets for sparkling wines, compiled by the Center for International Trade Development (CITD), given in Exercise 2.45 (p. 61). (These data are saved in the **WINEEXPORTS** file.) The Minitab descriptive statistics printout for the amount exported (thousands of dollars) and three-year percentage change for the 30 countries is reproduced below.

Descriptive Statistics: EXPORT, CHANGE

Variable	N	N*	Mean	StDev	Minimum	Q1	Median	Q3	Maximum	IQR
EXPORT	30	0	653	1113	70	105	231	523	4952	418
CHANGE	28	2	481	1098	-49	21	156	499	5750	478

a. Use the information on the printout to find the range of the amount exported.

b. Locate the standard deviation of the amount exported on the printout.

c. Use the result, part **b,** to find the variance of the amount exported.

2.66 **Is honey a cough remedy?** Refer to the *Archives of Pediatrics and Adolescent Medicine* (Dec. 2007) study of honey as a remedy for coughing, Exercises 2.28 and 2.47 (pp. 51, 62). The coughing improvement scores (as determined by the children's parents) for the patients in the over-the-counter cough medicine dosage (DM) group, honey dosage group, and control group are reproduced in the accompanying table. (These data are saved in the **HONEYCOUGH** file.)

a. Find the standard deviation of the improvement scores for the honey dosage group.

b. Find the standard deviation of the improvement scores for the DM dosage group.

c. Find the standard deviation of the improvement scores for the control group.

d. Based on the results, parts **a–c,** which group appears to have the most variability in coughing improvement scores? The least variability?

Honey Dosage:	12	11	15	11	10	13	10	4	15	16	9
	14	10	6	10	8	11	12	12	8		
	12	9	11	15	10	15	9	13	8	12	10
	8	9	5	12							
DM Dosage:	4	6	9	4	7	7	7	9	12	10	11	6
	3	4	9	12	7	6	8	12	12	4	12	
	13	7	10	13	9	4	4	10	15	9		
No Dosage (Control):	5	8	6	1	0	8	12	8	7	7	1	6
	7	7	12	7	9	7	9	5	11	9	5	
	6	8	8	6	7	10	9	4	8	7	3	1	4	3

Source: Paul, I. M., et al. "Effect of honey, dextromethorphan, and no treatment on nocturnal cough and sleep quality for coughing children and their parents," Archives of Pediatrics and Adolescent Medicine, Vol. 161, No. 12, Dec. 2007 (data simulated).

Applying the Concepts—Intermediate

2.67 **Size of diamonds sold at retail.** Refer to Exercise 2.25 (p. 50) and the *Journal of Statistics Education* data on diamonds saved in the **DIAMONDS** file. Consider the data on the number of carats for each of the 308 diamonds.

a. Find the range of the data set.

b. Find the variance of the data set.

c. Find the standard deviation of the data set.

d. Which measure of variation best describes the spread of the 308 carat values? Explain.

2.68   Most powerful women in America. Refer to Exercise 2.48 (p. 62) and *Fortune*'s (Oct. 16, 2008) list of the 50 most powerful women in America. The data are stored in the **WPOWER50** file.

a. Find the range of the ages for these 50 women.

b. Find the variance of the ages for these 50 women.

c. Find the standard deviation of the ages for these 50 women.

d. Suppose the standard deviation of the ages of the most powerful women in Europe is 10 years. For which location, the United States or Europe, is the age data more variable?

2.69   Active nuclear power plants. Refer to Exercise 2.54 (p. 63) and the U.S. Energy Information Administration's data on the number of nuclear power plants operating in each of 20 states. The data are saved in the **NUCLEAR** file.

a. Find the range, variance, and standard deviation of this data set.

b. Eliminate the largest value from the data set and repeat part **a**. What effect does dropping this measurement have on the measures of variation found in part **a**?

c. Eliminate the smallest and largest value from the data set and repeat part **a**. What effect does dropping both of these measurements have on the measures of variation found in part **a**?

Applying the Concepts—Advanced

2.70   Estimating production time. A widely used technique for estimating the length of time it takes workers to produce a product is the **time study.** In a time study, the task to be

studied is divided into measurable parts, and each is timed with a stopwatch or filmed for later analysis. For each worker, this process is repeated many times for each subtask. Then the average and standard deviation of the time required to complete each subtask are computed for each worker. A worker's overall time to complete the task under study is then determined by adding his or her subtask-time averages (Gaither and Frazier, *Operations Management*, 2001). The data (in minutes) given in the table are the result of a time study of a production operation involving two subtasks. (These data are saved in the **TIMESTUDY** file.)

a. Find the overall time it took each worker to complete the manufacturing operation under study.

b. For each worker, find the standard deviation of the seven times for subtask 1.

c. In the context of this problem, what are the standard deviations you computed in part **b** measuring?

d. Repeat part **b** for subtask 2.

e. If you could choose workers similar to A or workers similar to B to perform subtasks 1 and 2, which type would you assign to each subtask? Explain your decisions on the basis of your answers to parts **a–d.**

	Worker A		Worker B	
Repetition	Subtask 1	Subtask 2	Subtask 1	Subtask 2
1	30	2	31	7
2	28	4	30	2
3	31	3	32	6
4	38	3	30	5
5	25	2	29	4
6	29	4	30	1
7	30	3	31	4

2.6 Interpreting the Standard Deviation

We've seen that if we are comparing the variability of two samples selected from a population, the sample with the larger standard deviation is the more variable of the two. Thus, we know how to interpret the standard deviation on a relative or comparative basis, but we haven't explained how it provides a measure of variability for a single sample.

To understand how the standard deviation provides a measure of variability of a data set, consider a specific data set and answer the following questions: How many measurements are within 1 standard deviation of the mean? How many measurements are within 2 standard deviations? For a specific data set, we can answer these questions by counting the number of measurements in each of the intervals. However, if we are interested in obtaining a general answer to these questions, the problem is more difficult.

Tables 2.6 and 2.7 give two sets of answers to the questions of how many measurements fall within 1, 2, and 3 standard deviations of the mean. The first, which applies to *any* set of data, is derived from a theorem proved by the Russian mathematician P. L. Chebyshev. The second, which applies to **mound-shaped,** symmetric distributions of data (where the mean, median, and mode are all about the same), is based upon empirical evidence that has accumulated over the years. However, the percentages given for the intervals in Table 2.7 provide remarkably good approximations even when the distribution of the data is slightly skewed or asymmetric. Note that both rules apply to either population data sets or sample data sets.

Table 2.6	Interpreting the Standard Deviation: Chebyshev's Rule

Chebyshev's Rule applies to any data set, regardless of the shape of the frequency distribution of the data.

a. No useful information is provided on the fraction of measurements that fall within 1 standard deviation of the mean [i.e., within the interval $(\bar{x} - s, \bar{x} + s)$ for samples and $(\mu - \sigma, \mu + \sigma)$ for populations].

b. At least $3/4$ will fall within 2 standard deviations of the mean [i.e., within the interval $(\bar{x} - 2s, \bar{x} + 2s)$ for samples and $(\mu - 2\sigma, \mu + 2\sigma)$ for populations].

c. At least $8/9$ of the measurements will fall within 3 standard deviations of the mean [i.e., within the interval $(\bar{x} - 3s, \bar{x} + 3s)$ for samples and $(\mu - 3\sigma, \mu + 3\sigma)$ for populations].

d. Generally, for any number k greater than 1, at least $(1 - 1/k^2)$ of the measurements will fall within k standard deviations of the mean [i.e., within the interval $(\bar{x} - ks, \bar{x} + ks)$ for samples and $(\mu - k\sigma, \mu + k\sigma)$ for populations].

Table 2.7	Interpreting the Standard Deviation: The Empirical Rule

The **Empirical Rule** is a rule of thumb that applies to data sets with frequency distributions that are mound-shaped and symmetric, as shown below.

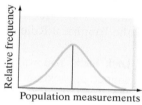

a. Approximately 68% of the measurements will fall within 1 standard deviation of the mean [i.e., within the interval $(\bar{x} - s, \bar{x} + s)$ for samples and $(\mu - \sigma, \mu + \sigma)$ for populations].

b. Approximately 95% of the measurements will fall within 2 standard deviations of the mean [i.e., within the interval $(\bar{x} - 2s, \bar{x} + 2s)$ for samples and $(\mu - 2\sigma, \mu + 2\sigma)$ for populations].

c. Approximately 99.7% (essentially all) of the measurements will fall within 3 standard deviations of the mean [i.e., within the interval $(\bar{x} - 3s, \bar{x} + 3s)$ for samples and $(\mu - 3\sigma, \mu + 3\sigma)$ for populations].

BIOGRAPHY PAFNUTY L. CHEBYSHEV (1821–1894)

The Splendid Russian Mathematician

P. L. Chebyshev was educated in mathematical science at Moscow University, eventually earning his master's degree. Following his graduation, Chebyshev joined St. Petersburg (Russia) University as a professor, becoming part of the well-known "Petersburg mathematical school." It was here that Chebyshev proved his famous theorem about the probability of a measurement being within k standard deviations of the mean (Table 2.6). His fluency in French allowed him to gain international recognition in probability theory. In fact, Chebyshev once objected to being described as a "splendid Russian mathematician," saying he surely was a "worldwide mathematician." One student remembered Chebyshev as "a wonderful lecturer" who "was always prompt for class," and "as soon as the bell sounded, he immediately dropped the chalk, and, limping, left the auditorium." ■

Example 2.11

Interpreting the Standard Deviation

Problem The 50 companies' percentages of revenues spent on R&D are repeated in Table 2.8. We have previously shown (see Figure 2.20, p. 67) that the mean and standard deviation of these data (rounded) are 8.49 and 1.98, respectively. Calculate the fraction of these measurements that lie within the intervals $\bar{x} \pm s$, $\bar{x} \pm 2s$, and $\bar{x} \pm 3s$ and compare the results with those predicted in Tables 2.6 and 2.7.

Solution We first form the interval

$$(\bar{x} - s, \bar{x} + s) = (8.49 - 1.98, 8.49 + 1.98) = (6.51, 10.47)$$

A check of the measurements reveals that 34 of the 50 measurements, or 68%, are within 1 standard deviation of the mean.

Table 2.8		R&D Percentages for 50 Companies							
13.5	9.5	8.2	6.5	8.4	8.1	6.9	7.5	10.5	13.5
7.2	7.1	9.0	9.9	8.2	13.2	9.2	6.9	9.6	7.7
9.7	7.5	7.2	5.9	6.6	11.1	8.8	5.2	10.6	8.2
11.3	5.6	10.1	8.0	8.5	11.7	7.1	7.7	9.4	6.0
8.0	7.4	10.5	7.8	7.9	6.5	6.9	6.5	6.8	9.5

🔵 Data Set: R&D

The next interval of interest,

$$(\bar{x} - 2s, \bar{x} + 2s) = (8.49 - 3.96, 8.49 + 3.96) = (4.53, 12.45),$$

contains 47 of the 50 measurements, or 94%.

Finally, the 3-standard-deviation interval around $\bar{x}$,

$$(\bar{x} - 3s, \bar{x} + 3s) = (8.49 - 5.94, 8.49 + 5.94) = (2.55, 14.43),$$

contains all, or 100%, of the measurements.

In spite of the fact that the distribution of these data is skewed to the right (see Figure 2.10, p. 44), the percentages within 1, 2, and 3 standard deviations (68%, 94%, and 100%) agree very well with the approximations of 68%, 95%, and 99.7% given by the Empirical Rule (Table 2.7).

Look Back You will find that unless the distribution is extremely skewed, the mound-shaped approximations will be reasonably accurate. Of course, no matter what the shape of the distribution, Chebyshev's Rule (Table 2.6) assures that at least 75% and at least 89% of the measurements will lie within 2 and 3 standard deviations of the mean, respectively.

Now Work Exercise 2.74

Example 2.12

Check on the Calculation of s

Problem Chebyshev's Rule and the Empirical Rule are useful as a check on the calculation of the standard deviation. For example, suppose we calculated the standard deviation for the R&D percentages (Table 2.8) to be 3.92. Are there any "clues" in the data that enable us to judge whether this number is reasonable?

Solution The range of the R&D percentages in Table 2.8 is $13.5 - 5.2 = 8.3$. From Chebyshev's Rule and the Empirical Rule we know that most of the measurements (approximately 95% if the distribution is mound-shaped) will be within 2 standard deviations of the mean. And, regardless of the shape of the distribution and the number of measurements, almost all of them will fall within 3 standard deviations of the mean. Consequently, we would expect the range of the measurements to be between 4 (i.e., $\pm 2s$) and 6 (i.e., $\pm 3s$) standard deviations in length (see Figure 2.21).

For the R&D data, this means that s should fall between

$$\frac{\text{Range}}{6} = \frac{8.3}{6} = 1.38 \quad \text{and} \quad \frac{\text{Range}}{4} = \frac{8.3}{4} = 2.08$$

In particular, the standard deviation should not be much larger than $1/4$ of the range, particularly for the data set with 50 measurements. Thus, we have reason to believe that the calculation of 3.92 is too large. A check of our work reveals that 3.92 is the variance s^2, not the standard deviation s (see Example 2.10). We "forgot" to take the square root (a common error); the correct value is $s = 1.98$. Note that this value is between $1/6$ and $1/4$ of the range.

Look Back In examples and exercises we'll sometimes use $s \approx \text{range}/4$ to obtain a crude, and usually conservatively large, approximation for s. However, we stress that this is no substitute for calculating the exact value of s when possible.

Now Work Exercise 2.75

Figure 2.21
The relation between the range and the standard deviation

In the next example, we use the concepts in Chebyshev's Rule and the Empirical Rule to build the foundation for statistical inference making.

Example 2.13

Making a Statistical Inference

Problem A manufacturer of automobile batteries claims that the average length of life for its grade A battery is 60 months. However, the guarantee on this brand is for just 36 months. Suppose the standard deviation of the life length is known to be 10 months, and the frequency distribution of the life-length data is known to be mound-shaped.

a. Approximately what percentage of the manufacturer's grade A batteries will last more than 50 months, assuming the manufacturer's claim is true?

b. Approximately what percentage of the manufacturer's batteries will last less than 40 months, assuming the manufacturer's claim is true?

c. Suppose your battery lasts 37 months. What could you infer about the manufacturer's claim?

Solution If the distribution of life length is assumed to be mound-shaped with a mean of 60 months and a standard deviation of 10 months, it would appear as shown in Figure 2.22. Note that we can take advantage of the fact that mound-shaped distributions are (approximately) symmetric about the mean, so that the percentages given by the Empirical Rule can be split equally between the halves of the distribution on each side of the mean.

For example, because approximately 68% of the measurements will fall within 1 standard deviation of the mean, the distribution's symmetry implies that approximately $\frac{1}{2}(68\%) = 34\%$ of the measurements will fall between the mean and 1 standard deviation on each side. This concept is illustrated in Figure 2.22. The figure also shows that 2.5% of the measurements lie beyond 2 standard deviations in each direction from the mean. This result follows from the fact that if approximately 95% of the measurements fall within 2 standard deviations of the mean, then about 5% fall outside 2 standard deviations; if the distribution is approximately symmetric, then about 2.5% of the measurements fall beyond 2 standard deviations on each side of the mean.

a. It is easy to see in Figure 2.22 that the percentage of batteries lasting more than 50 months is approximately 34% (between 50 and 60 months) plus 50% (greater than 60 months). Thus, approximately 84% of the batteries should have life length exceeding 50 months.

b. The percentage of batteries that last less than 40 months can also be easily determined from Figure 2.22. Approximately 2.5% of the batteries should fail prior to 40 months, assuming the manufacturer's claim is true.

c. If you are so unfortunate that your grade A battery fails at 37 months, you can make one of two inferences: either your battery was one of the approximately 2.5% that fail prior to 40 months, or something about the manufacturer's claim is not true. Because the chances are so small that a battery fails before 40 months, you would have good reason to have serious doubts about the manufacturer's claim. A mean

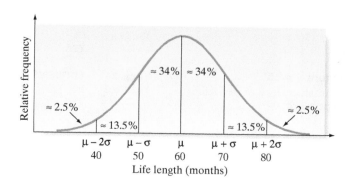

Figure 2.22

Battery life-length distribution: Manufacturer's claim assumed true smaller than 60 months and/or a standard deviation longer than 10 months would both increase the likelihood of failure prior to 40 months.*

Look Back The approximations given in Figure 2.22 are more dependent on the assumption of a mound-shaped distribution than those given by the Empirical Rule (Table 2.7) because the approximations in Figure 2.22 depend on the (approximate) symmetry of the mound-shaped distribution. We saw in Example 2.11 that the Empirical Rule can yield good approximations even for skewed distributions. This will *not* be true of the approximations in Figure 2.22; the distribution *must* be mound-shaped and approximately symmetric.

Example 2.13 is our initial demonstration of the statistical inference-making process. At this point you should realize that we'll use sample information (in Example 2.13, your battery's failure at 37 months) to make inferences about the population (in Example 2.13, the manufacturer's claim about the life length for the population of all batteries). We'll build on this foundation as we proceed.

Statistics IN Action   Revisited   Interpreting Numerical Descriptive Measures

We return to the analysis of length of time in practice for two groups of University Community Hospital physicians—those who indicate they are willing to use ethics consultation and those who would not use ethics consultation. Recall that the researchers propose that nonusers of ethics consultation will be more experienced than users. The Minitab descriptive statistics printout for the **ETHICS** data is displayed in Figure SIA2.5, with the means and standard deviations highlighted.

The sample mean for ethics consultation (EC) nonusers is 16.43, and the mean for EC users is 14.18. Our interpretation is that nonusers have slightly more experience (16.43 years, on average) than users (14.18 years, on average).

To interpret the standard deviation, we substitute into the formula, mean ± 2(standard deviation), to obtain the intervals:

EC Nonusers:

$$16.43 \pm 2(10.05) = 16.43 \pm 20.10 = (-3.67, 36.53)$$

EC Users:

$$14.18 \pm 2(8.95) = 14.18 \pm 17.90 = (-3.72, 32.08)$$

Because years of experience cannot take on a negative value, essentially the standard deviation intervals for EC nonusers and EC users are (0, 36.53) (0, 32.08), respectively.

From Chebyshev's Rule (Table 2.6), we know that at least 75% of the physicians who would not use ethics consultation will have anywhere between 0 and 36.5 years of experience. Similarly, we know that at least 75% of the EC users will have anywhere from 0 to 32.08 years of experience. Note that these ranges indicate that there is very little difference in the experience distributions of the two groups of physicians. However, if a physician on staff has 35 years of experience, it is very unlikely that the doctor would use ethics consultation because 35 years is above the mean ± 2(standard deviation) interval for EC users. Rather, the experience value of 35 is more likely to come from the distribution of years of experience for nonusers of ethics consultation.

 Data Set: ETHICS

Descriptive Statistics: YRSPRAC

Variable	FUTUREUSE	N	N*	Mean	SE Mean	StDev	Variance	Minimum	Q1
YRSPRAC	NO	21	2	16.43	2.19	10.05	100.96	1.00	7.50
	YES	91	4	14.176	0.938	8.950	80.102	1.000	7.000

Variable	FUTUREUSE	Median	Q3	Maximum
YRSPRAC	NO	18.00	25.00	35.00
	YES	14.000	20.000	40.000

Figure SIA2.5
Minitab analysis of physicians' experience

---

*The assumption that the distribution is mound-shaped and symmetric may also be incorrect. However, if the distribution were skewed to the right, as life-length distributions often tend to be, the percentage of measurements more than 2 standard deviations *below* the mean would be even less than 2.5%.

Exercises 2.71–2.87

Learning the Mechanics

2.71 The output from a statistical software package indicates that the mean and standard deviation of a data set consisting of 200 measurements are $1,500 and $300, respectively.

    a. What are the units of measurement of the variable of interest? Based on the units, what type of data is this: quantitative or qualitative?

    b. What can be said about the number of measurements between $900 and $2,100? Between $600 and $2,400? Between $1,200 and $1,800? Between $1,500 and $2,100?

2.72 For any set of data, what can be said about the percentage of the measurements contained in each of the following intervals?

    a. $\bar{x} - s$ to $\bar{x} + s$

    b. $\bar{x} - 2s$ to $\bar{x} + 2s$

    c. $\bar{x} - 3s$ to $\bar{x} + 3s$

2.73 For a set of data with a mound-shaped relative frequency distribution, what can be said about the percentage of the measurements contained in each of the intervals specified in Exercise 2.72?

2.74 The following (saved in the **LM2_74** file) is a sample of 25 [NW] measurements:

7	6	6	11	8	9	11	9	10	8	7	7	
5	9	10	7	7	7	7	9	12	10	10	8	6

    a. Compute $\bar{x}$, s^2, and s for this sample.

    b. Count the number of measurements in the intervals $\bar{x} \pm s$, $\bar{x} \pm 2s$, $\bar{x} \pm 3s$. Express each count as a percentage of the total number of measurements.

    c. Compare the percentages found in part **b** to the percentages given by the Empirical Rule and Chebyshev's Rule.

    d. Calculate the range and use it to obtain a rough approximation for s. Does the result compare favorably with the actual value for s found in part **a**?

2.75 Given a data set with a largest value of 760 and a smallest [NW] value of 135, what would you estimate the standard deviation to be? Explain the logic behind the procedure you used to estimate the standard deviation. Suppose the standard deviation is reported to be 25. Is this feasible? Explain.

Applying the Concepts—Basic

2.76 **Blogs for Fortune 500 firms.** Refer to the *Journal of Relationship Marketing* (Vol. 7, 2008) study of the prevalence of blogs and forums at Fortune 500 firms with both English and Chinese Web sites, Exercise 2.9 (p. 40). In a sample of firms that provide blogs and forums as marketing tools, the mean number of blogs/forums per site was 4.25, with a standard deviation of 12.02.

    a. Provide an interval that is likely to contain the number of blogs/forums per site for at least 75% of the Fortune 500 firms in the sample.

    b. Do you expect the distribution of the number of blogs/forums to be symmetric, skewed right, or skewed left? Explain.

2.77 **Semester hours taken by CPA candidates.** Refer to the *Journal of Accounting and Public Policy* (Spring 2002) study of 100,000 first-time candidates for the CPA exam, Exercise 2.51 (p. 63). Recall that the mean number of semester hours of college credit taken by the candidates was 141.31 hours. The standard deviation was reported to be 17.77 hours.

    a. Compute the 2-standard deviation interval around the mean.

    b. Make a statement about the proportion of first-time candidates for the CPA exam who have total college credit hours within the interval, part **a**.

    c. For the statement, part **b**, to be true, what must be known about the shape of the distribution of total semester hours?

2.78 **Size of diamonds sold at retail.** Refer to the *Journal of Statistics Education* data on diamonds saved in the **DIAMONDS** file. In Exercise 2.49 (p. 62) you found the mean number of carats for the 308 diamonds in the data set, and in Exercise 2.67 (p. 69) you found the standard deviation. Use the mean and standard deviation to form an interval that will contain at least 75% of the carat values in the data set.

2.79 **Vehicle use of an intersection.** For each day of last year, the number of vehicles passing through a certain intersection was recorded by a city engineer. One objective of this study was to determine the percentage of days that more than 425 vehicles used the intersection. Suppose the mean for the data was 375 vehicles per day and the standard deviation was 25 vehicles.

    a. What can you say about the percentage of days that more than 425 vehicles used the intersection? Assume you know nothing about the shape of the relative frequency distribution for the data.

    b. What is your answer to part **a** if you know that the relative frequency distribution for the data is mound-shaped?

Applying the Concepts—Intermediate

2.80 **Sanitation inspection of cruise ships.** Refer to the Centers for Disease Control and Prevention listing of the Dec. 2008 sanitation scores for 183 cruise ships, Exercise 2.22 (p. 49). The data are saved in the **SHIPSANIT** file.

    a. Find the mean and standard deviation of the sanitation scores.

    b. Calculate the intervals $\bar{x} \pm s$, $\bar{x} \pm 2s$, $\bar{x} \pm 3s$.

    c. Find the percentage of measurements in the data set that fall within each of the intervals, part **b**. Do these percentages agree with Chebyshev's Rule? The Empirical Rule?

2.81 **Bearing strength of concrete FRP strips.** Fiber reinforced polymer (FRP) composite materials are the standard for strengthening, retrofitting, and repairing concrete structures. Typically, FRP strips are fastened to the concrete with epoxy adhesive. Engineers at the University of Wisconsin-Madison have developed a new method of fastening the FRP strips using mechanical anchors (*Composites Fabrication Magazine,* Sep. 2004). To evaluate the new fastening method, 10 specimens of pultruded FRP strips mechanically fastened to highway bridges were tested for bearing strength. The strength measurements (recorded in mega pascal units, Mpa) are shown in the table and saved in the **FRP** file. Use the sample data to find an interval that is likely to contain the bearing strength of a pultruded FRP strip.

240.9	248.8	215.7	233.6	231.4	230.9	225.3	247.3	235.5	238.0

Source: Data are simulated from summary information provided in *Composites Fabrication Magazine*, Sep. 2004, p. 32 (Table 1).

2.82 **Time in bankruptcy.** Refer to the *Financial Management* (Spring 1995) study of 49 firms filing for prepackaged bankruptcy, Exercise 2.30 (p. 52). Data on the variable of interest, length of time (months) in bankruptcy for each firm, are saved in the **BANKRUPT** file.

  a. Construct a histogram for the 49 bankruptcy times. Comment on whether the Empirical Rule is applicable for describing the bankruptcy time distribution for firms filing for prepackaged bankruptcy.

  b. Find numerical descriptive statistics for the data set. Use this information to construct an interval that captures at least 75% of the bankruptcy times.

  c. Count the number of the 49 bankruptcy times that fall within the interval, part **b**, and convert the result to a percentage. Does the result agree with Chebyshev's Rule? The Empirical Rule?

  d. A firm is considering filing a prepackaged bankruptcy plan. Estimate the length of time the firm will be in bankruptcy.

2.83 **Velocity of Winchester bullets.** The *American Rifleman* (June 1993) reported on the velocity of ammunition fired from the FEG P9R pistol, a 9 mm gun manufactured in Hungary. Field tests revealed that Winchester bullets fired from the pistol had a mean velocity (at 15 feet) of 936 feet per second and a standard deviation of 10 feet per second. Tests were also conducted with Uzi and Black Hills ammunition.

  a. Describe the velocity distribution of Winchester bullets fired from the FEG P9R pistol.

  b. A bullet, brand unknown, is fired from the FEG P9R pistol. Suppose the velocity (at 15 feet) of the bullet is 1,000 feet per second. Is the bullet likely to be manufactured by Winchester? Explain.

2.84 **Buy-side vs. sell-side analysts' earnings forecasts.** Financial analysts are hired by investment companies to make forecasts of stock prices and recommendations about whether to buy, sell, or hold specific securities. These analysts can be categorized as either "buy-side" analysts or "sell-side" analysts based on a variety of factors, including scope of industry coverage, sources of information used, and target audience. A group of Harvard Business School professors compared earnings forecasts of buy-side and sell-side analysts (*Financial Analysts Journal,* Jul/Aug 2008). Data were collected on 3,526 forecasts made by buy-side analysts and 58,562 forecasts made by sell-side analysts, and the relative absolute forecast error was determined for each.

  a. Frequency distributions for buy-side and sell-side analysts forecast errors (with the sell-side distribution superimposed over the buy-side distribution) are shown in the accompanying figure. Based on the figure, the researchers concluded "that absolute forecast errors for buy-side analysts have a higher mean and

variance than those for the sell-side analysts." Do you agree? Explain.

  b. The mean and standard deviation of forecast errors for both buy-side and sell-side analysts are given in the following table. For each type of analyst, provide an interval that will contain approximately 95% of the forecast errors. Compare these intervals. Which type of analyst is likely to have a relative forecast error of +2.00 or higher?

	Buy-Side Analysts	Sell-Side Analysts
Mean	0.85	−0.05
Standard Deviation	1.93	0.85

Source: Groysberg, B., Healy, P., & Chapman, C. *Financial Analysts Journal,* Vol. 64, No. 4, Jul/Aug. 2008 (Table 2).

Applying the Concepts—Advanced

2.85 **Land purchase decision.** A buyer for a lumber company must decide whether to buy a piece of land containing 5,000 pine trees. If 1,000 of the trees are at least 40 feet tall, the buyer will purchase the land; otherwise, he won't. The owner of the land reports that the height of the trees has a mean of 30 feet and a standard deviation of 3 feet. Based on this information, what is the buyer's decision?

2.86 **Improving SAT scores.** The National Education Longitudinal Survey (NELS) tracks a nationally representative sample of U.S. students from eighth grade through high school and college. Research published in *Chance* (Winter 2001) examined the Standardized Assessment Test (SAT) scores of 265 NELS students who paid a private tutor to help them improve their scores. The table summarizes the changes in both the SAT–Mathematics and SAT–Verbal scores for these students.

	SAT–Math	SAT–Verbal
Mean change in score	19	7
Standard deviation of score changes	65	49

  a. Suppose one of the 265 students who paid a private tutor is selected at random. Give an interval that is likely to contain this student's change in the SAT–Math score.

  b. Repeat part **a** for the SAT–Verbal score.

  c. Suppose the selected student increased their score on one of the SAT tests by 140 points. Which test, the SAT–Math or SAT–Verbal, is the one most likely to have the 140-point increase? Explain.

2.87 Monitoring weights of flour bags. When it is working properly, a machine that fills 25-pound bags of flour dispenses an average of 25 pounds per fill; the standard deviation of the amount of fill is .1 pound. To monitor the performance of the machine, an inspector weighs the contents of a bag coming off the machine's conveyor belt every half hour during the day. If the contents of two consecutive bags fall more than 2 standard deviations from the mean (using the mean and standard deviation given above), the filling process is said to be out of control, and the machine is shut down briefly for adjustments. The data given in the following table (saved in the **FLOUR** file) are the weights measured by the inspector yesterday. Assume the machine is never shut down for more than 15 minutes at a time. At what times yesterday was the process shut down for adjustment? Justify your answer.

Time	Weight (pounds)
8:00 A.M.	25.10
8:30	25.15
9:00	24.81
9:30	24.75
10:00	25.00
10:30	25.05
11:00	25.23
11:30	25.25
12:00	25.01
12:30 P.M.	25.06
1:00	24.95
1:30	24.80
2:00	24.95
2:30	25.21
3:00	24.90
3:30	24.71
4:00	25.31
4:30	25.15
5:00	25.20

2.7 Numerical Measures of Relative Standing

We've seen that numerical measures of central tendency and variability describe the general nature of a quantitative data set (either a sample or a population). In addition, we may be interested in describing the *relative* quantitative location of a particular measurement within a data set. Descriptive measures of the relationship of a measurement to the rest of the data are called **measures of relative standing.**

One measure of the relative standing of a measurement is its **percentile ranking,** or **percentile score.** For example, if oil company A reports that its yearly sales are in the 90th percentile of all companies in the industry, the implication is that 90% of all oil companies have yearly sales less than company A's, and only 10% have yearly sales exceeding company A's. This is demonstrated in Figure 2.23. Similarly, if the oil company's yearly sales are in the 50th percentile (the median of the data set), 50% of all oil companies would have lower yearly sales and 50% would have higher yearly sales.

Percentile rankings are of practical value only for large data sets. Finding them involves a process similar to the one used in finding a median. The measurements are ranked in order, and a rule is selected to define the location of each percentile. Because we are primarily interested in interpreting the percentile rankings of measurements (rather than finding particular percentiles for a data set), we define the *pth percentile* of a data set.

Figure 2.23

Location of 90th percentile for yearly sales of oil companies

> For any set of *n* measurements (arranged in ascending or descending order), the *pth* **percentile** is a number such that $p\%$ of the measurements fall below the *pth* percentile and $(100 - p)\%$ fall above it.

Example 2.14

Finding and Interpreting Percentiles

Problem Refer to the percentages spent on R&D by the 50 high-technology firms listed in Table 2.8 (p. 72). A portion of the SPSS descriptive statistics printout is shown in Figure 2.24. Locate the 25th percentile and 95th percentile on the printout and interpret these values.

Solution Both the 25th percentile and 95th percentile are highlighted on the SPSS print-out, Figure 2.24. These values are 7.05 and 13.335, respectively. Our interpretations are as follows: 25% of the 50 R&D percentages fall below 7.05 and 95% of the R&D per-centages fall below 13.335.

Look Back The method for computing percentiles varies according to the software used. Some packages, like SPSS, give two different methods of computing percentiles. As the data set increases in size, these percentile values will converge to a single number.

Statistics

RDPCT

N	Valid		50
	Missing		0
Percentiles	5		5.765
	10		6.500
	25		7.050
	50		8.050
	75		9.625
	90		11.280
	95		13.335

Figure 2.24
SPSS percentiles for
50 R&D percentages

Now Work Exercise 2.89

Another measure of relative standing in popular use is the *z-score*. As you can see in the definition of z-score below, the z-score makes use of the mean and standard devi-ation of the data set in order to specify the relative location of a measurement. Note that the z-score is calculated by subtracting $\bar{x}$ (or μ) from the measurement x and then dividing the result by s (or σ). The final result, the z-score, represents the distance between a given measurement x and the mean, expressed in standard deviations.

The **sample z-score** for a measurement x is

$$z = \frac{x - \bar{x}}{s}$$

The **population z-score** for a measurement x is

$$z = \frac{x - \mu}{\sigma}$$

Example 2.15

Finding a z-Score

Problem Suppose 200 steelworkers are selected, and the annual income of each is deter-mined. The mean and standard deviation are $\bar{x} = \$54,000$ and $s = \$2,000$. Suppose Joe Smith's annual income is $52,000. What is his sample z-score?

Solution Joe Smith's annual income lies below the mean income of the 200 steelworkers (see Figure 2.25). We compute

$$z = \frac{x - \bar{x}}{s} = \frac{\$52,000 - \$54,000}{2,000} = -1.0$$

$$z = -1.0$$

which tells us that Joe Smith's annual income is 1.0 standard deviation *below* the sample mean, or, in short, his sample z-score is -1.0.

$48,000		$52,000	$54,000		$60,000
$\bar{x} - 3s$		Joe Smith's income	$\bar{x}$		$\bar{x} + 3s$

Figure 2.25
Annual income of steelworkers

Look Back The numerical value of the z-score reflects the relative standing of the measurement. A large positive z-score implies that the measurement is larger than almost all other measurements, whereas a large (in magnitude) negative z-score indicates that the measurement is smaller than almost every other measurement. If a z-score is 0 or near 0, the measurement is located at or near the mean of the sample or population.

Now Work Exercise 2.88

If we know that the frequency distribution of the measurements is mound-shaped, the following interpretation of the z-score can be given.

Interpretation of z-Scores for Mound-Shaped Distributions of Data

1. Approximately 68% of the measurements will have a z-score between -1 and 1.

2. Approximately 95% of the measurements will have a z-score between -2 and 2.

3. Approximately 99.7% (almost all) of the measurements will have a z-score between -3 and 3.

Note that this interpretation of z-scores is identical to that given by the Empirical Rule for mound-shaped distributions (Table 2.7). The statement that a measurement falls in the interval $(\mu - \sigma)$ to $(\mu + \sigma)$ is equivalent to the statement that a measurement has a population z-score between -1 and 1 because all measurements between $(\mu - \sigma)$ and $(\mu + \sigma)$ are within 1 standard deviation of μ. These z-scores are displayed in Figure 2.26.

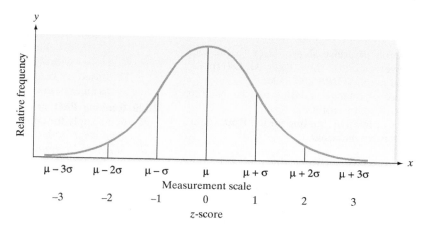

Figure 2.26

Population z-scores for a mound-shaped distribution

Exercises 2.88–2.102

Learning the Mechanics

2.88 Compute the z-score corresponding to each of the following values of x:
- **a.** $x = 40, s = 5, \bar{x} = 30$
- **b.** $x = 90, \mu = 89, \sigma = 2$
- **c.** $\mu = 50, \sigma = 5, x = 50$
- **d.** $s = 4, x = 20, \bar{x} = 30$
- **e.** In parts **a–d**, state whether the z-score locates x within a sample or a population.
- **f.** In parts **a–d**, state whether each value of x lies above or below the mean and by how many standard deviations.

2.89 Give the percentage of measurements in a data set that are above and below each of the following percentiles:
- **a.** 75th percentile
- **b.** 50th percentile

- **c.** 20th percentile
- **d.** 84th percentile

2.90 What is the 50th percentile of a quantitative data set called?

2.91 Compare the z-scores to decide which of the following x values lie the greatest distance above the mean and the greatest distance below the mean.
- **a.** $x = 100, \mu = 50, \sigma = 25$
- **b.** $x = 1, \mu = 4, \sigma = 1$
- **c.** $x = 0, \mu = 200, \sigma = 100$
- **d.** $x = 10, \mu = 5, \sigma = 3$

2.92 Suppose that 40 and 90 are two elements of a population data set and that their z-scores are -2 and 3, respectively. Using only this information, is it possible to determine the population's mean and standard deviation? If so, find them. If not, explain why it's not possible.

Applying the Concepts—Basic

2.93 Mathematics assessment test scores. According to the National Center for Education Statistics (2005), scores on a mathematics assessment test for United States eighth-graders have a mean of 279, a 10th percentile of 231, a 25th percentile of 255, a 75th percentile of 304, and a 90th percentile of 324. Interpret each of these numerical descriptive measures.

2.94 Drivers stopped by police. According to the Bureau of Justice Statistics (June 2006), 75% of all licensed drivers stopped by police are 25 years or older. Give a percentile ranking for the age of 25 years in the distribution of all ages of licensed drivers stopped by police.

2.95 Starting and mid-career salaries of bachelor's degree graduates. PayScale, Inc., an online provider of global compensation data, recently conducted a survey of 1.2 million bachelor's degree graduates with a minimum of ten years of work experience. Three of the many variables measured by PayScale were the graduate's starting salary, mid-career salary, and the college or university where they obtained their degree. A summary of the starting and mid-career salary data was reported in *The Wall Street Journal* (July 31, 2008). Descriptive statistics were provided for each of the over 300 colleges and universities that graduates attended. For example, graduates of the University of South Florida (USF) had a median starting salary of $41,100, a median mid-career salary of $71,100, and a mid-career 90th percentile salary of $131,000. Describe the salary distribution of USF bachelor's degree graduates by interpreting each of these summary statistics.

2.96 Sanitation inspection of cruise ships. Refer to the Dec. 2008 sanitation levels of cruise ships, Exercise 2.80 (p. 75). The data are saved in the **SHIPSANIT** file.
  a. Give a measure of relative standing for the Nautilus Explorer score of 74. Interpret the result.
  b. Give a measure of relative standing for the Rotterdam's score of 98. Interpret the result.

Applying the Concepts—Intermediate

2.97 Lead in drinking water. The U.S. Environmental Protection Agency (EPA) sets a limit on the amount of lead permitted in drinking water. The EPA *Action Level* for lead is .015 milligrams per liter (mg/L) of water. Under EPA guidelines, if 90% of a water system's study samples have a lead concentration less than .015 mg/L, the water is considered safe for drinking. I (coauthor Sincich) received a recent report on a study of lead levels in the drinking water of homes in my subdivision. The 90th percentile of the study sample had a lead concentration of .00372 mg/L. Are water customers in my subdivision at risk of drinking water with unhealthy lead levels? Explain.

2.98 Using z-scores for grades. At one university, the students are given z-scores at the end of each semester rather than the traditional GPAs. The mean and standard deviation of all students' cumulative GPAs, on which the z-scores are based, are 2.7 and .5, respectively.
  a. Translate each of the following z-scores to corresponding GPA: $z = 2.0$, $z = -1.0$, $z = .5$, $z = -2.5$.
  b. Students with z-scores below -1.6 are put on probation. What is the corresponding probationary GPA?
  c. The president of the university wishes to graduate the top 16% of the students with *cum laude* honors and the top 2.5% with *summa cum laude* honors. Where

(approximately) should the limits be set in terms of z-scores? In terms of GPAs? What assumption, if any, did you make about the distribution of the GPAs at the university?

2.99 Hazardous waste cleanup in Arkansas. The Superfund Act was passed by Congress to encourage state participation in the implementation of a law relating to the release and cleanup of hazardous substances. Hazardous waste sites financed by the Superfund Act are called *Superfund sites.* A total of 393 Superfund sites are operated by waste management companies in Arkansas (Tabor and Stanwick, *Arkansas Business and Economic Review,* Summer 1995). The number of these Superfund sites in each of Arkansas's 75 counties, shown in the next table, are saved in the **ARKFUND** file.

3	3	2	1	2	0	5	3	5	2	1	8	2
12	3	5	3	1	3	0	8	0	9	6	8	6
2	16	0	6	0	5	5	0	1	25	0	0	0
6	2	10	12	3	10	3	17	2	4	2	1	21
4	2	1	11	5	2	2	7	2	3	1	8	2
0	0	0	2	3	10	2	3	48	21			

Source: Tabor, R. H., and Stanwick, S. D. "Arkansas: An environmental perspective," *Arkansas Business and Economic Review,* Vol. 28, No. 2, Summer 1995, pp. 22–32 (Table 4).

  a. Find the 10th percentile of the data set. Interpret the result.
  b. Find the 95th percentile of the data set. Interpret the result.
  c. Find the mean and standard deviation of the data; then use these values to calculate the z-score for an Arkansas county with 48 Superfund sites.
  d. Based on your answer to part **c**, would you classify 48 as an extreme number of Superfund sites?

2.100 Ranking PhD programs in economics. Thousands of students apply for admission to graduate schools in economics each year with the intention of obtaining a PhD. The *Southern Economic Journal* (Apr. 2008) published a guide to graduate study in economics by ranking the PhD programs at 129 colleges and universities. Each program was evaluated according to the number of publications published by faculty teaching in the PhD program and by the quality of the publications. Data obtained from the Social Science Citation Index (SSCI) were used to calculate an overall productivity score for each PhD program. The mean and standard deviation of these 129 productivity scores were then used to compute a z-score for each economics program. Harvard University had the highest z-score ($z = 5.08$) and, hence, was the top-ranked school; Howard University was ranked last because it had the lowest z-score ($z = -0.81$). The data (z-scores) for all 129 economic programs are saved in the **ECOPHD** file.
  a. Interpret the z-score for Harvard University.
  b. Interpret the z-score for Howard University.
  c. The authors of the *Southern Economic Journal* article note that "only 44 of the 129 schools have positive z-scores, indicating that the distribution of overall productivity is skewed to the right." Do you agree? (Check your answer by constructing a histogram for the z-scores in the **ECOPHD** file.)

Applying the Concepts—Advanced

2.101 Ranking PhD programs in economics (cont'd). Refer to the *Southern Economic Journal* (Apr. 2008) study of PhD programs in economics, Exercise 2.100. The authors also made the following observation: "A noticeable feature of this skewness is that distinction between schools diminishes as the rank declines. For example, the top-ranked school, Harvard, has a z-score of 5.08, and the fifth-ranked school, Yale, has a z-score of 2.18, a substantial difference. However, …, the 70th-ranked school, the University of Massachusetts, has a z-score of –0.43, and the 80th-ranked school, the University of Delaware, has a z-score of –0.50, a very small difference. [Consequently] the ordinal rankings presented in much of the literature that ranks economics departments miss the fact that below a relatively small group of top programs, the differences in [overall] productivity become fairly small." Do you agree?

2.102 **Blue versus red-colored exam study.** In a study of how external clues influence performance, professors at the University of Alberta and Pennsylvania State University gave two different forms of a midterm examination to a large group of introductory students. The questions on the exam were identical and in the same order, but one exam was printed on blue paper and the other on red paper (*Teaching Psychology,* May 1998). Grading only the difficult questions on the exam, the researchers found that scores on the blue exam had a distribution with a mean of 53% and a standard deviation of 15%, while scores on the red exam had a distribution with a mean of 39% and a standard deviation of 12%. (Assume that both distributions are approximately mound-shaped and symmetric.)

a. Give an interpretation of the standard deviation for the students who took the blue exam.

b. Give an interpretation of the standard deviation for the students who took the red exam.

c. Suppose a student is selected at random from the group of students who participated in the study and the student's score on the difficult questions is 20%. Which exam form is the student more likely to have taken, the blue or the red exam? Explain.

● Applet Exercise 2.7

Use the applet *Standard Deviation* to determine whether an item in a data set may be an outlier. Begin by setting appropriate limits and plotting the data below on the number line provided in the applet.

10 80 80 85 85 85 85 90 90 90 90 90 95 95 95 95 100 100

a. The green arrow shows the approximate location of the mean. Multiply the standard deviation given by the applet by 3. Is the data item 10 more than three standard deviations away from the green arrow (the mean)? Can you conclude that the 10 is an outlier?

b. Using the mean and standard deviation from part **a,** move the point at 10 on your plot to a point that appears to be about three standard deviations from the mean. Repeat the process in part **a** for the new plot and the new suspected outlier.

c. When you replaced the extreme value in part **a** with a number that appeared to be within three standard deviations of the mean, the standard deviation got smaller and the mean moved to the right, yielding a new data set where the extreme value was not within three standard deviations of the mean. Continue to replace the extreme value with higher numbers until the new value is within three standard deviations of the mean in the new data set. Use trial and error to estimate the smallest number that can replace the 10 in the original data set so that the replacement is not considered to be an outlier.

2.8 Methods for Detecting Outliers: Box Plots and z-Scores

Sometimes it is important to identify inconsistent or unusual measurements in a data set. An observation that is unusually large or small relative to the data values we want to describe is called an *outlier.*

Outliers are often attributable to one of several causes. First, the measurement associated with the outlier may be invalid. For example, the experimental procedure used to generate the measurement may have malfunctioned, the experimenter may have misrecorded the measurement, or the data might have been coded incorrectly in the computer. Second, the outlier may be the result of a misclassified measurement—that is, the measurement belongs to a population different from which the rest of the sample was drawn. Finally, the measurement associated with the outlier may be recorded correctly and from the same population as the rest of the sample but represents a rare (chance) event. Such outliers occur most often when the relative frequency distribution of the sample data is extremely skewed because such a distribution has a tendency to include extremely large or small observations relative to the others in the data set.

An observation (or measurement) that is unusually large or small relative to the other values in a data set is called an **outlier.** Outliers typically are attributable to one of the following causes:

1. The measurement is observed, recorded, or entered into the computer incorrectly.
2. The measurement comes from a different population.
3. The measurement is correct but represents a rare (chance) event.

Two useful methods for detecting outliers, one graphical and one numerical, are **box plots** and z-scores. The box plot is based on the *quartiles* of a data set. **Quartiles** are values that partition the data set into four groups, each containing 25% of the measurements. The *lower quartile* Q_L is the 25th percentile, the *middle quartile* is the median m (the 50th percentile), and the *upper quartile* Q_U is the 75th percentile (see Figure 2.27).

Figure 2.27
The quartiles for a data set

The **lower quartile** Q_L is the 25th percentile of a data set. The **middle quartile** m is the median. The **upper quartile** Q_U is the 75th percentile.

A box plot is based on the *interquartile range* (IQR), the distance between the lower and upper quartiles:

$$IQR = Q_U - Q_L$$

The **interquartile range (IQR)** is the distance between the lower and upper quartiles:

$$IQR = Q_U - Q_L$$

An annotated Minitab box plot for the 50 companies' percentages of revenues spent on R&D (Table 2.2) is shown in Figure 2.28.* Note that a rectangle (the box) is drawn, with the top and bottom sides of the rectangle (the **hinges**) drawn at the quartiles Q_L and Q_U, respectively. By definition, then, the "middle" 50% of the observations—those between Q_L and Q_U—fall inside the box. For the R&D data, these quartiles are at 7.05 and 9.625 (see Figure 2.24, p. 78). Thus,

$$IQR = 9.625 - 7.05 = 2.575$$

The median is shown at 8.05 by a horizontal line within the box.

To guide the construction of the "tails" of the box plot, two sets of limits, called **inner fences** and **outer fences,** are used. Neither set of fences actually appears on the box plot. Inner fences are located at a distance of 1.5(IQR) from the hinges. Emanating from the hinges of the box are vertical lines called the **whiskers.** The two whiskers extend to the most extreme observation inside the inner fences. For example, the inner fence on the lower side (bottom) of the R&D percentage box plot is

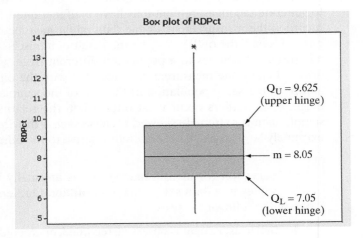

Figure 2.28
Annotated Minitab box plot for 50 R&D percentages

*Although box plots can be generated by hand, the amount of detail required makes them particularly well suited for computer generation. We use computer software to generate the box plots in this section.

$$\text{Lower inner fence} = \text{Lower hinge} - 1.5(\text{IQR})$$
$$= 7.05 - 1.5(2.575)$$
$$= 7.05 - 3.863 = 3.187$$

The smallest measurement in the data set is 5.2, which is well inside this inner fence. Thus, the lower whisker extends to 5.2. Similarly, the upper whisker extends to the most extreme observation inside the upper inner fence, where

$$\text{Upper inner fence} = \text{Upper hinge} + 1.5(\text{IQR})$$
$$= 9.625 + 1.5(2.575)$$
$$= 9.625 + 3.863 = 13.488$$

The largest measurement inside this fence is the third largest measurement, 13.2. Note that the longer upper whisker reveals the rightward skewness of the R&D distribution.

Values that are beyond the inner fences are deemed *potential outliers* because they are extreme values that represent relatively rare occurrences. In fact, for mound-shaped distributions, fewer than 1% of the observations are expected to fall outside the inner fences. Two of the 50 R&D measurements, both at 13.5, fall outside the upper inner fence. Each of these potential outliers is represented by the asterisk (*) at 13.5.

The other two imaginary fences, the outer fences, are defined at a distance 3(IQR) from each end of the box. Measurements that fall beyond the outer fence are represented by 0s (zeros) and are very extreme measurements that require special analysis. Because less than one-hundredth of 1% (.01% or .0001) of the measurements from mound-shaped distributions are expected to fall beyond the outer fence, these measurements are considered to be *outliers*. No measurement in the R&D percentage box plot (Figure 2.28) is represented by a 0; thus there are no outliers.

Recall that outliers are extreme measurements that stand out from the rest of the sample and may be faulty: They may be incorrectly recorded observations, members of a population different from the rest of the sample, or, at the least, very unusual measurements from the same population. For example, the two R&D measurements at 13.5 (identified by an asterisk) may be considered outliers. When we analyze these measurements, we find that they are correctly recorded. However, it turns out that both represent R&D expenditures of relatively young and fast-growing companies. Thus, the outlier analysis may have revealed important factors that relate to the R&D expenditures of high-tech companies: their age and rate of growth. Outlier analysis often reveals useful information of this kind and therefore plays an important role in the statistical inference-making process.

In addition to detecting outliers, box plots provide useful information on the variation in a data set. The elements (and nomenclature) of box plots are summarized in the next box. Some aids to the interpretation of box plots are also given.

Elements of a Box Plot

1. A rectangle (the **box**) is drawn with the ends (the **hinges**) drawn at the lower and upper quartiles (Q_L and Q_U). The median of the data is shown in the box, usually by a line or a symbol (such as "+").

2. The points at distances 1.5(IQR) from each hinge define the **inner fences** of the data set. Lines (the **whiskers**) are drawn from each hinge to the most extreme measurement inside the inner fence.

3. A second pair of fences, the **outer fences,** are defined at a distance of 3 interquartile ranges, 3(IQR) from the hinges. One symbol (usually "*") is used to represent measurements falling between the inner and outer fences, and another (usually "0") is used to represent measurements beyond the outer fences.

4. The symbols used to represent the median and the extreme data points (those beyond the fences) will vary depending on the software you use to construct the box plot. (You may use your own symbols if you are constructing a box plot by hand.) You should consult the program's documentation to determine exactly which symbols are used.

Aids to the Interpretation of Box Plots

1. Examine the length of the box. The IQR is a measure of the sample's variability and is especially useful for the comparison of two samples (see Example 2.17).

2. Visually compare the lengths of the whiskers. If one is clearly longer, the distribution of the data is probably skewed in the direction of the longer whisker.

3. Analyze any measurements that lie beyond the fences. Fewer than 5% should fall beyond the inner fences, even for very skewed distributions. Measurements beyond the outer fences are probably outliers, with one of the following explanations:
   a. The measurement is incorrect. It may have been observed, recorded, or entered into the computer incorrectly.
   b. The measurement belongs to a population different from the population that the rest of the sample was drawn from (see Example 2.17).
   c. The measurement is correct *and* from the same population as the rest. Generally, we accept this explanation only after carefully ruling out all others.

Example 2.16
Interpreting a Box Plot

Problem In Example 2.2 (p. 45) we analyzed 50 processing times (listed in Table 2.4) for the development of price quotes by the manufacturer of industrial wheels. The intent was to determine whether the success or failure in obtaining the order was related to the amount of time to process the price quotes. Each quote that corresponds to "lost" business was so classified. Use a statistical software package to draw a box plot for all 50 processing times. What does the box plot reveal about the data?

Solution The Minitab box plot printout for these data is shown in Figure 2.29. Note that the upper whisker is much longer than the lower whisker, indicating rightward skewness of the data. However, the most important feature of the data is made very obvious by the box plot: There are four measurements (indicated by asterisks) that are beyond the upper inner fence. Thus, the distribution is extremely skewed to the right, and several measurements—or outliers—need special attention in our analysis.

Look Back Before removing outliers from the data set, a good analyst will make a concerted effort to find the cause of the outliers. We offer an explanation for these processing time outliers in the next example.

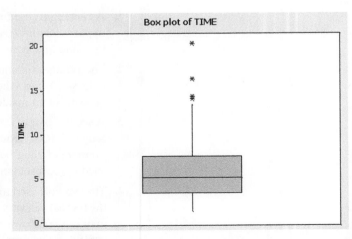

Figure 2.29
Minitab box plot for
processing time data

Example 2.17
Comparing Box Plots

Problem The box plot for the 50 processing times (Figure 2.29) does not explicitly reveal the differences, if any, between the set of times corresponding to the success and the set of times corresponding to the failure to obtain the business. Box plots corresponding to the 39 "won" and 11 "lost" bids were generated using SPSS and are shown in Figure 2.30. Interpret them.

Solution The division of the data set into two parts, corresponding to won and lost bids eliminates any observations that are beyond the inner fences. Furthermore, the skewness in the distributions has been reduced, as evidenced by the fact that the upper

Figure 2.30
SPSS box plots of processing times for won and lost bids

whiskers are only slightly longer than the lower. The box plots also reveal that the processing times corresponding to the lost bids tend to exceed those of the won bids. A plausible explanation for the outliers in the combined box plot (Figure 2.29) is that they are from a different population than the bulk of the times. In other words, there are two populations represented by the sample of processing times—one corresponding to lost bids and the other to won bids.

Look Back The box plots lend support to the conclusion that the price quote processing time and the success of acquiring the business are related. However, whether the visual differences between the box plots generalize to inferences about the populations corresponding to these two samples is a matter for inferential statistics, not graphical descriptions. We'll discuss how to use samples to compare two populations using inferential statistics in Chapter 7.

The following example illustrates how z-scores can be used to detect outliers and make inferences.

Example 2.18
Inference Using z-Scores

Problem Suppose a female bank employee believes that her salary is low as a result of sex discrimination. To substantiate her belief, she collects information on the salaries of her male counterparts in the banking business. She finds that their salaries have a mean of $64,000 and a standard deviation of $2,000. Her salary is $57,000. Does this information support her claim of sex discrimination?

Solution The analysis might proceed as follows: First, we calculate the z-score for the woman's salary with respect to those of her male counterparts. Thus,

$$z = \frac{\$57,000 - \$64,000}{\$2,000} = -3.5$$

The implication is that the woman's salary is 3.5 standard deviations *below* the mean of the male salary distribution. Furthermore, if a check of the male salary data shows that the frequency distribution is mound-shaped, we can infer that very few salaries in this distribution should have a z-score less than -3, as shown in Figure 2.31. Clearly, a z-score of -3.5 represents an outlier.

Figure 2.31
Male salary distribution

Either this female's salary is from a distribution different from the male salary distribution, or it is a very unusual (highly improbable) measurement from a distribution that is no different from the male salary distribution.

Look Back Which of the two situations do you think prevails? Statistical thinking would lead us to conclude that her salary does not come from the male salary distribution, lending support to the female bank employee's claim of sex discrimination. A careful investigator should aquire more information before inferring sex discrimination as the cause. We would want to know more about the data-collection technique the woman used and more about her competence at her job. Also, perhaps other factors such as length of employment should be considered in the analysis.

Now Work Exercise 2.103

Examples 2.17 and 2.18 exemplify an approach to statistical inference that might be called the **rare-event approach.** An experimenter hypothesizes a specific frequency distribution to describe a population of measurements. Then a sample of measurements is drawn from the population. If the experimenter finds it unlikely that the sample came from the hypothesized distribution, the hypothesis is concluded to be false. Thus, in Example 2.18, the woman believes her salary reflects discrimination. She hypothesizes that her salary should be just another measurement in the distribution of her male counterparts' salaries if no discrimination exists. However, it is so unlikely that the sample (in this case, her salary) came from the male frequency distribution that she rejects that hypothesis, concluding that the distribution from which her salary was drawn is different from the distribution for the men.

This rare-event approach to inference-making is discussed further in later chapters. Proper application of the approach requires a knowledge of probability, the subject of our next chapter.

We conclude this section with some rules of thumb for detecting outliers.

Rules of Thumb for Detecting Outliers*

Box Plots: Observations falling between the inner and outer fences are deemed *suspect outliers*. Observations falling beyond the outer fence are deemed *highly suspect outliers*.

z-scores: Observations with z-scores greater than 3 in absolute value are considered outliers. (For some highly skewed data sets, observations with z-scores greater than 2 in absolute value may be outliers.)

---

*The z-score and box plot methods both establish rule-of-thumb limits outside of which a measurement is deemed to be an outlier. Usually, the two methods produce similar results. However, the presence of one or more outliers in a data set can inflate the computed value of s. Consequently, it will be less likely that an errant observation would have a z-score larger than 3 in absolute value. In contrast, the values of the quartiles used to calculate the intervals for a box plot are not affected by the presence of outliers.

| Statistics ɪɴ Action | Revisited | Detecting Outliers |

In the ethics survey of University Community Hospital physicians, the medical researchers measured two quantitative variables: *Length of time in practice* (number of years) and *Amount of exposure to ethics in medical school* (number of hours). Are there any unusual values of these variables in the **ETHICS** data set? We will employ both the box plot and z-score methods to aid in identifying outliers in the data.

Descriptive statistics for these two variables, produced using Minitab, are shown in Figure SIA2.6. To employ the z-score method, we need the means and standard deviations. These values are highlighted on Figure SIA2.6. Then the 3-standard-deviation intervals are

$$
\begin{aligned}
\text{YRSPRAC:} \qquad & 14.6 \pm 3(9.2) = 14.6 \pm 27.6 \\
& \qquad\qquad\qquad = (-13.0, 42.2) \\
\text{EDHRS:} \qquad & 23.9 \pm 3(109.6) = 23.9 \pm 328.8 \\
& \qquad\qquad\qquad = (-304.9, 352.7)
\end{aligned}
$$

[*Note:* Because neither of the variables can be negative, for practical purposes the intervals all begin at 0.]

In this application, we will focus on only the three largest values of the variables in the data set. For length of time in practice, these values are 35, 40, and 40 years. Note that all three values fall within the 3-standard-deviation interval—that is, they all have z-scores less than 3 in absolute value. Consequently, no outliers exist for the data on length of time in practice.

For ethics exposure, the three largest values are 75, 80, and 1,000 hours. Note that only one of these values, 1,000, falls beyond the 3-standard-deviation interval. Thus, the data for the physician who was exposed to 1,000 hours of ethics in medical school is considered an outlier using the z-score approach. However, notice that the standard deviation for the variable (109.6) is much larger than the mean (23.9). Typically, when S exceeds $\bar{x}$ (for a non-negative variable), a high degree

of skewness exists. This skewness is due, in large part, to the extreme value of 1,000 hours. When such an extreme outlier occurs in the data, the standard deviation is inflated and the z-score method is less likely to detect unusual observations. (See the footnote on p. 86.) When this occurs, the box plot method for detecting outliers is preferred.

Rather than produce a box plot for the ethics exposure variable, we'll use the descriptive statistics in Figure SIA2.6 to find the inner and outer fences. From the Minitab printout, we see that $Q_L = 1$, $Q_U = 20$, and IQR = 19. Then the upper inner and outer fence boundaries of the box plot are

Upper inner fence:

$$ Q_U + (1.5)\text{IQR} = 20 + (1.5)(19) = 48.5 $$

Upper outer fence:

$$ Q_U + (3)\text{IQR} = 20 + (3)(19) = 77.0 $$

Now we see that the ethics exposure value of 80 hours is, indeed, a highly suspect outlier because it falls beyond the upper outer fence. Also, the exposure value of 75 hours is a suspect outlier because it falls beyond the upper inner fence. Thus, the box plot method detected an additional two outliers.

Before any type of inference is made concerning the population of ethics exposure values, we should consider whether these three outliers are legitimate observations (in which case they will remain in the data set) or are associated with physicians who are not members of the population of interest (in which case they will be removed from the data set).

Data Set: ETHICS

Figure SIA2.6

Minitab descriptive statistics for practice experience and ethics exposure

Descriptive Statistics: YRSPRAC, EDHRS

Variable	N	N*	Mean	StDev	Q1	Median	Q3	IQR
YRSPRAC	112	6	14.598	9.161	7.000	14.000	20.000	13.000
EDHRS	83	35	23.9	109.6	1.0	5.0	20.0	19.0

Exercises 2.103–2.116

Learning the Mechanics

2.103 A sample data set has a mean of 57 and a standard deviation
[NW] of 11. Determine whether each of the following sample measurements are outliers.
  a. 65
  b. 21
  c. 72
  d. 98

2.104 Define the 25th, 50th, and 75th percentiles of a data set. Explain how they provide a description of the data.

2.105 Suppose a data set consisting of exam scores has a lower quartile $Q_L = 60$, a median $m = 75$, and an upper quartile $Q_U = 85$. The scores on the exam range from 18 to 100. Without having the actual scores available to you, construct as much of the box plot as possible.

2.106 Consider the horizontal box plot shown below.

[NW] **a.** What is the median of the data set (approximately)?

b. What are the upper and lower quartiles of the data set (approximately)?

c. What is the interquartile range of the data set (approximately)?

d. Is the data set skewed to the left, skewed to the right, or symmetric?

e. What percentage of the measurements in the data set lie to the right of the median? To the left of the upper quartile?

f. Identify any outliers in the data.

Applying the Concepts—Basic

2.107 Budget lapsing at army hospitals. Accountants use the term *budget lapsing* to describe the situation that occurs when unspent funds do not carry over from one budgeting period to the next. Due to budget lapsing, U.S. army hospitals tend to stockpile pharmaceuticals and other supplies toward the end of the fiscal year, leading to a spike in expenditures. This phenomenon was investigated in the *Journal of Management Accounting Research* (Vol. 19, 2007). Data on expenses per full-time equivalent employees for a sample of 1,751 army hospitals yielded the following summary statistics: $\bar{x} = \$6,563$, $m = \$6,232$, $s = \$2,484$, $Q_L = \$5,309$, and $Q_U = \$7,216$.

a. Interpret, practically, the measures of relative standing.

b. Compute the interquartile range, IQR, for the data.

c. What proportion of the 1,751 army hospitals have expenses between $5,309 and $7,216?

2.108 Treating psoriasis with the "Doctorfish of Kangal." Psoriasis is a skin disorder with no known cure and no proven effective pharmacological treatment. An alternative treatment for psoriasis is ichthyotherapy, also known as therapy with the "Doctorfish of Kangal." Fish from the hot pools of Kangal, Turkey, feed on the skin scales of bathers, reportedly reducing the symptoms of psoriasis. In one study, 67 patients diagnosed with psoriasis underwent three weeks of ichthyotherapy (*Evidence-Based Research in Complementary and Alternative Medicine*, Dec. 2006). The Psoriasis Area Severity Index (PASI) of each patient was measured both before and after treatment. (The lower the PASI score, the better is the skin condition.) Box plots of the PASI scores, both before (baseline) and after three weeks of ichthyotherapy treatment, are shown in the accompanying diagram.

a. Find the approximate 25th percentile, the median, and the 75th percentile for the PASI scores before treatment.

b. Find the approximate 25th percentile, the median, and the 75th percentile for the PASI scores after treatment.

c. Comment on the effectiveness of ichthyotherapy in treating psoriasis.

2.109 Semester hours taken by CPA candidates. Refer to the *Journal of Accounting and Public Policy* (Spring 2002)

Output for Exercise 2.108

Baseline   After 3 weeks

study of 100,000 first-time candidates for the CPA exam, Exercise 2.51 (p. 63). The number of semester hours of college credit earned by the candidates had a mean of 141.31 hours and a standard deviation of 17.77 hours.

a. Find the z-score for a first-time candidate for the CPA exam who earned 160 semester hours of college credit. Is this observation considered an outlier?

b. Give a value of number of semester hours that would, in fact, be considered an outlier in this data set.

2.110 Salary offers to MBAs. The **MBASAL** file contains the top salary offer (in thousands of dollars) received by each member of a sample of 50 MBA students who graduated from the Graduate School of Management at Rutgers, the state university of New Jersey. Descriptive statistics and a box plot for the data are shown on the accompanying DDXL printouts on p. 89.

a. Find and interpret the z-score associated with the highest salary offer, the lowest salary offer, and the mean salary offer. Would you consider the highest offer to be unusually high? Why or why not?

b. Based on the box plot for this data set, which salary offers (if any) are suspect or highly suspect outliers?

Applying the Concepts—Intermediate

2.111 Time in bankruptcy. Refer to the *Financial Management* (Spring 1995) study of 49 firms filing for prepackaged bankruptcies, Exercise 2.30 (p. 52). Recall that three types of "prepack" firms exist: (1) those who hold no prefiling vote, (2) those who vote their preference for a joint solution; and (3) those who vote their preference for a prepack. (These data are saved in the **BANKRUPT** file.)

a. Construct a box plot for the time in bankruptcy (months) for each type of firm.

b. Find the median bankruptcy times for the three types.

c. How do the variabilities of the bankruptcy times compare for the three types?

d. The standard deviations of the bankruptcy times are 2.47 for "none," 1.72 for "joint," and 0.96 for "prepack." Do the standard deviations agree with the interquartile

DDXL output for Exercise 2.110

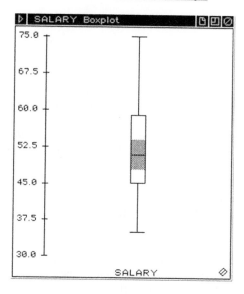

ranges with regard to the comparison of the variabilities of the bankruptcy times?

e. Is there evidence of outliers in any of the three distributions?

2.112 Most powerful women in America. Refer to the *Fortune* (Oct. 16, 2008) ranking of the 50 most powerful women in America, Exercise 2.48 (p. 62). The data are saved in the **WPOWER50** file. Use side-by-side box plots to compare the ages of the women in three groups based on their position within the firm: Group 1 (CEO/ chairman, CEO/president, COO/ president, EVP/president, or CFO/president); Group 2 (CEO, CFO, EVP/COO, CFO/EVP, CIO/EVP, chairman, COO, CRO, or president); Group 3 (EVP, executive, founder, SVP, treasurer, VP, director, or vice chair). Do you detect any outliers?

2.113 Sanitation inspection of cruise ships. Refer to Exercise 2.80 (p. 75) and the data on the sanitation levels of passenger cruise ships. The data are saved in the **SHIPSANIT** file.

a. Use the box plot method to detect any outliers in the data set.

b. Use the *z*-score method to detect any outliers in the data set.

c. Do the two methods agree? If not, explain why.

2.114 Hazardous waste cleanup in Arkansas. Refer to Exercise 2.99 (p. 80) and the data on the number of Superfund sites

in each of 75 Arkansas counties. The data are saved in the **ARKFUND** file.

a. There is at least one outlier in the data. Use the methods of this chapter to detect the outliers.

b. Delete the outlier(s) found in part **a** from the data set and recalculate measures of central tendency and variation. Which measures are most affected by the removal of the outlier(s)?

2.115 Network server downtime. A manufacturer of network computer server systems is interested in improving its customer support services. As a first step, its marketing department has been charged with the responsibility of summarizing the extent of customer problems in terms of system downtime. The 40 most recent customers were surveyed to determine the amount of downtime (in hours) they had experienced during the previous month. These data are listed in the table and saved in the **DOWNTIME** file.

Customer Number	Downtime	Customer Number	Downtime
230	12	250	4
231	16	251	10
232	5	252	15
233	16	253	7
234	21	254	20
235	29	255	9
236	38	256	22
237	14	257	18
238	47	258	28
239	0	259	19
240	24	260	34
241	15	261	26
242	13	262	17
243	8	263	11
244	2	264	64
245	11	265	19
246	22	266	18
247	17	267	24
248	31	268	49
249	10	269	50

a. Construct a box plot for these data. Use the information reflected in the box plot to describe the frequency distribution of the data set. Your description should address central tendency, variation, and skewness.

b. Use your box plot to determine which customers are having unusually lengthy downtimes.

c. Find and interpret the *z*-scores associated with the customers you identified in part **b**.

Applying the Concepts — Advanced

2.116 Sensor motion of a robot. Researchers at Carnegie Mellon University developed an algorithm for estimating the sensor motion of a robotic arm by mounting a camera with inertia sensors on the arm (*International Journal of Robotics Research*, Dec. 2004). One variable of interest is the error of estimating arm translation (measured in centimeters). Data for 10 experiments are listed in the following table and saved in the **SENSOR**

Trial	Perturbed Intrinsics	Perturbed Projections	Translation Error (cm)
1	Yes	No	1.0
2	Yes	No	1.3
3	Yes	No	3.0
4	Yes	No	1.5
5	Yes	No	1.3
6	No	Yes	22.9
7	No	Yes	21.0
8	No	Yes	34.4
9	No	Yes	29.8
10	No	Yes	17.7

Source: Strelow, D. and Singh, S. "Motion estimation form image and inertial measurements," *International Journal of Robotics Research,* Vol. 23, No. 12, Dec. 2004 (Table 4). Copyright © 2004 SAGE Publications.

file. In each experiment, the perturbation of camera intrinsics and projections were varied. Suppose a trial resulted in a translation error of 4.5 cm. Is this value an outlier for trials with perturbed intrinsics but no perturbed projections? For trials with perturbed projections but no perturbed intrinsics? What type of camera perturbation most likely occurred for this trial?

2.9 Graphing Bivariate Relationships*

The claim is often made that the crime rate and the unemployment rate are "highly correlated." Another popular belief is that the gross domestic product (GDP) and the rate of inflation are "related." Some people even believe that the Dow Jones Industrial Average and the lengths of fashionable skirts are "associated." The words *correlated, related,* and *associated* imply a relationship between two variables—in the examples above, two *quantitative* variables.

One way to describe the relationship between two quantitative variables—called a **bivariate relationship**—is to plot the data in a **scattergram** (or **scatterplot**). A scattergram is a two-dimensional plot, with one variable's values plotted along the vertical axis and the other along the horizontal axis. For example, Figure 2.32 is a scattergram relating (1) the cost of mechanical work (heating, ventilating, and plumbing) to (2) the floor area of the building for a sample of 26 factory and warehouse buildings. Note that the scattergram suggests a general tendency for mechanical cost to increase as building floor area increases.

When an increase in one variable is generally associated with an increase in the second variable, we say that the two variables are "positively related" or "positively correlated."* Figure 2.32 implies that mechanical cost and floor area are positively correlated. Alternatively, if one variable has a tendency to decrease as the other increases, we say the

Figure 2.32
Scattergram of cost vs. floor area

*A formal definition of correlation is given in Chapter 10. We will learn that correlation measures the strength of the linear (or straight-line) relationship between two quantitative variables.

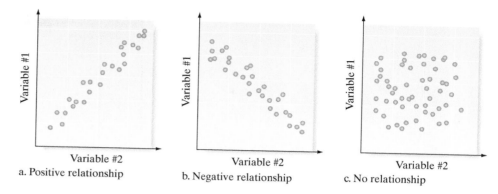

Figure 2.33
Hypothetical bivariate relationship

a. Positive relationship

b. Negative relationship

c. No relationship

variables are "negatively correlated." Figure 2.33 shows several hypothetical scattergrams that portray a positive bivariate relationship (Figure 2.33a), a negative bivariate relationship (Figure 2.33b), and a situation where the two variables are unrelated (Figure 2.33c).

Example 2.19

Graphing Bivariate Data from a Hospital

Problem A medical item used to treat a hospital patient is called a *factor*. For example, factors can be intravenous (IV) tubing, IV fluid, needles, shave kits, bedpans, diapers, dressings, medications, and even code carts. The coronary care unit at Bayonet Point Hospital (St. Petersburg, Florida) recently investigated the relationship between the number of factors used per patient and the patient's length of stay (in days). Data on these two variables for a sample of 50 coronary care patients are given in Table 2.9. Use a scattergram to describe the relationship between the two variables of interest: number of factors and length of stay.

Solution Rather than construct the plot by hand, we resort to a statistical software package. The Excel plot of the data in Table 2.9, with length of stay (LOS) on the vertical axis and number of factors (FACTORS) on the horizontal axis, is shown in Figure 2.34.

Table 2.9 **Data on Patient's Factors and Length of Stay**

Number of Factors	Length of Stay (days)	Number of Factors	Length of Stay (days)
231	9	354	11
323	7	142	7
113	8	286	9
208	5	341	10
162	4	201	5
117	4	158	11
159	6	243	6
169	9	156	6
55	6	184	7
77	3	115	4
103	4	202	6
147	6	206	5
230	6	360	6
78	3	84	3
525	9	331	9
121	7	302	7
248	5	60	2
233	8	110	2
260	4	131	5
224	7	364	4
472	12	180	7
220	8	134	6
383	6	401	15
301	9	155	4
262	7	338	8

Source: Bayonet Point Hospital, Coronary Care Unit.

Data Set: MEDFACTORS

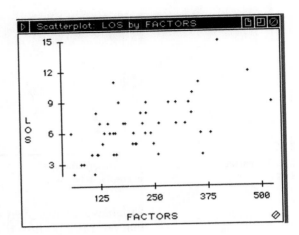

Figure 2.34
DDXL scatterplot of data
in Table 2.9

Although the plotted points exhibit a fair amount of variation, the scattergram clearly shows an increasing trend. It appears that a patient's length of stay is positively correlated with the number of factors used in the patient's care.

Look Back If hospital administrators can be confident that the sample trend shown in Figure 2.34 accurately describes the trend in the population, then they may use this information to improve their forecasts of lengths of stay for future patients.

Now Work Exercise 2.120

The scattergram is a simple but powerful tool for describing a bivariate relationship. However, keep in mind that it is only a graph. No measure of reliability can be attached to inferences made about bivariate populations based on scattergrams of sample data. The statistical tools that enable us to make inferences about bivariate relationships are presented in Chapter 10.

Statistics IN Action Revisited | **Interpreting Scatterplots**

Consider the two quantitative variables, *Length of time in practice* (number of years) and *Amount of exposure to ethics in medical school* (number of hours), measured on a sample of University Community Hospital physicians. To investigate a possible relationship between these two variables, we created a scatterplot for the data in Figure SIA2.7 using Minitab.

At first glance, the graph appears to show almost no relationship between the variables. However, note the outlying data point to the far right of the scatterplot. This point corresponds to a physician

Figure SIA2.7
Minitab scatterplot of practice
experience versus ethics
exposure

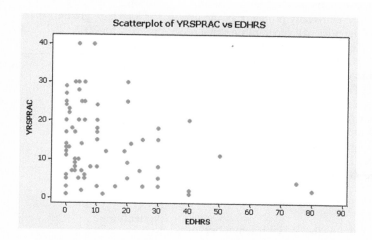

Figure SIA2.8

Minitab scatterplot of practice experience versus ethics exposure—outlier deleted

who reported 1,000 hours of exposure to ethics in medical school. Recall that we classified this data point as a highly suspect outlier in the previous SIA Revisited section (p. 89). If we remove this observation from the data set and rerun the scatterplot option of Minitab, the graph shown in Figure SIA2.8 is produced. Now the trend in the relationship is more apparent. For physicians with 20 or fewer hours of

ethics exposure, there is little or no trend. However, for physicians with more than 20 hours of exposure to ethics, there appears to be a decreasing trend; that is, for physicians with high exposure to ethics, practice experience and exposure time are apparently negatively related.

Data Set: ETHICS

Exercises 2.117–2.126

Learning the Mechanics

2.117 Construct a scattergram for the data in the following table.

Variable 1:	5	1	1.5	2	2.5	3	3.5	4	4.5	5
Variable 2:	2	1	3	4	6	10	9	12	17	17

2.118 Construct a scattergram for the data in the following table.

Variable 1:	5	3	−1	2	7	6	4	0	8
Variable 2:	14	3	10	1	8	5	3	2	12

Applying the Concepts—Basic

2.119 Does elevation impact hitting performance in baseball? The Colorado Rockies play their major league home baseball games at Coors Field, Denver. Each year, the Rockies are among the leaders in team batting statistics (e.g., home runs, batting average, and slugging percentage). Many baseball experts attribute this phenomenon to the "thin air" of Denver—called the "mile-high" city due to its elevation. *Chance* (Winter 2006) investigated the effects of elevation on slugging percentage in Major League Baseball. Data were compiled on players' composite slugging percentage at each of 29 cities for the 2003 season, as well as each city's elevation (feet above sea level). The data are saved in the **MLBPARKS** file. (Selected observations are shown in the table.) Construct a scattergram for the data. Do you detect a trend?

City	Slug Pct.	Elevation
Anaheim	.480	160
Arlington	.605	616
Atlanta	.530	1,050
Baltimore	.505	130
Boston	.505	20
⋮	⋮	⋮
Denver	.625	5,277
⋮	⋮	⋮
Seattle	.550	350
San Francisco	.510	63
St. Louis	.570	465
Tampa	.500	10
Toronto	.535	566

Source: Schaffer, J. & Heiny, E.L. "The effects of elevation on slugging percentage in Major League Baseball." *Chance*, Vol. 19, No. 1, Winter 2006 (adapted from Figure 2, p. 30). Reprinted with permission from *Chance*. © 2006 by the American Statistical Association. All rights reserved.

2.120 State SAT scores. Refer to Exercise 2.29 (p. 52) and the data on state SAT scores saved in the **SATSCORES** file. Construct a scatterplot for the data, with 2000 SAT score on the horizontal axis and 2007 SAT score on the vertical axis. What type of trend do you detect?

2.121 Characteristics of diamonds sold at retail. Refer to the *Journal of Statistics Education* data on diamonds saved in the **DIAMONDS** file. In addition to the number of carats, the asking price for the each of the 308 diamonds for sale on the open market was recorded. Construct a scatterplot for the data, with number of carats on the horizontal axis and price on the vertical axis. What type of trend do you detect?

2.122 **Are geography journals worth their cost?** In *Geoforum* (Vol. 37, 2006), Simon Fraser University professor Nicholas Blomley assessed whether the price of a geography journal is correlated with quality. He collected pricing data (cost for a 1-year subscription in U.S. dollars) for a sample of 28 geography journals. In addition to cost, three other variables were measured: Journal Impact Factor (JIF), defined as the average number of times articles from the journal have been cited; number of citations for a journal over the past five years; and Relative Price Index (RPI), a measure developed by economists. [Note: A journal with an RPI less than 1.25 is considered a "good value."] The data for the 28 geography journals are saved in the **GEOJRNL** file and listed in the next table.

  a. Construct a scatterplot for the variables JIF and cost. Do you detect a trend?

  b. Construct a scatterplot for the variables number of cites and cost. Do you detect a trend?

  c. Construct a scatterplot for the variables RPI and cost. Do you detect a trend?

Journal	Cost ($)	JIF	Cites	RPI
J. Econ. Geogr.	468	3.139	207	1.16
Prog. Hum. Geog.	624	2.943	544	0.77
T. I. Brit. Geogr.	499	2.388	249	1.11
Econ. Geogr.	90	2.325	173	0.30
A. A. A. Geogr.	698	2.115	377	0.93
Antipode	717	1.922	333	0.96
Reg. Stud.	1,312	1.652	445	1.49
Environ. Plan A	1,297	1.622	773	0.91
Environ. Plan D	479	1.591	297	0.99
Geoforum	1,118	1.560	298	1.58
Area	242	1.475	215	0.53
Polit. Geogr.	1,099	1.316	282	1.92
Int. J. Geogr. IS	1,733	1.234	240	3.42
Landscape. Ur. Plan	1,619	1.204	446	1.56
Sing. J. Trop. Geo.	197	1.029	62	1.13
Aust. Geogr.	345	0.947	72	1.83
Eur. Geogr. Eco.	499	0.780	62	1.99
Urban. Geogr.	530	0.667	135	1.81
J. Hist. Geogr.	388	0.661	96	1.44
Tij. Eco. Soc. Geo	343	0.518	99	1.00
Cult. Geogr.	538	0.500	24	NA
Pap. Reg. Sci.	397	0.481	89	1.36
Can. Geo. Can.	253	0.429	74	1.05
J. Geo. High. Ed.	1,115	0.413	79	4.33
Cartogr. J.	266	0.295	18	3.11
Geogr. Anal.	213	0.902	106	0.88
Geogr. J.	223	0.857	81	0.94
Appl. Geogr.	646	0.853	74	3.38

Source: Blomley, N. "Is this journal worth US$1118?," *Geoforum*, Vol. 37, 2006. Copyright © 2006 Elsevier Ltd. All rights reserved.

Applying the Concepts—Intermediate

2.123 **Performance ratings of government agencies.** The U.S. Office of Management and Budget (OMB) requires government agencies to produce annual performance and accounting reports (PARS) each year. A research team at George Mason University evaluated the quality of the PARS for 24 government agencies (*The Public Manager*, Summer 2008). Evaluation scores ranged from 12 (lowest) to 60 (highest). The PARS evaluation scores for 2007 and 2008, shown in the accompanying table, are saved in the **PARS** file.

  a. Construct a scattergram for the data. Do you detect a trend in the data?

  b. Based on the graph, identify one or two agencies that had greater than expected PARS evaluation scores for 2008.

Agency	Score07	Score08
Transportation	55	53
Labor	53	51
Veterans	51	51
NRC	39	34
Commerce	37	36
HHS	37	35
DHS	37	30
Justice	35	37
Treasury	35	35
GSA	34	40
Agriculture	33	35
EPA	33	36
Social Security	33	33
USAID	32	42
Education	32	36
Interior	32	31
NASA	32	32
Energy	31	34
HUD	31	30
NSF	31	31
State	31	50
OPM	27	28
SBA	22	31
Defense	17	32

Source: Ellig, J. & Wray, H. "Measuring performance reporting quality," *The Public Manager*, Vol. 37, No. 2, Summer 2008 (p. 66).

2.124 **Spreading rate of spilled liquid.** A contract engineer at DuPont Corp. studied the rate at which a spilled volatile liquid will spread across a surface (*Chemical Engineering*

Time (minutes)	Mass (pounds)
0	6.64
1	6.34
2	6.04
4	5.47
6	4.94
8	4.44
10	3.98
12	3.55
14	3.15
16	2.79
18	2.45
20	2.14
22	1.86
24	1.60
26	1.37
28	1.17
30	0.98
35	0.60
40	0.34
45	0.17
50	0.06
55	0.02
60	0.00

Source: Barry, J. "Estimating rates of spreading and evaporation of volatile liquids," *Chemical Engineering Progress*, Vol. 101, No. 1, Jan. 2005. Reproduced with permission. Copyright © 2005 AICHE.

Progress, Jan. 2005). Assume 50 gallons of methanol spills onto a level surface outdoors. The engineer used derived empirical formulas (assuming a state of turbulent-free convection) to calculate the mass (in pounds) of the spill after a period of time ranging from 0 to 60 minutes. The calculated mass values, given in the table on page 94, are saved in the **LIQUIDSPILL** file. Is there evidence to indicate that the mass of the spill tends to diminish as time increases? Support your answer with a scatterplot.

2.125 Most valuable NFL teams. Refer to the *Forbes* listing of the 2008 values of the 32 teams in the National Football League (NFL), Exercise 2.24 (p. 50). Access the data saved in the **NFLTEAMVALUES** file and construct a scattergram to investigate the relationship between 2008 value ($ millions) and operating income ($ millions). Would you recommend that an NFL executive use operating income to predict a team's current value? Explain.

Applying the Concepts–Advanced

2.126 Ranking driving performance of professional golfers. Refer to *The Sport Journal* (Winter 2007) analysis of a new method for ranking the total driving performance of golfers on the PGA tour, Exercise 2.50 (p. 63). Recall that the method uses both the average driving distance (yards) and driving accuracy (percent of drives that land in the fairway). Data on these two variables for the top 40 PGA golfers are saved in the **PGADRIVER** file. A professional golfer is practicing a new swing to increase his average driving distance. However, he is concerned that his driving accuracy will be lower. Is his concern a valid one? Explain.

2.10 The Time Series Plot

Each of the previous sections has been concerned with describing the information contained in a sample or population of data. Often these data are viewed as having been produced at essentially the same point in time. Thus, time has not been a factor in any of the graphical methods described so far.

Data of interest to managers are often produced and monitored over time. Examples include the daily closing price of their company's common stock, the company's weekly sales volume and quarterly profits, and characteristics—such as weight and length—of products produced by the company.

> Data that are produced and monitored over time are called **time series data.**

Recall from Section 1.4 that a process is a series of actions or operations that generates output over time. Accordingly, measurements taken of a sequence of units produced by a process—such as a production process—are time series data. In general, any sequence of numbers produced over time can be thought of as being generated by a process.

When measurements are made over time, it is important to record both the numerical value and the time or the time period associated with each measurement. With this information, a **time series plot**—sometimes called a **run chart**—can be constructed to describe the time series data and to learn about the process that generated the data. A time series plot is simply a scatterplot with the measurements on the vertical axis and time or the order in which the measurements were made on the horizontal axis. The plotted points are usually connected by straight lines to make it easier to see the changes and movement in the measurements over time. For example, Figure 2.35 is a time series plot of a particular company's monthly sales (number of units sold per month). And Figure 2.36 is a time series plot of the weights of 30 one-gallon paint cans that were consecutively filled by the same filling head. Notice that the weights are plotted against the order in which the cans were filled rather than some unit of time. When monitoring production processes, it is often more convenient to record the order rather than the exact time at which each measurement was made.

Time series plots reveal the movement (trend) and changes (variation) in the variable being monitored. Notice how sales trend upward in the summer and how the variation in the weights of the paint cans increases over time. This kind of information would not be revealed by stem-and-leaf displays or histograms, as the following example illustrates.

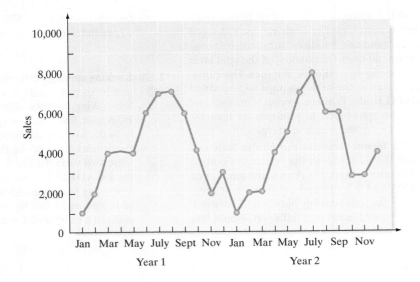

Figure 2.35
Time series plot
of company sales

Figure 2.36
Time series plot
of paint can weights

Example 2.20
Time Series Plot
versus a Histogram

Problem W. Edwards Deming was one of America's most famous statisticians. He was best known for the role he played after World War II in teaching the Japanese how to improve the quality of their products by monitoring and continually improving their production processes. In his book *Out of the Crisis* (1986), Deming warned against the knee-jerk (i.e., automatic) use of histograms to display and extract information from data. As evidence, he offered the following example.

Fifty camera springs were tested in the order in which they were produced. The elongation of each spring was measured under the pull of 20 grams. Both a time series plot and a histogram were constructed from the measurements. They are shown in Figure 2.37, which has been reproduced from Deming's book. If you had to predict the elongation measurement of the next spring to be produced (i.e., spring 51) and could use only one of the two plots to guide your prediction, which would you use? Why?

Solution Only the time series plot describes the behavior *over time* of the process that produces the springs. The fact that the elongation measurements are decreasing over time can be gleaned only from the time series plot. Because the histogram does not reflect the order in which the springs were produced, it in effect represents all observations as having been produced simultaneously. Using the histogram to predict the elongation of the 51st spring would very likely lead to an overestimate.

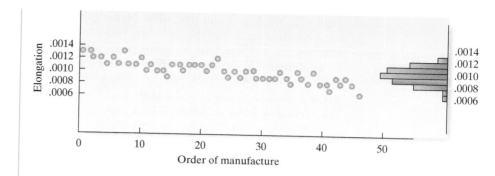

Figure 2.37
Deming's time series plot and histogram

Look Back The lesson from Deming's example is this: For displaying and analyzing data that have been generated over time by a process, the primary graphical tool is the time series plot, not the histogram.

We cover many other aspects of the statistical analysis of time series data in Chapter 13 (available on a CD that accompanies the text).

2.11 Distorting the Truth with Descriptive Techniques

A picture may be "worth a thousand words," but pictures can also color messages or distort them. In fact, the pictures in statistics (e.g., histograms, bar charts, time series plots, etc.) are susceptible to distortion, whether unintentional or as a result of unethical statistical practices. In this section, we will mention a few of the pitfalls to watch for when interpreting a chart, graph, or numerical descriptive measure.

Graphical Distortions

One common way to change the impression conveyed by a graph is to change the scale on the vertical axis, the horizontal axis, or both. For example, Figure 2.38 is a bar graph that shows the market share of sales for a company for each of the years 2004 to 2009. If you want to show that the change in firm A's market share over time is moderate, you should pack in a large number of units per inch on the vertical axis—that is, make the distance between successive units on the vertical scale small, as shown in Figure 2.38. You can see that a change in the firm's market share over time is barely apparent.

If you want to use the same data to make the changes in firm A's market share appear large, you should increase the distance between successive units on the vertical axis—that is, stretch the vertical axis by graphing only a few units per inch, as in

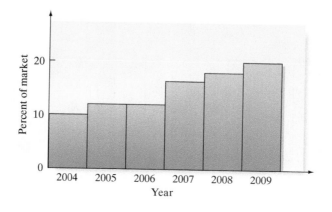

Figure 2.38
Firm A's market share from 2004 to 2009—packed vertical axis

Figure 2.39. A telltale sign of stretching is a long vertical axis, but this is often hidden by starting the vertical axis at some point above 0, as shown in the time series plot, Figure 2.40(a). The same effect can be achieved by using a broken line—called a *scale break*—for the vertical axis, as shown in Figure 2.40(b).

Stretching the horizontal axis (increasing the distance between successive units) may also lead you to incorrect conclusions. With bar graphs, a visual distortion can be achieved by making the width of the bars proportional to the height. For example, look at the bar chart in Figure 2.41(a), which depicts the percentage of a year's total automobile sales attributable to each of four major manufacturers. Now suppose we make both the width and the height grow as the market share grows. This change is shown in Figure 2.41(b). The reader may tend to equate the *area* of the bars with the relative market share of each manufacturer. But the fact is the true relative market share is proportional only to the *height* of the bars.

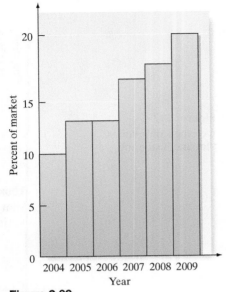

Figure 2.39
Firm A's market share from 2004 to 2009—stretched vertical axis

Ethics ɪɴ Statistics

Intentionally distorting a graph to portray a particular viewpoint is considered *unethical statistical practice*.

Sometimes we do not need to manipulate the graph to distort the impression it creates. Modifying the verbal description that accompanies the graph can change the interpretation that will be made by the viewer. Figure 2.42 provides good illustration of this ploy.

Although we've discussed only a few of the ways that graphs can be used to convey misleading pictures of phenomena, the lesson is clear. Look at all graphical descriptions of data with a critical eye. Particularly, check the axes and the size of the units on each axis. Ignore the visual changes and concentrate on the actual numerical changes indicated by the graph or chart.

Misleading Numerical Descriptive Statistics

The information in a data set can also be distorted by using numerical descriptive measures, as Example 2.21 indicates.

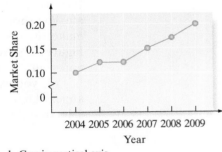

Figure 2.40

Firm A's market share from 2004 to 2009

a. Vertical axis started at a point greater than 0

b. Gap in vertical axis

Figure 2.41

Relative share of the automobile market for each of four major manufacturers

a. Bar chart

b. Width of bars grows with height

Production declines again

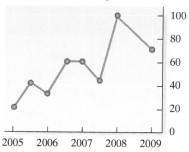

For our production, we need not even change the chart, so we can't be accused of fudging the data. Here we'll simply change the title so that for the Senate subcommittee, we'll indicate that we're not doing as well as in the past . . .

2009: 2nd best year for production

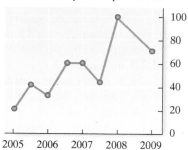

whereas for the general public, we'll tell them that we're still in the prime years.

Figure 2.42

Changing the verbal description to change a viewer's interpretation *Source:* Adapted from Selazny, G. "Grappling with Graphics," *Management Review,* Oct. 1975, p. 7.

Example 2.21

Misleading Descriptive Statistics

Problem Suppose you're considering working for a small law firm—one that currently has a senior member and three junior members. You inquire about the salary you could expect to earn if you join the firm. Unfortunately, you receive two answers:

> *Answer A:* The senior member tells you that an "average employee" earns $107,500.
> *Answer B:* One of the junior members later tells you that an "average employee" earns $95,000.

Which answer can you believe?

Solution The confusion exists because the phrase "average employee" has not been clearly defined. Suppose the four salaries paid are $95,000 for each of the three junior members and $145,000 for the senior member. Thus,

$$\text{Mean} = \frac{3(\$95,000) + \$145,000}{4} = \frac{\$430,000}{4} = \$107,500$$

$$\text{Median} = \$95,000$$

You can now see how the two answers were obtained. The senior member reported the mean of the four salaries, and the junior member reported the median. The information you received was distorted because neither person stated which measure of central tendency was being used.

Look Back Based on our earlier discussion of the mean and median, we would probably prefer the median as the measure that best describes the salary of the "average" employee.

Another distortion of information in a sample occurs when *only* a measure of central tendency is reported. Both a measure of central tendency and a measure of variability are needed to obtain an accurate mental image of a data set.

Suppose you want to buy a new car and are trying to decide which of two models to purchase. Because energy and economy are both important issues, you decide to purchase

Figure 2.43
Mileage distributions
for two car models

model A because its EPA mileage rating is 32 miles per gallon in the city, whereas the mileage rating for model B is only 30 miles per gallon in the city.

However, you may have acted too quickly. How much variability is associated with the ratings? As an extreme example, suppose that further investigation reveals that the standard deviation for model A mileages is 5 miles per gallon, whereas that for model B is only 1 mile per gallon. If the mileages form a mound-shaped distribution, they might appear as shown in Figure 2.43. Note that the larger amount of variability associated with model A implies that more risk is involved in purchasing model A—that is, the particular car you purchase is more likely to have a mileage rating that will greatly differ from the EPA rating of 32 miles per gallon if you purchase model A, while a model B car is not likely to vary from the 30-miles-per-gallon rating by more than 2 miles per gallon.

We conclude this section with another example on distorting the truth with numerical descriptive measures.

Example 2.22
More Misleading Descriptive Statistics

Problem *Children out of School in America* is a report on delinquency of school-age children prepared by the Children's Defense Fund (CDF), a government-sponsored organization. Consider the following three reported results of the CDF survey.

- Reported result 1: 25 percent of the 16- and 17-year-olds in the Portland, Maine, Bayside East Housing Project were out of school. Fact: *Only eight children were surveyed; two were found to be out of school.*

- Reported result 2: Of all the secondary-school students who had been suspended more than once in census tract 22 in Columbia, South Carolina, 33% had been suspended two times and 67% had been suspended three or more times. Fact: *CDF found only three children in that entire census tract who had been suspended; one child was suspended twice and the other two children, three or more times.*

- Reported result 3: In the Portland Bayside East Housing Project, 50% of all the secondary-school children who had been suspended more than once had been suspended three or more times. Fact: *The survey found two secondary-school children had been suspended in that area; one of them had been suspended three or more times.*

Identify the potential distortions in the results reported by the CDF.

Solution In each of these examples, the reporting of percentages (i.e., relative frequencies) instead of the numbers themselves is misleading. No inference we might draw from the cited examples would be reliable. (We'll see how to measure the reliability of estimated percentages in Chapter 5.) In short, either the report should state the numbers alone instead of percentages, or, better yet, it should state that the numbers were too small to report by region.

Look Back If several regions were combined, the numbers (and percentages) would be more meaningful.

CHAPTER NOTES

Key Terms

Bar graph 35
Bivariate relationship 90
Box plots 82, 83
Central tendency 54
Chebyshev's Rule 71
Class 33
Class frequency 33
Class interval 43
Class percentage 33
Class relative frequency 33
Dot plot 42, 47
Empirical Rule 71
Hinges 82, 83
Histogram 43, 47
Inner fences 82, 83
Interquartile range 82
Lower quartile 82
Mean 55
Measures of central
  tendency 54
Measures of relative
  standing 77
Measures of variability or
  spread 64
Median 56
Middle quartile 82
Modal class 59
Mode 58
Mound-shaped distribution 70, 79
Numerical descriptive
  measures 54
Outer fences 82, 83

Outliers 81
p^{th} percentile 77
Pareto diagram 35
Percentile ranking/score 77
Pie chart 35
Population z-score 78
Quartiles 82
Range 64
Rare-event approach 86
Relative frequency
  histogram 43
Run chart 95
Sample standard
  deviation 66
Sample variance 66
Sample z-score 78
Scattergram 90
Scatterplot 90
Skewness 58
Spread 64
Standard deviation 66
Stem-and-leaf display 42, 47
Summation notation 54
Symmetric distribution 70
Time series data 95
Time series plot 95
Time study 70
Upper quartile 82
Variability 54
Variance 66
Whiskers 82, 83
z-score 78

Key Symbols

	Sample	Population
Mean:	$\overline{x}$	μ
Variance:	s^2	σ^2
Std. Dev.:	s	σ
Median:	m	
Lower Quartile:	Q_L	
Upper Quartile:	Q_U	
Interquartile Range:	IQR	

Key Ideas

Describing Qualitative Data

1. Identify **category classes**
2. Determine **class frequencies**
3. **Class relative frequency** = (class frequency)/n
4. **Graph** relative frequencies

Pie Chart:

Bar Graph:

Pareto Diagram:

Graphing Quantitative Data

1 Variable
1. Identify class intervals
2. Determine **class interval frequencies**
3. **Class interval relative frequency** =
(class interval frequency)/n
4. **Graph** class interval relative frequencies

Dot Plot:

Stem-and-Leaf Display:

```
1 | 3
2 | 2489
3 | 126678
4 | 37
5 | 2
```

Histogram:

Box Plot:

2 Variables

Scatterplot:

Numerical Description of Quantitative Data

Central Tendency
Mean: $\bar{x} = (\Sigma x_i)/n$
Median: Middle value when data
ranked in order
Mode: Value that occurs most often

Variation
Range: Difference between largest and
smallest value
Variance:

$$s^2 = \frac{\Sigma(x_i - \bar{x})^2}{n - 1} = \frac{\Sigma x_i^2 - \dfrac{(\Sigma x_i)^2}{n}}{n - 1}$$

Std Dev.: $s = \sqrt{s^2}$
Interquartile Range: $\text{IQR} = Q_U - Q_L$

Relative Standing
Percentile Score: Percentage of values
that fall below *x*-score
z-score:

$$z = (x - \bar{x})/s$$

Rules for Detecting Quantitative Outliers

Interval	Chebyshev's Rule	Empirical Rule
$\bar{x} \pm s$	At least 0%	$\approx 68\%$
$\bar{x} \pm 2s$	At least 75%	$\approx 95\%$
$\bar{x} \pm 3s$	At least 89%	$\approx$ All

Rules for Detecting Quantitative Outliers

Method	Suspect	Highly Suspect
Box plot:	Values between inner & outer fences	Values beyond outer fences
z-score:	$2 < |z| < 3$	$|z| > 3$

Guide to Selecting the Data Description Method

Supplementary Exercises 2.127–2.159

Learning the Mechanics

2.127 Construct a relative frequency histogram for the data summarized in the accompanying table.

Measurement Class	Relative Frequency
.00–.75	.02
.75–1.50	.01
1.50–2.25	.03
2.25–3.00	.05
3.00–3.75	.10
3.75–4.50	.14
4.50–5.25	.19
5.25–6.00	.15
6.00–6.75	.12
6.75–7.50	.09
7.50–8.25	.05
8.25–9.00	.04
9.00–9.75	.01

2.128 Discuss the conditions under which the median is preferred to the mean as a measure of central tendency.

2.129 Consider the following three measurements: 50, 70, 80. Find the z-score for each measurement if they are from a population with a mean and standard deviation equal to

a. $\mu = 60, \sigma = 10$ b. $\mu = 50, \sigma = 5$
c. $\mu = 40, \sigma = 10$ d. $\mu = 40, \sigma = 100$

2.130 Refer to Exercise 2.129. For parts **a–d**, determine whether the values 50, 70, and 80 are outliers.

2.131 For each of the following data sets, compute $\bar{x}$, s^2, and s:
a. 13, 1, 10, 3, 3
b. 13, 6, 6, 0
c. 1, 0, 1, 10, 11, 11, 15
d. 3, 3, 3, 3

2.132 For each of the following data sets, compute $\bar{x}$, s^2, and s. If appropriate, specify the units in which your answers are expressed.
a. 4, 6, 6, 5, 6, 7
b. −$1, $4, −$3, $0, −$3, −$6
c. $\frac{3}{5}\%, \frac{4}{5}\%, \frac{2}{5}\%, \frac{1}{5}\%, \frac{1}{16}\%$
d. Calculate the range of each data set in parts **a–c**.

2.133 Explain why we generally prefer the standard deviation to the range as a measure of variability for quantitative data.

2.134 If the range of a set of data is 20, find a rough approximation to the standard deviation of the data set.

2.135 Construct a scattergram for the data in the following table.

Variable 1:	174	268	345	119	400	520	190	448	307	252
Variable 2:	8	10	15	7	22	31	15	20	11	9

Applying the Concepts—Basic

2.136 **National firearms survey.** In the journal *Injury Prevention* (Jan. 2007), researchers from the Harvard School of

Public Health reported on the size and composition of privately held firearm stock in the United States. In a representative household telephone survey of 2,770 adults, 26% reported that they own at least one gun. The accompanying graphic summarizes the types of firearms owned.
a. What type of graph is shown?
b. Identify the qualitative variable described in the graph.
c. From the graph, identify the most common type of firearms.
d. Convert the graph into a Pareto diagram. Interpret the results.

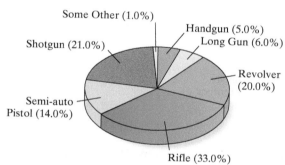

Some Other (1.0%)
Handgun (5.0%)
Long Gun (6.0%)
Shotgun (21.0%)
Revolver (20.0%)
Semi-auto Pistol (14.0%)
Rifle (33.0%)

Source: Hepburn, M., Miller, D. A., and Hemenway, D. "The U.S. gun stock: Results from the 2004 national firearms survey," *Injury Prevention*, Vol. 13, No. 1, Jan. 2007 (Figure 1).

2.137 **Business marketing publications.** Business-to-business marketing describes the field of marketing between multiple business entities. The *Journal of Business-to-Business Marketing* (Vol. 15, 2008) produced a pie chart describing the number of business-to-business marketing articles published in all journals, by topical area, between 1971 and 2006. The data used to produce the pie chart are shown in the table and saved in the **MARPUB** file.
a. Compute the relative frequencies for the nine topical areas shown in the table. Interpret the relative frequency for Buyer Behavior.
b. Use the relative frequencies, part **a**, to construct a pie chart for the data. Why is the slice for Marketing Research smaller than the slice for Sales Management?

Area	Number
Global Marketing	235
Sales Management	494
Buyer Behavior	478
Relationships	498
Innovation	398
Marketing Strategy	280
Channels/Distribution	213
Marketing Research	131
Services	136
Total	2,863

Source: "Commentary on 'The essence of business marketing…' by Lichtenthal, Mummalaneni, and Wilson: The JBBM Comes of Age," by Peter J. LaPlaca, *Journal of Business-to-Business Marketing*, Vol. 15, No. 2, 2008 (Figure 4, p. 187). Copyright © 2008 Routledge.

2.138　A boom in U.S. bankruptcies. The American Bankruptcy Institute and the National Bankruptcy Research Center monitor the number of consumer bankruptcy filings each month. The table lists the number of bankruptcy filings for each of the first 10 months of 2008.

a. Explain why the data in the table represent time series data.

b. Construct a time series plot for the monthly number of bankruptcy filings.

c. Do you detect a trend in the time series plot? Explain.

Month in 2008	Number of bankruptcy filings
January	66,050
February	76,120
March	86,165
April	92,291
May	91,214
June	82,770
July	94,124
August	96,413
September	88,663
October	106,266

Source: CardData (www.carddata.com), Nov. 5, 2008.

2.139　Crash tests on new cars. The National Highway Traffic Safety Administration (NHTSA) crash-tests new car models to determine how well they protect the driver and front-seat passenger in a head-on collision. The NHTSA has developed a "star" scoring system for the frontal crash test, with results ranging from one star (*) to five stars (*****). The more stars in the rating, the better the level of crash protection in a head-on collision. The NHTSA crash test results for 98 cars (in a recent model year) are stored in the data file named **CRASH**. The driver-side star ratings for the 98 cars are summarized in the Minitab printout shown below. Use the information in the printout to form a pie chart. Interpret the graph.

Tally for Discrete Variables: DRIVSTAR

DRIVSTAR	Count	Percent
2	4	4.08
3	17	17.35
4	59	60.20
5	18	18.37
N=	98	

2.140　Crash tests on new cars (cont'd). Refer to Exercise 2.139. One quantitative variable recorded by the NHTSA is driver's severity of head injury (measured on a scale from 0 to 1,500). The mean and standard deviation for the 98 driver head-injury ratings in the **CRASH** file are displayed in the Minitab printout below. Use these values to find the z-score for a driver head-injury rating of 408. Interpret the result.

Descriptive Statistics: DRIVHEAD

Variable	N	Mean	StDev	Minimum	Q1	Median	Q3	Maximum
DRIVHEAD	98	603.7	185.4	216.0	475.0	605.0	724.3	1240.0

2.141　Defects in new automobiles. Consider the following data from the automobile industry (adapted from Kane 1989).

All cars produced on a particular day were inspected for defects. The 145 defects found were categorized by type as shown in the accompanying table.

Defect Type	Number
Accessories	50
Body	70
Electrical	10
Engine	5
Transmission	10

a. Construct a Pareto diagram for the data. Use the graph to identify the most frequently observed type of defect.

b. All 70 car body defects were further classified as to type. The frequencies are provided in the following table. Form a Pareto diagram for type of body defect. (Adding this graph to the original Pareto diagram of part **a** is called *exploding the Pareto diagram*.) Interpret the result. What type of body defect should be targeted for special attention?

Body Defect	Number
Chrome	2
Dents	25
Paint	30
Upholstery	10
Windshield	3

2.142　Switching off air bags. Driver-side and passenger-side air bags are installed in all new cars to prevent serious or fatal injury in an automobile crash. However, air bags have been found to cause deaths in children and small people or people with handicaps in low-speed crashes. Consequently, in 1998, the federal government began allowing vehicle owners to request installation of an on–off switch for air bags. The table describes the reasons for requesting the installation of passenger-side on–off switches given by car owners over a two-year period.

Reason	Number of Requests
Infant	1,852
Child	17,148
Medical	8,377
Infant & medical	44
Child & medical	903
Infant & child	1,878
Infant & child & medical	135
Total	30,337

Source: National Highway Transportation Safety Administration, September 2000.

a. What type of variable, quantitative or qualitative, is summarized in the table? Give the values that the variable could assume.

b. Calculate the relative frequencies for each reason.

c. Display the information in the table in an appropriate graph.

d. What proportion of the car owners who requested on–off air bag switches gave medical as one of the reasons?

2.143 Orlando theme park prices. The entrance fees for adults to 14 theme parks and attractions in Orlando, Florida, are listed in the following table. (These data are saved in the **PARKFEES** file.) Find and interpret the mean, median, and mode of the entrance fees. Which measure of central tendency best describes the entrance-fee distribution of the data?

Theme Park/Attraction	Entrance Fee ($)
Blue Water Hot Air Balloons	185.00
Disney Animal Kingdom	56.70
Disney EPCOT Center	56.70
Disney Magic Kingdom	56.70
Disney MGM Studios	56.70
Disney Pleasure Island	20.95
Disney Wide World of Sports Complex	9.00
DisneyQuest	35.00
Gatorland	21.95
Holy Land Experience	29.99
SeaWorld Adventure Park	61.95
Universal CityWalk	11.95
Universal Islands of Adventure	63.00
Universal Studios	63.00

Source: American Automobile Association, 2006.

2.144 Collecting Beanie Babies. Beanie Babies are toy stuffed animals that have become valuable collector's items. *Beanie World Magazine* provided the age, retired status, and value of 50 Beanie Babies. The data are saved in the **BEANIE** file, with several of the observations shown in the table (in the next column).

a. Summarize the retired/current status of the 50 Beanie Babies with an appropriate graph. Interpret the graph.

b. Summarize the values of the 50 Beanie Babies with an appropriate graph. Interpret the graph.

Name	Age (Months)	Retired (R) Current (C)	Value ($)
1. Ally the Alligator	52	R	55.00
2. Batty the Bat	12	C	12.00
3. Bongo the Brown Monkey	28	R	40.00
4. Blackie the Bear	52	C	10.00
5. Bucky the Beaver	40	R	45.00
⋮	⋮	⋮	⋮
46. Stripes the Tiger(Gold/Black)	40	R	400.00
47. Teddy the 1997 Holiday Bear	12	R	50.00
48. Tuffy the Terrier	17	C	10.00
49. Tracker the Basset Hound	5	C	15.00
50. Zip the Black Cat	28	R	40.00

Source: Beanie World Magazine, Sept. 1998.

c. Use a graph to portray the relationship between a Beanie Baby's value and its age. Do you detect a trend?

d. According to Chebyshev's Rule, what percentage of the age measurements would you expect to find in the intervals $\bar{x} \pm .75s$, $\bar{x} \pm 2.5s$, $\bar{x} \pm 4s$?

e. What percentage of the age measurements actually fall in the intervals of part **d**? Compare your results with those of part **d**.

f. Repeat parts **d** and **e** for the value measurements.

2.145 Top Florida law firms. Data on the top-ranked law firms in Florida, obtained from *Florida Trend* magazine (April 2002), are provided in the table and saved in the **FLALAW** file.

a. Find the mean, median, and mode for the number of lawyers at the top-ranked Florida law firms. Interpret these values.

Rank	Firm	Headquarters	Number of Lawyers	Number of Offices
1	Holland & Knight	Tallahassee	529	11
2	Akerman Senterfit	Orlando	355	9
3	Greenberg Traurig	Miami	301	6
4	Carlton Fields	Tampa	207	6
5	Ruden McClosky Smit	Ft. Lauderdale	175	9
6	Fowler White Boggs	Tampa	175	7
7	Foley & Lardner	Orlando	159	5
8	Gray Harris	Orlando	158	6
9	Broad and Cassel	Orlando	150	7
10	Shutts & Bowen	Miami	144	5
11	Steel, Hector & Davis	Miami	141	5
12	Gunster Yoakley	W. Palm Beach	140	6
13	Adorno & Zeder	Miami	105	4
14	Becker & Poliakoff	Ft. Lauderdale	100	12
15	Lowndes Drosdick	Orlando	100	1
16	Conroy Simberg Ganon	Hollywood	91	6
17	Stearns Weaver	Miami	85	3
18	Wicker Smith O'Hara	Miami	85	6
19	Rogers Towers Bailey	Jacksonville	80	2
20	Butler Burnette	Tampa	77	3
21	Bilzin Sumberg Dunn	Miami	70	1
22	Morgan Colling	Orlando	70	4
23	White & Case	Miami	70	1
24	Fowler White Burnett	Miami	64	4
25	Rissman Weisberg	Orlando	63	3
26	Rumberger Kirk	Orlando	63	4

Source: Florida Trend magazine, April 2002, p. 105.

Data Set: FLALAW

b. Find the mean, median, and mode for the number of offices open by top-ranked Florida law firms. Interpret these values.

c. Construct a histogram for the number of lawyers. Which measure of central tendency best describes this distribution?

d. Construct a stem-and-leaf display for the number of offices. Which measure of central tendency best describes this distribution?

e. Construct a scatterplot for the data, with number of law offices on the horizontal axis and number of lawyers on the vertical axis. What type of trend do you detect?

Applying the Concepts—Intermediate

2.146 Survey of computer crime. Refer to the Computer Security Institute (CSI) annual survey of computer crime at U.S. businesses, Exercise 1.20 (p. 23). One question asked, "Did your business suffer unauthorized use of computer systems within the past year?" The responses are summarized in the next table for two survey years, 1999 and 2006. Compare the responses for the 2 years using side-by-side bar charts. What inference can be made from the charts?

Unauthorized Use of Computer Systems	Percentage in 1999	Percentage in 2006
Yes	62	52
No	17	38
Don't know	21	10
Totals	100	100

Source: "2006 CSI/FBI computer crime and security survey," *Computer Security Issues & Trends,* Spring 2006. Adapted from Fig. 12, p. 10.

2.147 Hull failures of oil tankers. Owing to several major ocean oil spills by tank vessels, Congress passed the 1990 Oil Pollution Act, which requires all tankers to be designed with thicker hulls. Further improvements in the structural design of a tank vessel have been proposed since then, each with the objective of reducing the likelihood of an oil spill and decreasing the amount of outflow in the event of a hull puncture. To aid in this development, *Marine Technology* (Jan. 1995) reported on the spillage amount (in thousands of metric tons) and cause of puncture for 42 recent major oil spills from tankers and carriers. [*Note:* Cause of puncture is classified as either collision (C), fire/explosion (FE), hull failure (HF), or grounding (G).] The data are saved in the **OILSPILL** file.

a. Use a graphical method to describe the cause of oil spillage for the 42 tankers. Does the graph suggest that any one cause is more likely to occur than any other? How is this information of value to the design engineers?

b. Find and interpret descriptive statistics for the 42 spillage amounts. Use this information to form an interval that can be used to predict the spillage amount of the next major oil spill.

2.148 Software defects. The Promise Software Engineering Repository is a collection of data sets available to serve businesses in building predictive software models. One such data set, saved in the **SWDEFECTS** file, contains information on 498 modules of software code. Each module was analyzed for defects and classified as "true" if it contained defective code and "false" if not. Access the

data file and produce a bar graph or a pie chart for the defect variable. Use the graph to make a statement about the likelihood of defective software code.

2.149 Evaluating toothpaste brands. *Consumer Reports,* published by Consumers Union, is a magazine that contains ratings and reports for consumers on goods, services, health, and personal finances. Consumers Union reported on the testing of 46 brands of toothpaste (*Consumer Reports,* Sept. 1992). Each was rated on package design, flavor, cleaning ability, fluoride content, and cost per month (a cost estimate based on brushing with half-inch of toothpaste twice daily). The data in the next table (saved in the **TOOTHPASTE** file) are costs per month for the 46 brands. Costs marked by an asterisk represent those brands that carry the American Dental Association (ADA) seal verifying effective decay prevention.

a. Construct a stem-and-leaf display for the data.

b. Circle the individual leaves that represent those brands that carry the ADA seal.

c. What does the pattern of circles suggest about the costs of those brands approved by the ADA?

.58	.66	1.02	1.11	1.77	1.40	.73*	53*	.57*	1.34
1.29	.89*	.49	.53*	.52	3.90	4.73	1.26	.71*	.55*
.59*	.97	.44*	.74*	.51*	.68*	.67	1.22	.39	.55
.62	.66*	1.07	.64	1.32*	1.77*	.80*	.79	.89*	.64
.81*	.79*	.44*	1.09	1.04	1.12				

2.150 Time to develop price quotes. A manufacturer of industrial wheels is losing many profitable orders because of the long time it takes the firm's marketing, engineering, and accounting departments to develop price quotes for potential customers. To remedy this problem, the firm's management would like to set guidelines for the length of time each department should spend developing price quotes. To help develop these guidelines, 50 requests for price quotes were randomly selected from the set of price quotes made last year: the processing time (in days) was determined for each price quote for each department. These times are saved in the **LOSTQUOTES** file. Several observations are displayed in the table below. The price quotes are also classified by whether or not they were "lost" (i.e., whether or not the customer placed an order after receiving the price quote).

Request Number	Marketing	Engineering	Accounting	Lost?
1	7.0	6.2	.1	No
2	.4	5.2	.1	No
3	2.4	4.6	.6	No
4	6.2	13.0	.8	Yes
5	4.7	.9	.5	No
⋮	⋮	⋮	⋮	⋮
46	6.4	1.3	6.2	No
47	4.0	2.4	13.5	Yes
48	10.0	5.3	.1	No
49	8.0	14.4	1.9	Yes
50	7.0	10.0	2.0	No

a. Construct a stem-and-leaf display for the total processing time for each department. Shade the leaves that correspond to "lost" orders in each of the displays, and interpret each of the displays.

b. Using your results from part **a,** develop "maximum processing time" guidelines for each department that, if followed, will help the firm reduce the number of lost orders.

c. Generate summary statistics for the processing times. Interpret the results.

d. Calculate the z-score corresponding to the maximum processing time guideline you developed in part **b** for each department, and for the total processing time.

e. Calculate the maximum processing time corresponding to a z-score of 3 for each of the departments. What percentage of the orders exceed these guidelines? How does this agree with Chebyshev's Rule and the Empirical Rule?

f. Repeat part **e** using a z-score of 2.

g. Compare the percentage of "lost" quotes with corresponding times that exceed at least one of the guidelines in part **e** to the same percentage using the guidelines in part **f.** Which set of guidelines would you recommend be adopted? Why?

2.151 Misleading advertisement. A time series plot similar to the one shown next appeared in a recent advertisement for a well-known golf magazine. One person might interpret the plot's message as the longer you subscribe to the magazine, the better golfer you should become. Another person might interpret it as indicating that if you subscribe for 3 years, your game should improve dramatically.

a. Explain why the plot can be interpreted in more than one way.

b. How could the plot be altered to rectify the current distortion?

2.152 History of corporate acquisitions. Refer to the *Academy of Management Journal* (Aug. 2008) study of corporate acquisitions from 1980 to 2000, Exercise 2.12 (p. 40). The data are saved in the **ACQUISITIONS** file.

a. Construct a time series plot of the number of firms with at least one acquisition.

b. For each year, compute the percentage of sampled firms with at least one acquisition. Then construct a time series plot of these percentages.

c. Which time series plot, part **a** or part **b,** is more informative about the history of corporate acquisitions over time? Explain.

2.153 Radiation levels in homes. In some locations, radiation levels in homes are measured at well above normal background levels in the environment. As a result, many architects and builders are making design changes to ensure adequate air exchange so that radiation will not be "trapped" in homes. In one such location, 50 homes levels were measured, and the mean level was 10 parts per billion (ppb), the median was 8 ppb, and the standard

deviation was 3 ppb. Background levels in this location are at about 4 ppb.

a. Based on these results, is the distribution of the 50 homes' radiation levels symmetric, skewed to the left, or skewed to the right? Why?

b. Use both Chebyshev's Rule and the Empirical Rule to describe the distribution of radiation levels. Which do you think is most appropriate in this case? Why?

c. Use the results from part **b** to approximate the number of homes in this sample that have radiation levels above the background level.

d. Suppose another home is measured at a location 10 miles from the one sampled and has a level of 20 ppb. What is the z-score for this measurement relative to the 50 homes sampled in the other location? Is it likely that this new measurement comes from the same distribution of radiation levels as the other 50? Why? How would you go about confirming your conclusion?

2.154 Amount of zinc phosphide in commercial rat poison. A chemical company produces a substance composed of 98% cracked corn particles and 2% zinc phosphide for use in controlling rat populations in sugarcane fields. Production must be carefully controlled to maintain the 2% zinc phosphide because too much zinc phosphide will cause damage to the sugarcane and too little will be ineffective in controlling the rat population. Records from past production indicate that the distribution of the actual percentage of zinc phosphide present in the substance is approximately mound-shaped, with a mean of 2.0% and a standard deviation of .08%.

a. If the production line is operating correctly, approximately what proportion of batches from a day's production will contain less than 1.84% of zinc phosphide?

b. Suppose one batch chosen randomly actually contains 1.80% zinc phosphide. Does this indicate that there is too little zinc phosphide in today's production? Explain your reasoning.

2.155 U.S. peanut production. If not examined carefully, the graphical description of U.S. peanut production shown on the next page can be misleading.

a. Explain why the graph may mislead some readers.

b. Construct an undistorted graph of U.S. peanut production for the given years.

Applying the Concepts—Advanced

2.156 Investigating the claims of weight-loss clinics. The U.S. Federal Trade Commission assesses fines and other penalties against weight-loss clinics that make unsupported or misleading claims about the effectiveness of their programs. Brochures from two weight-loss clinics both advertise "statistical evidence" about the effectiveness of their programs. Clinic A claims that the *mean* weight loss during the first month is 15 pounds; Clinic B claims a *median* weight loss of 10 pounds.

a. Assuming the statistics are accurately calculated, which clinic would you recommend if you had no other information? Why?

b. Upon further research, the median and standard deviation for Clinic A are found to be 10 pounds and 20 pounds, respectively, while the mean and standard deviation for Clinic B are found to be 10 and 5 pounds,

Graph for Exercise 2.155

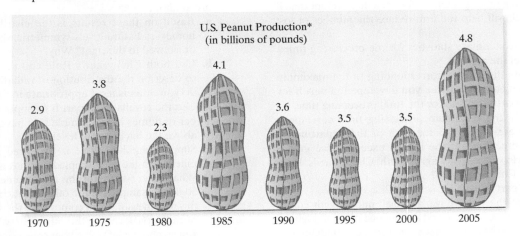

respectively. Both are based on samples of more than 100 clients. Describe the two clinics' weight-loss distributions as completely as possible given this additional information. What would you recommend to a prospective client now? Why?

c. Note that nothing has been said about how the sample of clients upon which the statistics are based was selected. What additional information would be important regarding the sampling techniques employed by the clinics?

2.157 **Age discrimination study.** The Age Discrimination in Employment Act mandates that workers 40 years of age or older be treated without regard to age in all phases of employment (hiring, promotions, firing, etc.). Age discrimination cases are of two types: *disparate treatment* and *disparate impact.* In the former, the issue is whether workers have been intentionally discriminated against. In the latter, the issue is whether employment practices adversely affect the protected class (i.e., workers 40 and over) even though no such effect was intended by the employer (Zabel 1989). A small computer manufacturer laid off 10 of its 20 software engineers. The ages of all engineers at the time of the layoff, shown below, are saved in the **LAYOFF** file. Analyze the data to determine whether the company may be vulnerable to a disparate impact claim.

| Not laid off: | 34 | 55 | 42 | 38 | 42 | 32 | 40 | 40 | 46 | 29 |
| Laid off: | 52 | 35 | 40 | 41 | 40 | 39 | 40 | 64 | 47 | 44 |

Critical Thinking Challenges

2.158 **No Child Left Behind Act.** According to the government, federal spending on K-12 education has increased dramatically over the past 20 years, but student performance has essentially stayed the same. Hence, in 2002, President George Bush signed into law the No Child Left Behind Act, a bill that promised improved student achievement for all U.S. children. *Chance* (Fall 2003) reported on a graphic obtained from the U.S. Department of Education Web site (www.ed.gov) that was designed to support the new legislation. The graphic is reproduced here. The bars in the graph represent annual federal spending on education, in billions of dollars (left-side vertical axis). The horizontal line represents the annual average fourth-grade children's reading ability score (right-side vertical axis). Critically assess the

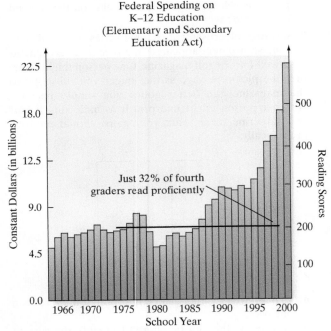

Source: U.S. Department of Education.

information portrayed in the graph. Does it, in fact, support the government's position that our children are not making classroom improvements despite federal spending on education? Use the following facts (divulged in the *Chance* article) to help you frame your answer: (1) The U.S. student population has also increased dramatically over the past 20 years, (2) fourth-grade reading test scores are designed to have an average of 250 with a standard deviation of 50, and (3) the reading test scores of seventh and twelfth grades and the mathematics scores of fourth graders did improve substantially over the past 20 years.

2.159 **Steel rod quality.** In his essay "Making Things Right," W. Edwards Deming considered the role of statistics in the quality control of industrial products.* In one example, Deming examined the quality-control process for a manufacturer of steel rods. Rods produced with diameters smaller than 1 centimeter fit too loosely in their bearings

*From Tanur, J., et al., eds. *Statistics: A Guide to the Unknown.* San Francisco: Holden-Day, 1978, pp. 279–81.

and ultimately must be rejected (thrown out). To determine whether the diameter setting of the machine that produces the rods is correct, 500 rods are selected from the day's production and their diameters are recorded. The distribution of the 500 diameters for one day's production is shown in the accompanying figure. Note that the symbol LSL in the figure represents the 1-centimeter lower specification limit of the steel rod diameters. There has been speculation that some of the inspectors are unaware of the trouble that an undersized rod diameter would cause later in the manufacturing process. Consequently, these inspectors may be passing rods with diameters that were barely below the lower specification limit and recording them in the interval centered at 1.000 centimeter. According to the figure, is there any evidence to support this claim? Explain.

References

Deming, W. E. *Out of the Crisis.* Cambridge, Mass.: M.I.T. Center for Advanced Engineering Study, 1986.

Gitlow, H., Oppenheim, A., Oppenheim, R., and Levine, D. *Quality Management,* 3rd ed. Homewood, Ill.: Irwin, 2004.

Huff, D. *How to Lie with Statistics.* New York: Norton, 1954.

Ishikawa, K. *Guide to Quality Control,* 2nd ed. Asian Productivity Organization, 1986.

Juran, J. M. *Juran on Quality by Design: The New Steps for Planning Quality into Goods and Services.* New York: The Free Press, 1992.

Mendenhall, W., Beaver, R. J., and Beaver, B. M. *Introduction to Probability and Statistics,* 12th ed. North Scituate, Mass.: Duxbury, 2006.

Tufte, E. R. *Beautiful Evidence.* Cheshire Conn.: Graphics Press, 2006.

Tufte, E. R. *Envisioning Information.* Cheshire, Conn.: Graphics Press, 1990.

Tufte, E. R. *Visual Display of Quantiative Information.* Cheshire, Conn.: Graphics Press, 1983.

Tufte, E. R. *Visual Explanations.* Cheshire, Conn.: Graphics Press, 1997.

Tukey, J. *Exploratory Data Analysis.* Reading, Mass.: Addison-Wesley, 1977.

Zabel, S. L. "Statistical Proof of Employment Discrimination." *Statistics: A Guide to the Unknown,* 3rd ed. Pacific Grove, Calif.: Wadsworth, 1989.

USING TECHNOLOGY

SPSS: Describing Data

Graphing Data

Step 1 Click on the "Graphs" button on the SPSS menu bar and then select "Legacy Dialogs."

Step 2 Click on the graph of your choice (bar, pie, boxplot, scatter/dotplot, or histogram) to view the appropriate dialog box. The dialog box for a histogram is shown in Figure 2.S.1.

Figure 2.S.1 SPSS histogram dialog box

Step 3 Make the appropriate variable selections and click "OK" to view the graph.

Stem-and-Leaf Plots

Step 1 Select "Analyze" from the main SPSS menu, then "Descriptive Statistics," and then "Explore."

Step 2 In the "Explore" dialog box, select the variable to be analyzed in the "Dependent List" box, as shown in Figure 2.S.2.

Figure 2.S.2 SPSS explore dialog box

Step 3 Click on either "Both" or "Plots" in the "Display" options and then click "OK" to display the stem-and-leaf graph.

Pareto Diagrams

Step 1 Select "Analyze" from the main SPSS menu, then "Quality Control," and then "Pareto Charts."

Step 2 Click "Define" on the resulting menu and then select the variable to be analyzed and move it to the "Category Axis" box, as shown in Figure 2.S.3.

Figure 2.S.3 SPSS Pareto chart dialog box

Step 3 Click "OK" to display the Pareto diagram.

Numerical Descriptive Statistics

Step 1 Click on the "Analyze" button on the main menu bar and then click on "Descriptive Statistics."

Step 2 Select "Descriptives;" the dialog box is shown in Figure 2.S.4.

Figure 2.S.4 SPSS descriptive statistics dialog box

Step 3 Select the quantitative variables you want to analyze and place them in the "Variable(s)" box. You can control which descriptive statistics appear by clicking the "Options" button on the dialog box and making your selections.

Step 4 Click "OK" to view the descriptive statistics printout.

Percentiles

Step 1 Select "Explore" from the main SPSS menu.

Step 2 In the resulting dialog box (see Figure 2.5.2), select the "Statistics" button and check the "Percentiles" box.

Step 3 Return to the "Explore" dialog box and click "OK" to generate the descriptive statistics.

Minitab: Describing Data

Graphing Data

Step 1 Click on the "Graph" button on the Minitab menu bar.

Step 2 Click on the graph of your choice (bar, pie, scatterplot, histogram, dotplot, or stem-and-leaf) to view the appropriate dialog box. The dialog box for a histogram is shown in Figure 2.M.1.

Figure 2.M.1 Minitab histogram dialog box

Step 3 Make the appropriate variable selections and then click "OK" to view the graph.

Numerical Descriptive Statistics

Step 1 Click on the "Stat" button on the main menu bar, click on "Basic Statistics," and then click on "Display Descriptive Statistics." The resulting dialog box appears in Figure 2.M.2.

Figure 2.M.2 Minitab descriptive statistics dialog box

Step 2 Select the quantitative variables you want to analyze and place them in the "Variables" box. You can control which descriptive statistics appear by clicking the "Statistics" button on the dialog box and making your selections. (As an option, you can create histograms and dot plots for the data by clicking the "Graphs" button and making the appropriate selections.)

Step 3 Click "OK" to view the descriptive statistics printout.

Excel/DDXL: Describing Data

Graphing Data

Step 1 Highlight (select) the data columns you want to graph.

Step 2 Click the "Add-Ins" button on the Excel main menu bar and then click "DDXL."

Step 3 From the resulting menu select "Charts and Plots." The "Charts and Plots" dialog box will appear (as shown in Figure 2.E.1).

Figure 2.E.1 DDXL charts and plots menu options

Step 4 Click on the graph of your choice to view the appropriate dialog box. The dialog box for a histogram is shown in Figure 2.E.2.

Figure 2.E.2 DDXL charts and plots menu for a histogram

Step 5 Move the variable of interest into the "Quantitative (or Qualitative) Variable" box and then click "OK" to view the graph.

Numerical Descriptive Statistics

Step 1 Highlight (select) the data columns you want to analyze, then click on "Add-Ins" in the main Excel menu bar and select "DDXL." On the resulting menu select "Summaries."

Step 2 Select "Summary of One Variable" to view the dialog box shown in Figure 2.E.3.

Figure 2.E.3 Excel/DDXL summary of one variable dialog box

Step 3 Move the variable of interest into the "Quantitative Variable" box and then click "OK" to view the summary statistics.

TI-84 Graphing Calculator: Describing Data

Histogram from Raw Data

Step 1 *Enter the data*

• Press **STAT** and select **1:Edit**

Note: If the list already contains data, clear the old data. Use the up arrow to highlight "**L1.**" Press **CLEAR ENTER.**

Use the arrow and **ENTER** keys to enter the data set into **L1.**

Step 2 *Set up the histogram plot*

• Press **2nd** and press **Y =** for **STAT PLOT**

• Press **1** for **Plot 1**

• Set the cursor so that **ON** is flashing

• For **Type,** use the arrow and Enter keys to highlight and select the histogram

• For **Xlist,** choose the column containing the data (in most cases, L1)

Note: Press **2nd 1** for **L1.**

Freq should be set to 1.

Step 3 *Select your window settings*

- Press **WINDOW** and adjust the settings as follows:

$$X \min = \text{lowest class boundary}$$
$$X \max = \text{highest class boundary}$$
$$X \text{ sel} = \text{class width}$$
$$Y \min = 0$$
$$Y \max \geq \text{greatest class frequency}$$
$$Y \text{ scl} = 1$$
$$X \text{ res} = 1$$

Step 4 *View the graph*

- Press **GRAPH**

Optional *Read class frequencies and class boundaries*

Step You can press **TRACE** to read the class frequencies and class boundaries. Use the arrow keys to move between bars.

Example The following figures show TI-84 window settings and histogram for the following sample data:

86, 70, 62, 98, 73, 56, 53, 92, 86, 37, 62, 83, 78, 49, 78, 37, 67, 79, 57

Histogram from a Frequency Table

Step 1 *Enter the data*

- Press **STAT** and select **1:Edit**

Note: If a list already contains data, clear the old data. Use the up arrow to highlight the list name, "**L1**" or "**L2**."

- Press **CLEAR ENTER**
- Enter the midpoint of each class into **L1**
- Enter the class frequencies or relative frequencies into **L2**

Step 2 *Set up the histogram plot*

- Press **2nd** and **Y** = for **STAT PLOT**
- Press **1** for **Plot 1**
- Set the cursor so that **ON** is flashing
- For **Type,** use the arrow and Enter keys to highlight and select the histogram
- For **Xlist,** choose the column containing the midpoints
- For **Freq,** choose the column containing the frequencies or relative frequencies

Step 3–4 *Follow steps 3–4 given above.*

Note: To set up the Window for relative frequencies, be sure to set **Ymax** to a value that is greater than or equal to the largest relative frequency.

One–Variable Descriptive Statistics

Step 1 *Enter the data*

- Press STAT and select **1:Edit**

Note: If the list already contains data, clear the old data. Use the up arrow to highlight "**L1.**" Press **CLEAR ENTER.**

- Use the arrow and **ENTER** keys to enter the data set into L1

Step 2 *Calculate descriptive statistics*

- Press **STAT**
- Press the right arrow key to highlight **CALC**
- Press **ENTER** for **1-Var Stats**
- Enter the name of the list containing your data
- Press **2nd 1** for **L1** (or **2nd 2** for **L2,** etc.)
- Press **ENTER**

You should see the statistics on your screen. Some of the statistics are off the bottom of the screen. Use the down arrow to scroll through to see the remaining statistics. Use the up arrow to scroll back up.

Example The descriptive statistics for the sample data set

86, 70, 62, 98, 73, 56, 53, 92, 86, 37, 62, 83, 78, 49, 78, 37, 67, 79, 57

The output screens for this example are shown below.

Sorting Data (to find the Mode)

The descriptive statistics do not include the mode. To find the mode, sort your data as follows:

- Press **STAT**
- Press **2** for **SORTA(**
- Enter the name of the list your data are in. If your data are in **L1,** press **2nd 1**
- Press **ENTER**
- The screen will say: **DONE**
- To see the sorted data, press **STAT** and select **1:Edit**
- Scroll down through the list and locate the data value that occurs most frequently

Box Plot

Step 1 *Enter the data*

- Press **STAT** and select **1:Edit**

Note: If the list already contains data, clear the old data. Use the up arrow to highlight "**L1**." Press **CLEAR ENTER.**

- Use the arrow and **ENTER** keys to enter the data set into **L1**

Step 2 *Set up the box plot*

- Press **2nd Y =** for **STAT PLOT**
- Press **1** for **Plot 1**
- Set the cursor so that "**ON**" is flashing
- For **TYPE,** use the right arrow to scroll through the plot icons and select the box plot in the middle of the second row
- For **XLIST,** choose **L1**
- Set **FREQ** to **1**

Step 3 *View the graph*

- Press **ZOOM** and select **9:ZoomStat**

Optional *Read the five number summary*

- Press **TRACE**
- Use the left and right arrow keys to move between **minX, Q1, Med, Q3,** and **maxX**

Example Make a box plot for the given data:

86, 70, 62, 98, 73, 56, 53, 92, 86, 37, 62, 83, 78, 49, 78, 37, 67, 79, 57

The output screen for this example is shown below.

Scatterplots

Step 1 *Enter the data*

- Press **STAT** and select **1:Edit**

Note: If a list already contains data, clear the old data. Use the up arrow to highlight the list name, "**L1**" or "**L2**."

- Press **CLEAR ENTER**
- Enter your *x*-data in **L1** and your *y*-data in **L2**

Step 2 *Set up the scatterplot*

- Press **2nd Y =** for **STAT PLOT**
- Press **1** for **Plot1**
- Set the cursor so that **ON** is flashing
- For **Type,** use the arrow and Enter keys to highlight and select the scatterplot (first icon in the first row)
- For **Xlist,** choose the column containing the *x*-data
- For **Ylist,** choose the column containing the *y*-data

Step 3 *View the scatterplot*

- Press **ZOOM 9** for **ZoomStat**

Example The figures below show a table of data entered on the T1-84 and the scatterplot of the data obtained using the steps given above.

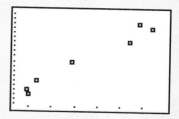

The Kentucky Milk Case—Part 1

Covers Chapters 1 and 2 – Many products and services are purchased by governments, cities, states, and businesses on the basis of scaled bids, and contracts are awarded to the lowest bidders. This process works extremely well in competitive markets, but it has the potential to increase the cost of purchasing if the markets are noncompetitive or if collusive practices are present. An investigation that began with a statistical analysis of bids in the Florida school milk market led to the recovery of more than $33,000,000 from dairies that had conspired to rig the bids there. The investigation spread quickly to other states, and to date, settlements and fines from dairies exceed $100.000,000 for school milk bidrigging in 20 other states. This case concerns a school milk bidrigging investigation in Kentucky.

Each year, the Commonwealth of Kentucky invites bids from dairies to supply half-pint containers of fluid milk products for its school districts. The products include whole white milk, low-fat white milk, and low-fat chocolate milk. In 13 school districts in northern Kentucky, the suppliers (dairies) were accused of "price-fixing" that is conspiring to allocate the districts so that the "winner" was predetermined. Because these districts are located in Boone, Campbell, and Kenton counties, the geographic market they represent is designated as the "tri-county" market. Over a 9-year period, two dairies—Meyer Dairy and Trauth Dairy—were the only bidders on the milk contracts in the school districts in the tri-county market. Consequently, these two companies were awarded all the milk contracts in the market. (In contrast, a large number of different dairies won the milk contracts for the school districts in the remainder of the northern Kentucky market—called the "surrounding" market.) The Commonwealth of Kentucky alleged that Meyer and Trauth conspired to allocate the districts in the tri-county market. To date, one of the dairies (Meyer) has admitted guilt, while the other (Trauth) steadfastly maintains its innocence.

The Commonwealth of Kentucky maintains a database on all bids received from the dairies competing for the milk contracts. Some of these data have been made available to you to analyze to determine whether there is empirical evidence of bid collusion in the tri-county market. The data, saved in the **MILK** file, are described in detail below. Some background information on the data and important economic theory regarding bid collusion is also provided. Use this information to guide your analysis. Prepare a professional document that presents the results of your analysis and gives your opinion regarding collusion.

Variable	Type	Description
YEAR	QN	Year in which milk contract awarded
MARKET	QL	Northern Kentucky Market (TRI-COUNTY or SURROUND)
WINNER	QL	Name of winning dairy
WWBID	QN	Winning bid price of whole white milk (dollars per half-pint)
WWQTY	QN	Quantity of whole white milk purchased (number of half-pints)
LFWBID	QN	Winning bid price of low-fat white milk (dollars per half-pints)
LFWQTY	QN	Quantity of low-fat white milk purchased (number of half-pints)
LFCBID	QN	Winning bid price of low-fat chocolate milk (dollars per half-pint)
LFCQTY	QN	Quantity of low-fat chocolate milk purchased (number of half-pints)
DISTRICT	QL	School district number
KYFMO	QN	FMO minimum raw cost of milk (dollars per half-pint)
MILESM	QN	Distance (miles) from Meyer processing plant to school district
MILEST	QN	Distance (miles) from Trauth processing plant to school district
LETDATE	QL	Date on which bidding on milk contract began (month/day/year)

🔘 *Data Set:* MILK

(Number of observations: 392)

Background Information

Collusive Market Environment

Certain economic features of a market create an environment in which collusion may be found. These basic features include the following:

1. *Few sellers and high concentration.* Only a few dairies control all or nearly all of the milk business in the market.

2. *Homogeneous products.* The products sold are essentially the same from the standpoint of the buyer (i.e., the school district).

3. *Inelastic demand.* Demand is relatively insensitive to price. (*Note:* The quantity of milk required by a school district is primarily determined by school enrollment, not price.)

4. *Similar costs.* The dairies bidding for the milk contracts face similar cost conditions. (*Note:* Approximately 60% of a dairy's production cost is raw milk, which is federally regulated. Meyer and Trauth are dairies of similar size, and both bought their raw milk from the same supplier.)

Although these market structure characteristics create an environment that makes collusive behavior easier, they do not necessarily indicate the existence of collusion. An analysis of the actual bid prices may provide additional information about the degree of competition in the market.

Collusive Bidding Patterns

The analyses of patterns in sealed bids reveal much about the level of competition, or lack thereof, among the vendors serving the market. Consider the following bid analyses:

1. *Market shares.* A market share for a dairy is the number of milk half-pints supplied by the dairy over a given school year, divided by the total number of half-pints supplied to the entire market.

One sign of potential collusive behavior is stable, nearly equal market shares over time for the dairies under investigation.

2. *Incumbency rates.* Market allocation is a common form of collusive behavior in bidrigging conspiracies. Typically, the same dairy controls the same school districts year after year. The incumbency rate for a market in a given school year is defined as the percentage of school districts that are won by the same vendor who won the previous year. An incumbency rate that exceeds 70% has been considered a sign of collusive behavior.

3. *Bid levels and dispersion.* In competitive sealed bid markets, vendors do not share information about their bids. Consequently, more dispersion or variability among the bids is observed than in collusive markets, where vendors communicate about their bids and have a tendency to submit bids in close proximity to one another in an attempt to make the bidding appear competitive. Furthermore, in competitive markets the bid dispersion tends to be directly proportional to the level of the bid: When bids are submitted at relatively high levels, there is more variability among the bids than when they are submitted at or near marginal cost, which will be approximately the same among dairies in the same geographic market.

4. *Price versus cost/distance.* In competitive markets, bid prices are expected to track costs over time. Thus, if the market is competitive, the bid price of milk should be highly correlated with the raw milk cost. Lack of such a relationship is another sign of collusion. Similarly, bid price should be correlated to the distance the product must travel from the processing plant to the school (due to delivery costs) in a competitive market.

5. *Bid sequence.* School milk bids are submitted over the spring and summer months, generally at the end of one school year and before the beginning of the next. When the bids are examined in sequence in competitive markets, the level of bidding is expected to fall as the bidding season progresses. (This phenomenon is attributable to the learning process that occurs during the season, with bids adjusted accordingly. Dairies may submit relatively high bids early in the season to "test the market," confident that volume can be picked up later if the early high bids lose. But, dairies who do not win much business early in the season are likely to become more aggressive in their bidding as the season progresses, driving price levels down.) Constant or slightly increasing price patterns of sequential bids in a market where a single dairy wins year after year is considered another indication of collusive behavior.

6. *Comparison of average winning bid prices.* Consider two similar markets, one in which bids are possibly rigged and the other in which bids are competitively determined. In theory, the mean winning price in the "rigged" market will be significantly higher than the mean price in the competitive market for each year in which collusion occurs.

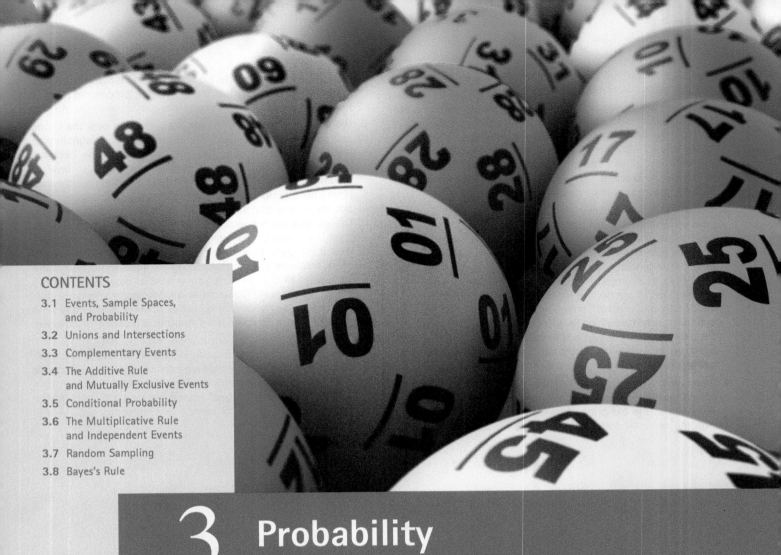

CONTENTS

3 Probability

Where We've Been

- Identified the objective of inferential statistics: to make inferences about a population based on information in a sample.

- Introduced graphical and numerical descriptive measures for both quantitative and qualitative data.

Where We're Going

- Develop probability as a measure of uncertainty.

- Introduce basic rules for finding probabilities.

- Use probability as a measure of reliability for an inference.

Statistics IN Action Lotto Buster!

"Welcome to the Wonderful World of Lottery Bu$ters." So began the premier issue of Lottery Buster, *a monthly publication for players of the state lottery games.* Lottery Buster *provides interesting facts and figures on the 42 state lotteries and 2 multistate lotteries currently operating in the United States and, more importantly, tips on how to increase a player's odds of winning the lottery.*

New Hampshire, in 1963, was the first state in modern times to authorize a state lottery as an alternative to increasing taxes. (Prior to this time, beginning in 1895, lotteries were banned in America because of corruption.) Since then, lotteries have become immensely popular for two reasons: (1) They lure you with the opportunity to win millions of dollars with a $1 investment, and (2) when you lose, at least you believe your money is going to a good cause. Many state lotteries, such as Florida, designate a high percentage of lottery revenues to fund state education.

The popularity of the state lottery has brought with it an avalanche of "experts" and "mathematical wizards" (such as the editors of *Lottery Buster*) who provide advice on how to win the lottery—for a fee, of course! Many offer guaranteed *(continued)* "systems" of winning through computer software products with catchy names such as Lotto Wizard, Lottorobics, Win4d, and Lotto-luck.

For example, most knowledgeable lottery players would agree that the "golden rule" or "first rule" in winning lotteries is *game selection*. State lotteries generally offer three types of games: an Instant (scratch-off tickets or online) game, Daily Numbers (Pick-3 or Pick-4), and a weekly Pick-6 Lotto game.

One version of the Instant game involves scratching off the thin opaque covering on a ticket with the edge of a coin to determine whether you have won or lost. The cost of a ticket ranges from 50¢ to $5, and the amount won ranges from $1 to $100,000 in most states, and to as much as $1 million in others. *Lottery Buster* advises against playing the Instant game because it is "a pure chance play, and you can win only by dumb luck. No skill can be applied to this game."

The Daily Numbers game permits you to choose either a three-digit (Pick-3) or four-digit (Pick-4) number at a cost of $1 per ticket. Each night, the winning number is drawn. If your number matches the winning number, you win a large sum of money, usually $100,000. You do have some control over the Daily Numbers game (because you pick the numbers that you play), and, consequently, there are strategies available to increase your chances of winning. However, the Daily Numbers game, like the Instant game, is not available for out-of-state play.

To play Pick-6 Lotto, you select six numbers of your choice from a field of numbers ranging from 1 to N, where N depends on which state's game you are playing. For example, Florida's current Lotto game involves picking six numbers ranging from 1 to 53. (See Figure SIA3.1.) The cost of a ticket is $1, and the payoff, if your six numbers match the winning numbers drawn, is $7 million or more, depending on the number of tickets purchased. (To date, Florida has had the largest individual state weekly payoff of over $200 million.) In addition to the grand prize, you can win second-, third-, and fourth-prize payoffs by matching five, four, and three of the six numbers drawn, respectively. And you don't have to be a resident of the state to play the state's Lotto game.

In this chapter, several Statistics in Action Revisited examples demonstrate how to use the basic concepts of probability to compute the odds of winning a state lottery game and to assess the validity of the strategies suggested by lottery "experts."

Figure SIA3.1
Reproduction of Florida's 6/53 Lotto ticket

Statistics in Action Revisited

- The Probability of Winning Lotto (p. 127)
- The Probability of Winning A Wheel System (p. 136)
- The Probability of Winning Cash 3 or Play 4 (p. 150)

Recall that one branch of statistics is concerned with decisions about a population based on sample information. You can see how this is accomplished more easily if you understand the relationship between population and sample—a relationship that becomes clearer if we reverse the statistical procedure of making inferences from sample to population. In this chapter, then, we assume that the population is known and calculate the chances of obtaining various samples from the population. Thus, we show that probability is the reverse of statistics: **In probability, we use the population information to infer the probable nature of the sample.**

Probability plays an important role in inference making. Suppose, for example, you have an opportunity to invest in an oil exploration company. Past records show that out of 10 previous oil drillings (a sample of the company's experiences), all 10 came up dry. What do you conclude? Do you think the chances are better than 50:50 that the company will hit a gusher? Should you invest in this company? Chances are, your answer to these questions will be an emphatic "no." If the company's exploratory prowess is sufficient to hit a producing well 50% of the time, a record of 10 dry wells out of 10 drilled is an event that is just too improbable.

Or suppose you're playing poker with what your opponents assure you is a well-shuffled deck of cards. In three consecutive five-card hands, the person on your right is dealt four aces. Based on this sample of three deals, do you think the cards are being adequately shuffled? Again, your answer is likely to be "no" because dealing three hands of four aces is just too improbable if the cards were properly shuffled.

Note that the decisions concerning the potential success of the oil drilling company and the adequacy of card shuffling both involve knowing the chance—or probability—of a certain sample result. Both situations were contrived so that you could easily conclude that the probabilities of the sample results were small. Unfortunately, the probabilities of many observed sample results are not so easy to evaluate intuitively. For these cases we will need the assistance of a theory of probability.

3.1 Events, Sample Spaces, and Probability

Let's begin our treatment of probability with simple examples that are easily described. With the aid of simple examples, we can introduce important definitions that will help us develop the notion of probability more easily.

Suppose a coin is tossed once and the up face is recorded. The result we see and record is called an *observation*, or *measurement*, and the process of making an observation is called an *experiment*. Notice that our definition of *experiment* is broader than the one used in the physical sciences, where you would picture test tubes, microscopes, and other laboratory equipment. Among other things, statistical experiments may include recording an Internet user's preference for a Web browser, recording a change in the Dow Jones Industrial Average from one day to the next, recording the weekly sales of a business firm, and counting the number of errors on a page of an accountant's ledger. The point is that a statistical experiment can be almost any act of observation as long as the outcome is uncertain.

> An **experiment** is an act or process of observation that leads to a single outcome that cannot be predicted with certainty.

Consider another simple experiment consisting of tossing a die and observing the number on the up face. The six basic possible outcomes to this experiment are as follows:

1. Observe a 1
2. Observe a 2
3. Observe a 3
4. Observe a 4
5. Observe a 5
6. Observe a 6

Note that if this experiment is conducted once, *you can observe one and only one of these six basic outcomes, and the outcome cannot be predicted with certainty*. Also, these possibilities cannot be decomposed into more basic outcomes. Because observing the outcome of an experiment is similar to selecting a sample from a population, the basic possible outcomes to an experiment are called *sample points*.*

> A **sample point** is the most basic outcome of an experiment.

Example 3.1

Listing the Sample Points for a Coin-Tossing Experiment

Problem Two coins are tossed, and their up faces are recorded. List all the sample points for this experiment.

Solution Even for a seemingly trivial experiment, we must be careful when listing the sample points. At first glance, we might expect three basic outcomes: Observe two heads, Observe two tails, or Observe one head and one tail. However, further reflection reveals that the last of these, Observe one head and one tail, can be decomposed into two outcomes: Head on coin 1, Tail on coin 2; and Tail on coin 1, Head on coin 2.

A useful tool for illustrating this notion is a **tree diagram.** Figure 3.1 shows a tree diagram for this experiment. At the top of the "tree," there are two branches,

---

*Alternatively, the term *simple event* can be used.

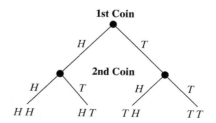

Figure 3.1
Tree diagram for the coin-tossing experiment

representing the two outcomes (*H* or *T*) for the first tossed coin. Each of these outcomes results in two more branches, representing the two outcomes (*H* or *T*) for the second tossed coin. Consequently, after tossing both coins, you can see that we have four sample points.

1. Observe *HH*

2. Observe *HT*

3. Observe *TH*

4. Observe *TT*

where *H* in the first position means "Head on coin 1," *H* in the second position means "Head on coin 2," and so on.

Look Back Even if the coins are identical in appearance, there are, in fact, two distinct coins. Thus, the sample points must account for this distinction.

Now Work Exercise 3.7a

We often wish to refer to the collection of all the sample points of an experiment. This collection is called the *sample space* of the experiment. For example, there are six sample points in the sample space associated with the die-toss experiment. The sample spaces for the experiments discussed thus far are shown in Table 3.1.

Table 3.1   Experiments and Their Sample Spaces

Experiment: Observe the up face on a coin.
Sample space: **1.** Observe a head
                              2. Observe a tail
This sample space can be represented in set notation as a set containing two sample points:

$$S: \{H, T\}$$

where *H* represents the sample point Observe a head and *T* represents the sample point Observe a tail.

Experiment: Observe the up face on a die.
Sample space: **1.** Observe a 1
                              2. Observe a 2
                              3. Observe a 3
                              4. Observe a 4
                              5. Observe a 5
                              6. Observe a 6
This sample space can be represented in set notation as a set of six sample points:

$$S: \{1, 2, 3, 4, 5, 6\}$$

Experiment: Observe the up faces on two coins.
Sample space: **1.** Observe *HH*
                              2. Observe *HT*
                              3. Observe *TH*
                              4. Observe *TT*
This sample space can be represented in set notation as a set of four sample points:

$$S: \{HH, HT, TH, TT\}$$

a. Experiment: Observe
   the up face on a coin

b. Experiment: Observe the
   up face on a die

c. Experiment: Observe the
   up faces on two coins

Figure 3.2
Venn diagrams for the three
experiments from Table 3.1

JOHN VENN (1834–1923)

The English Logician

Born in Hull, England, John Venn is
probably best known for his
pictorial representation of unions
and intersections (the Venn
diagram). While lecturing in Moral
Science at Cambridge University,
Venn wrote *The Logic of Chance*
and two other treatises on logic.
In these works, Venn probably had
his greatest contribution to the
field of probability and statistics—
the notion that the probability of an
event is simply the long-run
proportion of times the event
occurs. Besides being a well-
known mathematician, Venn was
also a historian, philosopher,
priest, and skilled machine builder.
(His machine for bowling cricket
balls once beat a top star on the
Australian cricket team.) ∎

> The **sample space** of an experiment is the collection of all its sample points.

Just as graphs are useful in describing sets of data, a pictorial method for presenting the sample space will often be useful. Figure 3.2 shows such a representation for
each of the experiments in Table 3.1. In each case, the sample space is shown as a closed
figure, labeled *S*, containing all possible sample points. Each sample point is represented
by a solid dot (i.e., a "point") and labeled accordingly. Such graphical representations
are called **Venn diagrams.**

Now that we know that an experiment will result in *only one* basic outcome—
called a *sample point*—and that the sample space is the collection of all possible sample points, we're ready to discuss the probabilities of the sample points. You've
undoubtedly used the term *probability* and have some intuitive idea about its meaning.
Probability is generally used synonymously with "chance," "odds," and similar concepts. For example, if a fair coin is tossed, we might reason that both the sample points,
Observe a head and Observe a tail, have the same *chance* of occurring. Thus, we might
state that "the probability of observing a head is 50%" or "the *odds* of seeing a head
are 50:50." Both of these statements are based on an informal knowledge of probability. We'll begin our treatment of probability by using such informal concepts and then
solidify what we mean later.

*The probability of a sample point is a number between 0 and 1 inclusive that
measures the likelihood that the outcome will occur when the experiment is performed.*
This number is usually taken to be the relative frequency of the occurrence of a sample point in a very long series of repetitions of an experiment.* For example, if we are
assigning probabilities to the two sample points (Observe a head and Observe a tail)
in the coin-toss experiment, we might reason that if we toss a balanced coin a very
large number of times, the sample points Observe a head and Observe a tail will occur
with the same relative frequency of .5.

Our reasoning is supported by Figure 3.3. The figure plots the relative frequency of the number of times that a head occurs when simulating (by computer) the
toss of a coin *N* times, where *N* ranges from as few as 25 tosses to as many as
1,500 tosses of the coin. You can see that when *N* is large (i.e., *N* = 1,500), the relative frequency is converging to .5. Thus, the probability of each sample point in the
coin-tossing experiment is .5.

For some experiments, we may have little or no information on the relative frequency of occurrence of the sample points; consequently, we must assign probabilities
to the sample points based on general information about the experiment. For example,
if the experiment is to invest in a business venture and to observe whether it succeeds
or fails, the sample space would appear as in Figure 3.4.

We are unlikely to be able to assign probabilities to the sample points of this
experiment based on a long series of repetitions because unique factors govern each
performance of this kind of experiment. Instead, we may consider factors such as the
personnel managing the venture, the general state of the economy at the time, the
rate of success of similar ventures, and any other pertinent information. If we finally
decide that the venture has an 80% chance of succeeding, we assign a probability of
.8 to the sample point Success. This probability can be interpreted as a measure of
our degree of belief in the outcome of the business venture; that is, it is a subjective
probability. Notice, however, that such probabilities should be based on expert information that is carefully assessed. If not, we may be misled on any decisions based on
these probabilities or based on any calculations in which they appear. [*Note:* For a
text that deals in detail with the subjective evaluation of probabilities, see Winkler
(1972) or Lindley (1985).]

---

*The result derives from an axiom in probability theory called the **Law of Large Numbers.** Phrased informally, this law states that the relative frequency of the number of times that an outcome occurs when an
experiment is replicated over and over again (i.e., a large number of times) approaches the theoretical
probability of the outcome.

Figure 3.3
Proportion of heads
in N coin tosses

Figure 3.4
Experiment: Invest in a business
venture and observe whether it
succeeds (S) or fails (F)

No matter how you assign the probabilities to sample points, the probabilities assigned must obey two rules:

Probability Rules for Sample Points

Let p_i represent the probability of sample point i.

1. All sample point probabilities *must* lie between 0 and 1 (i.e., $0 \le p_i \le 1$).

2. The probabilities of all the sample points within a sample space *must* sum to 1 (i.e., $\sum p_i = 1$).

Assigning probabilities to sample points is easy for some experiments. For example, if the experiment is to toss a fair coin and observe the face, we would probably all agree to assign a probability of $\frac{1}{2}$ to the two sample points, Observe a head and Observe a tail. However, many experiments have sample points whose probabilities are more difficult to assign.

Example 3.2

Assigning Probabilities to the Sample Points for a Hotel Guest Room Survey

Problem Many American hotels offer complimentary shampoo in their guest rooms. Suppose you randomly select one hotel from a registry of all hotels in the United States and check whether the hotel offers complimentary shampoo. Show how this problem might be formulated in the framework of an experiment with sample points and a sample space. Indicate how probabilities might be assigned to the sample points.

Solution The experiment can be defined as the selection of an American hotel and the observation of whether complimentary shampoo is offered in the hotel's guest rooms. There are two sample points in the sample space corresponding to this experiment:

S: {The hotel offers complimentary shampoo.}

N: {No complimentary shampoo is offered by the hotel.}

The difference between this and the coin-toss experiment becomes apparent when we attempt to assign probabilities to the two sample points. What probability should we assign to the sample point S? If you answer .5, you are assuming that the events S and N

should occur with equal likelihood, just like the sample points Heads and Tails in the coin-toss experiment. But assignment of sample point probabilities for the hotel-shampoo experiment is not so easy. In fact, a recent survey of American hotels found that 80% now offer complimentary shampoo to guests. Then it might be reasonable to approximate the probability of the sample point S as .8 and that of the sample point N as .2.

Look Back Here we see that sample points are not always equally likely, so assigning probabilities to them can be complicated—particularly for experiments that represent real applications (as opposed to coin- and die-toss experiments).

Now Work Exercise 3.9

Although the probabilities of sample points are often of interest in their own right, it is usually probabilities of collections of sample points that are important. Example 3.3 demonstrates this point.

Example 3.3

Finding the Probability of a Collection of Sample Points from a Die-Tossing Experiment

Problem A fair die is tossed, and the up face is observed. If the face is even, you win $1. Otherwise, you lose $1. What is the probability that you win?

Solution Recall that the sample space for this experiment contains six sample points:

$$S: \{1, 2, 3, 4, 5, 6\}$$

Because the die is balanced, we assign a probability of $\frac{1}{6}$ to each of the sample points in this sample space. An even number will occur if one of the sample points, Observe a 2, Observe a 4, or Observe a 6, occurs. A collection of sample points such as this is called an *event*, which we denote by the letter A. Because the event A contains three sample points—each with probability $\frac{1}{6}$—and because no sample points can occur simultaneously, we reason that the probability of A is the sum of the probabilities of the sample points in A. Thus, the probability of A (i.e., the probability that you will win) is $\frac{1}{6} + \frac{1}{6} + \frac{1}{6} = \frac{1}{2}$.

Look Back Based on our notion of probability, $P(A) = \frac{1}{2}$ implies that, *in the long run*, you will win $1 half the time and lose $1 half the time.

Now Work Exercise 3.6

Figure 3.5

Die-toss experiment with event A: Observe an even number

Figure 3.5 is a Venn diagram depicting the sample space associated with a die-toss experiment and the event A, Observe an even number. The event A is represented by the closed figure inside the sample space S. This closed figure A contains all the sample points that comprise it.

To decide which sample points belong to the set associated with an event A, test each sample point in the sample space S. If event A occurs, then that sample point is in the event A. For example, the event A, Observe an even number, in the die-toss experiment will occur if the sample point Observe a 2 occurs. By the same reasoning, the sample points Observe a 4 and Observe a 6 are also in event A.

To summarize, we have demonstrated that an event can be defined in words or it can be defined as a specific set of sample points. This leads us to the following general definition of an event:

An **event** is a specific collection of sample points. Further, a **simple event** contains only a single sample point, while a **compound event** contains two or more sample points.

Example 3.4

The Probability of an Event in a Coin-Tossing Experiment

Problem Consider the experiment of tossing two *unbalanced* coins. Because the coins are *not* balanced, their outcomes (*H* or *T*) are not equiprobable. Suppose the correct probabilities associated with the sample points are given in the table. [*Note:* The necessary properties for assigning probabilities to sample points are satisfied.]

Consider the events

A: {Observe exactly one head}

B: {Observe at least one head}

Calculate the probability of A and the probability of B.

Sample Point	Probability
HH	$\frac{4}{9}$
HT	$\frac{2}{9}$
TH	$\frac{2}{9}$
TT	$\frac{1}{9}$

Solution Event A contains the sample points *HT* and *TH*. Because two or more sample points cannot occur at the same time, we can easily calculate the probability of event A by summing the probabilities of the two sample points. Thus, the probability of observing exactly one head (event A), denoted by the symbol $P(A)$, is

$$P(A) = P(\text{Observe } HT) + P(\text{Observe } TH) = \frac{2}{9} + \frac{2}{9} = \frac{4}{9}$$

Similarly, because B contains the sample points *HH*, *HT*, and *TH*,

$$P(B) = \frac{4}{9} + \frac{2}{9} + \frac{2}{9} = \frac{8}{9}$$

Look Back Again, these probabilities should be interpreted *in the long run*. For example, $P(B) = \frac{8}{9} \approx .89$ implies that if we were to toss two coins an infinite number of times, we would observe at least 2 heads on about 89% of the tosses.

Now Work Exercise 3.3

The preceding example leads us to a general procedure for finding the probability of an event A:

Probability of an Event

The probability of an event A is calculated by summing the probabilities of the sample points in the sample space for A.

Thus, we can summarize the steps for calculating the probability of any event, as indicated in the next box.

Steps for Calculating Probabilities of Events

Step 1 Define the experiment; that is, describe the process used to make an observation and the type of observation that will be recorded.

Step 2 List the sample points.

Step 3 Assign probabilities to the sample points.

Step 4 Determine the collection of sample points contained in the event of interest.

Step 5 Sum the sample point probabilities to get the event probability.

Example 3.5

Applying the Five Steps to Find a Probability in Diversity Training

Problem Diversity training of employees is the latest trend in U.S. business. *USA Today* reported on the primary reasons businesses give for making diversity training part of their strategic planning process. The reasons are summarized in Table 3.2. Assume that one business is selected at random from all U.S. businesses that use diversity training, and the primary reason is determined.

Table 3.2	Primary Reasons for Diversity Training
Reason	Percentage
Comply with personnel policies (CPP)	7
Increase productivity (IP)	47
Stay competitive (SC)	38
Social responsibility (SR)	4
Other (O)	4
Total	100%

a. Define the experiment that generated the data in Table 3.2 and list the sample points.

b. Assign probabilities to the sample points.

c. What is the probability that the primary reason for diversity training is business related, that is, related to competition or productivity?

d. What is the probability that social responsibility is not a primary reason for diversity training?

Solution

a. The experiment is the act of determining the primary reason for diversity training of employees at a U.S. business. The sample points, the simplest outcomes of the experiment, are the five response categories listed in Table 3.2. These sample points are shown in the Venn diagram in Figure 3.6.

b. If, as in Example 3.1, we were to assign equal probabilities in this case, each of the response categories would have a probability of one-fifth $\frac{1}{5}$, or .20. But, by examining Table 3.2 you can see that equal probabilities are not reasonable here because the response percentages were not even approximately the same in the five classifications. It is more reasonable to assign a probability equal to the response percentage in each class, as shown in Table 3.3.*

c. Let the symbol B represent the event that the primary reason for diversity training is business related. B is not a sample point because it consists of more than one of the response classifications (the sample points). In fact, as shown in Figure 3.6, B consists of two sample points, IP and SC. The probability of B is defined to be the sum of the probabilities of the sample points in B.

$$P(B) = P(\text{IP}) + P(\text{SC}) = .47 + .38 = .85$$

d. Let NSR represent the event that social responsibility is not a primary reason for diversity training. Then NSR consists of all sample points except SR, and the probability is the sum of the corresponding sample point probabilities:

$$P(NSR) = P(\text{CPP}) + P(\text{IP}) + P(\text{SC}) + P(\text{O})$$
$$= .07 + .47 + .38 + .04 = .96$$

Look Back The key to solving this problem is to follow the steps outlined in the box. We defined the experiment (Step 1) and listed the sample points (Step 2) in part **a.** The assignment of probabilities to the sample points (Step 3) was done in part **b.** For each probability in parts **c** and **d,** we identified the collection of points in the event (Step 4) and summed their probabilities (Step 5).

Now Work Exercise 3.17

Figure 3.6
Venn diagram for diversity training survey

Table 3.3   Sample Point Probabilities for Diversity Training Survey

Sample Point	Probability
CPP	.07
IP	.47
SC	.38
SR	.04
O	.04

*The response percentages were based on a sample of U.S. businesses; consequently, these assigned probabilities are estimates of the true population-response percentages. You'll learn how to measure the reliability of probability estimates in Chapter 5.

Example 3.6

The Probability of Investing in a Successful Venture

Problem You have the capital to invest in two of four ventures, each of which requires approximately the same amount of investment capital. Unknown to you, two of the investments will eventually fail and two will be successful. You research the four ventures because you think that your research will increase your probability of a successful choice over a purely random selection, and you eventually decide on two. If you used none of the information generated by your research and selected two ventures at random, what is the probability that you would select at least one successful venture?

Solution

Step 1: Denote the two successful enterprises as S_1 and S_2 and the two failing enterprises as F_1 and F_2. The experiment involves a random selection of two out of the four ventures, and each possible pair of ventures represents a sample point.

Step 2: The six sample points that make up the sample space are

1. (S_1, S_2)
2. (S_1, F_1)
3. (S_1, F_2)
4. (S_2, F_1)
5. (S_2, F_2)
6. (F_1, F_2)

Step 3: Next, we assign probabilities to the sample points. If we assume that the choice of any one pair is as likely as any other, then the probability of each sample point is $\frac{1}{6}$.

Step 4: The event of selecting at least one of the two successful ventures includes all the sample points except (F_1, F_2).

Step 5: Now, we find

$$P(\text{Select at least one success}) = P(S_1, S_2) + P(S_1, F_1) + P(S_1, F_2) +$$
$$P(s_2, F_1) + P(S_2, F_2)$$
$$= \frac{1}{6} + \frac{1}{6} + \frac{1}{6} + \frac{1}{6} + \frac{1}{6} = \frac{5}{6}$$

Therefore, with a random selection, the probability of selecting at least one successful venture out of two is $\frac{5}{6}$.

The preceding examples have one thing in common: The number of sample points in each of the sample spaces was small; hence, the sample points were easy to identify and list. How can we manage this when the sample points run into the thousands or millions? For example, suppose you wish to select five business ventures from a group of 1,000. Then each different group of five ventures would represent a sample point. How can you determine the number of sample points associated with this experiment?

One method of determining the number of sample points for a complex experiment is to develop a counting system. Start by examining a simple version of the experiment. For example, see if you can develop a system for counting the number of ways to select two ventures from a total of four (this is exactly what was done in Example 3.6). If the ventures are represented by the symbols V_1, V_2, V_3, and V_4, the sample points could be listed in the following pattern:

$$(V_1, V_2) \quad (V_2, V_3) \quad (V_3, V_4)$$
$$(V_1, V_3) \quad (V_2, V_4)$$
$$(V_1, V_4)$$

Note the pattern and now try a more complex situation—say, sampling three ventures out of five. List the sample points and observe the pattern. Finally, see if you can deduce the pattern for the general case. Perhaps you can program a computer to produce the matching and counting for the number of samples of 5 selected from a total of 1,000.

A second method of determining the number of sample points for an experiment is to use **combinatorial mathematics.** This branch of mathematics is concerned with developing counting rules for given situations. For example, there is a simple rule for finding the number of different samples of five ventures selected from 1,000. This rule, called the **Combinations Rule,** is given in the box.

Combinations Rule

A sample of n elements is to be drawn from a set of N elements. Then, the number of different samples possible is denoted by $\binom{N}{n}$ and is equal to

$$\binom{N}{n} = \frac{N!}{n!(N-n)!}$$

where the factorial symbol (!) means that

$$n! = n(n-1)(n-2)\cdots(3)(2)(1)$$

For example, $5! = 5 \cdot 4 \cdot 3 \cdot 2 \cdot 1$. [*Note:* The quantity 0! is defined to be equal to 1.]

Example 3.7

Using the Combinations Rule to Determine the Number of Possible Investments: Selecting 2 from 4

Problem Refer to Example 3.6, where we selected two ventures from four in which to invest. Use the Combinations Rule to determine how many different selections can be made.

Solution For this example, $N = 4$, $n = 2$, and

$$\binom{4}{2} = \frac{4!}{2!2!} = \frac{4 \cdot 3 \cdot 2 \cdot 1}{(2 \cdot 1)(2 \cdot 1)} = \frac{4 \cdot 3}{2 \cdot 1} = \frac{12}{2} = 6$$

Look Back You can see that this agrees with the number of sample points obtained in Example 3.6.

Now Work Exercise 3.4

Example 3.8

Using the Combinations Rule to Determine the Number of Possible Investments: Selecting 5 from 20

Problem Suppose you plan to invest equal amounts of money in each of five business ventures. If you have 20 ventures from which to make the selection, how many different samples of five ventures can be selected from the 20?

Solution For this example, $N = 20$ and $n = 5$. Then the number of different samples of 5 that can be selected from the 20 ventures is

$$\binom{20}{5} = \frac{20!}{5!(20-5)!} = \frac{20!}{5!15!}$$

$$= \frac{20 \cdot 19 \cdot 18 \cdot \cdots \cdot 3 \cdot 2 \cdot 1}{(5 \cdot 4 \cdot 3 \cdot 2 \cdot 1)(15 \cdot 14 \cdot 13 \cdot \cdots \cdot 3 \cdot 2 \cdot 1)} = \frac{20 \cdot 19 \cdot 18 \cdot 17 \cdot 16}{5 \cdot 4 \cdot 3 \cdot 2 \cdot 1} = 15,504$$

Look Back You can see that attempting to list all the sample points for this experiment would be an extremely tedious and time consuming, if not practically impossible, task.

The Combinations Rule is just one of a large number of counting rules that have been developed by combinatorial mathematicians. This counting rule applies to situations in which the experiment calls for selecting n elements from a total of N elements, without replacing each element before the next is selected. If you are interested in learning other methods for counting sample points for various types of experiments, you will find a few of the basic counting rules in Appendix A. Others can be found in the chapter references.

Statistics IN Action | **Revisited** | The Probability of Winning Lotto

In Florida's state lottery game, called Pick-6 Lotto, you select six numbers of your choice from a set of numbers ranging from 1 to 53. We can apply the Combinations Rule to determine the total number of combinations of 6 numbers selected from 53 (i.e., the total number of sample points [or possible winning tickets]). Here, $N = 53$ and $n = 6$: therefore, we have

$$\binom{N}{n} = \frac{N!}{n!(N - n)!} = \frac{53!}{6!47!}$$

$$= \frac{(53)(52)(51)(50)(49)(48)(47!)}{(6)(5)(4)(3)(2)(1)(47!)}$$

$$= 22,957,480$$

Now, since the Lotto balls are selected at random, each of these 22,957,480 combinations is equally likely to occur. Therefore, the probability of winning Lotto is

$$P(\text{Win6/53 Lotto}) = 1/(22,957,480) = .00000004356$$

This probability is often stated as follows: The odds of winning the game with a single ticket are 1 in 22,957,480, or 1 in approximately 23 million. For all practical purposes, this probability is 0, implying that you have almost no chance of winning the lottery with a single ticket. Yet each

week there is almost always a winner in the Florida Lotto. This apparent contradiction can be explained with the following analogy.

Suppose there is a line of Smart cars, front-to-back, from New York City to Los Angeles, California. Based on the distance between the two cities and the length of a standard minivan, there would be approximately 23 million Smart cars in line. Lottery officials will select, at random, one of the Smart cars and put a check for $10 million dollars in the glove compartment. For a cost of $1, you may roam the country and select one (and only one) Smart car and check the glove compartment. Do you think you will find $10 million in the Smart car you choose? You can be almost certain that you won't. But now permit anyone to enter the lottery for $1 and suppose that 50 million people do so. With such a large number of participants, it is very likely that someone will find the Smart car with the $10 million—but it almost certainly won't be you! (This example illustrates an axiom in statistics called the Law of Large Numbers. See the footnote at the bottom of p. 120.)

Exercises 3.1–3.21

Learning the Mechanics

3.1 An experiment results in one of the following sample points: E_1, E_2, E_3, E_4, or E_5.
   a. Find $P(E_3)$ if $P(E_1) = .1$, $P(E_2) = .2$, $P(E_4) = .1$, and $P(E_5) = .1$.
   b. Find $P(E_3)$ if $P(E_1) = P(E_3)$, $P(E_2) = .1$, $P(E_4) = .2$, and $P(E_5) = .1$.
   c. Find $P(E_3)$ if $P(E_1) = P(E_2) = P(E_4) = P(E_5) = .1$.

3.2 The diagram below describes the sample space of a particular experiment and events A and B.
   a. What is this type of diagram called?
   b. Suppose the sample points are equally likely. Find $P(A)$ and $P(B)$.
   c. Suppose $P(1) = P(2) = P(3) = P(4) = P(5) = \frac{1}{20}$ and $P(6) = P(7) = P(8) = P(9) = P(10) = \frac{3}{20}$. Find $P(A)$ and $P(B)$.

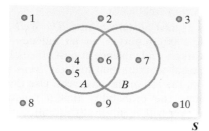

3.3 The sample space for an experiment contains five sample
   [NW] points with probabilities as shown in the table. Find the probability of each of the following events:

Sample Points	Probabilities
1	.05
2	.20
3	.30
4	.30
5	.15

   A: {Either 1, 2, or 3 occurs}
   B: {Either 1, 3, or 5 occurs}
   C: {4 does not occur}

3.4 Compute each of the following:
   [NW]
   a. $\binom{9}{4}$ **b.** $\binom{7}{2}$ **c.** $\binom{4}{4}$

   d. $\binom{5}{0}$ **e.** $\binom{6}{5}$

3.5 Compute the number of ways you can select n elements from N elements for each of the following:
   a. $n = 2, N = 5$
   b. $n = 3, N = 6$
   c. $n = 5, N = 20$

3.6 Two fair dice are tossed, and the face on each die is observed.

[NW]   **a.** Use a tree diagram to find the 36 sample points contained in the sample space.

b. Assign probabilities to the sample points in part **a.**

c. Find the probability of each of the following events:

A = {3 showing on each die}

B = {sum of two numbers showing is 7}

C = {sum of two numbers showing is even}

3.7 Two marbles are drawn at random and without replace-

[NW]   ment from a box containing two blue marbles and three red marbles.

a. List the sample points for this experiment.

b. Assign probabilities to the sample points.

c. Determine the probability of observing each of the following events:

A: {Two blue marbles are drawn.}

B: {A red and a blue marble are drawn.}

C: {Two red marbles are drawn.}

3.8 Simulate the experiment described in Exercise 3.7 using any five identically shaped objects, two of which are one color and three another color. Mix the objects, draw two, record the results, and then replace the objects. Repeat the experiment a large number of times (at least 100). Calculate the proportion of time events A, B, and C occur. How do these proportions compare with the probabilities you calculated in Exercise 3.7? Should these proportions equal the probabilities? Explain.

⚙ Applet Exercise 3.1

Use the applet *Simulating the Probability of Rolling a 6* to explore the relationship between the proportion of 6s rolled on several rolls of a die and the theoretical probability of rolling a 6 on a fair die.

a. To simulate rolling a die one time, click on the *Roll* button on the screen while $n = 1$. The outcome of the roll appears in the list at the right, and the cumulative proportion of 6s for one roll is shown above the graph and as a point on the graph corresponding to 1. Click *Reset* and repeat the process with $n = 1$ several times. What are the possible values of the cumulative proportion of 6s for one roll of a die? Can the cumulative proportion of 6s for one roll of a die equal the theoretical probability of rolling a 6 on a fair die? Explain.

b. Set $n = 10$ and click the *Roll* button. Repeat this several times, resetting after each time. Record the cumulative proportion of 6s for each roll. Compare the cumulative proportions for $n = 10$ to those for $n = 1$ in part **a.** Which tend to be closer to the theoretical probability of rolling a 6 on a fair die?

c. Repeat part **b** for $n = 1,000$, comparing the cumulative proportions for $n = 1,000$ to those for $n = 1$ in part **a** and for $n = 10$ in part **b.**

d. Based on your results for parts **a, b,** and **c,** do you believe that we could justifiably conclude that a die is unfair because we rolled it 10 times and didn't roll any 6s? Explain.

⚙ Applet Exercise 3.2

Use the applet *Simulating the Probability of a Head with a Fair Coin* to explore the relationship between the proportion of heads on several flips of a coin and the theoretical probability of getting heads on one flip of a fair coin.

a. Repeat parts **a–c** of Applet Exercise 3.1 for the experiment of flipping a coin and the event of getting heads.

b. Based on your results for part **a,** do you believe that we could justifiably conclude that a coin is unfair because we flipped it 10 times and didn't roll any heads? Explain.

Applying the Concepts—Basic

3.9 **Colors of M&M's candies.** In 1940, Forrest E. Mars Sr.,

[NW]   formed the Mars Corporation to produce chocolate candies with a sugar shell that could be sold throughout the year and wouldn't melt during the summer. Originally, M&M's Plain Chocolate Candies came in only a brown color. Today, M&M's in standard bags come in six colors: brown, yellow, red, blue, orange, and green. According to Mars Corporation, today 24% of all M&M's produced are blue, 20% are orange, 16% are green, 14% are yellow, 13% are brown, and 13% are red. Suppose you purchase a randomly selected bag of M&M's Plain Chocolate Candies and randomly select one of the M&M's from the bag. The color of the selected M&M is of interest.

a. Identify the outcomes (sample points) of this experiment.

b. Assign reasonable probabilities to the outcomes, part **a.**

c. What is the probability that the selected M&M is brown (the original color)?

d. In 1960, the colors red, green, and yellow were added to brown M&Ms. What is the probability that the selected M&M is either red, green, or yellow?

e. In 1995, based on voting by American consumers, the color blue was added to the M&M mix. What is the probability that the selected M&M is not blue?

3.10 **Workers' unscheduled absence survey.** Each year CCH, Inc., a firm that provides human resources and employment law information, conducts a survey on absenteeism in the workplace. The *2007 CCH Unscheduled Absence Survey* found that of all unscheduled work absences, 34% are due to "personal illness," 22% for "family issues," 18% for "personal needs," 13% for "entitlement mentality," and 13% due to "stress." Consider a randomly selected employee who has an unscheduled work absence.

a. List the sample points for this experiment.

b. Assign reasonable probabilities to the sample points.

c. What is the probability that the absence is due to something other than "personal illness"?

3.11 **Male nannies.** In a recent survey conducted by the International Nanny Association (INA) and reported at the INA Web site (www.nanny.org), 4,176 nannies were placed in a job in a given year. Only 24 of the nannies placed were men. Find the probability that a randomly selected nanny who was placed during the last year is a male nanny (a "mannie").

3.12 **Assaults against postal workers.** *The Wall Street Journal* (Sept. 1, 2000) reported on an independent study of postal workers and violence at post offices. In a sample of 12,000 postal workers, 600 of them were physically assaulted on the job in the past year. Use this information to estimate the probability that a randomly selected postal worker will be physically assaulted on the job during the year.

3.13 Going online for health information. A *cyberchondriac* is defined as a person who regularly searches the Web for health care information (see Exercise 1.18, p. 23). A 2008 Harris Poll surveyed 1,010 U.S. adults by telephone and asked each respondent how often (in the past month) he/she looked for health care information online. The results are summarized in the following table. Consider the response category of a randomly selected person who participated in the Harris Poll.

Response (# per Month)	Percentage of Respondents
None	25
1 or 2	31
3–5	25
6–9	5
10 or more	14
Total	100%

Source: The Harris Poll, July 29, 2008 (Table 3).

a. List the sample points for the experiment.
b. Assign reasonable probabilities to the sample points.
c. Find the probability that the respondent looks for health care information online more than two times per month.

3.14 Incorrectly filed and lost documents. Since the introduction of e-mail into organizations, the use of paper has increased dramatically. The amount of paperwork generated at large organizations can be overwhelming, leading to lack of storage space, incorrectly filed papers, and lost documents. An article in the *Communications of the ACM* (Vol. 43, 2000) reported that 3% of all documents produced at organizations are incorrectly filed, and 7.5% of all documents are lost forever. What is more likely to occur at a large organization, an incorrectly filed document or a document that is lost forever? Explain.

Applying the Concepts—Intermediate

3.15 USDA chicken inspection. The U.S. Department of Agriculture (USDA) reports that, under its standard inspection system, one in every 100 slaughtered chickens pass inspection with fecal contamination. (*Tampa Tribune,* Mar. 31, 2000.)
a. If a slaughtered chicken is selected at random, what is the probability that it passes inspection with fecal contamination?
b. The probability of part **a** was based on a USDA study that found that 306 of 32,075 chicken carcasses passed inspection with fecal contamination. Do you agree with the USDA's statement about the likelihood of a slaughtered chicken passing inspection with fecal contamination?

3.16 PIN pad shipments. Personal identification number (PIN) pads are devices that connect to point-of-sale electronic cash registers for debit and credit card purchases. Refer to *The Nilson Report* (Oct. 2008) listing of the volume of PIN pad shipments by manufacturers worldwide, Exercise 2.5 (p. 39). Recall that for the 12 manufacturers listed in the table, a total of 334,039 PIN pads were shipped in 2007. (The data are saved in the **PINPADS** file.) Suppose you randomly select one of these PIN pads and identify the manufacturer.

Manufacturer	Number Shipped (units)
Bitel	13,500
CyberNet	16,200
Fujian Landi	119,000
Glintt (ParaRede)	5,990
Intelligent	4,562
KwangWoo	42,000
Omron	20,000
Pax Tech.	10,072
ProvencoCadmus	20,000
SZZT Electronics	67,300
Toshiba TEC	12,415
Urmet	3,000

Source: The Nilson Report, No. 912, October 2008 (p. 9).

a. List the sample points for this experiment.
b. Explain why the probability of each sample point is not 1/12, then calculate the probability of each sample point.
c. Find the probability that the PIN pad is shipped by either Fujian Landi or SZZT Electronics.
d. Suppose that 1,000 of the PIN pads shipped in 2007 were found to be defective. Find the probability that the PIN pad selected is one of the defectives.

3.17 Management system failures. Refer to the *Process Safety Progress* (Dec. 2004) study of 83 industrial accidents caused by management system failures, Exercise 2.6 (p. 39). A summary of the root causes of these 83 incidents is reproduced in the following table.

Management System Cause Category	Number of Incidents
Engineering and Design	27
Procedures and Practices	24
Management and Oversight	22
Training and Communication	10
Total	83

Source: Blair, A. S. "Management system failures identified in incidents investigated by the U.S. Chemical Safety and Hazard Investigation Board," *Process Safety Progress,* Vol. 23, No. 4, Dec. 2004, pp. 232–236 (Table 1). Reprinted with permission of John Wiley & Sons, Inc.

a. Find and interpret the probability that an industrial accident is caused by faulty engineering and design.
b. Find and interpret the probability that an industrial accident is caused by something other than faulty procedures and practices.

3.18 Jai-alai bets. The Quinella bet at the paramutual game of jai-alai consists of picking the jai-alai players that will place first and second in a game *irrespective* of order. In jai-alai, eight players (numbered 1, 2, 3, ..., 8) compete in every game.
a. How many different Quinella bets are possible?
b. Suppose you bet the Quinella combination of 2–7. If the players are of equal ability, what is the probability that you win the bet?

3.19 Investing in stocks. From a list of 15 preferred stocks recommended by your broker, you will select three to invest in. How many different ways can you select the three stocks from the 15 recommended stocks?

3.20 Groundwater contamination in wells. Refer to the *Environmental Science & Technology* (Jan. 2005) study of methyl *tert*-butyl ether (MTBE) contamination in New Hampshire wells, Exercise 2.15 (p. 41). Data collected for a sample of 223 wells are saved in the **MTBE** file. Recall that each well was classified according to well class (public or private), aquifier (bedrock or unconsolidated), and detectable level of MTBE (below limit or detect).

a. Consider an experiment in which the well class, aquifier, and detectable MTBE level of a well are observed. List the sample points for this experiment. [Hint: One sample point is private/bedrock/below limit.]

b. Use statistical software to find the number of the 223 wells in each sample point outcome. Then use this information to compute probabilities for the sample points.

c. Find and interpret the probability that a well has a detectable level of MTBE.

3.21 Choosing portable grill displays. University of Maryland marketing professor R. W. Hamilton studied how people attempt to influence the choices of others by offering undesirable alternatives (*Journal of Consumer Research,* Mar. 2003). Such a phenomenon typically occurs when family members propose a vacation spot, friends recommend a restaurant for dinner, and realtors show the buyer potential homes. In one phase of the study, the researcher had each of 124 college students select showroom displays for portable grills. Five different displays (representing five different-sized grills) were available, but only three displays would be selected. The students were instructed to select the displays to maximize purchases of Grill #2 (a smaller-sized grill).

a. In how many possible ways can the three grill displays be selected from the five displays? List the possibilities.

b. The table shows the grill display combinations and the number of each selected by the 124 students. Use this information to assign reasonable probabilities to the different display combinations.

c. Find the probability that a student who participated in the study selected a display combination involving Grill #1.

Grill Display Combination	Number of Students
1-2-3	35
1-2-4	8
1-2-5	42
2-3-4	4
2-3-5	1
2-4-5	34

Source: Hamilton, R. W. "Why do people suggest what they do not want? Using context effects to influence others' choices," *Journal of Consumer Research,* Vol. 29, No. 4, Mar. 2003 (Table 1). Copyright © 2003 JCR, Inc.

3.22 Highest-rated new cars. *Consumer Reports* magazine annually asks readers to evaluate their experiences in buying a new car during the previous year. Analysis of the questionnaires for a recent year revealed that readers were most satisfied with the following three new cars (in no particular order): Infiniti M35, Toyota Prius, and Chevrolet Corvette (*Consumer Reports,* Apr. 2006).

a. List all possible sets of rankings for these top three cars.

b. Assuming that each set of rankings in part **a** is equally likely, what is the probability that readers ranked Toyota Prius first? That readers ranked Infiniti M35 third? That

readers ranked Toyota Prius first and Chevrolet Corvette second (which is, in fact, what they did)?

Applying the Concepts—Advanced

3.23 Odds of winning a race. Handicappers for greyhound races express their belief about the probabilities that each greyhound will win a race in terms of **odds.** If the probability of event E is $P(E)$, then the *odds in favor of E* are $P(E)$ to $1 - P(E)$. Thus, if a handicapper assesses a probability of .25 that Oxford Shoes will win its next race, the odds in favor of Oxford Shoes are $^{25}/_{100}$ to $^{75}/_{100}$, or 1 to 3. It follows that the *odds against E* are $1 - P(E)$ to $P(E)$, or 3 to 1 against a win by Oxford Shoes. In general, if the odds in favor of event E are a to b, then $P(E) = a/(a + b)$.

a. A second handicapper assesses the probability of a win by Oxford Shoes to be $^{1}/_{3}$. According to the second handicapper, what are the odds in favor of Oxford Shoes winning?

b. A third handicapper assesses the odds in favor of Oxford Shoes to be 1 to 1. According to the third handicapper, what is the probability of Oxford Shoes winning?

c. A fourth handicapper assesses the odds against Oxford Shoes winning to be 3 to 2. Find this handicapper's assessment of the probability that Oxford Shoes will win.

3.24 Lead bullets as forensic evidence. *Chance* (Summer 2004) published an article on the use of lead bullets as forensic evidence in a federal criminal case. Typically, the Federal Bureau of Investigation (FBI) will use a laboratory method to match the lead in a bullet found at the crime scene with unexpended lead cartridges found in possession of the suspect. The value of this evidence depends on the chance of a *false positive* (i.e., the probability that the FBI finds a match given that the lead at the crime scene and the lead in possession of the suspect are actually from two different "melts," or sources). To estimate the false-positive rate, the FBI collected 1,837 bullets that they were confident all came from different melts. The FBI then examined every possible pair of bullets and counted the number of matches using its established criteria. According to *Chance,* the FBI found 693 matches. Use this information to compute the chance of a false positive. Is this probability small enough for you to have confidence in the FBI's forensic evidence?

3.25 Making your vote count. The recent Democratic and Republican presidential state primary elections were highlighted by the difference in the way winning candidates were awarded delegates. In Republican states, the winner is awarded all the state's delegates; conversely, the Democratic state winner is awarded delegates in proportion to the percentage of votes. This led to a *Chance* (Fall 2007) article on making your vote count. Consider the following scenario where you are one of five voters (for example, on a county commission where you are one of the five commissioners voting on an issue).

a. Determine the number of ways the five commissioners can vote, where each commissioner votes either for or against. (These outcomes represent the sample points for the experiment.)

b. Assume each commissioner is equally likely to vote for or against. Assign reasonable probabilities to the sample points, part **a**.

c. Your vote counts (i.e., is the decisive vote) only if the other four voters split, two in favor and two against.

Assuming you are commissioner number 5, how many of the sample points in part **a** result in a 2-2 split for the other four commissioners?

d. Use your answers to parts **a–c** to find the probability that your vote counts.

e. Now, suppose you convince two other commissioners to "vote in bloc," i.e., you all agree to vote among yourselves first, and whatever the majority decides is the way all three will vote. With only five total voters, this guarantees that the bloc vote will determine the outcome. In this scenario, your vote counts only if the other two commissioners in the bloc split votes, one in favor and one against. Find the probability that your vote counts.

3.2 Unions and Intersections

An event can often be viewed as a composition of two or more other events. Such events, which are called **compound events,** can be formed (composed) in two ways, as defined and illustrated here.

> The **union** of two events A and B is the event that occurs if either A or B or both occur on a single performance of the experiment. We denote the union of events A and B by the symbol $A \cup B$. $A \cup B$ consists of all the sample points that belong to A or B or both. (See Figure 3.7a.)

> The **intersection** of two events A and B is the event that occurs if both A and B occur on a single performance of the experiment. We write $A \cap B$ for the intersection of A and B. $A \cap B$ consists of all the sample points belonging to *both A and B*. (See Figure 3.7b.)

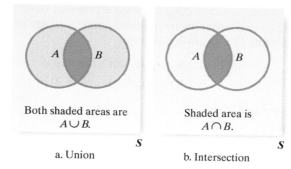

Both shaded areas are
$A \cup B$.

Shaded area is
$A \cap B$.

a. Union

b. Intersection

Figure 3.7
Venn diagrams for union and intersection

Example 3.9

Probabilities of Unions and Intersections in a Die-Toss Experiment

Problem Consider the die-toss experiment. Define the following events:

  A: {Toss an even number}

  B: {Toss a number less than or equal to 3}

a. Describe $A \cup B$ for this experiment.

b. Describe $A \cap B$ for this experiment.

c. Calculate $P(A \cup B)$ and $P(A \cap B)$ assuming the die is fair.

Solution Draw the Venn diagram as shown in Figure 3.8.

a. The union of A and B is the event that occurs if we observe either an even number, a number less than or equal to 3, or both on a single throw of the die. Consequently, the sample points in the event $A \cup B$ are those for which A occurs, B occurs, or both A and B occur. Checking the sample points in the entire sample space, we find that the collection of sample points in the union of A and B is

$$A \cup B = \{1, 2, 3, 4, 6\}$$

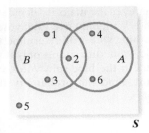

Figure 3.8
Venn diagram for die toss

b. The intersection of A and B is the event that occurs if we observe *both* an even number and a number less than or equal to 3 on a single throw of the die. Checking the sample points to see which imply the occurrence of *both* events A and B, we see that the intersection contains only one sample point:

$$A \cap B = \{2\}$$

In other words, the intersection of A and B is the sample point Observe a 2.

c. Recalling that the probability of an event is the sum of the probabilities of the sample points of which the event is composed, we have

$$P(A \cup B) = P(1) + P(2) + P(3) + P(4) + P(6)$$
$$= \tfrac{1}{6} + \tfrac{1}{6} + \tfrac{1}{6} + \tfrac{1}{6} + \tfrac{1}{6} = \tfrac{5}{6}$$

and

$$P(A \cup B) = P(2) = \tfrac{1}{6}$$

Now Work Exercise 3.25a–d

Example 3.10

Finding Probabilities in a Two–Way Table for a Mass Mailing: Income Versus Age

Problem Many firms undertake direct marketing campaigns to promote their products. The campaigns typically involve mailing information to millions of households. The response rates are carefully monitored to determine the demographic characteristics of respondents. By studying tendencies to respond, the firms can better target future mailings to those segments of the population most likely to purchase their products.

Suppose a distributor of mail-order tools is analyzing the results of a recent mailing. The probability of response is believed to be related to income and age. The percentages of the total number of respondents to the mailing are given by income and age classification in Table 3.4. This table is called a **two-way table** because responses are classified according to two variables, income (columns) and age (rows).

Define the following events:

$A:$ {A respondent's income is more than $50,000.}

$B:$ {A respondents age is 30 or more.}

a. Find $P(A)$ and $P(B)$.

b. Find $P(A \cup B)$.

c. Find $P(A \cap B)$.

Solution Following the steps for calculating probabilities of events, we first note that the objective is to characterize the income and age distribution of respondents to the mailing. To accomplish this, we define the experiment to consist of selecting a respondent from the collection of all respondents and observing which income and age class he or she occupies. The sample points are the nine different age-income classifications:

$E_1:$ {< 30 yrs, < \$25,000} $E_4:$ {< 30 yrs, \$25,000–\$50,000} $E_7:$ {< 30 yrs, > \$50,000}
$E_2:$ {30–50 yrs, < \$25,000} $E_5:$ {30–50 yrs, \$25,000–\$50,000} $E_8:$ {30–50 yrs, > \$50,000}
$E_3:$ {> 50 yrs, < \$25,000} $E_6:$ {> 50 yrs, \$25,000–\$50,000} $E_9:$ {> 50 yrs, > \$50,000}

Table 3.4	**Two-Way Table with Percentage of Respondents in Age-Income Classes**		
		Income	
Age	< \$25,000	\$25,000–\$50,000	> \$50,000
< 30 yrs	5%	12%	10%
30–50 yrs	14%	22%	16%
> 50 yrs	8%	10%	3%

Next, we assign probabilities to the sample points. If we blindly select one of the respondents, the probability that he or she will occupy a particular age-income classification is the proportion, or relative frequency, of respondents in the classification. These proportions are given (as percentages) in Table 3.4. Thus,

$$P(E_1) = \text{Relative frequency of respondents in age-income class}$$
$$\{< 30 \text{ yrs}, < \$25{,}000\} = .05$$
$$P(E_2) = .14$$
$$P(E_3) = .08$$
$$P(E_4) = .12$$
$$P(E_5) = .22$$
$$P(E_6) = .10$$
$$P(E_7) = .10$$
$$P(E_8) = .16$$
$$P(E_9) = .03$$

You may verify that the sample points probabilities add to 1.

a. To find $P(A)$, we first determine the collection of sample points contained in event A. Because A is defined as $\{> \$50{,}000\}$, we see from Table 3.4 that A contains the three sample points represented by the last column of the table. In other words, the event A consists of the income classification $\{> \$50{,}000\}$ in all three age classifications. The probability of A is the sum of the probabilities of the sample points in A:

$$P(A) = P(E_7) + P(E_8) + P(E_9) = .10 + .16 + .03 = .29$$

Similarly, $B = \{\geq 30 \text{ yrs}\}$ consists of the six sample points in the second and third rows of Table 3.4:

$$P(B) = P(E_2) + P(E_3) + P(E_5) + P(E_6) + P(E_8) + P(E_9)$$
$$= .14 + .08 + .22 + .10 + .16 + .03 = .73$$

b. The union of events A and B, $A \cup B$, consists of all the sample points in *either A or B or both*—that is, the union of A and B consists of all respondents whose income exceeds \$50,000 *or* whose age is 30 or more. In Table 3.4 this is any sample point found in the third column *or* the last two rows. Thus,

$$P(A \cup B) = .10 + .14 + .22 + .16 + .08 + .10 + .03 = .83$$

c. The intersection of events A and B, $A \cap B$, consists of all sample points in *both A and B*—that is, the intersection of A and B consists of all respondents whose income exceeds \$50,000 *and* whose age is 30 or more. In Table 3.4 this is any sample point found in the third column *and* the last two rows. Thus,

$$P(A \cap B) = .16 + .03 = .19$$

Look Back As with previous problems, the key to finding the probabilities of parts **b** and **c** is to identify the sample points that comprise the event of interest. In a two-way table like Table 3.4, the number of sample points will be equal to the number of rows times the number of columns.

Now Work Exercise 3.27f–g

3.3 Complementary Events

A very useful concept in the calculation of event probabilities is the notion of *complementary events:*

> The **complement** of an event A is the event that A does *not* occur—that is, the event consisting of all sample points that are not in event A. We denote the complement of A by A^c.

Figure 3.9
Venn diagram of
complementary events

An event A is a collection of sample points, and the sample points included in A^c are those not in A. Figure 3.9 demonstrates this idea. Note from the figure that all sample points in S are included in *either* A or A^c and that *no* sample point is in both A and A^c. This leads us to conclude that the probabilities of an event and its complement *must sum to 1*:

Rule of Complements

The sum of the probabilities of complementary events equals 1:
$$P(A) + P(A^c) = 1.$$

In many probability problems, calculating the probability of the complement of the event of interest is easier than calculating the event itself. Then, because

$$P(A) + P(A^c) = 1$$

we can calculate $P(A)$ by using the relationship

$$P(A) = 1 - P(A^c)$$

Example 3.11

Probabilities of
Complementary Events
in a Coin–Tossing
Experiment

Problem Consider the experiment of tossing two fair coins. Use the complementary relationship to calculate the probability of event A: {Observing at least one head}.

Solution We know that the event A: {Observing at least one head} consists of the sample points

$$A: \{HH, HT, TH\}$$

The complement of A is defined as the event that occurs when A does not occur. Therefore,

$$A^c: \{\text{Observe no heads}\} = \{TT\}$$

This complementary relationship is shown in Figure 3.10. Assuming the coins are balanced,

$$P(A^c) = P(TT) = \tfrac{1}{4}$$

and

$$P(A) = 1 - P(A^c) = 1 - \tfrac{1}{4} = \tfrac{3}{4}$$

Look Back Note that we could have found $P(A)$ by summing the probabilities of the sample points HH, HT, and TH in A. Many times, it is easier to find the probability of A^c and use the rule of complements.

Now Work Exercise 3.25e–f

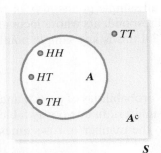

Figure 3.10
Complementary events in the
toss of two coins

3.4 The Additive Rule and Mutually Exclusive Events

In Section 3.2 we saw how to determine which sample points are contained in a union and how to calculate the probability of the union by adding the probabilities of the sample points in the union. It is also possible to obtain the probability of the union of two events by using the **additive rule of probability.**

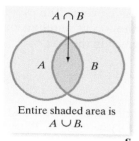

Figure 3.11
Venn diagram of union

The union of two events will often contain many sample points because the union occurs if either one or both of the events occur. By studying the Venn diagram in Figure 3.11, you can see that the probability of the union of two events, A and B, can be obtained by summing $P(A)$ and $P(B)$ and subtracting the probability corresponding to $A \cap B$. Therefore, the formula for calculating the probability of the union of two events is given in the next box.

Additive Rule of Probability

The probability of the union of events A and B is the sum of the probabilities of events A and B minus the probability of the intersection of events A and B—that is,

$$P(A \cup B) = P(A) + P(B) - P(A \cap B)$$

Example 3.12

Applying the Additive Rule to a Hospital Admission Study

Problem Hospital records show that 12% of all patients are admitted for surgical treatment, 16% are admitted for obstetrics, and 2% receive both obstetrics and surgical treatment. If a new patient is admitted to the hospital, what is the probability that the patient will be admitted either for surgery, obstetrics, or both? Use the additive rule of probability to arrive at the answer.

Solution Consider the following events:

A: {A patient admitted to the hospital receives surgical treatment.}
B: {A patient admitted to the hospital receives obstetrics treatment.}

Then, from the given information,

$$P(A) = .12$$
$$P(B) = .16$$

and the probability of the event that a patient receives both obstetrics and surgical treatment is

$$P(A \cap B) = .02$$

The event that a patient admitted to the hospital receives either surgical treatment, obstetrics treatment, or both is the union $A \cup B$. The probability of $A \cup B$ is given by the additive rule of probability:

$$P(A \cup B) = P(A) + P(B) - P(A \cap B) = .12 + .16 - .02 = .26$$

Thus, 26% of all patients admitted to the hospital receive either surgical treatment, obstetrics treatment, or both.

Look Back From the information given, it is not possible to list and assign probabilities to all the sample points. Consequently, we cannot proceed through the five-step process for finding the probability of an event and must use the additive rule.

Now Work Exercise 3.22

A very special relationship exists between events A and B when $A \cup B$ contains no sample points. In this case we call the events A and B *mutually exclusive events.*

Events A and B are **mutually exclusive** if $A \cap B$ contains no sample points—that is, if A and B have no sample points in common.

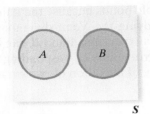

Figure 3.12
Venn diagram of mutually
exclusive events

Figure 3.12 shows a Venn diagram of two mutually exclusive events. The events A and B have no sample points in common—that is, A and B cannot occur simultaneously, and $P(A \cap B) = 0$ Thus, we have the important relationship given in the box.

Probability of Union of Two Mutually Exclusive Events

If two events A and B are *mutually exclusive*, the probability of the union of A and B equals the sum of the probabilities of A and B; that is, $P(A \cup B) = P(A) + P(B)$.

⚠ **CAUTION** The formula just shown is *false* if the events are *not* mutually exclusive. For two nonmutually exclusive events, you must apply the general additive rule of probability. ▲

Example 3.13

The Union of Two Mutually Exclusive Events in a Coin-Tossing Experiment

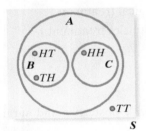

Figure 3.13
Venn diagram for coin-toss
experiment

Problem Consider the experiment of tossing two balanced coins. Find the probability of observing at *least* one head.

Solution Define the events

$$A: \{\text{Observe at least one head}\}$$
$$B: \{\text{Observe exactly one head}\}$$
$$C: \{\text{Observe exactly two heads}\}$$

Note that

$$A = B \cup C$$

and that $B \cap C$ contains no sample points (see Figure 3.13). Thus, B and C are mutually exclusive, so that

$$P(A) = B \cup C = P(B) + P(C) = {}^1/_2 + {}^1/_4 = {}^3/_4$$

Look Back Although this example is very simple, it shows us that writing events with verbal descriptions that include the phrases *at least* or *at most* as unions of mutually exclusive events is very useful. This practice enables us to find the probability of the event by adding the probabilities of the mutually exclusive events.

Statistics IN Action | **Revisited** | **The Probability of Winning a Wheeling System**

Refer to Florida's Pick-6 Lotto game in which you select six numbers of your choice from a field of numbers ranging from 1 to 53. In Section 3.1, we learned that the probability of winning Lotto on a single ticket is only 1 in approximately 23 million. The "experts" at Lotto Buster recommend many strategies for increasing the odds of winning the lottery. One strategy is to employ a wheeling system. In a complete wheeling system, you select more than six numbers, say, seven, and play every combination of six of those seven numbers.

Suppose you choose to "wheel" the following seven numbers: 2, 7, 18, 23, 30, 32, and 51. Every combination of six of these seven numbers is listed in Table SIA3.1. You can see that there are seven different possibilities. (Use the Combinations Rule with $N = 7$ and $n = 6$ to verify this.) Thus, we would purchase seven tickets (at a cost of $7)

corresponding to these different combinations in a complete wheeling system.

To determine if this strategy does, in fact, increase our odds of winning, we need to find the probability that one of these seven combinations occurs during the 6/53 Lotto draw—that is, we need to find the probability that either Ticket 1 or Ticket 2 or Ticket 3 or Ticket 4 or Ticket 5 or Ticket 6 or Ticket 7 is the winning combination. Note that this probability is stated using the word *or*, implying a union of seven events. Letting T1 represent the event that Ticket 1 wins, and defining T2, T3, ..., T7 in a similar fashion, we want to find

$$P(\text{T1 or T2 or T3 or T4 or T5 or T6 or T7})$$

Recall (Section 3.1, p. 127) that the 22,957,480 possible combinations in Pick-6 Lotto are mutually exclusive and equally likely to occur. Consequently, the probability of the union of the seven events is simply the sum of the probabilities of the individual events, where each event has probability of 1/(22,957,480):

P(win Lotto with 7 wheeled numbers)

$= P$(T1 or T2 or T3 or T4 or T5 or T6 or T7)

$= 7/(22,957,480) = .0000003$

In terms of odds, we now have 3 chances in 10 million of winning the Lotto with the complete wheeling system. The "experts" are correct—our odds of winning Lotto have increased (from 1 in 23 million). However, the probability of winning is so close to 0 we question whether the $7 spent on lottery tickets is worth the negligible increase in odds. In fact, it can be shown that to increase your chance of winning the 6/53 Lotto to 1 chance in 100 (i.e., .01) using a complete wheeling system, you would have to wheel 26 of your favorite numbers—a total of 230,230 combinations at a cost of $230,230!

Table SIA3.1	Wheeling the Six Numbers 2, 7, 18, 23, 30, 32, and 51					
Ticket 1:	2	7	18	23	30	32
Ticket 2:	2	7	18	23	30	51
Ticket 3:	2	7	18	23	32	51
Ticket 4:	2	7	18	30	32	51
Ticket 5:	2	7	23	30	32	51
Ticket 6:	2	18	23	30	32	51
Ticket 7:	7	18	23	30	32	51

Exercises 3.26–3.46

Learning the Mechanics

3.26 Suppose $P(A) = .4$, $P(B) = .7$, and $P(A \cap B) = .3$. Find [NW] the following probabilities:
  a. $P(B^c)$
  b. $P(A^c)$
  c. $P(A \cup B)$

3.27 A fair coin is tossed three times, and the events A and B are defined as follows:

  A: {At least one head is observed.}
  B: {The number of heads observed is odd.}

  a. Identify the sample points in the events A, B, $A \cup B$, A^c, and $A \cap B$.
  b. Find $P(A)$, $P(B)$, $P(A \cup B)$, $P(A^c)$, and $P(A \cap B)$ by summing the probabilities of the appropriate sample points.
  c. Find $P(A \cup B)$ using the additive rule. Compare your answer to the one you obtained in part **b.**
  d. Are the events A and B mutually exclusive? Why?

3.28 A pair of fair dice is tossed. Define the following events:

  A: {You will roll a 7.} (i.e., The sum of the dots on the up faces of the two dice is equal to 7.)
  B: {At least one of the two dice shows a 4.}

  a. Identify the sample points in the events A, B, $A \cap B$, $A \cup B$, and A^c.
  b. Find $P(A)$, $P(B)$, $P(A \cap B)$, $P(A \cup B)$, and $P(A^c)$ by summing the probabilities of the appropriate sample points.
  c. Find $P(A \cup B)$ using the additive rule. Compare your answer to that for the same event in part **b.**
  d. Are A and B mutually exclusive? Why?

3.29 Consider the Venn diagram below, where
[NW]
$$P(E_1) = P(E_2) = P(E_3) = 1/5, P(E_4) = P(E_5) = 1/20,$$
$$P(E_6) = 1/10, \text{ and } P(E_7) = 1/5.$$
Find each of the following probabilities:
  a. $P(A)$ **e.** $P(A^c)$
  b. $P(B)$ **f.** $P(B^c)$
  c. $P(A \cup B)$ **g.** $P(A \cup A^c)$
  d. $P(A \cap B)$ **h.** $P(A^c \cap B)$

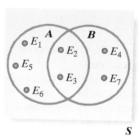

3.30 Consider the Venn diagram on the next page, where
$$P(E_1) = .10, P(E_2) = .05, P(E_3) = P(E_4) = .2,$$
$$P(E_5) = .06, P(E_6) = .3, P(E_7) = .06, \text{ and}$$
$$P(E_8) = .03.$$

Find the following probabilities:
  a. $P(A^c)$
  b. $P(B^c)$
  c. $P(A^c \cap B)$
  d. $P(A \cup B)$
  e. $P(A \cap B)$
  f. $P(A^c \cap B^c)$
  g. Are events A and B mutually exclusive? Why?

Venn Diagram for Exercise 3.30

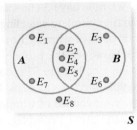

S

3.31 The outcomes of two variables are (Low, Medium, High) and (On, Off), respectively. An experiment is conducted in which the outcomes of each of the two variables are observed. The probabilities associated with each of the six possible outcome pairs are given in the accompanying two-way table.

	Low	Medium	High
On	.50	.10	.05
Off	.25	.07	.03

Consider the following events:

$A:$ {On}
$B:$ {Medium or On}
$C:$ {Off and Low}
$D:$ {High}

a. Find $P(A)$.
b. Find $P(B)$.
c. Find $P(C)$.
d. Find $P(D)$.
e. Find $P(A^c)$.
NW f. Find $P(A \cup B)$.
NW g. Find $P(A \cap C)$.
h. Consider each pair of events (A and B, A and C, A and D, B and C, B and D, C and D). List the pairs of events that are mutually exclusive. Justify your choices.

3.32 Refer to Exercise 3.31. Use the same event definitions to do the following exercises.
a. Write the event that the outcome is "On" and "High" as an intersection of two events.
b. Write the event that the outcome is "Low" or "Medium" as the complement of an event.

Applet Exercise 3.3

Use the applets *Simulating the Probability of Rolling a 6* and *Simulating the Probability of Rolling a 3 or 4* to explore the additive rule for probability.
a. Explain why the applet *Simulating the Probability of Rolling a 6* can also be used to simulate the probability of rolling a 3. Then use the applet with $n = 1,000$ to simulate the probability of rolling a 3. Record the cumulative proportion. Repeat the process to simulate the probability of rolling a 4.
b. Use the applet *Simulating the Probability of Rolling a 3 or 4* with $n = 1,000$ to simulate the probability of rolling a 3 or 4. Record the cumulative proportion.

c. Add the two cumulative proportions from part **a**. How does this sum compare to the cumulative proportion in part **b**? How does this illustrate the additive rule for probability?

Applet Exercise 3.4

Use the applets *Simulating the Probability of Rolling a 6* and *Simulating the Probability of Rolling a 3 or 4* to simulate the probability of the complement of an event.
a. Explain how the applet *Simulating the Probability of Rolling a 6* can also be used to simulate the probability of the event *rolling a 1, 2, 3, 4, or 5*. Then use the applet with $n = 1,000$ to simulate this probability.
b. Explain how the applet *Simulating the Probability of Rolling a 3 or 4* can also be used to simulate the probability of the event *rolling a 1, 2, 5, or 6*. Then use the applet with $n = 1,000$ to simulate this probability.
c. Which applet could be used to simulate the probability of the event *rolling a 1, 2, 3, or 4*? Explain.

Applying the Concepts—Basic

3.33 **Study of analysts' forecasts.** The *Journal of Accounting Research* (March 2008) published a study on relationship incentives and degree of optimism among analysts' forecasts. Participants were analysts at either a large or small brokerage firm who made their forecasts either early or late in the quarter. Also, some analysts were only concerned with making an accurate forecast, while others were also interested in their relationship with management. Suppose one of these analysts is randomly selected. Consider the following events:
$A = $ {The analyst is concerned only with making an accurate forecast.}
$B = $ {The analyst makes the forecast early in the quarter.}
$C = $ {The analyst is from a small brokerage firm.}
Describe each of the following events in terms of unions, intersections, and complements (e.g., $A \cup B$, $A \cap B$, A^c, etc.).
a. The analyst makes an early forecast and is concerned only with accuracy.
b. The analyst is not concerned only with accuracy.
c. The analyst is from a small brokerage firm or makes an early forecast.
d. The analyst makes a late forecast and is not concerned only with accuracy.

3.34 **Problems at major companies.** The *Organization Development Journal* (Summer 2006) reported on the results of a survey of human resource officers (HROs) at major employers located in a southeastern city. The focus of the study was employee behavior, namely absenteeism, promptness to work, and turnover. The study found that 55% of the HROs had problems with employee absenteeism; also, 41% had problems with turnover. Suppose that 22% of the HROs had problems with both absenteeism and turnover. Use this information to find the probability that an HRO officer selected from the group surveyed had problems with either employee absenteeism or employee turnover.

3.35 **Use of cellular phone features.** Harris Interactive conducted a survey of cellular phone owners to estimate the likelihood of using extra phone features, such as the calendar, address book, instant messaging, e-mail, and so on. The results were reported online at *BusinessWeek.com* (Aug. 17, 2005). The following table shows the percentage of 18- to 34-year-olds who use the extra cell phone features. (Note that the percentages in the table do not sum to 100% because a cell phone owner may use more than one feature.)

Cell Phone Feature	Percentage of 18- to 34-Year-Olds
Calendar and address book	56%
Download and/or play games	54%
Download ringtones	47%
Instant messaging	43%
Take pictures	35%
Send and receive e-mail	28%
Access the Internet	34%
None of the above	16%

Source: BusinessWeek.com, Aug. 17, 2005.

a. Estimate the probability that an 18- to 34-year-old cell phone owner uses instant messaging.
b. Estimate the probability that an 18- to 34-year-old cell phone owner uses at least one of the features listed in the table.

3.36 **Scanning errors at Wal-Mart.** The National Institute for Standards and Technology (NIST) mandates that for every 100 items scanned through the electronic checkout scanner at a retail store, no more than 2 should have an inaccurate price. A recent study of the accuracy of checkout scanners at Wal-Mart stores in California was conducted (*Tampa Tribune*, Nov. 22, 2005). Of the 60 Wal-Mart stores investigated, 52 violated the NIST scanner accuracy standard. If one of the 60 Wal-Mart stores is randomly selected, what is the probability that the store does not violate the NIST scanner accuracy standard?

3.37 **Inactive oil and gas structures.** U.S. federal regulations require that operating companies clear all inactive offshore oil and gas structures within 1 year after production ceases. Researchers at the Louisiana State University Center for Energy Studies gathered data on both active and inactive oil and gas structures in the Gulf of Mexico (*Oil & Gas Journal*, Jan. 3, 2005). They discovered that the Gulf of Mexico had 2,175 active and 1,225 idle (inactive) structures at the end of 2003. The following table breaks down these structures by type (caisson, well protector, or fixed platform). Consider the structure type and active status of one of these oil/gas structures.

	Structure Type			
	Caisson	Well Protector	Fixed Platform	Totals
Active	503	225	1,447	2,175
Inactive	598	177	450	1,225

Source: Kaiser, M., and Mesyanzhinov, D. "Study tabulates idle Gulf of Mexico structures," *Oil & Gas Journal*, Vol. 103, No. 1, Jan. 3, 2005 (Table 2).

a. List the simple events for this experiment.
b. Assign reasonable probabilities to the simple events.
c. Find the probability that the structure is active.
d. Find the probability that the structure is a well protector.
e. Find the probability that the structure is an inactive caisson.

f. Find the probability that the structure is either inactive or a fixed platform.
g. Find the probability that the structure is not a caisson.

3.38 **Social networking Web sites in the United Kingdom.** In the United States, MySpace and FaceBook are considered the two most popular social networking Web sites. In the United Kingdom (UK), the competition for social networking is between MySpace and Bebo. According to Nielsen/NetRatings (April 2006), 4% of UK citizens visit MySpace, 3% visit Bebo, and 1% visit both MySpace and Bebo.

a. Draw a Venn diagram to illustrate the use of social networking sites in the United Kingdom.
b. Find the probability that a UK citizen visits either the MySpace or Bebo social networking sites.
c. Use your answer to part **b** to find the probability that a UK citizen does not visit either social networking site.

Applying the Concepts—Intermediate

3.39 **Characteristics of a new product.** The long-run success of a business depends on its ability to market products with superior characteristics that maximize consumer satisfaction and that give the firm a competitive advantage (Kotler & Keller, *Marketing Management,* 2006). Ten new products have been developed by a food-products firm. Market research has indicated that the 10 products have the characteristics described by the following Venn diagram:

a. Write the event that a product possesses all the desired characteristics as an intersection of the events defined in the Venn diagram. Which products are contained in this intersection?
b. If one of the 10 products were selected at random to be marketed, what is the probability that it would possess all the desired characteristics?
c. Write the event that the randomly selected product would give the firm a competitive advantage or would satisfy consumers as a union of the events defined in the Venn diagram. Find the probability of this union.
d. Write the event that the randomly selected product would possess superior product characteristics and satisfy consumers. Find the probability of this intersection.

3.40 **Guilt in decision making.** The effect of guilt emotion on how a decision maker focuses on the problem was investigated in the Jan. 2007 issue of the *Journal of Behavioral Decision*

Making (see Exercise 1.26, p. 24). A total of 171 volunteer students participated in the experiment, where each was randomly assigned to one of three emotional states (guilt, anger, or neutral) through a reading/writing task. Immediately after the task, students were presented with a decision problem where the stated option has predominantly negative features (e.g., spending money on repairing a very old car). The results (number responding in each category) are summarized in the accompanying table. Suppose one of the 171 participants is selected at random.

Emotional State	Choose Stated Option	Do Not Choose Stated Option	Totals
Guilt	45	12	57
Anger	8	50	58
Neutral	7	49	56
Totals	60	111	171

Source: Gangemi, A., and Mancini, F. "Guilt and focusing in decision-making," *Journal of Behavioral Decision Making,* Vol. 20, Jan. 2007 (Table 2).

a. Find the probability that the respondent is assigned to the guilty state.
b. Find the probability that the respondent chooses the stated option (repair the car).
c. Find the probability that the respondent is assigned to the guilty state and chooses the stated option.
d. Find the probability that the respondent is assigned to the guilty state or chooses the stated option.

3.41 **Appeals of federal civil trials.** The *Journal of the American Law and Economics Association* (Vol. 3, 2001) published the results of a study of appeals of federal civil trials. The following table, extracted from the article, gives a breakdown of 2,143 civil cases that were appealed by either the plaintiff or the defendant. The outcome of the appeal, as well as the type of trial (judge or jury), was determined for each civil case. Suppose one of the 2,143 cases is selected at random and both the outcome of the appeal and type of trial are observed.

	Jury	Judge	Totals
Plaintiff trial win—reversed	194	71	265
Plaintiff trial win—affirmed/dismissed	429	240	669
Defendant trial win—reversed	111	68	179
Defendant trial win—affirmed/dismissed	731	299	1,030
Totals	1,465	678	2,143

a. Find $P(A)$, where A = {jury trial}.
b. Find $P(B)$, where B = {plaintiff trial win is reversed}.
c. Are A and B mutually exclusive events?

d. Find $P(A^c)$.
e. Find $P(A \cup B)$.
f. Find $P(A \cap B)$.

3.42 **Likelihood of a tax return audit.** At the beginning of each year, the Internal Revenue Service (IRS) releases information on the likelihood of a tax return being audited. In 2007, the IRS audited 1,384,563 individual tax returns from the total of 134,421,400 filed returns; also in 2007, the IRS audited 59,516 business returns from the total of 9,072,828 business returns filed (*IRS Fiscal Year 2007 Enforcement and Services Statistics*).

a. Suppose an individual tax return from 2007 is randomly selected. What is the probability that the return is audited by the IRS?
b. Refer to part **a.** Determine the probability that an individual return is not audited by the IRS.
c. Suppose a business tax return from 2007 is randomly selected. What is the probability that the return is audited by the IRS?
d. Refer to part **c.** Determine the probability that a business return is not audited by the IRS.

3.43 **Online securities trading.** E*TRADE Group Inc. was the first to provide online securities trading for its clients, offering an alternative to traditional investment firms. According to *Business Week,* online securities trading accounts for a significant share of the brokerage business. The table below reports the number of online and traditional accounts for five leading brokerages. Suppose a customer account is to be drawn at random from the population of accounts described in the table. Consider the following events:

A: {The account is with Merrill Lynch.}
B: {The account is an online account.}
C: {The account is with E*TRADE and is an online account.}
D: {The account is either with TD Waterhouse or E*TRADE and is an online account.}
E: { The account is with E*TRADE.}

a. Find the probability of each of the aforementioned events.
b. Find $P(A \cap B)$.
c. Find $P(A \cup B)$.
d. Find $P(B^c \cap E)$
e. Find $P(A \cup E)$.
f. Which pairs of events are mutually exclusive?

3.44 **Home modifications for wheelchair users.** The *American Journal of Public Health* (Jan. 2002) reported on a study of elderly wheelchair users who live at home. A sample of 306 wheelchair users, age 65 or older, were surveyed about whether they had an injurious fall during the year and whether their home features any one of five structural

Table for Exercise 3.43

Brokerage Firms	Online Accounts	Traditional Accounts	Total Accounts
Fidelity Investments	2.8 million	8.0 million	10.8 million
Merrill Lynch & Co.	0	8.0 million	8.0 million
Charles Schwab & Co.	2.8 million	3.5 million	6.3 million
TD Waterhouse Group Inc.	1.0 million	1.1 million	2.1 million
E*TRADE Group Inc.	1.24 million	0	1.24 million
Totals	7.84 million	20.6 million	28.44 million

Source: Business Week, Oct. 18, 1999, pp. 185–186.

modifications: bathroom modifications, widened door-ways/hallways, kitchen modifications, installed railings, and easy-open doors. The responses are summarized in the accompanying table. Suppose we select, at random, one of the 306 surveyed wheelchair users.

Home Features	Injurious Fall(s)	No Falls	Totals
All 5	2	7	9
At least 1 but not all	26	162	188
None	20	89	109
Totals	48	258	306

Source: Berg, K., Hines, M., and Allen, S. "Wheelchair users at home: Few home modifications and many injurious falls," *American Journal of Public Health*, Vol. 92, No. 1, Jan. 2002 (Table 1).

  a. Find the probability that the wheelchair user had an injurious fall.

  b. Find the probability that the wheelchair user had all five features installed in the home.

  c. Find the probability that the wheelchair user had no falls and none of the features installed in the home.

3.45 **Reliability of gas station air pumps.** Tire and automobile manufacturers and consumer safety experts all recommend that drivers maintain proper tire pressure in their cars. Consequently, many gas stations now provide air pumps and air gauges for their customers. In a *Research Note* (Nov. 2001), the National Highway Traffic Safety Administration studied the reliability of gas station air pumps. The next table gives the percentage of gas stations that provide air gauges that overreport the pressure level in the tire.

  a. If the gas station air pressure gauge reads 35 psi, what is the probability that the pressure is overreported by 6 psi or more?

Station Gauge Pressure	Overreport by 4 psi or More (%)	Overreport by 6 psi or More (%)	Overreport by 8 psi or More (%)
25 psi	16	2	0
35 psi	19	9	0
45 psi	19	14	5
55 psi	20	15	9

  b. If the gas station air pressure gauge reads 55 psi, what is the probability that the pressure is overreported by 8 psi or more?

  c. If the gas station air pressure gauge reads 25 psi, what is the probability that the pressure is not overreported by 4 psi or more?

  d. Are the events A = {overreport by 4 psi or more} and B = {overreport by 6 psi or more} mutually exclusive? Explain.

  e. Based on your answer to part **d**, why do the probabilities in the table not sum to 1?

Applying the Concepts—Advanced

3.46 **Galileo's Passedix game.** Passedix is a game of chance played with three fair dice. Players bet whether the sum of the faces shown on the dice will be above or below 10. During the late sixteenth century, the astronomer and mathematician Galileo Galilei was asked by the Grand Duke of Tuscany to explain why "the chance of throwing a total of 9 with three fair dice was less than that of throwing a total of 10" (*Interstat*, Jan. 2004). The grand duke believed that the chance should be the same because "there are an equal number of partitions of the numbers 9 and 10." Find the flaw in the grand duke's reasoning and answer the question posed to Galileo.

3.5 Conditional Probability

The event probabilities we've been discussing give the relative frequencies of the occurrences of the events when the experiment is repeated a very large number of times. Such probabilities are often called **unconditional probabilities** because no special conditions are assumed, other than those that define the experiment.

    Often, however, we have additional knowledge that might affect the likelihood of the outcome of an experiment, so we need to alter the probability of an event of interest. A probability that reflects such additional knowledge is called the **conditional probability** of the event. For example, we've seen that the probability of observing an even number (event A) on a toss of a fair die is $\frac{1}{2}$. But suppose we're given the information that on a particular throw of the die, the result was a number less than or equal to 3 (event B). Would the probability of observing an even number on that throw of the die still be equal to $\frac{1}{2}$? It can't be because making the assumption that B has occurred reduces the sample space from six sample points to three sample points (namely, those contained in event B). This reduced sample space is as shown in Figure 3.14.

    Because the sample points for the die-toss experiment are equally likely, each of the three sample points in the reduced sample space is assigned an equal *conditional probability* of $\frac{1}{3}$. Because the only even number of the three in the reduced sample space B is the number 2 and the die is fair, we conclude that the probability that A occurs *given that B occurs* is $\frac{1}{3}$. We use the symbol $P(A|B)$ to represent the probability of event A given that event B occurs. For the die-toss example, $P(A|B) = \frac{1}{3}$.

    To get the probability of event A given that event B occurs, we proceed as follows: We divide the probability of the part of A that falls within the reduced sample space B, namely $P(A \cap B)$, by the total probability of the reduced sample space, namely $P(B)$.

Figure 3.14

Reduced sample space for the die-toss experiment given that event B has occurred

Thus, for the die-toss example with event *A*: {Observe an even number} and event *B*: {Observe a number less than or equal to 3}, we find

$$P(A|B) = \frac{P(A \cap B)}{P(B)} = \frac{P(2)}{P(1) + P(2) + P(3)} = \frac{\frac{1}{6}}{\frac{3}{6}} = \frac{1}{3}$$

The formula for $P(A|B)$ is true in general:

Conditional Probability Formula

To find the *conditional probability that event A occurs given that event B occurs,* divide the probability that *both* A and B occur by the probability that B occurs—that is,

$$P(A|B) = \frac{P(A \cap B)}{P(B)} \qquad \text{[We assume that } P(B) \neq 0.]$$

This formula adjusts the probability of $A \cap B$ from its original value in the complete sample space *S* to a conditional probability in the reduced sample space *B*. If the sample points in the complete sample space are equally likely, then the formula will assign equal probabilities to the sample points in the reduced sample space, as in the die-toss experiment. If, on the other hand, the sample points have unequal probabilities, the formula will assign conditional probabilities proportional to the probabilities in the complete sample space. This is illustrated by the following practical examples.

Example 3.14

The Conditional Probability Formula Applied to Executives Who Cheat at Golf

Problem To develop programs for business travelers staying at convention hotels, a major hotel chain commissioned a study of executives who play golf. The study revealed that 55% of the executives admitted they had cheated at golf. Also, 20% of the executives admitted they had cheated at golf and had lied in business. Given an executive had cheated at golf, what is the probability that the executive also had lied in business?

Solution Let's define events *A* and *B* as follows:

$$A = \{\text{Executive who had cheated at golf}\}$$
$$B = \{\text{Executive who had lied in business}\}$$

From the study, we know that 55% of executives had cheated at golf, so $P(A) = .55$. Now, executives who both cheat at golf (event *A*) *and* lie in business (event *B*) represent the compound event $A \cap B$. From the study, $P(A \cap B) = .20$. We want to know the probability that an executive lied in business (event *B*), given he or she cheated at golf (event *A*)—that is, we want to know the conditional probability $P(A|B)$. Applying the preceding conditional probability formula, we have

$$P(B|A) = \frac{P(A \cap B)}{P(A)} = \frac{.20}{.55} = .364$$

Thus, given an executive had cheated at golf, the probability that the executive also had lied in business is .364.

Look Back One of the keys to correctly applying the formula is to write the information in the study in the form of probability statements involving the events of interest. The word *and* in the statement "cheat at golf *and* lie in business" implies an intersection of the two events, *A* and *B*. The word *given* in the phrase "*given* an executive cheats at golf" implies that event *A* is the given event.

Now Work Exercise 3.56

Example 3.15

Applying the Conditional
Probability Formula to a
Two-Way Table on
Customer Desire to Buy

Figure 3.15
Sample space for contacting a
sales prospect

Problem Suppose you are interested in the probability of the sale of a large piece of earthmoving equipment. A single prospect is contacted. Let F be the event that the buyer has sufficient money (or credit) to buy the product and let F^c denote the complement of F (the event that the prospect does not have the financial capability to buy the product). Similarly, let B be the event that the buyer wishes to buy the product and let B^c be the complement of that event. Then the four sample points associated with the experiment are shown in Figure 3.15, and their probabilities are given in Table 3.5. Use the sample point probabilities to find the probability that a single prospect will buy, given that the prospect is able to finance the purchase.

Table 3.5	**Probabilities of Customer Desire to Buy and Ability to Finance**		
		Desire	
		To Buy, B	Not to Buy, B^c
Able to Finance	Yes, F	.2	.1
	No, F^c	.4	.3

Solution Suppose you consider the large collection of prospects for the sale of your product and randomly select one person from this collection. What is the probability that the person selected will buy the product? In order to buy the product, the customer must be financially able *and* have the desire to buy, so this probability would correspond to the entry in Table 3.5 {To buy, B} and next to {Yes, F}, or $P(B \cap F) = .2$. This is the unconditional probability of the event $B \cap F$.

In contrast, suppose you know that the prospect selected has the financial capability for purchasing the product. Now you are seeking the probability that the customer will buy given (the condition) that the customer has the financial ability to pay. This probability, the conditional probability of B given that F has occurred and denoted by the symbol $P(B|F)$, would be determined by considering only the sample points in the reduced sample space containing the sample points $B \cap F$ and $B^c \cap F$—that is, sample points that imply the prospect is financially able to buy. (This subspace is shaded in Figure 3.16.) From our definition of conditional probability,

$$P(B|F) = \frac{P(B \cap F)}{P(F)}$$

where $P(F)$ is the sum of the probabilities of the two sample points corresponding to $B \cap F$ and $B^c \cap F$ (given in Table 3.5). Then

$$P(F) = P(B \cap F) + P(B^c \cap F) = .2 + .1 = .3$$

and the conditional probability that a prospect buys, given that the prospect is financially able, is

$$P(B|F) = \frac{P(B \cap F)}{P(F)} = \frac{.2}{.3} = .667$$

As we would expect, the probability that the prospect will buy, given that he or she is financially able, is higher than the unconditional probability of selecting a prospect who will buy.

Figure 3.16

Subspace (shaded) containing
sample points implying a
financially able prospect

Look Back Note that the conditional probability formula assigns a probability to the event $(B \cap F)$ in the reduced sample space that is proportional to the probability of the event in the complete sample space. To see this, note that the two sample points in the reduced sample space, $(B \cap F)$ and $(B^c \cap F)$, have probabilities of .2 and .1, respectively, in the complete sample space S. The formula assigns conditional probabilities $2/3$ and $1/3$ (use the formula to check the second one) to these sample points in the reduced sample space F so that the conditional probabilities retain the 2-to-1 proportionality of the original sample point probabilities.

Now Work Exercise 3.47a–b

Example 3.16

Applying the Conditional Probability Formula to a Two-Way Table on Customer Complaints

Problem The investigation of consumer product complaints by the Federal Trade Commission (FTC) has generated much interest by manufacturers in the quality of their products. A manufacturer of an electromechanical kitchen utensil conducted an analysis of a large number of consumer complaints and found that they fell into the six categories shown in Table 3.6. If a consumer complaint is received, what is the probability that the cause of the complaint was product appearance given that the complaint originated during the guarantee period?

Table 3.6   Distribution of Product Complaints

	Reason for Complaint			
Complaint Origin	Electrical	Mechanical	Appearance	Totals
During Guarantee Period	18%	13%	32%	63%
After Guarantee Period	12%	22%	3%	37%
Totals	30%	35%	35%	100%

Solution Let A represent the event that the cause of a particular complaint is product appearance and let B represent the event that the complaint occurred during the guarantee period. Checking Table 3.6, you can see that $(18 + 13 + 32)\% = 63\%$ of the complaints occur during the guarantee period. Hence, $P(B) = .63$. The percentage of complaints that were caused by appearance and occurred during the guarantee period (the event $A \cap B$) is 32%. Therefore, $P(A \cap B) = .32$.

Using these probability values, we can calculate the conditional probability $P(A|B)$ that the cause of a complaint is appearance, given that the complaint occurred during the guarantee time:

$$P(A|B) = \frac{P(A \cap B)}{P(B)} = \frac{.32}{.63} = .51$$

Consequently, we can see that slightly more than half the complaints that occurred during the guarantee period were due to scratches, dents, or other imperfections in the surface of the kitchen devices.

Look Back Note that the answer, $\dfrac{.32}{.63}$, is the proportion for the event of interest A (.32) divided by the row total proportion for the given event B (.63)—that is, it is the proportion of the time A occurs within the given event B.

Now Work Exercise 3.58

3.6 The Multiplicative Rule and Independent Events

The probability of an intersection of two events can be calculated using the multiplicative rule, which employs the conditional probabilities we defined in the previous section. Actually, we have already developed the formula in another context (Section 3.5). You will recall that the formula for calculating the conditional probability of A given B is

$$P(A|B) = \frac{P(A \cap B)}{P(B)}$$

Multiplying both sides of this equation by $P(B)$, we obtain a formula for the probability of the intersection of events A and B. This is often called the **multiplicative rule of probability.**

Multiplicative Rule of Probability

$P(A \cap B) = P(A)P(B|A)$ or, equivalently, $P(A \cap B) = P(B)P(A|B)$

Example 3.17

Applying the Multiplicative Rule to Find a Probability Associated with Wheat Futures

Problem An investor in wheat futures is concerned with the following events:

B: {U.S. production of wheat will be profitable next year.}

A: {A serious drought will occur next year.}

Based on available information, the investor believes that the probability is .01 that production of wheat will be profitable *assuming* a serious drought will occur in the same year and that the probability is .05 that a serious drought will occur—that is,

$$P(B|A) = .01 \text{ and } P(A) = .05$$

Based on the information provided, what is the probability that a serious drought will occur and that a profit will be made? That is, find $P(A \cap B)$, the probability of the intersection of events A and B.

Solution We want to calculate $P(A \cap B)$. Using the formula for the multiplicative rule, we obtain

$$P(A \cap B) = P(A)P(B|A) = (.05)(.01) = .0005$$

The probability that a serious drought occurs and the production of wheat is profitable is only .0005. As we might expect, this intersection is a very rare event.

Look Back The multiplicative rule can be expressed in two ways: $P(A \cap B) = P(A) \cdot P(B|A)$ or $P(A \cap B) = P(B) \cdot P(A|B)$. Select the formula that involves a given event for which you know the probability (e.g., event B in the example).

Now Work Exercise 3.60

Intersections often contain only a few sample points. In this case, the probability of an intersection is easy to calculate by summing the appropriate sample point probabilities. However, the formula for calculating intersection probabilities is invaluable when the intersection contains numerous sample points, as the next example illustrates.

Example 3.18

Applying the Multiplicative Rule to a Study of Welfare Workers

Problem A county welfare agency employs 10 welfare workers who interview prospective food stamp recipients. Periodically the supervisor selects, at random, the forms completed by 2 workers to audit for illegal deductions. Unknown to the supervisor, 3 of the workers have regularly been giving illegal deductions to applicants. What is the probability that both of the 2 workers chosen have been giving illegal deductions?

Solution Define the following two events:

A: {First worker selected gives illegal deductions}

B: {Second worker selected gives illegal deductions}

We want to find the probability of the event that both selected workers have been giving illegal deductions. This event can be restated as {First worker gives illegal deductions *and* second worker gives illegal deductions}. Thus, we want to find the probability of the intersection, $A \cap B$. Applying the multiplicative rule, we have

$$P(A \cap B) = P(A)P(B|A)$$

Figure 3.17
Venn diagram for finding $P(A)$

Figure 3.18
Venn diagram for finding
$P(B|A)$

To find $P(A)$, it is helpful to consider the experiment as selecting 1 worker from the 10. Then the sample space for the experiment contains 10 sample points (representing the 10 welfare workers), where the 3 workers giving illegal deductions are denoted by the symbol I (I_1, I_2, I_3), and the 7 workers not giving illegal deductions are denoted by the symbol N $(N_1, \ldots, N_7)$. The resulting Venn diagram is illustrated in Figure 3.17.

Because the first worker is selected at random from the 10, it is reasonable to assign equal probabilities to the 10 sample points. Thus, each sample point has a probability of $1/10$. The sample points in event A are $\{I_1, I_2, I_3,\}$—the 3 workers who are giving illegal deductions. Thus,

$$P(A) = P(I_1) + P(I_2) + P(I_3) = \frac{1}{10} + \frac{1}{10} + \frac{1}{10} = \frac{3}{10}$$

To find the conditional probability, $P(B|A)$, we need to alter the sample space S. Because we know A has occurred [the first worker selected is giving illegal deductions (say I_3), only 2 of the 9 remaining workers in the sample space are giving illegal deductions]. The Venn diagram for this new sample space (S') is shown in Figure 3.18. Each of these nine sample points are equally likely, so each is assigned a probability of $1/9$. Because the event $(B|A)$ contains the sample points $\{I_1, I_2\}$, we have

$$P(B|A) = P(I_1) + P(I_2) = \frac{1}{9} + \frac{1}{9} = \frac{2}{9}$$

Substituting $P(A) = 3/10$ and $P(B|A) = 2/9$ into the formula for the multiplicative rule, we find

$$P(A \cap B) = P(A)P(B|A) = (\tfrac{3}{10})(\tfrac{2}{9}) = \frac{6}{90} = \frac{1}{15}$$

Thus, there is a 1 in 15 chance that both workers chosen by the supervisor have been giving illegal deductions to food stamp recipients.

Look Back The key words *both* and *and* in the statement "both A and B occur" imply an intersection of two events, which in turn implies that we should *multiply* probabilities to obtain the probability of interest.

Now Work Exercise 3.51c

The sample space approach is only one way to solve the problem posed in Example 3.18. An alternative method employs the tree diagram (introduced in Example 3.1). Tree diagrams are helpful for calculating the probability of an intersection.

To illustrate, a tree diagram for Example 3.18 is displayed in Figure 3.19. The tree begins at the far left with two branches. These branches represent the two possible outcomes

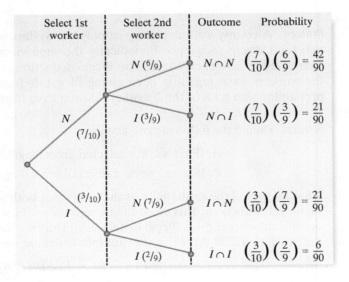

Figure 3.19
Tree diagram for Example 3.18

N (no illegal deductions) and I (illegal deductions) for the first worker selected. The unconditional probability of each outcome is given (in parentheses) on the appropriate branch—that is, for the first worker selected, $P(N) = \frac{7}{10}$ and $P(I) = \frac{3}{10}$. (These can be obtained by summing sample point probabilities as in Example 3.18.)

The next level of the tree diagram (moving to the right) represents the outcomes for the second worker selected. The probabilities shown here are conditional probabilities because the outcome for the first worker is assumed to be known. For example, if the first worker is giving illegal deductions (I), the probability that the second worker is also giving illegal deductions (I) is $\frac{2}{9}$ because of the 9 workers left to be selected, only 2 remain who are giving illegal deductions. This conditional probability, $\frac{2}{9}$, is shown in parentheses on the bottom branch of Figure 3.18.

Finally, the four possible outcomes of the experiment are shown at the end of each of the four tree branches. These events are intersections of two events (outcome of first worker and outcome of second worker). Consequently, the multiplicative rule is applied to calculate each probability, as shown in Figure 3.18. You can see that the intersection $\{I \cap I\}$ (i.e., the event that both workers selected are giving illegal deductions) has probability $\frac{6}{90} = \frac{1}{15}$—the same value obtained in Example 3.18.

In Section 3.5 we showed that the probability of an event A may be substantially altered by the knowledge that an event B has occurred. However, this will not always be the case. In some instances, the assumption that event B has occurred will *not* alter the probability of event A at all. When this is true, we say that the two events A and B are *independent events*.

Events A and B are **independent events** if the occurrence of B does not alter the probability that A has occurred; that is, events A and B are independent if

$$P(A|B) = P(A)$$

When events A and B are independent, it is also true that

$$P(B|A) = P(B)$$

Events that are not independent are said to be **dependent.**

Example 3.19

Checking for Independence in a Die-Tossing Experiment

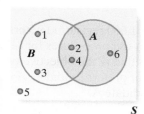

Figure 3.20
Venn diagram for die-toss experiment

Problem Consider the experiment of tossing a fair die and let

> A: {Observe an even number.}
> B: {Observe a number less than or equal to 4.}

Are events A and B independent?

Solution The Venn diagram for this experiment is shown in Figure 3.20. We first calculate

$$P(A) = P(2) + P(4) + P(6) = \tfrac{1}{2}$$
$$P(B) = P(1) + P(2) + P(3) + P(4) = \tfrac{2}{3}$$
$$P(A \cap B) = P(2) + P(4) = \tfrac{1}{3}$$

Now assuming B has occurred, the conditional probability of A given B is

$$P(A|B) = \frac{P(A \cap B)}{P(B)} = \frac{\frac{1}{3}}{\frac{2}{3}} = \frac{1}{2} = P(A)$$

Thus, assuming that event B occurring does not alter the probability of observing an even number, $P(A)$ remains $\frac{1}{2}$. Therefore, the events A and B are independent.

Look Back Note that if we calculate the conditional probability of B given A, our conclusion is the same:

$$P(B|A) = \frac{P(A \cap B)}{P(A)} = \frac{\frac{1}{3}}{\frac{1}{2}} = \frac{2}{3} = P(B)$$

Solver of Chevalier's Dilemma

As a precocious child growing up in France, Blaise Pascal showed an early inclination toward mathematics. Although his father would not permit Pascal to study mathematics before the age of 15 (removing all math texts from his house), at age 12 Blaise discovered on his own that the sum of the angles of a triangle are two right triangles.

Pascal went on to become a distinguished mathematician, as well as a physicist, theologian, and the inventor of the first digital calculator. Most historians attribute the beginning of the study of probability to the correspondence between Pascal and Pierre de Fermat in 1654. The two solved the Chevalier's dilemma—a gambling problem related to Pascal by his friend and Paris gambler the Chevalier de Mere. The problem involved determining the expected number of times one could roll two dice without throwing a double 6. (Pascal proved that the breakeven point was 25 rolls.) ▧

Example 3.20

Checking for Independence in the Consumer Product Complaint Study

Problem Refer to the consumer product complaint study in Example 3.16. The percentages of complaints of various types during and after the guarantee period are shown in Table 3.6. Define the following events:

A: {Cause of complaint is product appearance.}

B: {Complaint occurred during the guarantee term.}

Are A and B independent events?

Solution Events A and B are independent if $P(A|B) = P(A)$. We calculated $P(A|B)$ in Example 3.16 to be .51, and from Table 3.6 we see that

$$P(A) = .32 + .03 = .35$$

Therefore, $P(A|B)$ is not equal to $P(A)$, and A and B are dependent events.

Now Work Exercise 3.47c

To gain an intuitive understanding of independence, think of situations in which the occurrence of one event does not alter the probability that a second event will occur. For example, suppose two small companies are being monitored by a financier for possible investment. If the businesses are in different industries and they are otherwise unrelated, then the success or failure of one company may be *independent* of the success or failure of the other—that is, the event that company A fails may not alter the probability that company B will fail.

As a second example, consider an election poll in which 1,000 registered voters are asked their preference between two candidates. Pollsters try to use procedures for selecting a sample of voters so that the responses are independent—that is, the objective of the pollster is to select the sample so the event that one polled voter prefers candidate A does not alter the probability that a second polled voter prefers candidate A.

We will make three final points about independence. The first is that the property of independence, unlike the mutually exclusive property, cannot be shown on or gleaned from a Venn diagram. This means *you can't trust your intuition*. In general, the only way to check for independence is by performing the calculations of the probabilities in the definition.

The second point concerns the relationship between the mutually exclusive and independence properties. Suppose that events A and B are mutually exclusive, as shown in Figure 3.21, and both events have nonzero probabilities. Are these events independent or dependent? That is, does the assumption that B occurs alter the probability of the occurrence of A? It certainly does, because if we assume that B has occurred, it is impossible for A to have occurred simultaneously—that is, $P(A|B) = 0$. Thus, *mutually exclusive events are dependent events* because $P(A) \neq P(A|B)$.

S

Figure 3.21

Mutually exclusive events are dependent events

The third point is that the probability of the intersection of independent events is very easy to calculate. Referring to the formula for calculating the probability of an intersection, we find

$$P(A \cap B) = P(A)P(B \mid A)$$

Thus, because $P(B \mid A) = P(B)$ when A and B are independent, we have the following useful rule:

> **Probability of Intersection of Two Independent Events**
>
> If events A and B are independent, the probability of the intersection of A and B equals the product of the probabilities of A and B; that is,
>
> $$P(A \cap B) = P(A)P(B)$$
>
> The converse is also true: If $P(A \cap B) = P(A)P(B)$, then events A and B are independent.

In the die-toss experiment, we showed in Example 3.19 that the events A: {Observe an even number} and B: {Observe a number less than or equal to 4} are independent if the die is fair. Thus,

$$P(A \cap B) = P(A)P(B) = (\tfrac{1}{2})(\tfrac{2}{3}) = \tfrac{1}{3}$$

This agrees with the result that we obtained in the example:

$$P(A \cap B) = P(2) + P(4) = \tfrac{2}{6} = \tfrac{1}{3}$$

Example 3.21

Probability of Independent Events Occurring Simultaneously in the Diversity Training Study

Problem Refer to Example 3.5 (pp. 123–124). Recall that *USA Today* found that of all U.S. firms that use diversity training, 38% state that their primary reason for using it is to stay competitive.

a. What is the probability that in a sample of two firms that use diversity training, both primarily use it to stay competitive?

b. What is the probability that in a sample of 10 firms that use diversity training, all 10 primarily use it to stay competitive?

Solution

a. Let C_1 represent the event that firm 1 gives "stay competitive" as the primary reason for using diversity training. Define C_2 similarly for firm 2. The event that *both* firms give "stay competitive" as their primary reason is the intersection of the two events, $C_1 \cap C_2$. Based on the survey that found that 38% of U.S. firms use diversity training to stay competitive, we could reasonably conclude that $P(C_1) = .38$ and $P(C_2) = .38$. However, in order to compute the probability of $C_1 \cap C_2$ from the multiplicative rule, we must make the assumption that the two events are independent. Because the classification of any firm using diversity training is not likely to affect the classification of another firm, this assumption is reasonable. Assuming independence, we have

$$P(C_1 \cap C_2) = P(C_1)P(C_2) = (.38)(.38) = .1444$$

b. To see how to compute the probability that 10 of 10 firms will give "stay competitive" as their primary reason, first consider the event that 3 of 3 firms give "stay competitive" as the primary reason. Using the notation defined earlier, we want to compute the probability of the intersection $C_1 \cap C_2 \cap C_3$. Again assuming independence of the classifications, we have

$$P(C_1 \cap C_2 \cap C_3) = P(C_1)P(C_2)P(C_3) = (.38)(.38)(.38) = .054872$$

Similar reasoning leads us to the conclusion that the intersection of 10 such events can be calculated as follows:

$$P(C_1 \cap C_2 \cap C_3 \cap \ldots \cap C_{10}) = P(C_1)P(C_2)\ldots P(C_{10}) = (.38)^{10} = .0000628$$

Thus, the probability that 10 of 10 firms all give "stay competitive" as their primary reason for using diversity training is about 63 in 1 million, assuming the events (stated reasons for using diversity training) are independent.

Look Back The very small probability in part **b** makes it extremely unlikely that 10 of 10 firms would give "stay competitive" as their primary reason for diversity training. If this event should actually occur, we would need to reassess our estimate of the probability of .38 used in the calculation. If all 10 firms' reason is staying competitive, then the probability that any one firm gives staying competitive as their reason is much higher than .38. (This conclusion is another application of the rare event approach to statistical inference.)

Now Work Exercise 3.70a

Statistics IN Action Revisited   The Probability of Winning Cash 3 or Play 4

In addition to biweekly Lotto 6/53, the Florida Lottery runs several other games. Two popular daily games are "Cash 3" and "Play 4." In Cash 3, players pay $1 to select three numbers in sequential order, where each number ranges from 0 to 9. If the three numbers selected (e.g., 2-8-4) match exactly the order of the three numbers drawn, the player wins $500. Play 4 is similar to Cash 3, but players must match four numbers (each number ranging from 0 to 9). For a $1 Play 4 ticket (e.g., 3-8-3-0), the player will win $5,000 if the numbers match the order of the four numbers drawn.

During the official drawing for Cash 3, 10 Ping-Pong balls numbered 0, 1, 2, 3, 4, 5, 6, 7, 8, and 9 are placed into each of three chambers. The balls in the first chamber are colored pink, the balls in the second chamber are blue, and the balls in the third chamber are yellow. One ball of each color is randomly drawn, with the official order as pink-blue-yellow. In Play 4, a fourth chamber with orange balls is added, and the official order is pink-blue-yellow-orange. Because the draws of the colored balls are random and independent, we can apply an extension of the Probability Rule for the Intersection of Two Independent Events to find the odds of winning Cash 3 and Play 4. The probability of matching a numbered ball being drawn from a chamber is 1/10; therefore,

$$
\begin{aligned}
P(\text{Win Cash 3}) &= P(\text{match pink AND match blue AND match yellow}) \\
&= P(\text{match pink}) \times P(\text{match blue}) P(\text{match yellow}) \\
&= (1/10)(1/10)(1/10) = 1/1000 = .001
\end{aligned}
$$

$$
\begin{aligned}
P(\text{Win Play 4}) &= P(\text{match pink AND match blue AND match yellow AND match orange}) \\
&= P(\text{match pink}) \times P(\text{match blue}) \times P(\text{match yellow}) \times P(\text{match orange}) \\
&= (1/10)(1/10)(1/10)(1/10) \\
&= 1/10,000 = .0001
\end{aligned}
$$

Although the odds of winning one of these daily games is much better than the odds of winning Lotto 6/53, there is still only a 1 in 1,000 chance (for Cash 3) or 1 in 10,000 chance (for Play 4) of winning the daily game. And the payoffs ($500 or $5,000) are much smaller. In fact, it can be shown that you will lose an average of 50¢ every time you play either Cash 3 or Play 4!

Activity 3.1   *Exit Polls:* Conditional Probability

Exit polls are conducted in selected locations as voters leave their polling places after voting. In addition to being used to predict the outcome of elections before the votes are counted, these polls are used to gauge tendencies among voters. The results are usually stated in terms of conditional probabilities.

The table on the next page shows the results of exit polling that suggest men were almost evenly spit on voting for John McCain or Barack Obama, while women were more likely to vote

for Obama in the 2008 presidential election. In addition, the table also suggests that more women than men voted in the election. The six percentages in the last three columns represent conditional probabilities where the given event is gender.

1. Find similar exit poll results where the voters are categorized by race, income, education, or some other criterion for a recent national, state, or local election. Choose two different examples and interpret the percentages given as probabilities, or conditional probabilities where appropriate.

2008 Presidential Election, Vote by Gender

	Obama	McCain	Other
Male (47%)	49%	48%	3%
Female (53%)	56%	43%	1%

Source: www.cnn.com

2. Use the multiplicative rule of probability to find the probabilities related to the percentages given. [For example, in the table above find *P*(Obama and Male) using the multiplicative rule.] Then interpret each of these probabilities and use them to determine the total percentage of the electorate who voted for each candidate.

3. Describe a situation where a business might use a form of exit polling to gauge customer reaction to a new product or service. Identify the type of business, the product or service, the criterion used to categorize customers, and how the customers' reactions will be determined. Then describe how the results will be summarized as conditional probabilities. How might the results of the poll benefit the business?

Exercises 3.47–3.74

Learning the Mechanics

3.47 For two events, *A* and *B*, $P(A) = .4$, $P(B) = .2$, and $P(A \cap B) = .1$.
    a. Find $P(A|B)$.
    b. Find $P(B|A)$.
    c. Are *A* and *B* independent events?

3.48 For two events, *A* and *B*, $P(A) = .4$, $P(B) = .2$, and $P(A|B) = .6$.
    a. Find $P(A \cap B)$.
    b. Find $P(B|A)$.

3.49 For two independent events, *A* and *B*, $P(A) = .4$ and $P(B) = .2$.
    a. Find $P(A \cap B)$.
    b. Find $P(A|B)$.
    c. Find $P(A \cup B)$.

3.50 An experiment results in one of three mutually exclusive events, *A*, *B*, or *C*. It is known that $P(A) = .30$, $P(B) = .55$, and $P(C) = .15$. Find each of the following probabilities:
    a. $P(A \cup B)$
    b. $P(A \cap C)$
    c. $P(A|B)$
    d. $P(B \cup C)$
    e. Are *B* and *C* independent events? Explain.

3.51 Consider the experiment depicted by the Venn diagram, with the sample space *S* containing five sample points. The sample points are assigned the following probabilities: $P(E_1) = .20$, $P(E_2) = .30$, $P(E_3) = .30$, $P(E_4) = .10$, $P(E_5) = .10$.

S

    a. Calculate $P(A)$, $P(B)$, and $P(A \cap B)$.
    b. Suppose we know that event *A* has occurred, so that the reduced sample space consists of the three sample points in *A*—namely, E_1, E_2, and E_3. Use the formula for conditional probability to adjust the probabilities of these three sample points for the knowledge that *A* has occurred [i.e., $P(E_i|A)$]. Verify that the conditional probabilities are in the same proportion to one another as the original sample point probabilities.

c. Calculate the conditional probability $P(B|A)$ in two ways: (1) Add the adjusted (conditional) probabilities of the sample points in the intersection $A \cap B$, as these represent the event that *B* occurs given that *A* has occurred; (2) use the formula for conditional probability:
$$P(B|A) = \frac{P(A \cap B)}{P(A)}$$
    Verify that the two methods yield the same result.
    d. Are events *A* and *B* independent? Why or why not?

3.52 Two fair coins are tossed, and the following events are defined:

    A: {Observe at least one head}
    B: {Observe exactly one head}

    a. Draw a Venn diagram for the experiment, showing events *A* and *B*. Assign probabilities to the sample points.
    b. Find $P(A)$, $P(B)$, and $P(A \cap B)$.
    c. Use the formula for conditional probability to find $P(A|B)$ and $P(B|A)$. Verify your answer by inspecting the Venn diagram and using the concept of reduced sample spaces.

3.53 An experiment results in one of five sample points with the following probabilities: $P(E_1) = .22$, $P(E_2) = .31$, $P(E_3) = .15$, $P(E_4) = .22$, and $P(E_5) = .1$. The following events have been defined:

    A: $\{E_1, E_3\}$
    B: $\{E_2, E_3, E_4\}$
    C: $\{E_1, E_5\}$

    Find each of the following probabilities:
    a. $P(A)$
    b. $P(B)$
    c. $P(A \cap B)$
    d. $P(A|B)$
    e. $P(B \cap C)$
    f. $P(C|B)$
    g. Consider each pair of events: *A* and *B*, *A* and *C*, and *B* and *C*. Are any of the pairs of events independent? Why?

3.54 Two fair dice are tossed, and the following events are defined:

    A: {Sum of the numbers showing is odd}
    B: {Sum of the numbers showing is 9, 11, or 12}

    Are events *A* and *B* independent? Why?

3.55 A sample space contains six sample points and events *A*, *B*, and *C* as shown in the Venn diagram. The probabilities of the sample points are

$$P(1) = .20, P(2) = .05, P(3) = .30, P(4) = .10,$$
$$P(5) = .10, P(6) = .25.$$

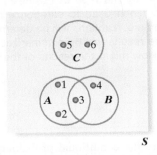

a. Which pairs of events, if any, are mutually exclusive? Why?
b. Which pairs of events, if any, are independent? Why?
c. Find $P(A \cup B)$ by adding the probabilities of the sample points and then by using the additive rule. Verify that the answers agree. Repeat for $P(A \cup C)$.

⦿ Applet Exercise 3.5

Use the applet *Simulating the Probability of Rolling a 6* to simulate conditional probabilities. Begin by running the applet twice with *n* = 10 without resetting between runs. The data on your screen represent 20 rolls of a die. The diagram above the *Roll* button shows the frequency of each of the six possible outcomes. Use this information to find each of the probabilities.

a. The probability of 6 given the outcome is 5 or 6
b. The probability of 6 given the outcome is even
c. The probability of 4 or 6 given the outcome is even
d. The probability of 4 or 6 given the outcome is odd

Applying the Concepts — Basic

3.56 **Speeding linked to fatal car crashes.** According to the National Highway Traffic and Safety Administration's National Center for Statistics and Analysis (NCSA), "speeding is one of the most prevalent factors contributing to fatal traffic crashes" (*NHTSA Technical Report*, Aug. 2005). The probability that speeding is a cause of a fatal crash is .3. Furthermore, the probability that speeding and missing a curve are causes of a fatal crash is .12. Given speeding is a cause of a fatal crash, what is the probability that the crash occurred on a curve?

3.57 **Largest nondomestic public companies.** *Forbes* (Mar. 30, 2006) conducted a survey of the 20 largest nondomestic public companies in the world. Of these 20 companies, 3 were banking companies based in the United Kingdom. A total of 5 UK companies were on the top 20 list. Suppose we select one of these 20 companies at random. Given the company is based in the UK, what is the probability that it is a banking company?

3.58 **Guilt in decision making.** Refer to the *Journal of Behavioral Decision Making* (Jan. 2007) study of the effect of guilt emotion on how a decision-maker focuses on the problem, Exercise 3.40 (p. 139). The results (number responding in each category) for the 171 study participants are reproduced in the table below. Suppose one of the 171 participants is selected at random.

Emotional State	Choose Stated Option	Do Not Choose Stated Option	Totals
Guilt	45	12	57
Anger	8	50	58
Neutral	7	49	56
Totals	60	111	171

Source: Gangemi, A., and Mancini, F. "Guilt and focusing in decision-making," *Journal of Behavioral Decision Making*, Vol. 20, Jan. 2007 (Table 2).

a. Given the respondent is assigned to the guilty state, what is the probability that the respondent chooses the stated option?
b. If the respondent does not choose to repair the car, what is the probability that the respondent is in the anger state?
c. Are the events {repair the car} and {guilty state} independent?

3.59 **National firearms survey.** Refer to the Harvard School of Public Health study of privately held firearm stock in the United States, Exercise 2.136 (p. 103). Recall that in a representative household telephone survey of 2,770 adults, 26% reported that they own at least one gun (*Injury Prevention*, Jan. 2007). Of those that own a gun 5% own a handgun. Suppose one of the 2,770 adults surveyed is randomly selected.
a. What is the probability that the adult owns at least one gun?
b. What is the probability that the adult owns at least one gun and the gun is a handgun?

3.60 **Monitoring quality of power equipment.** *Mechanical Engineering* (Feb. 2005) reported on the need for wireless networks to monitor the quality of industrial equipment. For example, consider Eaton Corp., a company that develops distribution products. Eaton estimates that 90% of the electrical switching devices it sells can monitor the quality of the power running through the device. Eaton further estimates that of the buyers of electrical switching devices capable of monitoring quality, 90% do not wire the equipment up for that purpose. Use this information to estimate the probability that an Eaton electrical switching device is capable of monitoring power quality and is wired up for that purpose.

3.61 **Internet user study.** In a study of Internet users, researchers discovered that 80% of the users own at least one computer and that 25% of the users log on to the Internet for more than 30 hours per week (*Internet Research*, Vol. 11, 2001). Suppose that 15% of the users own at least one computer and log on to the Internet for more than 30 hours per week.
a. Given an Internet user owns at least one computer, what is the probability that he or she logs on to the Internet for more than 30 hours per week?
b. Given an Internet user logs on to the Internet for more than 30 hours per week, what is the probability that he or she owns at least one computer?

Applying the Concepts — Intermediate

3.62 **Probability of winning a war.** Before a country enters into a war, a prudent government will assess the cost, utility, and probability of a victory. University of Georgia professor

P. L. Sullivan has developed a statistical model for determining the probability of winning a war based on a government's capabilities and resources (*Journal of Conflict Resolution,* Vol. 51, 2007). Now consider the current U.S.-Iraq conflict. One researcher used the model to estimate that the probability of a successful regime change in Iraq was .70 prior to the start of the war. Of course, we now know that the successful regime change was achieved. However, the model also estimates that given the mission is extended to support a weak Iraqi government, the probability of ultimate success is only .26. Assume these probabilities are accurate.

a. Prior to the start of the U.S.-Iraq war, what is the probability that a successful regime change is not achieved?

b. Given that the mission is extended to support a weak Iraqi government, what is the probability that a successful regime change is ultimately achieved?

c. Suppose the probability of the U.S. extending the mission to support a weak Iraqi government was .55. Find the probability that the mission is extended and results in a successful regime change.

3.63 Reversible errors in capital punishment cases. New York's Columbia University Law School released a report in February 2002 on all capital punishment (death penalty) cases that occurred over the past 25 years in the United States. Two of the findings are stated as follows: 68% of all capital punishment cases had a serious, reversible error. Of the cases that were overturned due to reversible error, 7% resulted in acquittal for the defendant during retrial.

a. Write each of these findings in the form of a probability.

b. Use the findings to find the probability that a capital case had a serious, reversible error and an innocent defendant.

3.64 Degrees of best-paid CEOs. Refer to the results of the *Forbes* (April 30, 2008) survey of the top 40 best-paid CEOs shown in Table 2.1 (p. 32). The data on highest degree obtained are summarized in the SPSS printout at the bottom of the page. Suppose you randomly select five of the CEOs (without replacement) and record the highest degree obtained by each.

a. What is the probability that the highest degree obtained by the first CEO you select is a bachelor's degree?

b. Suppose the highest degree obtained by each of the first four CEOs you select is a bachelor's degree. What is the probability that the highest degree obtained by the fifth CEO you select is a bachelor's degree?

3.65 Home modifications for wheelchair users. Refer to the *American Journal of Public Health* (Jan. 2002) study of elderly wheelchair users who live at home, Exercise 3.44

(p. 140). The table classifying a sample of 306 wheelchair users according to type of features installed in the home and whether or not they had an injurious fall follows. Suppose we select, at random, one of the 306 surveyed wheelchair users.

Home Features	Injurious Fall(s)	No Falls	Totals
All 5	2	7	9
At least 1	26	162	188
None	20	89	109
Totals	48	258	306

Source: Berg, K., Hines, M., and Allen, S. "Wheelchair users at home: Few home modifications and many injurious falls," *American Journal of Public Health,* Vol. 92, No. 1, Jan. 2002 (Table 1).

a. Given the wheelchair user had all five features installed, what is the probability that the user had an injurious fall?

b. Given the wheelchair user had none of the features installed, what is the probability that the user had an injurious fall?

3.66 Working mothers with children. The U.S. Census Bureau reports a decline in the percentage of mothers with infant children in the workforce. The following table gives a breakdown of the marital status and working status of the 3.9 million mothers with infant children in the year 2000. (The numbers in the table are reported in millions.) Consider the following events: A = {Mom with infant works}, B = {Mom with infant is married and living with husband}. Are A and B independent events?

	Working	Not Working
Married/living with husband	1,385	1,175
All other arrangements	786	588

Source: U.S. Census Bureau, *American Demographics,* Feb. 2002.

3.67 Intrusion detection systems. A computer intrusion detection system (IDS) is designed to provide an alarm whenever an intrusion (e.g., unauthorized access) is being attempted into a computer system. A probabilistic evaluation of a system with two independently operating intrusion detection systems (a double IDS) was published in the *Journal of Research of the National Institute of Standards and Technology* (November/December 2003). Consider a double IDS with system A and system B. If there is an intruder, system A sounds an alarm with probability .9, and system B sounds an alarm with probability .95. If there is no intruder, the probability that

SPSS Output for Exercise 3.64

DEGREE

		Frequency	Percent	Valid Percent	Cumulative Percent
Valid	Bachelors	14	35.0	35.0	35.0
	Law	6	15.0	15.0	50.0
	Masters	3	7.5	7.5	57.5
	MBA	12	30.0	30.0	87.5
	None	2	5.0	5.0	92.5
	PhD	3	7.5	7.5	100.0
	Total	40	100.0	100.0	

system A sounds an alarm (i.e., a false alarm) is .2, and the probability that system B sounds an alarm is .1. Assume that under a given condition (intruder or not), systems A and B operate independently.

a. Using symbols, express the four probabilities given in the example.

b. If there is an intruder, what is the probability that both systems sound an alarm?

c. If there is no intruder, what is the probability that both systems sound an alarm?

d. Given an intruder, what is the probability that at least one of the systems sounds an alarm?

3.68 **Detecting traces of TNT.** University of Florida researchers in the Department of Materials Science and Engineering have invented a technique to rapidly detect traces of TNT (*Today,* Spring 2005). The method, which involves shining a laser light on a potentially contaminated object, provides instantaneous results and gives no false positives. In this application, a false positive would occur if the laser light detects traces of TNT when, in fact, no TNT is actually present on the object. Let A be the event that the laser light detects traces of TNT. Let B be the event that the object contains no traces of TNT. The probability of a false positive is 0. Write this probability in terms of A and B using symbols such as $\cup, \cap$, and $|$.

3.69 **Are you really being served red snapper?** Red snapper is a rare and expensive reef fish served at upscale restaurants. Federal law prohibits restaurants from serving a cheaper look-alike variety of fish (e.g., vermillion snapper or lane snapper) to customers who order red snapper. Researchers at the University of North Carolina used DNA analysis to examine fish specimens labeled "red snapper" that were purchased from vendors across the country (*Nature,* July 15, 2004). The DNA tests revealed that 77% of the specimens were not red snapper but cheaper look-alike variety of fish.

a. Assuming the results of the DNA analysis are valid, what is the probability that you are actually served red snapper the next time you order it at a restaurant?

b. If there are five customers at a restaurant, all who have ordered red snapper, what is the probability that at least one customer is actually served red snapper?

3.70 **Lie detector test.** A new type of lie detector—called the computerized voice stress analyzer (CVSA)—has been developed. The manufacturer claims that the CVSA is 98% accurate, and, unlike a polygraph machine, will not be thrown off by drugs and medical factors. However, laboratory studies by the U.S. Defense Department found that the CVSA had an accuracy rate of 49.8%—slightly less than pure chance (*Tampa Tribune,* Jan. 10, 1999). Suppose the CVSA is used to test the veracity of four suspects. Assume the suspects' responses are independent.

[NW] **a.** If the manufacturer's claim is true, what is the probability that the CVSA will correctly determine the veracity of all four suspects?

b. If the manufacturer's claim is true, what is the probability that the CVSA will yield an incorrect result for at least one of the four suspects?

c. Suppose that in a laboratory experiment conducted by the U.S. Defense Department on four suspects, the CVSA yielded incorrect results for two of the suspects. Use this result to make an inference about the true accuracy rate of the new lie detector.

Applying the Concepts—Advanced

3.71 **Patient medical instruction sheets.** Physicians and pharmacists sometimes fail to inform patients adequately about the proper application of prescription drugs and about the precautions to take in order to avoid potential side effects. One method of increasing patients' awareness of the problem is for physicians to provide patient medication instruction (PMI) sheets. The American Medical Association, however, has found that only 20% of the doctors who prescribe drugs frequently distribute PMI sheets to their patients. Assume that 20% of all patients receive the PMI sheet with their prescriptions and that 12% receive the PMI sheet and are hospitalized because of a drug-related problem. What is the probability that a person will be hospitalized for a drug-related problem given that the person has received the PMI sheet?

3.72 **Risk of a natural gas pipeline accident.** *Process Safety Progress* (Dec. 2004) published a risk analysis for a natural gas pipeline between Bolivia and Brazil. The most likely scenario for an accident would be natural gas leakage from a hole in the pipeline. The probability that the leak ignites immediately (causing a jet fire) is .01. If the leak does not immediately ignite, it may result in a delayed ignition of a gas cloud. Given no immediate ignition, the probability of delayed ignition (causing a flash fire) is .01. If there is no delayed ignition, the gas cloud will harmlessly disperse. Suppose a leak occurs in the natural gas pipeline. Find the probability that either a jet fire or a flash fire will occur. Illustrate with a tree diagram.

3.73 **Most likely coin-tossing sequence.** In *Parade Magazine*'s (Nov. 26, 2000) column "Ask Marilyn," the following question was posed: "I have just tossed a [balanced] coin 10 times, and I ask you to guess which of the following three sequences was the result. One (and only one) of the sequences is genuine."

    (1) H H H H H H H H H H
    (2) H H T T H T T H H H
    (3) T T T T T T T T T T

a. Demonstrate that prior to actually tossing the coins, the three sequences are equally likely to occur.

b. Find the probability that the 10 coin tosses result in all heads or all tails.

c. Find the probability that the 10 coin tosses result in a mix of heads and tails.

d. Marilyn's answer to the question posed was "Though the chances of the three specific sequences occurring randomly are equal ... it's reasonable for us to choose sequence (2) as the most likely genuine result." If you know that only one of the three sequences actually occurred, explain why Marilyn's answer is correct. [*Hint:* Compare the probabilities in parts **b** and **c.**]

3.74 **Software defects in NASA spacecraft instrument code.** Portions of computer software code that may contain undetected defects are called *blind spots*. The issue of blind spots in software code evaluation was addressed at the *8th IEEE International Symposium on High Assurance Software Engineering* (March 2004). The researchers developed guidelines for assessing methods of predicting software defects using data on 498 modules of software code written in "C" language for a NASA spacecraft instrument. One simple prediction algorithm is to count the lines of code in the module; any module with more than 50 lines of code is predicted to have a defect. The **SWDEFECTS** file contains the predicted and actual defect status of all 498 modules. A standard approach to evaluating a software defect prediction algorithm is to form a two-way summary table similar to the one shown here. In the table, *a*, *b*, *c*, and *d* represent the number of modules in each cell. Software engineers use these table entries to compute several probability measures, called *accuracy, detection rate, false alarm rate,* and *precision.*

		Module Has Defects	
		False	True
Algorithm	No	*a*	*b*
Predicts Defects	Yes	*c*	*d*

a. *Accuracy* is defined as the probability that the prediction algorithm is correct. Write a formula for *accuracy* as a function of the table values *a*, *b*, *c*, and *d*.

b. The *detection rate* is defined as the probability that the algorithm predicts a defect, given that the module actually is a defect. Write a formula for *detection rate* as a function of the table values *a*, *b*, *c*, and *d*.

c. The *false alarm rate* is defined as the probability that the algorithm predicts a defect, given that the module actually has no defect. Write a formula for *false alarm rate* as a function of the table values *a*, *b*, *c*, and *d*.

d. *Precision* is defined as the probability that the module has a defect, given that the algorithm predicts a defect. Write a formula for *precision* as a function of the table values *a*, *b*, *c*, and *d*.

e. Access the **SWDEFECTS** file and compute the values of accuracy, detection rate, false alarm rate, and precision. Interpret the results.

3.7 Random Sampling

How a sample is selected from a population is of vital importance in statistical inference because the probability of an observed sample will be used to infer the characteristics of the sampled population. To illustrate, suppose you deal yourself four cards from a deck of 52 cards and all four cards are aces. Do you conclude that your deck is an ordinary bridge deck, containing only four aces, or do you conclude that the deck is stacked with more than four aces? It depends on how the cards were drawn. If the four aces were always placed at the top of a standard bridge deck, drawing four aces is not unusual—it is certain. On the other hand, if the cards are thoroughly mixed, drawing four aces in a sample of four cards is highly improbable. The point, of course, is that in order to use the observed sample of four cards to draw inferences about the population (the deck of 52 cards), you need to know how the sample was selected from the deck.

One of the simplest and most frequently employed sampling procedures is implied in many of the previous examples and exercises. It produces what is known as a *random sample.* We learned in Section 1.6 (p. 15) that a random sample is likely to be *representative* of the population that it is selected from.

> If *n* elements are selected from a population in such a way that every set of *n* elements in the population has an equal probability of being selected, the *n* elements are said to be a **random sample.***

If a population is not too large and the elements can be numbered on slips of paper, poker chips, and so on, you can physically mix the slips of paper or chips and remove *n* elements from the total. The numbers that appear on the chips selected would indicate the population elements to be included in the sample. Becuase it is often difficult to achieve a thorough mix, such a procedure provides only an approximation to random sampling. Most researchers rely on **random number generators** to automatically generate the random sample. Random number generators are available in table form, and they are built into most statistical software packages.

Example 3.22
Selecting a Random Sample of Households

Problem Suppose you wish to randomly sample five households from a population of 100,000 households to participate in a study.

a. How many different samples can be selected?

b. Use a random number generator to select a random sample.

---

*Strictly speaking, this is a **simple random sample.** There are many different types of random samples. The simple random sample is the most common.

Solution

a. To determine the number of samples, we'll apply the Combinations Rule of Section 3.1. In this case, $N = 100,000$ and $n = 5$. Then

$$\binom{N}{n} = \binom{100,000}{5} = \frac{100,000!}{5!\,99,995!}$$

$$= \frac{100,000 \cdot 99,999 \cdot 99,998 \cdot 99,997 \cdot 99,996}{5 \cdot 4 \cdot 3 \cdot 2 \cdot 1}$$

$$= 8.33 \times 10^{22}$$

Thus, there are 83.3 billion trillion different samples of five households that can be selected from 100,000.

b. To ensure that each of the possible samples has an equal chance of being selected, as required for random sampling, we can employ a **random number table,** as provided in Table I in Appendix B. Random number tables are constructed in such a way that every number occurs with (approximately) equal probability. Furthermore, the occurrence of any one number in a position is independent of any of the other numbers that appear in the table. To use a table of random numbers, number the N elements in the population from 1 to N. Then turn to Table I and select a starting number in the table. Proceeding from this number either across the row or down the column, remove and record n numbers from the table.

   To illustrate, first we number the households in the population from 1 to 100,000. Then, we turn to a page of Table I, say the first page. (A partial reproduction of the first page of Table I is shown in Table 3.7.) Now we arbitrarily select a starting number, say the random number appearing in the third row, second column. This number is 48,360. Then we proceed down the second column to obtain the remaining four random numbers. In this case we have selected five random numbers, which are shaded in Table 3.7. Using the first five digits to represent households from 1 to 99,999 and the number 00000 to represent household 100,000, we can see that the households numbered

48,360

93,093

39,975

6,907

72,905

should be included in our sample.

   Note: Use only the necessary number of digits in each random number to identify the element to be included in the sample. If, in the course of recording the n numbers from the table, you select a number that has already been selected, simply discard the

Table 3.7	Partial Reproduction of Table I in Appendix B					
Column Row	1	2	3	4	5	6
1	10480	15011	01536	02011	81647	91646
2	22368	46573	25595	85393	30995	89198
3	24130	48360	22527	97265	76393	64809
4	42167	93093	06243	61680	07856	16376
5	37570	39975	81837	16656	06121	91782
6	77921	06907	11008	42751	27756	53498
7	99562	72905	56420	69994	98872	31016
8	96301	91977	05463	07972	18876	20922
9	89579	14342	63661	10281	17453	18103
10	85475	36857	53342	53988	53060	59533
11	28918	69578	88231	33276	70997	79936
12	63553	40961	48235	03427	49626	69445
13	09429	93969	52636	92737	88974	33488

duplicate and select a replacement at the end of the sequence. Thus, you may have to record more than *n* numbers from the table to obtain a sample of *n* unique numbers.

Look Back Can we be perfectly sure that all 83.3 billion trillion samples have an equal chance of being selected? The fact is, we can't; but to the extent that the random number table contains truly random sequences of digits, the sample should be very close to random.

Now Work Exercise 3.76

Table I in Appendix B is just one example of a random number generator. For most scientific studies that require a large random sample, computers are used to generate the random sample. The EXCEL, Minitab, and SPSS statistical software packages all have easy-to-use random number generators.

For example, suppose we required a random sample of *n* = 50 households from the population of 100,000 households in Example 3.22. Here, we might employ the Minitab random number generator. Figure 3.22 shows a Minitab printout listing 50 random numbers (from a population of 100,000). The households with these identification numbers would be included in the random sample.

ASPIRIN-STUDY.M

	C1 Physician	C2 Treatment
1	1	3
2	2	11
3	3	10
4	4	14
5	5	2
6	6	7
7	7	6
8	8	16
9	9	17
10	10	9
11	11	
12	12	
13	13	
14	14	
15	15	
16	16	
17	17	
18	18	
19	19	
20	20	
21		

Figure 3.23

Minitab worksheet with random assignment of physicians

HOUSE50.MTW *

	C1 HouseID1	C2 HouseID2	C3 HouseID3	C4 HouseID4	C5 HouseID5
1	2036	22037	39884	62123	75750
2	3161	22055	44687	62421	80044
3	3930	22226	44689	63749	81857
4	9838	22773	45422	69079	81918
5	9961	22820	48104	69802	91680
6	11623	32989	50226	70895	94987
7	14114	33119	50443	71029	96110
8	17244	35045	50806	72879	97679
9	17598	35922	50813	73962	99232
10	18769	39272	61059	75517	99789
11					

Figure 3.22

Minitab worksheet with random sample of 50 households

Recall our discussion of designed experiments in Section 1.6 (p. 14). The notion of random selection and randomization is key to conducting good research with a designed experiment. The next example illustrates a basic application.

Example 3.23

Randomization in a Designed Experiment

Problem A designed experiment in the medical field involving human subjects is referred to as a *clinical trial*. One recent clinical trial was designed to determine the potential of using aspirin in preventing heart attacks. Volunteer physicians were randomly divided into two groups—the *treatment* group and the *control* group. Each physician in the treatment group took one aspirin tablet a day for one year, while the physicians in the control group took an aspirin-free placebo made to look identical to an aspirin tablet. Because the physicians did not know which group, treatment or control, they were assigned to, the clinical trial is called a *blind study*. Assume 20 physicians volunteered for the study. Use a random number generator to randomly assign half of the physicians to the treatment group and half to the control group.

Solution Essentially, we want to select a random sample of 10 physicians from the 20. The first 10 selected will be assigned to the treatment group; the remaining 10 will be assigned to the control group. (Alternatively, we could randomly assign each physician, one by one, to either the treatment or control group. However, this would not guarantee exactly 10 physicians in each group.)

Ethics in Statistics

Intentionally selecting a nonrandom sample in an effort to support a particular viewpoint is considered *unethical statistical practice*.

The Minitab random sample procedure was employed, producing the printout shown above in Figure 3.23. Numbering the physicians from 1 to 20, we see that physicians 3, 11, 10, 14, 2, 7, 6, 16, 17, and 9 are assigned to receive the aspirin (treatment). The remaining physicians are assigned the placebo (control).

Activity 3.2   *Keep the Change:* Independent Events

Once again we return to the Bank of America *Keep the Change* savings program, Activity 1.1 (p. 16). This time we look at whether certain events involving purchase totals and amounts transferred to savings are independent. Throughout this activity, the experiment consists of randomly selecting one purchase from a large group of purchases.

1. Define events A and B as follows:

   A: {Purchase total ends in $0.25.}
   B: {Amount transferred is less than $0.50.}

   Explain why events A and B are not independent. Are events A and B mutually exclusive? Use this example to explain the difference between independent events and mutually exclusive events.

2. Now define events A and B in this manner:

   A: {Purchase total is greater than $10.}
   B: {Amount transferred is less than $0.50.}

   Do you believe that these events are independent? Explain your reasoning.

3. To investigate numerically whether the events in Question 2 are independent, we will use the data collected in Activity 1.1, page 16. Pool your data with the data from other students or the entire class so that the combined data set represents at least 100 purchases. Complete the table by counting the number of purchases in each category.

Distribution of Purchases

	Purchase	Total	
Transfer Amount	≤ $10	> $10	Totals
$0.00–$0.49			
$0.99–$0.99			
Totals			

Compute appropriate probabilities based on your completed table to test whether the events of Question 2 are independent. If you conclude that the events are not independent, can you explain your conclusion in terms of the original data?

Exercises 3.75–3.83

Learning the Mechanics

3.75 How are random samples related to representative samples?

3.76 Suppose you wish to sample $n = 2$ elements from a total of $N = 10$ elements.
[NW]
   a. Count the number of different samples that can be drawn, first by listing them, and then by using combinatorial mathematics (see Section 3.1).
   b. If random sampling is to be employed, what is the probability that any particular sample will be selected?
   c. Show how to use the random number table, Table I in Appendix B, to select a random sample of 2 elements from a population of 10 elements. Perform the sampling procedure 20 times. Do any two of the samples contain the same 2 elements? Given your answer to part b, did you expect repeated samples?

3.77 Suppose you wish to sample $n = 3$ elements from a total of $N = 600$ elements.
   a. Count the number of different samples by using combinatorial mathematics (see Section 3.1).
   b. If random sampling is to be employed, what is the probability that any particular sample will be selected?
   c. Show how to use the random number table, Table I in Appendix B, to select a random sample of 3 elements from a population of 600 elements. Perform the sampling procedure 20 times. Do any two of the samples contain the same three elements? Given your answer to part b, did you expect repeated samples?
   d. Use a computer to generate a random sample of 3 from the population of 600 elements.

3.78 Suppose that a population contains $N = 200,000$ elements. Use a computer or Table I in Appendix B to select a random sample of $n = 10$ elements from the population. Explain how you selected your sample.

Applying the Concepts—Basic

3.79 **Random-digit dialing.** To ascertain the effectiveness of their advertising campaigns, firms frequently conduct telephone interviews with consumers using *random-digit dialing*. With this approach, a random number generator mechanically creates the sample of phone numbers to be called.
   a. Explain how the random number table (Table I in Appendix B) or a computer could be used to generate a sample of seven-digit telephone numbers.
   b. Use the procedure you described in part a to generate a sample of 10 seven-digit telephone numbers.
   c. Use the procedure you described in part a to generate five seven-digit telephone numbers whose first three digits are 373.

3.80 **Census sampling.** In addition to its decennial enumeration of the population, the U.S. Census Bureau regularly samples the population to estimate the level of and changes in a number of attributes, such as income, family size, employment, and marital status. Suppose the bureau plans to sample 1,000 households in a city that has a total of 534,322 households. Show how the bureau could use the random number table in Appendix B or a computer to generate the sample. Select the first 10 households to be included in the sample.

Applying the Concepts—Intermediate

3.81 **Auditing an accounting system.** In auditing a firm's financial statements, an auditor will (1) assess the capability of the firm's accounting system to accumulate, measure, and synthesize transactional data properly and (2) assess the operational effectiveness of the accounting system. In performing the second assessment, the auditor frequently relies on a random sample of actual transactions (Stickney and Weil, *Financial*

Accounting: An Introduction to Concepts, Methods, and Uses, 2002). A particular firm has 5,382 customer accounts that are numbered from 0001 to 5382.

a. One account is to be selected at random for audit. What is the probability that account number 3,241 is selected?

b. Draw a random sample of 10 accounts and explain in detail the procedure you used.

c. Refer to part **b.** The following are two possible random samples of size 10. Is one more likely to be selected than the other? Explain.

Sample Number 1				
5011	0082	0963	0772	3415
2663	1126	0008	0026	4189

Sample Number 2				
0001	0003	0005	0007	0009
0002	0004	0006	0008	0010

3.82 Sampling stocks on the NYSE. The results of the previous business day's transactions for stocks traded on the New York Stock Exchange (NYSE) and five regional exchanges—the Chicago, Pacific, Philadelphia, Boston, and Cincinnati stock exchanges—are summarized each business day in the NYSE–Composite Transactions table in the *Wall Street Journal.*

a. Examine the NYSE–Composite Transactions table in a recent issue of the *Wall Street Journal* and explain how to draw a random sample of stocks from the table.

b. Use the procedure you described in part **a** to draw a random sample of 20 stocks from a recent NYSE–Composite Transactions table. For each stock in the sample, list its name (i.e., the abbreviation given in the table), its sales volume, and its closing price.

Applying the Concepts—Advanced

3.83 Sampling TV markets for a court case. A recent court case involved a claim of satellite television subscribers obtaining illegal access to local TV stations. The defendant (the satellite TV company) wanted to sample TV markets nationwide and determine the percentage of its subscribers in each sampled market who have illegal access to local TV stations. To do this, defendant's expert witness drew a rectangular grid over the continental United States, with horizontal and vertical grid lines every .02 degrees of latitude and longitude, respectively. This created a total of 500 rows and 1,000 columns, or $(500)(1,000) = 500,000$ intersections. The plan was to randomly sample 900 intersection points and include the TV market at each intersection in the sample. Explain how you could use a random number generator to obtain a random sample of 900 intersections. Develop at least two plans: one that numbers the intersections from 1 to 500,000 prior to selection and another that selects the row and column of each sampled intersection (from the total of 500 rows and 1,000 columns).

3.8 Bayes's Rule

An early attempt to employ probability in making inferences is the basis for a branch of statistical methodology known as **Bayesian statistical methods.** The logic employed by the English philosopher Thomas Bayes in the mid-1700s involves converting an unknown conditional probability, say $P(B|A)$, to one involving a known conditional probability, say $P(A|B)$. The method is illustrated in the next example.

Example 3.24

Applying Bayes's Logic to an Intruder Detection System

Problem An unmanned monitoring system uses high-tech video equipment and microprocessors to detect intruders. A prototype system has been developed and is in use outdoors at a weapons munitions plant. The system is designed to detect intruders with a probability of .90. However, the design engineers expect this probability to vary with weather conditions. The system automatically records the weather condition each time an intruder is detected. Based on a series of controlled tests, in which an intruder was released at the plant under various weather conditions, the following information is available: Given the intruder was, in fact, detected by the system, the weather was clear 75% of the time, cloudy 20% of the time, and raining 5% of the time. When the system failed to detect the intruder, 60% of the days were clear, 30% cloudy, and 10% rainy. Use this information to find the probability of detecting an intruder, given rainy weather conditions. (Assume that an intruder has been released at the plant.)

Solution Define D to be the event that the intruder is detected by the system. Then D^c is the event that the system failed to detect the intruder. Our goal is to calculate the conditional probability, $P(D|\text{Rainy})$. From the statement of the problem, the following information is available:

$$P(D) = .90 \qquad\qquad P(D^c) = .10$$
$$P(\text{Clear}|D) = .75 \qquad P(\text{Clear}|D^c) = .60$$

$$P(\text{Cloudy}|D) = .20 \quad P(\text{Cloudy}|D^c) = .30$$
$$P(\text{Rainy}|D) = .05 \quad P(\text{Rainy}|D^c) = .10$$

Note that $P(D|\text{Rainy})$ is not one of the conditional probabilities that is known. However, we can find

$$P(\text{Rainy} \cap D) = P(D)P(\text{Rainy}|D) = (.90)(.05) = .045$$

and

$$P(\text{Rainy} \cap D^c) = P(D^c)P(\text{Rainy}|D^c) = (.10)(.10) = .01$$

using the multiplicative rule of probability. These two probabilities are highlighted on the tree diagram for the problem in Figure 3.24.

Now the event Rainy is the union of two mutually exclusive events, $(\text{Rainy} \cap D)$ and $(\text{Rainy} \cap D^c)$. Thus, applying the additive rule of probability, we have

$$P(\text{Rainy}) = P(\text{Rainy} \cap D) + P(\text{Rainy} \cap D^c) = .045 + .01 = .055$$

We now apply the formula for conditional probability to obtain

$$P(D|\text{Rainy}) = \frac{P(\text{Rainy} \cap D)}{P(\text{Rainy})} = \frac{P(\text{Rainy} \cap D)}{P(\text{Rainy} \cap D) + P(\text{Rainy} \cap D^c)}$$
$$= {}^{.045}/_{.055} = .818$$

Therefore, under rainy weather conditions, the prototype system can detect the intruder with a probability of .818—a value lower than the designed probability of .90.

Figure 3.24
Tree diagram for Example 3.24

Now Work Exercise 3.84

The technique utilized in Example 3.24, called **Bayes's Rule,** can be applied when an observed event A occurs with any one of several mutually exclusive and exhaustive events, $B_1, B_2, \ldots, B_k$. The formula for finding the appropriate conditional probabilities is given in the box.

BIOGRAPHY

THOMAS BAYES (1702–1761)

The Inverse Probabilist

The Reverend Thomas Bayes was an ordained English Presbyterian minister who became a Fellow of the Royal Statistical Society without benefit of any formal training in mathematics or any published papers in science during his lifetime. His manipulation of the formula for conditional probability in 1761 is now known as Bayes's Theorem. At the time and for 200 years afterward, use of Bayes's Theorem (or inverse probability, as it was called) was controversial and, to some, considered an inappropriate practice. It was not until the 1960s that the power of the Bayesian approach to decision making began to be tapped. ■

Bayes's Rule

Given k mutually exclusive and exhaustive events, $B_1, B_2, ..., B_k$, such that $P(B_1) + P(B_2) + \cdots + P(B_k) = 1$, and an observed event A, then

$$P(B_i | A) = \frac{P(B_i \cap A)}{P(A)}$$

$$= \frac{P(B_i)P(A|B_i)}{P(B_1)P(A|B_1) + P(B_2)P(A|B_2) + \cdots + P(B_k)P(A|B_k)}$$

In applying Bayes's Rule to Example 3.24, the observed event $A = \{$Rainy$\}$ and the $k = 2$ mutually exclusive and exhaustive events are the complementary events $D = \{$intruder detected$\}$ and $D^c = \{$intruder not detected$\}$. Hence, the formula

$$P(D|\text{Rainy}) = \frac{P(D)P(\text{Rainy}|D)}{P(D)P(\text{Rainy}|D) + P(D^c)P(\text{Rainy}|D^c)}$$

$$= \frac{(.90)(.05)}{(.90)(.05) + (.10)(.10)} = .818$$

Exercises 3.84–3.94

Learning the Mechanics

3.84 Suppose the events B_1 and B_2 are mutually exclusive and complementary events, such that $P(B_1) = .75$ and $P(B_2) = .25$. Consider another event A such that $P(A|B_1) = .3$ and $P(A|B_2) = .5$.
  a. Find $P(B_1 \cap A)$.
  b. Find $P(B_2 \cap A)$.
  c. Find $P(A)$ using the results in parts **a** and **b.**
  d. Find $P(B_1|A)$.
  e. Find $P(B_2|A)$.

3.85 Suppose the events B_1, B_2, and B_3 are mutually exclusive and complementary events, such that $P(B_1) = .2$, $P(B_2) = .15$, and $P(B_3) = .65$. Consider another event A such that $P(A|B_1) = .4$, $P(A|B_2) = .25$, and $P(A|B_3) = .6$. Use Bayes's Rule to find
  a. $P(B_1|A)$
  b. $P(B_2|A)$
  c. $P(B_3|A)$

3.86 Suppose the events B_1, B_2, and B_3 are mutually exclusive and complementary events, such that $P(B_1) = .2$, $P(B_2) = .15$, and $P(B_3) = .65$. Consider another event A such that $P(A) = .4$. If A is independent of B_1, B_2, and B_3, use Bayes's Rule to show that $P(B_1|A) = P(B_1) = .2$.

Applying the Concepts—Basic

3.87 **Tests for Down syndrome.** Currently, there are three diagnostic tests available for chromosome abnormalities in a developing fetus: triple serum marker screening, ultrasound, and amniocentesis. The safest (to both the mother and fetus) and least expensive of the three is the ultrasound test. Two San Diego State University statisticians investigated the accuracy of using ultrasound to test for Down syndrome (*Chance*, Summer 2007). Let D denote that the fetus has a genetic marker for Down syndrome and N denote that the ultrasound test is normal (i.e., no indication of chromosome abnormalities). Then, the statisticians desire the probability $P(D|N)$. Use Bayes's Rule and the following probabilities (provided in the article) to find the desired probability: $P(D) = 1/80$, $P(D^c) = 79/80$, $P(N|D) = 1/2$, $P(N^c|D) = 1/2$, $P(N|D^c) = 1$, and $P(N^c|D^c) = 0$.

3.88 **Errors in estimating job costs.** A construction company employs three sales engineers. Engineers 1, 2, and 3 estimate the costs of 30%, 20%, and 50%, respectively, of all jobs bid by the company. For $i = 1, 2, 3$, define E_i to be the event that a job is estimated by engineer i. The following probabilities describe the rates at which the engineers make serious errors in estimating costs:

$$P(\text{error} | E_1) = .01, P(\text{error} | E_2) = .03, \text{ and}$$
$$P(\text{error} | E_3) = .02$$

  a. If a particular bid results in a serious error in estimating job cost, what is the probability that the error was made by engineer 1?
  b. If a particular bid results in a serious error in estimating job cost, what is the probability that the error was made by engineer 2?
  c. If a particular bid results in a serious error in estimating job cost, what is the probability that the error was made by engineer 3?
  d. Based on the probabilities, parts **a–c,** which engineer is most likely responsible for making the serious error?

3.89 **Fish contaminated by a plant's toxic discharge.** Refer to the U.S. Army Corps of Engineers' study on the DDT contamination of fish in the Tennessee River (Alabama), Example 1.5 (p. 13). Part of the investigation focused on how far upstream the contaminated fish have migrated. (A fish is considered to be contaminated if its measured DDT concentration is greater than 5.0 parts per million.)

a. Considering only the contaminated fish captured from the Tennessee River, the data (saved in the **DDT** file) reveal that 52% of the fish are found between 275 and 300 miles upstream, 39% are found 305 to 325 miles upstream, and 9% are found 330 to 350 miles upstream. Use these percentages to determine the probabilities, $P(275-300)$, $P(305-325)$, and $P(330-350)$.

b. Given that a contaminated fish is found a certain distance upstream, the probability that it is a channel catfish (CC) is determined from the data as $P(CC|275-300) = .775$, $P(CC|305-325) = .77$, and $P(CC|330-350) = .86$. If a contaminated channel catfish is captured from the Tennessee River, what is the probability that it was captured 275-300 miles upstream?

3.90 **Drug testing in athletes.** Due to inaccuracies in drug-testing procedures (e.g., false positives and false negatives) in the medical field, the results of a drug test represent only one factor in a physician's diagnosis. Yet, when Olympic athletes are tested for illegal drug use (i.e., doping), the results of a single test are used to ban the athlete from competition. In *Chance* (Spring 2004), University of Texas biostatisticians D. A. Berry and L. Chastain demonstrated the application of Bayes's Rule for making inferences about testosterone abuse among Olympic athletes. They used the following example: In a population of 1,000 athletes, suppose 100 are illegally using testosterone. Of the users, suppose 50 would test positive for testosterone. Of the nonusers, suppose 9 would test positive.

a. Given that the athlete is a user, find the probability that a drug test for testosterone will yield a positive result. (This probability represents the *sensitivity* of the drug test.)

b. Given the athlete is a nonuser, find the probability that a drug test for testosterone will yield a negative result. (This probability represents the *specificity* of the drug test.)

c. If an athlete tests positive for testosterone, use Bayes's Rule to find the probability that the athlete is really doping. (This probability represents the *positive predictive value* of the drug test.)

Applying the Concepts—Intermediate

3.91 **Malfunctioning production lines.** A manufacturing operation utilizes two production lines to assemble electronic fuses. Both lines produce fuses at the same rate and generally produce 2.5% defective fuses. However, production line 1 recently suffered mechanical difficulty and produced 6.0% defectives during a 3-week period. This situation was not known until several lots of electronic fuses produced in this period were shipped to customers. If one of the two fuses tested by a customer was found to be defective, what is the probability that the lot from which it came was produced on malfunctioning line 1? (Assume all the fuses in the lot were produced on the same line.)

3.92 **Nondestructive evaluation.** Nondestructive evaluation (NDE) describes methods that quantitatively characterize materials, tissues, and structures by noninvasive means, such as X-ray computed tomography, ultrasonics, and acoustic emission. Recently, NDE was used to detect defects in steel castings (*JOM,* May 2005). Assume that the probability that NDE detects a "hit" (i.e., predicts a defect in a steel casting) when, in fact, a defect exists is .97. (This is often called the *probability of detection.*) Also assume that the probability that NDE detects a hit when, in fact, no defect exists is .005. (This is called the *probability of a false call.*) Past experience has shown a defect occurs once in every 100 steel castings. If NDE detects a hit for a particular steel casting, what is the probability that an actual defect exists?

3.93 **Purchasing microchips.** An important component of your desktop or laptop personal computer (PC) is a microchip. The table gives the proportions of microchips that a certain PC manufacturer purchases from seven suppliers.

Supplier	Proportion
S_1	.15
S_2	.05
S_3	.10
S_4	.20
S_5	.12
S_6	.20
S_7	.18

a. It is known that the proportions of defective microchips produced by the seven suppliers are .001, .0003, .0007, .006, .0002, .0002, and .001, respectively. If a single PC microchip failure is observed, which supplier is most likely responsible?

b. Suppose the seven suppliers produce defective microchips at the same rate, .0005. If a single PC microchip failure is observed, which supplier is most likely responsible?

3.94 **Intrusion detection systems.** Refer to the *Journal of Research of the National Institute of Standards and Technology* (Nov.–Dec. 2003) study of a double intrusion detection system with independent systems, Exercise 3.67 (p. 153). Recall that if there is an intruder, system A sounds an alarm with probability .9 and system B sounds an alarm with probability .95. If there is no intruder, system A sounds an alarm with probability .2, and system B sounds an alarm with probability .1. Now assume that the probability of an intruder is .4. Also assume that under a given condition (intruder or not), systems A and B operate independently. If both systems sound an alarm, what is the probability that an intruder is detected?

CHAPTER NOTES

Key Terms

Key Symbols

S	**sample space** (collection of all sample points)
$A: \{1, 2\}$	set of **sample points in event** A
$P(A)$	**probability** of event A
$A \cup B$	**union** of events A and B (either A or B can occur)
$A \cap B$	**intersection** of events A and B (both A and B occur)
A^c	**complement** of A (event A does not occur)
$A \mid B$	event A occurs, **given** event B occurs
$\binom{N}{n}$	number of **combinations** of N elements taken n at a time
$N!$	**N factorial** $= N(N-1)(N-2)\ldots(2)(1)$

Key Ideas

Probability Rules for k Sample Points, $S_1, S_2, S_3, \ldots, S_k$

1. $0 \leq P(S_i) \leq 1$
2. $\sum P(S_i) = 1$

Random Sample

All possible such samples have equal probability of being selected.

Combinations Rule

Counting number of samples of n elements selected from N elements

$$\binom{N}{n} = \frac{N!}{n!(N-n)!} = \frac{N(N-1)(N-2)\cdots(N-n+1)}{n(n-1)(n-2)\cdots(2)(1)}$$

Bayes's Rule

$$P(S_i \mid A) = \frac{P(S_i)P(A \mid S_i)}{P(S_1)P(A \mid S_1) + P(S_2)P(A \mid S_2) + \cdots + P(S_k)P(A \mid S_k)}$$

Guide to Selecting Probability Rules

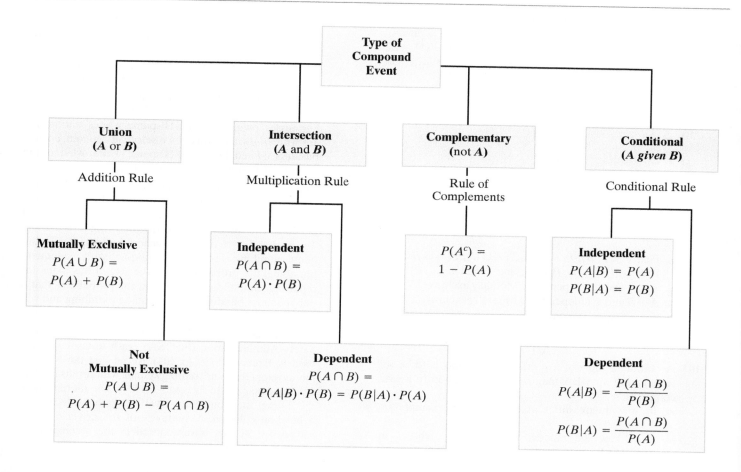

Supplementary Exercises 3.95–3.132

Learning the Mechanics

3.95 A sample space consists of four sample points, where $P(S_1) = .2$, $P(S_2) = .1$, $P(S_3) = .3$, and $P(S_4) = .4$.
  a. Show that the sample points obey the two probability rules for a sample space.
  b. If an event $A = \{S_1, S_4\}$, find $P(A)$.

3.96 For two events A and B, suppose $P(A) = .7$, $P(B) = .5$, and $P(A \cap B) = .4$. Find $P(A \cup B)$.

3.97 A and B are mutually exclusive events, with $P(A) = .2$ and $P(B) = .3$.
  a. Find $P(A|B)$.
  b. Are A and B independent events?

3.98 Which of the following pairs of events are mutually exclusive? Justify your response.
  a. {The Dow Jones Industrial Average increases on Monday.}, {A large New York bank decreases its prime interest rate on Monday.}
  b. {The next sale by a PC retailer is a laptop computer.}, {The next sale by a PC retailer is a desktop computer.}
  c. {You reinvest all your dividend income in a limited partnership.}, {You reinvest all your dividend income in a money market fund.}

3.99 Given that $P(A \cap B) = .4$ and $P(A|B) = .8$, find $P(B)$.

3.100 Two events, A and B, are independent, with $P(A) = .3$ and $P(B) = .1$.
  a. Are A and B mutually exclusive? Why?
  b. Find $P(A|B)$ and $P(B|A)$.
  c. Find $P(A \cup B)$.

3.101 The Venn diagram below illustrates a sample space containing six sample points and three events, A, B, and C. The probabilities of the sample points are $P(1) = .3$, $P(2) = .2$, $P(3) = .1$, $P(4) = .1$, $P(5) = .1$, and $P(6) = .2$.

S

  a. Find $P(A \cap B)$, $P(B \cap C)$, $P(A \cup C)$, $P(A \cup B \cup C)$, $P(B^c)$, $P(A^c \cap B)$, $P(B|C)$, and $P(B|A)$.
  b. Are A and B independent? Mutually exclusive? Why?
  c. Are B and C independent? Mutually exclusive? Why?

3.102 Find the numerical value of
  a. $6!$ **b.** $\binom{10}{9}$ **c.** $\binom{10}{1}$ **d.** $\binom{6}{3}$ **e.** $0!$

3.103 A random sample of five graduate students is to be selected from 50 MBA majors for participation in a case competition.
  a. In how many different ways can the sample be drawn?
  b. Show how the random number table, Table I in Appendix B, can be used to select the sample of students.

● Applet Exercise 3.6

Use the applet entitled *Random Numbers* to generate a list of 50 numbers between 1 and 100, inclusive. Use this list to find each of the probabilities.
  a. The probability that a number chosen from the list is less than or equal to 50
  b. The probability that a number chosen from the list is even
  c. The probability that a number chosen from the list is less than or equal to 50 and even
  d. The probability that a number chosen from the list is less than or equal to 50 given that the number is even
  e. Do your results from parts **a–d** support the conclusion that the events *less than or equal to 50* and *even* are independent? Explain.

Applying the Concepts — Basic

3.104 **Annual compensation and benefits report.** Each year, Hudson Institute conducts a survey of 10,000 U.S. workers about their total compensation packages. One question in Hudson's *2006 Compensation and Benefits Report* focused on employees who received raises in the past year. Of these employees, 35% reported that their raise was based on job performance, 50% reported that it was based on a standard cost of living, and the remainder (15%) were unsure how their raises were determined. Suppose we select (at random) one of the U.S. workers surveyed who received a raise last year and inquire about how that worker's raise was determined.
  a. List the sample points for this experiment.
  b. Assign reasonable probabilities to the sample points.
  c. Find the probability that the raise was based either on job performance or a standard cost of living.

3.105 **Ownership of small businesses.** According to the *Journal of Business Venturing* (Vol. 17, 2002), 27% of all small businesses owned by non-Hispanic whites nationwide are women-owned firms. If we select, at random, a small business owned by a non-Hispanic white, what is the probability that it is a male-owned firm?

3.106 **Condition of public school facilities.** The National Center for Education Statistics (NCES) conducted a survey on the condition of America's public school facilities. The survey revealed the following information. The probability that a public school building has inadequate plumbing is .25. Of the buildings with inadequate plumbing, the probability that the school has plans for repairing the building is .38. Find the probability that a public school building has inadequate plumbing and will be repaired.

3.107 **New car crash tests.** Refer to the National Highway Traffic Safety Administration (NHTSA) crash tests of new car models, Exercise 2.139 (p. 104). Recall that the NHTSA has developed a "star" scoring system, with results ranging from one star (*) to five stars (*****). The more stars in the rating, the better the level of crash protection in a head-on collision. A summary of the driver-side star ratings for 98 cars is reproduced in the accompanying Minitab printout. Assume that one of the 98 cars is selected at random. State whether each of the following is true or false.

a. The probability that the car has a rating of two stars is 4.

b. The probability that the car has a rating of four or five stars is .7857.

c. The probability that the car has a rating of one star is 0.

d. The car has a better chance of having a two-star rating than of having a five-star rating.

```
Tally for Discrete Variables: DRIVSTAR

DRIVSTAR    Count    Percent
       2        4       4.08
       3       17      17.35
       4       59      60.20
       5       18      18.37
      N=       98
```

3.108 ISO 9000 registered companies. The ISO 9000 is a series of standards for setting up and documenting quality systems, processes, and procedures. To gauge how managers view the standards or how the standards were achieved, a sample of 40 ISO 9000–registered companies in Colorado was selected, and the manager most responsible for ISO 9000 implementation was interviewed (*Quality Progress,* 1995). The following are some of the data obtained by the study:

Level of Top Management Involvement in the ISO 9000 Registration Process	Frequency
Very involved	9
Moderate involvement	16
Minimal involvement	12
Not involved	3

Length of Time to Achieve ISO 9000 Registration	Frequency
Less than 1 year	5
1–1.5 years	21
1.6–2 years	9
2.1–2.5 years	2
More than 2.5 years	3

Source: Weston, F. C. "What do managers really think of the ISO 9000 registration process?" *Quality Progress,* October 1995, pp. 68–69 (Tables 3 and 4). Reprinted with permission from *Quality Progress.* © 1995 American Society for Quality. No further distribution allowed without permission.

Suppose one of the 40 managers who were interviewed is to be randomly selected for additional questioning. Consider the events defined as follows:

A: {The manager was involved in the ISO 9000 registration.}

B: {The length of time to achieve ISO 9000 registration was more than 2 years.}

a. Find $P(A)$.

b. Find $P(B)$.

c. Explain why the preceding data are not sufficient to determine whether events *A* and *B* are independent.

3.109 Survey on energy conservation. A state energy agency mailed questionnaires on energy conservation to 1,000 homeowners in the state capital. Five hundred questionnaires were returned. Suppose an experiment consists of randomly selecting and reviewing one of the returned questionnaires. Consider the events:

A: {The home is constructed of brick.}

B: {The home is more than 30 years old.}

C: {The home is heated with oil.}

Describe each of the following events in terms of unions, intersections, and complements (i.e., $A \cup B$, $A \cap B$, A^c, etc.):

a. The home is more than 30 years old and is heated with oil.

b. The home is not constructed of brick.

c. The home is heated with oil or is more than 30 years old.

d. The home is constructed of brick and is not heated with oil.

3.110 Identifying urban counties. *Urban* and *rural* describe geographic areas for which land zoning regulations, school district policy, and public service policy are often set. However, the characteristics of urban/rural areas are not clearly defined. Researchers at the University of Nevada (Reno) asked a sample of county commissioners to give their perception of the single most important factor in identifying urban counties (*Professional Geographer,* Feb. 2000). In all, five factors were mentioned by the commissioners: total population, agricultural change, presence of industry, growth, and population concentration. The survey results are displayed in the pie chart below. Suppose one of the commissioners is selected at random and the most important factor specified by the commissioner is recorded.

a. List the sample points for this experiment.

b. Assign reasonable probabilities to the sample points.

c. Find the probability that the most important factor specified by the commissioner is population related.

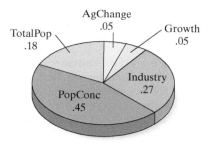

3.111 Use of country club facilities. A local country club has a membership of 600 and operates facilities that include an 18-hole championship golf course and 12 tennis courts. Before deciding whether to accept new members, the club president would like to know how many members regularly use each facility. A survey of the membership indicates that 70% regularly use the golf course, 50% regularly use the tennis courts, and 5% use neither of these facilities regularly.

a. Construct a Venn diagram to describe the results of the survey.

b. If one club member is chosen at random, what is the probability that the member uses either the golf course or the tennis courts or both?

c. If one member is chosen at random, what is the probability that the member uses both the golf and the tennis facilities?

d. A member is chosen at random from among those known to use the tennis courts regularly. What is the probability that the member also uses the golf course regularly?

3.112 Commodities shipped by rail. The following table, extracted from *Railway Age* (May 1999), lists the number of carloads of different types of commodities that were shipped by the major U.S. railroads during a week. Suppose the computer record for a carload shipped during the week is randomly selected from a masterfile of all carloads shipped that week and the commodity type shipped is identified.

Type of Commodity	Number of Carloads
Agricultural products	41,690
Chemicals	38,331
Coal	124,595
Forest products	21,929
Metallic ores and minerals	34,521
Motor vehicles and equipment	22,906
Nonmetallic minerals and products	37,416
Other carloads	14,382
Total	335,770

Source: Railway Age, May 1999, p. 1.

a. List or describe the sample points in this experiment.
b. Find the probability of each sample point.
c. What is the probability that the railcar was transporting automobiles? Nonagricultural products?
d. What is the probability that the railcar contained chemicals or coal?
e. One of the carloads shipped that week was in a boxcar with serial number 1003642. What is the probability that this particular carload would be the one randomly selected from the computer file? Justify your answer.

Applying the Concepts—Intermediate

3.113 Effect of stock market on consumer spending and saving. According to *Economic Inquiry* (Jan. 2002), 50% of all U.S. households own stock. A sample of these stockholders was asked what effect recent trends in the stock market have had on their saving and spending. The responses are summarized in the table. A U.S. household is selected at random.

Stock Market Effect on Spending/Saving	Percent of Stockholders
No effect	85.0
Spend more/save less	3.4
Spend less/save more	11.6
Total	100.0

Source: Starr-McCluer, M. "Stock market wealth and consumer spending," Economic Inquiry, Vol. 40, No. 1, Jan. 2002, pp. 69–79 (Table 3). Reprinted with permission of John Wiley & Sons, Inc.

a. What is the probability that the household does not own stock?

b. Given the household owns stock, what is the probability that the household spends more and saves less due to recent trends in the stock market?

c. What is the probability that the household owns stock but spends less and saves more due to recent trends in the stock market?

3.114 Assembling a panel of energy experts. The state legislature has appropriated $1 million to be distributed in the form of grants to individuals and organizations engaged in the research and development of alternative energy sources. You have been hired by the state's energy agency to assemble a panel of five energy experts whose task it will be to determine which individuals and organizations should receive the grant money. You have identified 11 equally qualified individuals who are willing to serve on the panel. How many different panels of five experts could be formed from these 11 individuals?

3.115 Testing a watch manufacturer's claim. A manufacturer of electronic digital watches claims that the probability of its watch running more than 1 minute slow or 1 minute fast after 1 year of use is .05. A consumer protection agency has purchased four of the manufacturer's watches with the intention of testing the claim.

a. Assuming that the manufacturer's claim is correct, what is the probability that none of the watches are as accurate as claimed?

b. Assuming that the manufacturer's claim is correct, what is the probability that exactly two of the four watches are as accurate as claimed?

c. Suppose that only one of the four tested watches is as accurate as claimed. What inference can be made about the manufacturer's claim? Explain.

d. Suppose that none of the watches tested are as accurate as claimed. Is it necessarily true that the manufacturer's claim is false? Explain.

3.116 Ranking razor blades. The corporations in the highly competitive razor blade industry do a tremendous amount of advertising each year. Corporation G gave a supply of three top-name brands, G, S, and W, to a consumer and asked her to use them and rank them in order of preference. The corporation was, of course, hoping the consumer would prefer its brand and rank it first, thereby giving them some material for a consumer interview advertising campaign. If the consumer did not prefer one blade over any other but was still required to rank the blades, what is the probability that

a. The consumer ranked brand G first?
b. The consumer ranked brand G last?
c. The consumer ranked brand G last and brand W second?
d. The consumer ranked brand W first, brand G second, and brand S third?

3.117 Link between cigar smoking and cancer. The *Journal of the National Cancer Institute* (Feb. 16, 2000) published the results of a study that investigated the association between cigar smoking and death from tobacco-related cancers. Data were obtained for a national sample of 137,243 American men. The results are summarized in the table on the next page. Each male in the study was classified according to his cigar-smoking status and whether or not he died from a tobacco-related cancer.

a. Find the probability that a man who never smoked cigars died from cancer.

b. Find the probability that a former cigar smoker died from cancer.

c. Find the probability that a current cigar smoker died from cancer.

	Died from Cancer	Did Not Die from Cancer	Totals
Never Smoked Cigars	782	120,747	121,529
Former Cigar Smoker	91	7,757	7,848
Current Cigar Smoker	141	7,725	7,866
Totals	1,014	136,229	137,243

Source: Shapiro, J. A., Jacobs, E. J., and Thun, M. J. "Cigar smoking in men and risk of death from tobacco-related cancers," *Journal of the National Cancer Institute*, Vol. 92, No. 4, Feb. 16, 2000, pp. 333–337 (Table 2). By permission of Oxford University Press.

3.118 Which events are independent? Use your intuitive understanding of independence to form an opinion about whether each of the following scenarios represent independent events.

a. The results of consecutive tosses of a coin

b. The opinions of randomly selected individuals in a preelection poll

c. A major league baseball player's results in two consecutive at-bats

d. The amount of gain or loss associated with investments in different stocks if these stocks are bought on the same day and sold on the same day one month later

e. The amount of gain or loss associated with investments in different stocks that are bought and sold in different time periods, 5 years apart

f. The prices bid by two different development firms in response to a building construction proposal

3.119 Employees' choices of health care plans. Most companies offer their employees a variety of health care plans to choose from—e.g., preferred provider organizations (PPOs) and health maintenance organizations (HMOs). A survey of 100 large, 100 medium, and 100 small companies that offer their employees HMOs, PPOs, and fee-for-service plans was conducted; each firm provided information on the plans chosen by their employees. These companies had a total employment of 833,303 people. A breakdown of the number of employees in each category by firm size and plan is provided in the table.

Company Size	Fee-for-Service	PPO	HMO	Totals
Small	1,808	1,757	1,456	5,021
Medium	8,953	6,491	6,938	22,382
Large	330,419	241,770	233,711	805,900
Totals	341,180	250,018	242,105	833,303

Source: Adapted from Bucci, M., and Grant, R. "Employer-sponsored health insurance: What's offered: What's chosen?" *Monthly Labor Review*, October 1995, Vol. 118, No. 10, pp. 38–43.

One employee from the 833,303 total employees is to be chosen at random for further analysis. Define the events A and B as follows:

A: {Observe an employee that chose fee-for-service}

B: {Observe an employee from a small company}

a. Find $P(B)$.

b. Find $P(A \cap B)$.

c. Find $P(A \cup B)$.

d. Find $P(A|B)$.

e. Are A and B independent? Justify your answer.

3.120 World Cup soccer match draws. Every four years the world's 32 best national soccer teams compete for the World Cup. The 2006 World Cup final between champion Italy and France was one of the most watched events in television history, with an estimated audience of 715 million people. Run by FIFA (Fédération Internationale de Football Association), national teams are placed into eight groups of four teams, with the group winners advancing to play for the World Cup. *Chance* (Spring 2007) investigated the fairness of the 2006 World Cup draw. Each of the top 8 seeded teams (teams ranked 1–8, called pot 1) were placed into one of the eight groups (named, Group A, B, C, D, E, F, G, and H). The remaining 24 teams were assigned to 3 pots of 8 teams each to achieve the best possible geographical distribution between the groups. The teams in pot 2 were assigned to groups as follows: The first team drawn was placed into Group A, the second team drawn was placed in Group B, etc. Teams in pots 3 and 4 were assigned to the groups in similar fashion. Because teams in pots 2–4 are not necessarily placed there based on their world ranking, this typically leads to a "group of death," i.e., a group involving at least two highly seeded teams where only one can advance.

a. In 2006, Germany (as the host country) was assigned as the top seed in Group A. What is the probability that Paraguay (with the highest ranking in pot 2) is assigned to Group A?

b. Many soccer experts view the South American teams (Ecuador and Paraguay) as the most dangerous teams in pot 2. What is the probability one of the South American teams is assigned to Group A?

c. In 2006, Group B was considered the "group of death," with England (world rank 2), Paraguay (highest rank in pot 2), Sweden (2nd highest rank in pot 3), and Trinidad and Tobago. What is the probability that Group B will include the team with the highest rank in pot 2 and the team with one of the top two ranks in pot 3?

d. In drawing teams from pot 2, there was a notable exception in 2006. If a South American team (either Ecuador or Paraguay) was drawn into a group with another South American team, it was automatically moved to the next group. This rule impacted Group C (Argentina as the top seed) and Group F (Brazil as the top seed), because they already have South American teams, and groups that follow these groups in the draw. Now Group D included the eventual champion Italy as its top seed. What is the probability that Group D was not assigned one of the dangerous South American teams in pot 2?

3.121 Chance of an Avon sale. The probability that an Avon salesperson sells beauty products to a prospective customer on the first visit to the customer is .4. If the salesperson fails to make the sale on the first visit, the probability that the sale will be made on the second visit is .65. The salesperson never visits a prospective customer more than twice. What is the probability that the salesperson will make a sale to a particular customer?

3.122 Repairing a computer network. The local area network (LAN) for the College of Business computing system at a large university is temporarily shut down for repairs. Previous shutdowns have been due to hardware failure, software failure, or power failure. Maintenance engineers have determined that the probabilities of hardware, software, and power problems are .01, .05, and .02, respectively. They have also determined that if the system experiences hardware problems, it shuts down 73% of the time. Similarly, if software problems occur, the system shuts down 12% of the time; and, if power failure occurs, the system shuts down 88% of the time. What is the probability that the current shutdown of the LAN is due to hardware failure? Software failure? Power failure?

3.123 Profile of a sustainable farmer. *Sustainable development* or *sustainable farming* means finding ways to live and work the Earth without jeopardizing the future. Studies were conducted in five Midwestern states to develop a profile of a sustainable farmer. The results revealed that farmers can be classified along a sustainability scale, depending on whether they are likely (L) or unlikely (U) to engage in the following practices: (1) Raise a broad mix of crops; (2) raise livestock; (3) use chemicals sparingly; and (4) use techniques for regenerating the soil, such as crop rotation.

  a. List the different sets of classifications that are possible for the four practices (e.g., LUUL).

  b. Suppose you are planning to interview farmers across the country to determine the frequency with which they fall into the classification sets you listed for part **a.** Because no information is yet available, assume initially that there is an equal chance of a farmer falling into any single classification set. Using that assumption, what is the probability that a farmer will be classified as unlikely on all four criteria (i.e., classified as a nonsustainable farmer)?

  c. Using the same assumption as in part **b,** what is the probability that a farmer will be classified as likely on at least three of the criteria (i.e., classified as a near-sustainable farmer)?

3.124 Evaluating the performance of quality inspectors. The performance of quality inspectors affects both the quality of outgoing products and the cost of the products. A product that passes inspection is assumed to meet quality standards; a product that fails inspection may be reworked, scrapped, or reinspected. Quality engineers at Westinghouse Electric Corporation evaluated performances of inspectors in judging the quality of solder joints by comparing each inspector's classifications of a set of 153 joints with the consensus evaluation of a panel of experts. The results for a particular inspector are shown in the table. One of the 153 solder joints is to be selected at random.

	Inspector's Judgment	
Committee's Judgment	Joint Acceptable	Joint Rejectable
Joint acceptable	101	10
Joint rejectable	23	19

Source: Meagher, J., and Scazzero, J., "Measuring inspector variability," pp. 75–81. Reprinted with permission from Proceedings from the 39th Annual Quality Congress. © 1985 American Society for Quality. No further distribution allowed without permission.

  a. What is the probability that the inspector judges the joint to be acceptable? That the committee judges the joint to be acceptable?

  b. What is the probability that both the inspector and the committee judge the joint to be acceptable? That neither judge the joint to be acceptable?

  c. What is the probability that the inspector and the committee disagree? Agree?

3.125 System components operating in series and parallel. Consider the two systems shown in the schematic below. System A operates properly only if all three components operate properly. (The three components are said to operate *in series.*) The probability of failure for system A components 1, 2, and 3 are .12, .09, and .11, respectively. Assume the components operate independently of each other. System B comprises two subsystems said to operate *in parallel.* Each subsystem has two components that operate in series. System B will operate properly as long as at least one of the subsystems functions properly. The probability of failure for each component in the system is .1. Assume the components operate independently of each other.

  a. Find the probability that System A operates properly.

  b. What is the probability that at least one of the components in system A will fail and therefore that the system will fail?

  c. Find the probability that System B operates properly.

  d. Find the probability that exactly one subsystem in system B fails.

  e. Find the probability that system B fails to operate properly.

  f. How many parallel subsystems like the two shown here would be required to guarantee that the system would operate properly at least 99% of the time?

Figures for Exercise 3.125

Applying the Concepts—Advanced

3.126 **Rejected bottles of a brewery.** A small brewery has two bottling machines. Machine A produces 75% of the bottles, and machine B produces 25%. 1 out of every 20 bottles filled by A is rejected for some reason, while 1 out of every 30 bottles from B is rejected. What proportion of bottles is rejected? What is the probability that a randomly selected bottle comes from machine A, given that it is accepted?

3.127 **Scrap rate of machine parts.** A press produces parts used in the manufacture of large-screen plasma televisions. If the press is correctly adjusted, it produces parts with a scrap rate of 5%. If it is not adjusted correctly, it produces scrap at a 50% rate. From past company records, the machine is known to be correctly adjusted 90% of the time. A quality control inspector randomly selects one part from those recently produced by the press and discovers it is defective. What is the probability that the machine is incorrectly adjusted?

3.128 **Chance of winning at "craps."** A version of the dice game "craps" is played in the following manner. A player starts by rolling two balanced dice. If the roll (the sum of the two numbers showing on the dice) results in a 7 or 11, the player wins. If the roll results in a 2 or a 3 (called *craps*), the player loses. For any other roll outcome, the player continues to throw the dice until the original roll outcome recurs (in which case the player wins) or until a 7 occurs (in which case the player loses).

a. What is the probability that a player wins the game on the first roll of the dice?

b. What is the probability that a player loses the game on the first roll of the dice?

c. If the player throws a total of 4 on the first roll, what is the probability that the game ends (win or lose) on the next roll?

3.129 **Chance of winning blackjack.** Blackjack, a favorite game of gamblers, is played by a dealer and at least one opponent (called a *player*). In one version of the game, 2 cards of a standard 52-card bridge deck are dealt to the player and 2 cards to the dealer. For this exercise, assume that drawing an ace and a face card is called *blackjack*. If the dealer does not draw a blackjack and the player does, the player wins. If both the dealer and player draw blackjack, a "push" (i.e., a tie) occurs.

a. What is the probability that the dealer will draw a blackjack?

b. What is the probability that the player wins with a blackjack?

3.130 **Strategy in the game "Go."** "Go" is one of the oldest and most popular strategic board games in the world, especially in Japan and Korea. The University of Virginia requires MBA students to learn Go to understand how the Japanese conduct business. This two-player game is played on a flat surface marked with 19 vertical and 19 horizontal lines. The objective is to control territory by placing pieces, called *stones*, on vacant points on the board. Players alternate placing their stones. The player using black stones goes first, followed by the player using white stones. *Chance* (Summer 1995) published an article that investigated the advantage of playing first (i.e., using the black

stones) in Go. The results of 577 games recently played by professional Go players were analyzed.

a. In the 577 games, the player with the black stones, won 319 times, and the player with the white stones won 258 times. Use this information to assess the probability of winning when you play first in Go.

b. Professional Go players are classified by level. Group C includes the top-level players, followed by Group B (middle-level) and Group A (low-level) players. The following table describes the number of games won by the player with the black stones, categorized by level of the black player and level of the opponent. Assess the probability of winning when you play first in Go for each combination of player and opponent level.

c. If the player with the black stones is ranked higher than the player with the white stones, what is the probability that black wins?

d. Given the players are of the same level, what is the probability that the player with the black stones wins?

Black Player Level	Opponent Level	Number of Wins	Number of Games
C	A	34	34
C	B	69	79
C	C	66	118
B	A	40	54
B	B	52	95
B	C	27	79
A	A	15	28
A	B	11	51
A	C	5	39
Totals		319	577

Source: Kim, J., and Kim, H. J. "The advantage of playing first in Go," *Chance,* Vol. 8, No. 3, Summer 1995, p. 26 (Table 3). Reprinted with permission from *Chance.* © 1995 by the American Statistical Association. All rights reserved.

Critical Thinking Challenges

3.131 **"Let's Make a Deal."** Marilyn vos Savant, who is listed in *Guinness Book of World Records Hall of Fame* for "Highest IQ," writes a weekly column in the Sunday newspaper supplement, *Parade Magazine.* Her column, "Ask Marilyn," is devoted to games of skill, puzzles, and mind-bending riddles. In one issue (*Parade Magazine,* Feb. 24, 1991), vos Savant posed the following question:

Suppose you're on a game show, and you're given a choice of three doors. Behind one door is a car; behind the others, goats. You pick a door—say, #1—and the host, who knows what's behind the doors, opens another door—say #3—which has a goat. He then says to you, "Do you want to pick door #2?" Is it to your advantage to switch your choice?

Marilyn's answer: "Yes, you should switch. The first door has a $1/3$ chance of winning [the car], but the second has a $2/3$ chance [of winning the car]." Predictably, vos Savant's surprising answer elicited thousands of critical letters, many of them from PhD mathematicians, who disagreed with her. Who is correct, the PhDs or Marilyn?

3.132 **Flawed Pentium computer chip.** In October 1994, a flaw was discovered in the Pentium microchip installed in personal computers. The chip produced an incorrect result when dividing two numbers. Intel, the manufacturer of the Pentium chip, initially announced that such an error would occur once in 9 billion divisions, or "once in every 27,000 years" for a typical user; consequently, it did not immediately offer to replace the chip.

Depending on the procedure, statistical software packages (e.g., Minitab) may perform an extremely large number of divisions to produce the required output. For heavy users of the software 1 billion divisions over a short time frame is not unusual. Will the flawed chip be a problem for a heavy Minitab user? [*Note:* Two months after the flaw was discovered, Intel agreed to replace all Pentium chips free of charge.]

References

Bennett, D. J. *Randomness.* Cambridge, Mass.: Harvard University Press, 1998.

Epstein, R. A. *The Theory of Gambling and Statistical Logic,* rev. ed. New York: Academic Press, 1977.

Feller, W. *An Introduction to Probability Theory and Its Applications,* 3rd ed., Vol. 1. New York: Wiley, 1968.

Lindley, D. V. *Making Decisions,* 2nd ed. London: Wiley, 1985.

Parzen, E. *Modern Probability Theory and Its Applications.* New York: Wiley, 1960.

Wackerly, D., Mendenhall, W., and Scheaffer, R. L. *Mathematical Statistics with Applications,* 7th ed. Boston: Duxbury, 2008.

Williams, B. *A Sampler on Sampling.* New York: Wiley, 1978.

Winkler, R. L. *An Introduction to Bayesian Inference and Decision.* New York: Holt, Rinehart and Winston, 1972.

Wright, G., and Ayton, P., eds. *Subjective Probability.* New York: Wiley, 1994.

USING TECHNOLOGY

SPSS: Generating a Random Sample

Step 1 Click on the "Data" button on the SPSS menu bar and then click on "Select Cases," as shown in Figure 3.S.1. The resulting menu list appears as shown in Figure 3.S.2.

Figure 3.S.2 SPSS options for selecting a random sample

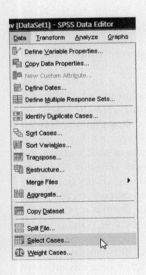

Figure 3.S.1 SPSS menu options for sampling from a data set

Step 2 Select "Random sample of cases" from the list and then click on the "Sample" button. The dialog box shown in Figure 3.S.3 will appear.

Step 3 Specify the sample size either as a percentage of cases or a raw number.

Step 4 Click "Continue" to return to the "Select Cases" dialog box (Figure 3.S.2) and then click "OK." The SPSS spreadsheet will reappear with the selected (sampled) cases.

Figure 3.S.3 SPSS random sample dialog box

Minitab: Generating a Random Sample

Step 1 Click on the "Calc" button on the Minitab menu bar and then click on "Random Data," and finally, click on "Sample From Columns," as shown in Figure 3.M.1. The resulting dialog box appears as shown in Figure 3.M.2.

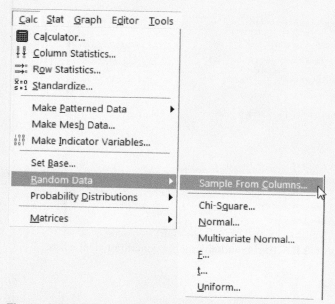

Figure 3.M.1 Minitab menu options for sampling from a data set

Figure 3.M.2 Minitab options for selecting a random sample from worksheet columns

Step 2 Specify the sample size (i.e., number of rows), the variable(s) to be sampled, and the column(s) where you want to save the sample.

Step 3 Click "OK" and the Minitab worksheet will reappear with the values of the variable for the selected (sampled) cases in the column specified.

In Minitab, you can also generate a sample of case numbers.

Step 1 From the Minitab menu, click on the "Calc" button and then click on "Random Data," and finally, click on the "Uniform" option (see Figure 3.M.1).

Step 2 In the resulting dialog box (shown in Figure 3.M.3), specify the number of cases (rows, i.e., the sample size), and the column where the case numbers selected will be stored.

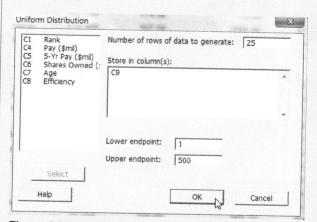

Figure 3.M.3 Minitab options for selecting a random sample of cases

Step 3 Click "OK" and the Minitab worksheet will reappear with the case numbers for the selected (sampled) cases in the column specified.

[*Note:* If you want the option of generating the same (identical) sample multiple times from the data set, then first click on the "Set Base" option shown in Figure 3.M.1. Specify an integer in the resulting dialog box. If you always select the same integer, Minitab will select the same sample when you choose the random sampling options.]

Excel: Generating a Random Sample

To obtain a random sample of numbers in EXCEL, perform the following:

Step 1 Select "Data," and then "Data Analysis" from the Excel main menu bar, as shown in Figure 3.E.1.

Step 2 Select "Random Number Generation" from the Data Analysis dialog box and then click "OK," as shown in Figure 3.E.2.

Step 3 In the resulting menu (shown in Figure 3.E.3), specify the number of variables and number of random numbers you want to generate and select "Uniform" for the distribution. Click "OK" to generate the random numbers.

Figure 3.E.1 Excel menu options for generating a random sample of numbers

Figure 3.E.2 Excel data analysis tools options: Random number generation

Figure 3.E.3 Excel random number generation dialog box

4 Random Variables and Probability Distributions

Where We've Been

- Used probability to make an inference about a population from data in an observed sample
- Used probability to measure the reliability of the inference

Where We're Going

- Develop the notion of a random variable
- Learn that numerical data are observed values of either discrete or continuous random variables
- Study two important types of random variables and their probability models: the binomial and normal model
- Define a sampling distribution as the probability distribution of a sample statistic
- Learn that the sampling distribution of $\bar{x}$ follows a normal model

Statistics IN Action — Super Weapons Development—Optimizing the Hit Ratio

The U.S. Army is working with a major defense contractor to develop a "super" weapon. The weapon is designed to fire a large number of sharp tungsten bullets—called flechettes—with a single shot that will destroy a large number of enemy soldiers. Flechettes are about the size of an average nail, with small fins at one end to stabilize them in flight. Since World War I, when France dropped them in large quantities from aircraft on masses of ground troops, munitions experts have experimented with using flechettes in a variety of guns. The problem with using flechettes as ammunition is accuracy—current weapons that fire large quantities of flechettes have unsatisfactory hit ratios when fired at long distances.

The defense contractor (not named here for both confidentiality and security reasons) has developed a prototype gun that fires 1,100 flechettes with a single round. In range tests, three 2-feet-wide targets were set up a distance of 500 meters (approximately 1,500 feet) from the weapon. Using a number line as a reference, the centers of the three targets were at 0, 5, and 10 feet, respectively, as shown in Figure SIA4.1. The prototype gun was aimed at the middle target (center at 5 feet) and fired once. The point where each *(continued)*

Statistics ɪɴ Action
(continued)

of the 1,100 flechettes landed at the 500-meter distance was measured using a horizontal and vertical grid. For the purposes of this application, only the horizontal measurements are considered. These 1,100 measurements are saved in the **MOAGUN** file. (The data are simulated for confidentiality reasons.) For example, a flechette with a value of $x = 5.5$ hit the middle target, but a flechette with a value of $x = 2.0$ did not hit any of the three targets (see Figure SIA4.1).

The defense contractor is interested in the likelihood of any one of the targets being hit by a flechette and, in particular, wants to set the gun specifications to maximize the number of target hits. The weapon is designed to have a mean horizontal value equal to the aim point (e.g., $\mu = 5$

feet when aimed at the center target). By changing specifications, the contractor can vary the standard deviation, σ. The **MOAGUN** file contains flechette measurements for three different range tests—one with a standard deviation of $\sigma = 1$ foot, one with $\sigma = 2$ feet, and one with $\sigma = 4$ feet.

In this chapter, three Statistics in Action Revisited examples demonstrate how we can use one of the probability models discussed in this chapter—the normal probability distribution—to aid the defense contractor in developing its "super" weapon.

Figure SIA4.1
Target placement on gun range

Statistics ɪɴ Action Revisited

- Using the Normal Model (p. 214)
- Assessing Fit of the Normal Distribution (p. 221)
- Making an Inference about Mean Accuracy (p. 250)

Data Set: MOAGUN

You may have noticed that many of the examples of experiments in Chapter 3 generated quantitative (numerical) observations. The Consumer Price Index, the unemployment rate, the number of sales made in a week, and the yearly profit of a company are all examples of numerical measurements of some phenomenon. Thus, most experiments have sample points that correspond to values of some numerical variable.

To illustrate, consider the coin-tossing experiment of Chapter 3. Figure 4.1 is a Venn diagram showing the sample points when two coins are tossed and the up faces (heads or tails) of the coins are observed. One possible numerical outcome is the total number of heads observed. These values (0, 1, or 2) are shown in parentheses on the Venn diagram, one numerical value associated with each sample point. In the jargon of probability, the variable "total number of heads observed when two coins are tossed" is called a *random variable*.

HH	HT
•	•
(2)	(1)
TT	TH
•	•
(0)	(1)

S

Figure 4.1
Venn diagram for coin-tossing experiment

> A **random variable** is a variable that assumes numerical values associated with the random outcomes of an experiment, where one (and only one) numerical value is assigned to each sample point.

The term *random variable* is more meaningful than the term *variable* because the adjective *random* indicates that the coin-tossing experiment may result in one of the several possible values of the variable—0, 1, and 2—according to the *random* outcome of the experiment, *HH, HT, TH,* and *TT*. Similarly, if the experiment is to count the number of customers who use the drive-up window of a bank each day, the random variable (the number of customers) will vary from day to day, partly because of random phenomena that influence whether customers use the drive-up window. Thus, the possible values of this random variable range from 0 to the maximum number of customers the window could possibly serve in a day.

We define two different types of random variables, *discrete* and *continuous*, in Section 4.1. Then we spend the remainder of this chapter discussing specific types of both discrete and continuous random variables and the aspects that make them important in business applications.

4.1 Two Types of Random Variables

Recall that the sample point probabilities corresponding to an experiment must sum to 1. Dividing one unit of probability among the sample points in a sample space and consequently assigning probabilities to the values of a random variable is not always as easy as the examples in Chapter 3 might lead you to believe. If the number of sample points can be completely listed, the job is straightforward. But if the experiment results in an infinite number of numerical sample points that are impossible to list, the task of assigning probabilities to the sample points is impossible without the aid of a probability model. The next three examples demonstrate the need for different probability models depending on the number of values that a random variable can assume.

Example 4.1

Values of a Discrete Random Variable—Wine Ratings

Problem A panel of 10 experts for the *Wine Spectator* (a national publication) is asked to taste a new white wine and assign a rating of 0, 1, 2, or 3. A score is then obtained by adding together the ratings of the 10 experts. How many values can this random variable assume?

Solution A sample point is a sequence of 10 numbers associated with the rating of each expert. For example, one sample point is

$$\{1, 0, 0, 1, 2, 0, 0, 3, 1, 0\}$$

The random variable assigns a score to each one of these sample points by adding the 10 numbers together. Thus, the smallest score is 0 (if all 10 ratings are 0), and the largest score is 30 (if all 10 ratings are 3). Because every integer between 0 and 30 is a possible score, the random variable denoted by the symbol x can assume 31 values. Note that the value of the random variable for the sample point above is $x = 8$.*

Look Back This is an example of a *discrete random variable* because there is a finite number of distinct possible values. Whenever all the possible values a random variable can assume can be listed (or counted), the random variable is discrete.

Example 4.2

Values of a Discrete Random Variable—EPA Application

Problem Suppose the Environmental Protection Agency (EPA) takes readings once a month on the amount of pesticide in the discharge water of a chemical company. If the amount of pesticide exceeds the maximum level set by the EPA, the company is forced to take corrective action and may be subject to penalty. Consider the random variable, x, number of months before the company's discharge exceeds the EPA's maximum level. What values can x assume?

Solution The company's discharge of pesticide may exceed the maximum allowable level on the first month of testing, the second month of testing, and so on. It is possible that the company's discharge will *never* exceed the maximum level. Thus, the set of possible values for the number of months until the level is first exceeded is the set of all positive integers

$$1, 2, 3, 4, \ldots$$

*The standard mathematical convention is to use a capital letter (e.g., X) to denote the theoretical random variable. The possible values (or realizations) of the random variable are typically denoted with a lowercase letter (e.g., x). Thus, in Example 4.1, the random variable X can take on the values $x = 0, 1, 2, \ldots, 30$. Because this notation can be confusing for introductory statistics students, we simplify the notation by using the lowercase x to represent the random variable throughout.

Look Back If we can list the values of a random variable x, even though the list is never ending, we call the list **countable** and the corresponding random variable *discrete*. Thus, the number of months until the company's discharge first exceeds the limit is a *discrete random variable*.

Now Work Exercise 4.4

Example 4.3

Values of a Continuous Random Variable— Another EPA Application

Problem Refer to Example 4.2. A second random variable of interest is the amount x of pesticide (in milligrams per liter) found in the monthly sample of discharge waters from the chemical company. What values can this random variable assume?

Solution Unlike the *number* of months before the company's discharge exceeds the EPA's maximum level, the set of all possible values for the *amount* of discharge *cannot be listed*—that is, it is not countable. The possible values for the amounts of pesticide would correspond to the points on the interval between 0 and the largest possible value the amount of the discharge could attain, the maximum number of milligrams that could occupy 1 liter of volume. (Practically, the interval would be much smaller, say, between 0 and 500 milligrams per liter.)

Look Back When the values of a random variable are not countable but instead correspond to the points on some interval, we call it a *continuous random variable*. Thus, the *amount* of pesticide in the chemical plant's discharge waters is a *continuous random variable*.

Now Work Exercise 4.5

> Random variables that can assume a *countable* number (finite or infinite) of values are called **discrete**.

> Random variables that can assume values corresponding to any of the points contained in one or more intervals (i.e., values that are infinite and *uncountable*) are called **continuous**.

Several more examples of discrete random variables follow:

1. The number of sales made by a salesperson in a given week: $x = 0, 1, 2, \ldots$

2. The number of consumers in a sample of 500 who favor a particular product over all competitors: $x = 0, 1, 2, \ldots, 500$

3. The number of bids received in a bond offering: $x = 0, 1, 2, \ldots$

4. The number of errors on a page of an accountant's ledger: $x = 0, 1, 2, \ldots$

5. The number of customers waiting to be served in a restaurant at a particular time: $x = 0, 1, 2, \ldots$

Note that each of the examples of discrete random variables begins with the words "The number of …." This wording is very common because the discrete random variables most frequently observed are counts.

We conclude this section with some more examples of continuous random variables:

1. The length of time between arrivals at a hospital clinic: $0 \leq x < \infty$ (infinity)

2. For a new apartment complex, the length of time from completion until a specified number of apartments are rented: $0 \leq x < \infty$

3. The amount of carbonated beverage loaded into a 12-ounce can in a can-filling operation: $0 \leq x \leq 12$

4. The depth at which a successful oil-drilling venture first strikes oil: $0 \leq x \leq c$, where c is the maximum depth obtainable

5. The weight of a food item bought in a supermarket: $0 \leq x \leq 500$
[*Note:* Theoretically, there is no upper limit on x, but it is unlikely that it would exceed 500 pounds.]

Discrete random variables and their probability distributions are discussed in Part I—Sections 4.2–4.4. Continuous random variables and their probability distributions are the topic of Part II—Sections 4.5–4.9.

Exercises 4.1–4.10

Applying the Concepts—Basic

4.1 **Types of random variables.** Which of the following describe continuous random variables? Which describe discrete random variables?

   a. The number of newspapers sold by the *New York Times* each month

   b. The amount of ink used in printing a Sunday edition of the *New York Times*

   c. The actual number of ounces in a one-gallon bottle of laundry detergent

   d. The number of defective parts in a shipment of nuts and bolts

   e. The number of people collecting unemployment insurance each month

4.2 **Types of finance random variables.** Security analysts are professionals who devote full-time efforts to evaluating the investment worth of a narrow list of stocks. The following variables are of interest to security analysts (Radcliffe, *Investments: Concepts, Analysis and Strategy,* 1997). Which are discrete and which are continuous random variables?

   a. The closing price of a particular stock on the New York Stock Exchange

   b. The number of shares of a particular stock that are traded each business day

   c. The quarterly earnings of a particular firm

   d. The percentage change in yearly earnings between 2008 and 2009 for a particular firm

   e. The number of new products introduced per year by a firm

   f. The time until a pharmaceutical company gains approval from the U.S. Food and Drug Administration to market a new drug

4.3 **NHTSA crash tests.** Refer to the National Highway Traffic Safety Administration (NHTSA) crash tests of new car models, Exercise 2.139 (p. 104). Recall that the NHTSA developed a driver-side "star" scoring system, with results ranging from one star (*) to five stars (*****). The more stars in the rating, the better the level of crash protection in a head-on collision. Suppose that a car is selected from the **CRASH** data and its driver-side star rating is determined. Let x equal the number of stars in the rating. Is x a discrete or continuous random variable?

4.4 **Customers in line at a Subway shop.** The number of customers, x, waiting in line to order sandwiches at a Subway shop at noon is of interest to the store manager. What values can x assume? Is x a discrete or continuous random variable?

4.5 **Executive Compensation Scoreboard.** Refer to *Forbes'* 2008 "Executive Compensation Scoreboard" (Table 1.1, p. 4). One variable saved in the **CEOPAY2008** file is the CEO's compensation (in $ millions) in 2008. Is x a discrete or continuous random variable?

Applying the Concepts—Intermediate

4.6 **Banking.** Give an example of a discrete random variable that would be of interest to a banker.

4.7 **Economics.** Give an example of a continuous random variable that would be of interest to an economist.

4.8 **Hotel management.** Give an example of a discrete random variable that would be of interest to the manager of a hotel.

4.9 **Retailing.** Give two examples of discrete random variables that would be of interest to the manager of a clothing store.

4.10 **Stock market.** Give an example of a continuous random variable that would be of interest to a stockbroker.

PART I: DISCRETE RANDOM VARIABLES

4.2 Probability Distributions for Discrete Random Variables

A complete description of a discrete random variable requires that we *specify the possible values the random variable can assume and the probability associated with each value.* To illustrate, consider Example 4.4.

Example 4.4

Finding a Probability Distribution for a Coin-Tossing Experiment

Problem Recall the experiment of tossing two coins (Section 4.1) and let x be the number of heads observed. Find the probability associated with each value of the random variable x, assuming the two coins are fair. Display these values in a table or graph.

Solution The sample space and sample points for this experiment are reproduced in Figure 4.2. Note that the random variable x can assume values 0, 1, and 2. Recall (from Chapter 3) that the probability associated with each of the four sample points is $\frac{1}{4}$.

Figure 4.2
Venn diagram for the two-coin-toss experiment

Then, identifying the probabilities of the sample points associated with each of these values of x, we have

$$P(x = 0) = P(TT) = \tfrac{1}{4}$$
$$P(x = 1) = P(TH) + P(HT) = \tfrac{1}{4} + \tfrac{1}{4} = \tfrac{1}{2}$$
$$P(x = 2) = P(HH) = \tfrac{1}{4}$$

Thus, we now know the values the random variable can assume $(0, 1, 2)$ and how the probability is *distributed over* these values $(\tfrac{1}{4}, \tfrac{1}{2}, \tfrac{1}{4})$. This completely describes the random variable and is referred to as the *probability distribution,* denoted by the symbol $p(x)$.* The probability distribution for the coin-toss example is shown in tabular form in Table 4.1 and in graphical form in Figure 4.3. Because the probability distribution for a discrete random variable is concentrated at specific points (values of x), the graph in Figure 4.3a represents the probabilities as the heights of vertical lines over the corresponding values of x. Although the representation of the probability distribution as a histogram, as in Figure 4.3b, is less precise (because the probability is spread over a unit interval), the histogram representation will prove useful when we approximate probabilities of certain discrete random variables in Section 4.4.

Table 4.1	Probability Distribution for Coin-Toss Experiment: Tabular Form
x	$p(x)$
0	$\tfrac{1}{4}$
1	$\tfrac{1}{2}$
2	$\tfrac{1}{4}$

Look Back We could also present the probability distribution for x as a formula, but this would unnecessarily complicate a very simple example. We give the formulas for the probability distributions of some common discrete random variables later in this chapter.

Now Work Exercise 4.15

> The **probability distribution** of a **discrete random variable** is a graph, table, or formula that specifies the probability associated with each possible value the random variable can assume.

Two requirements must be satisfied by all probability distributions for discrete random variables.

> **Requirements for the Probability Distribution of a Discrete Random Variable, x**
>
> 1. $p(x) \geq 0$ for all values of x
> 2. $\Sigma p(x) = 1$
>
> where the summation of $p(x)$ is over all possible values of x.**

a. Point representation of $p(x)$

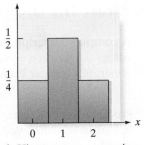

b. Histogram representation of $p(x)$

Figure 4.3
Probability distribution for coin-toss experiment: graphical form

*In standard mathematical notation, the probability that a random variable X takes on a value x is denoted $P(X = x) = p(x)$. Thus, $P(X = 0) = p(0)$, $P(X = 1) = p(1)$, etc. In this introductory text, we adopt the simpler $p(x)$ notation.
**Unless otherwise indicated, summations will always be over all possible values of x.

Example 4.4 illustrates how the probability distribution for a discrete random variable can be derived, but for many practical situations, the task is much more difficult. Fortunately, many experiments and associated discrete random variables observed in business possess identical characteristics. Thus, you might observe a random variable in a marketing experiment that would possess the same characteristics as a random variable observed in accounting, economics, or management. We classify random variables according to type of experiment, derive the probability distribution for each of the different types, and then use the appropriate probability distribution when a particular type of random variable is observed in a practical situation. The probability distributions for most commonly occurring discrete random variables have already been derived. This fact simplifies the problem of finding the appropriate probability distributions for the business analyst, as the next example illustrates.

Example 4.5

Probability Distribution for Texas Droughts Using a Formula

Problem A drought is a period of abnormal dry weather that causes serious problems in the farming industry of the region. University of Arizona researchers used historical annual data to study the severity of droughts in Texas (*Journal of Hydrologic Engineering*, Sept./Oct. 2003). The researchers showed that the distribution of x, the number of consecutive years that must be sampled until a dry (drought) year is observed, can be modeled using the formula

$$p(x) = (.3)(.7)^{x-1}, x = 1, 2, 3, \ldots$$

Find the probability that exactly 3 years must be sampled before a drought year occurs.

Solution We want to find the probability that $x = 3$. Using the formula, we have

$$p(3) = (.3)(.7)^{3-1} = (.3)(.7)^2 = (.3)(.49) = .147$$

Thus, there is about a 15% chance that exactly 3 years must be sampled before a drought year occurs in Texas.

Look Back The probability of interest can also be derived using the principles of probability developed in Chapter 3. The event of interest is $N_1 N_2 D_3$, where N_1 represents no drought occurs in the first sampled year, N_2 represents no drought occurs in the second sampled year, and D_3 represents a drought occurs in the third sampled year. The researchers discovered that the probability of a drought occurring in any sampled year is .3 (and, consequently, the probability of no drought occurring in any sampled year is .7). Using the multiplicative rule of probability for independent events, the probability of interest is $(.7)(.7)(.3) = .147$.

Because probability distributions are analogous to the relative frequency distributions of Chapter 2, it should be no surprise that the mean and standard deviation are useful descriptive measures.

If a discrete random variable x were observed a very large number of times, and the data generated were arranged in a relative frequency distribution, the relative frequency distribution would be indistinguishable from the probability distribution for the random variable. Thus, the probability distribution for a random variable is a theoretical model for the relative frequency distribution of a population. To the extent that the two distributions are equivalent (and we will assume they are), the probability distribution for x possesses a mean μ and a variance σ^2 that are identical to the corresponding descriptive measures for the population. How can you find the mean value for a random variable? We illustrate the procedure with an example.

Examine the probability distribution for x (the number of heads observed in the toss of two fair coins) in Figure 4.4. Try to locate the mean of the distribution intuitively. We may reason that the mean μ of this distribution is equal to 1 as follows: In a large number of experiments—say, 100,000—$\frac{1}{4}$ (or 25,000) should result in $x = 0$, $\frac{1}{2}$ (or 50,000) in $x = 1$, and $\frac{1}{4}$ (or 25,000) in $x = 2$ heads. Therefore, the average number of heads is

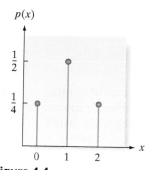

Figure 4.4
Probability distribution for a two-coin toss

$$\mu = \frac{0(25,000) + 1(50,000) + 2(25,000)}{100,000} = 0\left(\tfrac{1}{4}\right) + 1\left(\tfrac{1}{2}\right) + 2\left(\tfrac{1}{4}\right) = 0 + \tfrac{1}{2} + \tfrac{1}{2} = 1$$

Note that to get the population mean of the random variable x, we multiply each possible value of x by its probability $p(x)$ and then sum this product over all possible values of x. The *mean of x* is also referred to as the *expected value of x*, denoted $E(x)$.

The **mean,** or **expected value,** of a discrete random variable x is

$$\mu = E(x) = \sum x p(x)$$

Expected is a mathematical term and should not be interpreted as it is typically used. Specifically, a random variable might never be equal to its "expected value." Rather, the expected value is the mean of the probability distribution or a measure of its central tendency. You can think of μ as the mean value of x in a *very large* (actually, *infinite*) number of repetitions of the experiment, where the values of x occur in proportions equivalent to the probabilities of x.

Example 4.6

Finding an Expected Value—An Insurance Application

Problem Suppose you work for an insurance company, and you sell a $10,000 one-year term insurance policy at an annual premium of $290. Actuarial tables show that the probability of death during the next year for a person of your customer's age, sex, health, etc., is .001. What is the expected gain (amount of money made by the company) for a policy of this type?

Solution The experiment is to observe whether the customer survives the upcoming year. The probabilities associated with the two sample points, Live and Die, are .999 and .001, respectively. The random variable you are interested in is the gain x, which can assume the values shown in the following table.

Gain, x	Sample Point	Probability
$290	Customer lives	.999
−$9,710	Customer dies	.001

If the customer lives, the company gains the $290 premium as profit. If the customer dies, the gain is negative because the company must pay $10,000, for a net "gain" of $(290 − 10,000) = −\$9,710$. The expected gain is therefore

$$\mu = E(x) = \sum x p(x)$$
$$= (290)(.999) + (-9,710)(.001) = \$280$$

In other words, if the company were to sell a very large number of one-year $10,000 policies to customers possessing the characteristics previously described, it would (on the average) net $280 per sale in the next year.

Look Back Note that $E(x)$ need not equal a possible value of x—that is, the expected value is $280, but x will equal either $290 or $−$9,710 each time the experiment is performed (a policy is sold and a year elapses). The expected value is a measure of central tendency— and in this case represents the average over a very large number of one-year policies—but is not a possible value of x.

Now Work Exercise 4.28a

We learned in Chapter 2 that the mean and other measures of central tendency tell only part of the story about a set of data. The same is true about probability distributions. We need to measure variability as well. Because a probability distribution can be viewed as a representation of a population, we will use the population variance to measure its variability.

The *population variance* σ^2 is defined as the average of the squared distance of x from the population mean μ. Because x is a random variable, the squared distance, $(x - \mu)^2$, is also a random variable. Using the same logic used to find the mean value of

x, we find the mean value of $(x - \mu)^2$ by multiplying all possible values of $(x - \mu)^2$ by $p(x)$ and then summing over all possible x values.* This quantity,

$$E[(x - \mu)^2] = \sum (x - \mu)^2 p(x)$$

is also called the *expected value of the squared distance from the mean;* that is, $\sigma^2 = E[(x - \mu)^2]$. The standard deviation of x is defined as the square root of the variance σ^2.

> The **variance** of a **discrete random variable** x is
>
> $$\sigma^2 = E[(x - \mu)^2] = \sum (x - \mu)^2 p(x)$$

> The **standard deviation of a discrete random variable** is equal to the square root of the variance, i.e., $\sigma = \sqrt{\sigma^2}$.

Knowing the mean μ and standard deviation σ of the probability distribution of x, in conjunction with Chebyshev's Rule (Table 2.6, page 71) and the Empirical Rule (Table 2.7, page 71), we can make statements about the likelihood that values of x will fall within the intervals $\mu \pm \sigma$, $\mu \pm 2\sigma$, and $\mu \pm 3\sigma$. These probabilities are given in the box.

> **Probability Rules for a Discrete Random Variable**
>
> Let x be a discrete random variable with probability distribution $p(x)$, mean μ, and standard deviation σ. Then, depending on the shape of $p(x)$, the following probability statements can be made:
>
> | | Chebyshev's Rule | Empirical Rule |
> |---|---|---|
> | | Applies to any probability distribution (see Figure 4.5a) | Applies to probability distributions that are mound shaped and symmetric (see Figure 4.5b) |
> | $P(\mu - \sigma < x < \mu + \sigma)$ | ≥ 0 | $\approx .68$ |
> | $P(\mu - 2\sigma < x < \mu + 2\sigma)$ | $\geq \frac{3}{4}$ | $\approx .95$ |
> | $P(\mu - 3\sigma < x < \mu + 3\sigma)$ | $\geq \frac{8}{9}$ | ≈ 1.00 |

Figure 4.5

Shapes of two probability distributions for a discrete random variable x

a. Skewed distribution

b. Mound-shaped, symmetric

---

*It can be shown that $E[(x - \mu^2)] = E(x^2) - \mu^2$, where $E(x^2) = \sum x^2 p(x)$. Note the similarity between this expression and the shortcut formula $\sum(x - \overline{x})^2 = \sum x^2 - (\sum x)^2/n$ given in Chapter 2.

Example 4.7

Finding μ and σ for an Internet Business Venture

Problem Suppose you invest a fixed sum of money in each of five Internet business ventures. Assume you know that 70% of such ventures are successful, the outcomes of the ventures are independent of one another, and the probability distribution for the number, x, of successful ventures out of five is

x	0	1	2	3	4	5
$p(x)$	.002	.029	.132	.309	.360	.168

a. Find $\mu = E(x)$. Interpret the result.

b. Find $\sigma = \sqrt{E[(x - \mu)^2]}$. Interpret the result.

c. Graph $p(x)$. Locate μ and the interval $\mu \pm 2\sigma$ on the graph. Use either Chebyshev's Rule or the Empirical Rule to approximate the probability that x falls in this interval. Compare this result with the actual probability.

d. Would you expect to observe fewer than two successful ventures out of five?

Solution

a. Applying the formula,

$$\mu = E(x) = \sum xp(x) = 0(.002) + 1(.029) + 2(.132) + 3(.309)$$
$$+ 4(.360) + 5(.168) = 3.50$$

On average, the number of successful ventures out of five will equal 3.5. Remember that this expected value has meaning only when the experiment—investing in five Internet business ventures—is repeated a large number of times.

b. Now we calculate the variance of x:

$$\sigma^2 = E[(x - \mu)^2] = \sum (x - \mu)^2 p(x)$$
$$= (0 - 3.5)^2(.002) + (1 - 3.5)^2(.029) + (2 - 3.5)^2(.132)$$
$$+ (3 - 3.5)^2(.309) + (4 - 3.5)^2(.360) + (5 - 3.5)^2(.168)$$
$$= 1.05$$

Thus, the standard deviation is

$$\sigma = \sqrt{\sigma^2} = \sqrt{1.05} = 1.02$$

This value measures the spread of the probability distribution of x, the number of successful ventures out of five. A more useful interpretation is obtained by answering parts **c** and **d**.

c. The graph of $p(x)$ in histogram form is shown in Figure 4.6 with the mean μ and the interval $\mu \pm 2\sigma = 3.50 \pm 2(1.02) = 3.50 \pm 2.04 = (1.46, 5.54)$ shown on the graph. Note particularly that $\mu = 3.5$ locates the center of the probability distribution. Because this distribution is a theoretical relative frequency distribution that is moderately mound shaped (see Figure 4.6), we expect (from Chebyshev's Rule) at least 75% and, more likely (from the Empirical Rule), approximately 95% of observed x values to fall in the interval $\mu \pm 2\sigma$—that is, between 1.46 and 5.54. You can see from Figure 4.6 that the actual probability that x falls in the interval $\mu \pm 2\sigma$ includes the sum of $p(x)$ for the values $x = 2$,

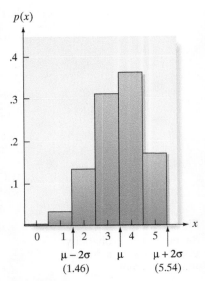

Figure 4.6

Graph of $p(x)$ for Example 4.6

$x = 3$, $x = 4$, and $x = 5$. This probability is $p(2) + p(3) + p(4) + p(5) = .132 + .309 + .360 + .168 = .969$. Therefore, 96.9% of the probability distribution lies within 2 standard deviations of the mean. This percentage is consistent with both Chebyshev's Rule and the Empirical Rule.

d. Fewer than two successful ventures out of five implies that $x = 0$ or $x = 1$. Because both these values of x lie outside the interval $\mu \pm 2\sigma$, we know from the Empirical Rule that such a result is unlikely (approximate probability of .05). The exact probability, $P(x \le 1)$, is $p(0) + p(1) = .002 + .029 = .031$. Consequently, in a single experiment where we invest in five Internet business ventures, we would not expect to observe fewer than two successful ones.

Now Work Exercise 4.17

Exercises 4.11–4.35

Learning the Mechanics

4.11 A die is tossed. Let x be the number of spots observed on the upturned face of the die.
  a. Find the probability distribution of x and display it in tabular form.
  b. Display the probability distribution of x in graphical form.

4.12 The random variable x has the following discrete probability distribution:

x	1	3	5	7	9
$p(x)$	.1	.2	.4	.2	.1

  a. List the values x may assume.
  b. What value of x is most probable?
  c. Display the probability distribution as a graph.
  d. Find $P(x = 7)$.
  e. Find $P(x \ge 5)$.
  f. Find $P(x > 2)$.

4.13 A discrete random variable x can assume five possible values: 2, 3, 5, 8, and 10. Its probability distribution is shown here:

x	2	3	5	8	10
$p(x)$	.15	.10	–	.25	.25

  a. What is $p(5)$?
  b. What is the probability that x equals 2 or 10?
  c. What is $P(x \le 8)$?

4.14 Explain why each of the following is or is not a valid probability distribution for a discrete random variable x:

a.

x	0	1	2	3
$p(x)$	.1	.3	.3	.2

b.

x	−2	−1	0
$p(x)$	.25	.50	.25

c.

x	4	9	20
$p(x)$	−.3	.4	.3

d.

x	2	3	5	6
$p(x)$	.15	.15	.45	.35

4.15 Toss three fair coins and let x equal the number of heads observed.
  a. Identify the sample points associated with this experiment and assign a value of x to each sample point.
  b. Calculate $p(x)$ for each value of x.
  c. Construct a graph for $p(x)$.
  d. What is $P(x = 2 \text{ or } x = 3)$?

● Applet Exercise 4.1

Use the applet *Random Numbers* to generate a list of 25 numbers between 1 and 3, inclusive. Let x represent a number chosen from this list.
  a. What are the possible values of x?
  b. Write a probability distribution for x in table form.
  c. Use the probability distribution in part **b** to find the expected value of x.
  d. Let y be a number randomly chosen from the set $\{1, 2, 3\}$. Write a probability distribution for y in table form and use it to find the expected value of y.
  e. Compare the expected values of x and y in parts **c** and **d.** Why should these two numbers be approximately the same?

● Applet Exercise 4.2

Run the applet *Simulating the Probability of a Head with a Fair Coin* ten times with $n = 2$, resetting between runs, to simulate flipping two coins ten times. Count and record the number of heads each time. Let x represent the number of heads on a single flip of the two coins.
  a. What are the possible values of x?
  b. Use the results of the simulation to write a probability distribution for x in table form and then use it to find the expected value of x.
  c. Explain why the expected value in part **b** should be close to 1.

4.16 Consider the probability distribution for the random variable x shown here:

x	10	20	30	40	50	60
$p(x)$	.05	.20	.30	.25	.10	.10

a. Find μ, σ^2, and σ.
b. Graph $p(x)$.
c. Locate μ and the interval $\mu \pm 2\sigma$ on your graph. What is the probability that x will fall within the interval $\mu \pm 2\sigma$?

4.17 Consider the probability distribution shown here:

NW

x	−4	−3	−2	−1	0	1	2	3	4
$p(x)$	.02	.07	.10	.15	.30	.18	.10	.06	.02

a. Calculate μ, σ^2, and σ.
b. Graph $p(x)$. Locate μ, $\mu - 2\sigma$, and $\mu + 2\sigma$ on the graph.
c. What is the probability that x is in the interval $\mu \pm 2\sigma$?

4.18 Consider the probability distributions shown here:

x	0	1	2		y	0	1	2
$p(x)$	.3	.4	.3		$p(y)$	.1	.8	.1

a. Use your intuition to find the mean for each distribution. How did you arrive at your choice?
b. Which distribution appears to be more variable? Why?
c. Calculate μ and σ^2 for each distribution. Compare these answers to your answers in parts **a** and **b**.

Applying the Concepts—Basic

4.19 **NHTSA crash tests.** Refer to the NHTSA crash tests of new car models, Exercise 4.3 (p. 177). A summary of the driver-side star ratings for the 98 cars in the **CRASH** file is reproduced in the accompanying Minitab printout. Assume that one of the 98 cars is selected at random and let x equal the number of stars in the car's driver-side star rating.

Tally for Discrete Variables: DRIVSTAR

DRIVSTAR	Count	Percent
2	4	4.08
3	17	17.35
4	59	60.20
5	18	18.37
N=	98	

a. Use the information in the printout to find the probability distribution for x.
b. Find $P(x = 5)$.
c. Find $P(x \leq 2)$.
d. Find $\mu = E(x)$ and practically interpret the result.

4.20 **Ages of "dot-com" employees.** The age distribution for the employees of a highly successful "dot-com" company

headquartered in Atlanta is shown in the next table. An employee is to be randomly selected from this population.

Age	20 21 22 23 24 25 26 27 28 29 30 31 32 33
Proportion	.02 .04 .05 .07 .04 .02 .07 .02 .11 .07 .09 .13 .15 .12

Source: Personal communication from P. George Benson.

a. Can the relative frequency distribution in the table be interpreted as a probability distribution? Explain.
b. Graph the probability distribution.
c. What is the probability that the randomly selected employee is over 30 years of age? Over 40 years of age? Under 30 years of age?
d. What is the probability that the randomly selected employee will be 25 or 26 years old?

4.21 **Customer arrivals at Wendy's.** The probability distribution for the number of customer arrivals per 15-minute period at a Wendy's in New Jersey is shown below.

x	5	6	7	8	9	10	11	12	13	14	15
$p(x)$	.01	.02	.03	.05	.08	.09	.11	.13	.12	.10	.08

x	16	17	18	19	20	21
$p(x)$	.06	.05	.03	.02	.01	.01

Source: Ford, R., Roberts, D., and Saxton. P. *Queuing Models.* Graduate School of Management, Rutgers University, 1992.

a. Does this distribution meet the two requirements for the probability distribution of a discrete random variable? Justify your answer.
b. What is the probability that exactly 16 customers enter the restaurant in the next 15 minutes?
c. Find $p(x \leq 10)$.
d. Find $p(5 \leq x \leq 15)$.

4.22 **Choosing portable grill displays.** Refer to the *Journal of Consumer Research* (Mar. 2003) marketing study of influencing consumer choices by offering undesirable alternatives, Exercise 3.21 (p. 130). Recall that each of 124 college students selected showroom displays for portable grills. Five different displays (representing five different-sized grills) were available, but the students were instructed to select only three displays in order to maximize purchases of Grill #2 (a smaller-sized grill). The table shows the grill display combinations and the number of times each was selected by the 124 students. Suppose one of the 124 students is selected at random. Let x represent the sum of the grill numbers selected by this student. (This value is an indicator of the size of the grills selected.)
a. Find the probability distribution for x.
b. What is the probability that x exceeds 10?

Grill Display Combination	Number of Students
1-2-3	35
1-2-4	8
1-2-5	42
2-3-4	4
2-3-5	1
2-4-5	34

Source: Hamilton, R. W. "Why do people suggest what they do not want? Using context effects to influence others' choices," *Journal of Consumer Research*, Vol. 29, Mar. 2003 (Table 1). Copyright © 2003 JCR, Inc.

4.23 **Solar energy cells.** According to *Wired* (June 2008), 35% of the world's solar energy cells are manufactured in China. Consider a random sample of five solar energy cells and let *x* represent the number in the sample that are manufactured in China. In the next section, we show that the probability distribution for *x* is given by the formula,

$$p(x) = \frac{(5!)(.35)^x(.65)^{5-x}}{(x!)(5-x)!}, \text{ where}$$

$$n! = (n)(n-1)(n-2)\cdots(2)(1)$$

a. Explain why *x* is a discrete random variable.
b. Find $p(x)$ for $x = 0, 1, 2, 3, 4,$ and 5.
c. Show that the properties for a discrete probability distribution are satisfied.
d. Find the probability that at least four of the five solar energy cells in the sample are manufactured in China.

Applying the Concepts—Intermediate

4.24 **USDA chicken inspection.** In Exercise 3.15 (p. 129) you learned that one in every 100 slaughtered chickens passes USDA inspection with fecal contamination. Consider a random sample of three slaughtered chickens that all pass USDA inspection. Let *x* equal the number of chickens in the sample that have fecal contamination.
a. Find $p(x)$ for $x = 0, 1, 2, 3$.
b. Graph $p(x)$.
c. Find $P(x \leq 1)$.

4.25 **Contaminated gun cartridges.** A weapons manufacturer uses a liquid propellant to produce gun cartridges. During the manufacturing process, the propellant can get mixed with another liquid to produce a contaminated cartridge. A University of South Florida statistician, hired by the company to investigate the level of contamination in the stored cartridges, found that 23% of the cartridges in a particular lot were contaminated. Suppose you randomly sample (without replacement) gun cartridges from this lot until you find a contaminated one. Let *x* be the number of cartridges sampled until a contaminated one is found. It is known that the probability distribution for *x* is given by the formula

$$p(x) = (.23)(.77)^{x-1}, x = 1, 2, 3, \ldots$$

a. Find $p(1)$. Interpret this result.
b. Find $p(5)$. Interpret this result.
c. Find $P(x \geq 2)$. Interpret this result.

4.26 **Appeals of federal civil trials.** Refer to the *Journal of the American Law and Economics Association* (Vol. 3, 2001) study of appeals of federal civil trials, Exercise 3.41 (p. 140). A breakdown of the 678 civil cases that were originally tried in front of a judge (rather than a jury) and appealed by either the plaintiff or defendant is reproduced in the next table. Suppose each civil case is awarded points (positive or negative) based on the outcome of the appeal for the purpose of evaluating federal judges. If the appeal is affirmed or dismissed, +5 points are awarded. If the appeal of a plaintiff trial win is reversed, −1 point is awarded. If the appeal of a defendant trial win is reversed, −3 points are awarded. Suppose one of the 678 cases is selected at random and the number, *x*, of points awarded is determined. Find and graph the probability distribution for *x*.

Outcome of Appeal	Number of Cases
Plaintiff trial win—reversed	71
Plaintiff trial win—affirmed/dismissed	240
Defendant trial win—reversed	68
Defendant trial win—affirmed/dismissed	299
Total	678

4.27 **Mailrooms contaminated with anthrax.** During autumn 2001, there was a highly publicized outbreak of anthrax cases among U.S. Postal Service workers. In *Chance* (Spring 2002), research statisticians discussed the problem of sampling mailrooms for the presence of anthrax spores. Let *x* equal the number of mailrooms contaminated with anthrax spores in a random sample of *n* mailrooms selected from a population of *N* mailrooms. The researchers showed that the probability distribution for *x* is given by the formula

$$p(x) = \frac{\binom{k}{x}\binom{N-k}{n-x}}{\binom{N}{n}}$$

where *k* is the number of contaminated mailrooms in the population. (In Section 4.4 we identify this probability distribution as the *hypergeometric distribution*.) Suppose $N = 100$, $n = 3$, and $k = 20$.
a. Find $p(0)$.   **b.** Find $p(1)$.
c. Find $p(2)$.   **d.** Find $p(3)$.

4.28 **Investment risk analysis.** The risk of a portfolio of financial assets is sometimes called *investment risk* (Radcliffe, 1997). In general, investment risk is typically measured by computing the variance or standard deviation of the probability distribution that describes the decision maker's potential outcomes (gains or losses). The greater the variation in potential outcomes, the greater the uncertainty faced by the decision maker; the smaller the variation in potential outcomes, the more predictable the decision maker's gains or losses. The two discrete probability distributions given in the next table were developed from historical data. They describe the potential total physical damage losses next year to the fleets of delivery trucks of two different firms.

Firm A		Firm B	
Loss Next Year	Probability	Loss Next Year	Probability
$ 0	.01	$ 0	.00
500	.01	200	.01
1,000	.01	700	.02
1,500	.02	1,200	.02
2,000	.35	1,700	.15
2,500	.30	2,200	.30
3,000	.25	2,700	.30
3,500	.02	3,200	.15
4,000	.01	3,700	.02
4,500	.01	4,200	.02
5,000	.01	4,700	.01

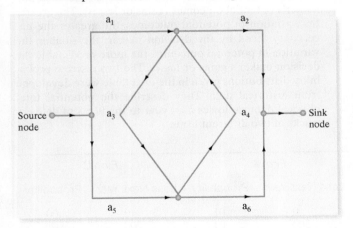

a. Verify that both firms have the same expected total physical damage loss.

b. Compute the standard deviation of each probability distribution and determine which firm faces the greater risk of physical damage to its fleet next year.

4.29 **Reliability of a bridge network.** The journal *Networks* periodically publishes studies on the reliability of flow networks. For example, *Networks* (Sep. 2007) gave applications in mobile ad hoc and sensor networks. Another network examined in a May issue, illustrated below, is a bridge network with arcs $a_1, a_2, a_3, a_4, a_5,$ and a_6. The probability distribution of the capacity x for each of the six arcs is provided in the following table.

Arc	Capacity (x)	p(x)	Arc	Capacity (x)	p(x)
a_1	3	.60	a_4	1	.90
	2	.25		0	.10
	1	.10			
	0	.05			
a_2	2	.60	a_5	1	.90
	1	.30		0	.10
	0	.10			
a_3	1	.90	a_6	2	.70
	0	.10		1	.25
				0	.05

Source: Lin, J., et al. "On reliability evaluation of capacitated-flow network in terms of minimal pathsets," *Networks*, Vol. 25, No. 3, May 1995, p. 135 (Table 1), 1995, John Wiley and Sons.

a. Verify that the properties of discrete probability distributions are satisfied for each arc capacity distribution.

b. Find the probability that the capacity for arc a_1 will exceed 1.

c. Repeat part **b** for each of the remaining five arcs.

d. Compute the mean capacity for each arc and interpret its value.

e. Compute σ for each arc and interpret the results.

4.30 **Checkout lanes at a supermarket.** A team of consultants working for a large national supermarket chain based in the New York metropolitan area developed a statistical model for predicting the annual sales of potential new store locations. Part of their analysis involved identifying variables that influence store sales, such as the size of the store (in square feet), the size of the surrounding population, and the number of checkout lanes. They surveyed 52 supermarkets in a particular region of the country and constructed the relative frequency distribution shown below to describe the number of checkout lanes per store, x.

x	1	2	3	4	5	6	7	8	9	10
Relative Frequency	.01	.04	.04	.08	.10	.15	.25	.20	.08	.05

Source: Adapted from Chow, W. et. al. "A model for predicting a supermarket's annual sales per square foot," Graduate School of Management, Rutgers University, 1994.

a. Why do the relative frequencies in the table represent the approximate probabilities of a randomly selected supermarket having x number of checkout lanes?

b. Find $E(x)$ and interpret its value in the context of the problem.

c. Find the standard deviation of x.

d. According to Chebyshev's Rule (Chapter 2, p. 71), what percentage of supermarkets would be expected to fall within $\mu \pm \sigma$? Within $\mu \pm 2\sigma$?

e. What is the actual number of supermarkets that fall within $\mu \pm \sigma$? $\mu \pm 2\sigma$? Compare your answers to those of part **d**. Are the answers consistent?

4.31 **Expected loss due to flood damage.** The National Weather Service issues precipitation forecasts that indicate the likelihood of measurable precipitation ($\geq .01$ inch) at a specific point (the official rain gauge) during a given time period. Suppose that if a measurable amount of rain falls during the next 24 hours, a river will reach flood stage and a business will incur damages of $300,000. The National Weather Service has indicated that there is a 30% chance of a measurable amount of rain during the next 24 hours.

a. Construct the probability distribution that describes the potential flood damages.

b. Find the firm's expected loss due to flood damage.

4.32 **Expected lotto winnings.** Most states offer weekly lotteries to generate revenue for the state. Despite the long odds of winning, residents continue to gamble on the lottery each week. In SIA, Chapter 3 (p. 116), you learned that the chance of winning Florida's Pick-6 Lotto game is 1 in approximately 23 million. Suppose you buy a $1 Lotto ticket in anticipation of winning the $7 million grand prize. Calculate your expected net winnings. Interpret the result.

4.33 **The showcase showdown.** On the popular television game show *The Price Is Right*, contestants can play "The Showcase Showdown." The game involves a large wheel with 20 nickel values, $5, 10, 15, 20, \ldots, 95, 100$, marked on it. Contestants spin the wheel once or twice, with the objective of obtaining the highest total score *without going over a dollar (100)*. [According to the *American Statistician* (Aug. 1995), the optimal strategy for the first spinner in a three-player game is to spin a second time only if the value of the initial spin is 65 or less.] Let x represent the total score for a single contestant playing "The Showcase Showdown." Assume a "fair" wheel (i.e., a wheel with equally likely outcomes). If the total of the player's spins exceeds 100, the total score is set to 0.

a. If the player is permitted only one spin of the wheel, find the probability distribution for x.

b. Refer to part **a**. Find $E(x)$ and interpret this value.

c. Refer to part **a**. Give a range of values within which x is likely to fall.

d. Suppose the player will spin the wheel twice, no matter what the outcome of the first spin. Find the probability distribution for x.

e. What assumption did you make to obtain the probability distribution, part **d**? Is it a reasonable assumption?

f. Find μ and σ for the probability distribution, part **d**, and interpret the results.

g. Refer to part **d**. What is the probability that in two spins the player's total score exceeds a dollar (i.e., is set to 0)?

h. Suppose the player obtains a 20 on the first spin and decides to spin again. Find the probability distribution for x.

i. Refer to part **h**, What is the probability that the player's total score exceeds a dollar?

j. Given the player obtains a 65 on the first spin and decides to spin again, find the probability that the player's total score exceeds a dollar.

k. Repeat part **j** for different first-spin outcomes. Use this information to suggest a strategy for the one-player game.

Applying the Concepts—Advanced

4.34 **Robot-sensor system configuration.** Engineers at Broadcom Corp. and Simon Fraser University collaborated on research involving a robot-sensor system in an unknown environment (*International Journal of Robotics Research*, Dec. 2004). As an example, the engineers presented the three-point, single-link robotic system shown in the accompanying figure. Each point (A, B, or C) in the physical space of the system has either an "obstacle" status or a "free" status. There are two single links in the system: A ↔ B and B ↔ C.

A link has a "free" status if and only if both points in the link are "free." Otherwise, the link has an "obstacle" status. Of interest is the random variable Y, the total number of links in the system that are "free."

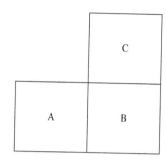

a. List the possible values of Y for the system.

b. The researchers stated that the probability of any point in the system having a "free" status is .5. Assuming the three points in the system operate independently, find the probability distribution for Y.

4.35 **Parlay card betting.** Odds makers try to predict which professional and college football teams will win and by how much (the *spread*). If the odds makers do this accurately, adding the spread to the underdog's score should make the final score a tie. Suppose a bookie will give you $6 for every $1 you risk if you pick the winners in three games (adjusted by the spread) on a "parlay" card. Thus, for every $1 bet, you will either lose $1 or gain $5. What is the bookie's expected earnings per dollar wagered?

4.3 The Binomial Distribution

Many experiments result in *dichotomous* responses—that is, responses for which there exist two possible alternatives, such as Yes-No, Pass-Fail, Defective-Nondefective, or Male-Female. A simple example of such an experiment is the coin-toss experiment. A coin is tossed a number of times, say 10. Each toss results in one of two outcomes, Head or Tail. Ultimately, we are interested in the probability distribution of x, the number of heads observed. Many other experiments are equivalent to tossing a coin (either balanced or unbalanced) a fixed number n of times and observing the number x of times that one of the two possible outcomes occurs. Random variables that possess these characteristics are called **binomial random variables.**

Public opinion and consumer preference polls (e.g., the CNN, Gallup, and Harris polls) frequently yield observations on binomial random variables. For example, suppose a sample of 100 current customers is selected from a firm's database and each person is asked whether he or she prefers the firm's product (a Head) or prefers a competitor's product (a Tail). Suppose we are interested in x, the number of customers in the sample who prefer the firm's product. Sampling 100 customers is analogous to tossing the coin 100 times. Thus, you can see that consumer preference polls like the one described here are real-life equivalents of coin-toss experiments. We have been describing a **binomial experiment**; it is identified by the following characteristics.

Characteristics of a Binomial Experiment

1. The experiment consists of n identical trials.

2. There are only two possible outcomes on each trial. We will denote one outcome by S (for success) and the other by F (for failure).

> **3.** The probability of S remains the same from trial to trial. This probability is denoted by p, and the probability of F is denoted by q. Note that $q = 1 - p$.
>
> **4.** The trials are independent.
>
> **5.** The binomial random variable x is the number of S's in n trials.

Example 4.8

Assessing Whether x Is Binomial

Problem For the following examples, decide whether x is a binomial random variable.

a. You randomly select 3 bonds out of a possible 10 for an investment portfolio. Unknown to you, 8 of the 10 will maintain their present value, and the other 2 will lose value due to a change in their ratings. Let x be the number of the 3 bonds you select that lose value.

b. Before marketing a new product on a large scale, many companies will conduct a consumer preference survey to determine whether the product is likely to be successful. Suppose a company develops a new diet soda and then conducts a taste preference survey in which 100 randomly chosen consumers state their preferences among the new soda and the two leading sellers. Let x be the number of the 100 who choose the new brand over the two others.

c. Some surveys are conducted by using a method of sampling other than simple random sampling (defined in Chapter 3). For example, suppose a television cable company plans to conduct a survey to determine the fraction of households in the city that would use the cable television service. The sampling method is to choose a city block at random and then survey every household on that block. This sampling technique is called *cluster sampling*. Suppose 10 blocks are so sampled, producing a total of 124 household responses. Let x be the number of the 124 households that would use the television cable service.

Solution

a. In checking the binomial characteristics in the box, a problem arises with both characteristic 3 (probabilities remaining the same from trial to trial) and characteristic 4 (independence). The probability that the first bond you pick loses value is clearly $^2/_{10}$. Now suppose the first bond you picked was 1 of the 2 that will lose value. This reduces the chance that the second bond you pick will lose value to $^1/_9$ because now only 1 of the 9 remaining bonds are in that category. Thus, the choices you make are dependent, and therefore x, the number of 3 bonds you select that lose value, is *not* a binomial random variable.

b. Surveys that produce dichotomous responses and use random sampling techniques are classic examples of binomial experiments. In our example, each randomly selected consumer either states a preference for the new diet soda or does not. The sample of 100 consumers is a very small proportion of the totality of potential consumers, so the response of one would be, for all practical purposes, independent of another.* Thus, x is a binomial random variable.

c. This example is a survey with dichotomous responses (Yes or No to the cable service), but the sampling method is not simple random sampling. Again, the binomial characteristic of independent trials would probably not be satisfied. The responses of households within a particular block would be dependent because the households within a block tend to be similar with respect to income, level of education, and general interests. Thus, the binomial model would not be satisfactory for x if the cluster sampling technique were employed.

Look Back Nonbinomial random variables with two outcomes on every trial typically occur because they do not satisfy characteristics 3 or 4 of a binomial distribution.

Now Work Exercise 4.43a

---

*In most real-life applications of the binomial distribution, the population of interest has a finite number of elements (trials), denoted N. When N is large and the sample size n is small relative to N, say $n/N \leq .05$, the sampling procedure, for all practical purposes, satisfies the conditions of a binomial experiment.

Example 4.9

Deriving the Binomial Probability Distribution in a PC Purchase Application

Problem A computer retailer sells both desktop and laptop personal computers (PCs) online. Assume that 80% of the PCs that the retailer sells online are desktops and 20% are laptops.

a. Use the steps given in Chapter 3 (box on page 123) to find the probability that all of the next four online PC purchases are laptops.

b. Find the probability that three of the next four online PC purchases are laptops.

c. Let x represent the number of the next four online PC purchases that are laptops. Explain why x is a binomial random variable.

d. Use the answers to parts **a** and **b** to derive a formula for $p(x)$, the probability distribution of the binomial random variable x.

Solution

a. **1.** The first step is to define the experiment. Here we are interested in observing the type of PC purchased online by each of the next four (buying) customers: desktop (D) or laptop (L).

2. Next, we list the sample points associated with the experiment. Each sample point consists of the purchase decisions made by the four online customers. For example, $DDDD$ represents the sample point that all four purchase desktop PCs, while $LDDD$ represents the sample point that customer 1 purchases a laptop, while customers 2, 3, and 4 purchase desktops. The 16 sample points are listed in Table 4.2.

3. We now assign probabilities to the sample points. Note that each sample point can be viewed as the intersection of four customers' decisions and, assuming the decisions are made independently, the probability of each sample point can be obtained using the multiplicative rule, as follows:

$$P(DDDD) = P[(\text{customer 1 chooses desktop}) \cap (\text{customer 2 chooses desktop})$$
$$\cap (\text{customer 3 chooses desktop}) \cap (\text{customer 4 chooses desktop})]$$
$$= P(\text{customer 1 chooses desktop}) \times P(\text{customer 2 chooses desktop}) \times P(\text{customer 3 chooses desktop})$$
$$\times P(\text{customer 4 chooses desktop})$$
$$= (.8)(.8)(.8)(.8) = (.8)^4 = .4096$$

All other sample point probabilities are calculated using similar reasoning. For example,

$$P(LDDD) = (.2)(.8)(.8)(.8) = (.2)(.8)^3 = .1024$$

You can check that this reasoning results in sample point probabilities that add to 1 over the 16 points in the sample space.

4. Finally, we add the appropriate sample point probabilities to obtain the desired event probability. The event of interest is that all four online customers purchase laptops. In Table 4.2 we find only one sample point, LLLL,

Table 4.2	Sample Points for PC Experiment of Example 4.9			
$DDDD$	$LDDD$	$LLDD$	$DLLL$	LLLL
	$DLDD$	$LDLD$	$LDLL$	
	$DDLD$	$LDDL$	$LLDL$	
	$DDDL$	$DLLD$	$LLLD$	
		$DLDL$		
		$DDLL$		

contained in this event. All other sample points imply that at least one desktop is purchased. Thus,

$$P(\text{All four purchase laptops}) = P(LLLL) = (.2)^4 = .0016$$

That is, the probability is only 16 in 10,000 that all four customers purchase laptop PCs.

b. The event that three of the next four online buyers purchase laptops consists of the four sample points in the fourth column of Table 4.2: *DLLL, LDLL, LLDL,* and *LLLD.* To obtain the event probability, we add the sample point probabilities:

$$P(\text{3 of next 4 customers purchase laptops})$$
$$= P(DLLL) + P(LDLL) + P(LLDL) + P(LLLD)$$
$$= (.2)^3(.8) + (.2)^3(.8) + (.2)^3(.8) + (.2)^3(.8)$$
$$= 4(.2)^3(.8) = .0256$$

Note that each of the four sample point probabilities is the same because each sample point consists of three *L*'s and one *D;* the order does not affect the probability because the customers' decisions are (assumed) independent.

c. We can characterize the experiment as consisting of four identical trials—the four customers' purchase decisions. There are two possible outcomes to each trial, *D* or *L,* and the probability of *L,* $p = .2$, is the same for each trial. Finally, we are assuming that each customer's purchase decision is independent of all others, so that the four trials are independent. Then it follows that *x,* the number of the next four purchases that are laptops, is a binomial random variable.

d. The event probabilities in parts **a** and **b** provide insight into the formula for the probability distribution $p(x)$. First, consider the event that three purchases are laptops (part **b**). We found that

$$P(x = 3) = (\text{Number of sample points for which } x = 3)$$
$$\times (.2)^{\text{Number of laptops purchased}} \times (.8)^{\text{Number of desktops purchased}}$$
$$= 4(.2)^3(.8)^1$$

In general, we can use combinatorial mathematics to count the number of sample points. For example,

Number of sample points for which $x = 3$

= Number of different ways of selecting 3 of the 4 trials for *L* purchases

$$= \binom{4}{3} = \frac{4!}{3!(4-3)!} = \frac{4 \cdot 3 \cdot 2 \cdot 1}{(3 \cdot 2 \cdot 1) \cdot 1} = 4$$

The formula that works for any value of *x* can be deduced as follows. Because

$$P(x = 3) = \binom{4}{3}(.2)^3(.8)^1,$$

then $p(x) = \binom{4}{x}(.2)^x(.8)^{4-x}$

The component $\binom{4}{x}$ counts the number of sample points with *x* laptops and the component $(.2)^x(.8)^{4-x}$ is the probability associated with each sample point having *x* laptops. For the general binomial experiment, with *n* trials and probability of success *p* on each trial, the probability of *x* successes is

$$p(x) = \binom{n}{x} \cdot p^x(1-p)^{n-x}$$

Number of
sample points
with *x* S's

Probability of *x* S's
and (*n* − *x*) F's in
any sample point

Look Back In theory, you could always resort to the principles developed in this example to calculate binomial probabilities; list the sample points and sum their probabilities. However, as the number of trials (n) increases, the number of sample points grows very rapidly (the number of sample points is 2^n). Thus, we prefer the formula for calculating binomial probabilities because its use avoids listing sample points.

The binomial distribution* is summarized in the box.

The Binomial Probability Distribution

$$p(x) = \binom{n}{x} p^x q^{n-x} \ (x = 0, 1, 2, \ldots, n)$$

where

p = Probability of a success on a single trial
$q = 1 - p$
n = Number of trials
x = Number of successes in n trials
$n - x$ = Number of failures in n trials
$$\binom{n}{x} = \frac{n!}{x!(n-x)!}$$

As noted in Chapter 3, the symbol 5! means $5 \cdot 4 \cdot 3 \cdot 2 \cdot 1 = 120$. Similarly, $n! = n(n-1)(n-2) \cdots 3 \cdot 2 \cdot 1$; remember, $0! = 1$.

Example 4.10

Applying the Binomial Distribution to the Manufacture of Automobiles

Problem A machine that produces stampings for automobile engines is malfunctioning and producing 10% defectives. The defective and nondefective stampings proceed from the machine in a random manner. If the next five stampings are tested, find the probability that three of them are defective.

Solution Let x equal the number of defectives in $n = 5$ trials. Then x is a binomial random variable with p, the probability that a single stamping will be defective, equal to .1, and $q = 1 - p = 1 - .1 = .9$. The probability distribution for x is given by the expression

$$p(x) = \binom{n}{x} p^x q^{n-x} = \binom{5}{x}(.1)^x(.9)^{5-x}$$

$$= \frac{5!}{x!(5-x)!}(.1)^x(.9)^{5-x} \quad (x = 0, 1, 2, 3, 4, 5)$$

To find the probability of observing $x = 3$ defectives in a sample of $n = 5$, substitute $x = 3$ into the formula for $p(x)$ to obtain

$$p(3) = \frac{5!}{3!(5-3)!}(.1)^3(.9)^{5-3} = \frac{5!}{3!2!}(.1)^3(.9)^2$$

$$= \frac{5 \cdot 4 \cdot 3 \cdot 2 \cdot 1}{(3 \cdot 2 \cdot 1)(2 \cdot 1)}(.1)^3(.9)^2 = 10(.1)^3(.9)^2$$

$$= .0081$$

Look Back Note that the binomial formula tells us that there are 10 sample points having 3 defectives (check this by listing them), each with probability $(.1)^3(.9)^2$.

Now Work Exercise 4.39

---

*The binomial distribution is so named because the probabilities, $p(x)$, $x = 0, 1, \ldots, n$, are terms of the binomial expansion $(q + p)^n$.

The mean, variance, and standard deviation for the binomial random variable x are shown in the box.

Mean, Variance, and Standard Deviation for a Binomial Random Variable

$$\text{Mean: } \mu = np$$
$$\text{Variance: } \sigma^2 = npq$$
$$\text{Standard deviation: } \sigma = \sqrt{npq}$$

As we demonstrated in Chapter 2, the mean and standard deviation provide measures of the central tendency and variability, respectively, of a distribution. Thus, we can use μ and σ to obtain a rough visualization of the probability distribution for x when the calculation of the probabilities is too tedious. The next example illustrates this idea.

Example 4.11

Finding μ and σ in the Automobile Manufacturing Application

Problem Refer to Example 4.10 and find the values of $p(0)$, $p(1)$, $p(2)$, $p(4)$, and $p(5)$. Graph $p(x)$. Calculate the mean μ and standard deviation σ. Locate μ and the interval $\mu - 2\sigma$ to $\mu + 2\sigma$ on the graph. If the experiment were to be repeated many times, what proportion of the x observations would fall within the interval $\mu - 2\sigma$ to $\mu + 2\sigma$?

Solution Again, $n = 5$, $p = .1$, and $q = .9$. Then, substituting into the formula for $p(x)$:

$$p(0) = \frac{5!}{0!(5-0)!}(.1)^0(.9)^{5-0} = \frac{5 \cdot 4 \cdot 3 \cdot 2 \cdot 1}{(1)(5 \cdot 4 \cdot 3 \cdot 2 \cdot 1)}(1)(.9)^4 = .59049$$

$$p(1) = \frac{5!}{1!(5-1)!}(.1)^1(.9)^{5-1} = 5(.1)(.9)^4 = .32805$$

$$p(2) = \frac{5!}{2!(5-2)!}(.1)^2(.9)^{5-2} = (10)(.1)^2(.9)^3 = .07290$$

$$p(3) = .0081 \text{ (from Example 4.10)}$$

$$p(4) = \frac{5!}{4!(5-4)!}(.1)^4(.9)^{5-4} = (5)(.1)^4(.9) = .00045$$

$$p(5) = \frac{5!}{5!(5-5)!}(.1)^5(.9)^{5-5} = (.1)^5 = .00001$$

The graph of $p(x)$ is shown as a probability histogram in Figure 4.7.

To calculate the values of μ and σ, substitute $n = 5$ and $p = .1$ into the following formulas:

$$\mu = np = (5)(.1) = .5$$
$$\sigma = \sqrt{npq} = \sqrt{(5)(.1)(.9)} = \sqrt{.45} = .67$$

To find the interval $\mu - 2\sigma$ to $\mu + 2\sigma$, we calculate

$$\mu - 2\sigma = .5 - 2(.67) = -.84$$
$$\mu + 2\sigma = .5 + 2(.67) = 1.84$$

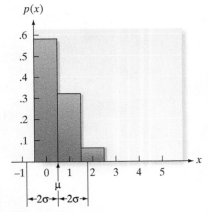

Figure 4.7
The binomial distribution: $n = 5$, $p = .1$

If the experiment was repeated a large number of times, what proportion of the x observations would fall within the interval $\mu - 2\sigma$ to $\mu + 2\sigma$? You can see from Figure 4.7 that all observations equal to 0 or 1 will fall within the interval. The probabilities corresponding to these values are .5905 and .3280, respectively. Consequently, you would expect $.5905 + .3280 = .9185$, or approximately 91.9%, of the observations to fall within the interval $\mu - 2\sigma$ to $\mu + 2\sigma$.

Look Back This result again emphasizes that for most probability distributions, observations rarely fall more than 2 standard deviations from μ.

Table 4.3	Reproduction of Part of Table II in Appendix B: Binomial Probabilities for $n = 10$												
	p												
k	.01	.05	.10	.20	.30	.40	.50	.60	.70	.80	.90	.95	.99
0	.904	.599	.349	.107	.028	.006	.001	.000	.000	.000	.000	.000	.000
1	.996	.914	.736	.376	.149	.046	.011	.002	.000	.000	.000	.000	.000
2	1.000	.988	.930	.678	.383	.167	.055	.012	.002	.000	.000	.000	.000
3	1.000	.999	.987	.879	.650	.382	.172	.055	.011	.001	.000	.000	.000
4	1.000	1.000	.998	.967	.850	.633	.377	.166	.047	.006	.000	.000	.000
5	1.000	1.000	1.000	.994	.953	.834	.623	.367	.150	.033	.002	.000	.000
6	1.000	1.000	1.000	.999	.989	.945	.828	.618	.350	.121	.013	.001	.000
7	1.000	1.000	1.000	1.000	.998	.988	.945	.833	.617	.322	.070	.012	.000
8	1.000	1.000	1.000	1.000	1.000	.998	.989	.954	.851	.624	.264	.086	.004
9	1.000	1.000	1.000	1.000	1.000	1.000	.999	.994	.972	.893	.651	.401	.096

Using Binomial Tables

Calculating binomial probabilities becomes tedious when n is large. For some values of n and p, the binomial probabilities have been tabulated in Table II in Appendix B. Part of Table II is shown in Table 4.3; a graph of the binomial probability distribution for $n = 10$ and $p = .10$ is shown in Figure 4.8. Table II actually contains a total of nine tables, labeled (a) through (i), each one corresponding to $n = 5, 6, 7, 8, 9, 10, 15, 20,$ and 25. In each of these tables, the columns correspond to values of p, and the rows correspond to values (k) of the random variable x. The entries in the table represent **cumulative binomial probabilities,** $p(x \leq k)$. Thus, for example, the entry in the column corresponding to $p = .10$ and the row corresponding to $k = 2$ is .930 (shaded), and its interpretation is

$$P(x \leq 2) = P(x = 0) + P(x = 1) + P(x = 2) = .930$$

This probability is also shaded in the graphical representation of the binomial distribution with $n = 10$ and $p = .10$ in Figure 4.8.

You can also use Table II to find the probability that x equals a specific value. For example, suppose you want to find the probability that $x = 2$ in the binomial distribution with $n = 10$ and $p = .10$. This is found by subtraction as follows:

$$P(x = 2) = [P(x = 0) + P(x = 1) + P(x = 2)] - [P(x = 0) + P(x = 1)]$$
$$= P(x \leq 2) - P(x \leq 1) = .930 - .736 = .194$$

The probability that a binomial random variable exceeds a specified value can be found using Table II and the notion of complementary events. For example, to find the probability that x exceeds 2 when $n = 10$ and $p = .10$, we use

$$P(x > 2) = 1 - P(x \leq 2) = .930 = .070$$

Note that this probability is represented by the unshaded portion of the graph in Figure 4.8.

All probabilities in Table II are rounded to three decimal places. Thus, although none of the binomial probabilities in the table is exactly zero, some are small enough (less than .0005) to round to .000. For example, using the formula to find $P(x = 0)$ when $n = 10$ and $p = .6$, we obtain

$$P(x = 0) = \binom{10}{0}(.6)^0(.4)^{10-0} = .4^{10} = .00010486$$

but this is rounded to .000 in Table II in Appendix B (see Table 4.3).

Similarly, none of the table entries is exactly 1.0, but when the cumulative probabilities exceed .9995, they are rounded to 1.000. The row corresponding to the largest possible value for x, $x = n$, is omitted because all the cumulative probabilities in that row are equal to 1.0 (exactly). For example, in Table 4.3, with $n = 10$, $P(x \leq 10) = 1.0$, no matter what the value of p.

The following example further illustrates the use of Table II.

Figure 4.8

Binomial probability distribution for $n = 10$ and $p = .10$; $P(x \leq 2)$ shaded

Example 4.12

Using the Binomial Table to Find Probabilities Associated with Worker Unionization

Problem Suppose a poll of 20 employees is taken in a large company. The purpose is to determine x, the number who favor unionization. Suppose that 60% of all the company's employees favor unionization.

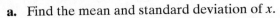

a. Find the mean and standard deviation of x.

b. Use Table II in Appendix B to find the probability that $x \le 10$.

c. Use Table II to find the probability that $x > 12$.

d. Use Table II to find the probability that $x = 11$.

e. Graph the probability distribution of x and locate the interval $\mu \pm 2\sigma$ on the graph.

Solution

a. The number of employees polled is presumably small compared with the total number of employees in this company. Thus, we may treat x, the number of the 20 who favor unionization, as a binomial random variable. The value of p is the fraction of the total employees who favor unionization; that is, $p = .6$. Therefore, we calculate the mean and variance:

$$\mu = np = 20(.6) = 12$$
$$\sigma^2 = npq = 20(.6)(.4) = 4.8$$
$$\sigma = \sqrt{4.8} = 2.19$$

b. Looking in the $k = 10$ row and the $p = .6$ column of Table II (Appendix B) for $n = 20$, we find the value of .245. Thus,

$$P(x \le 10) = .245$$

c. To find the probability

$$P(x > 12) = \sum_{x=13}^{20} p(x)$$

we use the fact that for all probability distributions, $\sum_{\text{All } x} p(x) = 1$. Therefore,

$$P(x > 12) = 1 - P(x \le 12) = 1 - \sum_{x=0}^{12} p(x)$$

Consulting Table II, we find the entry in row $k = 12$, column $p = .6$ to be .584. Thus,

$$P(x > 12) = 1 - .584 = .416$$

d. To find the probability that exactly 11 employees favor unionization, recall that the entries in Table II are cumulative probabilities and use the relationship

$$P(x = 11) = [p(0) + p(1) + \cdots + p(11)] - [p(0) + p(1) + \cdots + p(10)]$$
$$= P(x \le 11) - P(x \le 10)$$

Then

$$P(x = 11) = .404 - .245 = .159$$

Figure 4.9
The binomial probability distribution for x in Example 4.12: $n = 20$, $p = .6$

e. The probability distribution for x in this example is shown in Figure 4.9. Note that

$$\mu - 2\sigma = 12 - 2(2.2) = 7.6$$
$$\mu + 2\sigma = 12 + 2(2.2) = 16.4$$

The interval $(7.6, 16.4)$ is also shown in Figure 4.9. The probability that x falls in this interval is $P(x = 8, 9, 10, \ldots, 16) = P(x \leq 16) - P(x \leq 7) = .984 - .021 = .963$. This probability is very close to the .95 given by the Empirical Rule. Thus, we expect the number of employees in the sample of 20 who favor unionization to be between 8 and 16.

Activity 4.1   *Warehouse Club Memberships:* Exploring a Binomial Random Variable

Warehouse clubs are retailers that offer lower prices than traditional retailers, but they sell only to customers who have purchased memberships and often merchandise must be purchased in large quantities. A warehouse club may offer more than one type of membership, such as a regular membership R for a low annual fee and an upgraded membership U for a higher annual fee. The upgraded membership has additional benefits that might include extended shopping hours, additional discounts on certain products, or cash back on purchases.

   A local warehouse club has determined that 20% of its customer base has the upgraded membership.

1. What is the probability $P(U)$ that a randomly chosen customer entering the store has an upgraded membership? What is the probability $P(R)$ that a randomly chosen customer entering the store has a regular (not upgraded) membership?

   In an effort to sell more upgraded memberships, sales associates are placed at the entrance to the store to explain the benefits of the upgraded membership to customers as they enter. Suppose that in a given time period five customers enter the store.

2. Given that 20% of the store's customers have an upgraded membership, how many of the five customers would you expect to have an upgraded membership?

3. Because there are five customers and each customer either has an upgraded membership (U) or does not (R), there are $2^5 = 32$ different possible combinations of membership types among the five customers. List these 32 possibilities.

4. Find the probability of each of the 32 outcomes. Assume that each of the five customers' membership type is independent of each of the other customers' membership type and use your probabilities $P(U)$ and $P(R)$ with the multiplicative rule. For example, $P(RRUUR) = P(R)P(R)P(U)P(U)P(R)$.

5. Notice that $P(URRRR) = P(RURRR) = P(RRURR) = P(RRRUR) = P(RRRRU) = P(U)^1 P(R)^4$ so that $P(\text{exactly one } U) = P(URRRR) + P(RURRR) + P(RRURR) + P(RRRUR) + P(RRRRU) = 5P(U)^1 P(R)^4$ where 5 is the number of ways that exactly one U can occur. Find $P(\text{exactly one } U)$. Use similar reasoning to establish that $P(\text{no } U\text{'s}) = 1P(U)^0 P(R)^5$, $P(\text{exactly two } U\text{'s}) = 10P(U)^2 P(R)^3$, $P(\text{exactly three } U\text{'s}) = 10P(U)^3 P(R)^2$, $P(\text{exactly four } U\text{'s}) = 5P(U)^4 P(R)^1$, and $P(\text{five } U\text{'s}) = 1P(U)^5 P(R)^0$.

6. Let x be the number of upgraded memberships U in a sample of five customers. Use the results of Part **5** to write a probability distribution for the random variable x in table form. Find the mean and standard deviation of the distribution using the formulas in Section 4.2.

7. Calculate np and $\sqrt{npq}$ where $n = 5$, $p = P(U)$, and $q = P(R)$. How do these numbers compare to the mean and standard deviation of the random variable x in Part **6** and to the expected number of customers with upgraded memberships in Part **1**?

8. Explain how the characteristics of a binomial random variable are illustrated in this activity.

Exercises 4.36–4.56

Learning the Mechanics

4.36 Compute the following:

    a. $\dfrac{6!}{2!(6-2)!}$ **b.** $\dbinom{5}{2}$ **c.** $\dbinom{7}{0}$ **d.** $\dbinom{6}{6}$ **e.** $\dbinom{4}{3}$

4.37 Consider the following probability distribution:

$$p(x) = \binom{5}{x}(.7)^x(.3)^{5-x} \quad (x = 0, 1, 2, \ldots, 5)$$

    a. Is x a discrete or a continuous random variable?
    b. What is the name of this probability distribution?
    c. Graph the probability distribution.
    d. Find the mean and standard deviation of x.
    e. Show the mean and the 2-standard-deviation interval on each side of the mean on the graph you drew in part **c.**

4.38 Suppose x is a binomial random variable with $n = 3$ and $p = .3$.
    a. Calculate the value of $p(x)$, $x = 0, 1, 2, 3$, using the formula for a binomial probability distribution.
    b. Using your answers to part **a,** give the probability distribution for x in tabular form.

4.39 If x is a binomial random variable, compute $p(x)$ for each
[NW] of the following cases:
    a. $n = 5, x = 1, p = .2$
    b. $n = 4, x = 2, q = .4$
    c. $n = 3, x = 0, p = .7$
    d. $n = 5, x = 3, p = .1$
    e. $n = 4, x = 2, q = .6$
    f. $n = 3, x = 1, p = .9$

4.40 If x is a binomial random variable, use Table II in Appendix B to find the following probabilities:
    a. $P(x = 2)$ for $n = 10, p = .4$
    b. $P(x \leq 5)$ for $n = 15, p = .6$
    c. $P(x > 1)$ for $n = 5, p = .1$
    d. $P(x < 10)$ for $n = 25, p = .7$
    e. $P(x \geq 10)$ for $n = 15, p = .9$
    f. $P(x = 2)$ for $n = 20, p = .2$

4.41 If x is a binomial random variable, calculate μ, σ^2, and σ for each of the following:
    a. $n = 25, p = .5$
    b. $n = 80, p = .2$
    c. $n = 100, p = .6$
    d. $n = 70, p = .9$
    e. $n = 60, p = .8$
    f. $n = 1,000, p = .04$

4.42 The binomial probability distribution is a family of probability distributions with each single distribution depending on the values of n and p. Assume that x is a binomial random variable with $n = 4$.
    a. Determine a value of p such that the probability distribution of x is symmetric.
    b. Determine a value of p such that the probability distribution of x is skewed to the right.
    c. Determine a value of p such that the probability distribution of x is skewed to the left.
    d. Graph each of the binomial distributions you obtained in parts **a, b,** and **c.** Locate the mean for each distribution on its graph.
    e. In general, for what values of p will a binomial distribution be symmetric? Skewed to the right? Skewed to the left?

Applet Exercise 4.3

Use the applets *Simulating the Probability of a Head with an Unfair Coin (P(H) = .2)*, and *Simulating the Probability of a Head with an Unfair Coin (P(H) = .8)* to study the mean μ of a binomial distribution.
    a. Run each applet mentioned above once with $n = 1,000$ and record the cumulative proportions. How does the cumulative proportion for each applet compare to the value of $P(H)$ given for the applet?
    b. Using the cumulative proportion from each applet as p, compute $\mu = np$ for each applet where $n = 1,000$. What does the value of μ represent in terms of the results from running each applet in part **a**?
    c. In your own words, describe what the mean μ of a binomial distribution represents.

Applet Exercise 4.4

Open the applet *Sample from a Population.* On the pull-down menu to the right of the top graph, select *Binary.* Set $n = 10$ as the sample size and repeatedly choose samples from the population. For each sample, record the number of 1s in the sample. Let x be the number of 1s in a sample of size 10. Explain why x is a binomial random variable.

Applet Exercise 4.5

Use the applet *Simulating the Stock Market* to estimate the probability that the stock market will go up each of the next two days. Repeatedly run the applet for $n = 2$, recording the number of up's each time. Use the proportion of 2s among your results as the estimate of the probability. Compare to the binomial probability where $x = 2, n = 2$, and $p = 0.5$.

Applying the Concepts—Basic

4.43 Using wireless Internet at home. According to a survey conducted by the *Pew Internet & American Life Project* (Feb. 2007), 20% of Internet users go online at home using a wireless network. In a random sample of 100 Internet users, let x be the number who go online at home using a wireless network.
    [NW] **a.** Explain why x is a binomial random variable (to a reasonable degree of approximation).
    b. What is the value of p? Interpret this value.
    c. What is the expected value of x? Interpret this value.

4.44 Analysis of bottled water. Is the bottled water you're drinking really purified water? A four-year study of bottled water brands conducted by the Natural Resources Defense Council found that 25% of bottled water is just tap water packaged in a bottle (*Scientific American,* July 2003). Consider a sample of five bottled water brands and let x equal the number of these brands that use tap water.
    a. Explain why x is (approximately) a binomial random variable.
    b. Give the probability distribution for x as a formula.
    c. Find $P(x = 2)$.
    d. Find $P(x \leq 1)$.

4.45 Women-owned businesses. According to the *Journal of Business Venturing* (Vol. 17, 2002), 27% of all small businesses owned by non-Hispanic whites nationwide are women-owned firms.

a. In a sample of 200 small businesses owned by non-Hispanic whites, how many would you expect to be female owned?

b. If eight small businesses owned by non-Hispanic whites were randomly selected, what is the probability that none are female owned? That half are female owned?

4.46 **Physicians' opinions on a career in medicine.** Many primary care doctors feel overworked and burdened by potential lawsuits. In fact, the Physicians' Foundation reported that 60% of all general practice physicians in the United States do not recommend medicine as a career (*Reuters*, Nov. 18, 2008). Let *x* represent the number of sampled general practice physicians who do not recommend medicine as a career.

a. Explain why *x* is approximately a binomial random variable.

b. Use the Physicians' Foundation report to estimate *p* for the binomial random variable.

c. Consider a random sample of 25 general practice physicians. Use *p* from part **b** to find the mean and standard deviation of *x,* the number who do not recommend medicine as a career.

d. For the sample of part **c,** find the probability that at least one general practice physician does not recommend medicine as a career.

4.47 **Tracking missiles with satellite imagery.** The U.S. government has devoted considerable funding to missile defense research over the past 20 years. The latest development is the Space-Based Infrared System (SBIRS), which uses satellite imagery to detect and track missiles (*Chance*, Summer 2005). The probability that an intruding object (e.g., a missile) will be detected on a flight track by SBIRS is .8. Consider a sample of 20 simulated tracks, each with an intruding object. Let *x* equal the number of these tracks where SBIRS detects the object.

a. Demonstrate that *x* is (approximately) a binomial random variable.

b. Give the values of *p* and *n* for the binomial distribution.

c. Find $P(x = 15)$, the probability that SBIRS will detect the object on exactly 15 tracks.

d. Find $P(x \geq 15)$, the probability that SBIRS will detect the object on at least 15 tracks.

e. Find $E(x)$ and interpret the result.

Applying the Concepts—Intermediate

4.48 **Making your vote count.** Refer to the *Chance* (Fall 2007) study on making your vote count, Exercise 3.25 (p. 130). Recall the scenario where you are one of five county commissioners voting on an issue, and each commissioner is equally likely to vote for or against.

a. Your vote counts (i.e., is the decisive vote) only if the other four voters split, two in favor and two against. Use the binomial distribution to find the probability that your vote counts.

b. If you convince two other commissioners to "vote in bloc" (i.e., you all agree to vote among yourselves first, and whatever the majority decides is the way all three will vote, guaranteeing that the issue is decided by the bloc), your vote counts only if these two commissioners split their bloc votes, one in favor and one against.

Again, use the binomial distribution to find the probability that your vote counts.

4.49 **Bridge inspection ratings.** According to the National Bridge Inspection Standard (NBIS), public bridges over 20 feet in length must be inspected and rated every 2 years. The NBIS rating scale ranges from 0 (poorest rating) to 9 (highest rating). University of Colorado engineers used a probabilistic model to forecast the inspection ratings of all major bridges in Denver (*Journal of Performance of Constructed Facilities,* Feb. 2005). For the year 2020, the engineers forecast that 9% of all major Denver bridges will have ratings of 4 or below.

a. Use the forecast to find the probability that in a random sample of 10 major Denver bridges, at least 3 will have an inspection rating of 4 or below in 2020.

b. Suppose that you actually observe 3 or more of the sample of 10 bridges with inspection ratings of 4 or below in 2020. What inference can you make? Why?

4.50 **Detecting a computer virus attack.** *Chance* (Winter 2004) presented basic methods for detecting virus attacks (e.g., Trojan programs or worms) on a network computer that are sent from a remote host. These viruses reach the network through requests for communication (e.g., e-mail, Web chat, or remote log-in) that are identified as "packets." For example, the "SYN flood" virus ties up the network computer by "flooding" the network with multiple packets. Cybersecurity experts can detect this type of virus attack if at least one packet is observed by a network sensor. Assume that the probability of observing a single packet sent from a new virus is only .001. If the virus actually sends 150 packets to a network computer, what is the probability that the virus is detected by the sensor?

4.51 **Tax returns audited by the IRS.** According to the Internal Revenue Service (IRS), the chances of your tax return being audited are about 1 in 100 if your income is less than $1 million and 9 in 100 if your income is $1 million or more (*IRS Fiscal Year 2007 Enforcement and Services Statistics*).

a. What is the probability that a taxpayer with income less than $1 million will be audited by the IRS? With income $1 million or more?

b. If five taxpayers with incomes under $1 million are randomly selected, what is the probability that exactly one will be audited? That more than one will be audited?

c. Repeat part **b** assuming that five taxpayers with incomes of $1 million or more are randomly selected.

d. If two taxpayers with incomes under $1 million are randomly selected and two with incomes more than $1 million are randomly selected, what is the probability that none of these taxpayers will be audited by the IRS?

e. What assumptions did you have to make in order to answer these questions using the methodology presented in this section?

4.52 **Student gambling on sports.** A study of gambling activity at the University of West Georgia (UWG) discovered that 60% of the male students wagered on sports in the past year (*The Sport Journal*, Fall 2006). Consider a random sample of 50 UWG male students. How many of these students would you expect to have gambled on sports in the past year? Give a range that is likely to include the number of male students who have gambled on sports.

4.53 FDA report on pesticides in food. Every quarter, the Food and Drug Administration (FDA) produces a report called the *Total Diet Study*. The FDA's report covers a variety of food items, each of which is analyzed for potentially harmful chemical compounds. A recent *Total Diet Study* reported that no pesticides at all were found in 70% of the domestically produced food samples (*FDA Pesticide Program: Residue Monitoring*, 2006). Consider a random sample of 800 food items analyzed for the presence of pesticides.

a. Compute μ and σ for the random variable x, the number of food items found that showed no trace of pesticide.

b. Based on a sample of 800 food items, is it likely you would observe less than half without any traces of pesticide? Explain.

Applying the Concepts—Advanced

4.54 Purchasing decision. Suppose you are a purchasing officer for a large company. You have purchased 5 million electrical switches, and your supplier has guaranteed that the shipment will contain no more than .1% defectives. To check the shipment, you randomly sample 500 switches, test them, and find that four are defective. Based on this evidence, do you think the supplier has complied with the guarantee? Explain.

4.55 USGA golf ball specifications. According to the U.S. Golf Association (USGA), "The weight of the [golf] ball shall not be greater than 1.620 ounces avoirdupois (45.93 grams). ... The diameter of the ball shall not be less than 1.680 inches. ... The velocity of the ball shall not be greater than 250 feet per second" (USGA 2002). The USGA periodically checks the specifications of golf balls sold in the United States by randomly sampling balls from pro shops around the country. Two dozen of each kind are sampled, and if more than three do not meet size and/or velocity requirements, that kind of ball is removed from the USGA's approved-ball list.

a. What assumptions must be made and what information must be known in order to use the binomial probability distribution to calculate the probability that the USGA will remove a particular kind of golf ball from its approved-ball list?

b. Suppose 10% of all balls produced by a particular manufacturer are less than 1.680 inches in diameter, and assume that the number of such balls, x, in a sample of two dozen balls can be adequately characterized by a binomial probability distribution. Find the mean and standard deviation of the binomial distribution.

c. Refer to part **b.** If x has a binomial distribution, then so does the number, y, of balls in the sample that meet the USGA's minimum diameter. [*Note:* $x + y = 24$.] Describe the distribution of y. In particular, what are p, q, and n? Also, find $E(y)$ and the standard deviation of y.

4.56 Reliability of a "one-shot" device. A "one-shot" device can be used only once; after use, the device (e.g., a nuclear weapon, space shuttle, automobile air bag) is either destroyed or must be rebuilt. The destructive nature of a one-shot device makes repeated testing either impractical or too costly. Hence, the reliability of such a device must be determined with minimal testing. Consider a one-shot device that has some probability, p, of failure. Of course, the true value of p is unknown, so designers will specify a value of p that is the largest defective rate they are willing to accept. Designers will conduct n tests of the device and determine the success or failure of each test. If the number of observed failures, x, is less than or equal to some specified value, K, then the device is considered to have the desired failure rate. Consequently, the designers want to know the minimum sample size n needed so that observing K or fewer defectives in the sample will demonstrate that the true probability of failure for the one-shot device is no greater than p.

a. Suppose the desired failure rate for a one-shot device is $p = .10$. Also, suppose designers will conduct $n = 20$ tests of the device and conclude that the device is performing to specifications if $K = 1$ (i.e., if 1 or no failures are observed in the sample). Find $P(x \leq 1)$.

b. In reliability analysis, $1 - P(x \leq K)$ is often called the *level of confidence* for concluding that the true failure rate is less than or equal to p. Find the level of confidence for the one-shot device described in part **a.** In your opinion, is this an acceptable level? Explain.

c. Demonstrate that the confidence level can be increased by either (1) increasing the sample size n or (2) decreasing the number K of failures allowed in the sample.

d. Typically, designers want a confidence level of .90, .95, or .99. Find the values of n and K to use so that the designers can conclude (with at least 95% confidence) that the failure rate for the one-shot device of part **a** is no greater than $p = .10$.

[*Note:* The U.S. Department of Defense Reliability Analysis Center (DoD RAC) provides designers with free access to tables and toolboxes that give the minimum sample size n required to obtain a desired confidence level for a specified number of observed failures in the sample.]

4.4 Other Discrete Distributions: Poisson and Hypergeometric

Poisson Random Variable

A type of discrete probability distribution that is often useful in describing the number of rare events that will occur in a specific period of time or in a specific area or volume is the **Poisson distribution** (named after the 18th-century physicist and mathematician, Siméon Poisson). Typical examples of random variables for which the Poisson probability distribution provides a good model are as follows:

1. The number of industrial accidents per month at a manufacturing plant

2. The number of noticeable surface defects (scratches, dents, etc.) found by quality inspectors on a new automobile

3. The parts per million of some toxin found in the water or air emission from a manufacturing plant

4. The number of customer arrivals per unit of time at a supermarket checkout counter

5. The number of death claims received per day by an insurance company

6. The number of errors per 100 invoices in the accounting records of a company

---

Characteristics of a Poisson Random Variable

1. The experiment consists of counting the number of times a certain event occurs during a given unit of time or in a given area or volume (or weight, distance, or any other unit of measurement).

2. The probability that an event occurs in a given unit of time, area, or volume is the same for all the units.

3. The number of events that occur in one unit of time, area, or volume is independent of the number that occur in any other mutually exclusive unit.

4. The mean (or expected) number of events in each unit is denoted by the Greek letter lambda, λ.

BIOGRAPHY

SIMÉON D. POISSON
(1781–1840)

A Lifetime Mathematician

Growing up in France during the French Revolution, Siméon Denis Poisson was sent away by his father to become an apprentice surgeon, but he lacked the manual dexterity to perform the delicate procedures required and returned home. He eventually enrolled in Ecole Polytechnique University to study mathematics. In his final year of study, Poisson wrote a paper on the theory of equations that was of such quality that he was allowed to graduate without taking the final examination. Two years later, Poisson was named a professor at the university. During his illustrious career, Poisson published between 300 and 400 mathematics papers. He is most known for his 1837 paper where the distribution of a rare event—the Poisson distribution—first appears. (In fact, the distribution was actually described years earlier by one of the Bernoulli brothers.) Poisson dedicated his life to mathematics, once stating that "life is good for only two things: to study mathematics and to teach it." ■

The characteristics of the Poisson random variable are usually difficult to verify for practical examples. The examples given satisfy them well enough that the Poisson distribution provides a good model in many instances. As with all probability models, the real test of the adequacy of the Poisson model is in whether it provides a reasonable approximation to reality—that is, whether empirical data support it.

The probability distribution, mean, and variance for a Poisson random variable are shown in the next box.

Probability Distribution, Mean, and Variance for a Poisson Random Variable*

$$p(x) = \frac{\lambda^x e^{-\lambda}}{x!} \quad (x = 0, 1, 2, \ldots)$$

$$\mu = \lambda$$
$$\sigma^2 = \lambda$$

where

λ = Mean number of events during given unit of time, area, volume, etc.

$e = 2.71828\ldots$

The calculation of Poisson probabilities is made easier by the use of Table III in Appendix B, which gives the cumulative probabilities $P(x \leq k)$ for various values of λ. The use of Table III is illustrated in Example 4.13.

Example 4.13

Finding Poisson Probabilities Associated with Worker Absenteeism

Problem Suppose the number, x, of a company's employees who are absent on Mondays has (approximately) a Poisson probability distribution. Furthermore, assume that the average number of Monday absentees is 2.6.

a. Find the mean and standard deviation of x, the number of employees absent on Monday.

b. Use Table III to find the probability that fewer than two employees are absent on a given Monday.

---

*The Poisson probability distribution also provides a good approximation to a binomial distribution with mean $\lambda = np$ when n is large and p is small (say, $np \leq 7$).

c. Use Table III to find the probability that more than five employees are absent on a given Monday.

d. Use Table III to find the probability that exactly five employees are absent on a given Monday.

Solution

a. The mean and variance of a Poisson random variable are both equal to λ. Thus, for this example,

$$\mu = \lambda = 2.6$$
$$\sigma^2 = \lambda = 2.6$$

Then the standard deviation of x is

$$\sigma = \sqrt{2.6} = 1.61$$

Remember that the mean measures the central tendency of the distribution and does not necessarily equal a possible value of x. In this example, the mean is 2.6 absences, and although there cannot be 2.6 absences on a given Monday, the average number of Monday absences is 2.6. Similarly, the standard deviation of 1.61 measures the variability of the number of absences per week. Perhaps a more helpful measure is the interval $\mu \pm 2\sigma$, which in this case stretches from −.62 to 5.82. We expect the number of absences to fall in this interval most of the time—with at least 75% relative frequency (according to Chebyshev's Rule) and probably with approximately 95% relative frequency (the Empirical Rule). The mean and the 2-standard-deviation interval around it are shown in Figure 4.10.

b. A partial reproduction of Table III is shown in Table 4.4. The rows of the table correspond to different values of λ, and the columns correspond to different values (k) of the Poisson random variable x. The entries in the table (like the binomial probabilities in Table II) give the cumulative probability $P(x \leq k)$. To find the probability that fewer than two employees are absent on Monday, we first note that

$$P(x < 2) = P(x \leq 1)$$

This probability is cumulative and therefore is the entry in Table III in the row corresponding to λ = 2.6 and the column corresponding to $k = 1$. The entry is .267, shown shaded in Table 4.4. This probability corresponds to the shaded area in Figure 4.10 and may be interpreted as meaning that there is a 26.7% chance that fewer than two employees will be absent on a given Monday.

c. To find the probability that more than five employees are absent on a given Monday, we consider the complementary event

$$P(x > 5) = 1 - P(x \leq 5) = 1 - .951 = .049$$

where .951 is the entry in Table III corresponding to λ = 2.6 and $k = 5$ (see Table 4.4). Note from Figure 4.10 that this is the area in the interval $\mu \pm 2\sigma$, or −.62 to 5.82. Then the number of absences should exceed 5—or, equivalently, should be more than 2 standard deviations from the mean—during only about 4.9% of all Mondays. Note that this percentage agrees remarkably well with that given by the Empirical Rule for

Figure 4.10
Probability distribution for number of Monday absences

Table 4.4		**Reproduction of Part of Table III in Appendix B**								
k λ	0	1	2	3	4	5	6	7	8	9
2.2	.111	.355	.623	.819	.928	.975	.993	.998	1.000	1.000
2.4	.091	.308	.570	.779	.904	.964	.988	.997	.999	1.000
2.6	.074	.267	.518	.736	.877	.951	.983	.995	.999	1.000
2.8	.061	.231	.469	.692	.848	.935	.976	.992	.998	.999
3.0	.050	.199	.423	.647	.815	.916	.966	.988	.996	.999
3.2	.041	.171	.380	.603	.781	.895	.955	.983	.994	.998
3.4	.033	.147	.340	.558	.744	.871	.942	.977	.992	.997
3.6	.027	.126	.303	.515	.706	.844	.927	.969	.988	.996
3.8	.022	.107	.269	.473	.668	.816	.909	.960	.984	.994
4.0	.018	.092	.238	.433	.629	.785	.889	.949	.979	.992
4.2	.015	.078	.210	.395	.590	.753	.867	.936	.972	.989
4.4	.012	.066	.185	.359	.551	.720	.844	.921	.964	.985
4.6	.010	.056	.163	.326	.513	.686	.818	.905	.955	.980
4.8	.008	.048	.143	.294	.476	.651	.791	.887	.944	.975
5.0	.007	.040	.125	.265	.440	.616	.762	.867	.932	.968
5.2	.006	.034	.109	.238	.406	.581	.732	.845	.918	.960
5.4	.005	.029	.095	.213	.373	.546	.702	.822	.903	.951
5.6	.004	.024	.082	.191	.342	.512	.670	.797	.886	.941
5.8	.003	.021	.072	.170	.313	.478	.638	.771	.867	.929
6.0	.002	.017	.062	.151	.285	.446	.606	.744	.847	.916

mound-shaped distributions, which tells us to expect approximately 5% of the measurements (values of the random variable) to lie farther than 2 standard deviations from the mean.

d. To use Table III to find the probability that *exactly* five employees are absent on a Monday, we must write the probability as the difference between two cumulative probabilities:

$$P(x = 5) = P(x \le 5) - P(x \le 4) = .951 - .877 = .074$$

Now Work Exercise 4.58

    Note that the probabilities in Table III are all rounded to three decimal places. Thus, although in theory a Poisson random variable can assume infinitely large values, the values of k in Table III are extended only until the cumulative probability is 1.000. This does not mean that x *cannot* assume larger values, but only that the likelihood is less than .001 (in fact, less than .0005) that it will do so.

    Finally, you may need to calculate Poisson probabilities for values of λ not found in Table III. You may be able to obtain an adequate approximation by interpolation, but if not, consult more extensive tables for the Poisson distribution.

Hypergeometric Random Variable

The **hypergeometric probability distribution** provides a realistic model for some types of enumerative (countable) data. The characteristics of the hypergeometric distribution are listed in the following box:

Characteristics of a Hypergeometric Random Variable

1. The experiment consists of randomly drawing n elements without replacement from a set of N elements, r of which are S's (for success) and $(N - r)$ of which are F's (for failure).

2. The hypergeometric random variable x is the number of S's in the draw of n elements.

Note that both the hypergeometric and binomial characteristics stipulate that each draw, or trial, results in one of two outcomes. The basic difference between these random variables is that the hypergeometric trials are dependent, while the binomial trials are independent. The draws are dependent because the probability of drawing an S (or an F) is dependent on what occurred on preceding draws.

To illustrate the dependence between trials, we note that the probability of drawing an S on the first draw is r/N. Then the probability of drawing an S on the second draw depends on the outcome of the first. It will be either $(r-1)/(N-1)$ or $r/(N-1)$, depending on whether the first draw was an S or an F. Consequently, the results of the draws represent dependent events.

For example, suppose we define x as the number of women hired in a random selection of three applicants from a total of six men and four women. This random variable satisfies the characteristics of a **hypergeometric random variable** with $N = 10$ and $n = 3$. The possible outcomes on each trial are either the selection of a female (S) or the selection of a male (F). Another example of a hypergeometric random variable is the number x of defective large-screen plasma televisions in a random selection of $n = 4$ from a shipment of $N = 8$. Finally, as a third example, suppose $n = 5$ stocks are randomly selected from a list of $N = 15$ stocks. Then the number x of the five companies selected that pay regular dividends to stockholders is a hypergeometric random variable.

The hypergeometric probability distribution is summarized in the following box:

Probability Distribution, Mean, and Variance of the Hypergeometric Random Variable

$$p(x) = \frac{\binom{r}{x}\binom{N-r}{n-x}}{\binom{N}{n}} \quad [x = \text{Maximum } [0, n - (N - r)], \ldots, \text{Minimum}(r, n)]$$

$$\mu = \frac{nr}{N} \qquad \sigma^2 = \frac{r(N-r)n(N-n)}{N^2(N-1)}$$

where

N = Total number of elements

r = Number of S's in the N elements

n = Number of elements drawn

x = Number of S's drawn in the n elements

Example 4.14

Applying the Hypergeometric Distribution—Selecting Teaching Assistants

Problem Suppose a marketing professor randomly selects three new teaching assistants from a total of ten applicants—six male and four female students. Let x be the number of females who are hired.

a. Find the mean and standard deviation of x.

b. Find the probability that no females are hired.

Solution

a. Because x is a hypergeometric random variable with $N = 10$, $n = 3$, and $r = 4$, the mean and variance are

$$\mu = \frac{nr}{N} = \frac{(3)(4)}{10} = 1.2$$

$$\sigma^2 = \frac{r(N-r)n(N-n)}{N^2(N-1)} = \frac{4(10-4)3(10-3)}{(10)^2(10-1)}$$

$$= \frac{(4)(6)(3)(7)}{(100)(9)} = .56$$

The standard deviation is

$$\sigma = \sqrt{.56} = .75$$

b. The probability that no female students are hired by the professor, assuming that the selection is truly random, is

$$P(x = 0) = p(0) = \frac{\binom{4}{0}\binom{10 - 4}{3 - 0}}{\binom{10}{3}}$$

$$= \frac{\dfrac{4!}{0!(4 - 0)!}\dfrac{6!}{3!(6 - 3)!}}{\dfrac{10!}{3!(10 - 3)!}} = \frac{(1)(20)}{120} = \frac{1}{6}$$

Look Back The entire probability distribution for x is shown in Figure 4.11. The mean $\mu = 1.2$ and the interval $\mu \pm 2\sigma = (-.3, 2.7)$ are indicated. You can see that if this random variable were to be observed over and over again a large number of times, most of the values of x would fall within the interval $\mu \pm 2\sigma$.

Now Work Exercise 4.73

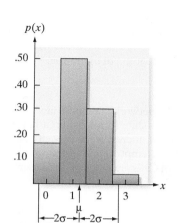

Figure 4.11
Probability distribution for x in Example 4.14

Exercises 4.57–4.78

Learning the Mechanics

4.57 Consider the probability distribution shown here:

$$p(x) = \frac{3^x e^{-3}}{x!} \quad (x = 0, 1, 2, \dots)$$

a. Is x a discrete or continuous random variable? Explain.
b. What is the name of this probability distribution?
c. Graph the probability distribution.
d. Find the mean and standard deviation of x.

4.58 Assume that x is a random variable having a Poisson probability distribution with a mean of 1.5. Use Table III to find the following probabilities:
a. $P(x \le 3)$ **b.** $P(x \ge 3)$
c. $P(x = 3)$ **d.** $P(x = 0)$
e. $P(x > 0)$ **f.** $P(x > 6)$

4.59 Given that x is a hypergeometric random variable, compute $p(x)$ for each of the following cases:
a. $N = 5, n = 3, r = 3, x = 1$
b. $N = 9, n = 5, r = 3, x = 3$
c. $N = 4, n = 2, r = 2, x = 2$
d. $N = 4, n = 2, r = 2, x = 0$

4.60 Given that x is a hypergeometric random variable with $N = 8, n = 3$, and $r = 5$, compute the following:
a. $P(x = 1)$ **b.** $P(x = 0)$
c. $P(x = 3)$ **d.** $P(x \ge 4)$

4.61 Given that x is a random variable for which a Poisson probability distribution provides a good approximation, use Table III to compute the following:
a. $P(x \le 2)$ when $\lambda = 1$
b. $P(x \le 2)$ when $\lambda = 2$
c. $P(x \le 2)$ when $\lambda = 3$

d. What happens to the probability of the event $\{x \le 2\}$ as λ increases from 1 to 3? Is this intuitively reasonable?

4.62 Suppose x is a random variable for which a Poisson probability distribution with $\lambda = 5$ provides a good characterization.
a. Graph $p(x)$ for $x = 0, 1, 2, \dots, 15$.
b. Find μ and σ for x and locate μ and the interval $\mu \pm 2\sigma$ on the graph.
c. What is the probability that x will fall within the interval $\mu \pm 2\sigma$?

4.63 Suppose you plan to sample 10 items from a population of 100 items and would like to determine the probability of observing 4 defective items in the sample. Which probability distribution should you use to compute this probability under the conditions listed here? Justify your answers.
a. The sample is drawn without replacement.
b. The sample is drawn with replacement.

4.64 Given that x is a hypergeometric random variable with $N = 10, n = 5$, and $r = 7$:
a. Display the probability distribution for x in tabular form.
b. Compute the mean and variance of x.
c. Graph $p(x)$ and locate μ and the interval $\mu \pm 2\sigma$ on the graph.
d. What is the probability that x will fall within the interval $\mu \pm 2\sigma$?

Applying the Concepts—Basic

4.65 **On-site treatment of hazardous waste.** The Resource Conservation and Recovery Act mandates the tracking and disposal of hazardous waste produced at U.S. facilities. *Professional Geographer* (Feb. 2000) reported the hazardous-waste generation and disposal characteristics of 209 facilities.

Only 8 of these facilities treated hazardous waste on-site. Use the hypergeometric distribution to answer the following:

a. In a random sample of 10 of the 209 facilities, what is the expected number in the sample that treat hazardous waste on-site? Interpret this result.

b. Find the probability that 4 of the 10 selected facilities treat hazardous waste on-site.

4.66 **FDIC bank failures.** The Federal Deposit Insurance Corporation (FDIC) normally insures deposits of up to $100,000 in banks that are members of the Federal Reserve System against losses due to bank failure or theft. Over the last 5 years, the average number of bank failures per year among insured banks was 3.8 (*FDIC Stats at a Glance*, Sep. 2008). Assume that x, the number of bank failures per year among insured banks, can be adequately characterized by a Poisson probability distribution with mean 4.

a. Find the expected value and standard deviation of x.

b. In 2005, no insured bank failed. How far (in standard deviations) does $x = 0$ lie below the mean of the Poisson distribution? That is, find the z-score for $x = 0$.

c. In 2002, 10 insured banks failed. Find $P(x \leq 10)$.

4.67 **Airline fatalities.** U.S. airlines average about 4.5 fatalities per month (*Statistical Abstract of the United States: 2008*). Assume the probability distribution for x, the number of fatalities per month, can be approximated by a Poisson probability distribution.

a. What is the probability that no fatalities will occur during any given month?

b. What is the probability that one fatality will occur during a month?

c. Find $E(x)$ and the standard deviation of x.

4.68 **Male nannies.** According to the International Nanny Association (INA), 4,176 nannies were placed in a job last year (www.nanny.org, 2007). Of these, only 24 were men. In Exercise 3.11 (p. 128) you found the probability that a randomly selected nanny who was placed last year is a man. Now use the hypergeometric distribution to find the probability that in a random sample of 10 nannies who were placed last year, at least 1 is a man.

4.69 **Contaminated gun cartridges.** Refer to the investigation of contaminated gun cartridges at a weapons manufacturer, presented in Exercise 4.25 (p. 185). In a sample of 158 cartridges from a certain lot, 36 were found to be contaminated and 122 were "clean." If you randomly select 5 of these 158 cartridges, what is the probability that all 5 will be "clean"?

4.70 **Spare line replacement units.** The DoD RAC publishes Selected Topics in Assurance Related Technologies (START) sheets to help improve the quality of manufactured components and systems. One START sheet, titled "Application of the Poisson Distribution" (Vol. 9, No. 1, 2002), focuses on a spare line replacement unit (LRU).

Failures of LRUs are assumed to follow a Poisson distribution with a mean failure rate of 1.2 failures per 10,000 hours.

a. Find the probability that there are no LRU failures during the next 10,000 hours of operation.

b. Find the probability that there are at least two LRU failures during the next 10,000 hours of operation.

Applying the Concepts—Intermediate

4.71 **LAN video conferencing.** A network administrator is installing a video conferencing module to a local area network (LAN) computer system. Of interest is the capacity of the LAN to handle users who attempt to call in for video conferencing during peak hours. Calls are blocked if the user finds all LAN lines are "busy." The capacity is directly related to the rate at which calls are blocked ("Traffic Engineering Model for LAN Video Conferencing," Intel, 2005). Let x equal the number of calls blocked during the peak hour (busy) video conferencing call time. The network administrator believes that x has a Poisson distribution with mean $\lambda = 5$.

a. Find the probability that fewer than 3 calls are blocked during the peak hour.

b. Find $E(x)$ and interpret its value.

4.72 **Lot inspection sampling.** Imagine that you are purchasing small lots of a manufactured product. If it is very costly to test a single item, it may be desirable to test a sample of items from the lot instead of testing every item in the lot. Suppose each lot contains 10 items. You decide to sample 4 items per lot and reject the lot if you observe 1 or more defectives.

a. If the lot contains 1 defective item, what is the probability that you will accept the lot?

b. What is the probability that you will accept the lot if it contains 2 defective items?

4.73 **Testing for spoiled wine.** Suppose that you are purchasing [NW] cases of wine (12 bottles per case) and that, periodically, you select a test case to determine the adequacy of the bottles' seals. To do this, you randomly select and test 3 bottles in the case. If a case contains 1 spoiled bottle of wine, what is the probability that this bottle will turn up in your sample?

4.74 **Customer arrivals at a bakery.** As part of a project targeted at improving the services of a local bakery, a management consultant (L. Lei of Rutgers University) monitored customer arrivals for several Saturdays and Sundays. Using the arrival data, she estimated the average number of customer arrivals per 10-minute period on Saturdays to be 6.2. She assumed that arrivals per 10-minute interval followed the Poisson distribution (some of whose values are missing) shown in the table below.

a. Compute the missing probabilities.

b. Plot the distribution.

c. Find μ and σ and plot the intervals $\mu \pm \sigma$, $\mu \pm 2\sigma$, and $\mu \pm 3\sigma$ on your plot of part **b**.

Probability Distribution for Exercise 4.74

x	0	1	2	3	4	5	6	7	8	9	10	11	12	13
$p(x)$	.002	.013	—	.081	.125	.155	—	.142	.110	.076	—	.026	.014	.007

Source: Lei, L. *Dorsi's Bakery: Modeling Service Operations.* Graduate School of Management, Rutgers University, 1993.

d. The owner of the bakery claims that more than 75 customers per hour enter the store on Saturdays. Based on the consultant's data, is this likely? Explain.

4.75 **Making high-stakes insurance decisions.** The *Journal of Economic Psychology* (Sep. 2008) published the results of a high stakes experiment where subjects were asked how much they would pay for insuring a valuable painting. The painting was threatened by fire and theft, hence, the need for insurance. To make the risk realistic, the subjects were informed that if it rained on exactly 24 days in July, the painting was considered to be stolen; if it rained on exactly 23 days in August, the painting was considered to be destroyed by fire. Although the probability of these two events, "fire" and "theft," was ambiguous for the subjects, the researchers estimated their probabilities of occurrence at .0001. Rain frequencies for the months of July and August were shown to follow a Poisson distribution with a mean of 10 days per month.

a. Find the probability that it will rain on exactly 24 days in July.

b. Find the probability that it will rain on exactly 23 days in August.

c. Are the probabilities, parts **a** and **b**, good approximations to the probabilities of "fire" and "theft"?

4.76 **Reliability of incandescent lightbulbs.** A large manufacturing plant has 3,200 incandescent lightbulbs illuminating the manufacturing floor. The rate at which the bulbs fail follows a Poisson distribution with a mean of 3 bulbs per hour. What is the probability that no bulbs fail in an 8-hour shift?

Applying the Concepts—Advanced

4.77 **Gender discrimination suit.** The *Journal of Business & Economic Statistics* (July 2000) presented a case in which a charge of gender discrimination was filed against the U.S. Postal Service. At the time, there were 302 U.S. Postal Service employees (229 men and 73 women) who applied for promotion. Of the 72 employees who were awarded promotion, 5 were female. Make an inference about whether or not females at the U.S. Postal Service were promoted fairly.

4.78 **Waiting for a car wash.** An automatic car wash takes exactly 5 minutes to wash a car. On average, 10 cars per hour arrive at the car wash. Suppose that 30 minutes before closing time, 5 cars are in line. If the car wash is in continuous use until closing time, is it likely anyone will be in line at closing time?

PART II: CONTINUOUS RANDOM VARIABLES

4.5 Probability Distributions for Continuous Random Variables

The graphical form of the probability distribution for a **continuous random variable** x is a smooth curve that might appear as shown in Figure 4.12. This curve, a function of x, is denoted by the symbol $f(x)$ and is variously called a **probability density function (pdf)**, a **frequency function**, or a **probability distribution.**

The areas under a probability distribution correspond to probabilities for x. For example, the area A beneath the curve between the two points a and b, as shown in Figure 4.12, is the probability that x assumes a value between a and b ($a < x < b$). Because there is no area over a point, say $x = a$, it follows that (according to our model) the probability associated with a particular value of x is equal to 0; that is, $P(x = a) = 0$ and hence $P(a < x < b) = P(a \le x \le b)$. In other words, the probability is the same whether or not you include the endpoints of the interval. Also, because areas over intervals represent probabilities, it follows that the total area under a probability distribution, the probability assigned to all values of x, should equal 1. Note that probability distributions for continuous random variables possess different shapes depending on the relative frequency distributions of real data that the probability distributions are supposed to model.

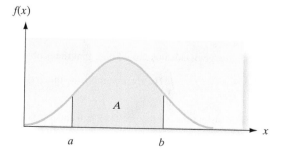

Figure 4.12

A probability distribution $f(x)$ for a continuous random variable x

The areas under most probability distributions are obtained by using calculus or numerical methods.* Because these methods often involve difficult procedures, we will give the areas for some of the most common probability distributions in tabular form in Appendix B. Then, to find the area between two values of x, say $x = a$ and $x = b$, you simply have to consult the appropriate table.

For each of the continuous random variables presented in this chapter, we will give the formula for the probability distribution along with its mean μ and standard deviation σ. These two numbers will enable you to make some approximate probability statements about a random variable even when you do not have access to a table of areas under the probability distribution.

4.6 The Normal Distribution

One of the most commonly observed continuous random variables has a **bell-shaped** probability distribution (or **bell curve**), as shown in Figure 4.13. It is known as a **normal random variable,** and its probability distribution is called a **normal distribution.**

The normal distribution plays a very important role in the science of statistical inference. Moreover, many business phenomena generate random variables with probability distributions that are very well approximated by a normal distribution. For example, the monthly rate of return for a particular stock is approximately a normal random variable, and the probability distribution for the weekly sales of a corporation might be approximated by a normal probability distribution. The normal distribution might also provide an accurate model for the distribution of scores on an employment aptitude test. You can determine the adequacy of the normal approximation to an existing population by comparing the relative frequency distribution of a large sample of the data to the normal probability distribution. Methods to detect disagreement between a set of data and the assumption of normality are presented in Section 4.7.

The normal distribution is perfectly symmetric about its mean μ, as can be seen in the examples in Figure 4.14. Its spread is determined by the value of its standard deviation σ. The formula for the normal probability distribution is showsn in the box. When plotted, this formula yields a curve like that shown in Figure 4.13.

Note that the mean μ and standard deviation σ appear in this formula, so no separate formulas for μ and σ are necessary. To graph the normal curve, we have to know the numerical values of μ and σ. Computing the area over intervals under the normal

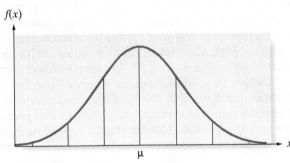

Figure 4.13
A normal probability distribution

Figure 4.14
Several normal distributions with different means and standard deviations

*Students with knowledge of calculus should note that the probability that x assumes a value in the interval $a < x < b$ is $P(a < x < b) = \int_a^b f(x)dx$, assuming the integral exists. Similar to the requirement for a discrete probability distribution, we require $f(x) \geq 0$ and $\int_{-\infty}^{\infty} f(x)dx = 1$.

THE GAUSSIAN DISTRIBUTION (1777–1855)

Carl F. Gauss

The normal distribution began in the 18th century as a theoretical distribution for errors in disciplines where fluctuations in nature were believed to behave randomly. Although he may not have been the first to discover the formula, the normal distribution was named the Gaussian distribution after Carl Friedrich Gauss. A well-known and respected German mathematician, physicist, and astronomer, Gauss applied the normal distribution while studying the motion of planets and stars. Gauss's prowess as a mathematician was exemplified by one of his most important discoveries. At the young age of 22, Gauss constructed a regular 17-gon by ruler and compasses — a feat that was the most major advance in mathematics since the time of the ancient Greeks. In addition to publishing close to 200 scientific papers, Gauss invented the heliograph as well as a primitive telegraph device. ∎

Probability Distribution for a Normal Random Variable x

Probability density function: $f(x) = \dfrac{1}{\sigma\sqrt{2\pi}} e^{-(1/2)[(x-\mu)/\sigma]^2}$

where

μ = Mean of the normal random variable x

σ = Standard deviation

$\pi = 3.1415\ldots$

$e = 2.71828\ldots$

$P(x < a)$ is obtained from a table of normal probabilities

---

probability distribution is a difficult task.* Consequently, we will use the computed areas listed in Table IV in Appendix B. Although there are an infinitely large number of normal curves—one for each pair of values for μ and σ—we have formed a single table that will apply to any normal curve.

Table IV is based on a normal distribution with mean $\mu = 0$ and standard deviation $\sigma = 1$, called a *standard normal distribution*. A random variable with a standard normal distribution is typically denoted by the symbol z. The formula for the probability distribution of z is given by

$$f(z) = \frac{1}{\sqrt{2\pi}} e^{-(1/2)z^2}$$

Figure 4.15 shows the graph of a standard normal distribution.

The **standard normal distribution** is a normal distribution with $\mu = 0$ and $\sigma = 1$. A random variable with a standard normal distribution, denoted by the symbol z, is called a *standard normal random variable*.

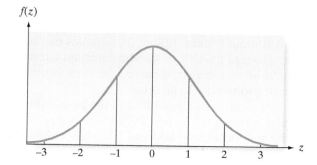

Figure 4.15

Standard normal distribution: $\mu = 0, \sigma = 1$

---

*The student with knowledge of calculus should note that there is not a closed-form expression for

$P(a < x < b) = \displaystyle\int_a^b f(x)\,dx$ for the normal probability distribution. The value of this definite integral can be

obtained to any desired degree of accuracy by numerical approximation procedures. For this reason, it is tabulated for the user.

Table 4.5	Reproduction of Part of Table IV in Appendix B

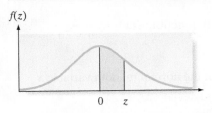

z	.00	.01	.02	.03	.04	.05	.06	.07	.08	.09
.0	.0000	.0040	.0080	.0120	.0160	.0199	.0239	.0279	.0319	.0359
.1	.0398	.0438	.0478	.0517	.0557	.0596	.0636	.0675	.0714	.0753
.2	.0793	.0832	.0871	.0910	.0948	.0987	.1026	.1064	.1103	.1141
.3	.1179	.1217	.1255	.1293	.1331	.1368	.1406	.1443	.1480	.1517
.4	.1554	.1591	.1628	.1664	.1700	.1736	.1772	.1808	.1844	.1879
.5	.1915	.1950	.1985	.2019	.2054	.2088	.2123	.2157	.2190	.2224
.6	.2257	.2291	.2324	.2357	.2389	.2422	.2454	.2486	.2517	.2549
.7	.2580	.2611	.2642	.2673	.2704	.2734	.2764	.2794	.2823	.2852
.8	.2881	.2910	.2939	.2967	.2995	.3023	.3051	.3078	.3106	.3133
.9	.3159	.3186	.3212	.3238	.3264	.3289	.3315	.3340	.3365	.3389
1.0	.3413	.3438	.3461	.3485	.3508	.3531	.3554	.3577	.3599	.3621
1.1	.3643	.3665	.3686	.3708	.3729	.3749	.3770	.3790	.3810	.3830
1.2	.3849	.3869	.3888	.3907	.3925	.3944	.3962	.3980	.3997	.4015
1.3	.4032	.4049	.4066	.4082	.4099	.4115	.4131	.4147	.4162	.4177
1.4	.4192	.4207	.4222	.4236	.4251	.4265	.4279	.4292	.4306	.4319
1.5	.4332	.4345	.4357	.4370	.4382	.4394	.4406	.4418	.4429	.4441

Because we will ultimately convert all normal random variables to standard normal in order to use Table IV to find probabilities, it is important that you learn to use Table IV well. A partial reproduction of Table IV is shown in Table 4.5. Note that the values of the standard normal random variable z are listed in the left-hand column. The entries in the body of the table give the area (probability) between 0 and z. Examples 4.15–4.18 illustrate the use of the table.

Example 4.15

Using the Standard Normal Table to Find $P(-z_0 < z < z_0)$

Problem Find the probability that the standard normal random variable z falls between -1.33 and 1.33.

Solution The standard normal distribution is shown again in Figure 4.16. Because all probabilities associated with standard normal random variables can be depicted as areas under the standard normal curve, you should always draw the curve and then equate the desired probability to an area.

In this example, we want to find the probability that z falls between -1.33 and 1.33, which is equivalent to the area between -1.33 and 1.33, shown shaded in Figure 4.16. Table IV provides the area between $z = 0$ and any value of z, so that if we look up $z = 1.33$, we find that the area between $z = 0$ and $z = 1.33$ is .4082. (The value of 1.33 and the area of .4082 are both highlighted in Table 4.5.) This is the area labeled A_1 in Figure 4.16. To find the area A_2 located between $z = 0$ and $z = -1.33$, we note that the symmetry of the normal distribution implies that the area between $z = 0$ and any point to the left is equal to the area between $z = 0$ and the point equidistant to the right. Thus, in this example, the area between $z = 0$ and $z = -1.33$ is equal to the area between $z = 0$ and $z = 1.33$. That is,

$$A_1 = A_2 = .4082$$

Figure 4.16

Areas under the standard normal curve for Example 4.15

The probability that z falls between -1.33 and 1.33 is the sum of the areas of A_1 and A_2. We summarize in probabilistic notation:

$$P(-1.33 < z < 1.33) = P(-1.33 < z < 0) + P(0 < z < 1.33)$$
$$= A_1 + A_2 = .4082 + .4082 = .8164$$

Look Back Remember that "$<$" and "$\leq$" are equivalent in events involving z because the inclusion (or exclusion) of a single point does not alter the probability of an event involving a continuous random variable.

Now Work Exercise 4.81

Example 4.16

Using the Standard Normal Table to Find $P(z > z_0)$

Problem Find the probability that a standard normal random variable exceeds 1.64; that is, find $P(z > 1.64)$.

Solution The area under the standard normal distribution to the right of 1.64 is the shaded area labeled A_1 in Figure 4.17. This area represents the desired probability that z exceeds 1.64. However, when we look up $z = 1.64$ in Table IV, we must remember that the probability given in the table corresponds to the area between $z = 0$ and $z = 1.64$ (the area labeled A_2 in Figure 4.17). From Table IV, we find that $A_2 = .4495$. To find the area A_1 to the right of 1.64, we make use of two facts:

Figure 4.17
Areas under the standard normal curve for Example 4.16

1. The standard normal distribution is symmetric about its mean, $z = 0$.

2. The total area under the standard normal probability distribution equals 1.

Taken together, these two facts imply that the areas on either side of the mean $z = 0$ equal .5; thus, the area to the right of $z = 0$ in Figure 4.17 is $A_1 + A_2 = .5$. Then

$$P(z > 1.64) = A_1 = .5 - A_2 = .5 - .4495 = .0505$$

Look Back To attach some practical significance to this probability, note that the implication is that the chance of a standard normal random variable exceeding 1.64 is approximately .05.

Now Work Exercise 4.79a

Example 4.17

Using the Standard Normal Table to Find $P(z < z_0)$

Problem Find the probability that a standard normal random variable lies to the left of .67.

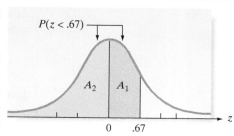

Solution The event is shown as the highlighted area in Figure 4.18. We want to find $P(z < .67)$. We divide the highlighted area into two parts: the area A_1 between $z = 0$ and $z = .67$ and the area A_2 to the left of $z = 0$. We must always make such a division when the desired area lies on both sides of the mean ($z = 0$) because Table IV contains areas between $z = 0$ and the point you look up. We look up $z = .67$ in Table IV to find that $A_1 = .2486$. The symmetry of the standard normal distribution also implies that half the distribution lies on each side of the mean, so the area A_2 to the left of $z = 0$ is .5. Then

Figure 4.18
Areas under the standard normal curve for Example 4.17

$$P(z < .67) = A_1 + A_2 = .2486 + .5 = .7486$$

Look Back Note that this probability is approximately .75. Thus, about 75% of the time the standard normal random variable z will fall below .67. This implies that $z = .67$ represents the approximate 75th percentile for the distribution.

Now Work Exercise 4.82f

Example 4.18

Using the Standard Normal Table to Find $P(|z| > z_0)$

Problem Find the probability that a standard normal random variable exceeds 1.96 in absolute value.

Solution We want to find

$$P(|z| > 1.96) = P(z < -1.96 \text{ or } z > 1.96)$$

Figure 4.19
Areas under the standard normal curve for Example 4.18

This probability is the shaded area in Figure 4.19. Note that the total shaded area is the sum of two areas, A_1 and A_2—areas that are equal because of the symmetry of the normal distribution.

We look up $z = 1.96$ and find the area between $z = 0$ and $z = 1.96$ to be .4750. Then the area to the right of 1.96, A_2, is $.5 - .4750 = .0250$, so that

$$P(|z| > 1.96) = A_1 + A_2 = .0250 + .0250 = .05$$

Look Back We emphasize, again, the importance of drawing the standard normal curve when finding normal probabilities.

To apply Table IV to a normal random variable x with any mean μ and any standard deviation σ, we must first convert the value of x to a z-score. The population z-score for a measurement was defined (in Section 2.7) as the *distance* between the measurement and the population mean, divided by the population standard deviation. Thus, the z-score gives the distance between a measurement and the mean in units equal to the standard deviation. In symbolic form, the z-score for the measurement x is

$$z = \frac{x - \mu}{\sigma}$$

Note that when $x = \mu$, we obtain $z = 0$.

An important property of the normal distribution is that if x is normally distributed with any mean and any standard deviation, z is always normally distributed with mean 0 and standard deviation 1. That is, z is a standard normal random variable.

Property of Normal Distributions

If x is a normal random variable with mean μ and standard deviation σ, then the random variable z, defined by the formula

$$z = \frac{x - \mu}{\sigma}$$

has a standard normal distribution. The value z describes the number of standard deviations between x and μ.

Recall from Example 4.18 that $P(|z| > 1.96) = .05$. This probability coupled with our interpretation of z implies that any normal random variable lies more than 1.96 standard deviations from its mean only 5% of the time. Compare this to the Empirical Rule (Chapter 2), which tells us that about 5% of the measurements in mound-shaped distributions will lie beyond 2 standard deviations from the mean. The normal distribution actually provides the model on which the Empirical Rule is based, along with much "empirical" experience with real data that often approximately obey the rule, whether drawn from a normal distribution or not.

Example 4.19

Finding the Probability of a Normal Random Variable—Cell Phone Application

Problem Assume that the length of time, x, between charges of a cellular phone is normally distributed with a mean of 10 hours and a standard deviation of 1.5 hours. Find the probability that the cell phone will last between 8 and 12 hours between charges.

Figure 4.20
Areas under the normal curve for Example 4.19

Solution The normal distribution with mean $\mu = 10$ and $\sigma = 1.5$ is shown in Figure 4.20. The desired probability that the charge lasts between 8 and 12 hours is shaded. In order to find the probability, we must first convert the distribution to standard normal, which we do by calculating the z-score:

$$z = \frac{x - \mu}{\sigma}$$

The z-scores corresponding to the important values of x are shown beneath the x values on the horizontal axis in Figure 4.20. Note that $z = 0$ corresponds to the mean of $\mu = 10$ hours, whereas the x values 8 and 12 yield z-scores of -1.33 and 1.33, respectively. Thus, the event that the cell phone charge lasts between 8 and 12 hours is equivalent to the event that a standard normal random variable lies between -1.33 and 1.33. We found this probability in Example 4.15 (see Figure 4.16) by doubling the area corresponding to $z = 1.33$ in Table IV. That is,

$$P(8 \leq x \leq 12) = P(-1.33 \leq z \leq 1.33) = 2(.4082) = .8164$$

Now Work Exercise 4.92a–c

The steps to follow when calculating a probability corresponding to a normal random variable are shown in the box.

Steps for Finding a Probability Corresponding to a Normal Random Variable

1. Sketch the normal distribution and indicate the mean of the random variable x. Then shade the area corresponding to the probability you want to find.

2. Convert the boundaries of the shaded area from x values to standard normal random variable z values using the formula

$$z = \frac{x - \mu}{\sigma}$$

Show the z values under the corresponding x values on your sketch.

3. Use Table IV in Appendix B to find the areas corresponding to the z values. If necessary, use the symmetry of the normal distribution to find areas corresponding to negative z values and the fact that the total area on each side of the mean equals .5 to convert the areas from Table IV to the probabilities of the event you have shaded.

Example 4.20

Using Normal Probabilities to Make an Inference about Advertised Gas Mileage

Problem Suppose an automobile manufacturer introduces a new model that has an advertised mean in-city mileage of 27 miles per gallon. Although such advertisements seldom report any measure of variability, suppose you write the manufacturer for the details of the tests, and you find that the standard deviation is 3 miles

per gallon. This information leads you to formulate a probability model for the random variable x, the in-city mileage for this car model. You believe that the probability distribution of x can be approximated by a normal distribution with a mean of 27 and a standard deviation of 3.

a. If you were to buy this model of automobile, what is the probability that you would purchase one that averages less than 20 miles per gallon for in-city driving? In other words, find $P(x < 20)$.

b. Suppose you purchase one of these new models and it does get less than 20 miles per gallon for in-city driving. Should you conclude that your probability model is incorrect?

Figure 4.21
Areas under the normal curve for Example 4.20

Solution

a. The probability model proposed for x, the in-city mileage, is shown in Figure 4.21.

We are interested in finding the area A to the left of 20 because this area corresponds to the probability that a measurement chosen from this distribution falls below 20. In other words, if this model is correct, the area A represents the fraction of cars that can be expected to get less than 20 miles per gallon for in-city driving. To find A, we first calculate the z-value corresponding to $x = 20$. That is,

$$z = \frac{x - \mu}{\sigma} = \frac{20 - 27}{3} = -\frac{7}{3} = -2.33$$

Then

$$P(x < 20) = P(z < -2.33)$$

as indicated by the shaded area in Figure 4.21. Because Table IV gives areas only to the right of the mean (and because the normal distribution is symmetric about its mean), we look up 2.33 in Table IV and find that the corresponding area is .4901. This is equal to the area between $z = 0$ and $z = -2.33$, so we find

$$P(x < 20) = A = .5 - .4901 = .0099 \approx .01$$

According to this probability model, you should have only about a 1% chance of purchasing a car of this make with an in-city mileage under 20 miles per gallon.

b. Now you are asked to make an inference based on a sample—the car you purchased. You are getting less than 20 miles per gallon for in-city driving. What do you infer? We think you will agree that one of two possibilities is true:

1. The probability model is correct. You simply were unfortunate to have purchased one of the cars in the 1% that get less than 20 miles per gallon in the city.
2. The probability model is incorrect. Perhaps the assumption of a normal distribution is unwarranted or the mean of 27 is an overestimate, or the standard deviation of 3 is an underestimate, or some combination of these errors was made. At any rate, the form of the actual probability model certainly merits further investigation.

You have no way of knowing with certainty which possibility is correct, but the evidence points to the second one. We are again relying on the rare-event approach to statistical inference that we introduced earlier. The sample (one measurement in this case) was so unlikely to have been drawn from the proposed probability model that it casts serious doubt on the model. We would be inclined to believe that the model is somehow in error.

Look Back When applying the rare event approach, the calculated probability must be small (say, less than or equal to .05) in order to infer that the observed event is, indeed, unlikely.

Now Work Exercise 4.92d

Occasionally you will be given a probability and will want to find the values of the normal random variable that correspond to the probability. For example, suppose the scores on a college entrance examination are known to be normally distributed, and a certain prestigious university will consider for admission only those applicants whose scores exceed the 90th percentile of the test score distribution. To determine the minimum score for admission consideration, you will need to be able to use Table IV in reverse, as demonstrated in the following example.

Example 4.21

Using the Normal Table in Reverse

Problem Find the value of z, call it z_0, in the standard normal distribution that will be exceeded only 10% of the time—that is, find z_0 such that $P(z \geq z_0) = .10$.

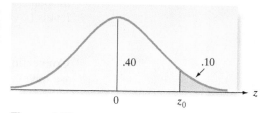

Figure 4.22
Area under the standard normal curve for Example 4.21

Solution In this case we are given a probability, or an area, and asked to find the value of the standard normal random variable that corresponds to the area. Specifically, we want to find the value z_0 such that only 10% of the standard normal distribution exceeds z_0 (see Figure 4.22).

We know that the total area to the right of the mean $z = 0$ is .5, which implies that z_0 must lie to the right of (above) 0. To pinpoint the value, we use the fact that the area to the right of z_0 is .10, which implies that the area between $z = 0$ and z_0 is $.5 - .1 = .4$. But areas between $z = 0$ and some other z-value are exactly the types given in Table IV. Therefore, we look up the area .4000 in the body of Table IV and find that the corresponding z-value is (to the closest approximation) $z_0 = 1.28$. The implication is that the point 1.28 standard deviations above the mean is the 90th percentile of a normal distribution.

Look Back As with earlier problems, it is critical to draw correctly the normal probability of interest on the normal curve. Placement of z_0 to the left or right of 0 is the key. Be sure to shade the probability (area) involving z_0. If it does not agree with the probability of interest (i.e., the shaded area is greater than .5 and the probability of interest is smaller than .5), then you need to place z_0 on the opposite side of 0.

Now Work Exercise 4.85

Example 4.22

Using the Normal Table in Reverse

Problem Find the value of z_0 such that 95% of the standard normal z values lie between $-z_0$ and z_0; that is, $P(-z_0 \leq z \leq z_0) = .95$.

Figure 4.23
Areas under the standard normal curve for Example 4.22

Solution Here we wish to move an equal distance z_0 in the positive and negative directions from the mean $z = 0$ until 95% of the standard normal distribution is enclosed. This means that the area on each side of the mean will be equal to $\frac{1}{2}(.95) = .475$, as shown in Figure 4.23. Because the area between $z = 0$ and z_0 is .475, we look up .475 in the body of Table IV to find the value $z_0 = 1.96$. Thus, as we found in the reverse order in Example 4.21, 95% of a normal distribution lies between -1.96 and 1.96 standard deviations of the mean.

Now Work Exercise 4.88

Now that you have learned to use Table IV to find a standard normal z-value that corresponds to a specified probability, we demonstrate a practical application in Example 4.23.

Example 4.23

Using the Normal Table in Reverse—Paint Manufacturing Application

Problem Suppose a paint manufacturer has a daily production, x, that is normally distributed with a mean of 100,000 gallons and a standard deviation of 10,000 gallons. Management wants to create an incentive bonus for the production crew when the daily production exceeds the 90th percentile of the distribution, in hopes that the crew will, in turn, become more productive. At what level of production should management pay the incentive bonus?

Solution In this example, we want to find a production level, x_0, such that 90% of the daily levels (x values) in the distribution fall below x_0 and only 10% fall above x_0—that is,

$$P(x \leq x_0) = .90$$

Converting x to a standard normal random variable, where $\mu = 100{,}000$ and $\sigma = 10{,}000$, we have

$$P(x \leq x_0) = P\left(z \leq \frac{x_0 - \mu}{\sigma}\right)$$

$$= P\left(z \leq \frac{x_0 - 100{,}000}{10{,}000}\right) = .90$$

In Example 4.21 (see Figure 4.22) we found the 90th percentile of the standard normal distribution to be $z_0 = 1.28$—that is, we found $P(z \leq 1.28) = .90$. Consequently, we know the production level x_0 at which the incentive bonus is paid corresponds to a z-score of 1.28; that is,

$$\frac{x_0 - 100{,}000}{10{,}000} = 1.28$$

If we solve this equation for x_0, we find

$$x_0 = 100{,}000 + 1.28(10{,}000) = 100{,}000 + 12{,}800 = 112{,}800$$

This x value is shown in Figure 4.24. Thus, the 90th percentile of the production distribution is 112,800 gallons. Management should pay an incentive bonus when a day's production exceeds this level if its objective is to pay only when production is in the top 10% of the current daily production distribution.

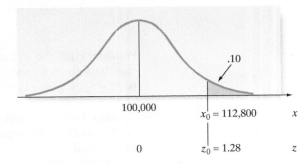

Figure 4.24
Area under the normal curve
for Example 4.23

Look Back As this example shows, in practical applications of the normal table in reverse, first find the value of z_0, then convert the value to the units of x using the z-score formula in reverse.

Statistics IN Action | **Revisited** | **Using the Normal Model**

Recall that a defense contractor has developed a prototype gun for the U.S. Army that fires 1,100 flechettes with a single round. The specifications of the weapon are set so that when the gun is aimed at a target 500 meters away, the mean horizontal grid value of the flechettes is equal to the aim point. In the range test, the weapon was aimed at the center target in Figure SIA4.1 (p. 174); thus, $\mu = 5$ feet. For three different tests, the standard deviation was set at $\sigma = 1$ feet, $\sigma = 2$ feet, and $\sigma = 4$ feet. From past experience, the defense contractor has found that the distribution of the horizontal hit point measurements is closely approximated by a normal distribution. Therefore, we can use the normal distribution to find the probability that a single flechette shot from the weapon will hit any one of the three targets. Recall from Figure SIA4.1 (p. 174) that the three targets range from −1 to 1, 4 to 6, and 9 to 11 feet on the horizontal grid.

Consider, first, the middle target. Letting x represent the horizontal measurement for a flechette shot from the gun, the flechette will hit the target if $4 \le x \le 6$. The probability that this flechette will hit the target when $\mu = 5$ and $\sigma = 1$ is, using the normal probability table (Table IV, Appendix B),

$$\underset{\sigma\,=\,1}{Middle:} \; P(4 \le x \le 6) = P\left(\frac{4-5}{1} < z < \frac{6-5}{1}\right)$$
$$= P(-1 < z < 1)$$
$$= 2(.3413) = .6826$$

Similarly, we find the probability that the flechette hits the left and right targets shown in Figure SIA4.1.

$$\underset{\sigma\,=\,1}{Left:} \; P(-1 \le x \le 1) = P\left(\frac{-1-5}{1} < z < \frac{1-5}{1}\right)$$
$$= P(-6 < z < -4) \approx 0$$
$$\underset{\sigma\,=\,1}{Right:} \; P(9 \le x \le 11) = P\left(\frac{9-5}{1} < z < \frac{11-5}{1}\right)$$
$$= P(4 < z < 6) \approx 0$$

You can see that there is about a 68% chance that a flechette will hit the middle target but virtually no chance that one will hit the left and right targets when the standard deviation is set at 1 foot.

To find these three probabilities for $\sigma = 2$ and $\sigma = 4$, we use the normal probability function in Minitab. Figure SIA4.2 is a Minitab worksheet giving the cumulative probabilities of a normal random variable (with $\mu = 5, \sigma = 1$) falling below the x values in the first column. The cumulative probabilities for $\sigma = 2$ and $\sigma = 4$ are given in the columns named "sigma2" and "sigma4," respectively.

Using the cumulative probabilities in the figure to find the three probabilities when $\sigma = 2$, we have

$$\underset{\sigma\,=\,2}{Middle:} \; P(4 \le x \le 6) = P(x \le 6) - P(x \le 4)$$
$$= .6915 - .3085 = .3830$$

↓	C1	C2	C3	C4
	x	sigma1	sigma2	sigma4
1	-1	0.00000	0.001350	0.066807
2	1	0.00003	0.022750	0.158655
3	4	0.15866	0.308538	0.401294
4	6	0.84134	0.691462	0.598706
5	9	0.99997	0.977250	0.841345
6	11	1.00000	0.998650	0.933193

Figure SIA4.2
Minitab worksheet with cumulative normal probabilities

$$\underset{\sigma\,=\,2}{Left:} \; P(-1 \le x \le 1) = P(x \le 1) - P(x \le -1)$$
$$= .0228 - .0014 = .0214$$

$$\underset{\sigma\,=\,2}{Right:} \; P(9 \le x \le 11) = P(x \le 11) - P(x \le 9)$$
$$= .9987 - .9773 = .0214$$

Thus, when $\sigma = 2$, there is about a 38% chance that a flechette will hit the middle target, a 2% chance that one will hit the left target, and a 2% chance that one will hit the right target. The probability that a flechette will hit either the middle or left or right target is simply the sum of these three probabilities (an application of the additive rule of probability). This sum is $.3830 + .0214 + .0214 = .4258$; consequently, there is about a 42% chance of hitting any one of the three targets when specifications are set so that $\sigma = 2$.

Now, we use the cumulative probabilities in Figure SIA4.2 to find the three hit probabilities when $\sigma = 4$:

$$\underset{\sigma\,=\,4}{Middle} \; P(4 \le x \le 6) = P(x \le 6) - P(x \le 4)$$
$$= .5987 - .4013 = .1974$$

$$\underset{\sigma\,=\,4}{Left:} \; P(-1 \le x \le 1) = P(x \le 1) - P(x \le -1)$$
$$= .1587 - .0668 = .0919$$

$$\underset{\sigma\,=\,9}{Right:} \; P(9 \le x \le 11) = P(x \le 11) - P(x \le 9)$$
$$= .9332 - .8413 = .0919$$

Thus, when $\sigma = 4$, there is about a 20% chance that a flechette will hit the middle target, a 9% chance that one will hit the left target, and a 9% chance that one will hit the right target. The probability that a flechette will hit any one of the three targets is $.1974 + .0919 + .0919 = .3812$.

These probability calculations reveal a few patterns. First, the probability of hitting the middle target (the target where the gun is aimed) is reduced as the standard deviation is increased. Obviously, if the U.S. Army wants to maximize the chance of hitting the target that the prototype gun is aimed at, it will want specifications set with a small value of σ. But if the Army wants to hit multiple targets with a single shot of the weapon, σ should be increased. With a larger σ, not as many of the flechettes will hit the target aimed at, but more will hit peripheral targets. Whether σ should be set at 4 or 6 (or some other value) depends on how high of a hit rate is required for the peripheral targets.

Data Set: MOAGUN

Exercises 4.79–4.104

Learning the Mechanics

4.79 Find the following probabilities for the standard normal random variable z:

`NW`
  a. $P(z > 1.46)$ **b.** $P(z < -1.56)$
  c. $P(.67 \le z < 2.41)$ **d.** $P(-1.96 \le z < -.33)$
  e. $P(z \ge 0)$ **f.** $P(-2.33 < z < 1.50)$

4.80 Find the area under the standard normal probability distribution between the following pairs of z-scores:
  a. $z = 0$ and $z = 2.00$ **b.** $z = 0$ and $z = 3$
  c. $z = 0$ and $z = 1.5$ **d.** $z = 0$ and $z = .80$

4.81 Find each of the following probabilities for the standard
`NW` normal random variable z:
  a. $P(-1 \le z \le 1)$ **b.** $P(-1.96 \le z \le 1.96)$
  c. $P(-1.645 \le z \le 1.645)$ **d.** $P(-2 \le z \le 2)$

4.82 Find the following probabilities for the standard normal random variable z:
  a. $P(-1 < z < 1)$ **b.** $P(-2 < z < 2)$
  c. $P(-2.16 \le z \le .55)$ **d.** $P(-.42 < z < 1.96)$
  e. $P(z \ge -2.33)$ `NW` **f.** $P(z < 2.33)$

4.83 Find each of the following probabilities for a standard normal random variable z:
  a. $P(z = 1)$ **b.** $P(z \le 1)$
  c. $P(z < 1)$ **d.** $P(z > 1)$

4.84 Find a value of the standard normal random variable z, call it z_0, such that
  a. $P(z \ge z_0) = .05$ **b.** $P(z \ge z_0) = .025$
  c. $P(z \le z_0) = .025$ **d.** $P(z \ge z_0) = .10$
  e. $P(z > z_0) = .10$

4.85 Find a value of the standard normal random variable z,
`NW` call it z_0, such that
  a. $P(z \le z_0) = .2090$
  b. $P(z \le z_0) = .7090$
  c. $P(-z_0 \le z < z_0) = .8472$
  d. $P(-z_0 \le z \le z_0) = .1664$
  e. $P(z_0 \le z \le 0) = .4798$
  f. $P(-1 < z < z_0) = .5328$

4.86 Give the z-score for a measurement from a normal distribution for the following:
  a. 1 standard deviation above the mean
  b. 1 standard deviation below the mean
  c. Equal to the mean
  d. 2.5 standard deviations below the mean
  e. 3 standard deviations above the mean

4.87 Suppose the random variable x is best described by a normal distribution with $\mu = 30$ and $\sigma = 4$. Find the z-score that corresponds to each of the following x values:
  a. $x = 20$ **b.** $x = 30$
  c. $x = 2.75$ **d.** $x = 15$
  e. $x = 35$ **f.** $x = 25$

4.88 The random variable x has a normal distribution with
`NW` $\mu = 1,000$ and $\sigma = 10$.
  a. Find the probability that x assumes a value more than 2 standard deviations from its mean. More than 3 standard deviations from μ.
  b. Find the probability that x assumes a value within 1 standard deviation of its mean. Within 2 standard deviations of μ.
  c. Find the value of x that represents the 80th percentile of this distribution. The 10th percentile.

4.89 Suppose x is a normally distributed random variable with $\mu = 11$ and $\sigma = 2$. Find each of the following:
  a. $P(10 \le x \le 12)$ **b.** $P(6 \le x \le 10)$
  c. $P(13 \le x \le 16)$ **d.** $P(7.8 \le x \le 12.6)$
  e. $P(x \ge 13.24)$ **f.** $P(x \ge 7.62)$

4.90 Suppose x is a normally distributed random variable with $\mu = 50$ and $\sigma = 3$. Find a value of the random variable, call it x_0, such that
  a. $P(x \le x_0) = .8413$
  b. $P(x > x_0) = .025$
  c. $P(x > x_0) = .95$
  d. $P(41 \le x < x_0) = .8630$
  e. 10% of the values of x are less than x_0.
  f. 1% of the values of x are greater than x_0.

🔵 Applet Exercise 4.6

Open the applet *Sample from a Population*. On the pull-down menu to the right of the top graph, select *Bell shaped*. The box to the left of the top graph displays the population mean, median, and standard deviation.
  a. Run the applet for each available value of n on the pull-down menu for the sample size. Go from the smallest to the largest value of n. For each value of n, observe the shape of the graph of the sample data and record the mean, median, and standard deviation of the sample.
  b. Describe what happens to the shape of the graph and the mean, median, and standard deviation of the sample as the sample size increases.

Applying the Concepts—Basic

4.91 **Most powerful business women in America.** Refer to the
  ⚽ *Fortune* (Oct. 16, 2008) list of the 50 most powerful women in America, Exercise 2.48 (p. 62). Recall that the data on age (in years) of each woman is stored in the **WPOWER50** file. The ages in the data set can be shown to be approximately normally distributed with a mean of 50 years and a standard deviation of 6 years. A powerful woman is randomly selected from the data, and her age is observed.
  a. Find the probability that her age will fall between 55 and 60 years.
  b. Find the probability that her age will fall between 48 and 52 years.
  c. Find the probability that her age will be less than 35 years.
  d. Find the probability that her age will exceed 40 years.

4.92 **The business of casino gaming.** Casino gaming yields over
`NW` $35 billion in revenue each year in the United States. In *Chance* (Spring 2005), University of Denver statistician R. C. Hannum discussed the business of casino gaming and its reliance on the laws of probability. Casino games of pure chance (e.g., craps, roulette, baccarat, and keno) always yield a "house advantage." For example, in the game of double-zero roulette, the expected casino win percentage is 5.26% on bets made on whether the outcome will be either black or red. (This implies that for every $5 bet on black or red, the casino will earn a net of about 25 cents.) It can be shown that in 100 roulette plays on black/red, the average casino win percentage is normally distributed with mean 5.26% and standard deviation 10%. Let x represent the average

casino win percentage after 100 bets on black/red in double-zero roulette.

   a. Find $P(x > 0)$. (This is the probability that the casino wins money.)

   b. Find $P(5 < x < 15)$.

   c. Find $P(x < 1)$.

   d. If you observed an average casino win percentage of -25% after 100 roulette bets on black/red, what would you conclude?

4.93 **Buy-side vs. sell-side analysts' earnings forecasts.** Financial analysts who make forecasts of stock prices are categorized as either "buy-side" analysts or "sell-side" analysts. Refer to the *Financial Analysts Journal* (Jul./Aug. 2008) comparison of earnings forecasts of buy-side and sell-side analysts, Exercise 2.84 (p. 76). The mean and standard deviation of forecast errors for both types of analysts are reproduced in the table. Assume that the distribution of forecast errors are approximately normally distributed.

   a. Find the probability that a buy-side analyst has a forecast error of +2.00 or higher.

   b. Find the probability that a sell-side analyst has a forecast error of +2.00 or higher.

	Buy-Side Analysts	Sell-Side Analysts
Mean	0.85	−0.05
Standard Deviation	1.93	0.85

Source: Groysberg, B., Healy, P., and Chapman, C. *Financial Analysts Journal,* Vol. 64, No. 4, Jul./Aug. 2008.

4.94 **NHTSA crash safety tests.** Refer to Exercise 4.19 (p. 184) and the NHTSA crash test data for new cars. One of the variables saved in the **CRASH** file is the severity of a driver's head injury when the car is in a head-on collision with a fixed barrier while traveling at 35 miles per hour. The more points assigned to the head injury rating, the more severe the injury. The head injury ratings can be shown to be approximately normally distributed with a mean of 605 points and a standard deviation of 185 points. One of the crash-tested cars is randomly selected from the data, and the driver's head injury rating is observed.

   a. Find the probability that the rating will fall between 500 and 700 points.

   b. Find the probability that the rating will fall between 400 and 500 points.

   c. Find the probability that the rating will be less than 850 points.

   d. Find the probability that the rating will exceed 1,000 points.

4.95 **Transmission delays in wireless technology.** Resource reservation protocol (RSVP) was originally designed to establish signaling links for stationary networks. In *Mobile Networks and Applications* (Dec. 2003), RSVP was applied to mobile wireless technology (e.g., a PC notebook with wireless LAN card for Internet access). A simulation study revealed that the transmission delay (measured in milliseconds) of an RSVP linked wireless device has an approximate normal distribution with mean $\mu = 48.5$ milliseconds and $\sigma = 8.5$ milliseconds.

   a. What is the probability that the transmission delay is less than 57 milliseconds?

   b. What is the probability that the transmission delay is between 40 and 60 milliseconds?

Applying the Concepts—Intermediate

4.96 **Mean shifts on a production line.** *Six Sigma* is a comprehensive approach to quality goal setting that involves statistics. An article in *Aircraft Engineering and Aerospace Technology* (Vol. 76, No. 6, 2004) demonstrated the use of the normal distribution in Six Sigma goal setting at Motorola Corporation. Motorola discovered that the average defect rate for parts produced on an assembly line varies from run-to-run and is approximately normally distributed with a mean equal to 3 defects per million. Assume that the goal at Motorola is for the average defect rate to vary no more than 1.5 standard deviations above or below the mean of 3. How likely is it that the goal will be met?

4.97 **Rating employee performance.** Almost all companies utilize some type of year-end performance review for their employees. Human Resources (HR) at the University of Texas Health Science Center provides guidelines for supervisors rating their subordinates. For example, raters are advised to examine their ratings for a tendency to be either too lenient or too harsh. According to HR, "if you have this tendency, consider using a normal distribution—10% of employees (rated) exemplary, 20% distinguished, 40% competent, 20% marginal, and 10% unacceptable." Suppose you are rating an employee's performance on a scale of 1 (lowest) to 100 (highest). Also, assume the ratings follow a normal distribution with a mean of 50 and a standard deviation of 15.

   a. What is the lowest rating you should give to an "exemplary" employee if you follow the University of Texas HR guidelines?

   b. What is the lowest rating you should give to a "competent" employee if you follow the University of Texas HR guidelines?

4.98 **Cotton crop yield study.** The crop yield for a particular farm in a particular year is typically measured as the amount of the crop produced per acre. For example, cotton is measured in pounds per acre. It has been demonstrated that the normal distribution can be used to characterize crop yields over time (*American Journal of Agricultural Economics,* May 1999). Historical data indicate that next summer's cotton yield for a particular Georgia farmer can be characterized by a normal distribution with mean 1,500 pounds per acre and standard deviation 250. The farm in question will be profitable if it produces at least 1,600 pounds per acre.

   a. What is the probability that the farm will lose money next summer?

   b. Assume the same normal distribution is appropriate for describing cotton yield in each of the next two summers. Also assume that the two yields are statistically independent. What is the probability that the farm will lose money for two straight years?

   c. What is the probability that the cotton yield falls within 2 standard deviations of 1,500 pounds per acre next summer?

4.99 **Personnel dexterity tests.** Personnel tests are designed to test a job applicant's cognitive and/or physical abilities. The Wonderlic IQ test is an example of the former; the Purdue Pegboard speed test involving the arrangement of pegs on a peg board is an example of the latter. A particular dexterity test is administered nationwide by a private testing service. It is known that for all tests administered last year, the distribution of scores was approximately normal with mean 75 and standard deviation 7.5.

a. A particular employer requires job candidates to score at least 80 on the dexterity test. Approximately what percentage of the test scores during the past year exceeded 80?

b. The testing service reported to a particular employer that one of its job candidate's scores fell at the 98th percentile of the distribution (i.e., approximately 98% of the scores were lower than the candidate's, and only 2% were higher). What was the candidate's score?

4.100 Manufacturing hourly pay rate. Government data indicate that the mean hourly wage for manufacturing workers in the United States is $17 (*Statistical Abstract of the United States: 2008*). Suppose the distribution of manufacturing wage rates nationwide can be approximated by a normal distribution with standard deviation $1.25 per hour. The first manufacturing firm contacted by a particular worker seeking a new job pays $18.30 per hour.

a. If the worker were to undertake a nationwide job search, approximately what proportion of the wage rates would be greater than $18.30 per hour?

b. If the worker were to randomly select a U.S. manufacturing firm, what is the probability the firm would pay more than $18.30 per hour?

c. The population median, call it η, of a continuous random variable x is the value such that $P(x \geq \eta) = P(x \leq \eta) = .5$—that is, the median is the value η such that half the area under the probability distribution lies above η and half lies below it. Find the median of the random variable corresponding to the wage rate and compare it to the mean wage rate.

4.101 Model for long-term construction cost. Before negotiating a long-term construction contract, building contractors must carefully estimate the total cost of completing the project. Benzion Barlev of New York University proposed a model for total cost of a long-term contract based on the normal distribution (*Journal of Business Finance and Accounting,* July 1995). For one particular construction contract, Barlev assumed total cost, x, to be normally distributed with mean $850,000 and standard deviation $170,000. The revenue, R, promised to the contractor is $1,000,000.

a. The contract will be profitable if revenue exceeds total cost. What is the probability that the contract will be profitable for the contractor?

b. What is the probability that the project will result in a loss for the contractor?

c. Suppose the contractor has the opportunity to renegotiate the contract. What value of R should the contractor strive for in order to have a .99 probability of making a profit?

Applying the Concepts—Advanced

4.102 Industrial filling process. The characteristics of an industrial filling process in which an expensive liquid is injected into a container was investigated in the *Journal of Quality Technology* (July 1999). The quantity injected per container is approximately normally distributed with mean 10 units and standard deviation .2 units. Each unit of fill costs $20 per unit. If a container contains less than 10 units (i.e., is underfilled), it must be reprocessed at a cost of $10. A properly filled container sells for $230.

a. Find the probability that a container is underfilled. Not underfilled.

b. A container is initially underfilled and must be reprocessed. Upon refilling, it contains 10.60 units. How much profit will the company make on this container?

c. The operations manager adjusts the mean of the filling process upward to 10.10 units in order to make the probability of underfilling approximately zero. Under these conditions, what is the expected profit per container?

4.103 Load on frame structures. In the *Journal of the International Association for Shell and Spatial Structures* (Apr. 2004), Japanese environmental researchers studied the performance of truss and frame structures subjected to uncertain loads. The load was assumed to have a normal distribution with a mean of 20,000 pounds. Also, the probability that the load is between 10,000 and 30,000 pounds is .95. Based on this information, find the standard deviation of the load distribution.

4.104 Box plots and the standard normal distribution. What relationship exists between the standard normal distribution and the box-plot methodology (Section 2.8) for describing distributions of data using quartiles? The answer depends on the true underlying probability distribution of the data. Assume for the remainder of this exercise that the distribution is normal.

a. Calculate the values of the standard normal random variable z, call them z_L and z_U, that correspond to the hinges of the box plot—that is, the lower and upper quartiles, Q_L and Q_U—of the probability distribution.

b. Calculate the z values that correspond to the inner fences of the box plot for a normal probability distribution.

c. Calculate the z values that correspond to the outer fences of the box plot for a normal probability distribution.

d. What is the probability that an observation lies beyond the inner fences of a normal probability distribution? The outer fences?

e. Can you better understand why the inner and outer fences of a box plot are used to detect outliers in a distribution? Explain.

4.7 Descriptive Methods for Assessing Normality

In the chapters that follow, we learn how to make inferences about the population based on information in the sample. Several of these techniques are based on the assumption that the population is approximately normally distributed. Consequently, it will be important to determine whether the sample data come from a normal population before we can properly apply these techniques.

Several descriptive methods can be used to check for normality. In this section, we consider the four methods summarized in the box.

Determining Whether the Data Are from an Approximately Normal Distribution

1. Construct either a histogram or stem-and-leaf display for the data and note the shape of the graph. If the data are approximately normal, the shape of the histogram or stem-and-leaf display will be similar to the normal curve, Figure 4.13 (i.e., mound shaped and symmetric about the mean).

2. Compute the intervals $\bar{x} \pm s$, $\bar{x} \pm 2s$, and $\bar{x} \pm 3s$, and determine the percentage of measurements falling in each. If the data are approximately normal, the percentages will be approximately equal to 68%, 95%, and 100%, respectively.

3. Find the interquartile range, IQR, and standard deviation, s, for the sample, then calculate the ratio IQR/s. If the data are approximately normal, then IQR/$s \approx 1.3$.

4. Examine a *normal probability plot* for the data. If the data are approximately normal, the points will fall (approximately) on a straight line.

The first two methods come directly from the properties of a normal distribution established in Section 4.6. Method 3 is based on the fact that for normal distributions, the z values corresponding to the 25th and 75th percentiles are $-.67$ and $.67$, respectively (see Example 4.17). Because $\sigma = 1$ for a standard normal distribution,

$$\frac{\text{IQR}}{\sigma} = \frac{Q_U - Q_L}{\sigma} = \frac{.67 - (-.67)}{1} = 1.34$$

The final descriptive method for checking normality is based on a *normal probability plot*. In such a plot, the observations in a data set are ordered from smallest to largest and then plotted against the expected z-scores of observations calculated under the assumption that the data come from a normal distribution. When the data are, in fact, normally distributed, a linear (straight-line) trend will result. A nonlinear trend in the plot suggests that the data are nonnormal.

A **normal probability plot** for a data set is a scatterplot with the ranked data values on one axis and their corresponding expected z-scores from a standard normal distribution on the other axis. [*Note:* Computation of the expected standard normal z-scores are beyond the scope of this text. Therefore, we will rely on available statistical software packages to generate a normal probability plot.]

Example 4.24

Checking for Normal Data—EPA Estimated Gas Mileages

Problem The Environmental Protection Agency (EPA) performs extensive tests on all new car models to determine their mileage ratings. The results of 100 EPA tests on a certain new car model are displayed in Table 4.6. Numerical and graphical descriptive measures for the data are shown on the Minitab and SPSS printouts, Figures 4.25a–c. Determine whether the EPA mileage ratings are from an approximate normal distribution.

Table 4.6	EPA Gas Mileage Ratings for 100 Cars (miles per gallon)								
36.3	41.0	36.9	37.1	44.9	36.8	30.0	37.2	42.1	36.7
32.7	37.3	41.2	36.6	32.9	36.5	33.2	37.4	37.5	33.6
40.5	36.5	37.6	33.9	40.2	36.4	37.7	37.7	40.0	34.2
36.2	37.9	36.0	37.9	35.9	38.2	38.3	35.7	35.6	35.1
38.5	39.0	35.5	34.8	38.6	39.4	35.3	34.4	38.8	39.7
36.3	36.8	32.5	36.4	40.5	36.6	36.1	38.2	38.4	39.3
41.0	31.8	37.3	33.1	37.0	37.6	37.0	38.7	39.0	35.8
37.0	37.2	40.7	37.4	37.1	37.8	35.9	35.6	36.7	34.5
37.1	40.3	36.7	37.0	33.9	40.1	38.0	35.2	34.8	39.5
39.9	36.9	32.9	33.8	39.8	34.0	36.8	35.0	38.1	36.9

Data Set: EPAGAS

Figure 4.25a
Minitab histogram for gas mileage data

Descriptive Statistics: MPG

Variable	N	Mean	StDev	Minimum	Q1	Median	Q3	Maximum
MPG	100	36.994	2.418	30.000	35.625	37.000	38.375	44.900

Figure 4.25b
Minitab descriptive statistics for gas mileage data

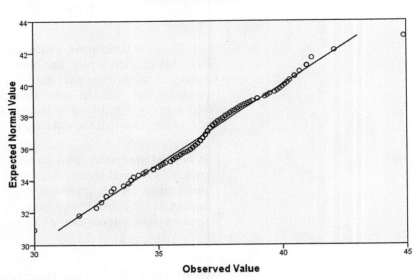

Figure 4.25c
SPSS normal probability plot for gas mileage data

Solution As a first check, we examine the Minitab histogram of the data shown in Figure 4.25a. Clearly, the mileages fall in an approximately mound-shaped, symmetric distribution centered around the mean of approximately 37 mpg. Note that a normal curve is superimposed on the figure. Therefore, using check #1 in the box, the data appear to be approximately normal.

To apply check #2, we obtain $\bar{x} = 37$ and $s = 2.4$ from the Minitab printout, Figure 4.25b. The intervals $\bar{x} \pm s$, $\bar{x} \pm 3s$, and $\bar{x} \pm 3s$ are shown in Table 4.7, as well as the percentage of mileage ratings that fall in each interval. These percentages agree almost exactly with those from a normal distribution.

Check #3 in the box requires that we find the ratio IQR/s. From Figure 4.25(b), the 25th percentile (called Q_1 by Minitab) is $Q_L = 35.625$, and the 75th percentile (labeled Q_3 by Minitab) is $Q_U = 38.375$. Then, IQR $= Q_U - Q_L = 2.75$, and the ratio is

$$\frac{\text{IQR}}{s} = \frac{2.75}{2.4} = 1.15$$

Table 4.7　**Describing the 100 EPA Mileage Ratings**

Interval	Percentage in Interval
$\bar{x} \pm s = (34.6, 39.4)$	68
$\bar{x} \pm 2s = (32.2, 41.8)$	96
$\bar{x} \pm 3s = (29.8, 44.2)$	99

Because this value is approximately equal to 1.3, we have further confirmation that the data are approximately normal.

A fourth descriptive method is to interpret a normal probability plot. An SPSS normal probability plot for the mileage data is shown in Figure 4.25c. Notice that the ordered mileage values (shown on the horizontal axis) fall reasonably close to a straight line when plotted against the expected z-scores from a normal distribution. Thus, check #4 also suggests that the EPA mileage data are likely to be approximately normally distributed.

Look Back The checks for normality given in the box are simple, yet powerful, techniques to apply, but they are only descriptive in nature. It is possible (although unlikely) that the data are nonnormal even when the checks are reasonably satisfied. Thus, we should be careful not to claim that the 100 EPA mileage ratings of Example 4.24 are, in fact, normally distributed. We can only state that it is reasonable to believe that the data are from a normal distribution.*

Now Work Exercise 4.108

As we will learn in the next chapter, several inferential methods of analysis require the data to be approximately normal. If the data are clearly nonnormal, inferences derived from the method may be invalid. Therefore, it is advisable to check the normality of the data prior to conducting the analysis.

Statistics in Action Revisited | Assessing Fit of the Normal Distribution

In Statistics in Action Revisited, Section 4.6, we used the normal distribution to find the probability that a single flechette from a super weapon that shoots 1,100 flechettes at once hits one of three targets at 500 meters. Recall that for three range tests, the weapon was always aimed at the center target (i.e., the specification mean was set at $\mu = 5$ feet), but the specification standard deviation was varied at $\sigma = 1$ foot, $\sigma = 2$ feet, and $\sigma = 4$ feet. Table SIA4.1 shows the calculated normal probabilities of hitting the three targets for the different values of σ, as well as the actual results of the three range tests. (Recall that the actual data are saved in the **MOAGUN** file.) You can see that the proportion of the 1,100

Table SIA4.1	**Summary of Normal Probability Calculations and Actual Range Test Results**			
Target	Specification	Normal Probability	Actual Number of Hits	Hit Ratio (Hits/1,100)
Left (–1 to 1)	$\sigma = 1$	.0000	0	.000
	$\sigma = 2$	.0214	30	.027
	$\sigma = 4$	.0919	73	.066
Middle (4 to 6)	$\sigma = 1$	.6826	764	.695
	$\sigma = 2$	.3820	409	.372
	$\sigma = 4$	.1974	242	.220
Right (9 to 11)	$\sigma = 1$	.0000	0	.000
	$\sigma = 2$	.0214	23	.021
	$\sigma = 4$	.0919	93	.085

Data Set: MOAGUN

*Statistical tests of normality that provide a measure of reliability for the inference are available. However, these tests tend to be very sensitive to slight departures from normality (i.e., they tend to reject the hypothesis of normality for any distribution that is not perfectly symmetrical and mound shaped). Consult the references (see Ramsey & Ramsey, 1990) if you want to learn more about these tests.

flechettes that actually hit each target—called the *hit ratio*—agrees very well with the estimated probability of a hit using the normal distribution.

Consequently, it appears that our assumption that the horizontal hit measurements are approximately normally distributed is reasonably satisfied. Further evidence of this is provided by the Minitab histograms of the horizontal hit measurements shown in Figures SIA4.3a–c. The normal curves superimposed on the histograms fit the data very well.

Figure SIA4.3a
Minitab histogram for the horizontal hit measurements when $\sigma = 1$

Figure SIA4.3b
Minitab histogram for the horizontal hit measurements when $\sigma = 2$

Figure SIA4.3c
Minitab histogram for the horizontal hit measurements when $\sigma = 4$

Exercises 4.105–4.117

Learning the Mechanics

4.105 If a population data set is normally distributed, what is the proportion of measurements you would expect to fall within the following intervals?

   a. $\mu \pm \sigma$

   b. $\mu \pm 2\sigma$

   c. $\mu \pm 3\sigma$

4.106 Consider a sample data set with the following summary statistics: $s = 95, Q_L = 72, Q_U = 195$.

   a. Calculate IQR.

   b. Calculate IQR/s.

   c. Is the value of IQR/s approximately equal to 1.3? What does this imply?

Normal probability plots for Exercise 4.107

a.   b.   c.

4.107 Normal probability plots for three data sets are shown above. Which plot indicates that the data are approximately normally distributed?

4.108 Examine the sample data saved in the **LM4_18** file.

[NW]

5.9	5.3	1.6	7.4	8.6	1.2	2.1
4.0	7.3	8.4	8.9	6.7	4.5	6.3
7.6	9.7	3.5	1.1	4.3	3.3	8.4
1.6	8.2	6.5	1.1	5.0	9.4	6.4

a. Construct a stem-and-leaf plot to assess whether the data are from an approximately normal distribution.

b. Compute s for the sample data.

c. Find the values of Q_L and Q_U and the value of s from part **b** to assess whether the data come from an approximately normal distribution.

d. Generate a normal probability plot for the data and use it to assess whether the data are approximately normal.

Applying the Concepts—Basic

4.109 Most powerful business women in America. Refer to the *Fortune* (Oct. 16, 2008) list of the 50 most powerful women in America. In Exercise 4.91 (p. 216), you assumed that the ages (in years) of these women are approximately normally distributed. An Excel/DDXL printout with summary statistics for the age variable saved in the **WPOWER50** file is reproduced below.

a. Use the relevant statistics on the printout to compute the IQR. Does the result agree with the value shown on the printout?

▷	Summary of AGE		
Count	50		
Mean	50.02		
Median	51		
Std Dev	6.444		
Variance	41.53		
Range	36		
Min	28		
Max	64		
IQR	7		
25th%	47		
75th%	54		

b. Locate the value of the standard deviation, s, on the printout.

c. Use the results, parts **a** and **b**, to demonstrate that the age distribution is approximately normal.

d. In Exercise 2.48 (p. 62) you constructed a relative frequency histogram for the age data. Use this graph to support your assumption of normality.

4.110 Ranking PhD programs in economics. Refer to the *Southern Economic Journal* (Apr. 2008) rankings of PhD programs in economics at 129 colleges and universities, Exercise 2.100 (p. 80). Recall that the number of publications published by faculty teaching in the PhD program and the quality of the publications were used to calculate an overall productivity score for each program. The mean and standard deviation of these 129 productivity scores were then used to compute a z-score for each economics program. The data (z-scores) for all 129 economic programs are saved in the **ECOPHD** file. A Minitab normal probability plot for the z-scores are shown below. Use the graph to assess whether the data are approximately normal.

Probability Plot of Z-Score
Normal - 95% CI

4.111 Software file updates. Software configuration management was used to monitor a software engineering team's performance at Motorola, Inc. (*Software Quality Professional*, Nov. 2004). One of the variables of interest was the number of updates to a file changed because of a problem report. Summary statistics for $n = 421$ files yielded the following results: $\bar{x} = 4.71$, $s = 6.09$, $Q_L = 1$, and $Q_U = 6$. Are these data approximately normally distributed? Explain.

Applying the Concepts—Intermediate

4.112 Wear-out of used display panels. Wear-out failure time of electronic components is often assumed to have a normal distribution. Can the normal distribution be applied to the wear-out of used manufactured products, such as colored display panels? A lot of 50 used display panels was purchased by an outlet store. Each panel displays 12 to 18 color characters. Prior to acquisition, the panels had been used for about one-third of their expected lifetimes. The data in the accompanying table (saved in the **PANELFAIL** file) give the failure times (in years) of the 50 used panels. Use the techniques of this section to determine whether the used panel wear-out times are approximately normally distributed.

0.01	1.21	1.71	2.30	2.96	0.19	1.22	1.75	2.30	2.98	0.51
1.24	1.77	2.41	3.19	0.57	1.48	1.79	2.44	3.25	0.70	1.54
1.88	2.57	3.31	0.73	1.59	1.90	2.61	1.19	0.75	1.61	1.93
2.62	3.50	0.75	1.61	2.01	2.72	3.50	1.11	1.62	2.16	2.76
3.50	1.16	1.62	2.18	2.84	3.50					

Source: Irony, T. Z., Lauretto, M., Pereira, C., and Stern, J. M. "A Weibull wearout test: Full Bayesian approach," paper presented at *Mathematical Sciences Colloquium,* Binghamton University, Binghamton, UK, December 2001.

4.113 NHTSA crash tests. Refer to the NHTSA crash test data for new cars. In Exercise 4.94 (p. 217), you assumed that the driver's head-injury rating is approximately normally distributed. Apply the methods of this chapter to the data saved in the **CRASH** file to support this assumption.

4.114 Sanitation inspection of cruise ships. Refer to the data on the Dec. 2008 sanitation scores for 183 cruise ships, first presented in Exercise 2.22 (p. 49). The data are saved in the **SHIPSANIT** file. Assess whether the sanitation scores are approximately normally distributed.

4.115 Ranking driving performance of professional golfers. Refer to *The Sport Journal* (Winter 2007) article on a new method for ranking the driving performance of PGA golfers, Exercise 2.50 (p. 63). Recall that the method incorporates a golfer's average driving distance (yards) and driving accuracy (percent of drives that land in the fairway) into a driving performance index. Data on these three variables for the top 40 PGA golfers are saved in the **PGADRIVER** file. Determine which of these variables—driving distance, driving accuracy, and driving performance index—are approximately normally distributed.

4.116 Department of Defense START sheets. The DoD RAC publishes START sheets for government and industry. These START sheets are designed to improve the reliability, maintainability, supportability, and quality of manufactured components and systems. In Volume 11 (2004), the DoD analyzed the following data set on tensile strength measurements taken at two different temperatures. (The data are saved in the **TENSILE** file.) In the START sheet, the DoD demonstrated that the data for the 11 tensile strength measurements were sampled from an approximately normal distribution. Do you agree?

Temperature	Strength
75	328.2
75	334.7
75	347.8
75	346.3
75	338.7
75	340.8
−67	343.6
−67	334.2
−67	348.7
−67	356.3
−67	344.1

Applying the Concepts—Advanced

4.117 Semester hours taken by CPA candidates. Refer to the *Journal of Accounting and Public Policy* (Spring 2002) study of first-time candidates for the CPA exam, Exercise 2.51 (p. 63). The variable of interest is the total semester hours of college credit for each candidate. Recall that the mean and median for the data set were 141.31 and 140 hours, respectively, and the standard deviation was 17.77 hours. Demonstrate why the probability distribution for the variable, total semester hours, is unlikely to be normally distributed.

4.8 Approximating a Binomial Distribution with a Normal Distribution

When the discrete binomial random variable (Section 4.3) can assume a large number of values, the calculation of its probabilities may become very tedious. To contend with this problem, we provide tables in Appendix B to give the probabilities for some values of n and p, but these tables are by necessity incomplete. Recall that the binomial probability table (Table II) can be used only for $n = 5, 6, 7, 8, 9, 10, 15, 20,$ or 25. To deal with this limitation, we seek approximation procedures for calculating the probabilities associated with a binomial probability distribution.

When n is large, a normal probability distribution may be used to provide a good approximation to the probability distribution of a binomial random variable. To show how this approximation works, we refer to Example 4.12, in which we used the binomial distribution to model the number x of 20 employees who favor unionization. We assumed that 60% of all the company's employees favored unionization. The mean and standard deviation of x were found to be $\mu = 12$ and $\sigma = 2.2$. The binomial distribution for $n = 20$ and $p = .6$ is shown in Figure 4.26, and the approximating normal distribution with mean $\mu = 12$ and standard deviation $\sigma = 2.2$ is superimposed.

As part of Example 4.12, we used Table II to find the probability that $x \leq 10$. This probability, which is equal to the sum of the areas contained in the rectangles (shown in Figure 4.26) that correspond to $p(0), p(1), p(2), \dots, p(10)$, was found to equal .245. The portion of the approximating normal curve that would be used to approximate the area $p(0) + p(1) + p(2) + \cdots + p(10)$ is shaded in Figure 4.26. Note that this shaded area lies to the left of 10.5 (not 10), so we may include all of the probability in the rectangle corresponding to $p(10)$. Because we are approximating a discrete distribution (the binomial) with a continuous distribution (the normal), we call the use of 10.5 (instead of 10 or 11) a **correction for continuity,** that is, we are correcting the discrete distribution so that it can be approximated by the continuous one. The use of the correction for continuity leads to the calculation of the following standard normal z-value:

$$z = \frac{x - \mu}{\sigma} = \frac{10.5 - 12}{2.2} = -.68$$

Using Table IV, we find the area between $z = 0$ and $z = .68$ to be .2517. Then the probability that x is less than or equal to 10 is approximated by the area under the normal distribution to the left of 10.5, shown shaded in Figure 4.26—that is,

$$P(x \leq 10) \approx P(z \leq -.68) = .5 - P(-.68 < z \leq 0) = .5 - .2517 = .2483$$

The approximation differs only slightly from the exact binomial probability, .245. Of course, when tables of exact binomial probabilities are available, we will use the exact value rather than a normal approximation.

Use of the normal distribution will not always provide a good approximation for binomial probabilities. The following is a useful rule of thumb to determine when n is large enough for the approximation to be effective: *The interval $\mu \pm 3\sigma$ should lie within the range of the binomial random variable* x *(i.e., 0 to* n*) in order for the normal approximation to be adequate.* The rule works well because almost all of the normal distribution falls within 3 standard deviations of the mean, so if this interval is contained within the range of x values, there is "room" for the normal approximation to work.

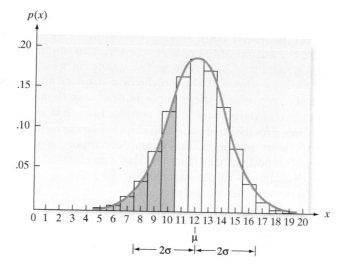

Figure 4.26

Binomial distribution for $n = 20$, $p = .6$ and normal distribution with $\mu = 12$, $\sigma = 2.2$

a. $n = 20, p = .6$: Normal approximation is good

b. $n = 10, p = .1$: Normal approximation is poor

Figure 4.27
Rule of thumb for normal approximation to binomial probabilities

As shown in Figure 4.27a for the preceding example with $n = 20$ and $p = .6$, the interval $\mu \pm 3\sigma = 12 \pm 3(2.2) = (5.4, 18.6)$ lies within the range 0 to 20. However, if we were to try to use the normal approximation with $n = 10$ and $p = .1$, the interval $\mu \pm 3\sigma$ is $1 \pm 3(.95)$, or $(-1.85, 3.85)$. As shown in Figure 4.27b, this interval is not contained within the range of x because $x = 0$ is the lower bound for a binomial random variable. Note in Figure 4.27b that the normal distribution will not "fit" in the range of x, and therefore it will not provide a good approximation to the binomial probabilities.

Example 4.25

Applying the Normal Approximation to a Binomial Probability—Lot Acceptance Sampling

Problem One problem with any product (e.g., a graphing calculator) that is mass produced is quality control. The process must somehow be monitored or audited to be sure the output of the process conforms to requirements. One method of dealing with this problem is *lot acceptance sampling*, in which items being produced are sampled at various stages of the production process and are carefully inspected. The lot of items from which the sample is drawn is then accepted or rejected, based on the number of defectives in the sample. Lots that are accepted may be sent forward for further processing or may be shipped to customers; lots that are rejected may be reworked or scrapped. For example, suppose a manufacturer of calculators chooses 200 stamped circuits from the day's production and determines x, the number of defective circuits in the sample. Suppose that up to a 6% rate of defectives is considered acceptable for the process.

a. Find the mean and standard deviation of x, assuming the defective rate is 6%.

b. Use the normal approximation to determine the probability that 20 or more defectives are observed in the sample of 200 circuits (i.e., find the approximate probability that $x \geq 20$).

Solution

a. The random variable x is binomial with $n = 200$ and the fraction defective $p = .06$. Thus,

$$\mu = np = 200(.06) = 12$$
$$\sigma = \sqrt{npq} = \sqrt{200(.06)(.94)} = \sqrt{11.28} = 3.36$$

We first note that

$$\mu \pm 3\sigma = 12 \pm 3(3.36) = 12 \pm 10.08 = (1.92, 22.08)$$

lies completely within the range from 0 to 200. Therefore, a normal probability distribution should provide an adequate approximation to this binomial distribution.

Figure 4.28
Normal approximation to the binomial distribution with $n = 200$, $p = .06$

b. Using the rule of complements, $P(x \geq 20) = 1 - P(x \leq 19)$. To find the approximating area corresponding to $x \leq 19$, refer to Figure 4.28. Note that we want to include all the binomial probability histogram from 0 to 19, inclusive. Because the event is of the form $x \leq a$, the proper correction for continuity is $a + .5 = 19 + .5 = 19.5$. Thus, the z-value of interest is

$$z = \frac{(a + .5) - \mu}{\sigma} = \frac{19.5 - 12}{3.36} = \frac{7.5}{3.36} = 2.23$$

Figure 4.29
Standard normal distribution

Referring to Table IV in Appendix B, we find that the area to the right of the mean 0 corresponding to $z = 2.23$ (see Figure 4.29) is .4871. So the area $A = P(z \leq 2.23)$ is

$$A = .5 + .4871 = .9871$$

Thus, the normal approximation to the binomial probability we seek is

$$P(x \geq 20) = 1 - P(x \leq 19) \approx 1 - .9871 = .0129$$

In other words, the probability is extremely small that 20 or more defectives will be observed in a sample of 200 circuits—*if in fact the true fraction of defectives is .06.*

Look Back If the manufacturer observes $x \geq 20$, the likely reason is that the process is producing more than the acceptable 6% defectives. The lot acceptance sampling procedure is another example of using the rare-event approach to make inferences.

Now Work Exercise 4.118

The steps for approximating a binomial probability by a normal probability are given in the next box.

Using a Normal Distribution to Approximate Binomial Probabilities

1. After you have determined n and p for the binomial distribution, calculate the interval

$$\mu \pm 3\sigma = np \pm 3\sqrt{npq}$$

If the interval lies in the range 0 to n, the normal distribution will provide a reasonable approximation to the probabilities of most binomial events.

2. Express the binomial probability to be approximated in the form $P(x \leq a)$ or $P(x \leq b) - P(x \leq a)$. For example,

$$P(x < 3) = P(x \leq 2)$$
$$P(x \geq 5) = 1 - P(x \leq 4)$$
$$P(7 \leq x \leq 10) = P(x \leq 10) - P(x \leq 6)$$

3. For each value of interest a, the correction for continuity is $(a + .5)$, and the corresponding standard normal z-value is

$$z = \frac{(a + .5) - \mu}{\sigma} \quad \text{(See Figure 4.30)}$$

4. Sketch the approximating normal distribution and shade the area corresponding to the probability of the event of interest, as in Figure 4.30. Verify that the rectangles you have included in the shaded area correspond to the event probability you wish to approximate. Using Table IV and the z-value(s) you calculated in step **3**, find the shaded area. This is the approximate probability of the binomial event.

Figure 4.30
Approximating binomial
probabilities by normal
probabilities

Exercises 4.118–4.132

Learning the Mechanics

4.118 Suppose x is a binomial random variable with $p = .4$ and
[NW] $n = 25$.
   a. Would it be appropriate to approximate the probability distribution of x with a normal distribution? Explain.
   b. Assuming that a normal distribution provides an adequate approximation to the distribution of x, what are the mean and variance of the approximating normal distribution?
   c. Use Table II in Appendix B to find the exact value of $P(x \geq 9)$.
   d. Use the normal approximation to find $P(x \geq 9)$.

4.119 Assume that x is a binomial random variable with n and p as specified in parts **a–f**. For which cases would it be appropriate to use a normal distribution to approximate the binomial distribution?
   a. $n = 100, p = .01$ **b.** $n = 20, p = .6$
   c. $n = 10, p = .4$ **d.** $n = 1,000, p = .05$
   e. $n = 100, p = .8$ **f.** $n = 35, p = .7$

4.120 Assume that x is a binomial random variable with $n = 1,000$ and $p = .50$. Use a normal approximation to find each of the following probabilities:
   a. $P(x > 500)$
   b. $P(490 \leq x < 500)$
   c. $P(x > 550)$

4.121 Assume that x is a binomial random variable with $n = 100$ and $p = .40$. Use a normal approximation to find the following:
   a. $P(x \leq 35)$
   b. $P(40 \leq x \leq 50)$
   c. $P(x \geq 38)$

Applying the Concepts—Basic

4.122 **Using wireless Internet at home.** In Exercise 4.43 (p. 196), you learned that 20% of Internet users go online at home using a wireless network (*Pew Internet & American Life Project,* Feb. 2007). In a random sample of 100 Internet users, let x be the number who go online at home using a wireless network.

a. Find the mean of x. (This value should agree with your answer to Exercise 4.43c.)

b. Find the standard deviation of x.

c. Find the z-score for the value $x = 27.5$.

d. Find the approximate probability that the number of Internet users who go online at home using a wireless network in a sample of 100 is less than or equal to 25.

4.123 LASIK surgery complications. According to recent studies, 1% of all patients who undergo laser surgery (i.e., LASIK) to correct their vision have serious postlaser vision problems (*All About Vision,* 2006). In a sample of 100,000 patients, what is the approximate probability that fewer than 950 will experience serious postlaser vision problems?

4.124 Women-owned businesses. In Exercise 4.45 (p. 196), you learned that 27% of all small businesses owned by non-Hispanic whites nationwide are women-owned firms (*Journal of Business Venturing,* Vol. 17, 2002). In a random sample of 350 small businesses owned by non-Hispanic whites, let x be the number that are owned by a woman.

a. Find the mean of x.

b. Find the standard deviation of x.

c. Find the z-score for the value $x = 99.5$.

d. Find the approximate probability that the number of small businesses in the sample of 350 that are owned by a woman is 100 or more.

4.125 Using the Internet for banking. Security First Network Bank (SFNB), founded in 1995 in Atlanta, Georgia, is considered to be the first ever Internet bank. Today, almost all financial institutions offer services via the Internet. According to *Consumer Interests Annual* (2007), the proportion of U.S. households that do some or all of their banking on the Internet is .28. Consider a random sample of 1,000 U.S. households.

a. How many of these households would you expect to use Internet banking?

b. Find the approximate probability that more than 750 of these households use Internet banking.

Applying the Concepts—Intermediate

4.126 Defects in semiconductor wafers. The computer chips in today's notebook and laptop computers are produced from semiconductor wafers. Certain semiconductor wafers are exposed to an environment that generates up to 100 possible defects per wafer. The number of defects per wafer, x, was found to follow a binomial distribution if the manufacturing process is stable and generates defects that are randomly distributed on the wafers (*IEEE Transactions on Semiconductor Manufacturing,* May 1995). Let p represent the probability that a defect occurs at any one of the 100 points of the wafer. For each of the following cases, determine whether the normal approximation can be used to characterize x.

a. $p = .01$

b. $p = .50$

c. $p = .90$

4.127 Analysis of bottled water. Refer to the *Scientific American* (July 2003) report on whether bottled water is really purified water, Exercise 4.44 (p. 196). Recall that the Natural Resources Defense Council found that 25% of bottled water brands fill their bottles with just tap water. In a random sample of 65 bottled water brands, is it likely that 20 or more brands will contain tap water? Explain.

4.128 Credit card market shares. The following table reports the U.S. credit card industry's market share data for 2007. A random sample of 100 credit card users is to be questioned regarding their satisfaction with their credit card company. For simplification, assume that each credit card user carries just one credit card and that the market share percentages are the percentages of all credit card customers that carry each brand.

Credit Card	Market Share %
Visa	46
MasterCard	36
American Express	12
Discover	6

Source: Nilson Report, May 2008.

a. Propose a procedure for randomly selecting the 100 credit card users.

b. For random samples of 100 credit card users, what is the expected number of customers who carry Visa? Discover?

c. What is the probability that half or more of the sample of credit card users carry Visa? American Express?

d. Justify the use of the normal approximation to the binomial in answering the question in part **c.**

4.129 Testing a manufacturer's claim. A manufacturer of CD-ROMs claims that 99.4% of its CDs are defect-free. A large software company that buys and uses a large number of the CDs wants to verify this claim, so it selects 1,600 CDs to be tested. The tests reveal 12 CDs to be defective. Assuming that the manufacturer's claim is correct, what is the probability of finding 12 or more defective CDs in a sample of 1,600? Does your answer cast doubt on the manufacturer's claim? Explain.

4.130 Financial aid for college students. The *Chronicle of Higher Education Almanac* reports that the percentage of undergraduates in the United States receiving federal financial aid is 45% at public four-year institutions and 52% at private four-year institutions. The U.S. Department of Education is interested in questioning a random sample of 100 U.S. undergraduate students to assess their satisfaction with federal financial aid procedures and policies.

a. Explain the difficulties of obtaining the desired random sample.

b. Assume the appropriate percentage above applies to your institution. If a random sample of 100 students from your institution were contacted, what is the approximate probability that 50 or more receive financial aid? Less than 25?

c. What assumptions must be made in order to answer part **b** using the normal approximation to the binomial?

Applying the Concepts—Advanced

4.131 Waiting time at an emergency room. According to *Health Affairs* (Oct. 28, 2004), the median time a patient waits to see a doctor in a typical U.S. emergency room is 30 minutes. Consider a U.S. emergency room on a day when 150 patients visit. What is the probability that

a. more than half will wait more than 30 minutes?

b. more than 85 will wait more than 30 minutes?

c. more than 60, but fewer than 90, will wait more than 30 minutes?

4.132 Luggage inspection at Newark airport. *New Jersey Business* reports that Newark Liberty International Airport's new terminal handles an average of 3,000 international passengers an hour but is capable of handling twice that number. Also, after scanning all luggage, 20% of arriving international passengers are detained for intrusive luggage inspection. The inspection facility can handle 600 passengers an hour without unreasonable delays for the travelers.

a. When international passengers arrive at the rate of 1,500 per hour, what is the expected number of passengers who will be detained for luggage inspection?

b. In the future, it is expected that as many as 4,000 international passengers will arrive per hour. When that occurs, what is the expected number of passengers who will be detained for luggage inspection?

c. Refer to part **b.** Find the approximate probability that more than 600 international passengers will be detained for luggage inspection. (This is also the probability that travelers will experience unreasonable luggage inspection delays.)

4.9 Other Continuous Distributions: Uniform and Exponential

Uniform Random Variable

Continuous random variables that appear to have equally likely outcomes over their range of possible values possess a **uniform probability distribution.** For example, if a short exists in a 5-meter stretch of electrical wire, it may have an equal probability of being in any particular 1-centimeter segment along the line. Or if a safety inspector plans to choose a time at random during the four afternoon work hours to pay a surprise visit to a certain area of a plant, then each 1-minute time interval in this 4-work-hour period will have an equally likely chance of being selected for the visit.

Suppose the random variable x can assume values only in an interval $c \leq x \leq d$. Then the **uniform frequency function** has a rectangular shape, as shown in Figure 4.31. Note that the possible values of x consist of all points in the interval between point c and point d. The height of $f(x)$ is constant in that interval and equals $1/(d - c)$. Therefore, the total area under $f(x)$ is given by

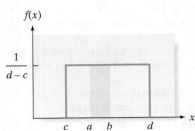

Figure 4.31

The uniform probability distribution

$$\text{Total area of rectangle} = (\text{Base})(\text{Height}) = (d - c)\left(\frac{1}{d - c}\right) = 1$$

The uniform probability distribution provides a model for continuous random variables that are *evenly distributed* over a certain interval—that is, a uniform random variable is one that is just as likely to assume a value in one interval as it is to assume a value in any other interval of equal size. There is no clustering of values around any value; instead, there is an even spread over the entire region of possible values.

The uniform distribution is sometimes referred to as the **randomness distribution** because one way of generating a uniform random variable is to perform an experiment in which a point is *randomly selected* on the horizontal axis between the points c and d. If we were to repeat this experiment infinitely often, we would create a uniform probability distribution like that shown in Figure 4.31. The random selection of points in an interval can also be used to generate random numbers such as those in Table I in Appendix B. Recall that random numbers are selected in such a way that every number would have an equal probability of selection. Therefore, random numbers are realizations of a uniform random variable. (Random numbers were used to draw random samples in Section 3.7.) The formulas for the uniform probability distribution, its mean, and standard deviation are shown in the next box.

Suppose the interval $a < x < b$ lies within the domain of x; that is, it falls within the larger interval $c \leq x \leq d$. Then the probability that x assumes a value within the

> **Probability Distribution for a Uniform Random Variable x**
>
> Probability density function: $f(x) = \dfrac{1}{d - c} \quad c \leq x \leq d$
>
> Mean: $\mu = \dfrac{c + d}{2}$ Standard deviation: $\sigma = \dfrac{d - c}{\sqrt{12}}$
>
> $P(a < x < b) = (b - a)/(d - c), c \leq a < b \leq d$

interval $a < x < b$ is equal to the area of the rectangle over the interval, namely, $(b - a)/(d - c)$.* (See the shaded area in Figure 4.31.)

Example 4.26

Applying the Uniform Distribution to Steel Manufacturing

Problem Suppose the research department of a steel manufacturer believes that one of the company's rolling machines is producing sheets of steel of varying thickness. The thickness is a uniform random variable with values between 150 and 200 millimeters. Any sheets less than 160 millimeters must be scrapped because they are unacceptable to buyers.

a. Calculate and interpret the mean and standard deviation of x, the thickness of the sheets produced by this machine.

b. Graph the probability distribution of x, and show the mean on the horizontal axis. Also show 1- and 2-standard-deviation intervals around the mean.

c. Calculate the fraction of steel sheets produced by this machine that have to be scrapped.

Solution

a. To calculate the mean and standard deviation for x, we substitute 150 and 200 millimeters for c and d, respectively, in the formulas for uniform random variables. Thus,

$$\mu = \frac{c + d}{2} = \frac{150 + 200}{2} = 175 \text{ millimeters}$$

and

$$\sigma = \frac{d - c}{\sqrt{12}} = \frac{200 - 150}{\sqrt{12}} = \frac{50}{3.464} = 14.43 \text{ millimeters}$$

Our interpretations follow:

The average thickness of all manufactured steel sheets is $\mu = 175$ millimeters. From Chebyshev's Rule (Table 2.6, p. 71), we know that at least 75% of the thickness values, x, in the distribution will fall in the interval

$$\mu \pm 2\sigma = 175 \pm 2(14.43)$$
$$= 175 \pm 28.86$$

or between 146.14 and 203.86 millimeters. (This demonstrates, once again, the conservativeness of Chebyshev's Rule because we know that all values of x fall between 150 and 200 millimeters.)

b. The uniform probability distribution is

$$f(x) = \frac{1}{d - c} = \frac{1}{200 - 150} = \frac{1}{50} \ (150 \leq x \leq 200)$$

*The student with knowledge of calculus should note that

$$P(a < x < b) \int_a^b f(x)d(x) = \int_a^b 1/(d - c)dx = (b - a)/(d - c)$$

Figure 4.32
Distribution for x in
Example 4.26

The graph of this function is shown in Figure 4.32. The mean and 1- and 2-standard-deviation intervals around the mean are shown on the horizontal axis.

c. To find the fraction of steel sheets produced by the machine that have to be scrapped, we must find the probability that x, the thickness, is less than 160 millimeters. As indicated in Figure 4.33, we need to calculate the area under the frequency function $f(x)$ between the points $x = 150$ and $x = 160$. Therefore, in this case, $a = 150$ and $b = 160$. Applying the formula in the box, we have

$$P(x < 160) = P(150 < x < 160)$$

$$= \frac{b - a}{d - c} = \frac{160 - 150}{200 - 150} = \frac{10}{50} = \frac{1}{5}$$

That is, 20% of all the sheets made by this machine must be scrapped.

Figure 4.33
Probability that sheet thickness,
x, is between 150 and
160 millimeters

Look Back The calculated probability in part **c** is the area of a rectangle with base $160 - 150 = 10$ and height $1/50$. Alternatively, we can find the fraction that has to be scrapped as

$$P(x < 160) = (\text{Base})(\text{Height}) = (10)\left(\frac{1}{50}\right) = \frac{1}{5}$$

Now Work Exercise 4.142

Exponential Random Variable

The length of time between emergency arrivals at a hospital, the length of time between breakdowns of manufacturing equipment, and the length of time between catastrophic events (e.g., a stockmarket crash), are all continuous random phenomena that we might want to describe probabilistically. The length of time or the distance between occurrences of random events like these can often be described by the **exponential probability distribution.** For this reason, the exponential distribution is sometimes called the **waiting-time distribution.** The formula for the exponential probability distribution is shown in the following box, along with its mean and standard deviation.

Probability Distribution for an Exponential Random Variable x

Probability density function: $f(x) = \frac{1}{\theta} e^{-x/\theta} (x > 0)$

Mean: $\mu = \theta$

Standard deviation: $\sigma = \theta$

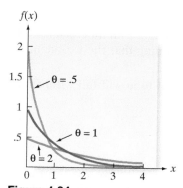

Figure 4.34
Exponential distributions

Unlike the normal distribution, which has a shape and location determined by the values of the two quantities μ and σ, the shape of the exponential distribution is governed by a single quantity: θ. Further, it is a probability distribution with the property that its mean equals its standard deviation. Exponential distributions corresponding to $\theta = .5, 1$, and 2 are shown in Figure 4.34.

To calculate probabilities of **exponential random variables,** we need to be able to find areas under the exponential probability distribution. Suppose we want to find the area A to the right of some number a, as shown in Figure 4.35. This area can be calculated by means of the formula shown in the box that follows. Use Table V in Appendix B or a calculator with an exponential function to find the value of $e^{-a/\theta}$ after substituting the appropriate numerical values for θ and a.

Finding the Area A to the Right of a Number a for an Exponential Distribution*

$$A = P(x \geq a) = e^{-a/\theta}$$

Figure 4.35
The area A to the right of a number a for an exponential distribution

---

Example 4.27

Finding an Exponential Probability—Hospital Emergency Arrivals

Figure 4.36
Area to the right of $a = 5$ for Example 4.27

Problem Suppose the length of time (in hours) between emergency arrivals at a certain hospital is modeled as an exponential distribution with $\theta = 2$. What is the probability that more than 5 hours pass without an emergency arrival?

Solution The probability we want is the area A to the right of $a = 5$ in Figure 4.36. To find this probability, we use the area formula:

$$A = e^{-a/\theta} = e^{-(5/2)} = e^{-2.5}$$

Referring to Table V, we find that

$$A = e^{-2.5} = .082085$$

Our exponential model indicates that the probability that more than 5 hours pass between emergency arrivals is about .08 for this hospital.

Look Back The value $e^{-2.5}$ can also be found with a standard calculator. Or you can find the desired probability with a statistical software package.

Now Work Exercise 4.137

Example 4.28

The Mean and Variance of an Exponential Random Variable—Length of Life of a Microwave Oven

Problem A manufacturer of microwave ovens is trying to determine the length of warranty period it should attach to its magnetron tube, the most critical component in the oven. Preliminary testing has shown that the length of life (in years), x, of a magnetron tube has an exponential probability distribution with $\theta = 6.25$.

---

*For students with a knowledge of calculus, the shaded area in Figure 4.35 corresponds to the integral

$$\int_a^b \frac{1}{\theta} e^{-x/\theta} dx = -e^{-x/\theta} \bigg|_a^\infty = e^{-a/\theta}.$$

a. Find the mean and standard deviation of x.

b. Suppose a warranty period of five years is attached to the magnetron tube. What fraction of tubes must the manufacturer plan to replace, assuming that the exponential model with $\theta = 6.25$ is correct?

c. Find the probability that the length of life of a magnetron tube will fall within the interval $\mu - 2\sigma$ to $\mu + 2\sigma$.

Solution

a. Because $\theta = \mu = \sigma$, both μ and σ equal 6.25.

b. To find the fraction of tubes that will have to be replaced before the five-year warranty period expires, we need to find the area between 0 and 5 under the distribution. This area, A, is shown in Figure 4.37. To find the required probability, we recall the formula

$$P(x > a) = e^{-a/\theta}$$

Using this formula, we find that

$$P(x > 5) = e^{-a/\theta} = e^{-5/6.25} = e^{-.80} = .449329$$

(See Table V.) To find the area A, we use the complementary relationship:

$$P(x \le 5) = 1 - P(x > 5) = 1 - .449329 = .550671$$

So approximately 55% of the magnetron tubes will have to be replaced during the five-year warranty period.

c. We would expect the probability that the life of a magnetron tube, x, falls within the interval $\mu - 2\sigma$ to $\mu + 2\sigma$ to be quite large. A graph of the exponential distribution showing the interval from $\mu - 2\sigma$ to $\mu + 2\sigma$ is given in Figure 4.38. Because the point $\mu - 2\sigma$ lies below $x = 0$, we need to find only the area between $x = 0$ and $x = \mu + 2\sigma = 6.25 + 2(6.25) = 18.75$.

This area, P, which is shaded in Figure 4.38, is

$$P = 1 - P(x > 18.75) = 1 - e^{-18.75/\theta} = 1 - e^{-18.75/6.25} = 1 - e^{-3}$$

Using Table V or a calculator, we find that $e^{-3} = .049787$. Therefore, the probability that the life x of a magnetron tube will fall within the interval $\mu - 2\sigma$ to $\mu + 2\sigma$ is

$$P = 1 - e^{-3} = 1 - .049787 = .950213$$

Figure 4.37
Area to the left of $a = 5$ for
Example 4.28

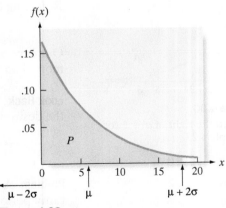

Figure 4.38
Area in the interval $\mu \pm 2\sigma$ for Example 4.28

Look Back You can see that this probability agrees well with the interpretation of a standard deviation given by the Empirical Rule (Table 2.7, p. 71), even though the probability distribution that we were given is not mound shaped. (It is strongly skewed to the right.)

Exercises 4.133–4.155

Learning the Mechanics

4.133 Suppose x is a random variable best described by a uniform probability distribution with $c = 20$ and $d = 45$.
   a. Find $f(x)$.
   b. Find the mean and standard deviation of x.
   c. Graph $f(x)$ and locate μ and the interval $\mu \pm 2\sigma$ on the graph. Note that the probability that x assumes a value within the interval $\mu \pm 2\sigma$ is equal to 1.

4.134 Refer to Exercise 4.133. Find the following probabilities:
   a. $P(20 \le x \le 30)$ **b.** $P(20 < x \le 30)$
   c. $P(x \ge 30)$ **d.** $P(x \ge 45)$
   e. $P(x \le 40)$ **f.** $P(x < 40)$
   g. $P(15 \le x \le 35)$ **h.** $P(21.5 \le x \le 31.5)$

4.135 Suppose x is a random variable best described by a uniform probability distribution with $c = 3$ and $d = 7$.
   a. Find $f(x)$.
   b. Find the mean and standard deviation of x.
   c. Find $P(\mu - \sigma \le x \le \mu + \sigma)$.

4.136 Use Table V in Appendix B to determine the value of $e^{-a/\theta}$ for each of the following cases:
   a. $\theta = 1, a = 1$ **b.** $\theta = 1, a = 2.5$
   c. $\theta = .4, a = 3$ **d.** $\theta = .2, a = .3$

4.137 Suppose x has an exponential distribution with $\theta = 1$. Find
[NW] the following probabilities:
   a. $P(x > 1)$ **b.** $P(x \le 3)$
   c. $P(x > 1.5)$ **d.** $P(x \le 5)$

4.138 Suppose x has an exponential distribution with $\theta = 2.5$. Find the following probabilities:
   a. $P(x \le 4)$ **b.** $P(x > 5)$
   c. $P(x \le 2)$ **d.** $P(x > 3)$

4.139 The random variable x is best described by a uniform probability distribution with $c = 100$ and $d = 200$. Find the probability that x assumes a value
   a. More than 2 standard deviations from μ.
   b. Less than 3 standard deviations from μ.
   c. Within 2 standard deviations of μ.

4.140 The random variable x can be adequately approximated by an exponential probability distribution with $\theta = 2$. Find the probability that x assumes a value
   a. More than 3 standard deviations from μ.
   b. Less than 2 standard deviations from μ.
   c. Within half a standard deviation of μ.

Applet Exercise 4.7

Open the applet *Sample from a Population*. On the pull-down menu to the right of the top graph, select *Uniform*. The box to the left of the top graph displays the population mean, median, and standard deviation.
   a. Run the applet for each available value of n on the pull-down menu for the sample size. Go from the smallest to the largest value of n. For each value of n, observe the shape of the graph of the sample data and record the mean, median, and standard deviation of the sample.
   b. Describe what happens to the shape of the graph and the mean, median, and standard deviation of the sample as the sample size increases.

Applet Exercise 4.8

Suppose we set the *Random Numbers* applet to generate one number between 1 and 100, inclusive. We let the value of the random variable x be the number generated when the *Sample* button is clicked. Explain why the distribution of x is approximately uniform even though x is a discrete rather than continuous random variable.

Applying the Concepts—Basic

4.141 Maintaining pipe wall temperature. Maintaining a constant pipe wall temperature in some hot-process applications is critical. A new technique that utilizes bolt-on trace elements to maintain temperature was presented in the *Journal of Heat Transfer* (Nov. 2000). Without bolt-on trace elements, the pipe wall temperature of a switch condenser used to produce plastic has a uniform distribution ranging from 260° to 290°F. When several bolt-on trace elements are attached to the piping, the wall temperature is uniform from 278° to 285°F.
   a. Ideally, the pipe wall temperature should range between 280° and 284°F. What is the probability that the temperature will fall in this ideal range when no bolt-on trace elements are used? When bolt-on trace elements are attached to the pipe?
   b. When the temperature is 268°F or lower, the hot liquid plastic hardens (or plates), causing a buildup in the piping. What is the probability of plastic plating when no bolt-on trace elements are used? When bolt-on trace elements are attached to the pipe?

4.142 New method for detecting anthrax. Researchers at the University of South Florida Center for Biological Defense have developed a safe method for rapidly detecting anthrax spores in powders and on surfaces (*USF Magazine*, Summer 2002). The method has been found to work well even when there are very few anthrax spores in a powder specimen. Consider a powder specimen that has exactly 10 anthrax spores. Suppose that the number of anthrax spores in the sample detected by the new method follows an approximate uniform distribution between 0 and 10.
   a. Find the probability that 8 or fewer anthrax spores are detected in the powder specimen.
   b. Find the probability that between 2 and 5 anthrax spores are detected in the powder specimen.

4.143 Lead in metal shredder residue. On the basis of data collected from metal shredders across the nation, the amount x of extractable lead in metal shredder residue has an approximate exponential distribution with mean $\theta = 2.5$ milligrams per liter (Florida Shredder's Association).
   a. Find the probability that x is greater than 2 milligrams per liter.
   b. Find the probability that x is less than 5 milligrams per liter.

4.144 Critical-part failures in NASCAR vehicles. In NASCAR races such as the Daytona 500, 43 drivers start the race; however, about 10% of the cars do not finish due to the failure of critical parts. University of Portland professors conducted a study of critical-part failures from 36 NASCAR races (*The Sport Journal*, Winter 2007). The researchers discovered that the time (in hours) until the first critical-part failure is exponentially distributed with a mean of .10 hour.

a. Find the probability that the time until the first critical-part failure is 1 hour or more.

b. Find the probability that the time until the first critical-part failure is less than 30 minutes.

4.145 Random numbers. The data set listed in the table was created using the Minitab random number generator and is saved in the **RANUNI** file. Construct a relative frequency histogram for the data. Except for the expected variation in relative frequencies among the class intervals, does your histogram suggest that the data are observations on a uniform random variable with $c = 0$ and $d = 100$? Explain.

38.8759	98.0716	64.5788	60.8422	.8413
88.3734	31.8792	32.9847	.7434	93.3017
12.4337	11.7828	87.4506	94.1727	23.0892
47.0121	43.3629	50.7119	88.2612	69.2875
62.6626	55.6267	78.3936	28.6777	71.6829
44.0466	57.8870	71.8318	28.9622	23.0278
35.6438	38.6584	46.7404	11.2159	96.1009
95.3660	21.5478	87.7819	12.0605	75.1015

Applying the Concepts—Intermediate

4.146 Marine losses for an oil company. The frequency distribution shown in the next table depicts the property and marine losses incurred by a large oil company over the last two years. This distribution can be used by the company to predict future losses and to help determine an appropriate level of insurance coverage. In analyzing the losses within an interval of the distribution, for simplification, analysts may treat the interval as a uniform probability distribution (*Research Review,* Summer 1998). In the insurance business, intervals like these are often called *layers*.

Layer	Property and Marine Losses (millions of $)	Frequency
1	0.00–0.01	668
2	0.01–0.05	38
3	0.05–0.10	7
4	0.10–0.25	4
5	0.25–0.50	2
6	0.50–1.00	1
7	1.00–2.50	0

Source: Cozzolino, J. M., and Mikolaj, P. J. "Applications of the piecewise constant pareto distribution," *Research Review,* Summer 1998.

a. Use a uniform distribution to model the loss amount in layer 2. Graph the distribution. Calculate and interpret its mean and variance.

b. Repeat part **a** for layer 6.

c. If a loss occurs in layer 2, what is the probability that it exceeds $10,000? That it is under $25,000?

d. If a layer-6 loss occurs, what is the probability that it is between $750,000 and $1,000,000? That it exceeds $900,000? That it is exactly $900,000?

4.147 Soft-drink dispenser. The manager of a local soft-drink bottling company believes that when a new beverage-dispensing machine is set to dispense 7 ounces, it in fact dispenses an amount x at random anywhere between 6.5 and 7.5 ounces inclusive. Suppose x has a uniform probability distribution.

a. Is the amount dispensed by the beverage machine a discrete or a continuous random variable? Explain.

b. Graph the frequency function for x, the amount of beverage the manager believes is dispensed by the new machine when it is set to dispense 7 ounces.

c. Find the mean and standard deviation for the distribution graphed in part **b** and locate the mean and the interval $\mu \pm 2\sigma$ on the graph.

d. Find $P(x \geq 7)$.

e. Find $P(x < 6)$.

f. Find $P(6.5 \leq x \leq 7.25)$.

g. What is the probability that each of the next six bottles filled by the new machine will contain more than 7.25 ounces of beverage? Assume that the amount of beverage dispensed in one bottle is independent of the amount dispensed in another bottle.

4.148 NHL overtime games. In the National Hockey League (NHL), games that are tied at the end of three periods are sent into "sudden-death" overtime. In overtime, the team to score the first goal wins. An analysis of NHL overtime games showed that the length of time elapsed before the winning goal is scored has an exponential distribution with mean 9.15 minutes (*Chance,* Winter 1995).

a. For a randomly selected overtime NHL game, find the probability that the winning goal is scored in 3 minutes or less.

b. In the NHL, each period (including overtime) lasts 20 minutes. If neither team scores a goal in overtime, the game is considered a tie. What is the probability of an NHL game ending in a tie?

4.149 Ship-to-shore transfer times. Lack of port facilities or shallow water may require cargo on a large ship to be transferred to a pier in smaller craft. The smaller craft may have to cycle back and forth from ship to shore many times. Researchers G. Horne (Center for Naval Analysis) and T. Irony (George Washington University) developed models of this transfer process that provide estimates of ship-to-shore transfer times (*Naval Research Logistics,* Vol. 41, 1994). They used an exponential distribution to model the time between arrivals of the smaller craft at the pier.

a. Assume that the mean time between arrivals at the pier is 17 minutes. Give the value of θ for this exponential distribution. Graph the distribution.

b. Suppose there is only one unloading zone at the pier available for the small craft to use. If the first craft docks at 10:00 A.M. and doesn't finish unloading until 10:15 A.M., what is the probability that the second craft will arrive at the unloading zone and have to wait before docking?

4.150 Cycle availability of a system. In the jargon of system maintenance, *cycle availability* is defined as the probability that the system is functioning at any point in time. The DoD developed a series of performance measures for assessing system cycle availability (START, Vol. 11, 2004). Under certain assumptions about the failure time and maintenance time of a system, cycle availability is shown to be uniformly distributed between 0 and 1. Find the following parameters for cycle availability: mean, standard deviation, 10th percentile, lower quartile, and upper quartile. Interpret the results.

4.151 Product failure behavior. An article in *Hotwire* (Dec. 2002) discussed the length of time till failure of a product produced at Hewlett-Packard. At the end of the product's lifetime, the time till failure is modeled using an exponential distribution with mean 500 thousand hours. In reliability jargon this is known as the "wear-out" distribution for the product. During its normal (useful) life, assume the product's time till failure is uniformly distributed over the range 100 thousand to 1 million hours.

a. At the end of the product's lifetime, find the probability that the product fails before 700 thousand hours.

b. During its normal (useful) life, find the probability that the product fails before 700 thousand hours.

c. Show that the probability of the product failing before 830 thousand hours is approximately the same for both the normal (useful) life distribution and the wear-out distribution.

4.152 Reliability of CD-ROMs. In *Reliability Ques* (March 2004), the exponential distribution was used to model the lengths of life of CD-ROM drives in a two-drive system. The two CD-ROM drives operate independently, and at least one drive must be operating for the system to operate successfully. Both drives have a mean length of life of 25,000 hours.

a. The reliability $R(t)$ of a single CD-ROM drive is the probability that the life of the drive exceeds t hours. Give a formula for $R(t)$.

b. Use the result from part **a** to find the probability that the life of the single CD-ROM drive exceeds 8,760 hours (the number of hours of operation in a year).

c. The reliability $S(t)$ of the two CD-ROM drive system is the probability that the life of at least one drive exceeds t hours. Give a formula for $S(t)$. [*Hint:* Use the rule of complements and the fact that the two drives operate independently.]

d. Use the result from part **c** to find the probability that the two-drive CD-ROM system has a life whose length exceeds 8,760 hours.

e. Compare the probabilities you found in parts **b** and **d**.

Applying the Concepts—Advanced

4.153 Gouges on a spindle. A tool-and-die machine shop produces extremely high-tolerance spindles. The spindles are 18-inch slender rods used in a variety of military equipment. A piece of equipment used in the manufacture of the spindles malfunctions on occasion and places a single gouge somewhere on the spindle. However, if the spindle can be cut so that it has 14 consecutive inches without a gouge, then the spindle can be salvaged for other purposes. Assuming that the location of the gouge along the spindle is random, what is the probability that a defective spindle can be salvaged?

4.154 Reliability of a robotic device. The *reliability* of a piece of equipment is frequently defined to be the probability, p, that the equipment performs its intended function successfully for a given period of time under specific conditions (Render and Heizer, *Principles of Operations Management*, 1995). Because p varies from one point in time to another, some reliability analysts treat p as if it were a random variable. Suppose an analyst characterizes the uncertainty about the reliability of a particular robotic device used in an automobile assembly line using the following distribution:

$$f(p) = \begin{cases} 1 & 0 \le p \le 1 \\ 0 & \text{otherwise} \end{cases}$$

a. Graph the analyst's probability distribution for p.

b. Find the mean and variance of p.

c. According to the analyst's probability distribution for p, what is the probability that p is greater than .95? Less than .95?

d. Suppose the analyst receives the additional information that p is definitely between .90 and .95, but that there is complete uncertainty about where it lies between these values. Describe the probability distribution the analyst should now use to describe p.

4.155 Length of life of a halogen bulb. For a certain type of halogen light bulb, an old bulb that has been in use for a while tends to have a longer life than a new bulb. Let x represent the life (in hours) of a new halogen light bulb and assume that x has an exponential distribution with mean $\theta = 250$ hours. According to *Microelectronics and Reliability* (Jan. 1986), the "life" distribution of x is considered *new better than used* (NBU) if

$$P(x > a + b) \le P(x > a)P(x > b)$$

Alternatively, a "life" distribution is considered *new worse than used* (NWU) if

$$P(x > a + b) \ge P(x > a)P(x > b)$$

a. Show that when $a = 300$ and $b = 200$, the exponential distribution is both NBU and NWU.

b. Choose any two positive numbers a and b and repeat part **a**.

c. Show that, in general, for any positive a and b, the exponential distribution with mean θ is both NBU and NWU. Such a "life" distribution is said to be *new same as used*, or *memoryless*. Explain why.

PART III: RANDOM VARIABLES BASED ON SAMPLING DISTRIBUTIONS

4.10 Sampling Distributions

In the previous sections, we assumed that we knew the probability distribution of a random variable, and using this knowledge we were able to compute the mean, variance, and probabilities associated with the random variable. However, in most practical applications, this information is not available. In reality, the true mean and standard deviation are unknown quantities that would have to be estimated. Numerical quantities that describe probability distributions are called *parameters*. Thus, p, the probability of a success in a binomial experiment, and μ and σ, the mean and standard deviation of a normal distribution, are examples of parameters.

A **parameter** is a numerical descriptive measure of a population. Because it is based on all the observations in the population, its value is almost always unknown.

We have also discussed the sample mean $\bar{x}$, sample variance s^2, sample standard deviation s, etc., which are numerical descriptive measures calculated from the sample. We will often use the information contained in these *sample statistics* to make inferences about the parameters of a population.

A **sample statistic** is a numerical descriptive measure of a sample. It is calculated from the observations in the sample.

Note that the term *statistic* refers to a *sample* quantity, and the term *parameter* refers to a *population* quantity, as shown in Table 4.8.

Table 4.8	List of Population Parameters and Corresponding Sample Statistics	
	Population Parameter	Sample Statistic
Mean	μ	$\bar{x}$
Variance	σ^2	s^2
Standard deviation	σ	s
Binomial proportion	p	$\hat{p}$

Before we can show you how to use sample statistics to make inferences about population parameters, we need to be able to evaluate their properties. Does one sample statistic contain more information than another about a population parameter? On what basis should we choose the "best" statistic for making inferences about a parameter? For example, if we want to estimate a parameter of a population—say, the population mean μ—we could use a number of sample statistics for our estimate. Two possibilities are the sample mean $\bar{x}$ and the sample median m. Which of these do you think will provide a better estimate of μ?

Before answering this question, consider the following example: Toss a fair die and let x equal the number of dots showing on the up face. Suppose the die is tossed three times, producing the sample measurements 2, 2, 6. The sample mean is $\bar{x} = 3.33$ and the sample median is $m = 2$. Because the population mean of x is $\mu = 3.5$, you can see that for this sample of three measurements, the sample mean $\bar{x}$ provides an estimate that falls closer to μ than does the sample median (see Figure 4.39a). Now suppose we toss the die three more times and obtain the sample measurements 3, 4, 6. The mean and median of this sample are $\bar{x} = 4.33$ and $m = 4$, respectively. This time m is closer to μ (see Figure 4.39b).

This simple example illustrates an important point: Neither the sample mean nor the sample median will *always* fall closer to the population mean. Consequently, we cannot compare these two sample statistics, or, in general, any

Figure 4.39

Comparing the sample mean ($\bar{x}$) and sample median (m) as estimators of the population mean (μ)

a. Sample 1: $\bar{x}$ is closer than m to μ

b. Sample 2: m is closer than $\bar{x}$ to μ

two sample statistics, on the basis of their performance for a single sample. Instead, we need to recognize that sample statistics are themselves random variables because different samples can lead to different values for the sample statistics. As random variables, sample statistics must be judged and compared on the basis of their probability distributions (i.e., the *collection* of values and associated probabilities of each statistic that would be obtained if the sampling experiment was repeated a *very large number of times*). We will illustrate this concept with another example.

Suppose it is known that the connector module manufactured for a certain brand of pacemaker has a mean length of $\mu = .3$ inch and a standard deviation of .005 inch. Consider an experiment consisting of randomly selecting 25 recently manufactured connector modules, measuring the length of each, and calculating the sample mean length $\bar{x}$. If this experiment was repeated a very large number of times, the value of $\bar{x}$ would vary from sample to sample. For example, the first sample of 25 length measurements might have a mean $\bar{x} = .301$, the second sample a mean $\bar{x} = .298$, the third sample a mean $\bar{x} = .303$, etc. If the sampling experiment was repeated a very large number of times, the resulting histogram of sample means would be approximately the probability distribution of $\bar{x}$. If $\bar{x}$ is a good estimator of μ, we would expect the values of $\bar{x}$ to cluster around μ, as shown in Figure 4.40. This probability distribution is called a *sampling distribution* because it is generated by repeating a sampling experiment a very large number of times.

> The **sampling distribution** of a sample statistic calculated from a sample of n measurements is the probability distribution of the statistic.

In actual practice, the sampling distribution of a statistic is obtained mathematically or (at least approximately) by simulating the sample on a computer using a procedure similar to that just described.

If $\bar{x}$ has been calculated from a sample of $n = 25$ measurements selected from a population with mean $\mu = .3$ and standard deviation $\sigma = .005$, the sampling distribution (Figure 4.40) provides information about the behavior of $\bar{x}$ in repeated sampling. For example, the probability that you will draw a sample of 25 length measurements and obtain a value of $\bar{x}$ in the interval $.299 \leq \bar{x} \leq .3$ will be the area under the sampling distribution over that interval.

Because the properties of a statistic are typified by its sampling distribution, it follows that to compare two sample statistics, you compare their sampling distributions. For example, if you have two statistics, A and B, for estimating the same parameter (for purposes of illustration, suppose the parameter is the population variance σ^2) and if their sampling distributions are as shown in Figure 4.41, you would choose statistic A in preference to statistic B. You would make this choice because the sampling distribution for statistic A centers over σ^2 and has less spread (variation) than the sampling distribution for statistic B. When you draw a single sample in a practical sampling situation, the probability is higher that statistic A will fall nearer σ^2.

Figure 4.40

Sampling distribution for $\bar{x}$ based on a sample of $n = 25$ length measurements

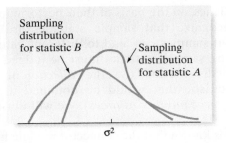

Figure 4.41
Two sampling distributions for estimating the population variance, σ^2

Remember that in practice we will not know the numerical value of the unknown parameter σ^2, so we will not know whether statistic A or statistic B is closer to σ^2 for a sample. We have to rely on our knowledge of the theoretical sampling distributions to choose the best sample statistic and then use it sample after sample. The procedure for finding the sampling distribution for a statistic is demonstrated in Example 4.29.

Example 4.29

Finding a Sampling Distribution

Problem Consider a game played with a standard 52-card bridge deck in which you can score 0, 3, or 12 points per hand. Suppose the population of points per hand is described by the probability distribution shown here. A random sample of $n = 3$ hands is selected from the population.

Points, x	0	3	12
$p(x)$	$1/2$	$1/4$	$1/4$

a. Find the sampling distribution of the sample mean number of points, $\bar{x}$.

b. Find the sampling distribution of the sample median number of points, m.

Solution Points for every possible sample of $n = 3$ hands listed in Table 4.9, along with the sample mean and median. The probability of each sample is obtained using the multiplicative rule. For example, the probability of the sample (0, 0, 3) is $p(0) \cdot p(0) \cdot p(3) = (1/2)(1/2)(1/4) = 1/16$. The probability for each sample is also listed in Table 4.9. Note that the sum of these probabilities is equal to 1.

a. From Table 4.9 you can see that $\bar{x}$ can assume the values 0, 1, 2, 3, 4, 5, 6, 8, 9, and 12. Because $\bar{x} = 0$ occurs in only the first listed sample, $P(\bar{x} = 0) = 8/64$. Similarly, $\bar{x} = 1$ occurs in 3 samples: (0, 0, 3), (0, 3, 0), and (3, 0, 0). Therefore, $P(\bar{x} = 1)$ is the sum of the probabilities for these 3 samples, i.e., $P(\bar{x} = 1) = 4/64 + 4/64 + 4/64 = 12/64$. Calculating the probabilities of the remaining values of $\bar{x}$ and arranging them in a table, we obtain the probability distribution shown below.

$\bar{x}$	0	1	2	3	4	5	6	8	9	12
$p(\bar{x})$	$8/64$	$12/64$	$6/64$	$1/64$	$12/64$	$12/64$	$3/64$	$6/64$	$3/64$	$1/64$

This is the sampling distribution for $\bar{x}$ because it specifies the probability associated with each possible value of $\bar{x}$.

b. In Table 4.9 you can see that the median m can assume one of the values 0, 3, or 12. The value $m = 0$ occurs in 7 different samples. Therefore, $P(m = 0)$ is the sum of the probabilities of these seven samples, i.e., $P(m = 0) = 8/64 + 4/64 + 4/64 + 4/64 + 4/64 + 4/64 + 4/64 = 32/64$. Similarly, $m = 3$ occurs in

Table 4.9	All Possible Samples of $n = 3$ Hands of a Card Game, Example 4.29		
Possible Samples	$\bar{x}$	m	Probability
0, 0, 0	0	0	$(\frac{1}{2})(\frac{1}{2})(\frac{1}{2}) = \frac{1}{8} = \frac{8}{64}$
0, 0, 3	1	0	$(\frac{1}{2})(\frac{1}{2})(\frac{1}{4}) = \frac{1}{16} = \frac{4}{64}$
0, 0, 12	4	0	$(\frac{1}{2})(\frac{1}{2})(\frac{1}{4}) = \frac{1}{16} = \frac{4}{64}$
0, 3, 0	1	0	$(\frac{1}{2})(\frac{1}{4})(\frac{1}{2}) = \frac{1}{16} = \frac{4}{64}$
0, 3, 3	2	3	$(\frac{1}{2})(\frac{1}{4})(\frac{1}{4}) = \frac{1}{32} = \frac{2}{64}$
0, 3, 12	5	3	$(\frac{1}{2})(\frac{1}{4})(\frac{1}{4}) = \frac{1}{32} = \frac{2}{64}$
0, 12, 0	4	0	$(\frac{1}{2})(\frac{1}{4})(\frac{1}{2}) = \frac{1}{16} = \frac{4}{64}$
0, 12, 3	5	3	$(\frac{1}{2})(\frac{1}{4})(\frac{1}{4}) = \frac{1}{32} = \frac{2}{64}$
0, 12, 12	8	12	$(\frac{1}{2})(\frac{1}{4})(\frac{1}{4}) = \frac{1}{32} = \frac{2}{64}$
3, 0, 0	1	0	$(\frac{1}{4})(\frac{1}{2})(\frac{1}{2}) = \frac{1}{16} = \frac{4}{64}$
3, 0, 3	2	3	$(\frac{1}{4})(\frac{1}{2})(\frac{1}{4}) = \frac{1}{32} = \frac{2}{64}$
3, 0, 12	5	3	$(\frac{1}{4})(\frac{1}{2})(\frac{1}{4}) = \frac{1}{32} = \frac{2}{64}$
3, 3, 0	2	3	$(\frac{1}{4})(\frac{1}{4})(\frac{1}{2}) = \frac{1}{32} = \frac{2}{64}$
3, 3, 3	3	3	$(\frac{1}{4})(\frac{1}{4})(\frac{1}{4}) = \frac{1}{64}$
3, 3, 12	6	3	$(\frac{1}{4})(\frac{1}{4})(\frac{1}{4}) = \frac{1}{64}$
3, 12, 0	5	3	$(\frac{1}{4})(\frac{1}{4})(\frac{1}{2}) = \frac{1}{32} = \frac{2}{64}$
3, 12, 3	6	3	$(\frac{1}{4})(\frac{1}{4})(\frac{1}{4}) = \frac{1}{64}$
3, 12, 12	9	12	$(\frac{1}{4})(\frac{1}{4})(\frac{1}{4}) = \frac{1}{64}$
12, 0, 0	4	0	$(\frac{1}{4})(\frac{1}{2})(\frac{1}{2}) = \frac{1}{16} = \frac{4}{64}$
12, 0, 3	5	3	$(\frac{1}{4})(\frac{1}{2})(\frac{1}{4}) = \frac{1}{32} = \frac{2}{64}$
12, 0, 12	8	12	$(\frac{1}{4})(\frac{1}{2})(\frac{1}{4}) = \frac{1}{32} = \frac{2}{64}$
12, 3, 0	5	3	$(\frac{1}{4})(\frac{1}{4})(\frac{1}{2}) = \frac{1}{32} = \frac{2}{64}$
12, 3, 3	6	3	$(\frac{1}{4})(\frac{1}{4})(\frac{1}{4}) = \frac{1}{64}$
12, 3, 12	9	12	$(\frac{1}{4})(\frac{1}{4})(\frac{1}{4}) = \frac{1}{64}$
12, 12, 0	8	12	$(\frac{1}{4})(\frac{1}{4})(\frac{1}{2}) = \frac{1}{32} = \frac{2}{64}$
12, 12, 3	9	12	$(\frac{1}{4})(\frac{1}{4})(\frac{1}{4}) = \frac{1}{64}$
12, 12, 12	12	12	$(\frac{1}{4})(\frac{1}{4})(\frac{1}{4}) = \frac{1}{64}$

$$Sum = \frac{64}{64} = 1$$

13 samples and $m = 12$ occurs in 7 samples, and these probabilities are obtained by summing the probabilities of their respective sample points. Therefore, the probability distribution (i.e., the sampling distribution) for the median m is as shown below.

m	0	3	12
$p(m)$	$\frac{32}{64}$	$\frac{22}{64}$	$\frac{10}{64}$

Look Back The sampling distributions of parts **a** and **b** are found by first listing all possible distinct values of the statistic and then calculating the probability of each value. Note that if the values of x were equally likely, then the 27 sample points in Table 4.9 would all have the same probability of occurring, namely $\frac{1}{27}$.

Now Work Exercise 4.156

Example 4.29 demonstrates the procedure for finding the exact sampling distribution of a statistic when the number of different samples that could be selected from the population is relatively small. In the real world, populations often consist of a large number of different values, making samples difficult (or impossible) to enumerate. When this situation occurs, we may choose to obtain the approximate sampling distribution for a statistic by simulating the sampling over and over again and recording the proportion of times different values of the statistic occur. Example 4.30 illustrates this procedure.

Example 4.30

Simulating a Sampling Distribution

$f(x)$

$\dfrac{1}{50}$

150   200

x

Figure 4.42

Uniform distribution for thickness of steel sheets

Problem Refer to Example 4.26 (p. 231). Recall that the thickness of a steel sheet follows a uniform distribution with values between 150 and 200 millimeters. Suppose we perform the following experiment over and over again: Randomly sample 11 steel sheets from the production line and record the thickness, x, of each. Calculate the two sample statistics

$$\bar{x} = \text{Sample mean} = \frac{\Sigma x}{11}$$

$m = \text{Median} = \text{Sixth sample measurement when the 11 thicknesses}$
$\text{are arranged in ascending order}$

Obtain approximations to the sampling distributions of $\bar{x}$ and m.

Solution Recall from Section 4.9 that the population of thicknesses follows the uniform distribution shown in Figure 4.42. We used Minitab to generate 1,000 samples from this population, each with $n = 11$ observations. Then we compute $\bar{x}$ and m for each sample. Our goal is to obtain approximations to the sampling distributions of $\bar{x}$ and m to find out which sample statistic ($\bar{x}$ or m) contains more information about μ. [*Note:* In this particular example, we *know* the population mean is $\mu = 175$ mm. (See Section 4.9.)] The first 10 of the 1,000 samples generated are presented in Table 4.10. For instance, the first computer-generated sample from the uniform distribution (arranged in ascending order) contained the following thickness measurements: 151, 157, 162, 169, 171, 173, 181, 182, 187, 188, and 193 millimeters. The sample mean $\bar{x}$ and median m computed for this sample are

$$\bar{x} = \frac{151 + 157 + \cdots + 193}{11} = 174.0$$

$m = \text{Sixth ordered measurement} = 173$

The Minitab relative frequency histograms for $\bar{x}$ and m for the 1,000 samples of size $n = 11$ are shown in Figure 4.43. These histograms represent approximations to the true sampling distributions of $\bar{x}$ and m.

Look Back You can see that the values of $\bar{x}$ tend to cluster around μ to a greater extent than do the values of m. Thus, on the basis of the observed sampling distributions, we conclude that $\bar{x}$ contains more information about μ than m does—at least for samples of $n = 11$ measurements from the uniform distribution.

Table 4.10	**First 10 Samples of $n = 11$ Thickness Measurements from Uniform Distribution**												
Sample					Thickness Measurements							Mean	Median
1	173	171	187	151	188	181	182	157	162	169	193	174.00	173
2	181	190	182	171	187	177	162	172	188	200	193	182.09	182
3	192	195	187	187	172	164	164	189	179	182	173	180.36	182
4	173	157	150	154	168	174	171	182	200	181	187	172.45	173
5	169	160	167	170	197	159	174	174	161	173	160	169.46	169
6	179	170	167	174	173	178	173	170	173	198	187	176.55	173
7	166	177	162	171	154	177	154	179	175	185	193	172.09	175
8	164	199	152	153	163	156	184	151	198	167	180	169.73	164
9	181	193	151	166	180	199	180	184	182	181	175	179.27	181
10	155	199	199	171	172	157	173	187	190	185	150	176.18	173

Data Set: SIMUNI

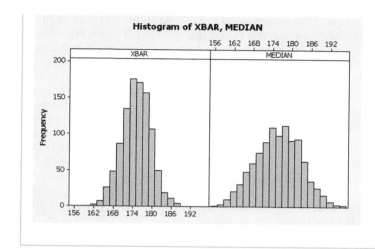

Figure 4.43
Minitab histograms for sample mean and sample median, Example 4.30

Now Work Exercise 4.161

As noted earlier, many sampling distributions can be derived mathematically, but the theory necessary to do this is beyond the scope of this text. Consequently, when we need to know the properties of a statistic, we will present its sampling distribution and simply describe its properties. The important properties of the sampling distribution of the sample mean are discussed in the next section.

Exercises 4.156–4.162

Learning the Mechanics

4.156 The probability distribution shown here describes a population of measurements that can assume values of 0, 2, 4, and 6, each of which occurs with the same relative frequency:

x	0	2	4	6
$p(x)$	$\frac{1}{4}$	$\frac{1}{4}$	$\frac{1}{4}$	$\frac{1}{4}$

a. List all the different samples of $n = 2$ measurements that can be selected from this population.
b. Calculate the mean of each different sample listed in part **a.**
c. If a sample of $n = 2$ measurements is randomly selected from the population, what is the probability that a specific sample will be selected?
d. Assume that a random sample of $n = 2$ measurements is selected from the population. List the different values of $\bar{x}$ found in part **b** and find the probability of each. Then give the sampling distribution of the sample mean $\bar{x}$ in tabular form.
e. Construct a probability histogram for the sampling distribution of $\bar{x}$.

4.157 Simulate sampling from the population described in Exercise 4.156 by marking the values of x, one on each of four identical coins (or poker chips, etc.). Place the coins (marked 0, 2, 4, and 6) into a bag, randomly select one, and observe its value. Replace this coin, draw a second coin, and observe its value. Finally, calculate the mean $\bar{x}$ for this sample of $n = 2$ observations randomly selected from the population (Exercise 4.156, part **b**). Replace the coins, mix, and using the same procedure, select a sample of $n = 2$ observations from the population. Record the numbers and calculate $\bar{x}$ for this sample. Repeat this sampling process until you acquire 100 values of $\bar{x}$. Construct a relative

frequency distribution for these 100 sample means. Compare this distribution to the exact sampling distribution of $\bar{x}$ found in part **e** of Exercise 4.156. [*Note:* The distribution obtained in this exercise is an approximation to the exact sampling distribution. But, if you were to repeat the sampling procedure, drawing two coins not 100 times but 10,000 times, the relative frequency distribution for the 10,000 sample means would be almost identical to the sampling distribution of $\bar{x}$ found in Exercise 4.156, part **e**.]

4.158 Consider the population described by the probability distribution shown below.

x	1	2	3	4	5
$p(x)$	.2	.3	.2	.2	.1

The random variable x is observed twice. If these observations are independent, verify that the different samples of size 2 and their probabilities are as shown below.

Sample	Probability	Sample	Probability
1, 1	.04	3, 4	.04
1, 2	.06	3, 5	.02
1, 3	.04	4, 1	.04
1, 4	.04	4, 2	.06
1, 5	.02	4, 3	.04
2, 1	.06	4, 4	.04
2, 2	.09	4, 5	.02
2, 3	.06	5, 1	.02
2, 4	.06	5, 2	.03
2, 5	.03	5, 3	.02
3, 1	.04	5, 4	.02
3, 2	.06	5, 5	.01
3, 3	.04		

a. Find the sampling distribution of the sample mean $\bar{x}$.
b. Construct a probability histogram for the sampling distribution of $\bar{x}$.
c. What is the probability that $\bar{x}$ is 4.5 or larger?
d. Would you expect to observe a value of $\bar{x}$ equal to 4.5 or larger? Explain.

4.159 Refer to Exercise 4.158 and find $E(x) = \mu$. Then use the sampling distribution of $\bar{x}$ found in Exercise 4.158 to find the expected value of $\bar{x}$. Note that $E(\bar{x}) = \mu$.

4.160 Refer to Exercise 4.158. Assume that a random sample of $n = 2$ measurements is randomly selected from the population.
a. List the different values that the sample median m may assume and find the probability of each. Then give the sampling distribution of the sample median.
b. Construct a probability histogram for the sampling distribution of the sample median and compare it with the probability histogram for the sample mean (Exercise 4.158, part **b**).

4.161 In Example 4.30 we used a computer to generate [NW] 1,000 samples, each containing $n = 11$ observations, from a uniform distribution over the interval from 150 to 200. For this exercise, use a computer to generate 500 samples, each containing $n = 15$ observations, from this population.
a. Calculate the sample mean for each sample. To approximate the sampling distribution of $\bar{x}$, construct a relative frequency histogram for the 500 values of $\bar{x}$.
b. Repeat part **a** for the sample median. Compare this approximate sampling distribution with the approximate sampling distribution of $\bar{x}$ found in part **a**.

4.162 Consider a population that contains values of x equal to 00, 01, 02, 03, ..., 96, 97, 98, 99. Assume that these values of x occur with equal probability. Use a computer to generate 500 samples, each containing $n = 25$ measurements, from this population. Calculate the sample mean $\bar{x}$ and sample variance s^2 for each of the 500 samples.
a. To approximate the sampling distribution of $\bar{x}$, construct a relative frequency histogram for the 500 values of $\bar{x}$.
b. Repeat part **a** for the 500 values of s^2.

4.11 The Sampling Distribution of a Sample Mean and the Central Limit Theorem

Estimating the mean useful life of automobiles, the mean monthly sales for all computer dealers in a large city, and the mean breaking strength of new plastic are practical problems with something in common. In each case, we are interested in making an inference about the mean μ of some population. As we mentioned in Chapter 2, the sample mean $\bar{x}$ is, in general, a good estimator of μ. We now develop pertinent information about the sampling distribution for this useful statistic.

Example 4.31

Describing the Sampling Distribution of $\bar{x}$

Problem Suppose a population has the uniform probability distribution given in Figure 4.44. The mean and standard deviation of this probability distribution are $\mu = 175$ and $\sigma = 14.43$. (See Section 4.9 for the formulas for μ and σ.) Now suppose a sample of 11 measurements is selected from this population. Describe the sampling distribution of the sample mean $\bar{x}$ based on the 1,000 sampling experiments discussed in Example 4.30.

Figure 4.44
Sampled uniform population

Solution You will recall that in Example 4.30 we generated 1,000 samples of $n = 11$ measurements each. The Minitab histogram for the 1,000 sample means is shown in Figure 4.45 with a normal probability distribution superimposed. You can see that this normal probability distribution approximates the computer-generated sampling distribution very well.

To fully describe a normal probability distribution, it is necessary to know its mean and standard deviation. Minitab gives these statistics for the 1,000 $\bar{x}$'s in the upper right corner of the histogram, Figure 4.45. You can see that the mean is 175.2, and the standard deviation is 4.383.

To summarize our findings based on 1,000 samples, each consisting of 11 measurements from a uniform population, the sampling distribution of $\bar{x}$ appears to be approximately normal with a mean of about 175 and a standard deviation of about 4.38.

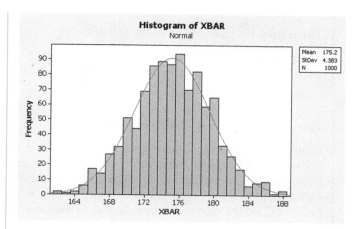

Figure 4.45

Minitab histogram for sample mean in 1,000 samples

Look Back Note that the simulated value $\mu_{\bar{x}} = 175.2$ is very close to $\mu = 175$ for the uniform distribution—that is, the simulated sampling distribution of $\bar{x}$ appears to provide an accurate estimate of μ.

The true sampling distribution of $\bar{x}$ has the properties given in the next box, assuming only that a random sample of n observations has been selected from *any* population.

Properties of the Sampling Distribution of $\bar{x}$

1. Mean of sampling distribution equals mean of sampled population*, that is, $\mu_{\bar{x}} = E(\bar{x}) = \mu$.

2. Standard deviation of sampling distribution equals

$$\frac{\text{Standard deviation of sampled population}}{\text{Square root of sample size}}$$

That is, $\sigma_{\bar{x}} = \sigma/\sqrt{n}.^{\dagger}$

The standard deviation $\sigma_{\bar{x}}$ is often referred to as the **standard error of the mean.**

You can see that our approximation to $\mu_{\bar{x}}$ in Example 4.31 was precise because property 1 assures us that the mean is the same as that of the sampled population: 175 mm. Property 2 tells us how to calculate the standard deviation of the sampling distribution of $\bar{x}$. Substituting $\sigma = 14.43$, the standard deviation of the sampled uniform distribution, and the sample size $n = 11$ into the formula for $\sigma_{\bar{x}}$, we find

$$\sigma_{\bar{x}} = \frac{\sigma}{\sqrt{n}} = \frac{14.43}{\sqrt{11}} = 4.35$$

Thus, the approximation we obtained in Example 4.31, $\sigma_{\bar{x}} = 4.38$, is very close to the exact value, $\sigma_{\bar{x}} = 4.35$.**

What can be said about the shape of the sampling distribution of $\bar{x}$? Two important theorems provide this information.

---

*When this property holds, we say that $\bar{x}$ is an *unbiased* estimate of μ.
†If the sample size, n, is large relative to the number, N, of elements in the population (e.g., 5% or more), $\sigma/\sqrt{n}$ must be multiplied by a finite population correction factor, $\sqrt{(N - n)/(N - 1)}$. For most sampling situations, this correction factor will be close to 1 and can be ignored.
**It can be shown (proof omitted) that the value of $\sigma_{\bar{x}}^2$ is the smallest variance among all unbiased estimators of μ—thus, $\bar{x}$ is the MVUE (minimum variance unbiased estimator) for μ.

Theorem 4.1

If a random sample of n observations is selected from a population with a normal distribution, the sampling distribution of $\bar{x}$ will be a normal distribution.

Theorem 4.2 (Central Limit Theorem)

Consider a random sample of n observations selected from a population (*any* probability distribution) with mean μ and standard deviation σ. Then, when n is sufficiently large, the sampling distribution of $\bar{x}$ will be approximately a normal distribution with mean $\mu_{\bar{x}} = \mu$ and standard deviation $\sigma_{\bar{x}} = \sigma/\sqrt{n}$. The larger the sample size, the better will be the normal approximation to the sampling distribution of $\bar{x}$.*

BIOGRAPHY

**PIERRE-SIMON LAPLACE
(1749–1827)**

The CLT Originator

As a boy growing up in Normandy, France, Pierre-Simon Laplace attended a Benedictine priory school. Upon graduation, he entered Caen University to study theology. During his two years there, he discovered his mathematical talents and began his career as an eminent mathematician. In fact, he considered himself the best mathematician in France. Laplace's contributions to mathematics ranged from introducing new methods of solving differential equations to complex analyses of motions of astronomical bodies. While studying the angles of inclination of comet orbits in 1778, Laplace showed that the sum of the angles were normally distributed. Consequently, he is considered to be the originator of the Central Limit Theorem. (A rigorous proof of the theorem, however, was not provided until the early 1930s by another French mathematician, Paul Levy.) Laplace also discovered Bayes's theorem and established Bayesian statistical analysis as a valid approach to many practical problems of his time. ■

Thus, for sufficiently large samples, the sampling distribution of $\bar{x}$ is approximately normal. How large must the sample size n be so that the normal distribution provides a good approximation for the sampling distribution of $\bar{x}$? The answer depends on the shape of the distribution of the sampled population, as shown by Figure 4.46. Generally speaking, the greater the skewness of the sampled population distribution, the larger the sample size must be before the normal distribution is an adequate approximation for the sampling distribution of $\bar{x}$. For most sampled populations, sample sizes of $n \geq 30$ will suffice for the normal approximation to be reasonable. We will use the normal approximation for the sampling distribution of $\bar{x}$ when the sample size is at least 30.

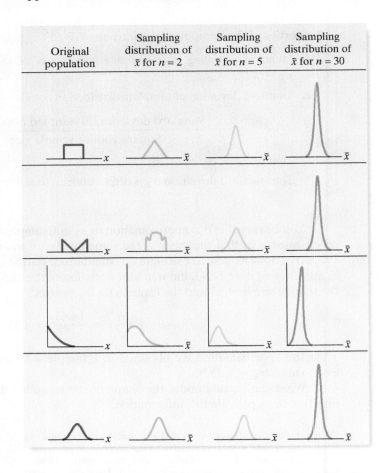

Figure 4.46

Sampling distributions of $\bar{x}$ for different populations and different sample sizes

*Moreover, because of the Central Limit Theorem, the sum of a random sample on n observations, Σx, will possess a sampling distribution that is approximately normal for large samples. This distribution will have a mean equal to $n\mu$ and a variance equal to $n\sigma^2$. Proof of the Central Limit Theorem is beyond the scope of this book, but it can be found in many mathematical statistics texts.

Example 4.32

Using the Central Limit Theorem to Find a Probability

Problem Suppose we have selected a random sample of $n = 36$ observations from a population with mean equal to 80 and standard deviation equal to 6. It is known that the population is not extremely skewed.

a. Sketch the relative frequency distributions for the population and for the sampling distribution of the sample mean, $\bar{x}$.

b. Find the probability that $\bar{x}$ will be larger than 82.

Solution

a. We do not know the exact shape of the population relative frequency distribution, but we do know that it should be centered about $\mu = 80$, its spread should be measured by $\sigma = 6$, and it is not highly skewed. One possibility is shown in Figure 4.47a. From the Central Limit Theorem, we know that the sampling distribution of $\bar{x}$ will be approximately normal because the sampled population distribution is not extremely skewed. We also know that the sampling distribution will have mean and standard deviation

$$\mu_{\bar{x}} = \mu = 80 \quad \text{and} \quad \sigma_{\bar{x}} = \frac{\sigma}{\sqrt{n}} = \frac{6}{\sqrt{36}} = 1$$

The sampling distribution of $\bar{x}$ is shown in Figure 4.47b.

b. The probability that $\bar{x}$ will exceed 82 is equal to the darker shaded area in Figure 4.48. To find this area, we need to find the z-value corresponding to $\bar{x} = 82$. Recall that the standard normal random variable z is the difference between any normally distributed random variable and its mean, expressed in units of its standard deviation. Because $\bar{x}$ is approximately a normally distributed random variable with mean $\mu_{\bar{x}} = \mu$ and $\sigma_{\bar{x}} = \sigma/\sqrt{n}$, it follows that the standard normal z-value corresponding to the sample mean, $\bar{x}$, is

$$z = \frac{(\text{Normal random variable}) - (\text{Mean})}{\text{Standard deviation}} = \frac{\bar{x} - \mu_{\bar{x}}}{\sigma_{\bar{x}}}$$

Therefore, for $\bar{x} = 82$, we have

$$z = \frac{\bar{x} - \mu_{\bar{x}}}{\sigma_{\bar{x}}} = \frac{82 - 80}{1} = 2$$

68   74   μ = 80   86   92

a. Population relative frequency distribution

77   $\mu_{\bar{x}} = 80$ 83

b. Sampling distribution of $\bar{x}$

Figure 4.47

A population relative frequency distribution and the sampling distribution for $\bar{x}$

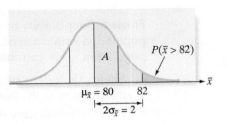

Figure 4.48
The sampling distribution of $\bar{x}$

The area A in Figure 4.48 corresponding to $z = 2$ is given in the table of areas under the normal curve (see Table IV in Appendix B) as .4772. Therefore, the tail area corresponding to the probability that $\bar{x}$ exceeds 82 is

$$P(\bar{x} > 82) = P(z > 2) = .5 - .4772 = .0228$$

Look Back The key to finding the probability, part **b**, is to recognize that the distribution of $\bar{x}$ is normal with mean $\mu_{\bar{x}} = \mu$ and $\sigma_{\bar{x}} = \sigma/\sqrt{n}$.

Now Work Exercises 4.166–4.167

Example 4.33

A Practical Application of the Central Limit Theorem to Test a Manufacturer's Claim

Problem A manufacturer of automobile batteries claims that the distribution of the lengths of life of its best battery has a mean of 54 months and a standard deviation of 6 months. Recently, the manufacturer has received a rash of complaints from unsatisfied customers whose batteries have died earlier than expected. Suppose a consumer group decides to check the manufacturer's claim by purchasing a sample of 50 of these batteries and subjecting them to tests that determine battery life.

a. Assuming that the manufacturer's claim is true, describe the sampling distribution of the mean lifetime of a sample of 50 batteries.

b. Assuming that the manufacturer's claim is true, what is the probability that the consumer group's sample has a mean life of 52 or fewer months?

Solution

a. Even though we have no information about the shape of the probability distribution of the lives of the batteries, we can use the Central Limit Theorem to deduce that the sampling distribution for a sample mean lifetime of 50 batteries is approximately normally distributed. Furthermore, the mean of this sampling distribution is the same as the mean of the sampled population, which is $\mu = 54$ months according to the manufacturer's claim. Finally, the standard deviation of the sampling distribution is given by

$$\sigma_{\bar{x}} = \frac{\sigma}{\sqrt{n}} = \frac{6}{\sqrt{50}} = .85 \text{ month}$$

Note that we used the claimed standard deviation of the sampled population, $\sigma = 6$ months. Thus, if we assume that the claim is true, the sampling distribution for the mean life of the 50 batteries sampled is as shown in Figure 4.49.

b. If the manufacturer's claim is true, the probability that the consumer group observes a mean battery life of 52 or fewer months for their sample of 50 batteries, $P(\bar{x} \le 52)$, is equivalent to the darker shaded area in Figure 4.49. Because the sampling distribution is approximately normal, we can find this area by computing the standard normal z-value:

$$z = \frac{\bar{x} - \mu_{\bar{x}}}{\sigma_{\bar{x}}} = \frac{52 - 54}{.85} = -2.35$$

Figure 4.49
Sampling distribution of $\bar{x}$ in
Example 4.33 for $n = 50$

$P(\bar{x} \le 52)$

A

52   54 $\bar{x}$

where $\mu_{\bar{x}}$, the mean of the sampling distribution of $\bar{x}$, is equal to μ, the mean of the lives of the sampled population, and $\sigma_{\bar{x}}$ is the standard deviation of the sampling distribution of $\bar{x}$. Note that z is the familiar standardized distance (z-score) of Section 2.7 and because $\bar{x}$ is approximately normally distributed, it will possess (approximately) the standard normal distribution of Section 4.6.

The area A shown in Figure 4.49 between $\bar{x} = 52$ and $\bar{x} = 54$ (corresponding to $z = -2.35$) is found in Table IV in Appendix B to be .4906. Therefore, the area to the left of $\bar{x} = 52$ is

$$P(\bar{x} \le 52) = .5 - A = .5 - .4906 = .0094$$

Thus, the probability that the consumer group will observe a sample mean of 52 or less is only .0094 if the manufacturer's claim is true.

Look Back If the 50 tested batteries do exhibit a mean of 52 or fewer months, the consumer group will have strong evidence that the manufacturer's claim is untrue because such an event is very unlikely to occur if the claim is true. (This is still another application of the *rare-event approach to statistical inference*.)

Now Work Exercise 4.172

We conclude this section with two final comments on the sampling distribution of $\bar{x}$. First, from the formula $\sigma_{\bar{x}} = \sigma/\sqrt{n}$, we see that the standard deviation of the sampling distribution of $\bar{x}$ gets smaller as the sample size n gets larger. For example, we computed $\sigma_{\bar{x}} = .85$ when $n = 50$ in Example 4.33. However, for $n = 100$, we obtain $\sigma_{\bar{x}} = \sigma/\sqrt{n} = 6/\sqrt{100} = .60$. This relationship will hold true for most of the sample statistics encountered in this text—that is, *the standard deviation of the sampling distribution decreases as the sample size increases*. Consequently, the larger the sample size, the more accurate the sample statistic (e.g., $\bar{x}$) is in estimating a population parameter (e.g., μ). We will use this result in Chapter 5 to help us determine the sample size needed to obtain a specified accuracy of estimation.

Our second comment concerns the Central Limit Theorem. In addition to providing a very useful approximation for the sampling distribution of a sample mean, the Central Limit Theorem offers an explanation for the fact that many relative frequency distributions of data possess mound-shaped distributions. Many of the measurements we take in business are really means or sums of a large number of small phenomena. For example, a company's sales for 1 year are the total of the many individual sales the company made during the year. Similarly, we can view the length of time a construction company takes to build a house as the total of the times taken to complete a multitude of distinct jobs, and we can regard the monthly demand for blood at a hospital as the total of the many individual patients' needs. Whether or not the observations entering into these sums satisfy the assumptions basic to the Central Limit Theorem is open to question. However, it is a fact that many distributions of data in nature are mound shaped and possess the appearance of normal distributions.

| Statistics in Action | Revisited | | **Making an Inference about Mean Accuracy** |

Consider, again, the prototype gun developed for the U.S. Army that fires over 1,000 flechettes with a single round. Suppose the specifications of the weapon are set so that when the gun is aimed at the center target (see Figure SIA4.1, page 174) from 500 meters away, the mean horizontal grid value is $\mu = 5$ feet (i.e., the aim point) and the standard deviation is $\sigma = 1$ foot. After firing one round of the super weapon, the U.S. Army randomly samples 100 of the discharged flechettes and records x, the horizontal measurement, for each. The sample mean was determined to be $\bar{x} = 5.3$. Is this result consistent with the gun specifications or is the true mean μ set higher than 5?

To answer this question, we need to examine the likelihood of obtaining the sample result, given that the gun specifications are met—that is, how likely is it to observe a sample mean of $\bar{x} = 5.3$ or higher for a sample of $n = 100$ flechettes when the mean and standard deviation of the population of horizontal grid measurements are set at $\mu = 5$ and $\sigma = 1$? Thus, the probability of interest is $P(\bar{x} > 5.3)$.

To find this probability, we invoke the Central Limit Theorem. According to the theorem, the sampling distribution of $\bar{x}$ is approximately normally distributed with the following mean and standard deviation:

$$\mu_{\bar{x}} = \mu = 5 \qquad \sigma_{\bar{x}} = \sigma/\sqrt{n} = 1/\sqrt{100} = .1$$

[Note that because we've already established (see SIA on pp. 214–215) that the population of horizontal grid measurements are normally distributed, Theorem 4.1 also guarantees

that the distribution of $\bar{x}$ will be normally distributed.] Therefore, we find the desired probability (using the standard normal table) as follows:

$$P(\bar{x} > 5.3) = P\left(z > \frac{5.3 - \mu_{\bar{x}}}{\sigma_{\bar{x}}}\right)$$

$$= P\left(z > \frac{5.3 - 5}{.1}\right) = P(z > 3) = .0013$$

In other words, the probability that we observe a sample mean at least as large as $\bar{x} = 5.3$ feet *if the mean and standard deviation of the horizontal grid measurements are $\mu = 5$ and $\sigma = 1$ (i.e., if the desired specifications are met) is almost 0.*

This small probability leads us to make one of two conclusions: Either the gun specifications are met and the U.S. Army has observed an extremely rare event (one with almost no chance of happening), or one or both of the gun specifications ($\mu = 5$ and $\sigma = 1$) are not being met. The *rare event approach* to making statistical inferences, of course, would favor the second conclusion. Possibly the gun specifications were set so that the true mean μ is higher than 5 feet, or the standard deviation was set at some number other than $\sigma = 1$. [In fact, you can show that if the specifications are set at $\sigma = 4$, $P(\bar{x} > 5.3) = .2266$. Thus, the observed sample mean has a reasonable chance of occurring if the standard deviation is inadvertently set at $\sigma = 4$.]

| **Activity 4.2** | *Keep the Change:* **Simulating a Sampling Distribution** |

In this activity, we will once again be working with the data set *Amounts Transferred* from Activity 1.1 on page 16. This activity is designed for small groups or the entire class.

1. Pool your *Amounts Transferred* data with other class members or the entire class so that the pooled data set has at least 100 data items. Have someone in the group calculate the mean and the standard deviation of the pooled data set.

2. Devise a convenient way to choose random samples from the pooled data set. You can assign each data item a number beginning with 1 and use a random number generator to select a sample, or you can write each data item on a small card and then draw cards without looking.

3. Choose a random sample of size $n = 30$ from the pooled data and find the mean of the sample, called a *sample mean*. Group members should repeat the process of choosing a sample of size $n = 30$ from the pooled data and finding the sample mean until the group has accumulated at least 25 sample means. Call this new data set *Sample Means*.

4. Find the mean and standard deviation of the data set *Sample Means*. Explain how the Central Limit Theorem is illustrated in this activity.

Keep the data set from this activity for use in future activities.

Exercises 4.163–4.181

Learning the Mechanics

4.163 Will the sampling distribution of $\bar{x}$ always be approximately normally distributed? Explain.

4.164 Suppose a random sample of $n = 25$ measurements is selected from a population with mean μ and standard deviation σ. For

each of the following values of μ and σ, give the values of $\mu_{\bar{x}}$ and $\sigma_{\bar{x}}$.

a. $\mu = 10, \sigma = 3$
b. $\mu = 100, \sigma = 25$
c. $\mu = 20, \sigma = 40$
d. $\mu = 10, \sigma = 100$

4.165 Suppose a random sample of n measurements is selected from a population with mean $\mu = 100$ and variance $\sigma^2 = 100$. For each of the following values of n, give the mean and standard deviation of the sampling distribution of the sample mean $\bar{x}$.

a. $n = 4$ b. $n = 25$
c. $n = 100$ d. $n = 50$
e. $n = 500$ f. $n = 1{,}000$

4.166 A random sample of $n = 64$ observations is drawn from a [NW] population with a mean equal to 20 and a standard deviation equal to 16.

a. Give the mean and standard deviation of the (repeated) sampling distribution of $\bar{x}$.
b. Describe the shape of the sampling distribution of $\bar{x}$. Does your answer depend on the sample size?
c. Calculate the standard normal z-score corresponding to a value of $\bar{x} = 15.5$.
d. Calculate the standard normal z-score corresponding to $\bar{x} = 23$.

4.167 Refer to Exercise 4.166. Find the probability that
[NW] a. $\bar{x}$ is less than 16.
b. $\bar{x}$ is greater than 23.
c. $\bar{x}$ is greater than 25.
d. $\bar{x}$ falls between 16 and 22.
e. $\bar{x}$ is less than 14.

4.168 A random sample of $n = 900$ observations is selected from a population with $\mu = 100$ and $\sigma = 10$.

a. What are the largest and smallest values of $\bar{x}$ that you would expect to see?
b. How far, at the most, would you expect $\bar{x}$ to deviate from μ?
c. Did you have to know μ to answer part **b**? Explain.

4.169 A random sample of $n = 100$ observations is selected from a population with $\mu = 30$ and $\sigma = 16$. Approximate the following probabilities:

a. $P(\bar{x} \geq 28)$ b. $P(22.1 \leq \bar{x} \leq 26.8)$
c. $P(\bar{x} \leq 28.2)$ d. $P(\bar{x} \geq 27.0)$

4.170 Consider a population that contains values of x equal to 0, 1, 2, ..., 97, 98, 99. Assume that the values of x are equally likely. For each of the following values of n, use a computer to generate 500 random samples and calculate $\bar{x}$ for each sample. For each sample size, construct a relative frequency histogram of the 500 values of $\bar{x}$. What changes occur in the histograms as the value of n increases? What similarities exist? Use $n = 2, n = 5, n = 10, n = 30$, and $n = 50$.

⬤ Applet Exercise 4.9

Open the applet *Sampling Distributions*. On the pull-down menu to the right of the top graph, select *Binary*.

a. Run the applet for the sample size $n = 10$ and the number of samples $N = 1{,}000$. Observe the shape of the graph of the sample proportions and record the mean, median, and standard deviation of the sample proportions.
b. How does the mean of the sample proportions compare to the mean $\mu = 0.5$ of the original distribution?
c. Compute the standard deviation of the original distribution using the formula $\sigma = \sqrt{np(1 - p)}$ where $n = 1$ and $p = 0.5$. Divide the result by $\sqrt{10}$, the square root of the sample size used in the sampling distribution. How does this result compare to the standard deviation of the sample proportions?

d. Explain how the graph of the distribution of sample proportions suggests that the distribution may be approximately normal.
e. Explain how the results of parts **b–d** illustrate the Central Limit Theorem.

⬤ Applet Exercise 4.10

Open the applet *Sampling Distributions*. On the pull-down menu to the right of the top graph, select *Uniform*. The box to the left of the top graph displays the population mean, median, and standard deviation of the original distribution.

a. Run the applet for the sample size $n = 30$ and the number of samples $N = 1{,}000$. Observe the shape of the graph of the sample means and record the mean, median, and standard deviation of the sample means.
b. How does the mean of the sample means compare to the mean of the original distribution?
c. Divide the standard deviation of the original distribution by $\sqrt{30}$, the square root of the sample size used in the sampling distribution. How does this result compare to the standard deviation of the sample proportions?
d. Explain how the graph of the distribution of sample means suggests that the distribution may be approximately normal.
e. Explain how the results of parts **b–d** illustrate the Central Limit Theorem.

Applying the Concepts—Basic

4.171 Semester hours taken by CPA candidates. Refer to the *Journal of Accounting and Public Policy* (Spring 2002) study of first-time candidates for the CPA exam, Exercise 2.51 (p. 63). The number of semester hours of college credit taken by candidates has a distribution with a mean of 141 hours and a standard deviation of 18 hours. Consider a random sample of 100 first-time candidates for the CPA exam and let $\bar{x}$ represent the mean number of hours of college credit taken for the sample.

a. What is $\mu_{\bar{x}}$?
b. What is $\sigma_{\bar{x}}$?
c. Describe the shape of the sampling distribution of $\bar{x}$.
d. Find the z-score for the value $\bar{x} = 142$ hours.
e. Find $P(\bar{x} > 142)$

4.172 Salary of a travel management professional. According to a [NW] National Business Travel Association (NBTA) 2008 survey, the average salary of a travel management professional is $97,300. Assume that the standard deviation of such salaries is $30,000. Consider a random sample of 50 travel management professionals and let $\bar{x}$ represent the mean salary for the sample.

a. What is $\mu_{\bar{x}}$?
b. What is $\sigma_{\bar{x}}$?
c. Describe the shape of the sampling distribution of $\bar{x}$.
d. Find the z-score for the value $\bar{x} = 89{,}500$.
e. Find $P(\bar{x} > 89{,}500)$.

4.173 Improving SAT scores. Refer to the *Chance* (Winter 2001) examination of Scholastic Assessment Test (SAT) scores of students who pay a private tutor to help them improve their results, Exercise 2.86 (p. 76). On the SAT–Mathematics test, these students had a mean score change of +19 points, with a standard deviation of 65 points. In a random sample of

100 students who pay a private tutor to help them improve their results, what is the likelihood that the sample mean score change is less than 10 points?

4.174 Critical part failures in NASCAR vehicles. Refer to *The Sport Journal* (Winter 2007) analysis of critical part failures at NASCAR races, Exercise 4.144 (p. 236). Recall that researchers found that the time x (in hours) until the first critical part failure is exponentially distributed with $\mu = .10$ and $\sigma = .10$. Now consider a random sample of $n = 50$ NASCAR races and let $\bar{x}$ represent the sample mean time until the first critical part failure.

a. Find $E(\bar{x})$ and $\text{Var}(\bar{x})$.
b. Although x has an exponential distribution, the sampling distribution of $\bar{x}$ is approximately normal. Why?
c. Find the probability that the sample mean time until the first critical part failure exceeds .13 hour.

Applying the Concepts—Intermediate

4.175 Levelness of concrete slabs. Geotechnical engineers use water-level "manometer" surveys to assess the levelness of newly constructed concrete slabs. Elevations are typically measured at eight points on the slab; of interest is the maximum differential between elevations. The *Journal of Performance of Constructed Facilities* (Feb. 2005) published an article on the levelness of slabs in California residential developments. Elevation data collected for over 1,300 concrete slabs *before tensioning* revealed that maximum differential, x, has a mean of $\mu = .53$ inch and a standard deviation of $\sigma = .193$ inch. Consider a sample of $n = 50$ slabs selected from those surveyed and let $\bar{x}$ represent the mean of the sample.

a. Fully describe the sampling distribution of $\bar{x}$.
b. Find $P(\bar{x} > .58)$.
c. The study also revealed that the mean maximum differential of concrete slabs measured *after tensioning and loading* is $\mu = .58$ inch. Suppose the sample data yield $\bar{x} = .59$ inch. Comment on whether the sample measurements were obtained before tensioning or after tensioning and loading.

4.176 Surface roughness of pipe. Refer to the *Anti-Corrosion Methods and Materials* (Vol. 50, 2003) study of the surface roughness of oil field pipes, Exercise 2.46 (p. 62). Recall that a scanning probe instrument was used to measure the surface roughness x (in micrometers) of 20 sampled sections of coated interior pipe. The data are saved in the **ROUGHPIPE** file. Consider the sample mean, $\bar{x}$.

a. Assume that the surface roughness distribution has a mean of $\mu = 1.8$ micrometers and a standard deviation of $\sigma = .5$ micrometer. Use this information to find the probability that $\bar{x}$ exceeds 1.85 micrometers.
b. The sample data are reproduced in the following table. Compute $\bar{x}$.
c. Based on the result, part **b**, comment on the validity of the assumptions made in part **a**.

1.72	2.50	2.16	2.13	1.06	2.24	2.31	2.03	1.09	1.40
2.57	2.64	1.26	2.05	1.19	2.13	1.27	1.51	2.41	1.95

Source: Farshad, F., and Pesacreta, T. "Coated pipe interior surface roughness as measured by three scanning probe instruments," *Anti-Corrosion Methods and Materials*, Vol. 50, No. 1, 2003 (Table III). Copyright © 2003 MCB UP Ltd.

4.177 Is exposure to a chemical in Teflon-coated cookware hazardous? Perfluorooctanoic acid (PFOA) is a chemical used in Teflon-coated cookware to prevent food from sticking. The EPA is investigating the potential risk of PFOA as a cancer-causing agent (*Science News Online*, August 27, 2005). It is known that the blood concentration of PFOA in people in the general population has a mean of $\mu = 6$ parts per billion (ppb) and a standard deviation of $\sigma = 10$ ppb. *Science News Online* reported on tests for PFOA exposure conducted on a sample of 326 people who live near DuPont's Teflon-making Washington (West Virginia) Works facility.

a. What is the probability that the average blood concentration of PFOA in the sample is greater than 7.5 ppb?
b. The actual study resulted in $\bar{x} = 300$ ppb. Use this information to make an inference about the true mean μ PFOA concentration for the population of people who live near DuPont's Teflon facility.

4.178 Rental car fleet evaluation. National Car Rental Systems, Inc., commissioned the U.S. Automobile Club (USAC) to conduct a survey of the general condition of the cars rented to the public by Hertz, Avis, National, and Budget Rent-a-Car.* USAC officials evaluate each company's cars using a demerit point system. Each car starts with a perfect score of 0 points and incurs demerit points for each discrepancy noted by the inspectors. One measure of the overall condition of a company's cars is the mean of all scores received by the company (i.e., the company's *fleet mean score*). To estimate the fleet mean score of each rental car company, 10 major airports were randomly selected, and 10 cars from each company were randomly rented for inspection from each airport by USAC officials (i.e., a sample of size $n = 100$ cars from each company's fleet was drawn and inspected).

a. Describe the sampling distribution of $\bar{x}$, the mean score of a sample of $n = 100$ rental cars.
b. Interpret the mean of $\bar{x}$ in the context of this problem.
c. Assume $\mu = 30$ and $\sigma = 60$ for one rental car company. For this company, find $P(\bar{x} \geq 45)$.
d. Refer to part **c**. The company claims that their true fleet mean score "couldn't possibly be as high as 30." The sample mean score tabulated by USAC for this company was Does this result tend to support or refute the claim? Explain.

4.179 Analysis of supplier lead time. In determining when to place orders to replenish depleted product inventories, a retailer should take into consideration the lead times for the products. *Lead time* is the time between placing the order and having the product available to satisfy customer demand. It includes time for placing the order, receiving the shipment from the supplier, inspecting the units received, and placing them in inventory (Clauss, *Applied Management Science and Spreadsheet Modeling*, 1996). Interested in average lead time, μ, for a particular supplier of men's apparel, the

*Information by personal communication with Rajiv Tandon, corporate vice president and general manager of the Car Rental Division, National Car Rental Systems, Inc., Minneapolis, Minnesota.

purchasing department of a national department store chain randomly sampled 50 of the supplier's lead times and found $\bar{x} = 44$ days.

a. Describe the shape of the sampling distribution of $\bar{x}$.

b. If μ and σ are really 40 and 12, respectively, what is the probability that a second random sample of size 50 would yield $\bar{x}$ greater than or equal to 44?

c. Using the values for μ and σ in part **b**, what is the probability that a sample of size 50 would yield a sample mean within the interval $\mu \pm 2\sigma/\sqrt{n}$?

Applying the Concepts—Advanced

4.180 Plastic fill process. University of Louisville researchers J. Usher, S. Alexander, and D. Duggins examined the process of filling plastic pouches of dry blended biscuit mix (*Quality Engineering*, Vol. 91, 1996). The current fill mean of the process is set at $\mu = 406$ grams, and the process fill standard deviation is $\sigma = 10.1$ grams. (According to the researchers, "The high level of variation is due to the fact that the product has poor flow properties and is, therefore, difficult to fill consistently from pouch to pouch.") Operators monitor the process by randomly sampling 36 pouches each day and measuring the amount of biscuit mix in each. Consider $\bar{x}$, the mean fill amount of the sample of 36 products. Suppose that on one particular day, the operators observe $\bar{x} = 400.8$. One of the operators believes that this indicates that the true process fill mean μ for that day is less than 406 grams. Another operator argues that $\mu = 406$, and the small value of $\bar{x}$ observed is due to random variation in the fill process. Which operator do you agree with? Why?

4.181 Handwashing versus handrubbing. The *British Medical Journal* (Aug. 17, 2002) published the results of a study to compare the effectiveness of handwashing with soap and handrubbing with alcohol. Health care workers who used handrubbing had a mean bacterial count of 35 per hand with a standard deviation of 59. Health care workers who used handwashing had a mean bacterial count of 69 per hand with a standard deviation of 106. In a random sample of 50 health care workers, all using the same method of cleaning their hands, the mean bacterial count per hand, $\bar{x}$, is less than 30. Give your opinion on whether this sample of workers used handrubbing with alcohol or handwashing with soap.

CHAPTER NOTES

Key Terms

Bell curve 206
Bell-shaped distribution 206
Binomial probability distribution 191
Binomial experiment 187
Binomial random variable 187
Central Limit Theorem 246
Continuous random variable 176
Correction for continuity 225
Countable 176
Cumulative binomial probabilities 193
Discrete random variable 176
Expected value 180
Exponential probability distribution 232
Exponential random variable 233
Frequency function 205
Hypergeometric probability distribution 201
Hypergeometric random variable 201
Mean of a binomial random variable 192
Mean of a discrete random variable 180
Mean of a hypergeometric random variable 202

Mean of a Poisson random variable 199
Normal distribution 206
Normal probability plot 219
Normal random variable 206
Parameter 238
Poisson distribution 198
Poisson random variable 199
Probability density function 205
Probability distribution 205
Probability distribution of a discrete random variable 178
Probability distribution of an exponential random variable 232
Probability distribution of a hypergeometric random variable 202
Probability distribution of a normal random variable 207
Probability distribution of a Poisson random variable 199
Probability distribution for a uniform random variable 231
Random variable 174
Randomness distribution 230
Sample statistic 238
Sampling distribution 239
Standard deviation of a binomial random variable 192

Standard deviation of a discrete random variable 181
Standard error of the mean 245
Standard normal distribution 207
Uniform frequency function 230
Uniform probability distribution 230
Uniform random variable 230

Variance of a binomial random variable 192
Variance of a discrete random variable 181
Variance of a hypergeometric random variable 202
Variance of a Poisson random variable 199
Waiting-time distribution 232

Key Symbols

$p(x)$	Probability distribution for discrete random variable, x
$f(x)$	Probability distribution for continuous random variable, x
S	Outcome of binomial trial denoted "success"
F	Outcome of binomial trial denoted "failure"
p	$P(S)$ in binomial trial
q	$P(F)$ in binomial trial $= 1 - p$
e	Constant used in normal and Poisson probability distributions, $e = 2.71828\ldots$
π	Constant used in normal probability distributions, $\pi = 3.1415\ldots$
$\mu_{\bar{x}}$	Mean of the population sampling distribution of $\bar{x}$
$\sigma_{\bar{x}}$	Standard deviation of the population sampling distribution of $\bar{x}$

Key Formulas

Random Variable	Probability Distribution	Mean	Variance
General Discrete:	Table, formula, or graph for $p(x)$	$\displaystyle\sum_{\text{all } x} x \cdot p(x)$	$\displaystyle\sum_{\text{all } x}(x - \mu)^2 \cdot p(x)$
Binomial:	$p(x) = \dbinom{n}{x} p^x q^{n-x}$ $x = 0, 1, 2, \ldots, n$	np	npq
Poisson:	$p(x) = \dfrac{\lambda^x e^{-\lambda}}{x!}$ $x = 0, 1, 2, \ldots$	λ	λ
Hypergeometric	$p(x) = \dfrac{\dbinom{r}{x}\dbinom{N-r}{n-x}}{\dbinom{N}{n}}$	$\dfrac{nr}{N}$	$\dfrac{r(N-r)n(N-n)}{N^2(N-1)}$
Uniform:	$f(x) = 1/(d - c)$ $(c \le x \le d)$	$(c + d)/2$	$(d - c)^2/12$
Normal:	$f(x) = \dfrac{1}{\sigma\sqrt{2\pi}} e^{-1/2[(x-\mu)/\sigma]^2}$	μ	σ^2
Exponential	$f(x) = \dfrac{1}{\theta} e^{-x/\theta}$	θ	θ
Standard Normal:	$f(z) = \dfrac{1}{\sqrt{2\pi}} e^{-1/2(z)^2}$ $z = (x - \mu)/\sigma$	$\mu = 0$	$\sigma^2 = 1$
Sample Mean: (large n)	$f(\bar{x}) = \dfrac{1}{\sigma_{\bar{x}}\sqrt{2\pi}} e^{-1/2[(x-\mu)/\sigma_{\bar{x}}]^2}$	$\mu_{\bar{x}} = \mu$	$\sigma_{\bar{x}}^2 = \sigma^2/n$

Key Ideas

Properties of Probability Distributions

Discrete Distributions

1. $p(x) \ge 0$

2. $\displaystyle\sum_{\text{all } x} p(x) = 1$

Continuous Distributions

1. $P(x = a) = 0$

2. $P(a < x < b)$ is area under curve between a and b

Normal Approximation to Binomial

x is binomial (n, p)

$P(x \le a) \approx P\{z < (a + .5) - \mu\}$

Methods for Assessing Normality

1. *Histogram*

2. *Stem-and-leaf display*

   ```
   1 | 7
   2 | 3389
   3 | 245677
   4 | 19
   5 | 2
   ```

3. $(IQR)/S \approx 1.3$

4. *Normal probability plot*

   z-scores

Generating the Sampling Distribution of $\bar{x}$

Select sample size n (large) from target population

Calculate $\bar{x}$

$\bar{x}_1$
$\bar{x}_2$
$\bar{x}_3$
$\vdots$

Population:
Mean = μ
Std. Dev. = σ
Unknown shape

Repeat this process an infinite number of times

Sampling distribution of $\bar{x}$
(i.e., theoretical population of $\bar{x}$'s)
Mean = $\mu_{\bar{x}} = \mu$
Std. Dev. = $\sigma_{\bar{x}} = \sigma/\sqrt{n}$
Normal distribution (Central Limit Theorem)

Guide to Selecting a Probability Distribution

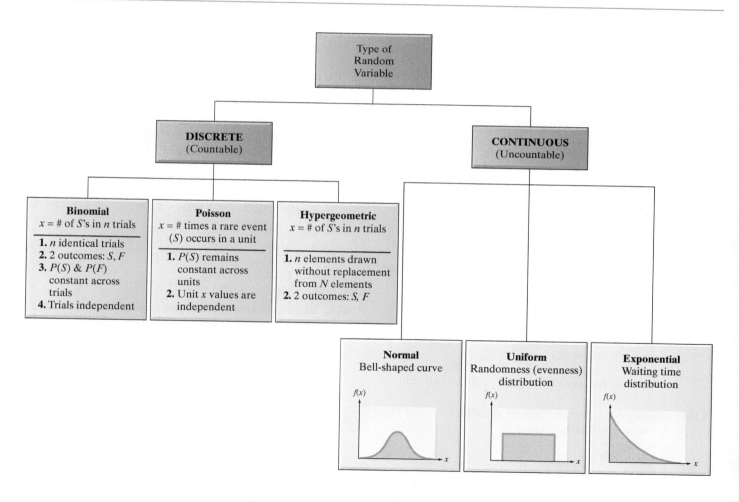

Type of Random Variable

DISCRETE (Countable)

CONTINUOUS (Uncountable)

Binomial
x = # of S's in n trials

1. n identical trials
2. 2 outcomes: S, F
3. $P(S)$ & $P(F)$ constant across trials
4. Trials independent

Poisson
x = # times a rare event (S) occurs in a unit

1. $P(S)$ remains constant across units
2. Unit x values are independent

Hypergeometric
x = # of S's in n trials

1. n elements drawn without replacement from N elements
2. 2 outcomes: S, F

Normal
Bell-shaped curve

$f(x)$

x

Uniform
Randomness (evenness) distribution

$f(x)$

x

Exponential
Waiting time distribution

$f(x)$

x

Supplementary Exercises 4.182–4.227

Learning the Mechanics

4.182 For each of the following examples, decide whether x is a binomial random variable and explain your decision:

a. A manufacturer of computer chips randomly selects 100 chips from each hour's production in order to estimate the proportion defective. Let x represent the number of defectives in the 100 sampled chips.

b. Of five applicants for a job, two will be selected. Although all applicants appear to be equally qualified, only three have the ability to fulfill the expectations of the company. Suppose that the two selections are made at random from the five applicants and let x be the number of qualified applicants selected.

c. A software developer establishes a support hotline for customers to call in with questions regarding use of the software. Let x represent the number of calls received on the support hotline during a specified workday.

d. Florida is one of a minority of states with no state income tax. A poll of 1,000 registered voters is conducted to determine how many would favor a state income tax in light of the state's current fiscal condition. Let x be the number in the sample who would favor the tax.

4.183 Given that x is a binomial random variable, compute $p(x)$ for each of the following cases:

a. $n = 7, x = 3, p = .5$
b. $n = 4, x = 3, p = .8$
c. $n = 15, x = 1, p = .1$

4.184 Consider the discrete probability distribution shown here.

x	10	12	18	20
$p(x)$	.2	.3	.1	.4

a. Calculate μ, σ^2, and σ.
b. What is $P(x < 15)$?
c. Calculate $\mu \pm 2\sigma$.
d. What is the probability that x is in the interval $\mu \pm 2\sigma$?

4.185 Suppose x is a binomial random variable with $n = 20$ and $p = .7$.

a. Find $P(x = 14)$.
b. Find $P(x \leq 12)$.
c. Find $P(x > 12)$.
d. Find $P(9 \leq x \leq 18)$.
e. Find $P(8 < x < 18)$.
f. Find μ, σ^2, and σ.
g. What is the probability that x is in the interval $\mu \pm 2\sigma$?

4.186 Suppose x is a Poisson random variable. Compute $p(x)$ for each of the following cases:

a. $\lambda = 2, x = 3$
b. $\lambda = 1, x = 4$
c. $\lambda = .5, x = 2$

4.187 Identify the type of random variable—binomial, Poisson, or hypergeometric—described by each of the following probability distributions:

a. $p(x) = \dfrac{.5^x e^{-5}}{x!}$ $(x = 0, 1, 2, \ldots)$

b. $p(x) = \dbinom{6}{x}(.2)^x(.8)^{6-x}$ $(x = 0,1,2,\ldots, 6)$

c. $p(x) = \dfrac{10!}{x!(10 - x)!}(.9)^x(.1)^{10-x}$
$(x = 0, 1, 2, \ldots, 10)$

4.188 Given that x is a hypergeometric random variable, compute $p(x)$ for each of the following cases:

a. $N = 8, n = 5, r = 3, x = 2$
b. $N = 6, n = 2, r = 2, x = 2$
c. $N = 5, n = 4, r = 4, x = 3$

4.189 Which of the following describe discrete random variables, and which describe continuous random variables?

a. The number of damaged inventory items
b. The average monthly sales revenue generated by a salesperson over the past year
c. Square feet of warehouse space a company rents
d. The length of time a firm must wait before its copying machine is fixed

4.190 Assume that x is a random variable best described by a uniform distribution with $c = 10$ and $d = 90$.

a. Find $f(x)$.
b. Find the mean and standard deviation of x.
c. Graph the probability distribution for x and locate its mean and the interval $\mu \pm 2\sigma$ on the graph.
d. Find $P(x \leq 60)$.
e. Find $P(x \geq 90)$.
f. Find $P(x \leq 80)$.
g. Find $P(\mu - \sigma \leq x \leq \mu + \sigma)$.
h. Find $P(x > 75)$.

4.191 Find the following probabilities for the standard normal random variable z:

a. $P(z \leq 2.1)$ **b.** $P(z \geq 2.1)$
c. $P(z \geq -1.65)$ **d.** $P(-2.13 \leq z \leq -.41)$
e. $P(-1.45 \leq z \leq 2.15)$ **f.** $P(z \leq -1.43)$

4.192 Find a z-score, call it z_0, such that

a. $P(z \leq z_0) = .5080$
b. $P(z \geq z_0) = .5517$
c. $P(z \geq z_0) = .1492$
d. $P(z_0 \leq z \leq .59) = .4773$

4.193 Identify the type of continuous random variable—uniform, normal, or exponential—described by each of the following probability density functions:

a. $f(x) = (e^{-x/7})/7, x > 0$
b. $f(x) = 1/20, 5 < x < 25$
c. $f(x) = \dfrac{e^{-.5[(x-10)/5]^2}}{5\sqrt{2\pi}}$

4.194 Assume that x has an exponential distribution with $\theta = 3$. Find

a. $P(x \leq 1)$ **b.** $P(x > 1)$
c. $P(x = 1)$ **d.** $P(x \leq 6)$
e. $P(2 \leq x \leq 10)$

4.195 The random variable x has a normal distribution with $\mu = 75$ and $\sigma = 10$. Find the following probabilities:

a. $P(x \leq 80)$ **b.** $P(x \geq 85)$
c. $P(70 \leq x \leq 75)$ **d.** $P(x > 80)$
e. $P(x = 78)$ **f.** $P(x \leq 110)$

4.196 Assume that x is a binomial random variable with $n = 100$ and $p = .5$. Use the normal probability distribution to approximate the following probabilities:
  a. $P(x \leq 48)$ **b.** $P(50 \leq x \leq 65)$
  c. $P(x \geq 70)$ **d.** $P(55 \leq x \leq 58)$
  e. $P(x = 62)$ **f.** $P(x \leq 49$ or $x \geq 72)$

4.197 The random variable x has a normal distribution with $\mu = 40$ and $\sigma^2 = 36$. Find a value of x, call it x_0, such that
  a. $P(x \geq x_0) = .10$ **b.** $P(\mu \leq x < x_0) = .40$
  c. $P(x < x_0) = .05$ **d.** $P(x \geq x_0) = .40$
  e. $P(x_0 \leq x < \mu) = .45$

4.198 A random sample of 40 observations is to be drawn from a large population of measurements. It is known that 30% of the measurements in the population are 1s, 20% are 2s, 20% are 3s, and 30% are 4s.
  a. Give the mean and standard deviation of the (repeated) sampling distribution of $\bar{x}$, the sample mean of the 40 observations.
  b. Describe the shape of the sampling distribution of $\bar{x}$. Does your answer depend on the sample size?

4.199 A random sample of $n = 68$ observations is selected from a population with $\mu = 19.6$ and $\sigma = 3.2$. Approximate each of the following probabilities.
  a. $P(\bar{x} \leq 19.6)$ **b.** $P(\bar{x} \leq 19)$
  c. $P(\bar{x} \geq 20.1)$ **d.** $P(19.2 \leq \bar{x} \leq 20.6)$

4.200 Use a statistical software package to generate 100 random samples of size $n = 2$ from a population characterized by a uniform probability distribution (Section 4.9) with $c = 0$ and $d = 10$. Compute $\bar{x}$ for each sample and plot a frequency distribution for the 100 $\bar{x}$ values. Repeat this process for $n = 5, 10, 30,$ and 50. Explain how your plots illustrate the Central Limit Theorem.

4.201 A random sample of size n is to be drawn from a large population with mean 100 and standard deviation 10, and the sample mean $\bar{x}$ is to be calculated. To see the effect of different sample sizes on the standard deviation of the sampling distribution of $\bar{x}$, plot $\sigma/\sqrt{n}$ against n for $n = 1, 5, 10, 20, 30, 40,$ and 50.

Applying the Concepts — Basic

4.202 **Back injuries at work.** A poll by the Gallup Organization sponsored by Philadelphia-based CIGNA Integrated Care found that about 40% of employees have missed work due to a musculoskeletal (back) injury of some kind (*National Underwriter*, Apr. 5, 1999). Let x be the number of sampled workers who have missed work due to a back injury.
  a. Explain why x is approximately a binomial random variable.
  b. Use the Gallup poll data to estimate p for the binomial random variable of part **a.**
  c. A random sample of 10 workers is to be drawn from a particular manufacturing plant. Use the p from part **b** to find the mean and standard deviation of x, the number of workers who missed work due to back injuries.
  d. For the sample in part **c**, find the probability that exactly one worker missed work due to a back injury. That more than one worker missed work due to a back injury.

4.203 **Dentists' use of laughing gas.** According to the American Dental Association, 60% of all dentists use nitrous oxide in their practice. If x equals the number of dentists in a random sample of five dentists who use laughing gas in practice, then the probability distribution of x is

x	0	1	2	3	4	5
$p(x)$	.0102	.0768	.2304	.3456	.2592	.0778

  a. Verify that the probabilities for x sum to 1.
  b. Find $P(x = 4)$.
  c. Find $P(x < 2)$.
  d. Find $P(x \geq 3)$.
  e. Find $\mu = E(x)$ and practically interpret this value.

4.204 **Analysis of "no-hitters" in baseball.** In baseball, a *no-hitter* is a regulation nine-inning game in which the pitcher yields no hits to the opposing batters. *Chance* (Summer 1994) reported on a study of no-hitters in Major League Baseball (MLB). The initial analysis focused on the total number of hits yielded per game per team for nine-inning MLB games. The distribution of hits/nine-innings is approximately normal with mean 8.72 and standard deviation 1.10.
  a. What percentage of nine-inning MLB games result in fewer than six hits?
  b. Demonstrate, statistically, why a no-hitter is considered an extremely rare occurrence in MLB.

4.205 **Trajectory of an electrical circuit.** Researchers at the University of California–Berkeley have designed, built, and tested a switched-capacitor circuit for generating random signals (*International Journal of Circuit Theory and Applications,* May–June 1990). The circuit's trajectory was shown to be uniformly distributed on the interval $(0, 1)$.
  a. Give the mean and variance of the circuit's trajectory.
  b. Compute the probability that the trajectory falls between .2 and .4.
  c. Would you expect to observe a trajectory that exceeds .995? Explain.

4.206 **Deep-draft vessel casualties.** University of New Mexico economists Gawande and Wheeler modeled the number of casualties experienced by a deep-draft marine vessel over a 3-year period as a Poisson random variable, x. They estimated $E(x)$ to be .03 (*Management Science*, January 1999).
  a. Find the variance x.
  b. Discuss the conditions that would make the researchers' Poisson assumption plausible.
  c. What is the probability that a deep-draft U.S. flag vessel will have exactly one casualty in a 3-year time period? No casualties in a 3-year period?

4.207 **Ocean quahog harvesting.** The ocean quahog is a type of clam found in the coastal waters of New England and the mid-Atlantic states. A federal survey of offshore ocean quahog harvesting in New Jersey, conducted from 1980 to 1992, revealed an average catch per unit effort (CPUE) of 89.34 clams. The CPUE standard deviation was 7.74 (*Journal of Shellfish Research*, June 1995). Let represent the mean CPUE for a sample of 35 attempts to catch ocean quahogs off the New Jersey shore.
  a. Compute $\mu_{\bar{x}}$ and $\sigma_{\bar{x}}$. Interpret their values.
  b. Sketch the sampling distribution of $\bar{x}$.

c. Find $P(\bar{x} > 88)$.

d. Find $P(\bar{x} < 87)$.

4.208 Dutch elm disease. A nursery advertises that it has 10 elm trees for sale. Unknown to the nursery, 3 of the trees have already been infected with Dutch elm disease and will die within a year.

a. If a buyer purchases 2 trees, what is the probability that both trees will be healthy?

b. Refer to part **a.** What is the probability that at least 1 of the trees is infected?

4.209 Hospital patient interarrival times. The length of time between arrivals at a hospital clinic has an approximately exponential probability distribution. Suppose the mean time between arrivals for patients at a clinic is 4 minutes.

a. What is the probability that a particular interarrival time (the time between the arrival of two patients) is less than 1 minute?

b. What is the probability that the next four interarrival times are all less than 1 minute?

c. What is the probability that an interarrival time will exceed 10 minutes?

4.210 Switching banks after a merger. Banks that merge with others to form "mega-banks" sometimes leave customers dissatisfied with the impersonal service. A poll by the Gallup Organization found 20% of retail customers switched banks after their banks merged with another (*Bank Marketing*, Feb. 1999). One year after the acquisition of First Fidelity by First Union, a random sample of 25 retail customers who had banked with First Fidelity were questioned. Let x be the number of those customers who switched their business from First Union to a different bank.

a. What assumptions must hold in order for x to be a binomial random variable? In the remainder of this exercise, use the data from the Gallop Poll to estimate p.

b. What is the probability that $x \leq 10$?

c. Find $E(x)$ and the standard deviation of x.

d. Calculate the interval $\mu \pm 2\sigma$.

e. If samples of size 25 were drawn repeatedly a large number of times and x determined for each sample, what proportion of the x values would fall within the interval you calculated in part **d**?

4.211 Machine repair times. An article in *IEEE Transactions* (Mar. 1990) gave an example of a flexible manufacturing system with four machines operating independently. The repair rates for the machines (i.e., the time, in hours, it takes to repair a failed machine) are exponentially distributed with means $\mu_1 = 1$, $\mu_2 = 2$, $\mu_3 = .5$, and $\mu_4 = .5$, respectively.

a. Find the probability that the repair time for machine 1 exceeds 1 hour.

b. Repeat part **a** for machine 2.

c. Repeat part **a** for machines 3 and 4.

d. If all four machines fail simultaneously, find the probability that the repair time for the entire system exceeds 1 hour.

4.212 Estimating demand for white bread. A bakery has determined that the number of loaves of its white bread demanded daily has a normal distribution with mean 7,200 loaves and standard deviation 300 loaves. Based on cost considerations, the company has decided that its best strategy is to produce a sufficient number of loaves so that it will fully supply demand on 94% of all days.

a. How many loaves of bread should the company produce?

b. Based on the production in part **a,** on what percentage of days will the company be left with more than 500 loaves of unsold bread?

4.213 Millions of suburban commuters are finding railroads to be a convenient, time-saving, less stressful alternative to the automobile. While generally perceived as a safe mode of transportation, the average number of deaths per week due to railroad accidents is a surprisingly high 20 (U.S. National Center for Health Statistics, *Vital Statistics of the United States, 2001*).

a. Construct arguments both for and against the use of the Poisson distribution to characterize the number of deaths per week due to railroad accidents.

b. For the remainder of this exercise, assume the Poisson distribution is an adequate approximation for x, the number of deaths per week due to railroad accidents. Find $E(x)$ and the standard deviation of x.

c. Based strictly on your answers to part **b,** is it likely that only four or fewer deaths occur next week? Explain.

d. Find $P(x \leq 4)$. Is this probability consistent with your answer to part **c?** Explain.

4.214 Environmental failures of Arkansas companies. Refer to the study of 38 Arkansas corporations that were penalized for violating one or more environmental laws, Exercise 2.27 (p. 51). The financial penalties assessed to the companies are saved in the **CLEANAIR** file. Determine whether the financial penalties are approximately normally distributed.

4.215 Time in bankruptcy. Refer to the *Financial Management* (Spring 1995) study of 49 companies that filed for a prepackaged bankruptcy, Exercise 2.30 (p. 52). The time in bankruptcy (measured in months) for each company is saved in the **BANKRUPT** file. Determine whether the bankruptcy times are approximately normally distributed.

4.216 Length of time working for an employer. Workers are much less likely to remain with one employer for many years than their parents were a generation before (*Georgia Trend*, December 1999). Do today's college students understand that the workplace they are about to enter is vastly different than the one their parents entered? To help answer this question, researchers at the Terry College of Business at the University of Georgia sampled 344 business students and asked them this question: Over the course of your lifetime, what is the maximum number of years you expect to work for any one employer? The resulting sample had $\bar{x} = 19.1$ years and $s = 6$ years. Assume the sample of students was randomly selected from the 5,800 undergraduate students in the Terry College.

a. Describe the sampling distribution of $\bar{x}$.

b. If the population mean was 18.5 years, what is $P(\bar{x} \geq 19.1$ years)?

c. If the population mean was 19.5 years, what is $P(\bar{x} \geq 19.1$ years)?

d. If $P(\bar{x} \geq 19.1) = .5$, what is the population mean?

e. If $P(\bar{x} \geq 19.1) = .2$, is the population mean greater or less than 19.1 years? Justify your answer.

4.217 Errors in measuring truck weights. To help highway planners anticipate the need for road repairs and design future construction projects, data are collected on the estimated volume and weight of truck traffic on specific roadways (*Transportation Planning Handbook*, 2008) using specialized "weigh-in-motion" equipment. In an experiment performed by the Minnesota Department of Transportation involving repeated weighing of a 27,907-pound truck, it was found that the weights recorded by the weigh-in-motion equipment were approximately normally distributed with a mean of 27,315 and a standard deviation of 628 pounds (Minnesota Department of Transportation). It follows that the difference between the actual weight and recorded weight, the error of measurement, is normally distributed with a mean of 592 pounds and a standard deviation of 628 pounds.

a. What is the probability that the weigh-in-motion equipment understates the actual weight of the truck?

b. If a 27,907-pound truck was driven over the weigh-in-motion equipment 100 times, approximately how many times would the equipment overstate the truck's weight?

c. What is the probability that the error in the weight recorded by the weigh-in-motion equipment for a 27,907-pound truck exceeds 400 pounds?

d. It is possible to adjust (or *calibrate*) the weigh-in-motion equipment to control the mean error of measurement. At what level should the mean error be set so the equipment will understate the weight of a 27,907-pound truck 50% of the time? Only 40% of the time?

4.218 Errors in filling prescriptions A large number of preventable errors (e.g., overdoses, botched operations, misdiagnoses) are being made by doctors and nurses in U.S. hospitals (*New York Times*, July 18, 1995). A study of a major metropolitan hospital revealed that of every 100 medications prescribed or dispensed, 1 was in error, but only 1 in 500 resulted in an error that caused significant problems for the patient. It is known that the hospital prescribes and dispenses 60,000 medications per year.

a. What is the expected number of errors per year at this hospital? The expected number of significant errors per year?

b. Within what limits would you expect the number of significant errors per year to fall?

c. What assumptions did you need to make in order to answer these questions?

4.219 Whistle-blowing among federal employees. *Whistle-blowing* refers to an employee's reporting of wrongdoing by coworkers. A survey found that about 5% of employees contacted had reported wrongdoing during the past 12 months. Assume that a sample of 25 employees in one agency are contacted and let x be the number who have observed and reported wrongdoing in the last 12 months. Assume that the probability of whistle-blowing is .05 for any federal employee over the past 12 months.

a. Find the mean and standard deviation of x. Can x be equal to its expected value? Explain.

b. Write the event that at least 5 of the employees are whistle-blowers in terms of x. Find the probability of the event.

c. If 5 of the 25 contacted have been whistle-blowers over the past 12 months, what would you conclude

about the applicability of the 5% assumption to this agency? Use your answer to part **b** to justify your conclusion.

4.220 Piercing rating of fencing safety jackets. A manufacturer produces safety jackets for competitive fencers. These jackets are rated by the minimum force, in newtons, that will allow a weapon to pierce the jacket. When this process is operating correctly, it produces jackets that have ratings with an average of 840 newtons and a standard deviation of 15 newtons. FIE, the international governing body for fencing, requires jackets to be rated at a minimum of 800 newtons. To check whether the process is operating correctly, a manager takes a sample of 50 jackets from the process, rates them, and calculates $\bar{x}$, the mean rating for jackets in the sample. She assumes that the standard deviation of the process is fixed but is worried that the mean rating of the process may have changed.

a. What is the sampling distribution of $\bar{x}$ if the process is still operating correctly?

b. Suppose the manager's sample has a mean rating of 830 newtons. What is the probability of getting an $\bar{x}$ of 830 newtons or lower if the process is operating correctly?

c. Given the manager's assumption that the standard deviation of the process is fixed, what does your answer to part **b** suggest about the current state of the process (i.e., does it appear that the mean jacket rating is still 840 newtons)?

d. Now suppose that the mean of the process has not changed, but the standard deviation of the process has increased from 15 newtons to 45 newtons. What is the sampling distribution of $\bar{x}$ in this case? What is the probability of getting an $\bar{x}$ of 830 newtons or lower when $\bar{x}$ has this distribution?

4.221 Awarding of home improvement grants. A curious event was described in the *Minneapolis Star and Tribune*. The Minneapolis Community Development Agency (MCDA) makes home improvement grants each year to homeowners in depressed city neighborhoods. Of the $708,000 granted one year, $233,000 was awarded by the city council via a "random selection" of 140 homeowners' applications from among a total of 743 applications: 601 from the north side, and 142 from the south side, of Minneapolis. Oddly, all 140 grants awarded were from the north side—clearly a highly improbable outcome if, in fact, the 140 winners were randomly selected from among the 743 applicants.

a. Suppose the 140 winning applications were randomly selected from among the total of 743 and let x equal the number in the sample from the north side. Find the mean and standard deviation of x.

b. Use the results of part **a** to support a contention that the grant winners were not randomly selected.

4.222 Time delays at a bus stop. A bus is scheduled to stop at a certain bus stop every half hour on the hour and the half hour. At the end of the day, buses still stop after every 30 minutes, but because delays often occur earlier in the day, the bus is never early and likely to be late. The director of the bus line claims that the length of time a bus is late is uniformly distributed, and the maximum time that a bus is late is 20 minutes.

a. If the director's claim is true, what is the expected number of minutes a bus will be late?

b. If the director's claim is true, what is the probability that the last bus on a given day will be more than 19 minutes late?

c. If you arrive at the bus stop at the end of a day at exactly half past the hour and must wait more than 19 minutes for the bus, what would you conclude about the director's claim? Why?

Applying the Concepts—Advanced

4.223 **How many questionnaires to mail?** The probability that a consumer responds to a marketing department's mailed questionnaire is .4. How many questionnaires should be mailed if you want to be reasonably certain that at least 100 will be returned?

4.224 **Establishing tolerance limits.** The *tolerance limits* for a particular quality characteristic (e.g., length, weight, or strength) of a product are the minimum and/or maximum values at which the product will operate properly. Tolerance limits are set by the engineering design function of the manufacturing operation (Moss, *Applying TQM to Product Design and Development,* 1996). The tensile strength of a particular metal part can be characterized as being normally distributed with a mean of 25 pounds and a standard deviation of 2 pounds. The upper and lower tolerance limits for the part are 30 pounds and 21 pounds, respectively. A part that falls within the tolerance limits results in a profit of $10. A part that falls below the lower tolerance limit costs the company $2; a part that falls above the upper tolerance limit costs the company $1. Find the company's expected profit per metal part produced.

4.225 **Purchasing decision.** A building contractor has decided to purchase a load of factory-reject aluminum siding as long as the average number of flaws per piece of siding in a sample of size 35 from the factory's reject pile is 2.1 or less. If it is known that the number of flaws per piece of siding in the factory's reject pile has a Poisson probability distribution with a mean of 2.5, find the approximate probability that the contractor will not purchase a load of siding.

Critical Thinking Challenges

4.226 **Reverse cocaine sting.** *The American Statistician* (May 1991) described an interesting application of a probability distribution in a case involving illegal drugs. During a drug bust, police seized 496 foil packets of a white, powdery substance that appeared to be cocaine. The police laboratory randomly selected 4 packets and found that all 4 tested positive for cocaine. This finding led to the conviction of the drug traffickers. Following the conviction, the police used 2 of the remaining 492 foil

packets (i.e., those not tested) in a reverse sting operation. The 2 randomly selected packets were sold by undercover officers to a buyer who disposed of the evidence before being arrested. Is there beyond a reasonable doubt that the 2 packets contained cocaine? To solve the dilemma, assume that of the 496 original packets confiscated, 331 contained genuine cocaine and 165 contained an inert (legal) powder. (A statistician, hired as an expert witness on the case, showed that the chance of the defendant being found not guilty is maximized when 331 packets contain cocaine and 165 do not.) [Hint: First, find the probability that 4 packets randomly selected from the original 496 will test positive for cocaine. Next find the probability that the 2 packets sold in the reverse sting did not contain cocaine. Finally, find the probability that both events occur (i.e., that the first 4 packets selected test positive for cocaine but that the next 2 packets selected do not). In each of these probability calculations, apply the binomial probability distribution to approximate the probabilities.]

4.227 **The insomnia pill.** A research report published in the *Proceedings of the National Academy of Sciences* (Mar. 1994) brought encouraging news to insomniacs and international business travelers who suffer from jet lag. Neuroscientists at the Massachusetts Institute of Technology (MIT) have been experimenting with melatonin—a hormone secreted by the pineal gland in the brain—as a sleep-inducing hormone. Because the hormone is naturally produced, it is nonaddictive. The researchers believe melatonin may be effective in treating jet lag. In the MIT study, young male volunteers were given various doses of melatonin or a placebo (a dummy medication containing no melatonin). Then they were placed in a dark room at midday and told to close their eyes for 30 minutes. The variable of interest was the time (in minutes) elapsed before each volunteer fell asleep.

Now, consider a random sample of 40 young males, each of whom is given a dosage of the sleep-inducing hormone, melatonin. The times (in minutes) to fall asleep for these 40 males are listed in the table and saved in the **INSOMNIA** file. The researchers know that with the placebo (i.e., no hormone), the mean time to fall asleep is $\mu = 15$ minutes and the standard deviation is $\sigma = 10$ minutes. They want to use the data to make an inference about the true value of μ for those taking the melatonin. Is melatonin an effective drug against insomnia?

7.6	2.1	1.4	1.5	3.6	17.0	14.9	4.4	4.7	20.1
7.7	2.4	8.1	1.5	10.3	1.3	3.7	2.5	3.4	10.7
2.9	1.5	15.9	3.0	1.9	8.5	6.1	4.5	2.2	2.6
7.0	6.4	2.8	2.8	22.8	1.5	4.6	2.0	6.3	3.2

[Note: These data are simulated sleep times based on summary information provided in the MIT study.]

References

Deming, W. E. *Out of the Crisis.* Cambridge, Mass.: MIT Center for Advanced Engineering Study, 1986.

Hogg, R. V., McKean, J. W., and Craig, A. T. *Introduction to Mathematical Statistics,* 6th ed. Upper Saddle River, N.J.: Prentice Hall, 2005.

Larsen, R. J., and Marx, M. L. *An Introduction to Mathematical Statistics and Its Applications,* 4th ed. Upper Saddle River, N.J.: Prentice Hall, 2005.

Lindgren, B. W. *Statistical Theory,* 4th ed. New York: Chapman & Hall, 1993.

Ramsey, P. P., and Ramsey, P. H. "Simple tests of normality in small samples," *Journal of Quality Technology,* Vol. 22, 1990.

Wackerly, D., Mendenhall, W., and Scheaffer, R, *Mathematical Statistics with Applications,* 7th ed. North Scituate, Mass.: Duxbury, 2008.

USING TECHNOLOGY

SPSS: Discrete Probabilities, Continuous Probabilities, Normal Probability Plots, and Simulated Sampling Distributions

Discrete and Continuous Probabilities

Step 1 Select "Transform" on the SPSS menu bar and then click on "Compute Variable," as shown in Figure 4.S.1. The resulting dialog box appears as shown in Figure 4.S.2.

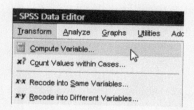

Figure 4.S.1 SPSS menu options for obtaining discrete and continuous probabilities

Figure 4.S.2 SPSS compute cumulative binomial probabilities dialog box

Step 2 Specify a name for the "Target Variable."

Step 3 Select either "CDF" (for cumulative probabilities) or "PDF" (for exact probabilities) in the "Function Group" box.

Step 4 Select the appropriate probability distribution in the "Functions and Special Variables" box. (For example, for cumulative probabilities of the binomial, use the function CDF.BINOM. For exact binomial probabilities, use the PDF.BINOM function.)

Step 5 Enter the parameters of the distribution in the "Numeric Expression" box. For example, Figure 4.S.2 shows the cumulative binomial function with parameters of $x = 3$ (the first number in the function), $n = 10$ (the second number), and $p = .2$ (the third number).

Step 6 Click "OK;" SPSS will compute the requested probability (in this example, the cumulative binomial probability that x is less than or equal to 3) and display it on the SPSS spreadsheet. Similarly, for example, Figure 4.S.3 shows the cumulative normal function with parameters of $x = 3.7$ (the first number in the function), $\mu = 5$ (the second number), and $\sigma = 2$ (the third number). When you click "OK," SPSS will compute the requested probability (in this example, the cumulative normal probability that x is less than 3.7) and display it on the SPSS spreadsheet.

Figure 4.S.3 SPSS compute cumulative normal probabilities dialog box

Normal Probability Plot

Step 1 Select "Analyze" on the SPSS menu bar, and then select "Descriptive Statistics" and "Q-Q Plots," as shown in Figure 4.S.4. The resulting dialog box appears as shown in Figure 4.S.5.

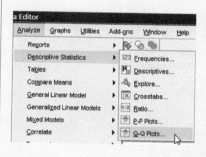

Figure 4.S.4 SPSS options for a normal probability plot

Figure 4.S.5 SPSS normal probability plot dialog box

Step 2 Specify the variable of interest in the "Variables" box and select "Normal" in the "Test Distribution" box.

Step 3 Click "OK" to generate the normal probability plot.

Sampling Distributions

Generating sampling distributions with SPSS is not a simple process. Consult the SPSS user's guide for help with this feature.

Minitab: Discrete Probabilities, Continuous Probabilities, Normal Probability Plots, and Simulated Sampling Distributions

Discrete and Continuous Probabilities

Step 1 Select the "Calc" button on the Minitab menu bar, click on "Probability Distributions" and then finally select the distribution of your choice (e.g., "Binomial"), as shown in Figure 4.M.1.

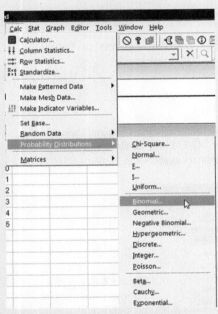

Figure 4.M.1 Minitab menu options for obtaining discrete and continuous probabilities

Step 2 Select either "Probability" or "Cumulative probability" on the resulting dialog box.

Step 3 Specify the parameters of the distribution (e.g., sample size n, probability of success p, μ or σ.)

Step 4 Specify the value of x of interest in the "Input constant" box.

Step 5 Click "OK." The probability for the value of x will appear on the Minitab session window.

[*Note:* Figure 4.M.2 gives the specifications for finding $P(x = 1)$ in a binomial distribution with $n = 5$ and $P = 2$. Figure 4.M.3 gives the specifications for finding $P(x \leq 20)$ in a normal distribution with $\mu = 24.5$ and $\sigma = 1$.]

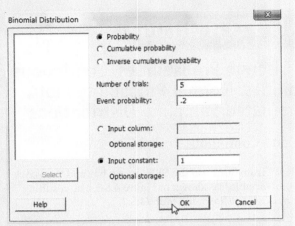

Figure 4.M.2 Minitab binomial distribution dialog box

Figure 4.M.3 Minitab normal distribution dialog box

Normal Probability Plot

Step 1 Select "Graph" on the Minitab menu bar and then click on "Probability Plot," as shown in Figure 4.M.4.

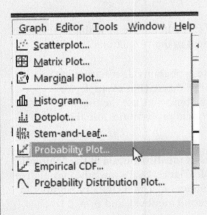

Figure 4.M.4 Minitab options for a normal probability plot

Step 2 Select "Single" (for one variable) on the next box, and the dialog box will appear as shown in Figure 4.M.5.

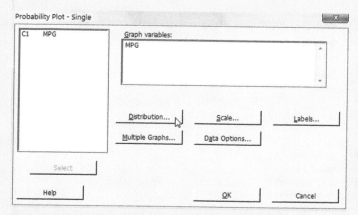

Figure 4.M.5 Minitab normal probability plot dialog box

Step 3 Specify the variable of interest in the "Graph variables" box and then click the "Distribution" button and select the "Normal" option. Click "OK" to return to the Probability Plot dialog box.

Step 4 Click "OK" to generate the normal probability plot.

Sampling Distributions

Step 1 Select "Calc" on the Minitab menu bar and then click on "Random Data" (see Figure 4.M.1).

Step 2 On the resulting menu list, click on the distribution of your choice (e.g., "Uniform"). A dialog box similar to the one (the Uniform Distribution) shown in Figure 4.M.6 will appear.

Figure 4.M.6 Minitab dialog box for simulating the uniform distribution

Step 3 Specify the number of samples (e.g., 1,000) to generate in the "Number of rows to generate" box and the columns where the data will be stored in the "Store in columns" box. (The number of columns will be equal to the sample size, e.g., 40.) Finally, specify the parameters of the distribution (e.g., the lower and upper range of the uniform distribution). When you click "OK," the simulated data will appear on the Minitab worksheet.

Step 4 Calculate the value of the sample statistic of interest for each sample. To do this, click on the "Calc" button on the Minitab menu bar and then click on "Row Statistics," as shown in Figure 4.M.7. The resulting dialog box appears in Figure 4.M.8.

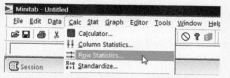

Figure 4.M.7 Minitab selections for generating sample statistics for the simulated data

Figure 4.M.8 Minitab row statistics dialog box

Step 5 Check the sample statistic (e.g., the mean) you want to calculate, specify the "Input variables" (or columns), and the column where you want the value of the sample statistic to be saved. Click "OK" and the value of the statistic for each sample will appear on the Minitab worksheet.

[*Note:* Use the Minitab menu choices provided in the Using Technology section in Chapter 2, p. 110 to generate a histogram of the sampling distribution of the statistic or to find the mean and variance of the sampling distribution.]

Excel/DDXL: Normal Probability Plot and Simulated Sampling Distributions

[*Note:* Discrete and continuous probability functions are unavailable in Excel and DDXL.]

Normal Probability Plot

Step 1 Highlight the cells (columns) with the data for the variable to be analyzed on the Excel spreadsheet.

Step 2 Click on the "Add-ins" button on the Excel menu bar, and then select "DDXL."

Step 3 Select "Charts and Plots" on the resulting menu, as shown in Figure 4.E.1.

Figure 4.E.1 Excel/DDXL options for a normal probability plot

Step 4 On the Charts and Plots dialog box (see Figure 4.E.2), specify "Normal Probability Plot" in the "Function Type" box, and select the variable to be analyzed in the "Quantitative Variable" box.

Figure 4.E.2 Excel/DDXL charts and plots dialog box

Step 5 Click "OK" to view the normal probability plot.

Sampling Distributions

Step 1 Select "Data" on the main menu bar and then click on "Data Analysis." The resulting menu is shown in Figure 4.E.3.

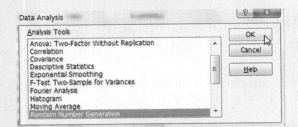

Figure 4.E.3 Excel data analysis menu options

Step 2 Select "Random Number Generation" from the Data Analysis menu and then click "OK." The dialog box in Figure 4.E.4 will appear.

Step 3 Specify the number of samples (e.g., 10) to generate in the "Number of Variables" box and the sample size of each (e.g., 100) in the "Number of Random Numbers" box.

Figure 4.E.4 Excel dialog box for generating uniform random numbers

Step 4 Specify the distribution (e.g., uniform) that the samples will be selected from and the parameters of the distribution.

Step 5 Click "OK;" the random numbers will appear on a new Excel spreadsheet (Figure 4.E.5).

Step 6 Specify a formula for the sample mean on the resulting Excel spreadsheet. For example, the formula "=AVERAGE (A2:J2)" in column "L" computes the mean of the 10 random numbers in each row of the spreadsheet shown in Figure 4.E.5.

Step 7 Once the means of the random samples are computed, you can generate a histogram or summary statistics for the mean by following the steps outlined in Using Technology, Chapter 2.

TI-84 Graphing Calculator: Discrete and Continuous Random Variables and Normal Probability Plots

Calculating the Mean and Standard Deviation of a Discrete Random Variable

Step 1 *Enter the data*

- Press **STAT** and select **1:Edit**

Note: If the lists already contain data, clear the old data. Use the up **ARROW** to highlight '**L1**'

- Press **CLEAR ENTER**

- Use the up **ARROW** to highlight '**L2**'

Figure 4.E.5 Excel formula for computing sample means from random numbers

- Press **CLEAR ENTER**
- Use the **ARROW** and **ENTER** keys to enter the x-values of the variable into **L1**
- Use the **ARROW** and **ENTER** keys to enter the probabilities, $P(x)$, into **L2**

Step 2 *Access the Calc Menu*

- Press **STAT**
- Arrow right to **CALC**
- Select **1-Var Stats**
- Press **ENTER**
- Press **2nd 1** for **L1**
- Press **COMMA**
- Select **2nd 2** for **L2**
- Press **ENTER**

The mean and standard deviation will be displayed on the screen, as well as the quartiles, min, and max.

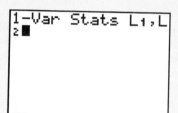

Calculating Binomial Probabilities

I. $P(x = k)$

To compute the probability of k successes in n trials, where p is the probability of success for each trial, use the **binompdf(** command. *Binompdf* stands for "binomial probability density function." This command is under the **DISTR**ibution menu and has the format **binompdf(n, p, k)**.

Example Compute the probability of 5 successes in 8 trials, where the probability of success for a single trial is 40%. In this example, $n = 8$, $p = .4$, and $k = 5$.

Step 1 *Enter the binomial parameters*

- Press **2nd VARS** for **DISTR**
- Press the down **ARROW** key until **binompdf** is highlighted
- Press **ENTER**
- After **binompdf(**, type **8, .4, 5)** (*Note:* be sure to use the **COMMA** key between each parameter)
- Press **ENTER**
- You should see

Thus, $P(x = 5)$ is about 12.4%.

II. $P(x \le k)$

To compute the probability of k or fewer successes in n trials, where p is the probability of success for each trial, use the **binomcdf(** command. *Binomcdf* stands for "binomial *cumulative* probability density function." This command is under the **DISTR**ibution menu and has the format **binomcdf(n, p, k)**.

Example Compute the probability of 5 or fewer successes in 8 trials, where the probability of success for a single trial is 40%. In this example, $n = 8$, $p = .4$, and $k = 5$.

Step 2 *Enter the binomial parameters*

- Press **2nd VARS** for **DISTR**
- Press down the **ARROW** key until **binomcdf** is highlighted
- Press **ENTER**
- After **binomcdf(**, type **8, .4, 5)**
- Press **ENTER**
- You should see

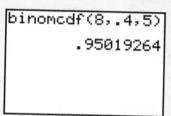

Thus, $P(x \le k)$ is about 95%.

III. $P(x < k)$, $P(x > k)$, $P(x \ge k)$

To find the probability of less than k successes $P(x < k)$, more than k successes $P(x > k)$, or at least k successes $P(x \ge k)$, variations of the **binomcdf(** command must be used as shown below.

- $P(x < k)$ use **binomcdf(n, p, k − 1)**
- $P(x > k)$ use **1 − binomcdf(n, p, k)**
- $P(x \ge k)$ use **1 − binomcdf(n, p, k − 1)**

Calculating Poisson Probabilities

I. $P(x = k)$

To compute $P(x = k)$, the probability of exactly k successes in a specified interval where λ is the mean number of successes in the interval, use the **poissonpdf(** command. *Poissonpdf* stands for "Poisson probability density function." This command is under the **DISTR**ibution menu and has the format **poissonpdf( )**.

Example Suppose that the number, x, of reported sightings per week of blue whales is recorded. Assume that x has approximately a Poisson probability distribution and that the average number of weekly sightings is 2.6. Compute the probability that exactly five sightings are made during a given week. In this example, $\lambda = 2.6$ and $k = 5$.

Step 1 *Enter the poisson parameters*

- Press **2nd VARS** for **DISTR**
- Press the down **ARROW** key until **poissonpdf** is highlighted
- Press **ENTER**
- After **poissonpdf(**, type **2.6, 5)** (*Note:* be sure to use the **COMMA** key between each parameter)
- Press **ENTER**
- You should see

Thus, the $P(x = 5)$ is about 7.4%.

II. $P(x \le k)$

To compute the probability of k or fewer successes in a specified interval, where λ is the mean number of successes in the interval, use the **poissoncdf(** command. *Poissoncdf* stands for "Poisson *cumulative* probability density function." This command is under the **DISTR**ibution menu and has the format **poissoncdf(**.

Example In the preceding example, compute the probability that five or fewer sightings are made during a given week. In this example, $\lambda = 2.6$ and $k = 5$.

Step 1 *Enter the poisson parameters*

- Press **2nd VARS** for **DISTR**
- Press the down **ARROW** key until **poissoncdf** is highlighted
- Press **ENTER**
- After **poissoncdf(**, type **2.6, 5**
- Press **ENTER**
- You should see:

Thus, the $P(x = 5)$ is about 95.1%.

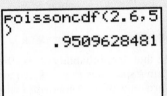

III. $P(x < k)$, $P(x > k)$, $P(x \geq k)$

To find the probability of less than k successes, more than k successes, or at least k successes, variations of the **poissoncdf(** command must be used as shown below.

- $P(x < k)$ use **poissoncdf(** $\lambda, k - 1$)
- $P(x > k)$ use 1 – **poissoncdf(** λ, k)
- $P(x \geq k)$ use 1 – **poissoncdf(** $\lambda, k - 1$)

Graphing the Area under the Standard Normal Curve

Step 1 *Turn off all plots*

- Press **2nd PRGM** and select **1:ClrDraw**
- Press **ENTER** and "Done" will appear on the screen
- Press **2nd Y=** and select **4:PlotsOff**
- Press **ENTER** and "Done" will appear on the screen

Step 2 *Set the viewing window (Recall that almost all of the area under the standard normal curve falls between −5 and 5. A height of 0.5 is a good choice for Ymax.)*

Note: When entering a negative number, be sure to use the negative sign (−), not the minus sign.

- Set **Xmin** = −5
- **Xmax** = 5
- **Xscl** = 1
- **Ymin** = 0
- **Ymax** = .5
- **Yscl** = 0
- **Xres** = 1

Step 3 *View graph*

- Press **2nd VARS**
- Arrow right to **DRAW**
- Press **ENTER** to select **1:ShadeNorm(**
- Enter your lower limit (e.g., −5)

- Press **COMMA**
- Enter your upper limit (e.g., 1.5)
- Press **)**
- Press **ENTER**

The graph will be displayed along with the area, lower limit, and upper limit.

Thus, $P(z < 1.5) = .9332$.

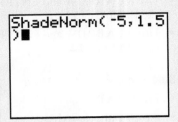

Nonstandard Normal Probabilities

I. Finding Normal Probabilities without a Graph

To compute probabilities for a normal distribution, use the **normalcdf(** command. *Normalcdf* stands for "normal cumulative density function." This command is under the **DISTR**ibution menu and has the format **normalcdf(***lower limit, upper limit, mean, standard deviation*).

Step 1 *Find probability*

- Press **2nd VARS** for **DISTR** and select **Normalcdf(**
- After **Normalcdf(**, type in the lower limit
- Press **COMMA**
- Enter the upper limit
- Press **COMMA**
- Enter the mean
- Press **COMMA**
- Enter the standard deviation
- Press **)**
- Press **ENTER**

The probability will be displayed on the screen.

Example What is $P(x < 115)$ for a normal distribution with $\mu = 100$ and $\sigma = 10$? In this example, the lower limit is $-\infty$, the upper limit is 115, the mean is 100, and the standard deviation is 10. To represent $-\infty$ on the calculator, enter **(−) 1**, press **2nd** and press the **COMMA** key for **EE,** and then press **99**. The screen appears as follows:

Thus, $P(x < 115)$ is .9332.

II. Finding Normal Probabilities with a Graph

Step 1 *Turn off all plots*

- Press **Y=** and **CLEAR** all functions from the Y registers
- Press **2nd Y=** and select **4:PlotsOff**
- Press **ENTER ENTER,** and 'Done' will appear on the screen

Step 2 *Set the viewing window (These values depend on the mean and standard deviation of the data.) Note:* When entering a negative number, be sure to use the negative sign (−), not the minus sign.

- Press **WINDOW**
- Set **Xmin** = $\mu - 5\sigma$

- **Xmax** = $\mu + 5\sigma$
- **Xscl** = σ
- **Ymin** = $-.125/\sigma$
- **Ymax** = $.5/\sigma$
- **Yscl** = 1
- **Xres** = 1

Step 3 *View graph*

- Press **2nd VARS**
- **ARROW** right to **DRAW**
- Press **ENTER** to select **1:ShadeNorm(**
- Enter the lower limit
- Press **COMMA**
- Enter the upper limit
- Press **COMMA**
- Enter the mean
- Press **COMMA**
- Enter the standard deviation
- Press **)**
- Press **ENTER**

The graph will be displayed along with the area, lower limit, and upper limit.

Example What is $P(x < 115)$ for a normal distribution with $\mu = 100$ and $\sigma = 10$? In this example, the lower limit is $-\infty$, the upper limit is 115, the mean is 100, and the standard deviation is 10. To represent $-\infty$ on the calculator, enter $(-)$ **1**, press **2nd** and press the **comma** key for **EE,** and then press **99**. The screens appear as follows:

Graphing a Normal Probability Plot

Step 1 *Enter the data*

- Press **STAT** and select **1:Edit**

Note: If the list already contains data, clear the old data. Use the up arrow to highlight **L1**.

- Press **CLEAR ENTER**
- Use the **ARROW** and **ENTER** keys to enter the data set into **L1**

Step 2 *Set up the normal probability plot*

- Press **Y=** and **CLEAR** all functions from the Y registers
- Press **2nd** and press **Y=** for **STAT PLOT**
- Press **1** for **Plot 1**
- Set the cursor so that **ON** is flashing
- For **Type,** use the **ARROW** and **ENTER** keys to highlight and select the last graph in the bottom row
- For **Data List,** choose the column containing the data (in most cases, L1) (Note: Press **2nd** 1 for **L1**)
- For **Data Axis,** choose **X** and press **ENTER**

Step 3 *View plot*

- Press **ZOOM 9**

Your data will be displayed against the expected z-scores from a normal distribution. If you see a "generally" linear relationship, your data set is approximately normal.

The Furniture Fire Case

Covers Chapters 3 and 4 — A wholesale furniture retailer stores in-stock items at a large warehouse located in Tampa, Florida. Early in the year, a fire destroyed the warehouse and all the furniture in it. After determining the fire was an accident, the retailer sought to recover costs by submitting a claim to its insurance company.

As is typical in a fire insurance policy of this type, the furniture retailer must provide the insurance company with an estimate of "lost" profit for the destroyed items. Retailers calculate profit margin in percentage form using the Gross Profit Factor (GPF). By definition, the GPF for a single sold item is the ratio of the profit to the item's selling price measured as a percentage, that is,

Item GPF = (Profit/Sales price) × 100%

Of interest to both the retailer and the insurance company is the average GPF for all of the items in the warehouse. Because these furniture pieces were all destroyed, their eventual selling prices and profit values are obviously unknown. Consequently, the average GPF for all the warehouse items is unknown.

One way to estimate the mean GPF of the destroyed items is to use the mean GPF of similar, recently sold items. The retailer sold 3,005 furniture items in the year prior to the fire and kept paper invoices on all sales. Rather than calculate the mean GPF for all 3,005 items (the data were not computerized), the retailer sampled a total of 253 of the invoices and computed the mean GPF for these items. The 253 items were obtained by first selecting a sample of 134 items and then augmenting this sample with a second sample of 119 items. The mean GPFs for the two subsamples were calculated to be 50.6% and 51.0%, respectively, yielding an overall average GPF of 50.8%. This average GPF can be applied to the costs of the furniture items destroyed in the fire to obtain an estimate of the "lost" profit.

According to experienced claims adjusters at the insurance company, the GPF for sale items of the type destroyed in the fire rarely exceeds 48%. Consequently, the estimate of 50.8% appeared to be unusually high. (A 1% increase in GPF for items of this type equates to, approximately, an additional $16,000 in profit.) When the insurance company questioned the retailer on this issue, the retailer responded "Our estimate was based on selecting two independent, random samples from the population of 3,005 invoices. Because the samples were selected randomly and the total sample size is large, the mean GPF estimate of 50.8% is valid."

A dispute arose between the furniture retailer and the insurance company, and a lawsuit was filed. In one portion of the suit, the insurance company accused the retailer of fraudulently representing their sampling methodology. Rather than selecting the samples randomly, the retailer was accused of selecting an unusual number of "high-profit" items from the population in order to increase the average GPF of the overall sample.

To support their claim of fraud, the insurance company hired a CPA firm to independently assess the retailer's Gross Profit Factor. Through the discovery process, the CPA firm legally obtained the paper invoices for the entire population of 3,005 items sold and input the information into a computer. The selling price, profit, profit margin, and month sold for these 3,005 furniture items are stored in the **FIRE** file, described below.

Your objective in this case is to use these data to determine the likelihood of fraud. Is it likely that a random sample of 253 items selected from the population of 3,005 items would yield a mean GPF of at least 50.8%? Or, is it likely that two independent, random samples of sizes 134 and 119 will yield mean GPFs of at least 50.6% and 51.0%, respectively? (These were the questions posed to a statistician retained by the CPA firm.) Use the ideas of probability and sampling distributions to guide your analysis.

Prepare a professional document that presents the results of your analysis and gives your opinion regarding fraud. Be sure to describe the assumptions and methodology used to arrive at your findings.

Variable	Type	Description
MONTH	QL	Month in which item was sold in 1991
INVOICE	QN	Invoice number
SALES	QN	Sales price of item in dollars
PROFIT	QN	Profit amount of item in dollars
MARGIN	QN	Profit margin of item = (Profit/Sales) × 100%

Data Set: FIRE

5 Inferences Based on a Single Sample
Estimation with Confidence Intervals

Where We've Been

- Learned that populations are characterized by numerical descriptive measures called *parameters*

- Found that decisions about population parameters are based on *statistics* computed from the sample

- Discovered that *inferences* about parameters are subject to uncertainty and that this uncertainty is reflected in the *sampling distribution* of a statistic

Where We're Going

- Estimate a population parameter (means or proportion) based on a large sample selected from the population

- Use the sampling distribution of a statistic to form a confidence interval for the population parameter

- Show how to select the proper sample size for estimating a population parameter

Statistics IN Action   Medicare Fraud Investigations

United States Department of Justice (USDOJ) press release (May 8, 2008): *Eleven people have been indicted in … a targeted criminal, civil and administrative effort against individuals and health care companies that fraudulently bill the Medicare program. The indictments in the Central District of California resulted from the creation of a multi-agency team of federal, state and local investigators designed specifically to combat Medicare fraud through the use of real-time analysis of Medicare billing data.*

USDOJ press release (Jun 27, 2008): *The owners of four Miami-based healthcare corporations were sentenced and remanded to prison yesterday for their roles in schemes to defraud the Medicare program. Collectively, the three defendants through their companies collected more than $14 million from the Medicare program for unnecessary medicine, durable medical equipment (DME) and home health care services.*

USDOJ press release (Oct. 7, 2008): *Eight Miami-Dade County residents have been charged in a 16-count indictment for their alleged roles in a Medicare fraud scheme involving fake HIV infusion treatments.*   *(continued)*

Statistics ɪɴ Action
(continued)

As the above press releases imply, the U.S. Department of Justice (USDOJ) and its Medicare Fraud Strike Force conducts investigations into suspected fraud and abuse of the Medicare system by health care providers. According to published reports, the Strike Force was responsible for almost 25% of the Medicare fraud charges brought nationwide in 2007.

One way in which Medicare fraud occurs is through the use of "upcoding," which refers to the practice of providers coding Medicare claims at a higher level of care than was actually provided to the patient. For example, suppose a particular kind of claim can be coded at three levels, where Level 1 is a routine office visit, Level 2 is a thorough examination involving advanced diagnostic tests, and Level 3 involves performing minor surgery. The amount of Medicare payment is higher for each increased level of claim. Thus, upcoding would occur if Level 1 services were billed at Level 2 or Level 3 payments, or if Level 2 services were billed at Level 3 payment.

The USDOJ relies on sound statistical methods to help identify Medicare fraud. Once the USDOJ has determined that possible upcoding has occurred, it next seeks to further investigate whether it is the result of legitimate practice (perhaps the provider is a specialist giving higher levels of care) or the result of fraudulent action on the part of the provider. To further its investigation, the USDOJ will next ask a statistician to select a sample of the provider's claims. For example, the statistician might determine that a random sample of 52 claims from the 1,000 claims in question will provide a sufficient sample to estimate the overcharge reliably. The USDOJ then asks a health care expert to audit each of the medical files corresponding to

the sampled claims and determine whether the level of care matches the level billed by the provider, and, if not, to determine what level should have been billed. Once the audit has been completed, the USDOJ will calculate the overcharge.

In this chapter, we present a recent Medicare fraud case investigated by the USDOJ. Results for the audit of 52 sampled claims, with the amount paid for each claim, the amount disallowed by the auditor, and the amount that should have been paid for each claim, are saved in the **MCFRAUD** file.* Knowing that a total of $103,500 was paid for the 1,000 claims, the USDOJ wants to use the sample results to extrapolate the overpayment amount to the entire population of 1,000 claims.

Statistics ɪɴ **Action Revisited**

- Estimating the Mean Overpayment (p. 286)
- Estimating the Coding Error Rate (p. 294)
- Determining Sample Size (p. 301)

Data Set: MCFRAUD

5.1 Identifying and Estimating the Target Parameter

In this chapter, our goal is to estimate the value of an unknown population parameter, such as a population mean or a proportion from a binomial population. For example, we might want to know the mean gas mileage for a new car model, the average expected life of a flat-screen computer monitor, or the proportion of dot-com companies that fail within a year of start-up.

You'll see that different techniques are used for estimating a mean or proportion, depending on whether a sample contains a large or small number of measurements. Nevertheless, our objectives remain the same. We want to use the sample information to estimate the population parameter of interest (called the **target parameter**) and assess the reliability of the estimate.

> The unknown population parameter (e.g., mean or proportion) that we are interested in estimating is called the **target parameter.**

Often, there are one or more key words in the statement of the problem that indicate the appropriate target parameter. Some key words associated with the two parameters covered in this section are listed in the table on the next page.

*Data provided (with permission) from Info Tech, Inc., Gainesville, Florida.

Determining the Target Parameter

Parameter	Key Words or Phrases	Type of Data
μ	Mean; average	Quantitative
p	Proportion; percentage; fraction; rate	Qualitative

For the examples given above, the words *mean* in *mean gas mileage* and *average* in *average life expectancy* imply that the target parameter is the population mean, μ. The word *proportion* in *proportion of dot-com companies that fail within one year of start-up* indicates that the target parameter is the binomial proportion, p.

In addition to key words and phrases, the type of data (quantitative or qualitative) collected is indicative of the target parameter. With quantitative data, you are likely to be estimating the mean of the data. With qualitative data with two outcomes (success or failure), the binomial proportion of successes is likely to be the parameter of interest.

A single number calculated from the sample that estimates a target population parameter is called a **point estimator.** For example, we'll use the sample mean, $\bar{x}$, to estimate the population mean μ. Consequently, $\bar{x}$ is a point estimator. Similarly, we'll learn that the sample proportion of successes, denoted $\hat{p}$, is a point estimator for the binomial proportion p. Also, we will attach a measure of reliability to our estimate by obtaining an **interval estimator**—a range of numbers that contain the target parameter with a high degree of confidence. For this reason the interval estimate is also called a **confidence interval.**

> A **point estimator** of a population parameter is a rule or formula that tells us how to use the sample data to calculate a *single* number that can be used as an *estimate* of the target parameter.

> An **interval estimator** (or **confidence interval**) is a formula that tells us how to use the sample data to calculate an *interval* that *estimates* the target parameter.

We consider confidence intervals for estimating a population mean using a large sample in Section 5.2 and a small sample in Section 5.3. Confidence intervals for a population proportion are presented in Section 5.4. In Section 5.5, we show how to determine the sample sizes necessary for reliable estimates of the target parameters based on simple random sampling. Finally, in Sections 5.6 and 5.7 we introduce more complex sample survey designs and their application to business.

5.2 Confidence Interval for a Population Mean: Normal (z) Statistic

Suppose a large bank wants to estimate the average amount of money owed by its delinquent debtors (i.e., debtors who are more than 2 months behind in payment). To accomplish this objective, the bank plans to randomly sample 100 of its delinquent accounts and use the sample mean, $\bar{x}$, of the amounts overdue to estimate μ, the mean for *all* delinquent accounts. Because the sample mean $\bar{x}$ represents a single number estimator, it is the *point estimator* of the target parameter μ. How can we assess the accuracy of this point estimator?

According to the Central Limit Theorem, the sampling distribution of the sample mean is approximately normal for large samples, as shown in Figure 5.1. Let us calculate the interval estimator:

$$\bar{x} \pm 1.96\sigma_{\bar{x}} = \bar{x} \pm \frac{1.96\sigma}{\sqrt{n}}$$

That is, we form an interval from 1.96 standard deviations below the sample mean to 1.96 standard deviations above the mean. *Prior to drawing the sample*, what are the chances that this interval will enclose μ, the population mean?

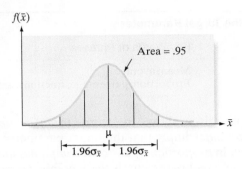

Figure 5.1
Sampling distribution of $\bar{x}$

To answer this question, refer to Figure 5.1. If the 100 measurements yield a value of $\bar{x}$ that falls between the two lines on either side of μ (i.e., within 1.96 standard deviations of μ), then the interval $\bar{x} \pm 1.96\sigma_{\bar{x}}$ will contain μ; if $\bar{x}$ falls outside these boundaries, the interval $\bar{x} \pm 1.96\sigma_{\bar{x}}$ will not contain μ. From Section 4.7, we know that the area under the normal curve (the sampling distribution of $\bar{x}$) between these boundaries is exactly .95. Thus, the probability that a randomly selected interval, $\bar{x} \pm 1.96\sigma_{\bar{x}}$, will contain μ is equal to .95.

Example 5.1

Estimating the Mean Overdue Amount, σ Known

Problem Consider the large bank that wants to estimate the average amount of money owed by its delinquent debtors, μ. The bank randomly samples $n = 100$ of its delinquent accounts and finds that the sample mean amount owed is $\bar{x} = \$230$. Also, suppose it is known that the standard deviation of the amount owed for all delinquent accounts is $\sigma = \$90$. Use the interval estimator $\bar{x} \pm 1.96\sigma_{\bar{x}}$ to calculate a confidence interval for the target parameter, μ.

Solution Substituting $\bar{x} = 230$ and $\sigma = 90$ into the interval estimator formula, we obtain:

$$\bar{x} \pm 1.96\sigma_{\bar{x}} = \bar{x} \pm (1.96)\sigma/\sqrt{n} = 230 \pm (1.96)(90/\sqrt{100}) = 230 \pm 17.64$$

Or, $(212.36, 247.64)$

Look Back Because we know the probability that the interval $\bar{x} \pm 1.96\sigma_{\bar{x}}$ will contain μ is .95, we call the interval estimator a *95% confidence interval* for μ.

Now Work Exercise 5.3a

The interval $\bar{x} \pm 1.96\sigma_{\bar{x}}$ in Example 5.1 is called a *large-sample* 95% confidence interval for the population mean μ. The term *large-sample* refers to the sample being of sufficiently large size that we can apply the Central Limit Theorem and the normal (z) statistic to determine the form of the sampling distribution of $\bar{x}$. Empirical research suggests that a sample size n exceeding a value between 20 and 30 will usually yield a sampling distribution of $\bar{x}$ that is approximately normal. This result led many practitioners to adopt the rule of thumb that a sample size of $n \geq 30$ is required to use large-sample confidence interval procedures. Keep in mind, though, that 30 is not a magical number and, in fact, is quite arbitrary.

Also, note that the large-sample interval estimator requires knowing the value of the population standard deviation, σ. In most (if not nearly all) practical business applications, however, the value of σ will be unknown. For large samples, the fact that σ is unknown poses only a minor problem because the sample standard deviation s provides a very good approximation to σ. The next example illustrates the more realistic large-sample confidence interval procedure.

Example 5.2

Estimating the Mean Overdue Amount, σ Unknown

Problem Refer to Example 5.1 and the problem of estimating μ, the average amount of money owed by a bank's delinquent debtors. The overdue amounts for the $n = 100$ delinquent accounts are shown in Table 5.1. Use the data to find a 95% confidence interval for μ and interpret the result.

Table 5.1		Overdue Amounts (in Dollars) for 100 Delinquent Accounts							
195	243	132	133	209	400	142	312	221	289
221	162	134	275	355	293	242	458	378	148
278	222	236	178	202	222	334	208	194	135
363	221	449	265	146	215	113	229	221	243
512	193	134	138	209	207	206	310	293	310
237	135	252	365	371	238	232	271	121	134
203	178	180	148	162	160	86	234	244	266
119	259	108	289	328	331	330	227	162	354
304	141	158	240	82	17	357	187	364	268
368	274	278	190	344	157	219	77	171	280

Data Set: OVERDUE

	A	B
1	AMOUNT	
2		
3	Mean	233.28
4	Standard Error	9.033988347
5	Median	222
6	Mode	221
7	Standard Deviation	90.33988347
8	Sample Variance	8161.294545
9	Kurtosis	0.254810234
10	Skewness	0.476799829
11	Range	495
12	Minimum	17
13	Maximum	512
14	Sum	23328
15	Count	100

Figure 5.2a

Excel summary statistics for overdue amounts

Solution The large bank almost surely does not know the true standard deviation, σ, of the population of overdue amounts. However, because the sample size is large, we will use the sample standard deviation, s, as an estimate for σ in the confidence interval formula. An Excel printout of summary statistics for the sample of 100 overdue amounts is shown in Figure 5.2a. From the shaded portion of the printout, we find $\bar{x} = 233.28$ and $s = 90.34$. Substituting these values into the interval estimator formula, we obtain:

$$\bar{x} \pm (1.96)\sigma/\sqrt{n} \approx \bar{x} \pm (1.96)s/\sqrt{n} = 233.28 \pm (1.96)(90.34)/\sqrt{100} = 233.28 \pm 17.71$$

Or, (215.57, 250.99). That is, we estimate the mean amount of delinquency for all accounts to fall within the interval \$215.57 to \$250.99.

Look Back The confidence interval is also shown at the bottom of the Excel/DDXL printout, Figure 5.2b. Note that the end-points of the interval vary slightly from those computed in the example. This is due to the fact that when σ is unknown and n is large,

```
▷ | AMOUNT Confidence Interval            🔲🔲
  ▷ | Summary Statistics                    🔲
   Count      Mean      Std Dev     df
   100        233.28    90.34       99


  ▷ | Interval Results                      🔲
   Confidence Interval
   With 95% Confidence, 215.355 < μ < 251.205
```

Figure 5.2b

Excel/DDXL 95% confidence interval for mean overdue amount

the sampling distribution of $\bar{x}$ will deviate slightly from the normal (z) distribution. In practice, these differences can be ignored.

Now Work Exercise 5.10

Can we be sure that μ, the true mean, is in the interval (215.57, 250.99) in Example 5.2? We cannot be certain, but we can be reasonably confident that it is. This confidence is derived from the knowledge that if we were to draw repeated random samples of 100 measurements from this population and form the interval $\bar{x} \pm 1.96\sigma_{\bar{x}}$ each time, 95% of the intervals would contain μ. We have no way of knowing (without looking at all the delinquent accounts) whether our sample interval is one of the 95% that contains μ or one of the 5% that does not, but the odds certainly favor its containing μ. The probability, .95, that measures the confidence we can place in the interval estimate is called a *confidence coefficient*. The percentage, 95%, is called the *confidence level* for the interval estimate.

The **confidence coefficient** is the probability that a randomly selected confidence interval encloses the population parameter—that is, the relative frequency with which similarly constructed intervals enclose the population parameter when the estimator is used repeatedly a very large number of times. The **confidence level** is the confidence coefficient expressed as a percentage.

Figure 5.3
Confidence intervals for μ: 10 samples

Now we have seen how an interval can be used to estimate a population mean. When we use an interval estimator, we can usually calculate the probability that the estimation *process* will result in an interval that contains the true value of the population mean—that is, the probability that the interval contains the parameter in repeated usage is usually known. Figure 5.3 shows what happens when 10 different samples are drawn from a population, and a confidence interval for μ is calculated from each. The location of μ is indicated by the vertical line in the figure. Ten confidence intervals, each based on one of 10 samples, are shown as horizontal line segments. Note that the confidence intervals move from sample to sample—sometimes containing μ and other times missing μ. *If our confidence level is 95%, then in the long run, 95% of our confidence intervals will contain μ and 5% will not.*

Suppose you wish to choose a confidence coefficient other than .95. Notice in Figure 5.1 that the confidence coefficient .95 is equal to the total area under the sampling distribution, less .05 of the area, which is divided equally between the two tails. Using this idea, we can construct a confidence interval with any desired confidence coefficient by increasing or decreasing the area (call it α) assigned to the tails of the sampling distribution (see Figure 5.4). For example, if we place area $\alpha/2$ in each tail and if $z_{\alpha/2}$ is the z-value such that the area $\alpha/2$ lies to its right, then the confidence interval with confidence coefficient $(1 - \alpha)$ is

$$\bar{x} \pm (z_{\alpha/2})\sigma_{\bar{x}}$$

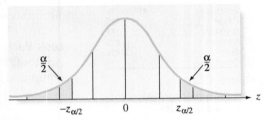

Figure 5.4
Locating $z_{\alpha/2}$ on the standard normal curve

Conditions Required for a Valid Large-Sample Confidence Interval for μ

1. A random sample is selected from the target population.

2. The sample size n is large (i.e., $n \geq 30$). Due to the Central Limit Theorem, this condition guarantees that the sampling distribution of $\bar{x}$ is approximately normal. Also, for large n, s will be a good estimator of σ.)

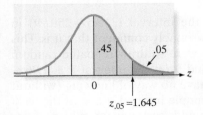

Figure 5.5
The z-value ($z_{.05}$) corresponding to an area equal to .05 in the upper tail of the z-distribution

To illustrate, for a confidence coefficient of .90, we have $(1 - \alpha) = .90$, $\alpha = .10$, and $\alpha/2 = .05$; $z_{.05}$ is the z-value that locates area .05 in the upper tail of the sampling distribution. Recall that Table IV in Appendix B gives the areas between the mean and a specified z-value. Because the total area to the right of the mean is .5, we find that $z_{.05}$ will be the z-value corresponding to an area of $.5 - .05 = .45$ to the right of the mean (see Figure 5.5). This z-value is $z_{.05} = 1.645$.

Confidence coefficients used in practice usually range from .90 to .99. The most commonly used confidence coefficients with corresponding values of α and $z_{\alpha/2}$ are shown in Table 5.2.

BIOGRAPHY   **JERZEY NEYMAN (1894–1981)**

Speaking Statistics with a Polish Accent

Polish-born Jerzey Neyman was educated at the University of Kharkov (Russia) in elementary mathematics but taught himself graduate mathematics by studying journal articles on the subject. After receiving his doctorate in 1924 from the University of Warsaw (Poland), Neyman accepted a position at University College (London). There, he developed a friendship with Egon Pearson; Neyman and Pearson together developed the theory of hypothesis testing (Chapter 6). In 1934, in a talk to the Royal Statistical Society, Neyman first proposed the idea of interval estimation, which he called *confidence intervals.* (It is interesting that Neyman rarely receives credit in textbooks as the originator of the confidence interval procedure.) In 1938, he emigrated to the United States and the University of California at Berkeley. At Berkeley, he built one of the strongest statistics departments in the country. Jerzey Neyman is considered one of the great founders of modern statistics. He was a superb teacher and innovative researcher who loved his students, always sharing his ideas with them. Neyman's influence on those he met is best expressed by a quote from prominent statistician David Salsburg: "We have all learned to speak statistics with a Polish accent." ∎

Table 5.2   **Commonly Used Values of $z_{\alpha/2}$**

Confidence Level			
$100(1 - \alpha)$	α	$\alpha/2$	$z_{\alpha/2}$
90%	.10	.05	1.645
95%	.05	.025	1.96
99%	.01	.005	2.575

Large-Sample $(1 - \alpha)\%$ Confidence Interval for μ

$$\overline{x} \pm z_{\alpha/2}\sigma_{\overline{x}} = \overline{x} \pm z_{\alpha/2}\left(\frac{\sigma}{\sqrt{n}}\right)$$

where $z_{\alpha/2}$ is the z-value with an area $\alpha/2$ to its right (see Figure 5.4) and $\sigma_{\overline{x}} = \sigma/\sqrt{n}$. The parameter σ is the standard deviation of the sampled population, and n is the sample size.

Note: When σ is unknown (as is almost always the case) and n is large (say, $n \geq 30$), the confidence interval is approximately equal to

$$\overline{x} \pm z_{\alpha/2}\left(\frac{s}{\sqrt{n}}\right)$$

where s is the sample standard deviation.

Example 5.3

Large–Sample Confidence Interval for the Mean Number of Unoccupied Seats per Flight, μ

Problem Unoccupied seats on flights cause airlines to lose revenue. Suppose a large airline wants to estimate its average number of unoccupied seats per flight over the past year. To accomplish this, the records of 225 flights are randomly selected, and the number of unoccupied seats is noted for each of the sampled flights. (The data are saved in the **AIRNOSHOWS** file.) Descriptive statistics for the data are displayed in the Minitab printout, Figure 5.6.

```
Variable     N     Mean    StDev   SE Mean        90% CI
NOSHOWS    225   11.5956   4.1026   0.2735   (11.1438, 12.0473)
```

Figure 5.6

Minitab confidence interval for mean, Example 5.3

Estimate μ, the mean number of unoccupied seats per flight during the past year, using a 90% confidence interval.

Solution The general form of the 90% confidence interval for a population mean is

$$\bar{x} \pm z_{\alpha/2}\sigma_{\bar{x}} = \bar{x} \pm z_{.05}\sigma_{\bar{x}} = \bar{x} \pm 1.645\left(\frac{\sigma}{\sqrt{n}}\right)$$

From Figure 5.6, we find (after rounding) $\bar{x} = 11.6$. Because we do not know the value of σ (the standard deviation of the number of unoccupied seats per flight for all flights of the year), we use our best approximation—the sample standard deviation s. Then the 90% confidence interval is, approximately,

$$11.6 \pm 1.645\left(\frac{4.1}{\sqrt{225}}\right) = 11.6 \pm .45$$

or from 11.15 to 12.05—that is, at the 90% confidence level, we estimate the mean number of unoccupied seats per flight to be between 11.15 and 12.05 during the sampled year. This result is verified (except for rounding) on the right side of the Minitab printout in Figure 5.6.

Look Back We stress that the confidence level for this example, 90%, refers to the procedure used. If we were to apply this procedure repeatedly to different samples, approximately 90% of the intervals would contain μ. Although we do not know whether this particular interval (11.15, 12.05) is one of the 90% that contain μ or one of the 10% that do not, our knowledge of probability gives us "confidence" that the interval contains μ.

Now Work Exercise 5.12

The interpretation of confidence intervals for a population mean is summarized in the next box.

Interpretation of a Confidence Interval for a Population Mean

When we form a $100(1 - \alpha)\%$ confidence interval for μ, we usually express our confidence in the interval with a statement such as, "We can be $100(1 - \alpha)\%$ confident that μ lies between the lower and upper bounds of the confidence interval," where for a particular application, we substitute the appropriate numerical values for the confidence and for the lower and upper bounds. *The statement reflects our confidence in the estimation process rather than in the particular interval that is calculated from the sample data.* We know that repeated application of the same procedure will result in different lower and upper bounds on the interval. Furthermore, we know that $100(1 - \alpha)\%$ of the resulting intervals will contain μ. There is (usually) no way to determine whether any particular interval is one of those that contain μ, or one that does not. However, unlike point estimators, confidence intervals have some measure of reliability, the confidence coefficient, associated with them. For that reason they are generally preferred to point estimators.

Sometimes, the estimation procedure yields a confidence interval that is too wide for our purposes. In this case, we will want to reduce the width of the interval to obtain a more precise estimate of μ. One way to accomplish this is to decrease the confidence coefficient, $1 - \alpha$. For example, reconsider the problem of estimating the mean amount owed, μ, for all delinquent accounts. Recall that for a sample of 100 accounts, $\bar{x} = \$233.28$ and $s = \$90.34$. A 90% confidence interval for μ is

$$\bar{x} \pm 1.645\sigma/\sqrt{n} \approx 233.28 \pm (1.645)(90.34/\sqrt{100}) = 233.28 \pm 14.86$$

or ($218.42, $248.14). You can see that this interval is narrower than the previously calculated 95% confidence interval ($215.57, $250.99). Unfortunately, we also have "less confidence" in the 90% confidence interval. An alternative method used to decrease the width of an interval without sacrificing "confidence" is to increase the sample size n. We demonstrate this method in Section 5.5.

Exercises 5.1–5.20

Learning the Mechanics

5.1 Find $z_{\alpha/2}$ for each of the following:
NW
  a. $\alpha = .10$ **b.** $\alpha = .01$
  c. $\alpha = .05$ **d.** $\alpha = .20$

5.2 What is the confidence level of each of the following confidence intervals for μ?

  a. $\bar{x} \pm 1.96\left(\dfrac{\sigma}{\sqrt{n}}\right)$ **b.** $\bar{x} \pm 1.645\left(\dfrac{\sigma}{\sqrt{n}}\right)$

  c. $\bar{x} \pm 2.575\left(\dfrac{\sigma}{\sqrt{n}}\right)$ **d.** $\bar{x} \pm 1.282\left(\dfrac{\sigma}{\sqrt{n}}\right)$

  e. $\bar{x} \pm .99\left(\dfrac{\sigma}{\sqrt{n}}\right)$

5.3 A random sample of n measurements was selected from a
NW population with unknown mean μ and known standard deviation σ. Calculate a 95% confidence interval for μ for each of the following situations:
  a. $n = 75, \bar{x} = 28, \sigma^2 = 12$
  b. $n = 200, \bar{x} = 102, \sigma^2 = 22$
  c. $n = 100, \bar{x} = 15, \sigma = .3$
  d. $n = 100, \bar{x} = 4.05, \sigma = .83$
  e. Is the assumption that the underlying population of measurements is normally distributed necessary to ensure the validity of the confidence intervals in parts **a–d**? Explain.

5.4 A random sample of 90 observations produced a mean $\bar{x} = 25.9$ and a standard deviation $s = 2.7$.
  a. Find an approximate 95% confidence interval for the population mean μ.
  b. Find an approximate 90% confidence interval for μ.
  c. Find an approximate 99% confidence interval for μ.

5.5 A random sample of 70 observations from a normally distributed population possesses a sample mean equal to 26.2 and a sample standard deviation equal to 4.1.
  a. Find an approximate 95% confidence interval for μ.
  b. What do you mean when you say that a confidence coefficient is .95?
  c. Find an approximate 99% confidence interval for μ.
  d. What happens to the width of a confidence interval as the value of the confidence coefficient is increased while the sample size is held fixed?
  e. Would your confidence intervals of parts **a** and **c** be valid if the distribution of the original population was not normal? Explain.

⚫ Applet Exercise 5.1

Use the applet *Confidence Intervals for a Mean (the impact of confidence level)* to investigate the situation in Exercise 5.5 further. For this exercise, assume that $\mu = 2.62$ is the population mean and $\sigma = 4.1$ is the population standard deviation.
  a. Using $n = 70$ and the normal distribution with the mean and standard deviation above, run the applet one time. How many of the 95% confidence intervals contain the mean? How many would you expect to contain the mean? How many of the 99% confidence intervals contain the mean? How many would you expect to contain the mean?
  b. Which confidence level has a greater frequency of intervals that contain the mean? Is this result what you would expect? Explain.
  c. Without clearing, run the applet several more times. What happens to the proportion of 95% confidence intervals that contain the mean as you run the applet more and more? What happens to the proportion of 99% confidence intervals that contain the mean as you run the applet more and more? Interpret these results in terms of the meanings of the 95% confidence interval and the 99% confidence interval.
  d. Change the distribution to *right skewed*, clear, and run the applet several more times. Do you get the same results as in part **c**? Would you change your answer to part **e** of Exercise 5.5? Explain.

⚫ Applet Exercise 5.2

Use the applet *Confidence Intervals for a Mean (the impact of confidence level)* to investigate the effect of the sample size on the proportion of confidence intervals that contain the mean when the underlying distribution is skewed. Set the distribution to *right skewed*, the mean to 10, and the standard deviation to 1.
  a. Using $n = 30$, run the applet several times without clearing. What happens to the proportion of 95% confidence intervals that contain the mean as you run the applet more and more? What happens to the proportion of 99% confidence intervals that contain the mean as you run the applet more and more? Do the proportions seem to be approaching the values that you would expect?
  b. Clear and run the applet several times using $n = 100$. What happens to the proportions of 95% confidence intervals and 99% confidence intervals that contain the mean this time? How do these results compare to your results in part **a**?
  c. Clear and run the applet several times using $n = 1,000$. How do the results compare to your results in parts **a** and **b**?
  d. Describe the effect of sample size on the likelihood that a confidence interval contains the mean for a skewed distribution.

5.6 Explain what is meant by the statement, "We are 95% confident that an interval estimate contains μ."

5.7 Explain the difference between an interval estimator and a point estimator for μ.

5.8 The mean and standard deviation of a random sample of n measurements are equal to 33.9 and 3.3, respectively.
  a. Find a 95% confidence interval for μ if $n = 100$.
  b. Find a 95% confidence interval for μ if $n = 400$.
  c. Find the widths of the confidence intervals found in parts **a** and **b.** What is the effect on the width of a confidence interval of quadrupling the sample size while holding the confidence coefficient fixed?

5.9 Will a large-sample confidence interval be valid if the population from which the sample is taken is not normally distributed? Explain.

Applying the Concepts—Basic

5.10 **Latex allergy in health care workers.** Health care workers who use latex gloves with glove powder on a daily basis are particularly susceptible to developing a latex allergy. Symptoms of a latex allergy include conjunctivitis, hand eczema, nasal congestion, skin rash, and shortness of breath. Each in a sample of 46 hospital employees who were diagnosed with latex allergy based on a skin-prick test reported on their exposure to latex gloves (*Current Allergy & Clinical Immunology,* Mar. 2004). Summary statistics for the number of latex gloves used per week are $\bar{x} = 19.3$, $s = 11.9$.
  a. Give a point estimate for the average number of latex gloves used per week by all health care workers with a latex allergy.
  b. Form a 95% confidence interval for the average number of latex gloves used per week by all health care workers with a latex allergy.
  c. Give a practical interpretation of the interval, part **b.**
  d. Give the conditions required for the interval, part **b,** to be valid.

5.11 **Budget lapsing at army hospitals.** Budget lapsing occurs when unspent funds do not carry over from one budgeting period to the next. Refer to the *Journal of Management Accounting Research* (Vol. 19, 2007) study on budget lapsing at U.S. army hospitals, Exercise 2.107 (p. 87). Because budget lapsing often leads to a spike in expenditures at the end of the fiscal year, the researchers recorded expenses per full-time equivalent employee for each in a sample of 1,751 army hospitals. The sample yielded the following summary statistics: $\bar{x} = \$6,563$ and $s = \$2,484$. Estimate the mean expenses per full-time equivalent employee of all U.S. army hospitals using a 90% confidence interval. Interpret the result.

5.12 **Tax-exempt charities.** Donations to tax-exempt organizations such as the Red Cross, the Salvation Army, the YMCA, and the American Cancer Society not only go to the stated charitable purpose but are also used to cover fund-raising expenses and overhead. The **CHARITY** file (see next table) contains the 2008 charitable commitments (i.e., the percentange of expenses that go toward the charitable purpose) for a sample of 30 charities. A Minitab analysis of the data is shown in the next column.
  a. Give a point estimate for the mean charitable commitment of tax-exempt organizations.
  b. Locate a 95% confidence interval for the true mean charitable commitment of tax-exempt organizations on the printout. Interpret the result.
  c. Why is the confidence interval of part **b** a better estimator of the mean charitable commitment than the point estimator of part **a?** Explain.

Variable	N	Mean	StDev	SE Mean	95% CI
COMMIT	30	79.67	10.25	1.87	(75.84, 83.49)

Organization	Charitable Commitment
American Cancer Society	71%
American National Red Cross	89
Big Brothers Big Sisters of America	78
Boy Scouts of America	87
Boys & Girls Clubs of America	80
CARE USA	90
Covenant House	67
Disabled American Veterans	69
Ducks Unlimited	86
Feed the Children	84
Girl Scouts of the USA	82
Goodwill Industries International	88
Habitat for Humanity International	83
Mayo Clinic	97
March of Dimes Foundation	77
Multiple Sclerosis Society	78
Museum of Modern Art	80
Nature Conservancy	80
Paralyzed Veterans of America	62
Planned Parenthood Federation	82
Salvation Army	82
Shriners Hospital for Children	92
Smithsonian Institution	82
Special Olympics	74
Trust for Public Land	89
United States Olympic Committee	71
United Way	86
WGBH Educational Foundation	79
World Trade Center Memorial Foundation	44
YMCA of the USA	81

Source: "America's 200 largest charities," *Forbes,* Nov. 19, 2008. Reprinted by permission of Forbes.com. © 2009 Forbes LLC.

5.13 **Blogs for Fortune 500 firms.** Refer to the *Journal of Relationship Marketing* (Vol. 7, 2008) study of the prevalence of blogs and forums at Fortune 500 firms with both English and Chinese Web sites, Exercise 2.76 (p. 75). In a sample of 56 firms that provide blogs and forums as marketing tools, the mean number of blogs/forums per site was 4.25, with a standard deviation of 12.02.
  a. Find a 99% confidence interval for the mean number of blogs/forums per site of all Fortune 500 firms that provide blogs and forums as marketing tools.
  b. Give a practical interpretation of the interval, part **a.**
  c. The number of blogs/forums per site is known to have a highly skewed distribution. Does this impact the validity of the inference, part **b?**

5.14 **Wear-out of used display panels.** Refer to Exercise 4.112 (p. 224) and the study of the wear-out failure time of used colored display panels purchased by an outlet store. Recall that prior to acquisition, the panels had been used for about one-third of their expected lifetimes. The failure times (in years) for a sample of 50 used panels (saved in the **PANELFAIL** file) are reproduced in the next table, followed by an SPSS printout of the analysis of the data.

SPSS Output for Exercise 5.14

Descriptives

			Statistic	Std. Error
FAILTIME	Mean		1.9350	.13133
	95% Confidence Interval for Mean	Lower Bound	1.6711	
		Upper Bound	2.1989	
	5% Trimmed Mean		1.9454	
	Median		1.8350	
	Variance		.862	
	Std. Deviation		.92865	
	Minimum		.01	
	Maximum		3.50	
	Range		3.49	
	Interquartile Range		1.43	
	Skewness		-.008	.337
	Kurtosis		-.755	.662

a. Locate a 95% confidence interval for the true mean failure time of used colored display panels on the printout.

b. Give a practical interpretation of the interval, part **a.**

c. In repeated sampling of the population of used colored display panels, where a 95% confidence interval for the mean failure time is computed for each sample, what proportion of all the confidence intervals generated will capture the true mean failure time?

0.01	1.21	1.71	2.30	2.96	0.19	1.22	1.75	2.30	2.98	0.51
1.24	1.77	2.41	3.19	0.57	1.48	1.79	2.44	3.25	0.70	1.54
1.88	2.57	3.31	0.73	1.59	1.90	2.61	1.19	0.75	1.61	1.93
2.62	3.50	0.75	1.61	2.01	2.72	3.50	1.11	1.62	2.16	2.76
3.50	1.16	1.62	2.18	2.84	3.50					

Source: Based on Irony, T. Z., Lauretto, M., Pereira, C., and Stern, J. M. "A Weibull wearout Test: Full Bayesian approach," paper presented at *Mathematical Sciences Colloquium,* Binghamton University, Binghamton, UK, December 2001.

Applying the Concepts—Intermediate

5.15 Executive Compensation Scoreboard. Refer to *Forbes'* 2008 "Executive Compensation Scoreboard." Recall that the **CEOPAY08** file contains the 2008 salaries (in $ millions) of the 500 CEOs that participated in the *Forbes'* survey. Suppose you are interested in estimating the mean 2008 salary for these 500 CEOs.

a. What is the target parameter?

b. Obtain a random sample of 50 salaries from the data set.

c. Find the mean of the 50 salaries, part **b.**

d. Verify that the standard deviation for the population of 500 salaries is $\sigma = \$18.5$ million.

e. Use the information, parts **c** and **d,** to form a 99% confidence interval for the true mean 2008 salary of the 500 CEOs in the *Forbes'* survey.

f. Give a practical interpretation of the interval, part **e.**

g. Find the true mean salary of the 500 CEOs and check to see if this value falls within the 99% confidence interval, part **e.**

5.16 401(k) Participation rates. Named for the section of the 1978 Internal Revenue Code that authorized them, 401(k) plans permit employees to shift part of their before-tax

salaries into investments such as mutual funds. Employers typically match 50% of the employee's contribution up to about 6% of salary. One company, concerned with what it believed was a low employee participation rate in its 401(k) plan, sampled 30 other companies with similar plans and asked for their 401(k) participation rates. The following rates (in percentages) were obtained and are saved in the **RATE401K** file.

80	76	81	77	82	80	85	60	80	79	82	70
88	85	80	79	83	75	87	78	80	84	72	75
90	84	82	77	75	86						

a. Construct a 90% confidence interval for the mean participation rate for all companies that have 401(k) plans.

b. Interpret the interval in the context of this problem.

c. What assumption is necessary to ensure the validity of this confidence interval?

d. If the company that conducted the sample has a 71% participation rate, can it safely conclude that its rate is below the population mean rate for all companies with 401(k) plans? Explain.

e. If in the data set the 60% had been 80%, how would the center and width of the confidence interval you constructed in part **a** be affected?

5.17 Accounting and Machiavellianism. Refer to the *Behavioral Research in Accounting* (Jan. 2008) study of Machiavellian traits in accountants, Exercise 1.27 (p. 24). Recall that *Machiavellian* describes negative character traits that include manipulation, cunning, duplicity, deception, and bad faith. A Machiavellian ("Mach") rating score was determined for each in a sample of accounting alumni of a large southwestern university. Scores range from a low of 40 to a high of 160, with the theoretical neutral Mach rating score of 100. The 122 purchasing managers in the sample had a mean Mach rating score of 99.6, with a standard deviation of 12.6.

a. From the sample, estimate the true mean Mach rating score of all purchasing managers.

b. Form a 95% confidence interval for the estimate, part **b.**

c. Give a practical interpretation of the interval, part **c.**

d. A director of purchasing at a major firm claims that the true mean Mach rating score of all purchasing managers is 85. Is there evidence to dispute this claim?

5.18   **Size of diamonds sold at retail.** Refer to Exercise 2.49 (p. 62) and the *Journal of Statistics Education* data on diamonds saved in the **DIAMONDS** file. Consider the quantitative variable, number of carats, recorded for each of the 308 diamonds for sale on the open market.

a. Select a random sample of 30 diamonds from the 308 diamonds.

b. Find the mean and standard deviation of the number of carats per diamond for the sample.

c. Use the sample information, part **b,** to construct a 95% confidence interval for the mean number of carats in the population of 308 diamonds.

d. Interpret the phrase *95% confidence* when applied to the interval, part **c.**

e. Refer to the mean of all 308 diamonds you calculated in Exercise 2.49. Does the "population" mean fall within the confidence interval of part **c?**

Applying the Concepts—Advanced

5.19   **Improving SAT scores.** Refer to the *Chance* (Winter 2001) and National Education Longitudinal Survey (NELS) study of 265 students who paid a private tutor to help them improve their SAT scores, Exercise 2.86

	SAT–Math	SAT–Verbal
Mean change in score	19	7
Standard deviation of score changes	65	49

(p. 76). The changes in both the SAT–Mathematics and SAT–Verbal scores for these students are reproduced in the table. Suppose the true population mean change in score on one of the SAT tests for all students who paid a private tutor is 15. Which of the two tests, SAT–Mathematics or SAT–Verbal, is most likely to have this mean change? Explain.

5.20   **The "Raid" test kitchen.** According to scientists, the cockroach has had 300 million years to develop a resistance to destruction. In a study conducted by researchers for S.C. Johnson & Son, Inc. (manufacturers of Raid and Off), 5,000 roaches (the expected number in a roach-infested house) were released in the Raid test kitchen. One week later, the kitchen was fumigated, and 16,298 dead roaches were counted, a gain of 11,298 roaches for the 1-week period. Assume that none of the original roaches died during the 1-week period and that the standard deviation of x, the number of roaches produced per roach in a 1-week period, is 1.5. Use the number of roaches produced by the sample of 5,000 roaches to find a 95% confidence interval for the mean number of roaches produced per week for each roach in a typical roach-infested house.

5.3 Confidence Interval for a Population Mean: Student's t-Statistic

Federal legislation requires pharmaceutical companies to perform extensive tests on new drugs before they can be marketed. Initially, a new drug is tested on animals. If the drug is deemed safe after this first phase of testing, the pharmaceutical company is then permitted to begin human testing on a limited basis. During this second phase, inferences must be made about the safety of the drug based on information in very small samples.

Suppose a pharmaceutical company must estimate the average increase in blood pressure of patients who take a certain new drug. Assume that only six patients (randomly selected from the population of all patients) can be used in the initial phase of human testing. The use of a *small sample* in making an inference about μ presents two immediate problems when we attempt to use the standard normal z as a test statistic.

BIOGRAPHY   **WILLIAM S. GOSSET (1876–1937)**

Student's t-Distribution

At the age of 23, William Gosset earned a degree in chemistry and mathematics at prestigious Oxford University. He was immediately hired by the Guinness Brewing Company in Dublin, Ireland, for his expertise in chemistry. However, Gosset's mathematical skills allowed him to solve numerous practical problems associated with brewing beer. For example, Gosset applied the Poisson distribution to model the number of yeast cells per unit volume in the fermentation process. His most important discovery was that of the t-distribution in 1908. Because most applied researchers worked with small samples, Gosset was interested in the behavior of the mean in the small sample case. He tediously took numerous small sets of numbers, calculated the mean and standard deviation, obtained their t-ratio, and plotted the results on graph paper. The shape of the distribution was always the same—the t-distribution. Under company policy, employees were forbidden to publish their research results, so Gosset used the pen name *Student* to publish a paper on the subject. Hence, the distribution has been called Student's t-distribution. ■

Problem 1   The shape of the sampling distribution of the sample mean $\bar{x}$ (and the *z*-statistic) now depends on the shape of the population that is sampled. We can no longer assume that the sampling distribution of $\bar{x}$ is approximately normal because the Central Limit Theorem ensures normality only for samples that are sufficiently large.

Solution to Problem 1   According to Theorem 4.1, the sampling distribution of $\bar{x}$ (and *z*) is exactly normal, even for small samples, if the sampled population is normal. It is approximately normal if the sampled population is approximately normal.

Problem 2   The population standard deviation σ is almost always unknown. Although it is still true that $\sigma_{\bar{x}} = \sigma/\sqrt{n}$, the sample standard deviation *s* may provide a poor approximation for σ when the sample size is small.

Solution to Problem 2   Instead of using the standard normal statistic

$$z = \frac{\bar{x} - \mu}{\sigma_{\bar{x}}} = \frac{\bar{x} - \mu}{\sigma/\sqrt{n}}$$

which requires knowledge of or a good approximation to σ, we define and use the statistic

$$t = \frac{\bar{x} - \mu}{s/\sqrt{n}}$$

in which the sample standard deviation, *s*, replaces the population standard deviation, σ.

If we are sampling from a normal distribution, the **t-statistic** has a sampling distribution very much like that of the *z*-statistic: mound-shaped, symmetric, with mean 0. The primary difference between the sampling distributions of *t* and *z* is that the *t*-statistic is more variable than the *z*, which follows intuitively when you realize that *t* contains two random quantities ($\bar{x}$ and *s*), whereas *z* contains only one ($\bar{x}$).

The actual amount of variability in the sampling distribution of *t* depends on the sample size *n*. A convenient way of expressing this dependence is to say that the *t*-statistic has $(n - 1)$ **degrees of freedom (df).** Recall that the quantity $(n - 1)$ is the divisor that appears in the formula for s^2. This number plays a key role in the sampling distribution of s^2 and appears in discussions of other statistics in later chapters. In particular, the smaller the number of degrees of freedom associated with the *t*-statistic, the more variable will be its sampling distribution.

In Figure 5.7 we show both the sampling distribution of *z* and the sampling distribution of a *t*-statistic with 4 df. You can see that the increased variability of the *t*-statistic means that the *t*-value, t_α, that locates an area α in the upper tail of the *t*-distribution is larger than the corresponding value z_α. For any given value of α, the *t*-value t_α increases as the df decreases. Values of *t* that will be used in forming small-sample confidence intervals of μ are given in Table V in Appendix B. A partial reproduction of this table is shown in Table 5.3.

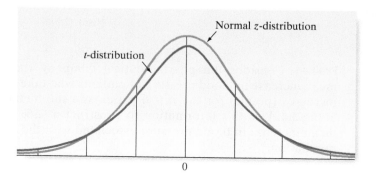

Figure 5.7
Standard normal (*z*) distribution and *t*-distribution with 4 df

Table 5.3	Reproduction of Part of Table V in Appendix B

Degrees of Freedom	$t_{.100}$	$t_{.050}$	$t_{.025}$	$t_{.010}$	$t_{.005}$	$t_{.001}$	$t_{.0005}$
1	3.078	6.314	12.706	31.821	63.657	318.13	636.62
2	1.886	2.920	4.303	6.965	9.925	22.326	21.598
3	1.638	2.353	3.182	4.541	5.841	10.213	12.924
4	1.533	2.132	2.776	3.747	4.604	7.173	8.610
5	1.476	2.015	2.571	3.365	4.032	5.893	6.869
6	1.440	1.943	2.447	3.132	3.707	5.208	5.959
7	1.415	1.895	2.365	2.998	3.499	4.785	5.408
8	1.397	1.860	2.306	2.896	3.355	4.501	5.041
9	1.383	1.833	2.262	2.821	3.250	4.297	4.781
10	1.372	1.812	2.228	2.764	3.169	4.144	4.587
11	1.363	1.796	2.201	2.718	3.106	4.025	4.437
12	1.356	1.782	2.179	2.681	3.055	3.930	4.318
13	1.350	1.771	2.160	2.650	3.012	3.852	4.221
14	1.345	1.761	2.145	2.624	2.977	3.787	4.140
15	1.341	1.753	2.131	2.602	2.947	3.733	4.073
⋮	⋮	⋮	⋮	⋮	⋮	⋮	⋮
∞	1.282	1.645	1.960	2.326	2.576	3.090	3.291

Note that t_α values are listed for various degrees of freedom, where α refers to the tail area under the t-distribution to the right of t_α. For example, if we want the t-value with an area of .025 to its right and 4 df, we look in the table under the column $t_{.025}$ for the entry in the row corresponding to 4 df. This entry is $t_{.025} = 2.776$, as shown in Figure 5.8. The corresponding standard normal z-score is $z_{.025} = 1.96$.

Note that the last row of Table V, where df = ∞ (infinity), contains the standard normal z-values. This follows from the fact that as the sample size n grows very large, s becomes closer to σ and thus t becomes closer in distribution to z. In fact, when df = 29, there is little difference between corresponding tabulated values of z and t. Thus, researchers often choose the arbitrary cutoff of $n = 30$ (df = 29) to distinguish between the large-sample and small-sample inferential techniques.

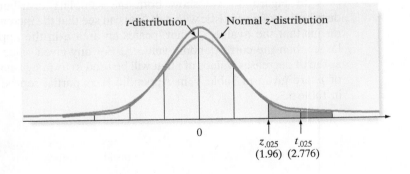

Figure 5.8

The $t_{.025}$ value in a t-distribution with 4 df and the corresponding $z_{.025}$ value

---

Example 5.4

A Confidence Interval for Mean Blood Pressure Increase Using the t-statistic

Problem Consider the pharmaceutical company that desires an estimate of the mean increase in blood pressure of patients who take a new drug. The blood pressure increases (points) for the $n = 6$ patients in the human testing phase are shown in Table 5.4. Use this information to construct a 95% confidence interval for μ, the mean increase in blood pressure associated with the new drug for all patients in the population.

Table 5.4	Blood Pressure Increases for $n = 6$ Patients

1.7   3.0   .8   3.4   2.7   2.1

Data Set: BPINCR

Solution First, note that we are dealing with a sample too small to assume that the sample mean $\bar{x}$ is approximately normally distributed by the Central Limit Theorem—that is, we do not get the normal distribution of $\bar{x}$ "automatically" from the Central Limit Theorem when the sample size is small. Instead, the measured variable, in this case the increase in blood pressure, must be normally distributed in order for the distribution of $\bar{x}$ to be normal.

Second, unless we are fortunate enough to know the population standard deviation σ, which in this case represents the standard deviation of *all* the patients' increases in blood pressure when they take the new drug, we cannot use the standard normal z-statistic to form our confidence interval for μ. Instead, we must use the t-distribution, with $(n - 1)$ degrees of freedom.

In this case, $n - 1 = 5$ df, and the t-value is found in Table 5.3 to be $t_{.025} = 2.571$ with 5 df. Recall that the large-sample confidence interval would have been of the form

$$\bar{x} \pm z_{\alpha/2}\sigma_{\bar{x}} = \bar{x} \pm z_{\alpha/2}\frac{\sigma}{\sqrt{n}} = \bar{x} \pm z_{.025}\frac{\sigma}{\sqrt{n}}$$

where 95% is the desired confidence level. To form the interval for a small sample from *a normal distribution, we simply substitute t for z and s for σ* in the preceding formula:

$$\bar{x} \pm t_{\alpha/2}\frac{s}{\sqrt{n}}$$

An SPSS printout showing descriptive statistics for the six blood pressure increases is displayed in Figure 5.9. Note that $\bar{x} = 2.283$ and $s = .950$. Substituting these numerical values into the confidence interval formula, we get

$$2.283 \pm (2.571)\left(\frac{.950}{\sqrt{6}}\right) = 2.283 \pm .997$$

or 1.286 to 3.280 points. Note that this interval agrees (except for rounding) with the confidence interval generated by SPSS in Figure 5.9.

We interpret the interval as follows: We can be 95% confident that the mean increase in blood pressure associated with taking this new drug is between 1.286 and 3.28 points. As with our large-sample interval estimates, our confidence is in the process, not in this particular interval. We know that if we were to repeatedly use this estimation procedure, 95% of the confidence intervals produced would contain the true mean μ, *assuming that the probability distribution of changes in blood pressure from which our sample was selected is normal.* The latter assumption is necessary for the small-sample interval to be valid.

Descriptives

			Statistic	Std. Error
BPINCR	Mean		2.283	.3877
	95% Confidence Interval for Mean	Lower Bound	1.287	
		Upper Bound	3.280	
	5% Trimmed Mean		2.304	
	Median		2.400	
	Variance		.902	
	Std. Deviation		.9496	
	Minimum		.8	
	Maximum		3.4	
	Range		2.6	
	Interquartile Range		1.625	
	Skewness		-.573	.845
	Kurtosis		-.389	1.741

Figure 5.9
SPSS confidence interval for mean blood pressure increase

Look Back What price did we pay for having to use a small sample to make the inference? First, we had to assume the underlying population is normally distributed, and if the assumption is invalid, our interval might also be invalid.* Second, we had to form the interval using a t-value of 2.571 rather than a z-value of 1.96, resulting in a wider interval to achieve the same 95% level of confidence. If the interval from 1.286 to 3.28 is too wide to be of use, then we know how to remedy the situation: increase the number of patients sampled to decrease the interval width (on average).

Now Work Exercise 5.22

The procedure for forming a small-sample confidence interval is summarized in the accompanying boxes.

Small-Sample Confidence Interval† for μ

$$\bar{x} \pm t_{\alpha/2}\left(\frac{s}{\sqrt{n}}\right)$$

where $t_{\alpha/2}$ is based on $(n - 1)$ degrees of freedom.

Conditions Required for a Valid Small-Sample Confidence Interval for μ

1. A random sample is selected from the target population.
2. The population has a relative frequency distribution that is approximately normal.

Example 5.5

A Small–Sample Confidence Interval for μ in Destructive Sampling

Problem Some quality-control experiments require *destructive sampling* (i.e., the test to determine whether the item is defective destroys the item) in order to measure some particular characteristic of the product. The cost of destructive sampling often dictates small samples. For example, suppose a manufacturer of printers for personal computers wishes to estimate the mean number of characters printed before the printhead fails. Suppose the printer manufacturer tests $n = 15$ randomly selected printheads and records the number of characters printed until failure for each. These 15 measurements (in millions of characters) are listed in Table 5.5, followed by an Excel/DDXL summary statistics printout in Figure 5.10.

a. Form a 99% confidence interval for the mean number of characters printed before the printhead fails. Interpret the result.

b. What assumption is required for the interval, part **a**, to be valid? Is it reasonably satisfied?

Table 5.5	Number of Characters (in Millions) for n = 15 Printhead Tests			
1.13	1.55	1.43	.92	1.25
1.36	1.32	.85	1.07	1.48
1.20	1.33	1.18	1.22	1.29

Data Set: PRINTHEAD

---

*By *invalid*, we mean that the probability that the procedure will yield an interval that contains μ is not equal to $(1 - \alpha)$. Generally, if the underlying population is approximately normal, then the confidence coefficient will approximate the probability that a randomly selected interval contains μ.

†The procedure given in the box assumes that the population standard deviation σ is unknown, which is almost always the case. If σ is known, we can form the small-sample confidence interval just as we would a large-sample confidence interval using a standard normal z-value instead of t. However, we must still assume that the underlying population is approximately normal.

Solution

a. For this small sample ($n = 15$), we use the *t*-statistic to form the confidence interval. We use a confidence coefficient of .99 and $n - 1 = 14$ degrees of freedom to find $t_{\alpha/2}$ in Table V:

$$t_{\alpha/2} = t_{.005} = 2.977$$

[*Note:* The small sample forces us to extend the interval almost 3 standard deviations (of $\bar{x}$) on each side of the sample mean in order to form the 99% confidence interval.] From the Excel/DDXL printout, Figure 5.10, we find $\bar{x} = 1.239$ and $s = .193$. Substituting these values into the confidence interval formula, we obtain

$$\bar{x} \pm t_{.005}\left(\frac{s}{\sqrt{n}}\right) = 1.239 \pm 2.977\left(\frac{.193}{\sqrt{15}}\right)$$

$$= 1.239 \pm .148 \text{ or } (1.091, 1.387)$$

This interval is shown at the bottom of the printout, Figure 5.10.

Our interpretation is as follows: The manufacturer can be 99% confident that the printhead has a mean life of between 1.091 and 1.387 million characters. If the manufacturer were to advertise that the mean life of its printheads is (at least) 1 million characters, the interval would support such a claim. Our confidence is derived from the fact that 99% of the intervals formed in repeated applications of this procedure would contain μ.

b. Because *n* is small, we must assume that the number of characters printed before printhead failure is a random variable from a normal distribution—that is, we assume that the population from which the sample of 15 measurements is selected is distributed normally. One way to check this assumption is to graph the distribution of data in Table 5.5. If the sample data are approximately normal, then the population from which the sample is selected is very likely to be normal. A Minitab stem-and-leaf plot for the sample data is displayed in Figure 5.11. The distribution is mound shaped and nearly symmetric. Therefore, the assumption of normality appears to be reasonably satisfied.

Look Back Other checks for normality, such as a normal probability plot and the ratio IQR/S, may also be used to verify the normality condition.

Figure 5.10
Excel/DDXL summary statistics and confidence interval for data in Table 5.5

Stem-and-Leaf Display: NUMBER

```
Stem-and-leaf of NUMBER   N  = 15
Leaf Unit = 0.010

   1    8    5
   2    9    2
   3   10    7
   5   11    38
  (4)  12    0259
   6   13    236
   3   14    38
   1   15    5
```

Figure 5.11
Minitab stem-and-leaf display of data in Table 5.5

Now Work Exercise 5.31

We have emphasized throughout this section that an assumption that the population is approximately normally distributed is necessary for making small-sample inferences about μ when using the *t*-statistic. Although many phenomena do have approximately normal distributions, it is also true that many random phenomena have distributions that are not normal or even mound shaped. Empirical evidence acquired over the years has shown that the *t*-distribution is rather insensitive to moderate departures from normality—that is, use of the *t*-statistic when sampling from slightly or moderately skewed mound shaped populations generally produces credible results; however, for cases in which the distribution is distinctly nonnormal, we must either take a large sample or use a *nonparametric method* (the topic of Chapter 14).

What Do You Do When the Population Relative Frequency Distribution Departs Greatly from Normality?

Answer: Use the nonparametric statistical methods of Chapter 14.

Statistics IN Action Revisited Estimating the Mean Overpayment

Refer to the Medicare fraud investigation described in the Statistics in Action (pp. 269–270). Recall that the United States Department of Justice (USDOJ) obtained a random sample of 52 claims from a population of 1,000 Medicare claims. For each claim, the amount paid, the amount disallowed (denied) by the auditor, and the amount that should have been paid (allowed) were recorded and saved in the **MCFRAUD** file. The USDOJ wants to use these data to calculate an estimate of the overpayment for all 1,000 claims in the population.

One way to do this is to first use the sample data to estimate the mean overpayment per claim for the population, then use the estimated mean to extrapolate the overpayment amount to the population of all 1,000 claims. The difference between the amount paid and the amount allowed by the auditor represents the overpayment for each claim. This value is recorded as the amount denied in the **MCFRAUD** file. These overpayment amounts are listed in the accompanying table.

Minitab software is used to find a 95% confidence interval for μ, the mean overpayment amount. The Minitab printout is displayed in Figure SIA5.1. The 95% confidence

interval for μ (highlighted on the printout) is (16.51, 27.13). Thus, the USDOJ can be 95% confident that the mean overpayment amount for the population of 1,000 claims is between $16.51 and $27.13.

Now, let x_i represent the overpayment amount for the *i*th claim. If the true mean μ were known, then the total overpayment amount for all 1,000 claims would be equal

$$\sum_{i=1}^{1,000} x_i = (1,000)\left[\sum_{i=1}^{1,000} x_i\right]/(1,000) = (1,000)\mu$$

Consequently, to estimate the total overpayment amount for the 1,000 claims, the USDOJ will simply multiply the end points of the interval by 1,000. This yields the 95% confidence interval ($16,510, $27,130).* Typically, the USDOJ is willing to give the Medicare provider in question the benefit of the doubt by demanding a repayment equal to the lower 95% confidence bound—in this case, $16,510.

Table SIA5.1	Overpayment Amounts for Sample of 52 Claims						
$0.00	$31.00	$0.00	$37.20	$37.20	$0.00	$43.40	$0.00
$37.20	$43.40	$0.00	$37.20	$0.00	$24.80	$0.00	$0.00
$37.20	$0.00	$37.20	$0.00	$37.20	$37.20	$37.20	$0.00
$37.20	$37.20	$0.00	$0.00	$37.20	$0.00	$43.40	$37.20
$0.00	$37.20	$0.00	$37.20	$37.20	$0.00	$37.20	$37.20
$0.00	$37.20	$43.40	$0.00	$37.20	$37.20	$37.20	$0.00
$43.40	$0.00	$43.40	$0.00				

Data Set: MCFRAUD

Figure SIA5.1
Minitab confidence interval for mean overpayment

```
Variable        N   Mean  StDev  SE Mean      95% CI
Denied_Amount  52  21.82  19.08     2.65  (16.51, 27.13)
```

*This interval represents an approximation to the true 95% confidence interval for the total amount of overpayment. The precise interval involves use of a continuity correction for population size (see Section 5.6).

Exercises 5.21–5.35

Learning the Mechanics

5.21 Suppose you have selected a random sample of $n = 5$ measurements from a normal distribution. Compare the standard normal z-values with the corresponding t-values if you were forming the following confidence intervals.
  a. 80% confidence interval
  b. 90% confidence interval
  c. 95% confidence interval
  d. 98% confidence interval
  e. 99% confidence interval
  f. Use the table values you obtained in parts **a–e** to sketch the z- and t-distributions. What are the similarities and differences?

⊙ **Applet Exercise 5.3**

Use the applet *Confidence Intervals for a Mean (the impact of not knowing the standard deviation)* to compare proportions of z-intervals and t-intervals that contain the mean for a population that is normally distributed.
  a. Using $n = 5$ and the normal distribution with mean 50 and standard deviation 10, run the applet several times. How do the proportions of z-intervals and t-intervals that contain the mean compare?
  b. Repeat part **a** first for $n = 10$ and then for $n = 20$. Compare your results to part **a**.
  c. Describe any patterns you observe between the proportion of z-intervals that contain the mean and the proportion of t-intervals that contain the mean as the sample size increases.

⊙ **Applet Exercise 5.4**

Use the applet *Confidence Intervals for a Mean (the impact of not knowing the standard deviation)* to compare proportions of z-intervals and t-intervals that contain the mean for a population with a skewed distribution.
  a. Using $n = 5$ and the right skewed distribution with mean 50 and standard deviation 10, run the applet several times. How do the proportions of z-intervals and t-intervals that contain the mean compare?
  b. Repeat part **a** first for $n = 10$ and then for $n = 20$. Compare your results to part **a**.
  c. Describe any patterns you observe between the proportion of z-intervals that contain the mean and the proportion of t-intervals that contain the mean as the sample size increases.
  d. How does skewedness of the underlying distribution affect the proportions of z-intervals and t-intervals that contain the mean?

5.22 Explain the differences in the sampling distributions of $\bar{x}$ for
[NW] large and small samples under the following assumptions.
  a. The variable of interest, x, is normally distributed.
  b. Nothing is known about the distribution of the variable x.

5.23 Let t_0 be a particular value of t. Use Table V in Appendix B to find t_0 values such that the following statements are true.
  a. $P(-t_0 < t < t_0) = .95$ where df $= 10$
  b. $P(t \leq -t_0 \text{ or } t \geq t_0) = .05$ where df $= 10$
  c. $P(t \leq t_0) = .05$ where df $= 10$
  d. $P(t \leq -t_0 \text{ or } t \geq t_0) = .10$ where df $= 20$
  e. $P(t \leq -t_0 \text{ or } t \geq t_0) = .01$ where df $= 5$

5.24 Let t_0 be a specific value of t. Use Table V in Appendix B to find t_0 values such that the following statements are true.
  a. $P(t \geq t_0) = .025$ where df $= 11$
  b. $P(t \geq t_0) = .01$ where df $= 9$
  c. $P(t \leq t_0) = .005$ where df $= 6$
  d. $P(t \leq t_0) = .05$ where df $= 18$

5.25 The following random sample was selected from a normal distribution: 4, 6, 3, 5, 9, 3.
  a. Construct a 90% confidence interval for the population mean μ.
  b. Construct a 95% confidence interval for the population mean μ.
  c. Construct a 99% confidence interval for the population mean μ.
  d. Assume that the sample mean $\bar{x}$ and sample standard deviation s remain exactly the same as those you just calculated but are based on a sample of $n = 25$ observations rather than $n = 6$ observations. Repeat parts **a–c**. What is the effect of increasing the sample size on the width of the confidence intervals?

5.26 The following sample of 16 measurements (saved in the
⊙ **LM5_26** file) was selected from a population that is approximately normally distributed:

91	80	99	110	95	106	78	121	106	100	97	82
100	83	115	104								

  a. Construct an 80% confidence interval for the population mean.
  b. Construct a 95% confidence interval for the population mean and compare the width of this interval with that of part **a**.
  c. Carefully interpret each of the confidence intervals and explain why the 80% confidence interval is narrower.

Applying the Concepts—Basic

5.27 **Assessing the bending strength of a wooden roof.** The white wood material used for the roof of an ancient Japanese temple is imported from Northern Europe. The wooden roof must withstand as much as 100 centimeters of snow in the winter. Architects at Tohoku University (Japan) conducted a study to estimate the mean bending strength of the white wood roof (*Journal of the International Association for Shell and Spatial Structures,* Aug. 2004). A sample of 25 pieces of the imported wood were tested and yielded the following statistics on breaking strength (MPa): $\bar{x} = 75.4$, $s = 10.9$. Estimate the true mean breaking strength of the white wood with a 90% confidence interval. Interpret the result.

5.28 **Hospital length of stay.** Health insurers and the federal government are both putting pressure on hospitals to shorten the average length of stay (LOS) of their patients. The average LOS for men in the United States is 5.2 days, and the average for women is 4.5 days (*Statistical Abstract of the United States: 2008*). A random sample of 20 hospitals in one state had a mean LOS for women of 3.8 days and a standard deviation of 1.2 days.
  a. Use a 90% confidence interval to estimate the population mean LOS for women for the state's hospitals.
  b. Interpret the interval in terms of this application.
  c. What is meant by the phrase "90% confidence interval"?

Minitab output for Exercise 5.29

One-Sample T: GrwthRate

```
Variable     N   Mean  StDev  SE Mean     95% CI
GrwthRate   12   2801   4912     1418  (-320, 5922)
```

5.29 Technology Fast 500. Deloitte & Touche rank the 500 fastest-growing technology companies in the United States based on percentage growth over a 5-year period. Consider a random sample of 12 companies similar to those ranked by D&T. The rankings and growth rates are shown in the table and saved in the **FAST500** file. A Minitab analysis of the data appears above.

Rank	5-year Revenue Growth Rate
19	15,554%
30	10,361
87	2,551
161	1,176
195	945
246	706
279	613
326	435
351	393
398	343
441	291
496	245

a. Locate a 95% confidence interval for the true mean 5-year revenue growth rate on the printout. Interpret the result.

b. In order to estimate the mean described in part **a** with a small-sample confidence interval, what characteristic must the population possess?

c. Explain why the required population characteristics may not hold in this case.

5.30 Surface roughness of pipe. Refer to the *Anti-corrosion Methods and Materials* (Vol. 50, 2003) study of the surface roughness of coated interior pipe used in oil fields, Exercise 2.46 (p. 62). The data (in micrometers) for 20 sampled pipe sections (saved in the **ROUGHPIPE** file) are reproduced in the next table; a Minitab analysis of the data appears below.

a. Locate a 95% confidence interval for the mean surface roughness of coated interior pipe on the accompanying Minitab printout.

b. Would you expect the average surface roughness to be as high as 2.5 micrometers? Explain.

1.72	2.50	2.16	2.13	1.06	2.24	2.31	2.03	1.09	1.40
2.57	2.64	1.26	2.05	1.19	2.13	1.27	1.51	2.41	1.95

Source: Farshad, F., and Pesacreta, T. "Coated pipe interior surface roughness as measured by three scanning probe instruments," *Anti-corrosion Methods and Materials*, Vol. 50, No. 1, 2003 (Table III). Copyright © 2003 MCB UP Ltd.

Applying the Concepts—Intermediate

5.31 Minimizing tractor skidding distance. When planning for a new forest road to be used for tree harvesting, planners must select the location to minimize tractor skidding distance. In the *Journal of Forest Engineering* (July 1999), researchers wanted to estimate the true mean skidding distance along a new road in a European forest. The skidding distances (in meters) were measured at 20 randomly selected road sites. These values are given in the accompanying table and saved in the **SKIDDING** file.

a. Estimate the true mean skidding distance for the road with a 95% confidence interval.

b. Give a practical interpretation of the interval, part **a**.

c. What conditions are required for the inference, part **b**, to be valid? Are these conditions reasonably satisfied?

d. A logger working on the road claims the mean skidding distance is at least 425 meters. Do you agree?

488	350	457	199	285	409	435	574	439	546
385	295	184	261	273	400	311	312	141	425

Source: Extracted from Tujek, J., and Pacola, E. "Algorithms for skidding distance modeling on a raster digital terrain model" *Journal of Forest Engineering*, Vol. 10, No. 1, July 1999 (Table 1).

One-Sample T: ROUGH

```
Variable     N      Mean    StDev   SE Mean      95% CI
ROUGH       20   1.88100  0.52391   0.11715  (1.63580, 2.12620)
```

5.32 **Contamination of New Jersey wells.** Methyl *t*-butyl ether (MTBE) is an organic water contaminant that often results from gasoline spills. The level of MTBE (in parts per billion) was measured for a sample of 12 well sites located near a gasoline service station in New Jersey (*Environmental Science & Technology,* Jan. 2005). The data are listed in the accompanying table and saved in the **NJGAS** file.

150	367	38	12	11	134
12	251	63	8	13	107

Source: Reprinted with permission from Kuder, T., et al. "Enrichment of stable carbon and hydrogen isotopes during anaerobic biodegradation of MTBE: Microcosm and field evidence," *Environmental Science & Technology,* Vol. 39, No. 1, Jan. 2005, pp. 213–220 (Table 1). © 2005 American Chemical Society

a. Give a point estimate for μ, the true mean MTBE level for all well sites located near the New Jersey gasoline service station.

b. Calculate and interpret a 99% confidence interval for μ.

c. What assumptions are required for the interval, part **b**, to be valid? Are these assumptions reasonably satisfied?

5.33 **Al Qaeda attacks on the United States.** *Studies in Conflict & Terrorism* (Vol. 29, 2006) published an empirical analysis of recent incidents involving suicide terrorist attacks. The data in the table (saved in the **ALQAEDA** file) are the number of individual suicide bombings and/or attacks for each in a sample of 21 incidents involving a transgression against the United States by the Al Qaeda terrorist group. (For example, the infamous 9/11/2001 Al Qaeda attack involved 4 separate hijacked airplane attacks—two planes crashed into the World Trade Center towers, one crashed into the Pentagon, and a fourth plane crashed in a field in Pennsylvania.)

a. Find the mean and standard deviation of the sample data.

b. Describe the population from which the sample is selected.

c. Use the information, part **a**, to find a 90% confidence interval for the mean, μ, of the population.

d. Give a practical interpretation of the result, part **c**.

e. In repeated sampling, where intervals similar to the one computed in part **c** are generated, what proportion of the intervals will enclose the true value of μ?

1	1	2	1	2	4	1	1	1	1	2	3	4	5	1	1	1	2	2	2	1

Source: Moghadam, A. "Suicide terrorism, occupation, and the globalization of martyrdom: A critique of *Dying to Win*," *Studies in Conflict & Terrorism,* Vol. 29, No. 8, 2006, pp. 707–729 (Table 3). Reprinted by permission of the publisher (Taylor & Francis Group www.informaworld.com).

5.34 **Overbooking policies for major airlines.** Airlines overbook flights in order to reduce the odds of flying with unused seats. An article in *Transportation Research* (Vol. 38, 2002) investigated the optimal overbooking policies for 10 major U.S. airlines. One of the variables measured for each airline was the compensation (in dollars) per bumped passenger required to maximize future revenue. These *threshold* levels of compensation for the 10 airlines are listed in the next table and saved in the **OVERBOOK** file. Suppose the data represent a sample of

threshold compensation levels selected from all major airlines. Estimate the true mean threshold compensation level for all major airlines using a 90% confidence interval. Interpret the result.

Airline	Threshold Compensation per Bumped Passenger
Alaska	$2,112
America West	752
American	1,312
Continental	1,264
Delta	2,048
Northwest	1,104
Southwest	720
Trans World	1,456
United	1,520
US Air	1,392

Source: Reprinted from Suzuki, Y. "An empirical analysis of the optimal overbooking policies for US major airlines," *Transportation Research, Part E,* Vol. 38, 2002, pp. 135–149 (Table 4). © 2002 with permission from Elsevier.

5.35 **Largest private companies.** IPOs—initial public offerings of stock—create billions of dollars of new wealth for owners, managers, and employees of companies that were previously privately owned. Nevertheless, hundreds of large and thousands of small companies remain privately owned. The revenues of a random sample of 15 firms from *Forbes* 441 Largest Private Companies list (saved in the **PRIVCOMP** file) is given in the table below.

Company	Revenue (in billions)
Enterprise Rent-A-Car	$13.10
Flying J	14.32
Tenaska Energy	11.60
Wawa	5.05
Ergon	4.49
Brookshire Grocery	2.20
BrightStar	3.66
Bose	2.18
Mary Kay	2.40
LL Bean	1.62
Rooms to Go	1.75
SAS Institute	2.15
Blue Tee	1.10
Printpack	1.36
US Oil	2.19

Source: "America's Largest Private Companies," *Forbes,* Nov. 3, 2008. Reprinted by permission of Forbes.com. © 2009 Forbes LLC.

a. Describe the population from which the random sample was drawn.

b. Use a 98% confidence interval to estimate the mean revenue of the population of companies in question.

c. Interpret your confidence interval in the context of the problem.

d. What characteristic must the population possess to ensure the appropriateness of the estimation procedure used in part **b**?

e. Suppose *Forbes* reports that the true mean revenue of the 441 companies on the list is $5.0 billion. Is the claim believable?

5.4 Large-Sample Confidence Interval for a Population Proportion

The number of public opinion polls has grown at an astounding rate in recent years. Almost daily, the news media report the results of some poll. Pollsters regularly determine the percentage of people who approve of the president's on-the-job performance, the fraction of voters in favor of a certain candidate, the fraction of customers who prefer a particular product, and the proportion of households that watch a particular TV program. In each case, we are interested in estimating the percentage (or proportion) of some group with a certain characteristic. In this section, we consider methods for making inferences about population proportions when the sample is large.

Example 5.6

Estimating a Population Proportion—Preference for Breakfast Cereal

Problem A food-products company conducted a market study by randomly sampling and interviewing 1,000 consumers to determine which brand of breakfast cereal they prefer. Suppose 313 consumers were found to prefer the company's brand. How would you estimate the true fraction of *all* consumers who prefer the company's cereal brand?

Solution In this study, consumers are asked which brand of breakfast cereal they prefer. Note that "brand" is a qualitative variable and what we are asking is how you would estimate the probability p of success in a binomial experiment, where p is the probability that a chosen consumer prefers the company's brand. One logical method of estimating p for the population is to use the proportion of successes in the sample—that is, we can estimate p by calculating

$$\hat{p} = \frac{\text{Number of consumers sampled who prefer the company's brand}}{\text{Number of consumers sampled}}$$

where $\hat{p}$ is read "p hat." Thus, in this case,

$$\hat{p} = \frac{313}{1,000} = .313$$

Look Back To determine the reliability of the estimator $\hat{p}$, we need to know its sampling distribution—that is, if we were to draw samples of 1,000 consumers over and over again, each time calculating a new estimate $\hat{p}$, what would be the frequency distribution of all the $\hat{p}$ values? The answer lies in viewing $\hat{p}$ as the average, or mean, number of successes per trial over the n trials. If each success is assigned a value equal to 1 and a failure is assigned a value of 0, then the sum of all n sample observations is x, the total number of successes, and $\hat{p} = x/n$ is the average, or mean, number of successes per trial in the n trials. The Central Limit Theorem tells us that the relative frequency distribution of the sample mean for any population is approximately normal for sufficiently large samples.

Now Work Exercise 5.45a

The repeated sampling distribution of $\hat{p}$ has the characteristics listed in the box on page 291 and shown in Figure 5.12.

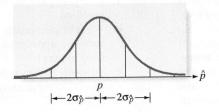

Figure 5.12
Sampling distribution of $\hat{p}$

Sampling Distribution of $\hat{p}$

1. The mean of the sampling distribution of $\hat{p}$ is p; that is, $\hat{p}$ is an unbiased estimator of p.

2. The standard deviation of the sampling distribution of $\hat{p}$ is $\sqrt{pq/n}$; that is, $\sigma\hat{p} = \sqrt{pq/n}$, where $q = 1 - p$.

3. For large samples, the sampling distribution of $\hat{p}$ is approximately normal. A sample size is considered large if both $n\hat{p} \geq 15$ and $n\hat{q} \geq 15$.

The fact that $\hat{p}$ is a "sample mean number of successes per trial" allows us to form confidence intervals about p in a manner that is completely analogous to that used for large-sample estimation of μ.

Large-Sample Confidence Interval for $\hat{p}$

$$\hat{p} \pm z_{\alpha/2}\sigma_{\hat{p}} = \hat{p} \pm z_{\alpha/2}\sqrt{\frac{pq}{n}} \approx \hat{p} \pm z_{\alpha/2}\sqrt{\frac{\hat{p}\hat{q}}{n}}$$

where $\hat{p} = \dfrac{x}{n}$ and $\hat{q} = 1 - \hat{p}$

Note: When n is large, $\hat{p}$ can approximate the value of p in the formula for $\sigma_{\hat{p}}$.

Conditions Required for a Valid Large-Sample Confidence Interval for p

1. A random sample is selected from the target population.

2. The sample size n is large. (This condition will be satisfied if both $n\hat{p} \geq 15$ and $n\hat{q} \geq 15$. Note that $n\hat{p}$ and $n\hat{q}$ are simply the number of successes and number of failures, respectively, in the sample.)

Thus, if 313 of 1,000 consumers prefer the company's cereal brand, a 95% confidence interval for the proportion of *all* consumers who prefer the company's brand is

$$\hat{p} \pm z_{\alpha/2}\sigma_{\hat{p}} = .313 \pm 1.96\sqrt{\frac{pq}{1,000}}$$

where $q = 1 - p$. Just as we needed an approximation for σ in calculating a large-sample confidence interval for μ, we now need an approximation for p. As Table 5.7 shows, the approximation for p does not have to be especially accurate because the value of $\sqrt{pq}$ needed for the confidence interval is relatively insensitive to changes in p. Therefore, we can use $\hat{p}$ to approximate p. Keeping in mind that $\hat{q} = 1 - \hat{p}$, we substitute these values into the formula for the confidence interval:

$$\hat{p} \pm 1.96\sqrt{\frac{pq}{1,000}} \approx \hat{p} \pm 1.96\sqrt{\frac{\hat{p}\hat{q}}{1,000}}$$

$$= .313 \pm 1.96\sqrt{\frac{(.313)(.687)}{1,000}}$$

$$= .313 \pm .029$$

$$= (.284, .342)$$

Table 5.7 Values of pq for Several Different Values of p

p	pq	$\sqrt{pq}$
.5	.25	.50
.6 or .4	.24	.49
.7 or .3	.21	.46
.8 or .2	.16	.40
.9 or .1	.09	.30

The company can be 95% confident that the interval from 28.4% to 34.2% contains the true percentage of *all* consumers who prefer its brand—that is, in repeated construction of confidence intervals, approximately 95% of all samples would produce confidence intervals that enclose p. Note that the guidelines for interpreting a confidence interval about μ also apply to interpreting a confidence interval for p because p is the "population fraction of successes" in a binomial experiment.

Example 5.7

Finding a Large-Sample Confidence Interval for p, the Proportion Optimistic about the Economy

Problem Many public polling agencies conduct surveys to determine the current consumer sentiment concerning the state of the economy. For example, the Bureau of Economic and Business Research (BEBR) at the University of Florida conducts quarterly surveys to gauge consumer sentiment in the Sunshine State. Suppose that the BEBR randomly samples 484 consumers and finds that 257 are optimistic about the state of the economy. Use a 90% confidence interval to estimate the proportion of all consumers in Florida who are optimistic about the state of the economy. Based on the confidence interval, can BEBR infer that the majority of Florida consumers are optimistic about the economy?

Solution The number, x, of the 484 sampled consumers who are optimistic about the Florida economy is a binomial random variable if we can assume that the sample was randomly selected from the population of Florida consumers and that the poll was conducted identically for each sampled consumer.

The point estimate of the proportion of Florida consumers who are optimistic about the economy is

$$\hat{p} = \frac{x}{n} = \frac{257}{484} = .531$$

We first check to be sure that the sample size is sufficiently large that the normal distribution provides a reasonable approximation for the sampling distribution of $\hat{p}$. We require both $n\hat{p}$ and $n\hat{q}$ to be at least 15. Now

$$n\hat{p} = 484(.531) = 257$$

and

$$n\hat{q} = 484(1 - .531) = 227$$

Because both of these values are at least 15, we may conclude that the normal approximation is reasonable.

We now proceed to form the 90% confidence interval for p, the true proportion of Florida consumers who are optimistic about the state of the economy:

$$\hat{p} \pm z_{\alpha/2}\sigma_{\hat{p}} = \hat{p} \pm z_{\alpha/2}\sqrt{\frac{pq}{n}} \approx \hat{p} \pm z_{\alpha/2}\sqrt{\frac{\hat{p}\hat{q}}{n}}$$

$$= .531 \pm 1.645\sqrt{\frac{(.531)(.469)}{484}} = .531 \pm .037 = (.494, .568)$$

(This interval is also shown on the Minitab printout, Figure 5.13.) Thus, we can be 90% confident that the proportion of all Florida consumers who are confident about the economy is between .494 and .568. As always, our confidence stems from the fact that 90% of all similarly formed intervals will contain the true proportion p and not from any knowledge about whether this particular interval does.

Can we conclude that the majority of Florida consumers are optimistic about the economy based on this interval? If we wished to use this interval to infer that a majority is optimistic, the interval would have to support the inference that p exceeds .5—that is, that more than 50% of the Florida consumers are optimistic about the economy. Note that the interval contains some values below .5 (as low as .494) as well as some above .5 (as high as .568). Therefore, we cannot conclude that the true value of p exceeds .5 based on this 90% confidence interval.

```
Sample    X    N   Sample p        90% CI
1        257  484  0.530992  (0.493681, 0.568303)
```

Figure 5.13

Portion of Minitab printout with 90% confidence interval for p

Look Back If the entire confidence interval fell above .5 (e.g., an interval from .52 to .54), then we could conclude (with 90% confidence) that the true proportion of consumers who are optimistic exceeds .5.

Now Work Exercise 5.45b,c

We conclude this section with a warning and an illustrative example.

⚠ **CAUTION** Unless n is extremely large, the large-sample procedure presented in this section performs poorly when p is near 0 or near 1. ▲

The problem stated in the above warning can be illustrated as follows. Suppose you want to estimate the proportion of executives who die from a work-related injury using a sample size of $n = 100$. This proportion is likely to be near 0, say $p \approx .001$. If so, then $np \approx 100(.001) = .1$ is less than the recommended value of 15 (see Conditions in the box on p. 291). Consequently, a confidence interval for p based on a sample of $n = 100$ will probably be misleading.

To overcome this potential problem, an *extremely* large sample size is required. Because the value of n required to satisfy "extremely large" is difficult to determine, statisticians (see Agresti & Coull, 1998) have proposed an alternative method, based on the Wilson (1927) point estimator of p. The procedure is outlined in the box below. Researchers have shown that this confidence interval works well for any p, even when the sample size n is very small.

Adjusted $(1 - \alpha)100\%$ Confidence Interval for a Population Proportion, p

$$\tilde{p} \pm z_{\alpha/2}\sqrt{\frac{\tilde{p}(1 - \tilde{p})}{n + 4}}$$

where $\tilde{p} = \frac{x + 2}{n + 4}$ is the adjusted sample proportion of observations with the characteristic of interest, x is the number of successes in the sample, and n is the sample size.

Example 5.8

Applying the Adjusted Confidence Interval Procedure for p, Proportion Who Are Victims of a Violent Crime

Problem According to *True Odds: How Risk Affects Your Everyday Life* (Walsh, 1997), the probability of being the victim of a violent crime is less than .01. Suppose that in a random sample of 200 Americans, 3 were victims of a violent crime. Estimate the true proportion of Americans who were victims of a violent crime using a 95% confidence interval.

Solution Let p represent the true proportion of Americans who were victims of a violent crime. Because p is near 0, an "extremely large" sample is required to estimate its value using the usual large-sample method. Note that the number of "successes," 3, is less than 15. Thus, we doubt whether the sample size of 200 is large enough to apply the large-sample method. Alternatively, we will apply the adjustment outlined in the box.

Because the number of "successes" (i.e., number of violent crime victims) in the sample is $x = 3$, the adjusted sample proportion is

$$\tilde{p} = \frac{x + 2}{n + 4} = \frac{3 + 2}{200 + 4} = \frac{5}{204} = .025$$

Note that this adjusted sample proportion is obtained by adding a total of four observations—two "successes" and two "failures"—to the sample data. Substituting $\tilde{p} = .025$ into the equation for a 95% confidence interval, we obtain

$$\tilde{p} \pm 1.96\sqrt{\frac{\tilde{p}(1 - \tilde{p})}{n + 4}} = .025 \pm 1.96\sqrt{\frac{(.025)(.975)}{204}}$$

$$= .025 \pm .021$$

or (.004, .046). Consequently, we are 95% confident that the true proportion of Americans who are victims of a violent crime falls between .004 and .046.

Look Back If we apply the standard large sample confidence interval formula, where $\hat{p} = 3/200 = .015$, we obtain

$$\hat{p} \pm 1.96\sqrt{\frac{\hat{p}\hat{q}}{200}} = .015 \pm 1.96\sqrt{\frac{(.015)(.985)}{200}}$$
$$= .015 \pm .017 \text{ or } (-.002, .032)$$

Note that the interval contains negative (nonsensical) values for the true proportion. Such a result is typical when the large-sample method is misapplied.

Now Work Exercise 5.52

Statistics IN Action Revisited   Estimating the Coding Error Rate

In the previous Statistics in Action Revisited (p. 286), we showed how to estimate the mean overpayment amount for claims in a Medicare fraud study. In addition to estimating overcharges, the USDOJ also is interested in estimating the *coding error rate* of a Medicare provider. The coding error rate is defined as the proportion of Medicare claims that are coded incorrectly. Thus, for this inference, the USDOJ is interested in estimating a population proportion, *p*. Typically, the USDOJ finds that about 50% of the claims in a Medicare fraud case are incorrectly coded.

If you examine the sample data in Table SIA5.1, you can verify that of the 52 audited claims, 31 were determined to be coded incorrectly, resulting in an overcharge. These are the claims with a disallowed amount greater than $0. Therefore, an estimate of the coding error rate, *p*, for this Medicare provider is

$$\hat{p} = 31/52 = .596$$

A 95% confidence interval for *p* can be obtained with the use of a confidence interval formula or with statistical software.

The **MCFRAUD** file includes a qualitative variable (called "Coding Error") at two levels, where "Yes" represents that the claim is coded incorrectly and "No" represents that the claim is coded correctly.

Thus, the USDOJ desires an estimate of the proportion of "Yes" values for the "Coding Error" variable. A confidence interval for the proportion of incorrectly coded claims is highlighted on the accompanying Minitab printout, Figure SIA5.2. The interval, (.45, .73), implies that the true coding error rate for the 1,000 claims in the population falls between .45 and .73, with 95% confidence. Note that the value .5 — the proportion of incorrectly coded claims expected by the USDOJ — falls within the 95% confidence interval.

Data Set: MCFRAUD

```
Event = Yes


Variable        X    N    Sample p        95% CI
Coding_Error   31   52    0.596154   (0.451016, 0.729940)
```

Figure SIA5.2
Minitab confidence interval for coding error rate

Exercises 5.36–5.55

Learning the Mechanics

5.36 Describe the sampling distribution of $\hat{p}$ based on large samples of size n — that is, give the mean, the standard deviation, and the (approximate) shape of the distribution of $\hat{p}$ when large samples of size n are (repeatedly) selected from the binomial distribution with probability of success p.

🟢 Applet Exercise 5.5

Use the applet *Confidence Intervals for a Proportion* to investigate the effect of the value of *p* on the number of confidence intervals that contain the population proportion *p* for a fixed sample size. For this exercise, use sample size $n = 10$.

   a. Run the applet several times without clearing for $p = .1$. What proportion of the 95% confidence intervals contain

p? What proportion of the 99% confidence intervals contain p? Do the results surprise you? Explain.

b. Repeat part **a** for each value of p: $p = .2, p = .3, p = .4,$ $p = .5, p = .6, p = .7, p = .8,$ and $p = .9$.

c. Which value of p yields the greatest proportion of each type of interval that contain p?

d. Based on your results, what values of p will yield more reliable confidence intervals for a fixed sample size n? Explain.

Applet Exercise 5.6

Use the applet *Confidence Intervals for a Proportion* to investigate the effect of the sample size on the number of confidence intervals that contain the population proportion p for a value of p close to 0 or 1.

a. Run the applet several times without clearing for $p = .5$ and $n = 50$. Record the proportion of the 99% confidence intervals containing p.

b. Now set $p = .1$ and run the applet several times without clearing for $n = 50$. How does the proportion of the 99% confidence intervals containing p compare to that in part **a**?

c. Repeat part **b** keeping $p = .1$ and increasing the sample size by 50 until you find a sample size that yields a similar proportion of the 99% confidence intervals containing p as that in part **a**.

d. Based on your results, describe how the value of p affects the sample size needed to guarantee a certain level of confidence.

5.37 For the binomial sample information summarized in each part, indicate whether the sample size is large enough to use the methods of this chapter to construct a confidence interval for p.

a. $n = 400, \hat{p} = .10$ **b.** $n = 50, \hat{p} = .10$
c. $n = 20, \hat{p} = .5$ **d.** $n = 20, \hat{p} = .3$

5.38 A random sample of size $n = 121$ yielded $\hat{p} = .88$.

a. Is the sample size large enough to use the methods of this section to construct a confidence interval for p? Explain.

b. Construct a 90% confidence interval for p.

c. What assumption is necessary to ensure the validity of this confidence interval?

5.39 A random sample of size $n = 225$ yielded $\hat{p} = .46$.

a. Is the sample size large enough to use the methods of this section to construct a confidence interval for p? Explain.

b. Construct a 95% confidence interval for p.

c. Interpret the 95% confidence interval.

d. Explain what is meant by the phrase "95% confidence interval."

5.40 A random sample of 50 consumers taste-tested a new snack food. Their responses were coded (0: do not like; 1: like; 2: indifferent), recorded, and saved in the **SNACK** file as follows:

1	0	0	1	2	0	1	1	0	0
0	1	0	2	0	2	2	0	0	1
1	0	0	0	0	1	0	2	0	0
0	1	0	0	1	0	0	1	0	1
0	2	0	0	1	1	0	0	0	1

a. Use an 80% confidence interval to estimate the proportion of consumers who like the snack food.

b. Provide a statistical interpretation for the confidence interval you constructed in part **a**.

Applying the Concepts—Basic

5.41 **Is Starbucks coffee overpriced?** The *Minneapolis Star Tribune* (August 12, 2008) reported that 73% of Americans say that Starbucks coffee is overpriced. The source of this information was a national telephone survey of 1,000 American adults conducted by Rasmussen Reports.

a. Identify the population of interest in this study.

b. Identify the sample for the study.

c. Identify the parameter of interest in the study.

d. Find and interpret a 95% confidence interval for the parameter of interest.

5.42 **Satellite radio in cars.** Refer to the June 2007 survey on satellite radio subscriber service and usage conducted for the National Association of Broadcasters, Exercise 1.21 (p. 23). Recall that a random sample of 501 satellite radio subscribers were asked, "Do you have a satellite radio receiver in your car?" The survey found that 396 subscribers did, in fact, have a satellite receiver in their car.

a. From the sample, calculate an estimate of the true proportion of satellite radio subscribers who have a satellite radio receiver in their car.

b. Form a 90% confidence interval for the estimate, part **a**.

c. Give a practical interpretation of the interval, part **b**.

5.43 **Contractors with a company Web site.** Each year, construction contractors and equipment distributors from across the United States participate in a survey called the CIT Construction Industry Forecast. Recently, 900 contractors were interviewed for the survey. Of these, 414 indicated that they either already have a company Web site or plan to have a company Web site by the end of the year (*Contractor Magazine*, Jan. 2005).

a. Use the survey information to find a point estimate for the true proportion of contractors in the United States who have a company Web site or who will have one by the end of the year.

b. Find an interval estimate for the proportion, part **a**. Use a 90% confidence interval.

c. Give a practical interpretation of the interval, part **b**. Your answer should begin with "We are 90% confident…."

d. Explain the meaning of the phrase, "90% confident."

5.44 **Material safety data sheets.** For over 20 years, the Occupational Safety & Health Administration has required companies that handle hazardous chemicals to complete material safety data sheets (MSDSs). These MSDSs have been criticized for being too hard to understand and complete by workers. Although improvements were implemented in 1990, a more recent study of 150 MSDSs revealed that only 11% were satisfactorily completed (*Chemical & Engineering News*, Feb. 7, 2005).

a. Give a point estimate of p, the true proportion of MSDSs that are satisfactorily completed.

b. Find a 95% confidence interval for p.

c. Give a practical interpretation of the interval, part **b**.

5.45 **Cell phone use by drivers.** In a July 2001 research note, the U.S. Department of Transportation reported the results of the *National Occupant Protection Use Survey*. One focus of the survey was to determine the level of cell phone use by drivers while they are in the act of driving a motor passenger vehicle. Data collected by observers at randomly selected intersections across the country revealed that in a sample of 1,165 drivers, 35 were using their cell phone.

a. Give a point estimate of *p*, the true driver cell phone use rate (i.e., the true proportion of drivers who are using a cell phone while driving).

b. Compute a 95% confidence interval for *p*.

c. Give a practical interpretation of the interval, part **b.**

5.46 **Products "Made in the USA."** Refer to Exercise 2.8 (p. 39) and the *Journal of Global Business* (Spring 2002) survey to determine what "Made in the USA" means to consumers. Recall that 106 shoppers at a shopping mall in Muncie, Indiana, responded to the question, " 'Made in the USA' means what percentage of U.S. labor and materials?" Sixty-four shoppers answered "100%."

a. Define the population of interest in the survey.

b. What is the characteristic of interest in the population?

c. Estimate the true proportion of consumers who believe "Made in the USA" means 100% U.S. labor and materials using a 90% confidence interval.

d. Give a practical interpretation of the interval, part **c.**

e. Explain what the phrase "90% confidence" means for this interval.

Applying the Concepts—Intermediate

5.47 **Adoption of high-speed Internet connection at home.** The Pew Internet & American Life Project reports periodically on the growth of home broadband adoption in the United States. A recent (May 2006) random-digit-dialing telephone survey of 4,000 American adults found that 42% have access to a high-speed Internet connection at home.

a. Give a point estimate of the true percentage of all American adults who have access to a high-speed Internet connection at home.

b. Construct a 95% confidence interval for the estimate, part **a,** and interpret the result.

c. In 2005, the Pew Internet & American Life Project reported that 30% of all American adults had access to a high-speed Internet connection at home. Is there evidence to conclude that the percentage has increased since 2005? Explain.

5.48 **Interviewing candidates for a job.** The costs associated with conducting interviews for a job opening have skyrocketed over the years. According to a Harris Interactive survey, 211 of 502 senior human resources executives at U.S. companies believe that their hiring managers are interviewing too many people to find qualified candidates for the job (*Business Wire*, June 8, 2006).

a. Describe the population of interest in this study.

b. Identify the population parameter of interest, *p*.

c. Is the sample size large enough to provide a reliable estimate of *p*?

d. Find and interpret an interval estimate for the true proportion of senior human resources executives who believe that their hiring managers interview too many candidates during a job search. Use a confidence level of 98%.

e. If you had constructed a 90% confidence interval, would it be wider or narrower?

5.49 **History of corporate acquisitions.** Refer to the *Academy of Management Journal* (Aug. 2008) investigation of the performance and timing of corporate acquisitions, Exercise 2.12 (p. 40). Recall that a corporate acquisition occurs when one corporation purchases all the stock shares of another. The investigation discovered that in a sample of 2,778 firms, 748 announced one or more acquisitions during the year 2000. Estimate the true percentage of all firms that announced one or more acquisitions during the year 2000 using a 90% confidence interval. Interpret the result.

5.50 **Diamonds sold on the open market.** Refer to the sample of 308 diamond stones that were listed for sale on the open market in Singapore's *Business Times*. The data are saved in the **DIAMONDS** file. Recall that the color of each diamond is classified as D, E, F, G, H, or I, while the clarity of each is classified as VVS1, VVS2, VS1, or VS2.

a. Find a 99% confidence interval for the proportion of all diamonds for sale on the open market that are classified as "D" color. Interpret the result.

b. Find a 99% confidence interval for the proportion of all diamonds for sale on the open market that are classified as "VS1" clarity. Interpret the result.

5.51 **Accuracy of price scanners at Wal-Mart.** The National Institute for Standards and Technology (NIST) mandates that for every 100 items scanned through the electronic checkout scanner at a retail store, no more than 2 should have an inaccurate price. A recent study of the accuracy of checkout scanners at Wal-Mart stores in California was conducted (*Tampa Tribune*, Nov. 22, 2005). At each of 60 randomly selected Wal-Mart stores, 100 random items were scanned. The researchers found that 52 of the 60 stores had more than 2 items that were inaccurately priced.

a. Give an estimate of *p*, the proportion of Wal-Mart stores in California that have more than 2 inaccurately priced items per 100 items scanned.

b. Construct a 95% confidence interval for *p*.

c. Give a practical interpretation of the interval, part **b.**

d. Suppose a Wal-Mart spokesperson claims that 99% of California Wal-Mart stores are in compliance with the NIST mandate on accuracy of price scanners. Comment on the believability of this claim.

e. Are the conditions required for a valid large-sample confidence interval for *p* satisfied in this application? If not, comment on the validity of the inference in part **d.**

5.52 **Male nannies.** The International Nanny Association reports that in a sample of 4,176 nannies who were placed in a job in 2007, only 24 were men (www.nanny.org). Use Wilson's adjustment to find a 95% confidence interval for the true proportion of all working nannies who are men. Interpret the resulting interval.

5.53 **Are you really being served red snapper?** Refer to the *Nature* (July 15, 2004) study of fish specimens labeled "red snapper," Exercise 3.69 (p. 154). Recall that federal law prohibits restaurants from serving a cheaper look-alike variety of fish (e.g., vermillion snapper or lane snapper) to customers who order red snapper. A team of University of North Carolina (UNC) researchers analyzed the meat from each in a sample of 22 "red snapper" fish fillets purchased from vendors across the United States in an effort to estimate the true proportion of fillets that are really red snapper. DNA tests revealed that 17 of the 22 fillets (or 77%) were not red snapper but the cheaper look-alike variety of fish.

a. Identify the parameter of interest to the UNC researchers.

b. Explain why a large-sample confidence interval is inappropriate to apply in this study.

c. Construct a 95% confidence interval for the parameter of interest using Wilson's adjustment.

d. Give a practical interpretation of the confidence interval.

Applying the Concepts—Advanced

5.54 **Latex allergy in health care workers.** Refer to the *Current Allergy & Clinical Immunology* (Mar. 2004) study of health care workers who use latex gloves, Exercise 5.10 (p. 278). In addition to the 46 hospital employees who were diagnosed with a latex allergy based on a skin-prick test, another 37 health care workers were diagnosed with the allergy using a latex-specific serum test. Of these 83 workers with confirmed latex allergy, only 36 suspected that they had the allergy when asked on a questionnaire. Make a statement about the likelihood that a health care worker with latex allergy suspects he or she actually has the allergy. Attach a measure of reliability to your inference.

5.55 **U.S. Postal Service's performance.** The accounting firm of Price Waterhouse annually monitors the U.S. Postal Service's performance. One parameter of interest is the percentage of mail delivered on time. In a sample of 332,000 items mailed between Dec. 10 and Mar. 3—the most difficult delivery season due to bad weather and holidays—Price Waterhouse determined that 282,200 items were delivered on time (*Tampa Tribune*, Mar. 26, 1995). Use this information to make a statement about the likelihood of an item being delivered on time by the U.S. Postal Service.

5.5 Determining the Sample Size

Recall (Section 1.6) that one way to collect the relevant data for a study used to make inferences about the population is to implement a designed (planned) experiment. Perhaps the most important design decision faced by the analyst is to determine the size of the sample. We show in this section that the appropriate sample size for making an inference about a population mean or proportion depends on the desired reliability.

Estimating a Population Mean

Consider the example from Section 5.2 in which we estimated the mean overdue amount for all delinquent accounts in a large credit corporation. A sample of 100 delinquent accounts produced the 95% confidence interval $\bar{x} \pm 1.96\sigma_{\bar{x}} \approx 233.28 \pm 17.71$. Consequently, our estimate $\bar{x}$ was within \$17.71 of the true mean amount due, μ, for all the delinquent accounts at the 95% confidence level—that is, the 95% confidence interval for μ was $2(17.71) = \$35.42$ wide when 100 accounts were sampled. This is illustrated in Figure 5.14(a).

a. $n = 100$

Figure 5.14

Relationship between sample size and width of confidence interval: delinquent debtors example

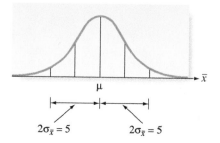

b. $n = 1,306$

Now suppose we want to estimate μ to within \$5 with 95% confidence—that is, we want to narrow the width of the confidence interval from \$35.42 to \$10, as shown in Figure 5.14(b). How much will the sample size have to be increased to accomplish this? If we want the estimator $\bar{x}$ to be within \$5 of μ, we must have

$$2\sigma_{\bar{x}} = 5 \quad \text{or, equivalently,} \quad 2\left(\frac{\sigma}{\sqrt{n}}\right) = 5$$

The necessary sample size is obtained by solving this equation for n. To do this, we need an approximation for σ. We have an approximation from the initial sample of 100 accounts—namely, the sample standard deviation, $s = 90.34$. Thus,

$$2\left(\frac{\sigma}{\sqrt{n}}\right) \approx 2\left(\frac{s}{\sqrt{n}}\right) = 2\left(\frac{90.34}{\sqrt{n}}\right) = 5$$

$$\sqrt{n} = \frac{2(90.34)}{5} = 36.136$$

$$n = (36.136)^2 = 1,305.81 \approx 1,306$$

Approximately 1,306 accounts will have to be randomly sampled to estimate the mean overdue amount μ to within \$5 with (approximately) 95% confidence. The confidence interval resulting from a sample of this size will be approximately \$10 wide (see Figure 5.14b).

In general, we express the reliability associated with a confidence interval for the population mean μ by specifying the **sampling error,** within which we want to estimate μ with $100(1 - \alpha)$% confidence. The sampling error (denoted SE), then, is equal to the half-width of the confidence interval, as shown in Figure 5.15.

Sample Size Determination for $100(1 - \alpha)$% Confidence Interval for μ

In order to estimate μ with a sampling error and with $100(1 - \alpha)$% confidence, the required sample size is found as follows:

$$z_{\alpha/2}\left(\frac{\sigma}{\sqrt{n}}\right) = SE$$

The solution for n is given by the equation

$$n = \frac{(z_{\alpha/2})^2 \sigma^2}{(SE)^2}$$

Note: The value of σ is usually unknown. It can be estimated by the standard deviation, s, from a prior sample. Alternatively, we may approximate the range R of observations in the population, and (conservatively) estimate $\sigma \approx R/4$. In any case, you should round the value of n obtained *upward* to ensure that the sample size will be sufficient to achieve the specified reliability.

Figure 5.15

Specifying the sampling error as the half-width of a confidence interval

Example 5.9

Finding the Sample Size for Estimating μ, the Mean Inflation Pressure of Footballs

Problem The manufacturer of official NFL footballs uses a machine to inflate its new balls to a pressure of 13.5 pounds. When the machine is properly calibrated, the mean inflation pressure is 13.5 pounds, but uncontrollable factors cause the pressures of individual footballs to vary randomly from about 13.3 to 13.7 pounds. For quality-control purposes, the manufacturer wishes to estimate the mean inflation pressure to within .025 pound of its true value with a 99% confidence interval. What sample size should be used?

Solution We desire a 99% confidence interval that estimates μ with a sampling error of SE = .025 pound. For a 99% confidence interval, we have $z_{\alpha/2} = z_{.005} = 2.575$. No previous estimate of s is available; however, we are given that the range of observations is $R = 13.7 - 13.3 = .4$. A conservative estimate (based on Chebychev's Rule) is $\sigma \approx R/4 = .1$. Now we use the formula derived in the box to find the sample size n:

$$n = \frac{(z_{\alpha/2})^2 \sigma^2}{(\text{SE})^2} \approx \frac{(2.575)^2(.1)^2}{(.025)^2} = 106.09$$

We round this up to $n = 107$. Realizing that σ was approximated by $R/4$, we might even advise that the sample size be specified as $n = 110$ to be more certain of attaining the objective of a 99% confidence interval with a sampling error of .025 pound or less.

Look Back To determine the value of the sampling error, look for the value that follows the key words "estimate μ to within. ..."

Now Work Exercise 5.64

Sometimes the formula will yield a small sample size (say, $n < 30$). Unfortunately, this solution is invalid because the procedures and assumptions for small samples differ from those for large samples, as we discovered in Section 5.3. Therefore, if the formulas yield a small sample size, one simple strategy is to select a sample size $n = 30$.

Estimating a Population Proportion

The method outlined above is easily applied to a population proportion p. For example, in Section 5.4, a company used a sample of 1,000 consumers to calculate a 95% confidence interval for the proportion of consumers who preferred its cereal brand, obtaining the interval .313 ± .029. Suppose the company wishes to estimate its market share more precisely, say to within .015 with a 95% confidence interval.

The company wants a confidence interval with a sampling error for the estimate of p of SE = .015. The sample size required to generate such an interval is found by solving the following equation for n (see Figure 5.16):

$$z_{\alpha/2}\sigma_{\hat{p}} = \text{SE} \qquad \text{or} \qquad z_{\alpha/2}\sqrt{\frac{pq}{n}} = .015$$

Because a 95% confidence interval is desired, the appropriate z-value is $z_{\alpha/2} = z_{.025} = 1.96 \approx 2$. We must approximate the value of the product pq before we can solve the

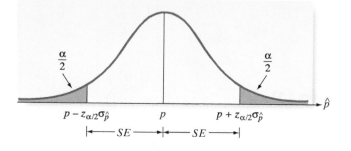

Figure 5.16

Specifying the sampling error of a confidence interval for a population proportion p

equation for n. As shown in Table 5.6, the closer the values of p and q to .5, the larger the product pq. Thus, to find a conservatively large sample size that will generate a confidence interval with the specified reliability, we generally choose an approximation of p close to .5. In the case of the food-products company, however, we have an initial sample estimate of $\hat{p} = .313$. A conservatively large estimate of pq can therefore be obtained by using, say, $p = .35$. We now substitute into the equation and solve for n:

$$2\sqrt{\frac{(.35)(.65)}{n}} = .015$$

$$n = \frac{(2)^2(.35)(.65)}{(.015)^2}$$

$$= 4{,}044.44 \approx 4{,}045$$

The company must sample about 4,045 consumers to estimate the percentage who prefer its brand to within .015 with a 95% confidence interval.

The procedure for finding the sample size necessary to estimate a population proportion p with a specified sampling error SE is given in the box.

Sample Size Determination for $100(1 - \alpha)$% Confidence Interval for p

In order to estimate a binomial probability p with sampling error SE and with $100(1 - \alpha)$ % confidence, the required sample size is found by solving the following equation for n:

$$z_{\alpha/2}\sqrt{\frac{pq}{n}} = SE$$

The solution for n can be written as follows:

$$n = \frac{(z_{\alpha/2})^2(pq)}{(SE)^2}$$

Note: Because the value of the product pq is unknown, it can be estimated by using the sample fraction of successes, $\hat{p}$, from a prior sample. Remember (Table 5.6) that the value of pq is at its maximum when p equals .5, so you can obtain conservatively large values of n by approximating p by .5 or values close to .5. In any case, you should round the value of n obtained *upward* to ensure that the sample size will be sufficient to achieve the specified reliability.

Example 5.10

Finding the Sample Size for Estimating p, the Fraction of Defective Cell Phones

Problem A cellular telephone manufacturer that entered the postregulation market too quickly has an initial problem with excessive customer complaints and consequent returns of the cell phones for repair or replacement. The manufacturer wants to determine the magnitude of the problem in order to estimate its warranty liability. How many cellular telephones should the company randomly sample from its warehouse and check in order to estimate the fraction defective, p, to within .01 with 90% confidence?

Solution In order to estimate p to within .01 of its true value, we set the half-width of the confidence interval equal to SE = .01, as shown in Figure 5.17.

Figure 5.17

Specified reliability for estimate of fraction defective in Example 5.10

The equation for the sample size n requires an estimate of the product pq. We could most conservatively estimate $pq = .25$ (i.e., use $p = .5$), but this may be overly conservative when estimating a fraction defective. A value of .1, corresponding to 10% defective, will probably be conservatively large for this application. The solution is therefore

$$n = \frac{(z_{\alpha/2})^2(pq)}{(SE)^2} = \frac{(1.645)^2(.1)(.9)}{(.01)^2} = 2{,}435.4 \approx 2{,}436$$

Thus, the manufacturer should sample 2,436 cellular telephones in order to estimate the fraction defective, p, to within .01 with 90% confidence.

Look Back Remember that this answer depends on our approximation for pq, where we used .09. If the fraction defective is closer to .05 than to .10, we can use a sample of 1,286 cell phones (check this) to estimate p to within .01 with 90% confidence.

Now Work Exercise 5.65

The cost of sampling will also play an important role in the final determination of the sample size to be selected to estimate either μ or p. Although more complex formulas can be derived to balance the reliability and cost considerations, we will solve for the necessary sample size and note that the sampling budget may be a limiting factor. Consult the references for a more complete treatment of this problem.

Statistics IN Action | Revisited | Determining Sample Size

In the previous Statistics in Action applications in this chapter, we used confidence intervals (1) to estimate μ, the mean overpayment amount for claims in a Medicare fraud study, and (2) to estimate p, the coding error rate (i.e., proportion of claims that are incorrectly coded) of a Medicare provider. Both of these confidence intervals were based on selecting a random sample of 52 claims from the population of claims handled by the Medicare provider. How does the USDOJ determine how many claims to sample for auditing?

Consider the problem of estimating the coding error rate, p. As stated in a previous Statistics in Action Revisited, the US-DOJ typically finds that about 50% of the claims in a Medicare fraud case are incorrectly coded. Suppose the USDOJ wants to estimate the true coding error rate of a Medicare provider to within .1 with 95% confidence. How many claims should be randomly sampled for audit in order to attain the desired estimate?

Here, the USDOJ desires a sampling error of SE = .1, a confidence level of $1 - \alpha = .95$ (for which $z_{\alpha/2} = 1.96$),

and uses an estimate $p \approx .50$. Substituting these values into the sample size formula (p. 300), we obtain:

$$\begin{aligned} n &= (z_{\alpha/2})^2(pq)/(SE)^2 \\ &= (1.96)^2(.5)(.5)/(.1)^2 \\ &= 96.04 \end{aligned}$$

Consequently, the USDOJ should audit about 97 randomly selected claims to attain a 95% confidence interval for p with a sampling error of .10.

[*Note:* You may wonder why the sample actually used in the fraud analysis included only 52 claims. The sampling strategy employed involved more than selecting a simple random sample; rather, it used a more sophisticated sampling scheme, called stratified random sampling. The 52 claims represented the sample for just one of the strata.]

Exercises 5.56–5.72

Learning the Mechanics

5.56 If you wish to estimate a population mean with a sampling error of SE = .3 using a 95% confidence interval, and you know from prior sampling that σ^2 is approximately equal to 7.2, how many observations would have to be included in your sample?

5.57 Suppose you wish to estimate a population mean correct to within .20 with probability equal to .90. You do not know σ^2, but you know that the observations will range in value between 30 and 34.

a. Find the approximate sample size that will produce the desired accuracy of the estimate. You wish to be conservative to ensure that the sample size will be ample to achieve the desired accuracy of the estimate. [*Hint:* Using your knowledge of data variation from Section 2.6, assume that the range of the observations will equal 4σ.]

b. Calculate the approximate sample size, making the less conservative assumption that the range of the observations is equal to 6σ.

5.58 In each case, find the approximate sample size required to construct a 95% confidence interval for p that has sampling error of SE = .08.

a. Assume p is near .2.

b. Assume you have no prior knowledge about p, but you wish to be certain that your sample is large enough to achieve the specified accuracy for the estimate.

5.59 The following is a 90% confidence interval for p: (.26, .54). How large was the sample used to construct this interval?

5.60 It costs you $10 to draw a sample of size $n = 1$ and measure the attribute of interest. You have a budget of $1,500.

a. Do you have sufficient funds to estimate the population mean for the attribute of interest with a 95% confidence interval 5 units in width? Assume $\sigma = 14$.

b. If you used a 90% confidence level, would your answer to part **a** change? Explain.

5.61 Suppose you wish to estimate the mean of a normal population using a 95% confidence interval, and you know from prior information that $\sigma^2 \approx 1$.

a. To see the effect of the sample size on the width of the confidence interval, calculate the width of the confidence interval for $n = 16, 25, 49, 100,$ and 400.

b. Plot the width as a function of sample size n on graph paper. Connect the points by a smooth curve and note how the width decreases as n increases.

5.62 If nothing is known about p, .5 can be substituted for p in the sample-size formula for a population proportion. But when this is done, the resulting sample size may be larger than needed. Under what circumstances will using $p = .5$ in the sample-size formula yield a sample size larger than needed to construct a confidence interval for p with a specified bound and a specified confidence level?

Applying the Concepts—Basic

5.63 **Assessing the bending strength of a wooden roof.** Refer to the *Journal of the International Association for Shell and Spatial Structures* (Aug. 2004) study to estimate the mean bending strength of imported white wood used on the roof of an ancient Japanese temple, Exercise 5.27 (p. 287). Suppose you want to estimate the true mean breaking strength of the white wood to within 4 MPa using a 90% confidence interval. How many pieces of the imported wood need to be tested? Recall that the sample standard deviation of the breaking strengths from the study was 10.9 MPa.

5.64 **Accounting and Machiavellianism.** Refer to the [NW] *Behavioral Research in Accounting* (Jan. 2008) study of Machiavellian traits in accountants, Exercise 5.17 (p. 279), where a Mach rating score was determined for each in a sample of accounting alumni who work as purchasing managers. Suppose you want to reduce the width of the 95% confidence interval for the true mean Mach rating score of all purchasing managers you obtained in Exercise 5.17b. How many purchasing managers should be included in the sample if you desire a sampling error of only 1.5 Mach rating points? Use $\sigma \approx 12$ in your calculations.

5.65 **Aluminum cans contaminated by fire.** A gigantic warehouse [NW] located in Tampa, Florida, stores approximately 60 million empty aluminum beer and soda cans. Recently, a fire occurred at the warehouse. The smoke from the fire contaminated many of the cans with blackspot, rendering them unusable. A University of South Florida statistician was hired by the insurance company to estimate p, the true proportion of cans in the warehouse that were contaminated by the fire. How many aluminum cans should be randomly sampled to estimate p to within .02 with 90% confidence?

5.66 **"Made in the USA" survey.** Refer to Exercise 5.46 (p. 296) and the *Journal of Global Business* (Spring 2002) survey to determine what "Made in the USA" means to consumers. Recall that 64 of 106 shoppers at a shopping mall in Muncie, Indiana, believe that "Made in the USA" implies all labor and materials are produced in the United States. Suppose the researchers want to increase the sample size in order to estimate the true proportion, p, to within .05 of its true value using a 90% confidence interval.

a. What is the confidence level desired by the researchers?

b. What is the sampling error desired by the researchers?

c. Compute the sample size necessary to obtain the desired estimate.

Applying the Concepts—Intermediate

5.67 **Bacteria in bottled water.** Is the bottled water you drink safe? The Natural Resources Defense Council warns that the bottled water you are drinking may contain more bacteria and other potentially carcinogenic chemicals than allowed by state and federal regulations. Of the more than 1,000 bottles studied, nearly one-third exceeded government levels (www.nrdc.org). Suppose that the Natural Resources Defense Council wants an updated estimate of the population proportion of bottled water that violates at least one government standard. Determine the sample size (number of bottles) needed to estimate this proportion to within ±0.01 with 99% confidence.

5.68 **Scanning errors at Wal-Mart.** Refer to the National Institute for Standards and Technology (NIST) study of the accuracy of checkout scanners at Wal-Mart stores in California, Exercise 5.51 (p. 296). Recall that in a sample of 60 Wal-Mart stores, 52 violated the NIST scanner accuracy standard (*Tampa Tribune,* Nov. 22, 2005). You demonstrated in Exercise 5.51e that the conditions for a valid large-sample confidence interval for the true proportion of Wal-Mart stores in California that violate the NIST standard were not met. Determine the number of Wal-Mart stores that must be sampled in order to estimate the true proportion to within .05 with 90% confidence using the large-sample method.

5.69 **Monitoring phone calls to a toll-free number.** A large food-products company receives about 100,000 phone calls a year from consumers on its toll-free number. A computer monitors and records how many rings it takes for an operator to answer, how much time each caller spends "on hold," and other data. However, the reliability of the monitoring system has been called into question by the operators and their labor union. As a check on the computer system, approximately how many calls should be manually monitored during the next year to estimate the true mean time that callers spend on hold to within 3 seconds with 95% confidence? Answer this question for the following values of the standard deviation of waiting times (in seconds): 10, 20, and 30.

5.70 USGA golf ball tests. The United States Golf Association USGA tests all new brands of golf balls to ensure that they meet USGA specifications. One test conducted is intended to measure the average distance traveled when the ball is hit by a machine called "Iron Byron," a name inspired by the swing of the famous golfer Byron Nelson. Suppose the USGA wishes to estimate the mean distance for a new brand to within 1 yard with 90% confidence. Assume that past tests have indicated that the standard deviation of the distances Iron Byron hits golf balls is approximately 10 yards. How many golf balls should be hit by Iron Byron to achieve the desired accuracy in estimating the mean?

Applying the Concepts—Advanced

5.71 Is caffeine addictive? Does the caffeine in coffee, tea, and cola induce an addiction similar to that induced by alcohol, tobacco, heroine, and cocaine? In an attempt to answer this question, researchers at Johns Hopkins University examined 27 caffeine drinkers and found 25 who displayed some type of withdrawal symptoms when abstaining from caffeine. [*Note:* The 27 caffeine drinkers volunteered for the study.] Furthermore, of 11 caffeine drinkers who were diagnosed as caffeine dependent, 8 displayed dramatic withdrawal symptoms (including impairment in normal functioning) when they consumed a caffeine-free diet in a controlled setting. The National Coffee Association claimed, however, that the study group was too small to draw conclusions. Is the sample large enough to estimate the true proportion of caffeine drinkers who are caffeine dependent to within .05 of the true value with 99% confidence? Explain.

5.72 Preventing production of defective items. It costs more to produce defective items—because they must be scrapped or reworked—than it does to produce nondefective items. This simple fact suggests that manufacturers should ensure the quality of their products by perfecting their production processes rather than through inspection of finished products (Deming, 1986). In order to better understand a particular metal-stamping process, a manufacturer wishes to estimate the mean length of items produced by the process during the past 24 hours.

a. How many parts should be sampled in order to estimate the population mean to within .1 millimeter (mm) with 90% confidence? Previous studies of this machine have indicated that the standard deviation of lengths produced by the stamping operation is about 2 mm.

b. Time permits the use of a sample size no larger than 100. If a 90% confidence interval for μ is constructed using $n = 100$, will it be wider or narrower than would have been obtained using the sample size determined in part **a**? Explain.

c. If management requires that μ be estimated to within .1 mm and that a sample size of no more than 100 be used, what is (approximately) the maximum confidence level that could be attained for a confidence interval that meets management's specifications?

5.6 Finite Population Correction for Simple Random Sampling

The large-sample confidence intervals for a population mean μ and a population proportion p presented in the previous sections are based on a simple random sample selected from the target population. Although we did not state it, the procedure also assumes that the number N of measurements (i.e., sampling units) in the population is large relative to the sample size n.

In some sampling situations, the sample size n may represent 5% or perhaps 10% of the total number N of sampling units in the population. When the sample size is large relative to the number of measurements in the population (see the next box), the standard errors of the estimators of μ and p given in Sections 5.2 and 5.4, respectively, should be multiplied by a **finite population correction factor.**

The form of the finite population correction factor depends on how the population variance σ^2 is defined. In order to simplify the formulas of the standard errors, it is common to define σ^2 as division of the sum of squares of deviations by $N - 1$ rather than by N (analogous to the way we defined the sample variance). If we adopt this convention, the finite population correction factor becomes $\sqrt{(N - n)/N}$. Then the estimated standard errors of $\bar{x}$ (the estimator of μ) and $\hat{p}$ (the estimator of p) are as shown in the box on page 304.*

> **Rule of Thumb for Finite Population Correction Factor**
>
> Use the finite population correction factor (shown in the next box) when $n/N > .05$.

*For most surveys and opinion polls, the finite population correction factor is approximately equal to 1 and, if desired, can be safely ignored. However, if $n/N > .05$, the finite population correction factor should be included in the calculation of the standard error.

Simple Random Sampling with Finite Population of Size N
Estimation of the Population Mean

Estimated standard error:

$$\hat{\sigma}_{\bar{x}} = \frac{s}{\sqrt{n}}\sqrt{\frac{N - n}{N}}$$

Approximate 95% confidence interval: $\bar{x} \pm 2\hat{\sigma}_{\bar{x}}$

Estimation of the Population Proportion

Estimated standard error:

$$\hat{\sigma}_{\hat{p}} = \sqrt{\frac{\hat{p}(1 - \hat{p})}{n}}\sqrt{\frac{N - n}{N}}$$

Approximate 95% confidence interval: $\hat{p} \pm 2\,\hat{\sigma}_{\hat{p}}$

Note: The confidence intervals are "approximate" because we are using 2 to approximate the value $z_{.025} = 1.96$.

Example 5.11

Applying the Finite Population Correction Factor in the Manufacture of Sheet Aluminum Foil

Problem A specialty manufacturer wants to purchase remnants of sheet aluminum foil. The foil, all of which is the same thickness, is stored on 1,462 rolls, each containing a varying amount of foil. To obtain an estimate of the total number of square feet of foil on all the rolls, the manufacturer randomly sampled 100 rolls and measured the number of square feet on each roll. The sample mean was 47.4, and the sample standard deviation was 12.4.

a. Find an approximate 95% confidence interval for the mean amount of foil on the 1,462 rolls.

b. Estimate the total number of square feet of foil on all the rolls by multiplying the confidence interval, part **a**, by 1,462. Interpret the result.

Solution

a. Each roll of foil is a sampling unit, and there are $N = 1{,}462$ units in the population, and the sample size is $n = 100$. Because $n/N = 100/1{,}462 = .068$ exceeds .05, we need to apply the finite population correction factor. We have $n = 100$, $\bar{x} = 47.4$, and $s = 12.4$. Substituting these quantities, we obtain the approximate 95% confidence interval:

$$\bar{x} \pm 2\frac{s}{\sqrt{n}}\sqrt{\frac{(N - n)}{N}} = (47.4) \pm 2\frac{12.4}{\sqrt{100}}\sqrt{\frac{(1{,}462 - 100)}{1{,}462}}$$

$$= 47.4 \pm 2.39$$

or, (45.01, 49.79).

b. For finite populations of size N, the sum of all measurements in the population—called a *population total*—is

$$\sum_{i=1}^{N} x_i = N\mu$$

Because the confidence interval, part **a**, estimates μ, an estimate of the population total is obtained by multiplying the endpoints of the interval by N. For we have

Lower Limit = $N(45.01) = 1{,}462(45.01) = 65{,}804.6$
Upper Limit = $N(49.79) = 1{,}462(49.79) = 72{,}793.0$

Consequently, the manufacturer estimates the total amount of foil to be in the interval of 65,805 square feet to 72,793 square feet with 95% confidence.

Look Back If the manufacturer wants to adopt a conservative approach, the bid for the foil will be based on the lower confidence limit, 65,805 square feet of foil.

Now Work Exercise 5.80a

Exercises 5.73–5.85

Learning the Mechanics

5.73 Calculate the percentage of the population sampled and the finite population correction factor for each of the following situations.
   a. $n = 1,000, N = 2,500$
   b. $n = 1,000, N = 5,000$
   c. $n = 1,000, N = 10,000$
   d. $n = 1,000, N = 100,000$

5.74 Suppose the standard deviation of the population is known to be $\sigma = 200$. Calculate the standard error of $\bar{x}$ for each of the situations described in Exercise 5.73.

5.75 Suppose $N = 10,000$, $n = 2,000$, and $s = 50$.
   a. Compute the standard error of $\bar{x}$ using the finite population correction factor.
   b. Repeat part **a** assuming $n = 4,000$.
   c. Repeat part **a** assuming $n = 10,000$.
   d. Compare parts **a, b,** and **c** and describe what happens to the standard error of $\bar{x}$ as n increased.
   e. The answer to part **c** is 0. This indicates that there is no sampling error in this case. Explain.

5.76 Suppose $N = 5,000$, $n = 64$, and $s = 24$.
   a. Compare the size of the standard error of $\bar{x}$ computed with and without the finite population correction factor.
   b. Repeat part **a**, but this time assume $n = 400$.
   c. Theoretically, when sampling from a finite population, the finite population correction factor should always be used in computing the standard error of $\bar{x}$. However, when n is small relative to N, the finite population correction factor is close to 1 and can safely be ignored. Explain how parts **a** and **b** illustrate this point.

5.77 Suppose you want to estimate a population proportion, p, and $\hat{p} = .42$, $N = 6,000$, and $n = 1,600$. Find an approximate 95% confidence interval for p.

5.78 Suppose you want to estimate a population mean, μ, and $\bar{x} = 422$, $s = 14$, $N = 375$, and $n = 40$. Find an approximate 95% confidence interval for μ.

5.79 A random sample of size $n = 30$ was drawn from a population of size $N = 300$. The following measurements were obtained and are saved in the **LM5_79** file.

21	33	19	29	22	38	58	29	52	36	37	30
53	37	29	18	35	42	36	41	35	36	33	38
29	38	39	54	42	42						

   a. Estimate μ with an approximate 95% confidence interval.
   b. Estimate p, the proportion of measurements in the population that are greater than 30, with an approximate 95% confidence interval.

Applying the Concepts—Basic

5.80 **Magazine subscriber salaries.** Each year, the trade magazine *Quality Progress* publishes a study of subscribers' salaries. One year, the 223 vice presidents sampled had a mean salary of $116,754 and a standard deviation of $39,185. Suppose the goal of the study is to estimate the true mean salary of all vice presidents who subscribe to *Quality Progress*.
   a. If 2,193 vice presidents subscribe to *Quality Progress*, estimate the mean with an approximate 95% confidence interval.
   b. Interpret the result.

5.81 **NFL player survey.** Researchers at the University of Pennsylvania's Wharton Sports Business Initiative collaborated with the National Football League Players Association (NFLPA) to produce the first NFL Player Survey in 2007. Of the 1,696 active NFL players, 1,355 (almost 80%) responded to the survey. One of the survey questions asked, "Who is the coach—professional, college, or high school—that has been the most influential in your career?" Of the 1,355 respondents, 759 selected an NFL (professional) coach.
   a. Construct a 95% confidence interval for the true proportion of active NFL players who select a professional coach as the most influential in their careers.
   b. Why is it necessary to use the continuity correction factor in the construction of the interval, part **a**?
   c. Give a practical interpretation of the interval, part **a**.

Applying the Concepts—Intermediate

5.82 **Furniture brand familiarity.** A brand name that consumers recognize is a highly valued commodity in any industry. To assess brand familiarity in the furniture industry, NPD (a market research firm) surveyed 1,333 women who head U.S. households that have incomes of $25,000 or more. The sample was drawn from a database of 25,000 households that match the criteria listed above. Of the 10 furniture brands evaluated, La-Z-Boy was the most recognized brand; 70.8% of the respondents indicated they were "very familiar" with La-Z-Boy (*HFN*, Oct. 11, 1999).
   a. Describe the population being investigated by NPD.
   b. In constructing a confidence interval to estimate the proportion of households that are very familiar with the La-Z-Boy brand, is it necessary to use the finite population correction factor? Explain
   c. What estimate of the standard error of $\hat{p}$ should be used in constructing the confidence interval of part **b**?
   d. Construct a 90% confidence interval for the true proportion and interpret it in the context of the problem.

5.83 **Auditing sampling methods.** Since the early 1950s, auditors have relied to a great extent on sampling techniques, rather than 100% audits, to help them test and evaluate the financial records of a client firm. When sampling is used to obtain an estimate of the total dollar value of an account—the account balance—the examination is known as *a substantive test* (*Audit Sampling—AICPA Audit Guide*, 2008). In order to evaluate the reasonableness of a firm's stated total value of its parts inventory, an auditor randomly samples 100 of the total of 500 parts in stock, prices each part, and reports the results shown in the next table. These data are saved in the **AUDPARTS** file.

Part Number	Part Price	Sample Size
002	$ 108	3
101	55	2
832	500	1
077	73	10
688	300	1
910	54	4
839	92	6
121	833	5
271	50	9
399	125	12
761	1,000	2
093	62	8
505	205	7
597	88	11
830	100	19

a. Give a point estimate of the mean value of the parts inventory.
b. Find the estimated standard error of the point estimate of part **a.**
c. Construct an approximate 95% confidence interval for the mean value of the parts inventory.
d. The firm reported a mean parts inventory value of $300. What does your confidence interval of part **c** suggest

about the reasonableness of the firm's reported figure? Explain.

5.84 Invoice errors in a billing system. In a study of invoice errors in a company's new billing system, an auditor randomly sampled 35 invoices produced by the new system and recorded actual amount (A), invoice amount (I), and the difference (or error), $x = (A - I)$. The results were $\bar{x} = \$1$ and $s = \$124$. At the time that the sample was drawn, the new system had produced 1,500 invoices. Use this information to find an approximate 95% confidence interval for the true mean error per invoice of the new system. Interpret the result.

Applying the Concepts—Advanced

5.85 Pesticide residue in corn products. The U.S. Environmental Protection Agency (EPA) bans use of the cancer-causing pesticide ethylene dibromide (EDB) as a fumigant for grain- and flour-milling equipment. EDB was once used to protect against infestation by microscopic roundworms called *nematodes*. The EPA sets maximum safe levels for EDB presence in raw grain, flour, cake mixes, cereals, bread, and other grain products on supermarket shelves and in warehouses. Of the 3,000 corn-related products sold in one state, tests indicated that 15 of a random sample of 175 had EDB residues above the safe level. Will more than 7% of the corn-related products in this state have to be removed from shelves and warehouses? Explain.

5.7 Sample Survey Designs*

The confidence interval methodology developed in Sections 5.2–5.5 is based on simple random sampling (Chapter 3). A (simple) random sample is just one of several different sampling designs used in *sample surveys*.

The term *sample survey* is used in conjunction with the sampling of populations (i.e., collections of people, households, businesses, etc.). A consumer preference poll is an example of a sample survey. Samplings conducted to estimate the general level of business inventories or to estimate the proportion of households that watched a particular television program are also examples of sample surveys.

Sample surveys cost time and money, and sometimes they are almost impossible to conduct. For example, suppose we want to obtain an estimate of the proportion of U.S. households that plan to purchase new television sets next year, and we plan to base our estimate on the intentions of a random sample of 3,000 households. What are the problems associated with collecting these data? In order to use a random number generator (Chapter 3) to select the sample, we would need a list of all the households in the United States. Obtaining such a list would be a monumental obstacle. After we obtain a list of households, we need to contact each of the 3,000 selected for the sample. Will all be at home when the surveyor reaches the household? And will all answer the surveyor's question? You can see that collecting a random sample is easier said than done.

The large body of knowledge underlying **survey sampling** or **sample survey design** was developed to help solve some of the problems we have noted. It includes sample survey designs that help reduce the cost and time involved in conducting a sample survey, and it includes the confidence interval procedures associated with those designs. Because survey sampling is a course in itself, we will present only a few of the most widely used sample survey designs and address only a few of the problems you might encounter in this optional section. Further information on this important subject can be found in the references at the end of the text.

One of the most common sampling designs (besides random sampling) is called *stratified random sampling*. **Stratified random sampling** is used when the sampling units (i.e., the units that are sampled) associated with the population can be physically separated into two or more groups of sampling units (called **strata**) where the within-stratum response variation is less than the variation within the entire population. For example, suppose we want to estimate the average amount of rent paid for a two-bedroom apartment in New York City. Because the variation in rent paid within New York City is likely to be large, we may want to divide the city into regions (strata) where the rents within each stratum are relatively homogeneous. Then we would estimate the population mean by selecting random samples from within each stratum and combining the stratum estimates.

Stratified random sampling often produces estimators with smaller standard errors than those achieved using simple random sampling. Furthermore, by sampling from each stratum, we are more likely to obtain a sample representative of the entire population. In addition, the administrative and labor costs of selecting the stratum samples are often less than those for simple random sampling.

Sometimes it is difficult or too costly to select random samples. For example, it would be easier to obtain a sample of student opinions at a large university by systematically selecting every hundredth name from the student directory. This type of sample design is called a **systematic sample.** Although systematic samples are usually easier to select than other types of samples, one difficulty is the possibility of a systematic sampling bias. For example, if every fifth item in an assembly line is selected for quality-control inspection, and if five different machines are sequentially producing the items, all the items sampled may have been manufactured by the same machine. If we use systematic sampling, we must be certain that no cycles (like every fifth item manufactured by the same machine) exist in the list of the sampling units.

A third alternative to the simple random sampling design is *randomized response sampling*. **Randomized response sampling** is particularly useful when the questions of the pollsters are likely to elicit false answers. For example, suppose each person in a sample of wage earners is asked whether he or she cheated on an income tax return. A person who has not cheated most likely would give an honest answer to this question. A cheater might lie, thus biasing an estimate of what proportion of persons cheats on their income tax returns.

One method of coping with the false responses produced by sensitive questions is randomized response sampling. Each person is presented *two* questions; one question is the object of the survey, and the other is an innocuous question to which the interviewee will give an honest answer. For example, each person might be asked these two questions:

1. Did you cheat on your income tax return?

2. Did you drink coffee this morning?

Then a procedure is used to select randomly which of the two questions the person is to answer. For example, the interviewee might be asked to flip a coin. If the coin shows a head, the interviewee answers the sensitive question, 1. If the coin shows a tail, the interviewee answers the innocuous question, 2. Because the interviewer never has the opportunity to see the coin, the interviewee can answer the question and feel assured that his or her guilt (if guilty) will not be exposed. Consequently, the random response procedure can elicit an honest response to a sensitive question. Sophisticated methodology is then used to derive an estimate of the percentage of "yes" responses to the sensitive question.

As mentioned earlier, in any sample survey design, cost (either in time, labor, or money) may be an issue. Two methods for reducing the cost of random sampling are to use a telephone survey or a mailed survey. Although this type of sampling eliminates transportation costs and reduces labor costs, it introduces a serious difficulty—the problem of **nonresponse.** By this, we mean that sampling units contained in a sample do not produce sample observations. For example, an individual may not be at home when telephoned or may refuse to complete and mail back a questionnaire.

Nonresponse is a serious problem because it may lead to very biased results. There may be a high association between the type of response and whether or not a person responds. For example, most citizens in a community might have an opinion on a school bond issue, but the respondents in a mail survey might very well be those with vested interests in the outcome of the survey—say, parents with children of school age, school teachers, or those whose taxes might be substantially affected. Others with no vested interests might have opinions on the issue but might not take the time to respond. For this example, the absence of the nonrespondents' data could lead to a larger estimate of the percentage in favor of the issue than was actually the case. In other words, the absence of the nonrespondents' data could lead to a biased estimate.

Nonresponse is a very important sampling problem. If your sampling plan calls for a specific collection of sampling units, failure to acquire the responses from those units may violate your sampling plan and lead to biased estimates. If you intend to select a random sample and you cannot obtain responses from some of the sampling units, then your sampling procedure is *no longer random*, and the methodology based on it (e.g., confidence intervals) and the product of the methodology (e.g., inferences) are suspect.

There are ways for coping with nonresponse. Most involve tracking down and questioning all or part of the nonrespondents and using the additional information to adjust for the missing nonrespondent data. For mailed surveys, however, it has been found that the inclusion of a monetary incentive with the questionnaire—even as little as 25¢—will substantially increase the response rate of the survey.

There are many sampling designs available to a sample surveyor; some are variations on simple random sampling and stratified random sampling, and others are completely different. In addition, different types of estimators can be used with these designs. In this brief introduction to survey sampling, our intent was to present only a few of the most important sample survey designs and some of their inherent problems. Thorough presentations of the different sample survey designs are given in textbooks devoted to this topic (see the references on page 314).

Ethics IN Statistics

In survey sampling, intentional omission of a group of respondents in order to bias the results toward a particular view or outcome is considered *unethical statistical practice*.

CHAPTER NOTES

Key Terms

Adjusted $(1 - \alpha)100\%$ confidence interval for a population parameter, p 293
Confidence coefficient 274
Confidence interval 271
Confidence level 274
Degrees of freedom 281
Finite population correction factor 303
Interval estimator 271
Large-sample confidence interval for μ 291
Nonresponse 307
Point estimator 271
Randomized response sampling 307

Sample survey design 306
Sampling error 298
Small-sample confidence interval for μ 284
Sample size determination for $100(1 - \alpha)\%$ confidence interval for μ 298
Sample size determination for $100(1 - \alpha)\%$ confidence interval for p 300
Strata 307
Stratified random sampling 306
Survey sampling 306
Systematic sampling 307
Target parameter 270
t-statistic 281

Key Symbols

μ	Population mean
σ	Population standard deviation
p	Population proportion; P(Success) in binomial trial
q	$1 - p$
$\bar{x}$	Sample mean (estimator of μ)
$\hat{p}$	Sample proportion (estimator of p)
$\mu_{\bar{x}}$	Mean of the population sampling distribution of $\bar{x}$
$\sigma_{\bar{x}}$	Standard deviation of the sampling distribution of $\bar{x}$
$\sigma_{\hat{p}}$	Standard deviation of the sampling distribution of $\hat{p}$

SE	Sampling error in estimation
α	$(1 - \alpha)$ represents the confidence coefficient
$z_{\alpha/2}$	z-value used in a $100(1 - \alpha)\%$ large-sample confidence interval
$t_{\alpha/2}$	Student's t-value used in a $100(1 - \alpha)\%$ small-sample confidence interval
N	Number of observations in the target population

Key Ideas

Population Parameters, Estimators, and Standard Errors

Parameter (θ)	Estimator $(\hat{\theta})$	Standard Error of Estimator $(\sigma_{\hat{\theta}})$	Estimated Std. Error $(\hat{\sigma}_{\hat{\theta}})$
Mean, μ	$\bar{x}$	$\sigma/\sqrt{n}$	$s/\sqrt{n}$
Proportion, p	$\hat{p}$	$\sqrt{pq/n}$	$\sqrt{\hat{p}\hat{q}/n}$

Confidence Interval: An interval that encloses an unknown population parameter with a certain level of confidence $(1 - \alpha)$

Confidence Coefficient: The probability $(1 - \alpha)$ that a randomly selected confidence interval encloses the true value of the population parameter.

Key Words for Identifying the Target Parameter

μ—Mean, Average
p—Proportion, Fraction, Percentage, Rate, Probability

Sample Survey Designs

1. *Simple random sampling*
2. *Stratified random sampling*
3. *Systematic sampling*
4. *Random response sampling*

Commonly Used z-Values for a Large-Sample Confidence Interval

90% CI: $(1 - \alpha) = .10$ $z_{.05} = 1.645$
95% CI: $(1 - \alpha) = .05$ $z_{.025} = 1.96$
99% CI: $(1 - \alpha) = .01$ $z_{.005} = 2.575$

Determining the Sample Size n

Estimating μ: $n = (z_{\alpha/2})^2(\sigma^2)/(SE)^2$
Estimating p: $n = (z_{\alpha/2})^2(pq)/(SE)^2$

Finite Population Correction Factor

Required when $n/N > .05$

Illustrating the Notion of "95% Confidence"

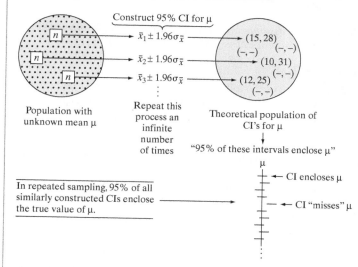

Guide to Forming a Confidence Interval

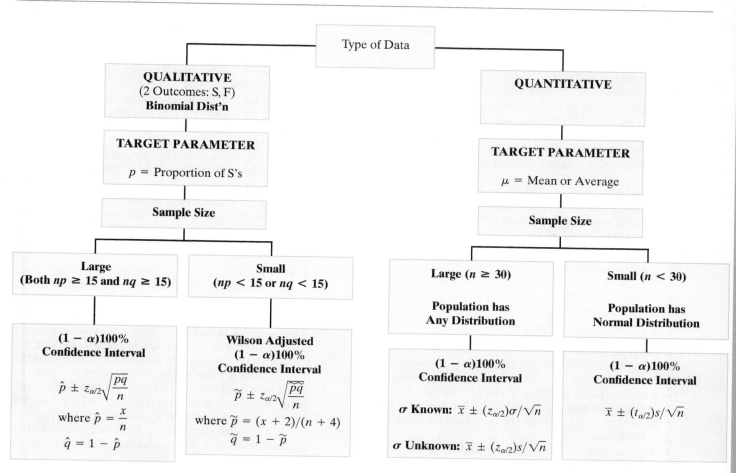

Supplementary Exercises 5.86–5.115

Note: List the assumptions necessary for the valid implementation of the statistical procedures you use in solving all these exercises.

Learning the Mechanics

5.86 In each of the following instances, determine whether you would use a z- or t-statistic (or neither) to form a 95% confidence interval and then look up the appropriate z- or t-value.

a. Random sample of size $n = 23$ from a normal distribution with unknown mean μ and standard deviation σ

b. Random sample of size $n = 135$ from a normal distribution with unknown mean μ and standard deviation σ

c. Random sample of size $n = 10$ from a normal distribution with unknown mean μ and standard deviation $\sigma = 5$

d. Random sample of size $n = 73$ from a distribution about which nothing is known

e. Random sample of size $n = 12$ from a distribution about which nothing is known

5.87 Let t_0 represent a particular value of t from Table V in Appendix B. Find the table values such that the following statements are true.

a. $P(t \le t_0) = .05$ where df = 20

b. $P(t \ge t_0) = .005$ where df = 9

c. $P(t \le -t_0 \text{ or } t \ge t_0) = .10$ where df = 8

d. $P(t \le -t_0 \text{ or } t \ge t_0) = .01$ where df = 17

5.88 In a random sample of 400 measurements, 227 of the measurements possess the characteristic of interest, A.

a. Use a 95% confidence interval to estimate the true proportion p of measurements in the population with characteristic A.

b. How large a sample would be needed to estimate p to within .02 with 95% confidence?

5.89 A random sample of 225 measurements is selected from a population, and the sample mean and standard deviation are $\bar{x} = 32.5$ and $s = 30.0$, respectively.

a. Use a 99% confidence interval to estimate the mean of the population, μ.

b. How large a sample would be needed to estimate μ to within .5 with 99% confidence?

c. What is meant by the phrase *99% confidence* as it is used in this exercise?

5.90 Calculate the finite population correction factor for each of the following situations:

a. $n = 50, N = 2,000$

b. $n = 20, N = 100$

c. $n = 300, N = 1,500$

Applying the Concepts—Basic

5.91 **General health survey.** The Centers for Disease Control and Prevention (CDCP) in Atlanta, Georgia, conducts an annual survey of the general health of the U.S. population as part of its Behavioral Risk Factor Surveillance System. Using random-digit dialing, the CDCP telephones U.S. citizens over 18 years of age and asks them the following four questions:

1. Is your health generally excellent, very good, good, fair, or poor?

2. How many days during the previous 30 days was your physical health not good because of injury or illness?

3. How many days during the previous 30 days was your mental health not good because of stress, depression, or emotional problems?

4. How many days during the previous 30 days did your physical or mental health prevent you from performing your usual activities?

Identify the parameter of interest for each question.

5.92 **Semester hours taken by CPA candidates.** Refer to the *Journal of Accounting and Public Policy* (Spring 2002) study of 100,000 first-time candidates for the CPA exam, Exercise 2.51 (p. 63). Recall that the mean number of semester hours of college credit taken by the candidates was 141.31 hours. The standard deviation was reported to be 17.77 hours.

a. Compute a 99% confidence interval for the mean number of semester hours taken by all first-time candidates for the CPA exam.

b. Give a practical interpretation of the interval, part **a**.

c. For the interpretation, part **b**, to be valid, what conditions must hold?

5.93 **Security of information submitted over the Internet.** As Internet usage proliferates, so do questions of security and confidentiality of personal information, including such things as social security and credit card numbers. NCR Corporation surveyed 1,000 U.S. adults and asked them under what circumstances they would give personal information to a company. Twenty-nine percent said they would never give personal data to a company, while 51% said they would if the company had strict privacy guidelines in place (*Precision Marketing,* Oct. 4, 1999).

a. Verify that the sample size is large enough to construct a valid confidence interval for p, the proportion of all U.S. adults who would never give personal information to a company.

b. Construct a 95% confidence interval for p and interpret your result in the context of the problem.

5.94 **Homicide on the job.** In a study of homicide on the job, University of North Carolina researchers collected data on workplaces where an employee was murdered (*American Journal of Epidemiology,* Vol. 154, 2001). In a sample of 105 cases, 67 of the homicides occurred during night hours (between 9:00 P.M. and 6:00 A.M.).

a. Give a point estimate of p, the true proportion of on-the-job homicide cases that occurred at night.

b. Compute a 95% confidence interval for p.

c. Give a practical interpretation of the interval, part **b**.

5.95 **Water pollution testing.** The EPA wants to test a randomly selected sample of n water specimens and estimate the mean daily rate of pollution produced by a mining operation. If the EPA wants a 95% confidence interval estimate with a sampling error of 1 milligram per liter (mg/L), how many water specimens are required in the sample? Assume prior knowledge indicates that pollution readings in water samples taken during a day are approximately normally distributed with a standard deviation equal to 5 mg/L.

5.96 Lead and copper in drinking water. Periodically, the Hillsborough County (Florida) Water Department tests the drinking water of homeowners for contaminants such as lead and copper. The lead and copper levels in water specimens collected for a sample of 10 residents of the Crystal Lakes Manors subdivision (saved in the **LEADCOPP** file) are shown below, followed by a Minitab printout analyzing the data at the bottom of this page.

Lead (µg/L)	Copper (mg/L)
1.32	.508
0	.279
13.1	.320
.919	.904
.657	.221
3.0	.283
1.32	.475
4.09	.130
4.45	.220
0	.743

Source: Hillsborough County Water Department Environmental Laboratory, Tampa, Florida.

a. Locate a 90% confidence interval for the mean lead level in water specimens from Crystal Lakes Manors on the printout.

b. Locate a 90% confidence interval for the mean copper level in water specimens from Crystal Lakes Manors on the printout.

c. Interpret the intervals, parts **a** and **b**, in the words of the problem.

d. Discuss the meaning of the phrase, "90% confident."

5.97 Employees with substance abuse problems. According to the New Jersey *Governor's Council for a Drug-Free Workplace Report,* 50 of the 72 sampled businesses that are members of the council admitted that they had employees with substance abuse problems. At the time of the survey, 251 New Jersey businesses were members of the Governor's Council. Use the finite population correction factor to find a 95% confidence interval for the proportion of all New Jersey Governor's Council business members who have employees with substance abuse problems. Interpret the resulting interval.

5.98 Sick leave taken by employees. A company is interested in estimating μ, the mean number of days of sick leave taken by all its employees. The firm's statistician selects at random 100 personnel files and notes the number of sick days taken by each employee. The following sample statistics are computed: $\bar{x} = 12.2$ days, $s = 10$ days.

a. Estimate μ using a 90% confidence interval. Interpret the result.

b. How many personnel files would the statistician have to select in order to estimate μ to within 2 days with a 99% confidence interval?

5.99 Fish contaminated by a plant's discharge. Refer (Ex 1.5 p. 13) to the U.S. Army Corps of Engineers data on a sample of 144 contaminated fish collected from the river adjacent to a chemical plant. The data are saved in the **DDT** file. Estimate the proportion of contaminated fish that are of the channel catfish species. Use a 90% confidence interval and interpret the result.

Applying the Concepts—Intermediate

5.100 Improving the productivity of chickens. Farmers have discovered that the more domestic chickens peck at objects placed in their environment, the healthier and more productive the chickens seem to be. White string has been found to be a particularly attractive pecking stimulus. In one experiment, 72 chickens were exposed to a string stimulus. Instead of white string, blue-colored string was used. The number of pecks each chicken took at the blue string over a specified time interval was recorded. Summary statistics for the 72 chickens were $\bar{x} = 1.13$ pecks, $s = 2.21$ pecks (*Applied Animal Behaviour Science,* Oct. 2000).

a. Estimate the population mean number of pecks made by chickens pecking at blue string using a 99% confidence interval. Interpret the result.

b. Previous research has shown that $\mu = 7.5$ pecks if chickens are exposed to white string. Based on the results, part **a,** is there evidence that chickens are more apt to peck at white string than blue string? Explain.

5.101 Petroleum waste contamination. Accidental spillage and misguided disposal of petroleum wastes have resulted in extensive contamination of soils across the country. A common hazardous compound found in the contaminated soil is benzo(a)pyrene [B(a)p]. An experiment was conducted to determine the effectiveness of a method designed to remove B(a)p from soil (*Journal of Hazardous Materials,* June 1995). Three soil specimens contaminated with a known amount of B(a)p were treated with a toxin that inhibits microbial growth. After 95 days of incubation, the percentage of B(a)p removed from each soil specimen was measured. The experiment produced the following summary statistics: $\bar{x} = 49.3$ and $s = 1.5$.

a. Use a 99% confidence interval to estimate the mean percentage of B(a)p removed from a soil specimen in which the toxin was used.

b. Interpret the interval in terms of this application.

c. What assumption is necessary to ensure the validity of this confidence interval?

d. Comment on whether the true mean percent removed could be as high as 50%.

5.102 IRS answers to gift tax questions. According to estimates made by the General Accounting Office, the Internal Revenue Service (IRS) answered 18.3 million telephone inquiries during a recent tax season, and 17% of the IRS

Minitab output for Exercise 5.96

Variable	N	Mean	StDev	SE Mean	90% CI
LEAD	10	2.89	3.92	1.24	(0.61, 5.16)
COPPER	10	0.4083	0.2495	0.0789	(0.2637, 0.5529)

offices provided wrong answers. These estimates were based on data collected from sample calls to numerous IRS offices. How many IRS offices should be randomly selected and contacted in order to estimate the proportion of IRS offices that fail to correctly answer questions about gift taxes with a 90% confidence interval of width .06?

5.103 **IQ comparison of older vs. younger workers.** The 1967 Age Discrimination in Employment Act (ADEA) made it illegal to discriminate against workers 40 years of age and older. Opponents of the law argue that there are sound economic reasons why employers would not want to hire and train workers who are very close to retirement. They also argue that people's abilities tend to deteriorate with age. In fact, *Forbes* (Dec. 13, 1999) reported that 25-year-olds did significantly better than 60-year-olds on the Wechsler Adult Intelligence Scale, the most popular IQ test. The following data (saved in the **IQ25** and **IQ60** files) are raw test scores (i.e., not the familiar normalized IQ scores) for a sample of thirty-six 25-year-olds and thirty-six 60-year-olds:

a. Estimate the mean raw test score for all 25-year-olds using a 99% confidence interval. Give a practical interpretation of the confidence interval.

b. What assumption(s) must hold for the method of estimation used in part **a** to be appropriate?

c. Find a 95% confidence interval for the mean raw score of all 60-year-olds and interpret your result.

25-Year-Olds					
54	61	80	92	41	63
59	68	66	76	82	80
82	47	81	77	88	94
49	86	55	82	45	51
70	72	63	50	52	67
75	60	58	49	63	68

60-Year-Olds					
42	54	38	22	58	37
60	49	51	60	45	42
73	28	65	65	60	34
34	33	40	28	36	60
45	61	47	30	45	45
45	37	27	40	37	58

Source: Adapted from "The case for age discrimination," *Forbes,* Dec. 13, 1999, p. 13. Reprinted by permission of Forbes.com. © 2009 Forbes LLC.

5.104 **Air bags pose danger for children.** By law, all new cars must be equipped with both driver-side and passenger-side safety air bags. There is concern, however, over whether air bags pose a danger for children sitting on the passenger side. In a National Highway Traffic Safety Administration (NHTSA) study of 55 people killed by the explosive force of air bags, 35 were children seated on the front-passenger side (www.nhtsa.org). This study led some car owners with children to disconnect the passenger-side air bag. Consider all fatal automobile accidents in which it is determined that air bags were the cause of death. Let p represent the true proportion of these accidents involving children seated on the front-passenger side.

a. Use the data from the NHTSA study to estimate p.

b. Construct a 99% confidence interval for p.

c. Interpret the interval, part **b,** in the words of the problem.

d. NHTSA investigators determined that 24 of 35 children killed by the air bags were not wearing seat belts or were improperly restrained. How does this information impact your assessment of the risk of an air bag fatality?

5.105 **Air bags pose danger for children (cont'd).** Refer to Exercise 5.104. How many fatal accidents should the NHTSA sample in order to estimate the proportion to within .1 of its true value using a 99% confidence interval?

5.106 **Laying off cancer patients.** According to the U.S. Bureau of Labor Statistics, 1 of every 80 American workers (i.e., 1.3%) is fired or laid off. Are employees with cancer fired or laid off at the same rate? To answer this question, *Working Women* magazine and Amgen—a company that makes drugs to lessen chemotherapy side effects—conducted a telephone survey of 100 cancer survivors who worked while undergoing treatment. Of these 100 cancer patients, 7 were fired or laid off due to their illness.

a. Construct a 90% confidence interval for the true percentage of all cancer patients who are fired or laid off due to their illness.

b. Give a practical interpretation of the interval, part **a.**

c. Are employees with cancer fired or laid off at the same rate as all U.S. workers? Explain.

5.107 **Vacation times at major companies.** The primary determinant of the amount of vacation time U.S. employees receive is their length of service. According to data released by Hewitt Associates (*Management Review,* Nov. 1995), more than 8 of 10 employers provide 2 weeks of vacation after the first year. After 5 years, 75% of employers provide 3 weeks, and after 15 years most provide 4-week vacations. To more accurately estimate p, the proportion of U.S. employers who provide only 2 weeks of vacation to new hires, a random sample of 24 major U.S. companies was contacted. The following vacation times reported (in days) are saved in the **VACTIMES** file.

10	12	10	10	10	10
15	10	10	10	10	10
10	10	10	10	10	15
10	10	15	10	10	10

a. Construct a 95% confidence interval for p.

b. Is the sample size large enough to ensure that the normal distribution provides a reasonable approximation to the sampling distribution of $\hat{p}$? Justify your answer.

c. How large a sample would be required to estimate p to within .02 with 95% confidence?

5.108 **Performance appraisal process.** The relationship between an employee's participation in the performance appraisal process and subsequent subordinate reactions toward the appraisal was investigated in the *Journal of Applied Psychology* (Aug. 1998). In Chapter 10 we will discuss a quantitative measure of the relationship between two variables, called the *coefficient* of *correlation r.* The researchers obtained r for a sample of 34 studies that examined the relationship between appraisal participation and a subordinate's satisfaction with the appraisal. These correlations are listed in the table and saved in the **CORR34** file. (Values of r near +1 reflect a strong positive relationship between the variables.) Find a 95% confidence interval for the mean of the data and interpret it in the words of the problem.

.50	.58	.71	.46	.63	.66	.31	.35	.51	.06	.35	.19
.40	.63	.43	.16	–.08	.51	.59	.43	.30	.69	.25	.20
.39	.20	.51	.68	.74	.65	.34	.45	.31	.27		

Source: Cawley, B. D., Keeping, L. M., and Levy, P. E. "Participation in the performance appraisal process and employee reactions: A meta-analytic review of field investigations," *Journal of Applied Psychology,* Vol. 83, No. 4, Aug. 1998, pp. 632–633 (Appendix). Copyright © 1998 by the American Psychological Association. Reproduced with permission. The use of APA information does not imply endorsement by APA.

5.109 Interpreting sampling error. When a poll reports, for example, that 61% of the public supports a program of national health insurance, it usually also reports the sampling error. For example, a poll might report that the estimate is accurate to within plus or minus 3%. A classic essay in *Time* magazine ("How not to read polls," Apr. 28, 1980) points out the following:

> *Readers consistently misinterpret the meaning of this "warning label."…[The sampling error warning] says nothing about errors that might be caused by a sloppily worded question or a biased one or a single question that evokes complex feelings. Example: "Are you satisfied with your job?" Most important of all, warning labels about sampling error say nothing about whether or not the public is conflict-ridden or has given a subject much thought. This is the most serious source of opinion poll misinterpretation.*

Carefully explain the difference between sampling error and nonsampling error, both in general and in the context of the above quotation.

5.110 Salmonella poisoning from eating an ice cream bar. Recently, a case of salmonella (bacterial) poisoning was traced to a particular brand of ice cream bar, and the manufacturer removed the bars from the market. Despite this response, many consumers refused to purchase *any* brand of ice cream bars for some period of time after the event (McClave, personal consulting). One manufacturer conducted a survey of consumers 6 months after the outbreak. A sample of 244 ice cream bar consumers was contacted, and 23 respondents indicated that they would not purchase ice cream bars because of the potential for food poisoning.

a. What is the point estimate of the true fraction of the entire market who refuse to purchase bars 6 months after the outbreak?

b. Is the sample size large enough to use the normal approximation for the sampling distribution of the estimator of the binomial probability? Justify your response.

c. Construct a 95% confidence interval for the true proportion of the market who still refuse to purchase ice cream bars 6 months after the event.

d. Interpret both the point estimate and confidence interval in terms of this application.

5.111 Salmonella poisoning from eating an ice cream bar (cont'd). Refer to Exercise 5.110. Suppose it is now 1 year after the outbreak of food poisoning was traced to ice cream bars.

The manufacturer wishes to estimate the proportion who still will not purchase bars to within .02 using a 95% confidence interval. How many consumers should be sampled?

Applying the Concepts—Advanced

5.112 Accountants salary survey. Each year, *Management Accounting* reports the results of a salary survey of the members of the Institute of Management Accountants (IMA). One year, the 2,112 members responding had a salary distribution with a 20th percentile of $35,100; a median of $50,000; and an 80th percentile of $73,000.

a. Use this information to determine the minimum sample size that could be used in next year's survey to estimate the mean salary of IMA members to within $2,000 with 98% confidence. [*Hint:* To estimate s, first apply Chebyshev's Theorem to find k such that at least 60% of the data fall within k standard deviations of μ. Then find $s \approx$ (80th percentile – 20th percentile)$/2k$.]

b. Explain how you estimated the standard deviation required for the sample size calculation.

c. List any assumptions you make.

5.113 Internal auditing of invoices. A firm's president, vice presidents, department managers, and others use financial data generated by the firm's accounting system to help them make decisions regarding such things as pricing, budgeting, and plant expansion. To provide reasonable certainty that the system provides reliable data, internal auditors periodically perform various checks of the system (Horngren, Foster, and Datar, *Cost Accounting: A Managerial Emphasis,* 2005). Suppose an internal auditor is interested in determining the proportion of sales invoices in a population of 5,000 sales invoices for which the "total sales" figure is in error. She plans to estimate the true proportion of invoices in error based on a random sample of size 100.

a. Assume that the population of invoices is numbered from 1 to 5,000 and that every invoice ending with a 0 is in error (i.e., 10% are in error). Use a random number generator to draw a random sample of 100 invoices from the population of 5,000 invoices. For example, random number 456 stands for invoice number 456. List the invoice numbers in your sample and indicate which of your sampled invoices are in error (i.e., those ending in a 0).

b. Use the results of your sample of part **a** to construct a 90% confidence interval for the true proportion of invoices in error.

c. Recall that the true population proportion of invoices in error is equal to .1. Compare the true proportion with the estimate of the true proportion you developed in part **b**. Does your confidence interval include the true proportion?

Critical Thinking Challenge

5.114 "Out of control" production process. When companies employ control charts to monitor the quality of their products, a series of small samples is typically used to determine if the process is "in control" during the period of time in which each sample is selected. (We cover quality-control charts in Chapter 12.) Suppose a concrete-block manufacturer samples nine blocks per hour and tests the breaking strength of each. During 1 hour's test, the mean and standard deviation are 985.6 pounds per square inch (psi) and 22.9 psi, respectively. The process is to be considered "out of control" if the true mean strength differs from 1,000 psi. The manufacturer wants to be reasonably certain that the process is really out of control before shutting down the process and trying to determine the problem. What is your recommendation?

5.115 **Scallops, sampling, and the law.** In *Interfaces* (March–April 1995), the case involved a ship that fishes for scallops off the coast of New England. In order to protect baby scallops from being harvested, the U.S. Fisheries and Wildlife Service requires that "the average meat per scallop weigh at least $\frac{1}{36}$ of a pound." The ship was accused of violating this weight standard. Bennett lays out the scenario:

> *The vessel arrived at a Massachusetts port with 11,000 bags of scallops, from which the harbormaster randomly selected 18 bags for weighing. From each such bag, his agents took a large scoopful of scallops; then, to estimate the bag's average meat per scallop, they divided the total weight of meat in the scoopful by the number of scallops it contained. Based on the 18 [numbers] thus generated, the harbormaster estimated that each of the ship's scallops possessed an average of $\frac{1}{39}$ of a pound of meat (that is, they were about seven percent lighter than the minimum requirement). Viewing this outcome as conclusive evidence that the weight standard had been violated, federal authorities at once confiscated 95 percent of the catch (which they then sold at auction). The fishing voyage was thus transformed into a financial catastrophe for its participants.*

The actual scallop weight measurements for each of the 18 sampled bags are listed in the accompanying table and are saved in the **SCALLOPS** file. For ease of exposition, Bennett expressed each number as a multiple of $\frac{1}{36}$ of a pound, the minimum permissible average weight per scallop. Consequently, numbers below 1 indicate individual bags that do not meet the standard.

The ship's owner filed a lawsuit against the federal government, declaring that his vessel had fully complied with the weight standard. A Boston law firm was hired to represent the owner in legal proceedings, and Bennett was retained by the firm to provide statistical litigation support and, if necessary, expert witness testimony.

a. Recall that the harbormaster sampled only 18 of the ship's 11,000 bags of scallops. One of the questions the lawyers asked Bennett was, "Can a reliable estimate of the mean weight of all the scallops be obtained from a sample of size 18?" Give your opinion on this issue.

b. As stated in the article, the government's decision rule is to confiscate a catch if the sample mean weight of the scallops is less than $\frac{1}{36}$ of a pound. Do you see any flaws in this rule?

c. Develop your own procedure for determining whether a ship is in violation of the minimum-weight restriction. Apply your rule to the data. Draw a conclusion about the ship in question.

| .93 | .88 | .85 | .91 | .91 | .84 | .90 | .98 | .88 |
| .89 | .98 | .87 | .91 | .92 | .99 | 1.14 | 1.06 | .93 |

Source: Barnett, A. "Misapplications review: Jail terms," *Interfaces,* Vol. 25, No. 2, Mar.–Apr. 1995, p. 20.

References

Agresti, A., and Coull, B. A. "Approximate is better than 'exact' for interval estimation of binomial proportions" *The American Statistician,* Vol. 52, No. 2, May 1998, pp. 119–126.

Arkin, H. *Sampling Methods for the Auditor.* New York: McGraw-Hill, 1982.

Cochran, W. G. *Sampling Techniques,* 3rd ed. New York: Wiley, 1977.

Freedman, D., Pisani, R., and Purves, R. *Statistics.* New York: Norton, 1978.

Kish, L. *Survey Sampling.* New York: Wiley, 1965.

Mendenhall, W., Beaver, R. J., and Beaver, B. *Introduction to Probability and Statistics,* 13th ed. Belmont, CA: Brooks/Cole, 2009.

Wilson, E. G. "Probable inference, the law of succession, and statistical inference," *Journal of the American Statistical Association,* Vol. 22, 1927, pp. 209–212.

USING TECHNOLOGY

SPSS: Confidence Intervals

SPSS can be used to obtain one-sample confidence intervals for a population mean but cannot currently produce confidence intervals for a population proportion. To generate a confidence interval for the mean perform the following:

Step 1 Access the SPSS spreadsheet file that contains the sample data.

Step 2 Click on the "Analyze" button on the SPSS menu bar and then click on "Descriptive Statistics" and "Explore," as shown in Figure 5.S.1.

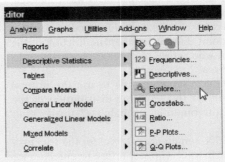

Figure 5.S.1 SPSS menu options—confidence interval for the mean

Step 3 On the resulting dialog box (shown in Figure 5.S.2.), specify the quantitative variable of interest in the "Dependent List" and then click on the "Statistics" button.

Figure 5.S.2 SPSS explore dialog box

Step 4 Specify the confidence level in the resulting dialog box, as shown in Figure 5.S.3.

Figure 5.S.3 SPSS explore statistics options

Step 5 Click "Continue" to return to the "Explore" dialog box and then click "OK" to produce the confidence interval.

Minitab: Confidence Intervals

Minitab can be used to obtain one-sample confidence intervals for both a population mean and a population proportion.

Confidence Interval for a Mean

Step 1 Access the Minitab data worksheet that contains the quantitative variable of interest.

Step 2 Click on the "Stat" button on the Minitab menu bar and then click on "Basic Statistics" and "1-Sample t," as shown in Figure 5.M.1.

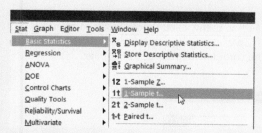

Figure 5.M.1 Minitab menu options—confidence interval for the mean

Step 3 On the resulting dialog box (shown in Figure 5.M.2.), click on "Samples in Columns," and then specify the quantitative variable of interest in the open box.

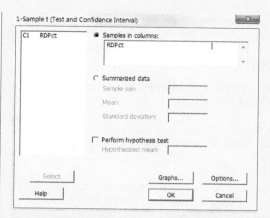

Figure 5.M.2 Minitab 1-sample t dialog box

Step 4 Click on the "Options" button at the bottom of the dialog box and specify the confidence level in the resulting dialog box, as shown in Figure 5.M.3.

Figure 5.M.3 Minitab 1-sample t options

Step 5 Click "OK" to return to the "1-Sample t" dialog box, and then click "OK" again to produce the confidence interval.

Note: If you want to produce a confidence interval for the mean from summary information (e.g., the sample mean, sample standard deviation, and sample size), click on "Summarized data" in the "1-Sample t" dialog box, as shown in Figure 5.M.4. Enter the values of the summary statistics and then click "OK."

Important: The Minitab 1-sample t procedure uses the *t*-statistic to generate the confidence interval. When the sample size *n* is small, this is the appropriate method. When the sample size *n* is large, the *t*-value will be approximately equal to the large-sample *z*-value and the resulting interval will still be valid. If you have a large sample and you know the value of the population standard deviation σ (which is rarely the case),

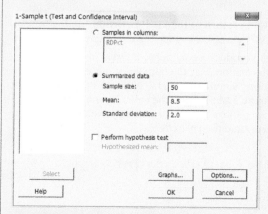

Figure 5.M.4 Minitab 1-sample t dialog box with summary statistics options

select "1-sample Z" from the "Basic Statistics" menu options (see Figure 5.M.1) and make the appropriate selections.

Confidence Interval for a Proportion

Step 1 Access the Minitab data worksheet that contains the qualitative variable of interest.

Step 2 Click on the "Stat" button on the Minitab menu bar and then click on "Basic Statistics" and "1 Proportion" (see Figure 5.M.1).

Step 3 On the resulting dialog box (shown in Figure 5.M.5.), click on "Samples in Columns" and then specify the qualitative variable of interest in the open box.

Figure 5.M.5 Minitab 1-proportion dialog box

Step 4 Click on the "Options" button at the bottom of the dialog box and specify the confidence level in the resulting dialog box, as shown in Figure 5.M.6. Also, check the "Use test and interval based on normal distribution" box at the bottom.

Figure 5.M.6 Minitab 1-proportion dialog box options

Step 5 Click "OK" to return to the "1- Proportion" dialog box and then click "OK" again to produce the confidence interval.

Note: If you want to produce a confidence interval for a proportion from summary information (e.g., the number of successes and the sample size), click on "Summarized data" in the "1-Proportion" dialog box (see Figure 5.M.5). Enter the value for the number of trials (i.e., the sample size) and the number of events (i.e., the number of successes) and then click "OK."

Excel/DDXL: Confidence Intervals

Confidence Interval for a Mean

To obtain a confidence interval for the mean of a quantitative variable, perform the following:

Step 1 Highlight (select) the data column you want to analyze on the Excel spreadsheet.

Step 2 Click on "Add-Ins" in the main Excel menu bar and select "DDXL." On the resulting menu, select "Confidence Intervals," as shown in Figure 5.E.1.

Figure 5.E.1 Excel/DDXL menu options—confidence intervals

Step 3 On the resulting menu, select "1 Var t Interval" in the Function Type box, as shown in Figure 5.E.2.

Figure 5.E.2 Excel/DDXL confidence intervals dialog box

Step 4 Move the variable of interest into the "Quantitative Variable" box and then click "OK," as shown in Figure 5.E.3.

Figure 5.E.3 Excel/DDXL confidence interval for mean options

Step 5 On the resulting menu, click the desired confidence level (e.g., 95%), then click "Compute Interval," as shown in Figure 5.E.4. The confidence interval will appear.

Figure 5.E.4 Excel/DDXL confidence interval for mean setup

Confidence Interval for a Proportion

To obtain a confidence interval for the proportion of successes for a qualitative variable, perform the following:

Step 1 Highlight (select) the data column you want to analyze on the Excel spreadsheet.

Step 2 Click on "Add-Ins" in the main Excel menu bar and select "DDXL." On the resulting menu select "Confidence Intervals," as shown in Figure 5.E.1.

Step 3 On the resulting menu, select "1 Var Prop Interval" in the Function Type box and move the variable of interest into the "Proportions Variable" box, as shown in Figure 5.E.5. Click "OK."

Figure 5.E.5 Excel/DDXL confidence interval for proportion options

Step 4 On the resulting menu, select the value of the qualitative variable that represents a success, click the desired confidence level (e.g., 95%), and click "Compute Interval," as shown in Figure 5.E.6. The confidence interval will appear.

Figure 5.E.6 Excel/DDXL confidence interval for proportion setup

TI-84 Graphing Calculator: Confidence Intervals

Creating a Confidence Interval for a Population Mean (Known σ or $n \geq 30$)

Step 1 *Enter the data (Skip to Step 2 if you have summary statistics, not raw data)*

• Press **STAT** and select **1:Edit**

Note: If the list already contains data, clear the old data. Use the up **ARROW** to highlight "**L1.**"

• Press **CLEAR ENTER**
• Use the **ARROW** and **ENTER** keys to enter the data set into **L1**

Step 2 *Access the Statistical Tests Menu*

• Press **STAT**
• Arrow right to **TESTS**
• Arrow down to **ZInterval**
• Press **ENTER**

Step 3 *Choose "Data," or "Stats." ("Data" is selected when you have entered the raw data into a List. "Stats" is selected when you are given only the mean, standard deviation, and sample size.)*

• Press **ENTER**

If you selected "Data," enter a value for σ (the best approximation is s, the sample standard deviation)

• Set **List** to **L1**
• Set **Freq** to **1**
• Set **C-Level** to the confidence level
• Arrow down to "**Calculate**"
• Press **ENTER**

If you selected "Stats," enter a value for σ (the best approximation is s, the sample standard deviation)

• Enter the sample mean and sample size
• Set **C-Level** to the confidence level
• Arrow down to "**Calculate**"
• Press **ENTER**

(The screen at right is set up for an example with a standard deviation of 20, a mean of 200, and a sample size of 40.) The confidence interval will be displayed along with the sample mean and the sample size.

Creating a Confidence Interval for a Population Mean ($n < 30$)

Step 1 *Enter the data (skip to Step 2 if you have summary statistics, not raw data)*

• Press **STAT** and select **1:Edit**

Note: If the list already contains data, clear the old data. Use the up **ARROW** to highlight "**L1.**"

• Press **CLEAR ENTER**
• Use the **ARROW** and **ENTER** keys to enter the data set into **L1**

Step 2 *Access the Statistical Tests Menu*

• Press **STAT**
• Arrow right to **TESTS**
• Arrow down to **TInterval**
• Press **ENTER**

Step 3 *Choose "Data" or "Stats." ("Data" is selected when you have entered the raw data into a List. "Stats" is selected*

when you are given only the mean, standard deviation, and sample size.)

- Press **ENTER**
- If you selected "Data," set **List** to **L1**
- Set **Freq** to **1**
- Set **C-Level** to the confidence level
- Arrow down to "**Calculate**"
- Press **ENTER**

If you selected "Stats," enter the mean, standard deviation, and sample size.

- Set **C-Level** to the confidence level
- Arrow down to "**Calculate**"
- Press **ENTER**

(The screen here is set up for an example with a mean of 100 and a standard deviation of 10.)

The confidence interval will be displayed with the mean, standard deviation, and sample size.

Creating a Confidence Interval for a Population Proportion (Large Samples)

Step 1 *Access the Statistical Tests Menu*

- Press **STAT**
- Arrow right to **TESTS**
- Arrow down to **1-PropZInt**
- Press **ENTER**

Step 2 *Enter the values for x, n, and C-Level*

- where **x** = number of successes
- **n** = sample size
- **C-Level** = level of confidence
- Arrow down to "**Calculate**"
- Press **ENTER**

(The screens at the right are set up for an example with $x = 532$, $n = 1,100$, and confidence level of .95.)

CONTENTS

6 Inferences Based on a Single Sample *Tests of Hypotheses*

Where We've Been

- Used sample information to provide a *point estimate* of a population parameter
- Used the sampling distribution of a statistic to assess the reliability of an estimate through a *confidence interval*

Where We're Going

- Test a specific value of a population parameter (mean or proportion), called a *test of hypothesis*
- Provide a measure of reliability for the hypothesis test, called the *significance level* of the test

Statistics IN Action   Diary of a Kleenex® User

In 1924, Kimberly-Clark Corporation invented a facial tissue for removing cold cream and began marketing it as Kleenex® brand tissues. Today, Kleenex® is recognized as the top-selling brand of tissue in the world. A wide variety of Kleenex® products are available, ranging from extra-large tissues to tissues with lotion. Over the past 80 years, Kimberly-Clark Corporation has packaged the tissues in boxes of different sizes and shapes and varied the number of tissues packaged in each box. For example, currently a family-size box contains 144 two-ply tissues, a cold-care box contains 70 tissues (coated with lotion), and a convenience pocket pack contains 15 miniature tissues.

How does Kimberly-Clark Corp. decide how many tissues to put in each box? According to the *Wall Street Journal*, marketing experts at the company use the results of a survey of Kleenex® customers to help determine how many tissues are packed in a box. In the mid-1980s, when Kimberly-Clark Corp. developed the cold-care box designed especially for people who have a cold, the company conducted their initial survey of customers for this purpose. Hundreds of customers were asked to keep *(continued)* count of their Kleenex® use in diaries. According to the *Wall Street Journal* report, the survey results left "little doubt that the company should put 60 tissues in each box." The number 60 was "the average number of times people blow their nose during a cold." (*Note:* In 2000, the company increased the number of tissues packaged in a cold-care box to 70.)

From summary information provided in the *Wall Street Journal* article, we constructed a data set that represents the results of a survey similar to the one described above. In the data file named **TISSUES,** we recorded the number of tissues used by each of 250 consumers during a period when they had a cold. We apply the hypothesis testing methodology

presented in this chapter to this data set in several Statistics in Action Revisited examples.

Statistics IN Action Revisited

- Key Elements of a Hypothesis Test (p. 329)
- Testing a Population Mean (p. 340)
- Testing a Population Proportion (p. 353)

Data Set: TISSUES

Suppose you wanted to determine whether the mean waiting time in the drive-through line of a fast-food restaurant is less than 5 minutes, or whether the majority of consumers are optimistic about the economy. In both cases you are interested in making an inference about how the value of a parameter relates to a specific numerical value. Is it less than, equal to, or greater than the specified number? This type of inference, called a **test of hypothesis,** is the subject of this chapter.

We introduce the elements of a test of hypothesis in Sections 6.1 and 6.2. We then show how to conduct a large-sample test of hypothesis about a population mean in Sections 6.3 and 6.4. In Section 6.5 we use small samples to conduct tests about means. Large-sample tests about binomial probabilities are the subject of Section 6.6, and some advanced methods for determining the reliability of a test are covered in Section 6.7. Finally, we show how to conduct a test about a population variance in Section 6.8.

6.1 The Elements of a Test of Hypothesis

Suppose building specifications in a certain city require that the average breaking strength of residential sewer pipe be more than 2,400 pounds per foot of length (i.e., per linear foot). Each manufacturer who wants to sell pipe in this city must demonstrate that its product meets the specification. Note that we are interested in making an inference about the mean μ of a population. However, in this example we are less interested in estimating the value of μ than we are in testing a **hypothesis** about its value—that is, *we want to decide whether the mean breaking strength of the pipe exceeds 2,400 pounds per linear foot.*

A statistical **hypothesis** is a statement about the numerical value of a population parameter.

The method used to reach a decision is based on the rare-event concept explained in earlier chapters. We define two hypotheses: (1) The **null hypothesis** is that which represents the status quo to the party performing the sampling experiment—the hypothesis that will be accepted unless the data provide convincing evidence that it is false. (2) The **alternative,** or **research, hypothesis** is that which will be accepted only if the data provide convincing evidence of its truth. From the point of view of the city conducting the tests, the null hypothesis is that the manufacturer's pipe does *not* meet specifications unless the tests provide convincing evidence otherwise. The null and alternative hypotheses are therefore

Null hypothesis (H_0): $\mu \leq 2{,}400$

(i.e., the manufacturer's pipe does not meet specifications)

Alternative (research) hypothesis (H_a): $\mu > 2{,}400$

(i.e., the manufacturer's pipe meets specifications)

> The **null hypothesis,** denoted H_0, represents the hypothesis that will be accepted unless the data provide convincing evidence that it is false. This usually represents the "status quo" or some claim about the population parameter that the researcher wants to test.

> The **alternative (research) hypothesis,** denoted H_a, represents the hypothesis that will be accepted only if the data provide convincing evidence of its truth. This usually represents the values of a population parameter for which the researcher wants to gather evidence to support.

How can the city decide when enough evidence exists to conclude that the manufacturer's pipe meets specifications? Because the hypotheses concern the value of the population mean μ, it is reasonable to use the sample mean $\bar{x}$ to make the inference, just as we did when forming confidence intervals for μ in Sections 5.2 and 5.3. The city will conclude that the pipe meets specifications only when the sample mean $\bar{x}$ convincingly indicates that the population mean exceeds 2,400 pounds per linear foot.

"Convincing" evidence in favor of the alternative hypothesis will exist when the value of $\bar{x}$ exceeds 2,400 by an amount that cannot be readily attributed to sampling variability. To decide, we compute a **test statistic,** i.e., a numerical value computed from the sample. Here, the test statistic is the z-value that measures the distance between the value of $\bar{x}$ and the value of μ specified in the null hypothesis. When the null hypothesis contains more than one value of μ, as in this case ($H_0: \mu \le 2,400$), we use the value of μ closest to the values specified in the alternative hypothesis. The idea is that if the hypothesis that μ *equals* 2,400 can be rejected in favor of $\mu > 2,400$, then μ *less than or equal to* 2,400 can certainly be rejected. Thus, the test statistic is

$$z = \frac{\bar{x} - 2,400}{\sigma_{\bar{x}}} = \frac{\bar{x} - 2,400}{\sigma/\sqrt{n}}$$

Note that a value of $z = 1$ means that $\bar{x}$ is 1 standard deviation above $\mu = 2,400$; a value of $z = 1.5$ means that $\bar{x}$ is 1.5 standard deviations above $\mu = 2,400$, and so on. How large must z be before the city can be convinced that the null hypothesis can be rejected in favor of the alternative and conclude that the pipe meets specifications?

> The **test statistic** is a sample statistic, computed from information provided in the sample, that the researcher uses to decide between the null and alternative hypotheses.

If you examine Figure 6.1, you will note that the chance of observing $\bar{x}$ more than 1.645 standard deviations above 2,400 is only .05—*if in fact the true mean μ is 2,400.*

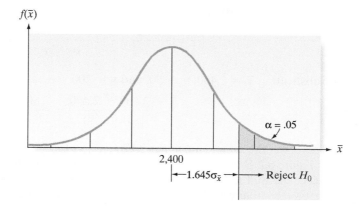

Figure 6.1

The sampling distribution of $\bar{x}$, assuming $\mu = 2,400$

Thus, if the sample mean is more than 1.645 standard deviations above 2,400, either H_0 is true and a relatively rare event has occurred (.05 probability), or H_a is true and the population mean exceeds 2,400. Because we would most likely reject the notion that a rare event has occurred, we would reject the null hypothesis ($\mu \le 2,400$) and conclude that the alternative hypothesis ($\mu > 2,400$) is true. What is the probability that this procedure will lead us to an incorrect decision?

Such an incorrect decision—deciding that the null hypothesis is false when in fact it is true—is called a **Type I error.** As indicated in Figure 6.1, the risk of making a Type I error is denoted by the symbol α—that is,

$$\alpha = P(\text{Type I error})$$

$$= P(\text{Rejecting the null hypothesis when in fact the null hypothesis is true})$$

> A **Type I error** occurs if the researcher rejects the null hypothesis in favor of the alternative hypothesis when, in fact, H_0 is true. The probability of committing a Type I error is denoted by α.

In our example,

$$\alpha = P(z > 1.645 \text{ when in fact } \mu = 2,400) = .05$$

We now summarize the elements of the test:

$$H_0: \mu \le 2,400 \quad \text{(Pipe does not meet specifications)}$$
$$H_a: \mu > 2,400 \quad \text{(Pipe meets specifications)}$$
$$\textit{Test statistic: } z = \frac{\bar{x} - 2,400}{\sigma_{\bar{x}}}$$
$$\textit{Rejection region: } z > 1.645, \text{ which corresponds to } \alpha = .05$$

Note that the **rejection region** refers to the values of the test statistic for which we will *reject the null hypothesis.*

> The **rejection region** of a statistical test is the set of possible values of the test statistic for which the researcher will reject H_0 in favor of H_a.

To illustrate the use of the test, suppose we test 50 sections of sewer pipe and find the mean and standard deviation for these 50 measurements to be

$$\bar{x} = 2,460 \text{ pounds per linear foot}$$
$$s = 200 \text{ pounds per linear foot}$$

As in the case of estimation, we can use s to approximate σ when s is calculated from a large set of sample measurements.

The test statistic is

$$z = \frac{\bar{x} - 2,400}{\sigma_{\bar{x}}} = \frac{\bar{x} - 2,400}{\sigma/\sqrt{n}} \approx \frac{\bar{x} - 2,400}{s/\sqrt{n}}$$

Substituting $\bar{x} = 2,460$, $n = 50$, and $s = 200$, we have

$$z \approx \frac{2,460 - 2,400}{200/\sqrt{50}} = \frac{60}{28.28} = 2.12$$

Therefore, the sample mean lies $2.12\sigma_{\bar{x}}$ above the hypothesized value of μ, 2,400, as shown in Figure 6.2. Because this value of z exceeds 1.645, it falls in the rejection region. That is, we reject the null hypothesis that $\mu = 2,400$ and conclude that $\mu > 2,400$. Thus, it appears that the company's pipe has a mean strength that exceeds 2,400 pounds per linear foot.

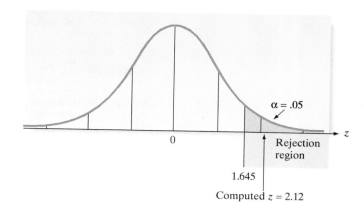

Figure 6.2

Location of the test statistic
for a test of the hypothesis
$H_0: \mu = 2,400$

How much faith can be placed in this conclusion? What is the probability that our statistical test could lead us to reject the null hypothesis (and conclude that the company's pipe meets the city's specifications) when in fact the null hypothesis is true? The answer is $\alpha = .05$—that is, we selected the level of risk, α, of making a Type I error when we constructed the test. Thus, the chance is only 1 in 20 that our test would lead us to conclude the manufacturer's pipe satisfies the city's specifications when in fact the pipe does *not* meet specifications.

Now, suppose the sample mean breaking strength for the 50 sections of sewer pipe turned out to be $\bar{x} = 2,430$ pounds per linear foot. Assuming that the sample standard deviation is still $s = 200$, the test statistic is

$$z = \frac{2,430 - 2,400}{200/\sqrt{50}} = \frac{30}{28.28} = 1.06$$

Therefore, the sample mean $\bar{x} = 2,430$ is only 1.06 standard deviations above the null hypothesized value of $\mu = 2,400$. As shown in Figure 6.3, this value does not fall into the rejection region ($z > 1.645$). Therefore, we know that we cannot reject H_0 using $\alpha = .05$. Even though the sample mean exceeds the city's specification of 2,400 by 30 pounds per linear foot, it does not exceed the specification by enough to provide *convincing* evidence that the *population mean* exceeds 2,400.

Should we accept the null hypothesis $H_0: \mu \leq 2,400$ and conclude that the manufacturer's pipe does not meet specifications? To do so would be to risk a **Type II error**—that of concluding that the null hypothesis is true (the pipe does not meet specifications) when in fact it is false (the pipe does meet specifications). We denote the probability of committing a Type II error by β, and we show in Section 6.7 that β is often difficult to determine

> A **Type II error** occurs if the researcher accepts the null hypothesis when, in fact, H_0 is false. The probability of committing a Type II error is denoted by β.

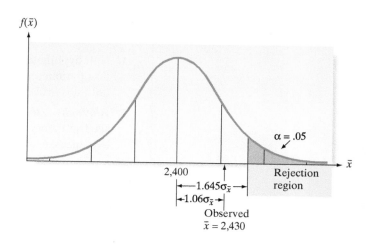

Figure 6.3

Location of test statistic
when $\bar{x} = 2,430$

Table 6.1	Conclusions and Consequences for a Test of Hypothesis	
	True State of Nature	
Conclusion	H_0 True	H_a True
Accept H_0 (Assume H_0 True)	Correct decision	Type II error (probability β)
Reject H_0 (Assume H_a True)	Type I error (probability α)	Correct decision

precisely. Rather than make a decision (accept H_0) for which the probability of error (β) is unknown, we avoid the potential Type II error by avoiding the conclusion that the null hypothesis is true. Instead, we will simply state that *the sample evidence is insufficient to reject H_0 at $\alpha = .05$.* Because the null hypothesis is the "status-quo" hypothesis, the effect of not rejecting H_0 is to maintain the status quo. In our pipe-testing example, the effect of having insufficient evidence to reject the null hypothesis that the pipe does not meet specifications is probably to prohibit the use of the manufacturer's pipe unless and until there is sufficient evidence that the pipe does meet specifications—that is, until the data indicate convincingly that the null hypothesis is false, we usually maintain the status quo implied by its truth.

Table 6.1 summarizes the four possible outcomes of a test of hypothesis. The "true state of nature" columns in Table 6.1 refer to the fact that either the null hypothesis H_0 is true or the alternative hypothesis H_a is true. Note that the true state of nature is unknown to the researcher conducting the test. The "decision" rows in Table 6.1 refer to the action of the researcher, assuming that he or she will either conclude that H_0 is true or that H_a is true, based on the results of the sampling experiment. Note that a Type I error can be made *only* when the null hypothesis is rejected in favor of the alternative hypothesis, and a Type II error can be made *only* when the null hypothesis is accepted. Our policy will be to make a decision only when we know the probability of making the error that corresponds to that decision. Because α is usually specified by the analyst, we will generally be able to reject H_0 (accept H_a) when the sample evidence supports that decision. However, because β is usually not specified, *we will generally avoid the decision to accept H_0, preferring instead to state that the sample evidence is insufficient to reject H_0 when the test statistic is not in the rejection region.*

⚠ CAUTION Be careful not to "accept H_0" when conducting a test of hypothesis because the measure of reliability, $\beta = P(\text{Type II error})$, is almost always unknown. If the test statistic does not fall into the rejection region, it is better to state the conclusion as "insufficient evidence to reject H_0."* ▲

The elements of a test of hypothesis are summarized in the following box. Note that the first four elements are all specified *before* the sampling experiment is performed. In no case will the results of the sample be used to determine the hypotheses; the data are collected to test the predetermined hypotheses, not to formulate them.

Elements of a Test of Hypothesis

1. **Null hypothesis** (H_0): A theory about the specific values of one or more population parameters. The theory generally represents the status quo, which we adopt until it is proven false. The theory is always stated as H_0: parameter = value.

2. *Alternative (research) hypothesis* (H_a): A theory that contradicts the null hypothesis. The theory generally represents that which we will adopt only when sufficient evidence exists to establish its truth.

---

*In many practical business applications of hypothesis testing, nonrejection leads management to behave as if the null hypothesis were accepted. Accordingly, the distinction between acceptance and nonrejection is frequently blurred in practice. We discuss the issues connected with the acceptance of the null hypothesis and the calculation of β in more detail in Section 6.7.

3. *Test statistic:* A sample statistic used to decide whether to reject the null hypothesis.

4. *Rejection region:* The numerical values of the test statistic for which the null hypothesis will be rejected. The rejection region is chosen so that the probability is α that it will contain the test statistic when the null hypothesis is true, thereby leading to a Type I error. The value of α is usually chosen to be small (e.g., .01, .05, or .10) and is referred to as the **level of significance** of the test.

5. *Assumptions:* Clear statement(s) of any assumptions made about the population(s) being sampled.

6. *Experiment and calculation of test statistic:* Performance of the sampling experiment and determination of the numerical value of the test statistic.

7. *Conclusion:*
   a. If the numerical value of the test statistic falls in the rejection region, we reject the null hypothesis and conclude that the alternative hypothesis is true. We know that the hypothesis-testing process will lead to this conclusion incorrectly (Type I error) only $100\alpha\%$ of the time when H_0 is true.
   b. If the test statistic does not fall in the rejection region, we do not reject H_0. Thus, we reserve judgment about which hypothesis is true. We do not conclude that the null hypothesis is true because we do not (in general) know the probability β that our test procedure will lead to an incorrect acceptance of H_0 (Type II error).

As with confidence intervals, the methodology for testing hypotheses varies depending on the target population parameter. In this chapter, we develop methods for testing a population mean, a population proportion, and a population variance. Some key words and the type of data associated with these target parameters are listed in the accompanying box.

Determining the Target Parameter

Parameter	Key Words or Phrases	Type of Data
μ	Mean; average	Quantitative
p	Proportion; percentage; fraction; rate	Qualitative
σ^2	Variance; variability; spread	Quantitative

6.2 Formulating Hypotheses and Setting Up the Rejection Region

In Section 6.1 we learned that the null and alternative hypotheses form the basis for inference using a test of hypothesis. The null and alternative hypotheses may take one of several forms. In the sewer pipe example, we tested the null hypothesis that the population mean strength of the pipe is less than or equal to 2,400 pounds per linear foot against the alternative hypothesis that the mean strength exceeds 2,400—that is, we tested

$$H_0: \mu \leq 2{,}400 \quad \text{(Pipe does not meet specifications)}$$

$$H_a: \mu > 2{,}400 \quad \text{(Pipe meets specifications)}$$

This is a **one-tailed** (or **one-sided**) **statistical test** because the alternative hypothesis specifies that the population parameter (the population mean μ in this example) is strictly greater than a specified value (2,400 in this example). If the null hypothesis had been $H_0: \mu \geq 2{,}400$ and the alternative hypothesis had been $H_a: \mu < 2{,}400$, the test would still be one-sided because the parameter is still specified to be on "one side" of the null hypothesis value. Some statistical investigations seek to show that the population parameter is *either larger or smaller* than some specified value. Such an alternative hypothesis is called a **two-tailed** (or **two-sided**) **hypothesis.**

While alternative hypotheses are always specified as strict inequalities, such as $\mu < 2{,}400$, $\mu > 2{,}400$, or $\mu \neq 2{,}400$, null hypotheses are usually specified as equalities, such as $\mu = 2{,}400$. Even when the null hypothesis is an inequality, such as $\mu \leq 2{,}400$, we specify $H_0: \mu = 2{,}400$, reasoning that if sufficient evidence exists to show that $H_a: \mu > 2{,}400$ is true when tested against $H_0: \mu = 2{,}400$, then surely sufficient evidence exists to reject $\mu < 2{,}400$ as well. Therefore, the null hypothesis is specified as the value of μ closest to a one-sided alternative hypothesis and as the only value *not* specified in a two-tailed alternative hypothesis. The steps for selecting the null and alternative hypotheses are summarized in the following box.

Steps for Selecting the Null and Alternative Hypotheses

1. Select the *alternative hypothesis* as that which the sampling experiment is intended to establish. The alternative hypothesis will assume one of three forms:
   a. One-tailed, upper-tailed   (e.g., $H_a: \mu > 2{,}400$)
   b. One-tailed, lower-tailed   (e.g., $H_a: \mu < 2{,}400$)
   c. Two-tailed   (e.g., $H_a: \mu \neq 2{,}400$)

2. Select the *null hypothesis* as the status quo, that which will be presumed true unless the sampling experiment conclusively establishes the alternative hypothesis. The null hypothesis will be specified as that parameter value closest to the alternative in one-tailed tests and as the complementary (or only unspecified) value in two-tailed tests.

$$(\text{e.g., } H_0: \mu = 2{,}400)$$

A **one-tailed test** of hypothesis is one in which the alternative hypothesis is directional and includes the symbol "<" or ">."

A **two-tailed test** of hypothesis is one in which the alternative hypothesis does not specify departure from H_0 in a particular direction and is written with the symbol " $\neq$."

Example 6.1

Formulating H_0 and H_a for a Test of a Population Mean

Problem A metal lathe is checked periodically by quality control inspectors to determine whether it is producing machine bearings with a mean diameter of .5 inch. If the mean diameter of the bearings is larger or smaller than .5 inch, then the process is out of control and must be adjusted. Formulate the null and alternative hypotheses for a test to determine whether the bearing production process is out of control.

Solution The hypotheses must be stated in terms of a population parameter. Here, we define μ as the true mean diameter (in inches) of all bearings produced by the metal lathe. If either $\mu > .5$ or $\mu < .5$, then the lathe's production process is out of control. Because the inspectors want to be able to detect either possibility (indicating that the process is in need of adjustment), these values of μ represent the alternative (or research) hypothesis. Alternatively, because $\mu = .5$ represents an in-control process (the status quo), this represents the null hypothesis. Therefore, we want to conduct the two-tailed test:

$$H_0: \mu = .5 \text{ (i.e., the process is in control)}$$
$$H_a: \mu \neq .5 \text{ (i.e., the process is out of control)}$$

Look Back Here, the alternative hypothesis is not necessarily the hypothesis that the quality control inspectors desire to support. However, they will make adjustments to the metal lathe settings only if there is strong evidence to indicate that the process is out of control. Consequently, $\mu \neq .5$ must be stated as the alternative hypothesis.

Now Work Exercise 6.10a

Example 6.2

Formulating H_0 and H_a for a Test of a Population Proportion

Problem Cigarette advertisements are required by federal law to carry the following statement: "Warning: The surgeon general has determined that cigarette smoking is dangerous to your health." However, this warning is often located in inconspicuous corners of the advertisements and printed in small type. Suppose the Federal Trade Commission (FTC) claims that 80% of cigarette consumers fail to see the warning. A marketer for a large tobacco firm wants to gather evidence to show that the FTC's claim is too high, i.e., that fewer than 80% of cigarette consumers fail to see the warning. Specify the null and alternative hypotheses for a test of the FTC's claim.

Solution The marketer wants to make an inference about p, the true proportion of all cigarette consumers who fail to see the surgeon general's warning. In particular, the marketer wants to collect data to show that fewer than 80% of cigarette consumers fail to see the warning, i.e., $p < .80$. Consequently, $p < .80$. represents the alternative hypothesis and $p = .80$ (the claim made by the FTC) represents the null hypothesis. That is, the marketer desires the one-tailed (lower-tailed) test:

$$H_0: p = .80 \text{ (i.e., the FTC's claim is true)}$$
$$H_a: p < .80 \text{ (i.e., the FTC's claim is false)}$$

Look Back Whenever a claim is made about the value of a particular population parameter and the researcher wants to test the claim, believing that it is false, the claimed value will represent the null hypothesis.

Now Work Exercise 6.11

The rejection region for a two-tailed test differs from that for a one-tailed test. When we are trying to detect departure from the null hypothesis in *either* direction, we must establish a rejection region in both tails of the sampling distribution of the test statistic. Figures 6.4a and 6.4b show the one-tailed rejection regions for lower- and upper-tailed tests, respectively. The two-tailed rejection region is illustrated in Figure 6.4c. Note that a rejection region is established in each tail of the sampling distribution for a two-tailed test.

The rejection regions corresponding to typical values selected for α are shown in Table 6.2 for one- and two-tailed tests. Note that the smaller α you select, the more evidence (the larger z) you will need before you can reject H_0.

Figure 6.4

Rejection regions corresponding to one- and two-tailed tests

a. Form of H_a: <   b. Form of H_a: >   c. Form of H_a: ≠

Table 6.2	**Rejection Regions for Common Values of α**		
	Alternative Hypotheses		
	Lower-Tailed	Upper-Tailed	Two-Tailed
$\alpha = .10$	$z < -1.28$	$z > 1.28$	$z < -1.645$ or $z > 1.645$
$\alpha = .05$	$z < -1.645$	$z > 1.645$	$z < -1.96$ or $z > 1.96$
$\alpha = .01$	$z < -2.33$	$z > 2.33$	$z < -2.575$ or $z > 2.575$

Example 6.3

Setting Up a Hypothesis Test for μ, the Mean Amount of Cereal in a Box

Problem A manufacturer of cereal wants to test the performance of one of its filling machines. The machine is designed to discharge a mean amount of 12 ounces per box, and the manufacturer wants to detect any departure from this setting. This quality study calls for randomly sampling 100 boxes from today's production run and determining whether the mean fill for the run is 12 ounces per box. Set up a test of hypothesis for this study, using $\alpha = .01$.

Solution The key word *mean* in the statement of the problem implies that the target parameter is μ, the mean amount of cereal discharged into the box. Because the manufacturer wishes to detect a departure from the setting of $\mu = 12$ in either direction, $\mu < 12$ or $\mu > 12$, we conduct a two-tailed statistical test. Following the procedure for selecting the null and alternative hypotheses, we specify as the alternative hypothesis that the mean differs from 12 ounces because detecting the machine's departure from specifications is the purpose of the quality control study. The null hypothesis is the presumption that the filling machine is operating properly unless the sample data indicate otherwise. Thus,

H_0: $\mu = 12$ (Population mean fill amount is 12 ounces)

H_a: $\mu \neq 12$ (i.e., $\mu < 12$ or $\mu > 12$; machine is under- or overfilling the box)

The test statistic measures the number of standard deviations between the observed value of $\bar{x}$ and the null hypothesized value $\mu = 12$:

$$Test\ statistic: z = \frac{\bar{x} - 12}{\sigma_{\bar{x}}}$$

The rejection region must be designated to detect a departure from $\mu = 12$ in *either* direction, so we will reject H_0 for values of z that are either too small (negative) or too large (positive). To determine the precise values of z that comprise the rejection region, we first select α, the probability that the test will lead to incorrect rejection of the null hypothesis. Then we divide α equally between the lower and upper tails of the distribution of z, as shown in Figure 6.5. In this example, $\alpha = .01$, so $\alpha/2 = .005$ is placed in each tail. The areas in the tails correspond to $z = -2.575$ and $z = 2.575$, respectively (from Table 6.2):

Rejection region: $z < -2.575$ or $z > 2.575$ (see Figure 6.5)

Assumptions: Because the sample size of the experiment is large enough ($n > 30$), the Central Limit Theorem will apply, and no assumptions need be made about the population of fill measurements. The sampling distribution of the sample mean fill of 100 boxes will be approximately normal regardless of the distribution of the individual boxes' fills.

Look Back Note that the test is set up *before* the sampling experiment is conducted. The data are not used to develop the test. Evidently, the manufacturer does not want to disrupt the filling process to adjust the machine, unless the sample data provide very convincing evidence that it is not meeting specifications, because the value of α has been set quite low at .01. If the sample evidence results in the rejection of H_0, the manufacturer will confidently conclude that the machine needs adjustment because there is only a .01 probability of a Type I error.

Figure 6.5

Two-tailed rejection region: $\alpha = .01$

Now Work Exercise 6.10b, c

Once the test is set up, the manufacturer is ready to perform the sampling experiment and conduct the test. The test is performed in the next section.

Statistics ᴵᴺ Action Revisited | Key Elements of a Hypothesis Test

In Kimberly-Clark Corp.'s survey of people with colds, each of 250 customers was asked to keep count of his or her use of Kleenex® tissues in diaries. One goal of the company was to determine how many tissues to package in a cold-care box of Kleenex®; consequently, the total number of tissues used was recorded for each person surveyed. Because number of tissues is a quantitative variable, the parameter of interest is μ, the mean number of tissues used by all customers with colds.

Now, according to a *Wall Street Journal* report, there was "little doubt that the company should put 60 tissues" in a cold-care box of Kleenex® tissues. This statement was based on a claim made by marketing experts that 60 is the average number of times a person will blow his or her nose during a

cold. Consequently, the marketers are claiming that $\mu = 60$. Suppose we disbelieve the claim that $\mu = 60$, believing instead that the population mean is smaller than 60 tissues. In order to test the claim against our belief, we set up the following null and alternative hypotheses:

$$H_0\colon \mu = 60 \qquad H_a\colon \mu < 60$$

We'll conduct this test in the next Statistics in Action Revisited on p. 340.

Activity 6.1 | *Challenging a Company's Claim:* Tests of Hypotheses

Use the Internet or a newspaper or magazine to find an example of a claim made by a company about the reliability or efficiency of one of its products. In this activity, you represent a consumer group that believes the claim may be false.

1. In your example, what kinds of evidence might exist that would cause one to suspect that the claim might be false and therefore worthy of a statistical study? Be specific. If the claim were false, how would consumers be hurt?

2. Explain the steps necessary to reject the company's claim at level α. State the null and alternative hypotheses. If you reject the claim, does it mean that the claim is false?

3. If you reject the claim when the claim is actually true, what type of error has occurred? What is the probability of this error occurring?

4. If you were to file a lawsuit against the company based on your rejection of its claim, how might the company use your results to defend itself?

Exercises 6.1–6.18

Learning the Mechanics

6.1 Which hypothesis, the null or the alternative, is the status-quo hypothesis? Which is the research hypothesis?

6.2 Which element of a test of hypothesis is used to decide whether to reject the null hypothesis in favor of the alternative hypothesis?

6.3 What is the level of significance of a test of hypothesis?

6.4 What is the difference between Type I and Type II errors in hypothesis testing? How do α and β relate to Type I and Type II errors?

6.5 List the four possible results of the combinations of decisions and true states of nature for a test of hypothesis.

6.6 We (generally) reject the null hypothesis when the test statistic falls in the rejection region, but we do not accept the null hypothesis when the test statistic does not fall in the rejection region. Why?

6.7 If you test a hypothesis and reject the null hypothesis in favor of the alternative hypothesis, does your test prove that the alternative hypothesis is correct? Explain.

6.8 For each of the following rejection regions, sketch the sampling distribution for z and indicate the location of the rejection region.

a. $z > 1.96$
b. $z > 1.645$
c. $z > 2.575$
d. $z < -1.28$
e. $z < -1.645$ or $z > 1.645$
f. $z < -2.575$ or $z > 2.575$
g. For each of the rejection regions specified in parts **a–f**, what is the probability that a Type I error will be made?

⏀ Applet Exercise 6.1

Use the applet *Hypothesis Test for a Mean* to investigate the frequency of Type I and Type II errors. For this exercise, use $n = 100$ and the normal distribution with mean 50 and standard deviation 10.

a. Set the null mean equal to 50 and the alternative to *not equal*. Run the applet one time. How many times was the null hypothesis rejected at level .05? In this case, the null hypothesis is true. Which type of error occurred each time the true null hypothesis was rejected? What is the probability of rejecting a true null hypothesis at level .05? How does the proportion of times the null hypothesis was rejected compare to this probability?

b. Clear the applet, then set the null mean equal to 47 and keep the alternative at *not equal*. Run the applet one time. How many times was the null hypothesis *not* rejected at level .05? In this case, the null hypothesis is false. Which type of error occurred each time the null hypothesis was *not* rejected? Run the applet several more times without clearing. Based on your results, what can you conclude about the probability of failing to reject the null hypothesis for the given conditions?

Applying the Concepts—Basic

6.9 **Effectiveness of online courses.** The Sloan Survey of Online Learning, "Making the Grade: Online Education in the United States," reported that 60% of college presidents believe that their online education courses are as good as or superior to courses that use traditional face-to-face instruction (*Inside Higher Ed*, Nov. 2006).
a. Give the null hypothesis for testing the claim made by the Sloan Survey.
b. Give the rejection region for a two-tailed test conducted at $\alpha = .01$.

6.10 **Play Golf America program.** The Professional Golf Association (PGA) and *Golf Digest* have developed the Play Golf America program, in which teaching professionals at participating golf clubs provide a free 10-minute lesson to new customers. According to *Golf Digest* (July 2008), golf facilities that participate in the program gain, on average, $2,400 in green fees, lessons, or equipment expenditures. A teaching professional at a golf club believes that the average gain in greens fees, lessons, or equipment expenditures for participating golf facilities exceeds $2,400.
a. In order to support the claim made by the teaching professional, what null and alternative hypotheses should you test?
b. Suppose you select $\alpha = .05$. Interpret this value in the words of the problem.
c. For $\alpha = .05$, specify the rejection region of a large-sample test.

6.11 **Student loan default rate.** The national student loan default rate has dropped steadily over the last decade. Five years ago, the Department of Education reported the default rate (i.e., the proportion of college students who default on their loans) at .045. Set up the null and alternative hypotheses if you want to determine if the student loan default rate this year is less than .045.

6.12 **Work travel policy.** American Express Consulting reported in *USA Today* (June 15, 2001) that 80% of U.S. companies have formal, written travel and entertainment policies for their employees. Give the null hypothesis for testing the claim made by American Express Consulting.

6.13 **Calories in school lunches.** A University of Florida economist conducted a study of Virginia elementary school lunch menus. During the state-mandated testing period, school lunches averaged 863 calories (National Bureau of Economic Research, Nov. 2002). The economist claims that after the testing period ends, the average caloric content of Virginia school lunches drops significantly. Set up the null and alternative hypotheses to test the economist's claim.

6.14 **Libor interest rate.** The interest rate at which London banks lend money to one another is called the *London*

interbank offered rate, or *Libor*. The British Bankers Association regularly surveys international banks for the Libor rate. One recent report (Bankrate.com, Aug. 23, 2006) had the average Libor rate at 5.40% for 3-month loans—a value considered high by many Western banks. Set up the null and alternative hypotheses for testing the reported value.

Applying the Concepts—Intermediate

6.15 **FDA certification of new drugs.** According to *Chemical Marketing Reporter*, pharmaceutical companies spend $15 billion per year on research and development of new drugs. The pharmaceutical company must subject each new drug to lengthy and involved testing before receiving the necessary permission from the Food and Drug Administration (FDA) to market the drug. The FDA's policy is that the pharmaceutical company must provide substantial evidence that a new drug is safe prior to receiving FDA approval, so that the FDA can confidently certify the safety of the drug to potential consumers.
a. If the new drug testing were to be placed in a test of hypothesis framework, would the null hypothesis be that the drug is safe or unsafe? The alternative hypothesis?
b. Given the choice of null and alternative hypotheses in part **a**, describe Type I and Type II errors in terms of this application. Define α and β in terms of this application.
c. If the FDA wants to be very confident that the drug is safe before permitting it to be marketed, is it more important that α or β be small? Explain.

6.16 **Authorizing computer users.** One of the most pressing problems in high-technology industries is computer security. Computer security is typically achieved by using a *password*—a collection of symbols (usually letters and numbers) that must be supplied by the user before the computer permits access to the account. The problem is that persistent hackers can create programs that enter millions of combinations of symbols into a target system until the correct password is found. The newest systems solve this problem by requiring authorized users to identify themselves by unique body characteristics. For example, a system developed by Palmguard, Inc. tests the hypothesis

H_0: The proposed user is authorized
H_a: The proposed user is unauthorized

by checking characteristics of the proposed user's palm against those stored in the authorized users' data bank (*Omni*, 1984).
a. Define a Type I error and Type II error for this test. Which is the more serious error? Why?
b. Palmguard reports that the Type I error rate for its system is less than 1%, whereas the Type II error rate is .00025%. Interpret these error rates.
c. Another successful security system, the EyeDentifyer, "spots authorized computer users by reading the one-of-a-kind patterns formed by the network of minute blood vessels across the retina at the back of the eye." The EyeDentifyer reports Type I and II error rates of .01% (1 in 10,000) and .005% (5 in 100,000), respectively. Interpret these rates.

Applying the Concepts—Advanced

6.17 **Jury trial outcomes.** Sometimes, the outcome of a jury trial defies the "common sense" expectations of the general public (e.g., the O. J. Simpson verdict in the "Trial of the Century"). Such a verdict is more acceptable if we understand that the jury trial of an accused murderer is analogous to the statistical hypothesis-testing process. The null hypothesis in a jury trial is that the accused is innocent. (The status-quo hypothesis in the U.S. system of justice is innocence, which is assumed to be true until proven *beyond a reasonable doubt*.) The alternative hypothesis is guilt, which is accepted only when sufficient evidence exists to establish its truth. If the vote of the jury is unanimous in favor of guilt, the null hypothesis of innocence is rejected, and the court concludes that the accused murderer is guilty. Any vote other than a unanimous one for guilt results in a "not guilty" verdict. The court never accepts the null hypothesis; that is, the court never declares the accused "innocent." A "not guilty" verdict (as in the O. J. Simpson case) implies that the court could not find the defendant guilty *beyond a reasonable doubt*.

a. Define Type I and Type II errors in a murder trial.

b. Which of the two errors is the more serious? Explain.

c. The court does not, in general, know the values of α and β; but ideally, both should be small. One of these probabilities is assumed to be smaller than the other in a jury trial. Which one, and why?

d. The court system relies on the belief that the value of α is made very small by requiring a unanimous vote before guilt is concluded. Explain why this is so.

e. For a jury prejudiced against a guilty verdict as the trial begins, will the value of α increase or decrease? Explain.

f. For a jury prejudiced against a guilty verdict as the trial begins, will the value of β increase or decrease? Explain.

6.18 **Intrusion detection systems.** Refer to the *Journal of Research of the National Institute of Standards and Technology* (Nov.–Dec. 2003) study of a computer intrusion detection system (IDS), Exercise 3.67 (p. 153). Recall that an IDS is designed to provide an alarm whenever unauthorized access (e.g., an intrusion) to a computer system occurs. The probability of the system giving a false alarm (i.e., providing a warning when no intrusion occurs) is defined by the symbol α, while the probability of a missed detection (i.e., no warning given when an intrusion occurs) is defined by the symbol β. These symbols are used to represent Type I and Type II error rates, respectively, in a hypothesis testing scenario.

a. What is the null hypothesis, H_0?

b. What is the alternative hypothesis, H_a?

c. According to actual data on the EMERALD system collected by the Massachusetts Institute of Technology Lincoln Laboratory, only 1 in 1,000 computer sessions with no intrusions resulted in a false alarm. For the same system, the laboratory found that only 500 of 1,000 intrusions were actually detected. Use this information to estimate the values of α and β.

6.3 Test of Hypothesis about a Population Mean: Normal (z) Statistic

When testing a hypothesis about a population mean μ, the test statistic we use will depend on whether the sample size n is large (say, $n \geq 30$) or small, and whether or not we know the value of the population standard deviation, σ. In this section, we consider the large-sample case.

Because the sample size is large, the Central Limit Theorem guarantees that the sampling distribution of $\bar{x}$ is approximately normal. Consequently, the test statistic for a test based on large samples will be based on the normal z-statistic. Although the z-statistic requires that we know the true population standard deviation σ, this is rarely, if ever, the case. However, we established in Chapter 5 that when n is large, the sample standard deviation s provides a good approximation to σ, and the z-statistic can be approximated as follows:

$$z = \frac{\bar{x} - \mu_0}{\sigma_{\bar{x}}} = \frac{\bar{x} - \mu_0}{\sigma/\sqrt{n}} \approx \frac{\bar{x} - \mu_0}{s/\sqrt{n}}$$

where μ_0 represents the value of μ specified in the null hypothesis.

The setup of a large-sample test of hypothesis about a population mean is summarized in the following boxes. Both the one- and two-tailed tests are shown.

Large-Sample Test of Hypothesis about μ

One-Tailed Test	Two-Tailed Test
$H_0: \mu = \mu_0$	$H_0: \mu = \mu_0$
$H_a: \mu < \mu_0$	$H_a: \mu \neq \mu_0$
(or $H_a: \mu > \mu_0$)	

$$\text{Test statistic: } z = \frac{\overline{x} - \mu_0}{\sigma_{\overline{x}}} \approx \frac{\overline{x} - \mu_0}{s/\sqrt{n}} \qquad \text{Test statistic: } z = \frac{\overline{x} - \mu_0}{\sigma_{\overline{x}}} \approx \frac{\overline{x} - \mu_0}{s/\sqrt{n}}$$

Rejection region: $z < -z_\alpha$ Rejection region: $|z| > z_{\alpha/2}$
 (or $z > z_\alpha$ when H_a: $\mu > \mu_0$)
where z_α is chosen so that   where $z_{\alpha/2}$ is chosen so that
 $P(z > z_\alpha) = \alpha$ $P(|z| > z_{\alpha/2}) = \alpha/2$

Note: μ_0 is the symbol for the numerical value assigned to μ under the null hypothesis.

Conditions Required for a Valid Large-Sample Hypothesis Test for μ

1. A random sample is selected from the target population.

2. The sample size n is large (i.e., $n \geq 30$). (Due to the Central Limit Theorem, this condition guarantees that the test statistic will be approximately normal regardless of the shape of the underlying probability distribution of the population.)

Once the test has been set up, the sampling experiment is performed and the test statistic calculated. The next box contains possible conclusions for a test of hypothesis, depending on the result of the sampling experiment.

Possible Conclusions for a Test of Hypothesis

1. If the calculated test statistic falls in the rejection region, reject H_0 and conclude that the alternative hypothesis H_a is true. State that you are rejecting H_0 at the α level of significance. Remember that the confidence is in the testing *process*, not the particular result of a single test.

2. If the test statistic does not fall in the rejection region, conclude that the sampling experiment does not provide sufficient evidence to reject H_0 at the α level of significance. [Generally, we will not "accept" the null hypothesis unless the probability β of a Type II error has been calculated (see Section 6.7).]

Example 6.4

Carrying Out a Hypothesis Test for μ, the Mean Amount of Cereal in a Box

Problem Refer to the quality control test set up in Example 6.3 (p. 328). Recall that a machine is designed to discharge a mean of 12 ounces of cereal per box. A sample of 100 boxes yielded the fill amounts (in ounces) shown in Table 6.3. Use these data to conduct the test.

$$H_0: \mu = 12 \quad \text{(Population mean fill amount is 12 ounces)}$$
$$H_a: \mu \neq 12 \quad \text{(Machine is under- or overfilling the box)}$$

Table 6.3	Fill Amounts from Quality Control Tests								
12.3	12.2	12.9	11.8	12.1	11.7	11.8	11.3	12.0	11.7
11.0	12.7	11.2	11.8	11.4	11.3	11.5	12.1	12.5	11.7
12.3	11.7	11.6	11.6	11.1	12.1	12.4	11.4	11.6	11.4
10.9	11.0	11.5	11.6	11.6	11.4	11.9	11.1	11.7	12.1
12.2	11.7	11.6	11.4	12.4	11.0	11.8	12.9	13.2	11.5
11.5	12.0	11.9	11.8	12.5	11.8	12.4	12.0	12.2	12.4
11.8	12.6	11.8	11.8	11.5	12.0	12.7	11.5	11.0	11.8
11.2	12.6	12.0	12.6	12.0	12.0	12.5	12.0	12.8	11.8
12.6	12.4	10.9	12.0	11.9	11.6	11.3	12.1	11.8	12.2
12.2	11.5	12.7	11.5	11.0	11.7	12.5	11.6	11.3	11.1

Data Set: CEREAL

Descriptive Statistics: FILL

Variable	N	Mean	StDev	Minimum	Q1	Median	Q3	Maximum
FILL	100	11.851	0.512	10.900	11.500	11.800	12.200	13.200

Figure 6.6
Minitab descriptive statistics for fill amounts, Example 6.4

Solution To carry out the test, we need to find the values of $\bar{x}$ and s. These values, $\bar{x} = 11.851$ and $s = .512$, are shown (highlighted) on the Minitab printout, Figure 6.6. Now, we substitute these sample statistics into the test statistic and obtain:

$$z = \frac{\bar{x} - 12}{\sigma_{\bar{x}}} = \frac{\bar{x} - 12}{\sigma/\sqrt{n}} = \frac{11.851 - 12}{\sigma/\sqrt{100}}$$

$$\approx \frac{11.851 - 12}{s/10} = \frac{-.149}{.512/10} = -2.91$$

The implication is that the sample mean, 11.851, is (approximately) 3 standard deviations below the null hypothesized value of 12.0 in the sampling distribution of $\bar{x}$. You can see in Figure 6.5 that this value of z is in the lower-tail rejection region, which consists of all values of $z < -2.575$. These sample data provide sufficient evidence to reject H_0 and conclude, at the $\alpha = .01$ level of significance, that the mean fill differs from the specification of $\mu = 12$ ounces. It appears that the machine is, on average, underfilling the boxes.

Look Back Three points about the test of hypothesis in this example apply to all statistical tests:

1. Because z is less than -2.575, it is tempting to state our conclusion at a significance level lower than $\alpha = .01$. We resist the temptation because the level of α is determined before the sampling experiment is performed. If we decide that we are willing to tolerate a 1% Type I error rate, the result of the sampling experiment should have no effect on that decision. In general, *the same data should not be used both to set up and to conduct the test.*

2. When we state our conclusion at the .01 level of significance, we are referring to the failure rate of the procedure, not the result of this particular test. We know that the test procedure will lead to the rejection of the null hypothesis only 1% of the time when in fact $\mu = 12$. Therefore, *when the test statistic falls in the rejection region, we infer that the alternative $\mu \neq 12$ is true and express our confidence in the procedure by quoting the α level of significance, or the $100(1 - \alpha)\%$ confidence level.*

3. Although a test may lead to a "statistically significant" result (i.e., rejecting H_0 at significance level α, as in the test above), it may not be "practically significant." For example, suppose the quality control study tested $n = 100,000$ cereal boxes, resulting in $\bar{x} = 11.995$ and $s = .5$. Now, a two-tailed hypothesis test of H_0: $\mu = 12$ results in a test statistic of $z = \dfrac{(11.995 - 12)}{.5/\sqrt{100,000}} = -3.16$.

This result at $\alpha = .01$ leads us to "reject H_0" and conclude that the mean, μ, is "statistically different" from 12. However, for all practical purposes, the sample mean, $\bar{x} = 11.995$, and hypothesized mean, $\mu = 12$, are the same. Because the result is not "practically significant," the company is not likely to spend money fixing a machine that, for all practical purposes, is dispensing an average of 12 ounces of cereal into the boxes. Consequently, *not all "statistically significant" results are "practically significant."*

Now Work Exercise 6.23

Exercises 6.19–6.33

Learning the Mechanics

6.19 Suppose you are interested in conducting the statistical test of $H_0: \mu = 255$ against $H_a: \mu > 255$, and you have decided to use the following decision rule: Reject H_0 if the sample mean of a random sample of 81 items is more than 270. Assume that the standard deviation of the population is 63.
   a. Express the decision rule in terms of z.
   b. Find α, the probability of making a Type I error, by using this decision rule.

6.20 A random sample of 100 observations from a population with standard deviation 60 yielded a sample mean of 110.
   a. Test the null hypothesis that $\mu = 100$ against the alternative hypothesis that $\mu > 100$ using $\alpha = .05$. Interpret the results of the test.
   b. Test the null hypothesis that $\mu = 100$ against the alternative hypothesis that $\mu \neq 100$ using $\alpha = .05$. Interpret the results of the test.
   c. Compare the results of the two tests you conducted. Explain why the results differ.

6.21 A random sample of 64 observations produced the following summary statistics: $\bar{x} = .323$ and $s^2 = .034$.
   a. Test the null hypothesis that $\mu = .36$ against the alternative hypothesis that $\mu < .36$ using $\alpha = .10$.
   b. Test the null hypothesis that $\mu = .36$ against the alternative hypothesis that $\mu \neq .36$ using $\alpha = .10$. Interpret the result.

Applet Exercise 6.2

Use the applet *Hypotheses Test for a Mean* to investigate the effect of the underlying distribution on the proportion of Type I errors. For this exercise use $n = 100$, mean $= 50$, standard deviation $= 10$, null mean $= 50$, and alternative $<$.
   a. Select the normal distribution and run the applet several times without clearing. What happens to the proportion of times the null hypothesis is rejected at the .05 level as the applet is run more and more times?
   b. Clear the applet and then repeat part **a** using the right skewed distribution. Do you get similar results? Explain.
   c. Describe the effect that the underlying distribution has on the probability of making a Type I error.

Applet Exercise 6.3

Use the applet *Hypotheses Test for a Mean* to investigate the effect of the underlying distribution on the proportion of Type II errors. For this exercise use $n = 100$, mean $= 50$, standard deviation $= 10$, null mean $= 52$, and alternative $<$.
   a. Select the normal distribution and run the applet several times without clearing. What happens to the proportion of times the null hypothesis is rejected at the .01 level as the applet is run more and more times? Is this what you would expect? Explain.
   b. Clear the applet and then repeat part **a** using the right skewed distribution. Do you get similar results? Explain.
   c. Describe the effect that the underlying distribution has on the probability of making a Type II error.

Applet Exercise 6.4

Use the applet *Hypotheses Test for a Mean* to investigate the effect of the null mean on the probability of making a Type II error. For this exercise use $n = 100$, mean $= 50$, standard deviation $= 10$, and alternative $<$ with the normal distribution. Set the null mean to 55 and run the applet several times without clearing. Record the proportion of Type II errors that occurred at the .01 level. Clear the applet and repeat for null means of 54, 53, 52, and 51. What can you conclude about the probability of a Type II error as the null mean gets closer to the actual mean? Can you offer a reasonable explanation for this?

Applying the Concepts—Basic

6.22 **Accounting and Machiavellianism.** Refer to the *Behavioral Research in Accounting* (Jan. 2008) study of Machiavellian traits in accountants, Exercise 5.17 (p. 279). A Mach rating score was determined for each in a random sample of 122 purchasing managers, with the following results: $\bar{x} = 99.6$, $s = 12.6$. Recall that a director of purchasing at a major firm claims that the true mean Mach rating score of all purchasing managers is 85.
   a. Suppose you want to test the director's claim. Specify the null and alternative hypothesis for the test.
   b. Give the rejection region for the test using $\alpha = .10$.
   c. Find the value of the test statistic.
   d. Use the result, part **c**, to make the appropriate conclusion.

6.23 **Latex allergy in health care workers.** Refer to the *Current Allergy & Clinical Immunology* (Mar. 2004) study of $n = 46$ hospital employees who were diagnosed with a latex allergy from exposure to the powder on latex gloves, Exercise 5.10 (p. 278). The number of latex gloves used per week by the sampled workers is summarized as follows: $\bar{x} = 19.3$ and $s = 11.9$. Let μ represent the mean number of latex gloves used per week by all hospital employees. Consider testing $H_0: \mu = 20$ against $H_a: \mu < 20$.
   a. Give the rejection region for the test at a significance level of $\alpha = .01$.
   b. Calculate the value of the test statistic.
   c. Use the results, parts **a** and **b**, to make the appropriate conclusion.

6.24 **Prices of hybrid cars.** *BusinessWeek.com* provides consumers with retail prices of new cars at dealers from across the country. The July 2006 prices for the hybrid Toyota Prius were obtained from a sample of 160 dealers. These 160 prices are saved in the **HYBRIDCARS** file.
   a. Give the null and alternative hypotheses for testing whether the mean July 2006 dealer price of the Toyota Prius, μ, differs from $25,000.
   b. Access the **HYBRIDCARS** file and find the sample mean and sample standard deviation.
   c. Use the information in part **b** to find the test statistic for the hypothesis test.
   d. Give the rejection region for the hypothesis test, using $\alpha = .05$.
   e. State the appropriate conclusion for the hypothesis test.

Table for Exercise 6.28									
14622	13196	11948	11289	11964	10526	10387	10592	10460	10086
14628	13396	11726	11252	12449	11030	10787	10603	10144	11674
11510	10946	10508	10604	10270	10529	10360	14796	12913	12270
11842	10656	11360	11136	10814	13523	11289	11183	10951	9722
10481	9812	9669	9643	9115	9115	11588	10888	9738	9295
9421	9105	10233	10186	9918	9209	9532	9933	9152	9295
16243	14628	12766	8714	9469	11948	12414			

6.25 **Identifying type of urban land cover.** For planning purposes, urban land-cover must be identified as either grassland, commercial, or residential. This is typically done using remote sensing data from satellite pictures. In *Geographical Analysis* (Oct. 2006), researchers from Arizona State, Florida State, and Louisiana State universities collaborated on a new method for analyzing remote sensing data. A satellite photograph of an urban area was divided into 4x4 meter areas (called pixels). Of interest is a numerical measure of the distribution of gaps or hole sizes in the pixel, called *lacunarity*. The mean and standard deviation of the lacunarity measurements for a sample of 100 pixels randomly selected from a specific urban area are 225 and 20, respectively. It is known that the mean lacunarity measurement for all grassland pixels is 220. Do the data suggest that the area sampled is grassland? Test at $\alpha = .01$.

6.26 **Size of diamonds sold at retail.** Refer to the *Journal of Statistics Education* data on diamonds saved in the **DIAMONDS** file. In Exercise 5.18 (p. 280) you selected a random sample of 30 diamonds from the 308 diamonds and found the mean and standard deviation of the number of carats per diamond for the sample. Let μ represent the mean number of carats in the population of 308 diamonds. Suppose you want to test $H_0: \mu = .6$ against $H_a: \mu \neq .6$.
  a. In the words of the problem, define a Type I error and a Type II error.
  b. Use the sample information to conduct the test at a significance level of $\alpha = .05$.
  c. Conduct the test, part **b**, using $\alpha = .10$.
  d. What do the results suggest about the choice of α in a test of hypothesis?

6.27 **Producer's and consumer's risk.** In quality control applications of hypothesis testing, the null and alternative hypotheses are frequently specified as

H_0: The production process is performing satisfactorily.

H_a: The process is performing in an unsatisfactory manner.

Accordingly, α is sometimes referred to as the *producer's risk*, while β is called the *consumer's risk* (Stevenson, *Operations Management*, 2008).

An injection molder produces plastic golf tees. The process is designed to produce tees with a mean weight of .250 ounce. To investigate whether the injection molder is operating satisfactorily, 40 tees were randomly sampled from the last hour's production. Their weights (in ounces) are listed in the following table and saved in the **TEES** file.
  a. Write H_0 and H_a in terms of the true mean weight of the golf tees, μ.

  b. Do the data provide sufficient evidence to conclude that the process is not operating satisfactorily? Test using $\alpha = .01$.
  c. In the context of this problem, explain why it makes sense to call α the producer's risk and β the consumer's risk.

Applying the Concepts—Intermediate

6.28 **Cooling method for gas turbines.** During periods of high electricity demand, especially during the hot summer months, the power output from a gas turbine engine can drop dramatically. One way to counter this drop in power is by cooling the inlet air to the gas turbine. An increasingly popular cooling method uses high pressure inlet fogging. The performance of a sample of 67 gas turbines augmented with high-pressure inlet fogging was investigated in the *Journal of Engineering for Gas Turbines and Power* (Jan. 2005). One measure of performance is heat rate (kilojoules per kilowatt per hour). Heat rates for the 67 gas turbines, saved in the **GASTURBINE** file, are listed in the table above. Suppose that a standard gas turbine has, on average, a heat rate of 10,000 kJ/kWh. Conduct a test to determine if the mean heat rate of gas turbines augmented with high-pressure inlet fogging exceeds 10,000 kJ/kWh. Use $\alpha = .05$.

6.29 **Point spreads of NFL games.** During the National Football League (NFL) season, Las Vegas oddsmakers establish a point spread on each game for betting purposes. For example, the champion Pittsburgh Steelers were established as 7-point favorites over the Arizona Cardinals in the 2009 Super Bowl. The final scores of NFL games were compared against the final point spreads established by the oddsmakers in *Chance* (Fall 1998). The difference between the game outcome and point spread (called a *point-spread error*) was calculated for 240 NFL games. The mean and standard deviation of the point-spread errors are $\bar{x} = -1.6$ and $s = 13.3$. Use this information to test the hypothesis that the true mean point-spread error for all NFL games differs from 0. Conduct the test at $\alpha = .01$ and interpret the result.

6.30 **Revenue for a full-service funeral.** According to the National Funeral Directors Association (NFDA), the nation's 22,000 funeral homes collected an average of $6,500 per full-service funeral in 2005 (*NFDA Fact Sheet*, 2009). A random sample of 36 funeral homes reported revenue data for 2009. Among other measures, each reported its average fee for a full-service funeral. These data (in thousands of dollars) are shown in the following table and saved in the **FUNERAL** file.

.247	.251	.254	.253	.253	.248	.253	.255	.256	.252
.253	.252	.253	.256	.254	.256	.252	.251	.253	.251
.253	.253	.248	.251	.253	.256	.254	.250	.254	.255
.249	.250	.254	.251	.251	.255	.251	.253	.252	.253

7.4	9.4	5.3	8.4	7.5	6.5	6.2	8.3	6.7
11.6	6.3	5.9	6.7	5.8	5.2	6.4	6.0	7.4
7.2	6.6	6.3	5.3	6.6	5.6	8.4	7.2	7.4
5.8	6.3	6.1	7.0	7.2	6.1	5.4	7.4	6.6

a. What are the appropriate null and alternative hypotheses to test whether the average full-service fee of U.S. funeral homes in 2009 exceeds $6,500?

b. Conduct the test at $\alpha = .05$. Do the sample data provide sufficient evidence to conclude that the average fee in 2009 was higher than in 2005?

c. In conducting the test, was it necessary to assume that the population of average full-service fees was normally distributed? Justify your answer.

6.31 **Salaries of postgraduates.** The *Economics of Education Review* (Vol. 21, 2002) published a paper on the relationship between education level and earnings. The data for the research were obtained from the National Adult Literacy Survey of over 25,000 respondents. The survey revealed that males with a postgraduate degree had a mean salary of $61,340 (with standard error $s_{\bar{x}} = \$2,185$), while females with a postgraduate degree had a mean of $32,227 (with standard error $s_{\bar{x}} = \$932$).

a. The article reports that a 95% confidence interval for μ_M, the population mean salary of all males with postgraduate degrees, is ($57,050, $65,631). Based on this interval, is there evidence to say that μ_M differs from $60,000? Explain.

b. Use the summary information to test the hypothesis that the true mean salary of males with postgraduate degrees differs from $60,000. Use $\alpha = .05$. (*Note:* $s_{\bar{x}} = s/\sqrt{n}$.)

c. Explain why the inferences in parts **a** and **b** agree.

d. The article reports that a 95% confidence interval for μ_F, the population mean salary of all females with postgraduate degrees, is ($30,396, $34,058). Based on this interval, is there evidence to say that μ_F differs from $33,000? Explain.

e. Use the summary information to test the hypothesis that the true mean salary of females with postgraduate degrees differs from $33,000. Use $\alpha = .05$. (*Note:* $s_{\bar{x}} = s/\sqrt{n}$.)

f. Explain why the inferences in parts **d** and **e** agree.

6.32 **Solder-joint inspections.** Current technology uses high resolution X-rays and lasers for inspection of solder-joint defects on printed circuit boards (PCBs) (*Global SMT & Packaging,* April 2008). A particular manufacturer of laser-based inspection equipment claims that its product can inspect on average at least 10 solder joints per second when the joints are spaced .1 inch apart. The equipment was tested by a potential buyer on 48 different PCBs. In each case, the equipment was operated for exactly 1 second. The number of solder joints inspected on each run follows (data are saved in the **PCB** file):

10	9	10	10	11	9	12	8	8	9	6	10
7	10	11	9	9	13	9	10	11	10	12	8
9	9	9	7	12	6	9	10	10	8	7	9
11	12	10	0	10	11	12	9	7	9	9	10

a. The potential buyer wants to know whether the sample data refute the manufacturer's claim. Specify the null and alternative hypotheses that the buyer should test.

b. In the context of this exercise, what is a Type I error? A Type II error?

c. Conduct the hypothesis test you described in part **a** and interpret the test's results in the context of this exercise. Use $\alpha = .05$.

Applying the Concepts—Advanced

6.33 **Why do small firms export?** What motivates small firms to export their products? To answer this question, California State University professor Ralph Pope conducted a survey of 137 exporting firms listed in the *California International Trade Register* (*Journal of Small Business Management,* Vol. 40, 2002.) Firm CEOs were asked to respond to the statement "Management believes that the firm can achieve economies of scale by exporting" on a scale of 1 (strongly disagree) to 5 (strongly agree). Summary statistics for the $n = 137$ scale scores were reported as $\bar{x} = 3.85$ and $s = 1.5$. In the journal article, the researcher hypothesized that if the true mean scale score exceeds 3.5, then CEOs at all California small firms generally agree with the statement.

a. Conduct the appropriate test using $\alpha = .05$. State your conclusion in the words of the problem.

b. Explain why the results of the study, although "statistically significant," may not be practically significant.

c. The scale scores for the sample of 137 small firms are unlikely to be normally distributed. Does this invalidate the inference you made in part **a**? Explain.

6.4 Observed Significance Levels: *p*-Values

According to the statistical test procedure described in Section 6.2, the rejection region and, correspondingly, the value of α are selected prior to conducting the test, and the conclusions are stated in terms of rejecting or not rejecting the null hypothesis. A second method of presenting the results of a statistical test is one that reports the extent to which the test statistic disagrees with the null hypothesis and leaves to the reader the task of deciding whether to reject the null hypothesis. This measure of disagreement is called the *observed significance level* (or *p-value*) for the test.

> The **observed significance level,** or *p*-value, for a specific statistical test is the probability (assuming H_0 is true) of observing a value of the test statistic that is at least as contradictory to the null hypothesis, and supportive of the alternative hypothesis, as the actual one computed from the sample data.

For example, the value of the test statistic computed for the sample of $n = 50$ sections of sewer pipe was $z = 2.12$. Because the test is one-tailed—that is, the alternative (research) hypothesis of interest is $H_a: \mu > 2,400$—values of the test statistic even more contradictory to H_0 than the one observed would be values larger than $z = 2.12$. Therefore, the observed significance level (*p*-value) for this test is

$$p\text{-value} = P(z > 2.12)$$

or, equivalently, the area under the standard normal curve to the right of $z = 2.12$ (see Figure 6.7).

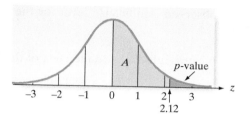

Figure 6.7

Finding the *p*-value for an upper-tailed test when $z = 2.12$

The area A in Figure 6.7 is given in Table IV in Appendix B as .4830. Therefore, the upper-tail area corresponding to $z = 2.12$ is

$$p\text{-value} = .5 - .4830 = .0170$$

Consequently, we say that these test results are "very significant" (i.e., they disagree rather strongly with the null hypothesis, $H_0: \mu = 2,400$, and favor $H_a: \mu > 2,400$). The probability of observing a z-value as large as 2.12 is only .0170, if in fact the true value of μ is 2,400.

If you are inclined to select $\alpha = .05$ for this test, then you would reject the null hypothesis because the *p*-value for the test, .0170, is less than .05. In contrast, if you choose $\alpha = .01$, you would not reject the null hypothesis because the *p*-value for the test is larger than .01. Thus, the use of the observed significance level is identical to the test procedure described in the preceding sections except that the choice of α is left to you.

The steps for calculating the *p*-value corresponding to a test statistic for a population mean are given in the next box.

Steps for Calculating the *p*-value for a Test of Hypothesis

1. Determine the value of the test statistic z corresponding to the result of the sampling experiment.

2. a. If the test is one-tailed, the *p*-value is equal to the tail area beyond z in the same direction as the alternative hypothesis. Thus, if the alternative hypothesis is of the form $>$, the *p*-value is the area to the right of, or above, the observed z-value. Conversely, if the alternative is of the form $<$, the *p*-value is the area to the left of, or below, the observed z-value. (See Figure 6.8.)

   b. If the test is two-tailed, the *p*-value is equal to twice the tail area beyond the observed z-value in the direction of the sign of z—that is, if z is positive, the *p*-value is twice the area to the right of, or above, the observed z-value. Conversely, if z is negative, the *p*-value is twice the area to the left of, or below, the observed z-value. (See Figure 6.9.)

Figure 6.8

Finding the *p*-value for a one-tailed test

a. Lower-tailed test, $H_a: \mu < \mu_0$

b. Upper-tailed test, $H_a: \mu > \mu_0$

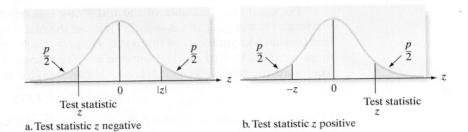

Figure 6.9
Finding the p-value for a
two-tailed test: p-value $= 2(p/2)$

Example 6.5

**Computing a p–Value
for the Test of Mean
Filling Weight**

Problem Find the observed significance level for the test of the mean filling weight in Examples 6.3 and 6.4.

Solution Example 6.3 presented a two-tailed test of the hypothesis

$$H_0: \mu = 12 \text{ ounces}$$

against the alternative hypothesis

$$H_a: \mu \neq 12 \text{ ounces}$$

The observed value of the test statistic in Example 6.4 was $z = -2.91$, and any value of z less than -2.91 or greater than 2.91 (because this is a two-tailed test) would be even more contradictory to H_0. Therefore, the observed significance level for the test is

$$p\text{-value} = P(z < -2.91 \text{ or } z > 2.91) = P(|z| > 2.91)$$

Thus, we calculate the area below the observed z-value, $z = -2.91$, and double it. Consulting Table IV in Appendix B, we find that $P(z < -2.91) = .5 - .4982 = .0018$. Therefore, the p-value for this two-tailed test is

$$2P(z < -2.91) = 2(.0018) = .0036$$

This p-value can also be obtained using statistical software. The rounded p-value is shown (highlighted) on the Minitab printout, Figure 6.10.

```
Test of mu = 12 vs not = 12
```

Variable	N	Mean	StDev	SE Mean	95% CI	T	P
FILL	100	11.8510	0.5118	0.0512	(11.7495, 11.9525)	-2.91	0.004

Figure 6.10
Minitab test of mean fill amount, Example 6.5

Look Back We can interpret this p-value as a strong indication that the machine is not filling the boxes according to specifications because we would observe a test statistic this extreme or more extreme only 36 in 10,000 times if the machine were meeting specifications ($\mu = 12$). The extent to which the mean differs from 12 could be better determined by calculating a confidence interval for μ.

Now Work Exercise 6.39

When publishing the results of a statistical test of hypothesis in journals, case studies, reports, and so on, many researchers make use of p-values. Instead of selecting α beforehand and then conducting a test, as outlined in this chapter, the researcher computes (usually with the aid of a statistical software package) and reports the value of the appropriate test statistic and its associated p-value. It is left to the reader of the report to judge the significance of the result (i.e., the reader must determine whether to reject the null hypothesis in favor of the alternative hypothesis, based on the reported p-value). Usually, the null hypothesis is rejected if the observed significance level is *less than* the fixed significance level, α, chosen by the reader. The inherent advantage of reporting test results in this manner are twofold: (1) Readers are permitted to select the maximum value of α that they would be willing to tolerate if they actually carried out a standard test of hypothesis in the manner outlined in this chapter, and (2) a measure of the degree of significance of the result (i.e., the *p*-value) is provided.

Ethics ɪɴ Statistics

Selecting the value of α *after* computing the observed significance level (*p*-value) in order to guarantee a preferred conclusion is considered *unethical statistical practice*.

> **Reporting Test Results as *p*-Values: How to Decide Whether to Reject H_0**
>
> 1. Choose the maximum value of α that you are willing to tolerate.
>
> 2. If the observed significance level (*p*-value) of the test is less than the chosen value of α, reject the null hypothesis. Otherwise, do not reject the null hypothesis.

Example 6.6

Using *p*–Values to Test Mean Hospital Length of Stay

Problem Knowledge of the amount of time a patient occupies a hospital bed—called *length of stay* (LOS)—is important for allocating resources. At one hospital, the mean LOS was determined to be 5 days. A hospital administrator believes that the mean LOS may now be less than 5 days due to a newly adopted managed care system. To check this, the LOSs (in days) for 100 randomly selected hospital patients were recorded; these are listed in Table 6.4. Test the hypothesis that the true mean LOS at the hospital is less than 5 days; that is,

$$H_0: \mu = 5 \quad \text{(Mean LOS is 5 days.)}$$
$$H_a: \mu < 5 \quad \text{(Mean LOS is less than 5 days.)}$$

Use the data in the table to conduct the test at $\alpha = .05$.

Solution The data were entered into a computer, and Excel/DDXL was used to conduct the analysis. The DDXL printout for the lower-tailed test is displayed in Figure 6.11. Both the test statistic, $z \approx -1.28$, and *p*-value of the test, $p = .102$, are highlighted

Table 6.4		Lengths of Stay for 100 Hospital Patients							
2	3	8	6	4	4	6	4	2	5
8	10	4	4	4	2	1	3	2	10
1	3	2	3	4	3	5	2	4	1
2	9	1	7	17	9	9	9	4	4
1	1	1	3	1	6	3	3	2	5
1	3	3	14	2	3	9	6	6	3
5	1	4	6	11	22	1	9	6	5
2	2	5	4	3	6	1	5	1	6
17	1	2	4	5	4	4	3	2	3
3	5	2	3	3	2	10	2	4	2

Data Set: HOSPLOS

```
LOS t Test

  Summary Statistics          Test Summary

     Count     100                 Ho:              μ = 5
     Mean      4.53                Ha:    Lower tail: μ < 5
     Std Dev   3.678               df:              99
     Std Error 0.368       t Statistic:           -1.28
                               p-value:           0.1021


                             Test Results

                             Conclusion

                             Fail to reject Ho at alpha = 0.05
```

Figure 6.11

Excel/DDXL printout for the hypothesis test of Example 6.6

on the printout. Because the p-value exceeds our selected α value, $\alpha = .05$, we cannot reject the null hypothesis. Hence, there is insufficient evidence (at $\alpha = .05$) to conclude that the true mean LOS at the hospital is less than 5 days.

Now Work Exercise 6.42

Note: Some statistical software packages (e.g., SPSS) will conduct only two-tailed tests of hypothesis. For these packages, you obtain the p-value for a one-tailed test as shown in the box:

Converting a Two-Tailed p-Value from a Printout to a One-Tailed p-value

$$p = \frac{\text{Reported } p\text{-value}}{2} \quad \text{if} \begin{cases} H_a \text{ is of form} > \text{ and } z \text{ is positive} \\ H_a \text{ is of form} < \text{ and } z \text{ is negative} \end{cases}$$

$$p = 1 - \left(\frac{\text{Reported } p\text{-value}}{2} \right) \quad \text{if} \begin{cases} H_a \text{ is of form} > \text{ and } z \text{ is negative} \\ H_a \text{ is of form} < \text{ and } z \text{ is positive} \end{cases}$$

Statistics IN Action | **Revisited** | **Testing a Population Mean**

Refer to Kimberly-Clark Corp.'s survey of 250 people who kept a count of their use of Kleenex® tissues in diaries (pp. 319–320). We want to test the claim made by marketing experts that $\mu = 60$ is the average number of tissues used by people with colds against our belief that the population mean is smaller than 60 tissues—that is, we want to test

$$H_0 : \mu = 60 \quad H_a : \mu < 60$$

We will select $\alpha = .05$ as the level of significance for the test.

The survey results for the 250 sampled Kleenex® users are stored in the **TISSUES** data file. A Minitab analysis of the data yielded the printout displayed in Figure SIA6.1.

The observed significance level of the test, highlighted on the printout, is p-value $= .018$. Because this p-value is

less than $\alpha = .05$, we have sufficient evidence to reject H_0; therefore, we conclude that the mean number of tissues used by a person with a cold is less than 60 tissues.

[*Note:* If we conduct the same test using $\alpha = .01$ as the level of significance, we would have insufficient evidence to reject H_0 because the p-value $= .018$ is greater than $\alpha = .01$. Thus, at $\alpha = .01$, there is not sufficient evidence to support our alternative that the population mean is less than 60.]

🔘 *Data Set:* TISSUES

```
Test of mu = 60 vs < 60
```

Figure SIA6.1
Minitab test of $\mu = 60$ for Kleenex® survey

Variable	N	Mean	StDev	SE Mean	95% Upper Bound	T	P
NUMUSED	250	56.6760	25.0343	1.5833	59.2900	-2.10	0.018

Exercises 6.34–6.48

Learning the Mechanics

6.34 If a hypothesis test were conducted using $\alpha = .05$, for which of the following p-values would the null hypothesis be rejected?
  a. .06   **b.** .10
  c. .01   **d.** .001
  e. .251   **f.** .042

6.35 For each α and observed significance level (p-value) pair, indicate whether the null hypothesis would be rejected.
  a. $\alpha = .05$, p-value $= .10$

  b. $\alpha = .10$, p-value $= .05$
  c. $\alpha = .01$, p-value $= .001$
  d. $\alpha = .025$, p-value $= .05$
  e. $\alpha = .10$, p-value $= .45$

6.36 In a test of the hypothesis $H_0 : \mu = 50$ versus $H_a : \mu > 50$, a sample of $n = 100$ observations possessed mean $\bar{x} = 49.4$ and standard deviation $s = 4.1$. Find and interpret the p-value for this test.

6.37 In a test of $H_0 : \mu = 100$ against $H_a : \mu > 100$, the sample data yielded the test statistic $z = 2.17$. Find and interpret the p-value for the test.

6.38 In a test of the hypothesis $H_0: \mu = 10$ versus $H_a: \mu \neq 10$, a sample of $n = 50$ observations possessed mean $\bar{x} = 10.7$ and standard deviation $s = 3.1$. Find and interpret the *p*-value for this test.

6.39 In a test of $H_0: \mu = 100$ against $H_a: \mu \neq 100$, the sample data yielded the test statistic $z = 2.17$. Find the *p*-value for the test.

6.40 In a test of $H_0: \mu = 75$ performed using the computer, SPSS reports a two-tailed *p*-value of .1032. Make the appropriate conclusion for each of the following situations:
  a. $H_a: \mu < 75$, $z = -1.63$, $\alpha = .05$
  b. $H_a: \mu < 75$, $z = 1.63$, $\alpha = .10$
  c. $H_a: \mu > 75$, $z = 1.63$, $\alpha = .10$
  d. $H_a: \mu \neq 75$, $z = -1.63$, $\alpha = .01$

6.41 An analyst tested the null hypothesis $\mu \geq 20$ against the alternative hypothesis that $\mu < 20$. The analyst reported a *p*-value of .06. What is the smallest value of α for which the null hypothesis would be rejected?

Applying the Concepts—Basic

6.42 **Prices of hybrid cars.** Refer to the *BusinessWeek.com* listing of the July 2006 dealer prices for the hybrid Toyota Prius, Exercise 6.24 (p. 334). Recall that the data are saved in the **HYBRIDCARS** file. The results of the test of $H_0: \mu = 25,000$ versus $H_a: \mu \neq 25.000$ is shown in the Minitab printout below. Find and interpret the *p*-value of the test.

6.43 **Size of diamonds sold at retail.** Refer to the carat data for 308 diamonds saved in the **DIAMONDS** file. In Exercise 6.26 (p. 335), you tested $H_0: \mu = .6$ against $H_a: \mu \neq .6$ based on a random sample of 30 diamonds.
  a. Use a statistical software package to find the *p*-value of the test.
  b. Compare the *p*-value to $\alpha = .05$ and make the appropriate conclusion.

6.44 **Testing mean weight of golf tees.** In Exercise 6.27 (p. 335), you tested $H_0: \mu = .250$ versus $H_a: \mu \neq .250$, where μ is the population mean weight of plastic golf tees. Recall that the data are saved in the **TEES** file. An SPSS printout for the hypothesis test is shown below. Locate the *p*-value on the printout and interpret its value.

6.45 **Revenue for a full-service funeral.** Refer to the National Funeral Directors Association study of the average fee charged for a full-service funeral, Exercise 6.30 (p. 335). Recall that a test was conducted to determine if the true mean fee charged exceeds \$6,500. The data (saved in the **FUNERAL** file) for the sample of 36 funeral homes were analyzed using Excel/DDXL. The resulting printout of the test of hypothesis is shown below.
  a. Locate the *p*-value for this upper-tailed test of hypothesis.
  b. Use the *p*-value to make a decision regarding the null hypothesis tested. Does the decision agree with your decision in Exercise 6.30?

Minitab Output for Exercise 6.42

```
Test of mu = 25000 vs not = 25000


Variable    N      Mean    StDev   SE Mean       95% CI           T      P
PRICE      160   25476.7   2429.8    192.1   (25097.3, 25856.1)  2.48   0.014
```

SPSS Output for Exercise 6.44

One-Sample Test

	\multicolumn{6}{c}{Test Value = .250}				
	t	df	Sig. (2-tailed)	Mean Difference	95% Confidence Interval of the Difference Lower	95% Confidence Interval of the Difference Upper
WEIGHT	7.019	39	.000	.002475	.00176	.00319

Excel/DDXL Output for Exercise 6.45

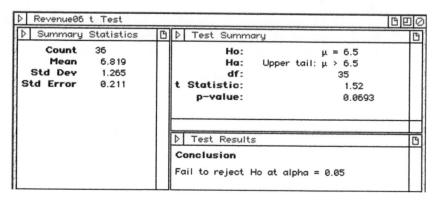

Applying the Concepts—Intermediate

6.46 **Feminized faces in TV commercials.** Television commercials most often employ females, or "feminized" males, to pitch a company's product. Research published in *Nature* (Aug. 27, 1998) revealed that people are, in fact, more attracted to "feminized" faces, regardless of gender. In one experiment, 50 human subjects viewed both a Japanese female face and a Caucasian male face on a computer. Using special computer graphics, each subject could morph the faces (by making them more feminine or more masculine) until they attained the "most attractive" face. The level of feminization x (measured as a percentage) was measured.

   a. For the Japanese female face, $\bar{x} = 10.2\%$ and $s = 31.3\%$. The researchers used this sample information to test the null hypothesis of a mean level of feminization equal to 0%. Verify that the test statistic is equal to 2.3.

   b. Refer to part **a.** The researchers reported the p-value of the test as $p = .021$. Verify and interpret this result.

   c. For the Caucasian male face, $\bar{x} = 15.0\%$ and $s = 25.1\%$. The researchers reported the test statistic (for the test of the null hypothesis stated in part **a**) as 4.23 with an associated p-value of approximately 0. Verify and interpret these results.

6.47 **Buy-side vs. sell-side analysts' earnings forecasts.** Refer to the *Financial Analysts Journal* (Jul./Aug. 2008) study of earnings forecasts of buy-side and sell-side analysts, Exercise 2.84 (p. 76). Buy-side analysts differ from sell-side analysts on a variety of factors, including scope of industry coverage, sources of information used, and target audience. Recall that data were collected on 3,526 forecasts made by buy-side analysts and 58,562 forecasts made by sell-side analysts, and the relative absolute forecast error was determined for each. A positive forecast error indicates that the analyst is overestimating earnings, while a negative forecast error implies that the analyst is underestimating earnings. Summary statistics for the forecast errors in the two samples are reproduced in the next table.

	Buy-Side Analysts	Sell-Side Analysts
Mean	0.85	−0.05
Standard Deviation	1.93	0.85

Source: Groysberg, B., Healy, P., and Chapman, C. "Buy-side vs. sell-side analysts' earnings forecast," *Financial Analysts Journal*, Vol. 64, No. 4, Jul./Aug. 2008.

   a. Conduct a test (at $\alpha = .01$) to determine if the true mean forecast error for buy-side analysts is positive. Use the observed significance level (p-value) of the test to make your decision and state your conclusion in the words of the problem.

   b. Conduct a test (at $\alpha = .01$) to determine if the true mean forecast error for sell-side analysts is negative. Use the observed significance level (p-value) of the test to make your decision and state your conclusion in the words of the problem.

Applying the Concepts—Advanced

6.48 **Ages of cable TV shoppers.** In a paper presented at the 2000 Conference of the International Association for Time Use Research, Professor Margaret Sanik of Ohio State University reported the results of her study on American cable TV viewers who purchase items from one of the home shopping channels. She found that the average age of these cable TV shoppers was 51 years. Suppose you want to test the null hypothesis, $H_0: \mu = 51$, using a sample of $n = 50$ cable TV shoppers.

   a. Find the p-value of a two-tailed test if $\bar{x} = 52.3$ and $s = 7.1$.

   b. Find the p-value of an upper-tailed test if $\bar{x} = 52.3$ and $s = 7.1$.

   c. Find the p-value of a two-tailed test if $\bar{x} = 52.3$ and $s = 10.4$,

   d. For each of the tests, parts **a–c**, give a value of α that will lead to a rejection of the null hypothesis.

   e. If $\bar{x} = 52.3$, give a value of s that will yield a two-tailed p-value of .01 or less.

6.5 Test of Hypothesis about a Population Mean: Student's t-Statistic

A manufacturing operation consists of a single-machine-tool system that produces an average of 15.5 transformer parts every hour. After undergoing a complete overhaul, the system was monitored by observing the number of parts produced in each of 17 randomly selected 1-hour periods. The mean and standard deviation for the 17 production runs are

$$\bar{x} = 15.42 \qquad s = .16$$

Does this sample provide sufficient evidence to conclude that the true mean number of parts produced every hour by the overhauled system differs from 15.5?

   This inference can be placed in a test of hypothesis framework. We establish the preoverhaul mean as the null hypothesized value and use a two-tailed alternative that the true mean of the overhauled system differs from the preoverhaul mean:

   $H_0: \mu = 15.5$ (Mean of overhauled system equals 15.5 parts per hour.)

   $H_a: \mu \neq 15.5$ (Mean of overhauled system differs from 15.5 parts per hour.)

   Recall from Section 5.3 that when we are faced with making inferences about a population mean using the information in a small sample, two problems emerge:

   1. The normality of the sampling distribution for $\bar{x}$ does not follow from the Central Limit Theorem when the sample size is small. We must assume that the distribution of measurements from which the sample was selected is approximately normally distributed in order to ensure the approximate normality of the sampling distribution of $\bar{x}$.

2. If the population standard deviation σ is unknown, as is usually the case, then we cannot assume that s will provide a good approximation for σ when the sample size is small. Instead, we must use the *t*-distribution rather than the standard normal *z*-distribution to make inferences about the population mean μ.

Therefore, as the test statistic of a small-sample test of a population mean, we use the *t*-statistic:

$$Test\ statistic:\ t = \frac{\bar{x} - \mu_0}{s/\sqrt{n}} = \frac{\bar{x} - 15.5}{s/\sqrt{n}}$$

where μ_0 is the null hypothesized value of the population mean μ. In our example, $\mu_0 = 15.5$.

To find the rejection region, we must specify the value of α, the probability that the test will lead to rejection of the null hypothesis when it is true, and then consult the *t*-table (Table V in Appendix B). Using $\alpha = .05$, the two-tailed rejection region is

$$Rejection\ region:\ t_{\alpha/2} = t_{.025} = 2.120 \text{ with } n - 1 = 16 \text{ df}$$
$$Reject\ H_0 \text{ if } t < -2.120 \text{ or } t > 2.120$$

The rejection region is shown in Figure 6.12.

We are now prepared to calculate the test statistic and reach a conclusion:

$$t = \frac{\bar{x} - \mu_0}{s/\sqrt{n}} = \frac{15.42 - 15.50}{.16/\sqrt{n}} = \frac{-.08}{.0388} = -2.06$$

Because the calculated value of *t* does not fall in the rejection region (Figure 6.12), we cannot reject H_0 at the $\alpha = .05$ level of significance. Based on the sample evidence, we should not conclude that the mean number of parts produced per hour by the overhauled system differs from 15.5.

It is interesting to note that the calculated *t*-value, -2.06, is *less than* $-z_{.05} = -1.96$. The implication is that if we had *incorrectly* used a *z*-statistic for this test, we would have rejected the null hypothesis at $\alpha = .05$, concluding that the mean production per hour of the overhauled system differs from 15.5 parts. The important point is that the statistical procedure to be used must always be closely scrutinized, with all the assumptions understood. Many statistical distortions are the result of misapplications of otherwise valid procedures.

Figure 6.12
Two-tailed rejection region for small-sample *t*-test

The technique for conducting a small-sample test of hypothesis about a population mean is summarized in the following box.

Small-Sample Test of Hypothesis about μ

One-Tailed Test	Two-Tailed Test
$H_0: \mu = \mu_0$	$H_0: \mu = \mu_0$
$H_a: \mu < \mu_0$ (or $H_a: \mu > \mu_0$)	$H_a: \mu \neq \mu_0$
Test statistic: $t = \dfrac{\bar{x} - \mu_0}{s/\sqrt{n}}$	Test statistic: $t = \dfrac{\bar{x} - \mu_0}{s/\sqrt{n}}$
Rejection region: $t < -t_\alpha$ (or $t > t_\alpha$ when $H_a: \mu > \mu_0$)	Rejection region: $\lvert t \rvert > t_{\alpha/2}$

where t_α and $t_{\alpha/2}$ are based on $(n - 1)$ degrees of freedom

> **Conditions Required for a Valid Small-Sample Hypothesis Test for μ**
>
> 1. A random sample is selected from the target population.
> 2. The population from which the sample is selected has a distribution that is approximately normal.

Example 6.7

Conducting a Small–Sample Test for μ—Does a New Engine Meet Air Pollution Standards?

Problem A major car manufacturer wants to test a new engine to determine whether it meets new air pollution standards. The mean emission μ of all engines of this type must be less than 20 parts per million of carbon. Ten engines are manufactured for testing purposes, and the emission level of each is determined. The data (in parts per million) are listed in Table 6.5.

Do the data supply sufficient evidence to allow the manufacturer to conclude that this type of engine meets the pollution standard? Assume that the production process is stable and the manufacturer is willing to risk a Type I error with probability $\alpha = .01$.

Table 6.5	Emission Levels for Ten Engines								
15.6	16.2	22.5	20.5	16.4	19.4	19.6	17.9	12.7	14.9

Data Set: EMISSIONS

Solution The manufacturer wants to support the research hypothesis that the mean emission level μ for all engines of this type is less than 20 parts per million. The elements of this small-sample one-tailed test are

$$H_0: \mu = 20 \qquad \text{(Mean emission level equals 20 ppm.)}$$
$$H_a: \mu < 20 \qquad \text{(Mean emission level is less than 20 ppm—i.e., engine meets pollution standard.)}$$

$$\text{Test statistic: } t = \frac{\bar{x} - 20}{s/\sqrt{n}}$$

Rejection region: For $\alpha = .01$ and df $= n - 1 = 9$, the one-tailed rejection region (see Figure 6.13) is $t < -t_{.01} = -2.821$.

Assumption: The relative frequency distribution of the population of emission levels for all engines of this type is approximately normal. Based on the shape of the Minitab stem-and-leaf display of the data shown in Figure 6.14, this assumption appears to be reasonably satisfied.

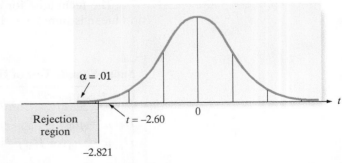

Figure 6.13

A *t*-distribution with 9 df and the rejection region for Example 6.7

To calculate the test statistic, we entered the data into a computer and analyzed it using Minitab. The Minitab printout is shown in Figure 6.14. From the printout, we obtain $\bar{x} = 17.57$, $s = 2.95$. Substituting these values into the test statistic formula, we get

$$t = \frac{\bar{x} - 20}{s/\sqrt{n}} = \frac{17.57 - 20}{2.95/\sqrt{10}} = -2.60$$

Stem-and-Leaf Display: E-LEVEL

```
Stem-and-leaf of E-LEVEL   N = 10
Leaf Unit = 1.0


   1     1   2
   3     1   45
  (3)    1   667
   4     1   99
   2     2   0
   1     2   2
```

One-Sample T: E-LEVEL

```
Test of mu = 20 vs < 20
```

					95% Upper		
Variable	N	Mean	StDev	SE Mean	Bound	T	P
E-LEVEL	10	17.5700	2.9522	0.9336	19.2814	-2.60	0.014

Figure 6.14
Minitab analysis of 10 emission levels, Example 6.7

Because the calculated *t* falls outside the rejection region (see Figure 6.13), the manufacturer cannot reject H_0. There is insufficient evidence to conclude that $\mu < 20$ parts per million. Consequently, we cannot conclude that the new engine type meets the pollution standard.

Look Back Are you satisfied with the reliability associated with this inference? The probability is only $\alpha = .01$ that the test would support the research hypothesis if, in fact, it were false.

Now Work Exercise 6.52a,b

Example 6.8

The *p*-Value for a Small-Sample Test of μ

Problem Find the observed significance level for the test described in Example 6.7. Interpret the result.

Solution The test of Example 6.7 was a lower-tailed test: H_0: $\mu = 20$ versus H_a: $\mu < 20$. Because the value of *t* computed from the sample data was $t = -2.60$, the observed significance level (or *p*-value) for the test is equal to the probability that *t* would assume a value less than or equal to −2.60 if, in fact, H_0 were true. This is equal to the area in the lower tail of the *t*-distribution (shaded in Figure 6.15).

One way to find this area (i.e., the *p*-value for the test) is to consult the *t*-table (Table V in Appendix B). Unlike the table of areas under the normal curve, Table V gives only the *t*-values corresponding to the areas .100, .050, .025, .010, .005, .001, and .0005. Therefore, we can only approximate the *p*-value for the test. Because the observed *t*-value was based on 9 degrees of freedom, we use the df = 9 row in Table V and move across the row until we reach the *t*-values that are closest to the observed $t = -2.60$. [*Note:* We ignore the minus sign.] The *t*-values corresponding to *p*-values of .010 and .025 are 2.821 and 2.262, respectively. Because the observed *t*-value falls between $t_{.010}$ and $t_{.025}$, the *p*-value for the test lies between .010 and .025. In other words, $.010 < p\text{-value} < .025$. Thus, we would reject the null hypothesis, H_0: $\mu = 20$ parts per million, for any value of α larger than .025 (the upper bound of the *p*-value).

A second, more accurate, way to obtain the *p*-value is to use a statistical software

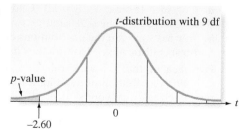

Figure 6.15
The observed significance level for the test of Example 6.7

package to conduct the test of hypothesis. The Minitab printout shown in Figure 6.14 gives both the test statistic (-2.60) and p-value (.014).

You can see that the actual p-value of the test falls within the bounds obtained from Table V. Based on the actual p-value, we will reject $H_0: \mu = 20$ in favor of $H_a: \mu < 20$ for any α level larger than .014.

Now Work Exercise 6.52c

Small-sample inferences typically require more assumptions and provide less information about the population parameter than do large-sample inferences. Nevertheless, the t-test is a method of testing a hypothesis about a population mean of a normal distribution when only a small number of observations are available. What can be done if you know that the population relative frequency distribution is decidedly nonnormal, say highly skewed?

What Can Be Done If the Population Relative Frequency Distribution Departs Greatly from Normal?

Answer: Use one of the nonparametric statistical methods of Chapter 14.

Activity 6.2   *Keep the Change:* Tests of Hypotheses

In this activity, we will test claims that the mean amount transferred for any single purchase is $0.50 and that the mean amount that Bank of America matches for a customer during the first 90 days of enrollment is at least $25. We will be working with data sets from Activity 1.1, p. 16 and Activity 4.2, p. 250.

1. Based on the assumption that all transfer amounts between $0.00 and $0.99 seem to be equally likely to occur, one may conclude that the mean of the amounts transferred is about $0.50. Explain how someone who doesn't believe this conclusion would use a test of hypothesis to argue that the conclusion is false.

2. Suppose that your original data set *Amounts Transferred* from Activity 1.1 represents a random sample of amounts transferred for all Bank of America customers' purchases. Does your sample meet the requirements for performing either a large-sample or a small-sample test of hypothesis about the population mean? Explain. If your data meet the criteria for one of the tests, perform that test at $\alpha = .05$.

3. Use the pooled data set of *Amounts Transferred* from Activity 4.2 to represent a random sample of amounts transferred for all Bank of America customers' purchases. Explain how the conditions for the large-sample test of hypothesis about a population mean are met. Then perform the test at $\alpha = .05$. Do your results suggest that the mean may be something other than $0.50? Explain.

4. A friend suggests to you that the mean amount the bank matches for a customer during the first 90 days is at least $25. Explain how you could use a test of hypothesis to argue that your friend is wrong.

5. Suppose that your data set *Bank Matching* from Activity 1.1 represents a random sample of all Bank of America customers' bank matching. Perform an appropriate test of hypotheses at $\alpha = .05$ against your friend's claim. Assume that the underlying distribution is normal, if necessary. Does the test provide evidence that your friend's claim is false?

Keep the results from this activity for use in other activities.

Exercises 6.49–6.63

Learning the Mechanics

6.49 **a.** Consider testing $H_0: \mu = 80$. Under what conditions should you use the t-distribution to conduct the test?
  b. In what ways are the distributions of the z-statistic and t-test statistic alike? How do they differ?

6.50 For each of the following rejection regions, sketch the sampling distribution of t and indicate the location of the rejection region on your sketch:
  a. $t > 1.440$ where df $= 6$
  b. $t < -1.782$ where df $= 12$
  c. $t < -2.060$ or $t > 2.060$ where df $= 25$
  d. For each of parts **a–c**, what is the probability that a Type I error will be made?

6.51 A random sample of n observations is selected from a normal population to test the null hypothesis that $\mu = 10$. Specify the rejection region for each of the following combinations of H_a, α, and n:
  a. $H_a: \mu \neq 10; \alpha = .05; n = 14$
  b. $H_a: \mu > 10; \alpha = .01; n = 24$
  c. $H_a: \mu > 10; \alpha = .10; n = 9$
  d. $H_a: \mu < 10; \alpha = .01; n = 12$
  e. $H_a: \mu \neq 10; \alpha = .10; n = 20$
  f. $H_a: \mu < 10; \alpha = .05; n = 4$

6.52 A sample of five measurements, randomly selected from a
NW normally distributed population, resulted in the following summary statistics: $\bar{x} = 4.8$, $s = 1.3$.

a. Test the null hypothesis that the mean of the population is 6 against the alternative hypothesis, $\mu < 6$. Use $\alpha = .05$.

b. Test the null hypothesis that the mean of the population is 6 against the alternative hypothesis, $\mu \neq 6$. Use $\alpha = .05$.

c. Find the observed significance level for each test.

6.53 Suppose you conduct a *t*-test for the null hypothesis $H_0: \mu = 1,000$ versus the alternative hypothesis $H_a: \mu > 1,000$ based on a sample of 17 observations. The test results are $t = 1.89$ and *p*-value $= .038$.

a. What assumptions are necessary for the validity of this procedure?

b. Interpret the results of the test.

c. Suppose the alternative hypothesis had been the two-tailed $H_a: \mu \neq 1,000$. If the *t*-statistic were unchanged, then what would the *p*-value be for this test? Interpret the *p*-value for the two-tailed test.

Applying the Concepts — Basic

6.54 **A new dental bonding agent.** When bonding teeth, orthodontists must maintain a dry field. A new bonding adhesive (called *Smartbond*) has been developed to eliminate the necessity of a dry field. However, there is concern that the new bonding adhesive is not as strong as the current standard, a composite adhesive (*Trends in Biomaterials & Artificial Organs*, Jan. 2003). Tests on a sample of 10 extracted teeth bonded with the new adhesive resulted in a mean breaking strength (after 24 hours) of $\bar{x} = 5.07$ Mpa and a standard deviation of $s = .46$ Mpa. Orthodontists want to know if the true mean breaking strength of the new bonding adhesive is less than 5.70 Mpa, the mean breaking strength of the composite adhesive.

a. Set up the null and alternative hypotheses for the test.

b. Find the rejection region for the test using $\alpha = .01$.

c. Compute the test statistic.

d. Give the appropriate conclusion for the test.

e. What conditions are required for the test results to be valid?

6.55 **Surface roughness of pipe.** Refer to the *Anti-corrosion Methods and Materials* (Vol. 50, 2003) study of the surface roughness of coated interior pipe used in oil fields, Exercise 5.30 (p. 288). The data (in micrometers) for 20 sampled pipe sections are reproduced in the next table and saved in the **ROUGHPIPE** file.

a. Give the null and alternative hypotheses for testing whether the mean surface roughness of coated interior pipe, μ, differs from 2 micrometers.

b. Find the test statistic for the hypothesis test.

c. Give the rejection region for the hypothesis test, using $\alpha = .05$.

d. State the appropriate conclusion for the hypothesis test.

e. A Minitab printout giving the test results is shown at the bottom of the page. Find and interpret the *p*-value of the test.

f. In Exercise 5.30 you found a 95% confidence interval for μ. Explain why the confidence interval and test lead to the same conclusion about μ.

1.72	2.50	2.16	2.13	1.06	2.24	2.31	2.03	1.09	1.40
2.57	2.64	1.26	2.05	1.19	2.13	1.27	1.51	2.41	1.95

Source: Farshad, F., and Pesacreta, T. "Coated pipe interior surface roughness as measured by three scanning probe instruments," *Anti-corrosion Methods and Materials*, Vol. 50, No. 1, 2003 (Table III). Copyright © 2003 MCB UP Ltd.

6.56 **Product usage index.** Information Resources, Inc., a Chicago-based research organization, tracks supermarket sales in 28 metropolitan markets in the United States. They convert their data for specific products to an index that measures product usage relative to the national average usage. For example, Green Bay, Wisconsin's, ketchup index is 143, the highest in the nation. This means that Green Bay residents consume 43% more ketchup, on average, than the mean national consumption rate. The table lists the salad dressings index for each in a sample of seven Southeastern cities. These data are saved in the **SALAD** file.

Salad Dressings Index (U.S. mean = 100)	
Charlotte, N.C.	124
Birmingham, Al.	99
Raleigh, N.C.	124
Knoxville, Tenn.	99
Memphis, Tenn.	90
Atlanta, Ga.	111
Nashville, Tenn.	89

Source: Wall Street Journal Interactive Edition, Jan. 5, 2000. Copyright 2000 by Dow Jones & Company Inc. Reproduced with permission of Dow Jones & Company, Inc. in the format Textbook via Copyright Clearance Center.

a. Specify the appropriate null and alternative hypotheses for testing whether the true mean consumption rate of salad dressings in the Southeastern United States is different than the mean national consumption rate of 100.

b. What assumptions about the sample and population must hold in order for it to be appropriate to use a *t*-statistic in conducting the hypothesis test?

Minitab Output for Exercise 6.55

One-Sample T: ROUGH

```
Test of mu = 2 vs not = 2


Variable    N     Mean    StDev   SE Mean        95% CI          T      P
ROUGH      20  1.88100  0.52391  0.11715  (1.63580, 2.12620)  -1.02  0.322
```

Excel/DDXL Output for Exercise 6.57

NUMBER t Test			
Summary Statistics		**Test Summary**	
Count	21	Ho:	$\mu = 2.5$
Mean	1.857	Ha: 2-tailed:	$\mu \neq 2.5$
Std Dev	1.195	df:	20
Std Error	0.261	t Statistic:	-2.46
		p-value:	0.0229

Test Results

Conclusion

Reject Ho at alpha = 0.10

c. Conduct the hypothesis test using $\alpha = .05$.

d. Is the observed significance level of the test greater or less than .05? Justify your answer.

6.57 **Al Qaeda attacks on the United States.** Refer to the *Studies in Conflict & Terrorism* (Vol. 29, 2006) analysis of recent incidents involving suicide terrorist attacks, Exercise 5.33 (p. 289). Data on the number of individual suicide bombings that occurred in each of 21 sampled Al Qaeda attacks against the United States is reproduced in the table. (Recall the data are saved in the **ALQAEDA** file).

a. Do the data indicate that the true mean number of suicide bombings for all Al Qaeda attacks against the United States differs from 2.5? Use $\alpha = .10$ and the accompanying Excel/DDXL printout to answer the question.

b. In Exercise 5.33 you found a 90% confidence interval for the mean, μ, of the population. Answer the question in part **a** based on the 90% confidence interval.

c. Do the inferences derived from the test (part **a**) and confidence interval (part **b**) agree? Explain why or why not.

d. What assumption about the data must be true for the inferences to be valid?

e. Use a graph to check whether the assumption, part **d**, is reasonably satisfied. Comment on the validity of the inference.

1	1	2	1	2	4	1	1	1	1	2	3	4	5	1	1	1	2	2	2	1

Source: Moghadam, A. "Suicide terrorism, occupation, and the globalization of martyrdom: A critique of *Dying to Win*," *Studies in Conflict & Terrorism*, Vol. 29, No. 8, 2006, pp. 707–729 (Table 3). Reprinted by permission of the publisher (Taylor & Francis Group, www.informaworld.com).

Applying the Concepts—Intermediate

6.58 **Spending by banks following acquisitions.** Refer to *The Nilson Report* (Oct. 2008) study of U.S. banks with recent acquisitions and mergers, Exercise 2.44 (p. 61). The amount charged to credit and debit cards issued by the banks was determined. The next table gives the total amount charged in 2007 for a sample of five banks. These data are saved in the **BANKCHARGE** file.

a. Give the null and alternative hypothesis for determining whether the mean amount charged to credit and debit cards in 2007 by all banks with recent acquisitions differs from $200 billion.

b. Use the results shown on the SPSS printout at the top of page 349 to conduct the test at $\alpha = .05$.

c. Repeat part **b**, but conduct the test at $\alpha = .10$.

d. You may recall from Exercise 2.44 that the five banks in the sample represent the top ranked banks in the United States with recent acquisitions. Explain how this sample may impact the validity of your conclusions in parts **b** and **c**.

U.S. Bank/Card Issuer	Amount Charged ($ billions)
Bank of America	462.20
JPMorgan Chase	458.84
American Express	445.32
Citigroup	240.58
Wells Fargo	192.68

Source: The Nilson Report, No. 912, October 2008 (p. 8).

6.59 **Minimizing tractor skidding distance.** Refer to the *Journal of Forest Engineering* (July 1999) study of minimizing tractor skidding distances along a new road in a European forest, Exercise 5.31 (p. 288). The skidding distances (in meters) were measured at 20 randomly selected road sites. The data (saved in the **SKIDDING** file) are repeated below. Recall that a logger working on the road claims the mean skidding distance is at least 425 meters. Is there sufficient evidence to refute this claim? Use $\alpha = .10$.

488	350	457	199	285	409	435	574	439	546
385	295	184	261	273	400	311	312	141	425

Source: Extracted from Tujek, J., and Pacola, E. "Algorithms for skidding distance modeling on a raster digital terrain model," *Journal of Forest Engineering*, Vol. 10, No. 1, July 1999 (Table 1).

SPSS Output for Exercise 6.58

One-Sample Statistics

	N	Mean	Std. Deviation	Std. Error Mean
AMOUNT	5	359.9240	132.05186	59.05539

One-Sample Test

	Test Value = 200					
					95% Confidence Interval of the Difference	
	t	df	Sig. (2-tailed)	Mean Difference	Lower	Upper
AMOUNT	2.708	4	.054	159.92400	-4.0400	323.8880

6.60 **Testing the effectiveness of a mosquito repellent.** A study was conducted to evaluate the effectiveness of a mosquito repellent designed by the U.S. Army to be applied as camouflage face paint (*Journal of the Mosquito Control Association,* June 1995). The repellent was applied to the forearms of five volunteers, and then the arms were exposed to 15 active mosquitoes for a 10-hour period. The percentage of the forearm surface area protected from bites (called *percent repellency*) was calculated for each of the five volunteers. For one color of paint (loam), the following summary statistics were obtained:

$$\bar{x} = 83\% \qquad s = 15\%$$

a. The new repellent is considered effective if it provides a percent repellency of at least 95. Conduct a test to determine whether the mean repellency percentage of the new mosquito repellent is less than 95. Test using $\alpha = .10$

b. What assumptions are required for the hypothesis test in part **a** to be valid?

6.61 **Crack intensity of paved highways.** The Mississippi Department of Transportation collected data on the number of cracks (called *crack intensity*) in an undivided two-lane highway using van-mounted, state-of-the-art video technology (*Journal of Infrastructure Systems,* Mar. 1995). The mean number of cracks found in a sample of eight 50-meter sections of the highway was $\bar{x} = .210$, with a variance of $s^2 = .011$. Suppose the American Association of State Highway and Transportation Officials (AASHTO) recommends a maximum mean crack intensity of .100 for safety purposes. Is there evidence to say that the true mean crack intensity of the Mississippi highway exceeds the AASHTO recommended maximum? Use $\alpha = .01$ in the test.

6.62 **Active nuclear power plants.** Refer to the U.S. Energy Information Administration's list of active nuclear power plants operating in each of a sample of 20 states, Exercise 2.54 (p. 63). The data, saved in the **NUCLEAR** file, are reproduced in the next table.

a. Is there sufficient evidence to claim that the mean number of active nuclear power plants operating in all states exceeds 3? Test using $\alpha = .10$.

b. Are the conditions required for a valid small-sample test reasonably satisfied? Explain.

c. Eliminate the lowest two values and the highest two values from the data set, then conduct the test of part **a** on the smaller data set. What impact does this have on the test results?

d. Why is it dangerous to eliminate data points in order to satisfy an assumption for a test of hypothesis?

State	Number of Power Plants	State	Number of Power Plants
Alabama	5	New Hampshire	1
Arizona	3	New York	6
California	4	North Carolina	5
Florida	5	Ohio	3
Georgia	4	Pennsylvania	9
Illinois	11	South Carolina	7
Kansas	1	Tennessee	3
Louisiana	2	Texas	4
Massachusetts	1	Vermont	1
Mississippi	3	Wisconsin	3

Source: Statistical Abstract of the United States, 2005 (Table 906). U.S. Energy Information Administration, Electric Power Annual.

Applying the Concepts—Advanced

6.63 **Arsenic in smelters.** The Occupational Safety and Health Act (OSHA) allows issuance of engineering standards to ensure safe workplaces for all Americans. The maximum allowable mean level of arsenic in smelters, herbicide production facilities, and other places where arsenic is used is .004 milligrams per cubic meter of air. Suppose smelters at two plants are being investigated to determine whether they are meeting OSHA standards. Two analyses of the air are made at each plant, and the results (in milligrams per cubic meter of air) are shown in the table. The data are saved in the **ARSENIC** file. A claim is made that the OSHA standard is violated at Plant 2 but not at Plant 1. Do you agree?

Plant 1		Plant 2	
Observation	Arsenic Level	Observation	Arsenic Level
1	.01	1	.05
2	.005	2	.09

6.6 Large–Sample Test of Hypothesis about a Population Proportion

Inferences about population proportions (or percentages) are often made in the context of the probability, p, of "success" for a binomial distribution. We saw how to use large samples from binomial distributions to form confidence intervals for p in Section 5.4. We now consider tests of hypotheses about p.

For example, consider the problem of *insider trading* in the stock market. Insider trading is the buying and selling of stock by an individual privy to inside information in a company, usually a high-level executive in the firm. The Securities and Exchange Commission (SEC) imposes strict guidelines about insider trading so that all investors can have equal access to information that may affect the stock's price. An investor wishing to test the effectiveness of the SEC guidelines monitors the market for a period of a year and records the number of times a stock price increases the day following a significant purchase of stock by an insider. For a total of 576 such transactions, the stock increased the following day 327 times. Does this sample provide evidence that the stock price may be affected by insider trading?

We first view this as a binomial experiment, with the 576 transactions as the trials, with success representing an increase in the stock's price the following day. Let p represent the probability that the stock price will increase following a large insider purchase. If the insider purchase has no effect on the stock price (that is, if the information available to the insider is identical to that available to the general market), then the investor expects the probability of a stock increase to be the same as that of a decrease, or $p = .5$. On the other hand, if insider trading affects the stock price (indicating that the market has not fully accounted for the information known to the insiders), then the investor expects the stock either to decrease or to increase more than half the time following significant insider transactions; that is, $p \neq .5$.

We can now place the problem in the context of a test of hypothesis:

$$H_0: p = .5 \text{ (Probability of stock increase equals .5—}$$
$$\text{i.e., insider purchase has no effect on stock price.)}$$

$$H_a: p \neq .5 \text{ (Probability of stock increase differs from .5—}$$
$$\text{i.e., insider trading effects stock price.)}$$

Recall that the sample proportion, $\hat{p}$, is really just the sample mean of the outcomes of the individual binomial trials and, as such, is approximately normally distributed (for large samples) according to the Central Limit Theorem. Thus, for large samples, we can use the standard normal z as the test statistic:

$$\textit{Test statistic: } z = \frac{\text{Sample proportion} - \text{Null hypothesized proportion}}{\text{Standard deviation of sample proportion}}$$

$$= \frac{\hat{p} - p_0}{\sigma_{\hat{p}}}$$

where we use the symbol p_0 to represent the null hypothesized value of p.

Rejection region: We use the standard normal distribution to find the appropriate rejection region for the specified value of α. Using $\alpha = .05$, the two-tailed rejection region is

$$z < -z_{\alpha/2} = -z_{.025} = -1.96 \text{ or } z > z_{\alpha/2} = z_{.025} = 1.96$$

See Figure 6.16.

We are now prepared to calculate the value of the test statistic. Before doing so, we want to be sure that the sample size is large enough to ensure that the normal approximation for the sampling distribution of $\hat{p}$ is reasonable. Recall from Section 5.4 that we require both np and nq to be at least 15. Because the null hypothesized value, p_0, is assumed to be the true value of p until our test procedure indicates otherwise, then we check to see if $np_0 \geq 15$ and $nq_0 \geq 15$ (where $q_0 = 1 - p_0$). Now, $np_0 = (576)(.5) = 288$ and $nq_0 = (576)(.5) = 288$;

Figure 6.16

Rejection region for insider trading example

therefore, the normal distribution will provide a reasonable approximation for the sampling distribution of $\hat{p}$.

Returning to the hypothesis test at hand, the proportion of the sampled transactions that resulted in a stock increase is

$$\hat{p} = \frac{327}{576} = .568$$

Finally, we calculate the number of standard deviations (the z-value) between the sampled and hypothesized value of the binomial proportion:

$$z = \frac{\hat{p} - p_0}{\sigma_{\hat{p}}} = \frac{\hat{p} - p_0}{\sqrt{p_0 q_0 / n}} = \frac{.568 - .5}{.021} = \frac{.068}{.021} = 3.24$$

The implication is that the observed sample proportion is (approximately) 3.24 standard deviations above the null hypothesized proportion .5 (Figure 6.16). Therefore, we reject the null hypothesis, concluding at the .05 level of significance that the true probability of an increase or decrease in a stock's price differs from .5 the day following insider purchase of the stock. It appears that an insider purchase significantly increases the probability that the stock price will increase the following day. (To estimate the magnitude of the probability of an increase, a confidence interval can be constructed.)

The test of hypothesis about a population proportion p is summarized in the next box. Note that the procedure is entirely analogous to that used for conducting large-sample tests about a population mean.

Large-Sample Test of Hypothesis about p

One-Tailed Test	Two-Tailed Test
H_0: $p = p_0$	H_0: $p = p_0$
H_a: $p < p_0$ (or H_a: $p > p_0$)	H_a: $p \neq p_0$
Test statistic: $z = \dfrac{\hat{p} - p_0}{\sigma_{\hat{p}}}$	Test statistic: $z = \dfrac{\hat{p} - p_0}{\sigma_{\hat{p}}}$

where, according to H_0, $\sigma_{\hat{p}} = \sqrt{p_0 q_0 / n}$ and $q_0 = 1 - p_0$

Rejection region:	Rejection region: $|z| > z_{\alpha/2}$
$z < -z_\alpha$ (or $z > z_\alpha$ when H_a: $p > p_0$)	

Note: p_0 is the symbol for the numerical value of p assigned in the null hypothesis.

Conditions Required for a Valid Large-Sample Hypothesis Test for p

1. A random sample is selected from a binomial population.

2. The sample size n is large. (This condition will be satisfied if both $np_0 \geq 15$ and $nq_0 \geq 15$.)

Example 6.9

Conducting a Hypothesis Test for p, the Proportion of Defective Batteries

Problem The reputations (and hence sales) of many businesses can be severely damaged by shipments of manufactured items that contain a large percentage of defectives. For example, a manufacturer of alkaline batteries may want to be reasonably certain that fewer than 5% of its batteries are defective. Suppose 300 batteries are randomly selected from a very large shipment; each is tested, and 10 defective batteries are found. Does this provide sufficient evidence for the manufacturer to conclude that the fraction defective in the entire shipment is less than .05? Use $\alpha = .01$.

Solution The objective of the sampling is to determine whether there is sufficient evidence to indicate that the fraction defective, p, is less than .05. Consequently, we will test the null hypothesis that $p = .05$ against the alternative hypothesis that $p < .05$. The elements of the test are

$$H_0: p = .05 \text{ (Fraction of defective batteries equals .05.)}$$

$$H_a: p < .05 \text{ (Fraction of defective batteries is less than .05.)}$$

$$\text{Test statistic: } z = \frac{\hat{p} - p_0}{\sigma_{\hat{p}}}$$

$$\text{Rejection region: } z < -z_{.01} = -2.33 \text{ (see Figure 6.17)}$$

Before conducting the test, we check to determine whether the sample size is large enough to use the normal approximation to the sampling distribution of $\hat{p}$. Because $np_0 = (300)(.05) = 15$ and $nq_0 = (300)(.95) = 285$ are both at least 15, the normal approximation will be adequate.

We now calculate the test statistic:

$$z = \frac{\hat{p} - .05}{\sigma_{\hat{p}}} = \frac{(10/300) - .05}{\sqrt{p_0 q_0/n}} = \frac{.03333 - .05}{\sqrt{p_0 q_0/300}}$$

Notice that we use p_0 to calculate $\sigma_{\hat{p}}$ because, in contrast to calculating $\sigma_{\hat{p}}$ for a confidence interval, the test statistic is computed on the assumption that the null hypothesis is true— that is, $p = p_0$. Therefore, substituting the values for $\hat{p}$ and p_0 into the z-statistic, we obtain

$$z \approx \frac{-.01667}{\sqrt{(.05)(.95)/300}} = \frac{-.01667}{.0126} = -1.32$$

As shown in Figure 6.17, the calculated z-value does not fall in the rejection region. Therefore, there is insufficient evidence at the .01 level of significance to indicate that the shipment contains fewer than 5% defective batteries.

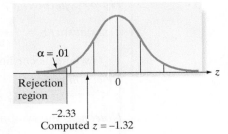

Figure 6.17
Rejection region for Example 6.9

Now Work Exercise 6.64a, b

Example 6.10

The p–Value for a Test about p

Problem In Example 6.9 we found that we did not have sufficient evidence, at the $\alpha = .01$ level of significance, to indicate that the fraction defective p of alkaline batteries was less than $p = .05$. How strong was the weight of evidence favoring the alternative hypothesis ($H_a: p < .05$)? Find the observed significance level for the test.

Solution The computed value of the test statistic z was $z = -1.32$. Therefore, for this lower-tailed test, the observed significance level is

$$\text{Observed significance level} = P(z \leq -1.32)$$

This lower-tail area is shown in Figure 6.18. The area between $z = 0$ and $z = 1.32$ is given in Table IV in Appendix B as .4066. Therefore, the observed significance level is $.5 - .4066 = .0934$.

Note: The observed significance level can also be obtained with statistical software. The Minitab printout shown in Figure 6.19 gives the p-value (highlighted).

Figure 6.18
The observed significance level for Example 6.10

Look Back Although we did not reject $H_0: p = .05$ at $\alpha = .01$, the probability of observing a z-value as small as or smaller than -1.32 is only .0934 if, in fact, H_0 is true.

Test and CI for One Proportion

Test of p = 0.05 vs p < 0.05

Sample	X	N	Sample p	95% Upper Bound	Z-Value	P-Value
1	10	300	0.033333	0.050380	-1.32	0.093

Using the normal approximation.

Figure 6.19
Minitab lower-tailed test of p, Example 6.10

Therefore, we would reject H_0 if we choose $\alpha = .10$ (because the observed significance level is less than .10), and we would not reject H_0 (the conclusion of Example 6.9) if we choose $\alpha = .05$ or $\alpha = .01$.

Now Work Exercise 6.64c

Small-sample test procedures are also available for p, although most surveys use samples that are large enough to employ the large-sample tests presented in this section. A test of proportions that can be applied to small samples is discussed in Chapter 9.

Statistics ɪN Action | **Revisited** | ## Testing a Population Proportion

In the previous "Statistics in Action Revisited" (p. 340), we investigated Kimberly-Clark Corp.'s assertion that the company should put 60 tissues in a cold-care box of Kleenex® tissues. We did this by testing the claim that the mean number of tissues used by a person with a cold is $\mu = 60$, using data collected from a survey of 250 Kleenex® users. Another approach to the problem is to consider the proportion of Kleenex® users who use fewer than 60 tissues when they have a cold. Now the population parameter of interest is p, the proportion of all Kleenex® users who use fewer than 60 tissues when they have a cold.

Kimberly-Clark Corp.'s belief that the company should put 60 tissues in a cold-care box will be supported if the *median* number of tissues used is 60. Now, if the true median is, in fact, 60, then half of the Kleenex® users will use less than 60 tissues and half will use more than 60 tissues (i.e., $p = .5$). Is there evidence to indicate that the population proportion differs from .5? To answer this question, we set up the following null and alternative hypotheses:

$$H_0: p = .5 \qquad H_a: p \neq .5$$

Recall that the survey results for the 250 sampled Kleenex® users are stored in the **TISSUES** data file. In addition to the number of tissues used by each person, the file contains a qualitative variable—called USED60—representing whether the person used fewer or more than 60 tissues. (The values of USED60 in the data set are "BELOW" or "ABOVE.") A Minitab analysis of this variable yielded the printout displayed in Figure SIA6.2.

On the Minitab printout, X represents the number of the 250 people with colds who used less than 60 tissues. Note that $X = 143$. This value is used to compute the test statistic, $z = 2.28$, highlighted on the printout. The p-value of the test, also highlighted on the printout, is .023. Because this value is less than $\alpha = .05$, there is sufficient evidence (at $\alpha = .05$) to reject H_0; we conclude that the proportion of all Kleenex® users who use fewer than 60 tissues when they have a cold differs from .5. However, if we test at $\alpha = .01$, there is insufficient evidence to reject H_0. Consequently, our choice of α (as in the previous "Statistics in the Action Revisited") is critical to our decision.

Data Set: TISSUES

Test of p = 0.5 vs p not = 0.5

Event = BELOW

Figure SIA6.2
Minitab test of $p = .5$ for Kleenex® survey

Variable	X	N	Sample p	95% CI	Z-Value	P-Value
USED60	143	250	0.572000	(0.510666, 0.633334)	2.28	0.023

Exercises 6.64–6.79

Learning the Mechanics

6.64 Suppose a random sample of 100 observations from a binomial population gives a value of $\hat{p} = .63$ and you wish to test the null hypothesis that the population parameter p is equal to .70 against the alternative hypothesis that p is less than .70.
   a. Noting that $\hat{p} = .63$, what does your intuition tell you? Does the value of $\hat{p}$ appear to contradict the null hypothesis?
   b. Use the large-sample z-test to test $H_0: p = .70$ against the alternative hypothesis, $H_a: p < .70$. Use $\alpha = .05$. How do the test results compare with your intuitive decision from part **a**?
   c. Find and interpret the observed significance level of the test you conducted in part **b**.

6.65 Suppose the sample in Exercise 6.64 has produced $\hat{p} = .83$ and we wish to test $H_0: p = .9$ against the alternative $H_a: p < .9$.
   a. Calculate the value of the z-statistic for this test.
   b. Note that the numerator of the z-statistic ($\hat{p} - p_0 = .83 - .90 = -.07$) is the same as for Exercise 6.64. Considering this, why is the absolute value of z for this exercise larger than that calculated in Exercise 6.64?
   c. Complete the test using $\alpha = .05$ and interpret the result.
   d. Find the observed significance level for the test and interpret its value.

6.66 A statistics student used a computer program to test the null hypothesis $H_0: p = .5$ against the one-tailed alternative, $H_a: p > .5$. A sample of 500 observations are input into SPSS, which returns the following results: $z = .44$, two-tailed p-value = .33.
   a. The student concludes, based on the p-value, that there is a 33% chance that the alternative hypothesis is true. Do you agree? If not, correct the interpretation.
   b. How would the p-value change if the alternative hypothesis was two-tailed, $H_a: p \neq .5$? Interpret this p-value.

6.67 Refer to Exercise 5.40 (p. 295), in which 50 consumers taste-tested a new snack food. Their responses (where $0 =$ do not like; $1 =$ like; $2 =$ indifferent) are reproduced below and saved in the **SNACK** file.
   a. Test $H_0: p = .5$ against $H_a: p > .5$, where p is the proportion of customers who do not like the snack food. Use $\alpha = .10$.
   b. Find the observed significance level of your test.

1	0	0	1	2	0	1	1	0	0	0	1
0	2	0	2	2	0	0	1	1	0	0	0
0	1	0	2	0	0	0	1	0	0	1	0
0	1	0	1	0	2	0	0	1	1	0	0
0	1

6.68 For the binomial sample sizes and null hypothesized values of p in each part, determine whether the sample size is large enough to use the normal approximation methodology presented in this section to conduct a test of the null hypothesis $H_0: p = p_0$.
   a. $n = 900, p_0 = .975$ **b.** $n = 125, p_0 = .01$
   c. $n = 40, p_0 = .75$ **d.** $n = 15, p_0 = .75$
   e. $n = 12, p_0 = .62$

⊙ **Applet Exercise 6.5**

Use the applet *Hypotheses Test for a Proportion* to investigate the relationships between the probabilities of Type I and Type II errors occurring at level .05 and .01. For this exercise, use $n = 100$, true $p = 0.5$, and alternative *not equal*.
   a. Set null $p = .5$. What happens to the proportion of times the null hypothesis is rejected at the .05 level and at the .01 level as the applet is run more and more times? What type of error has occurred when the null hypothesis is rejected in this situation? Based on your results, is this type of error more likely to occur at level .05 or at level .01? Explain.
   b. Set null $p = .6$. What happens to the proportion of times the null hypothesis is *not* rejected at the .05 level and at the .01 level as the applet is run more and more times? What type of error has occurred when the null hypothesis is *not* rejected in this situation? Based on your results, is this type of error more likely to occur at level .05 or at level .01? Explain.
   c. Use your results from parts **a** and **b** to make a general statement about the probabilities of Type I and Type II errors at levels .05 and .01.

⊙ **Applet Exercise 6.6**

Use the applet *Hypotheses Test for a Proportion* to investigate the effect of the true population proportion p on the probability of a Type I error occurring. For this exercise, use $n = 100$, and alternative *not equal*.
   a. Set true $p = .5$ and null $p = .5$. Run the applet several times and record the proportion of times the null hypothesis is rejected at the .01 level.
   b. Clear the applet and repeat part **a** for true $p = .1$ and null $p = .1$. Then repeat one more time for true $p = .01$ and null $p = .01$.
   c. Based on your results from parts **a** and **b**, what can you conclude about the probability of a Type I error occurring as the true population proportion gets closer to 0?

Applying the Concepts—Basic

6.69 **Adoption of high-speed Internet connection at home.** Refer to the Pew Internet & American Life Project report on the growth of home broadband adoption in the United States, Exercise 5.47 (p. 296). Recall that in a May 2006 random-digit-dialing telephone survey of 4,000 American adults, 42% of the sample had access to a high-speed Internet connection at home. Let p represent the true proportion of all American adults who had access to a high-speed Internet connection at home in 2006.

a. Compute a point estimate of p.

b. Recall that in 2005, the Pew Internet & American Life Project reported that 30% of all American adults had access to a high-speed Internet connection at home. Set up the null and alternative hypothesis to test whether p has increased since 2005.

c. Compute the test statistic for the test, part **b.**

d. Locate the rejection region for the test if $\alpha = .01$.

e. Use the results, parts **c** and **d,** to make the appropriate conclusion.

f. Find the observed significance level of the test and confirm the conclusion stated in part **e.**

6.70 **"Made in the USA" survey.** Refer to the *Journal of Global Business* (Spring 2002) study of what "Made in the USA" means to consumers, Exercise 2.8 (p. 39). Recall that 64 of 106 randomly selected shoppers believed "Made in the USA" means 100% of labor and materials are from the United States. Let p represent the true proportion of consumers who believe "Made in the USA" means 100% of labor and materials are from the United States.

a. Calculate a point estimate for p.

b. A claim is made that $p = .70$. Set up the null and alternative hypotheses to test this claim.

c. Calculate the test statistic for the test, part **b.**

d. Find the rejection region for the test if $\alpha = .01$.

e. Use the results, parts **c** and **d,** to make the appropriate conclusion.

6.71 **History of corporate acquisitions.** Refer to the *Academy of Management Journal* (Aug. 2008) investigation of the performance and timing of corporate acquisitions, Exercise 5.49 (p. 296). Recall that the investigation discovered that in a random sample of 2,778 firms, 748 announced one or more acquisitions during the year 2000. Does the sample provide sufficient evidence to indicate that the true percentage of all firms that announced one or more acquisitions during the year 2000 is less than 30%? Use $\alpha = .05$ to make your decision.

6.72 **Accuracy of price scanners at Wal-Mart.** Refer to Exercise 5.51 (p. 296) and the study of the accuracy of checkout scanners at Wal-Mart stores in California. Recall that the National Institute for Standards and Technology (NIST) mandates that for every 100 items scanned through the electronic checkout scanner at a retail store, no more than two should have an inaccurate price. A study of random items purchased at California Wal-Mart stores found that 8.3% had the wrong price (*Tampa Tribune,* Nov. 22, 2005). Assume that the study included 1,000 randomly selected items.

a. Identify the population parameter of interest in the study.

b. Set up H_0 and H_a for a test to determine if the true proportion of items scanned at California Wal-Mart stores exceeds the 2% NIST standard.

c. Find the test statistic and rejection region (at $\alpha = .05$) for the test.

d. Give a practical interpretation of the test.

e. What conditions are required for the inference, part **d,** to be valid? Are these conditions met?

6.73 **Toothpaste brands with the ADA seal.** *Consumer Reports* evaluated and rated 46 brands of toothpaste. One attribute examined in the study was whether or not a toothpaste brand carries an American Dental Association (ADA) seal verifying effective decay prevention. The data for the 46 brands (coded 1 = ADA seal, 0 = no ADA seal) are listed here and saved in the **ADA** file.

0	0	0	0	0	0	1	1	1	0	0	1
0	1	0	0	0	0	1	1	1	0	0	1
1	1	0	0	0	0	1	0	0	1	1
1	0	1	0	1	1	1	0	0	0

a. Give the null and alternative hypotheses for testing whether the true proportion of toothpaste brands with the ADA seal verifying effective decay prevention is less than .5.

b. Locate the p-value on the Minitab printout below.

c. Make the appropriate conclusion using $\alpha = .10$.

Minitab Output for Exercise 6.73

```
Test of p = 0.5 vs p < 0.5

Event = 1

                                    95%
                                  Upper     Exact
Variable   X   N   Sample p      Bound    P-Value
ADASEAL   20  46   0.434783    0.566289     0.231
```

6.74 **Minority vacation-home owners.** The *National Association of Realtors* (NAR) reported the results of a May 2006 survey of vacation-home owners. In a sample of 416 households that owned one or more vacation homes, 46 were minorities. Prior to 2003, 6% of vacation-home owners were minorities.

a. Do the survey results allow the NAR to conclude (at $\alpha = .01$) that the percentage of vacation-home owners in 2006 who are minorities is larger than 6%?

b. The NAR sent the survey questionnaire to a nationwide sample of 45,000 households that owned vacation homes. Only 416 of the households responded to the survey. How might this bias the survey results?

Applying the Concepts—Intermediate

6.75 **Effectiveness of skin cream.** Pond's Age-Defying Complex, a cream with alpha hydroxy acid, advertises that it can reduce wrinkles and improve the skin. In a study published in *Archives of Dermatology* (June 1996), 33 middle-aged women used a cream with alpha hydroxy acid for 22 weeks. At the end of the study period, a dermatologist judged whether each woman exhibited skin improvement. The results for the 33 women (where I = improved skin and N = no improvement) are listed in the next table and saved in the **SKINCREAM** file. [Note: Pond's recently discontinued the production of this cream product, replacing it with Age-Defying Towlettes.]

a. Do the data provide sufficient evidence to conclude that the cream will improve the skin of more than 60% of middle-aged women? Test using $\alpha = .05$.

b. Find and interpret the p-value of the test.

I	I	N	N	N	N	I	I	I	I	I
N	I	I	I	N	I	I	I	N	I	N	I
I	I	I	I	I	N	I	N	I	I	N

6.76 **Reporting company changes to the SEC.** The SEC requires a company to file Form 8-K to report material changes in its financial condition or operation. Common material events are changes in directors, auditors, and assets disposition. Up until 2004, companies had 15 business days to submit Form 8-K. Currently, the SEC requires that the form be submitted within 4 business days of the material event (*Sarbanes-Oxley Act,* Section 409). Previous research has indicated that as high as 10% of firms were in violation of the old, 15-day rule. Old Dominion University Accounting Professor Rob Pinsker conducted a study to determine if firms with material changes were able to comply with the new "4-day" rule (*Information Systems Mid-Year Meeting,* 2004). In a sample of 462 firms with material events, only 23 were in violation of the new 4-day requirement for filing. Are you able to conclude that the true percentage of firms in violation of the new 4-day rule for reporting material changes is less than 10%? Make your inference at a significance level of $\alpha = .01$.

6.77 **Graduation rates of student-athletes.** Are student-athletes at Division I universities poorer students than non-athletes? The National Collegiate Athletic Association (NCAA) measures the academic outcomes of student-athletes with the Graduation Success Rate (GSR). The GSR is measured as the percentage of eligible athletes who graduate within six years of entering college. According to the NCAA, the GSR for all scholarship athletes at Division I institutions is 63% (*Inside Higher Ed,* Nov. 10, 2006). It is well known that the GSR for all students at Division I colleges is 60%.

a. Suppose the NCAA report was based on a sample of 500 student-athletes, of which 315 graduated within six years. Is this sufficient information to conclude that the GSR for all scholarship athletes at Division I institutions differs from 60%? Test using $\alpha = .01$.

b. The GSR statistics were also broken down by gender and sport. For example, men's Division I college basketball players had a GSR of 42% (compared to a known GSR of 58% for all male college students). Suppose this statistic was based on a sample of 200 male basketball players, of which 84 graduated within six years. Is this sufficient information to conclude that the GSR for all male basketball players at Division I institutions differs from 58%? Test using $\alpha = .01$.

Applying the Concepts—Advanced

6.78 **Choosing portable grill displays.** Refer to the *Journal of Consumer Research* (Mar. 2003) experiment on influencing the choices of others by offering undesirable alternatives, Exercise 3.21 (p. 130). Recall that each of 124 college students selected three portable grills from five to display on the showroom floor. The students were instructed to include Grill #2 (a smaller-sized grill) and select the remaining two grills in the display to maximize purchases of Grill #2. If the six possible grill display combinations (1-2-3, 1-2-4, 1-2-5, 2-3-4, 2-3-5, and 2-4-5) are selected at random, then the proportion of students selecting any display will be $1/6 = .167$. One theory tested by the researcher is that the students will tend to choose the three-grill display so that Grill #2 is a compromise between a more desirable and a less desirable grill (i.e., display 1-2-3, 1-2-4, or 1-2-5). Of the 124 students, 85 selected a three-grill display that was consistent with this theory. Use this information to test the theory proposed by the researcher at $\alpha = .05$.

6.79 **The Pepsi Challenge.** "Take the Pepsi Challenge" was a famous marketing campaign used by the Pepsi-Cola Company. Coca-Cola drinkers participated in a blind taste test where they were asked to taste unmarked cups of Pepsi and Coke and were asked to select their favorite. In one Pepsi television commercial, an announcer states that "in recent blind taste tests, more than half the Diet Coke drinkers surveyed said they preferred the taste of Diet Pepsi." Suppose 100 Diet Coke drinkers took the Pepsi Challenge and 56 preferred the taste of Diet Pepsi. Determine if more than half of all Diet Coke drinkers will select Diet Pepsi in the blind taste test. Select α to minimize the probability of a Type I error. What are the consequences of the test results from Coca-Cola's perspective?

6.7 Calculating Type II Error Probabilities: More about β^*

In our introduction to hypothesis testing in Section 6.1, we showed that the probability of committing a Type I error, α, can be controlled by the selection of the rejection region for the test. Thus, when the test statistic falls in the rejection region and we make the decision to reject the null hypothesis, we do so knowing the error rate for incorrect rejections of H_0. The situation corresponding to accepting the null hypothesis, and thereby risking a Type II error, is not generally as controllable. For that reason, we adopted a policy of nonrejection of H_0 when the test statistic does not fall in the rejection region, rather than risking an error of unknown magnitude.

To see how β, the probability of a Type II error, can be calculated for a test of hypothesis, recall the example in Section 6.1 in which a city tests a manufacturer's pipe to see whether it meets the requirement that the mean strength exceeds 2,400 pounds per linear foot. The setup for the test is as follows:

$$H_0: \mu = 2,400$$
$$H_a: \mu > 2,400$$

Test statistic: $z = \dfrac{\bar{x} - 2,400}{\sigma/\sqrt{n}}$

Rejection region: $z > 1.645$ for $\alpha = .05$

Figure 6.20a shows the rejection region for the **null distribution**—that is, the distribution of the test statistic assuming the null hypothesis is true. The area in the rejection region is .05, and this area represents α, the probability that the test statistic leads to rejection of H_0 when in fact H_0 is true.

The Type II error probability β is calculated assuming that the null hypothesis is false because it is defined as the *probability of accepting H_0 when it is false.* Because H_0 is false for any value of μ exceeding 2,400, one value of β exists for each possible value of μ greater than 2,400 (an infinite number of possibilities). Figures 6.20b–d show three of the possibilities, corresponding to alternative hypothesis values of μ equal to 2,425, 2,450, and 2,475, respectively. Note that β is the area in the *nonrejection* (or *acceptance*) *region* in each of these distributions and that β decreases as the true value of μ moves farther from the null hypothesized value of $\mu = 2,400$. This is sensible because the probability of incorrectly accepting the null hypothesis should decrease as the distance between the null and alternative values of μ increases.

In order to calculate the value of β for a specific value of μ in H_a, we proceed as follows:

1. Calculate the value of $\bar{x}$ that corresponds to the border between the acceptance and rejection regions. For the sewer pipe example, this is the value of $\bar{x}$ that lies 1.645 standard deviations above $\mu = 2,400$ in the sampling distribution of $\bar{x}$. Denoting this value by $\bar{x}_0$, corresponding to the largest value of $\bar{x}$ that supports the null hypothesis, we find (recalling that $s = 200$ and $n = 50$)

$$\bar{x}_0 = \mu_0 + 1.645\sigma_{\bar{x}} = 2,400 + 1.645\left(\frac{\sigma}{\sqrt{n}}\right)$$

$$\approx 2,400 + 1.645\left(\frac{s}{\sqrt{n}}\right) = 2,400 + 1.645\left(\frac{200}{\sqrt{50}}\right)$$

$$= 2,400 + 1.645(28.28) = 2,446.5$$

2. For a particular alternative distribution corresponding to a value of μ, denoted by μ_a, we calculate the z-value corresponding to $\bar{x}_0$, the border between the rejection and acceptance regions. We then use this z-value and Table IV in Appendix B to determine the area in the *acceptance region* under the alternative distribution. This area is the value of β corresponding to the particular alternative μ_a. For example, for the alternative $\mu_a = 2,425$, we calculate

$$z = \frac{\bar{x}_0 - 2,425}{\sigma_{\bar{x}}} = \frac{\bar{x}_0 - 2,425}{\sigma/\sqrt{n}}$$

$$\approx \frac{\bar{x}_0 - 2,425}{\sigma_{\bar{x}}} = \frac{2,446.5 - 2,425}{28.28} = .76$$

Note in Figure 6.20b that the area in the acceptance region is the area to the left of $z = .76$. This area is

$$\beta = .5 + .2764 = .7764$$

Thus, the probability that the test procedure will lead to an incorrect acceptance of the null hypothesis $\mu = 2,400$ when in fact $\mu = 2,425$ is about .78. As the average strength of the pipe increases to 2,450, the value of β decreases to .4522 (Figure 6.20c). If the mean strength is further increased to 2,475, the value of β is

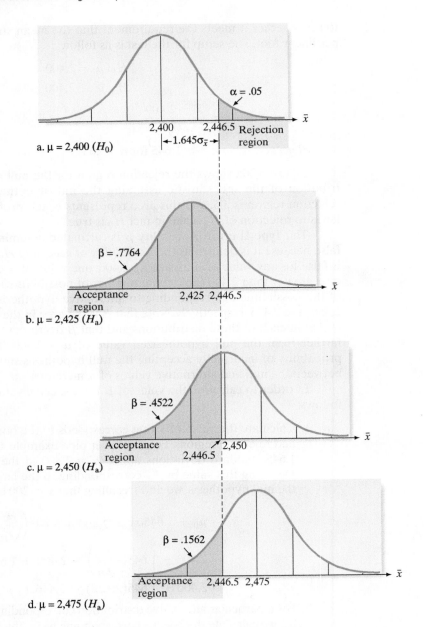

Figure 6.20

Values of α and β for various values of μ

further decreased to .1562 (Figure 6.20d). Thus, even if the true mean strength of the pipe exceeds the minimum specification by 75 pounds per linear foot, the test procedure will lead to an incorrect acceptance of the null hypothesis (rejection of the pipe) approximately 16% of the time. The upshot is that the pipe must be manufactured so that the mean strength well exceeds the minimum requirement if the manufacturer wants the probability of its acceptance by the city to be large (i.e., β to be small).

The steps for calculating β for a large-sample test about a population mean are summarized in the next box.

Steps for Calculating β for a Large-Sample Test about μ

1. Calculate the value(s) of $\bar{x}$ corresponding to the border(s) of the rejection region. There will be one border value for a one-tailed test and two for a two-tailed test. The formula is one of the following, corresponding to a test with level of significance α:

$$\text{Upper-tailed test: } \overline{x}_0 = \mu_0 + z_\alpha \sigma_{\overline{x}} \approx \mu_0 + z_\alpha\left(\frac{s}{\sqrt{n}}\right)$$

$$\text{Lower-tailed test: } \overline{x}_0 = \mu_0 - z_\alpha \sigma_{\overline{x}} \approx \mu_0 - z_\alpha\left(\frac{s}{\sqrt{n}}\right)$$

$$\text{Two-tailed test: } \overline{x}_{0,L} = \mu_0 - z_{\alpha/2} \sigma_{\overline{x}} \approx \mu_0 - z_{\alpha/2}\left(\frac{s}{\sqrt{n}}\right)$$

$$\overline{x}_{0,U} = \mu_0 + z_{\alpha/2} \sigma_{\overline{x}} \approx \mu_0 + z_{\alpha/2}\left(\frac{s}{\sqrt{n}}\right)$$

2. Specify the value of μ_a in the alternative hypothesis for which the value of β is to be calculated. Then convert the border value(s) of $\overline{x}_0$ to z-value(s) using the alternative distribution with mean μ_a. The general formula for the z-value is

$$z = \frac{\overline{x}_0 - \mu_a}{\sigma_{\overline{x}}}$$

Sketch the alternative distribution (centered at μ_a) and shade the area in the acceptance (nonrejection) region. Use the z-statistic(s) and Table IV in Appendix B to find the shaded area, which is β.

Following the calculation of β for a particular value of μ_a, you should interpret the value in the context of the hypothesis testing application. It is often useful to interpret the value of $1 - \beta$, which is known as the *power of the test* corresponding to a particular alternative, μ_a. Because β is the probability of accepting the null hypothesis when the alternative hypothesis is true with $\mu = \mu_a$, $1 - \beta$ is the probability of the complementary event, or the probability of rejecting the null hypothesis when the alternative $H_a: \mu = \mu_a$ is true—that is, the power $1 - \beta$ measures the likelihood that the test procedure will lead to the correct decision (reject H_0) for a particular value of the mean in the alternative hypothesis.

The **power of a test** is the probability that the test will correctly lead to the rejection of the null hypothesis for a particular value of μ in the alternative hypothesis. The power is equal to $1 - \beta$ for the particular alternative considered.

For example, in the sewer pipe example we found that $\beta = .7764$ when $\mu = 2,425$. This is the probability that the test leads to the (incorrect) acceptance of the null hypothesis when $\mu = 2,425$. Or, equivalently, the power of the test is $1 - .7764 = .2236$, which means that the test will lead to the (correct) rejection of the null hypothesis only 22% of the time when the pipe exceeds specifications by 25 pounds per linear foot. When the manufacturer's pipe has a mean strength of 2,475 (that is, 75 pounds per linear foot in excess of specifications), the power of the test increases to $1 - .1562 = .8438$—that is, the test will lead to the acceptance of the manufacturer's pipe 84% of the time if $\mu = 2,475$.

Example 6.11

Finding the Power of the Test

Problem Recall the quality control study in Examples 6.3 and 6.4, in which we tested to determine whether a cereal box filling machine was deviating from the specified mean fill of $\mu = 12$ ounces. The test setup is repeated here:

$$H_0: \mu = 12$$

$$H_a: \mu \neq 12 \text{ (i.e., } \mu < 12 \text{ or } \mu > 12)$$

Test statistic: $z = \dfrac{\bar{x} - 12}{\sigma_{\bar{x}}}$

Rejection region: $z < -1.96$ or $z > 1.96$ for $\alpha = .05$

$z < -2.575$ or $z > 2.575$ for $\alpha = .01$

Note that two rejection regions have been specified corresponding to values of $\alpha = .05$ and $\alpha = .01$, respectively. Assume that $n = 100$ and $s = .5$.

a. Suppose the machine is underfilling the boxes by an average of .1 ounce (i.e., $\mu = 11.9$). Calculate the values of β corresponding to the two rejection regions. Discuss the relationship between the values of α and β.

b. Calculate the power of the test for each of the rejection regions when $\mu = 11.9$.

Solution

a. We first consider the rejection region corresponding to $\alpha = .05$. The first step is to calculate the border values of $\bar{x}$ corresponding to the two-tailed rejection region, $z < -1.96$ or $z > 1.96$:

$$\bar{x}_{0.L} = \mu_0 - 1.96\sigma_{\bar{x}} \approx \mu_0 - 1.96\left(\frac{s}{\sqrt{n}}\right) = 12 - 1.96\left(\frac{.5}{10}\right) = 11.902$$

$$\bar{x}_{0.U} = \mu_0 + 1.96\sigma_{\bar{x}} \approx \mu_0 + 1.96\left(\frac{s}{\sqrt{n}}\right) = 12 + 1.96\left(\frac{.5}{10}\right) = 12.098$$

These border values are shown in Figure 6.21.

Next, we convert these values to z-values in the alternative distribution with $\mu_a = 11.9$:

$$z_L = \frac{x_{0.L} - \mu_a}{\sigma_{\bar{x}}} \approx \frac{11.902 - 11.9}{.05} = .04$$

$$z_U = \frac{x_{0.U} - \mu_a}{\sigma_{\bar{x}}} \approx \frac{12.098 - 11.9}{.05} = 3.96$$

These z-values are shown in Figure 6.21b: You can see that the acceptance (or non-rejection) region is the area between them. Using Table IV in Appendix B, we find that the area between $z = 0$ and $z = .04$ is .0160, and the area between $z = 0$ and $z = 3.96$ is (approximately) .5 (because $z = 3.96$ is off the scale of Table IV). Then the area between $z = .04$ and $z = 3.96$ is, approximately,

$$\beta = .5 - .0160 = .4840$$

Thus, the test with $\alpha = .05$ will lead to a Type II error about 48% of the time when the machine is underfilling, on average, by .1 ounce.

For the rejection region corresponding to $\alpha = .01$, $z < -2.575$, or $z > 2.575$, we find

$$\bar{x}_{0.L} = 12 - 2.575\left(\frac{.5}{10}\right) = 11.871$$

$$\bar{x}_{0.U} = 12 + 2.575\left(\frac{.5}{10}\right) = 12.129$$

These border values of the rejection region are shown in Figure 6.21c.

Converting these to z-values in the alternative distribution with $\mu_a = 11.9$, we find $z_L = -.58$ and $z_U = 4.58$. The area between these values is, approximately,

$$\beta = .2190 + .5 = .7190$$

Thus, the chance that the test procedure with $\alpha = .01$ will lead to an incorrect acceptance of H_0 is about 72%.

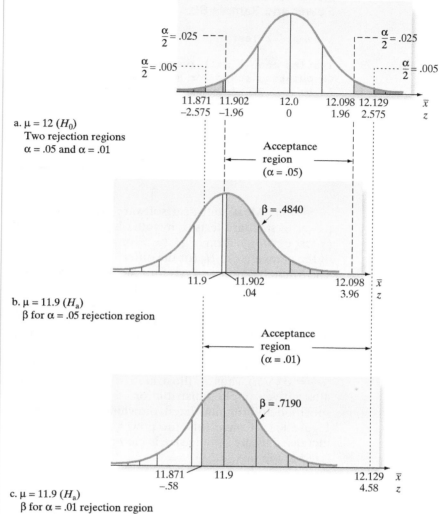

a. $\mu = 12$ (H_0)
Two rejection regions
$\alpha = .05$ and $\alpha = .01$

b. $\mu = 11.9$ (H_a)
β for $\alpha = .05$ rejection region

c. $\mu = 11.9$ (H_a)
β for $\alpha = .01$ rejection region

Figure 6.21
Calculation of β for filling machine example

Note that the value of β increases from .4840 to .7190 when we decrease the value of α from .05 to .01. This is a general property of the relationship between α and β: *as α is decreased (increased), β is increased (decreased)*.

b. The power is defined to be the probability of (correctly) rejecting the null hypothesis when the alternative is true. When $\mu = 11.9$ and $\alpha = .05$, we find

$$\text{Power} = 1 - \beta = 1 - .4840 = .5160$$

When $\mu = 11.9$ and $\alpha = .01$, we find

$$\text{Power} = 1 - \beta = 1 - .7190 = .2810$$

You can see that the power of the test is decreased as the level of α is decreased. This means that as the probability of incorrectly rejecting the null hypothesis is decreased, the probability of correctly accepting the null hypothesis for a given alternative is also decreased.

Look Back A key point of this example is that the value of α must be selected carefully, with the realization that a test is made less capable of detecting departures from the null hypothesis when the value of α is decreased.

Power and Sample Size

```
1-Sample Z Test

Testing mean = null (versus not = null)
Calculating power for mean = null + difference
Alpha = 0.05  Assumed standard deviation = 0.5
```

Figure 6.22
Minitab power analysis
for Example 6.11

```
              Sample
Difference     Size        Power
    0.1         100      0.516005
```

Note: Most statistical software packages now have options for computing the power of standard tests of hypothesis. Usually you will need to specify the type of test (z-test or t-test), form of H_a ($<$, $>$, or $\neq$), standard deviation, sample size, and the value of the parameter in H_a (or the difference between the value in H_0 and the value in H_a). The Minitab power analysis for Example 6.11 when $\alpha = .05$ is displayed in Figure 6.22. The power of the test (.516) is highlighted on the printout.

We have shown that the probability of committing a Type II error, β, is inversely related to α (Example 6.11) and that the value of β decreases as the value of μ_a moves farther from the null hypothesis value (sewer pipe example). The sample size n also affects β. Remember that the standard deviation of the sampling distribution of $\bar{x}$ is inversely proportional to the square root of the sample size $(\sigma_{\bar{x}} = \sigma/\sqrt{n})$ Thus, as illustrated in Figure 6.23, the variability of both the null and alternative sampling distributions is decreased as n is increased. If the value of α is specified and remains fixed, the value of β decreases as n increases, as illustrated in Figure 6.23. Conversely, the power of the test for a given alternative hypothesis is increased as the sample size is increased. The properties of β and power are summarized in the box.

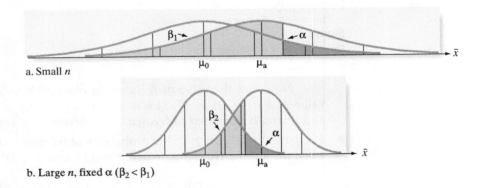

Figure 6.23
Relationship between
α, β, and n

a. Small n

b. Large n, fixed α ($\beta_2 < \beta_1$)

Properties of β and Power

1. For fixed n and α, the value of β decreases, and the power increases as the distance between the specified null value μ_0 and the specified alternative value μ_a increases (see Figure 6.20).

2. For fixed n and values of μ_0 and μ_a, the value of β increases, and the power decreases as the value of α is decreased (see Figure 6.21).

3. For fixed α and values of μ_0 and μ_a, the value of β decreases, and the power increases as the sample size n is increased (see Figure 6.23).

Exercises 6.80–6.89

Learning the Mechanics

6.80 **a.** List three factors that will increase the power of a test.
   b. What is the relationship between β, the probability of committing a Type II error, and the power of a test?

6.81 Suppose you want to test $H_0: \mu = 500$ against $H_a: \mu > 500$ using $\alpha = .05$. The population in question is normally distributed with standard deviation 100. A random sample of size $n = 25$ will be used.
   a. Sketch the sampling distribution of $\bar{x}$ assuming that H_0 is true.
   b. Find the value of $\bar{x}_0$, that value of $\bar{x}$ above which the null hypothesis will be rejected. Indicate the rejection region on your graph of part **a.** Shade the area above the rejection region and label it α.
   c. On your graph of part **a,** sketch the sampling distribution of $\bar{x}$ if $\mu = 550$. Shade the area under this distribution that corresponds to the probability that $\bar{x}$ falls in the nonrejection region when $\mu = 550$. Label this area β.
   d. Find β.
   e. Compute the power of this test for detecting the alternative $H_a: \mu = 550$.

6.82 Refer to Exercise 6.81.
   a. If $\mu = 575$ instead of 550, what is the probability that the hypothesis test will incorrectly fail to reject H_0? That is, what is β?
   b. If $\mu = 575$, what is the probability that the test will correctly reject the null hypothesis? That is, what is the power of the test?
   c. Compare β and the power of the test when $\mu = 575$ to the values you obtained in Exercise 6.81 for $\mu = 550$. Explain the differences.

6.83 It is desired to test $H_0: \mu = 75$ against $H_a: \mu < 75$ using $\alpha = .10$. The population in question is uniformly distributed with standard deviation 15. A random sample of size 49 will be drawn from the population.
   a. Describe the (approximate) sampling distribution of $\bar{x}$ under the assumption that H_0 is true.
   b. Describe the (approximate) sampling distribution of $\bar{x}$ under the assumption that the population mean is 70.
   c. If μ were really equal to 70, what is the probability that the hypothesis test would lead the investigator to commit a Type II error?
   d. What is the power of this test for detecting the alternative $H_a: \mu = 70$?

6.84 Refer to Exercise 6.83.
   a. Find β for each of the following values of the population mean: 74, 72, 70, 68, and 66.
   b. Plot each value of β you obtained in part **a** against its associated population mean. Show β on the vertical axis and μ on the horizontal axis. Draw a curve through the five points on your graph.
   c. Use your graph of part **b** to find the approximate probability that the hypothesis test will lead to a Type II error when $\mu = 73$.
   d. Convert each of the β values you calculated in part **a** to the power of the test at the specified value of μ. Plot

the power on the vertical axis against μ on the horizontal axis. Compare the graph of part **b** to the *power curve* of this part.
   e. Examine the graphs of parts **b** and **d.** Explain what they reveal about the relationships among the distance between the true mean μ and the null hypothesized mean μ_0, the value of β, and the power.

6.85 Suppose you want to conduct the two-tailed test of $H_0: \mu = 30$ against $H_a: \mu \neq 30$ using $\alpha = .05$. A random sample of size 121 will be drawn from the population in question. Assume the population has a standard deviation equal to 1.2.
   a. Describe the sampling distribution of $\bar{x}$ under the assumption that H_0 is true.
   b. Describe the sampling distribution of $\bar{x}$ under the assumption that $\mu = 29.8$.
   c. If μ were really equal to 29.8, find the value of β associated with the test.
   d. Find the value of β for the alternative $H_a: \mu = 30.4$.

Applying the Concepts—Intermediate

6.86 **Square-footage of new California homes.** The average size of single-family homes built in the United States is 2,230 square feet, an increase of over 200 square feet a decade earlier (*Wall Street Journal Interactive Edition,* Jan. 7, 2000). A random sample of 100 new homes sold in California yielded the following size information: $\bar{x} = 2{,}347$ square feet and $s = 257$ square feet.
   a. Assume the average size of U.S. homes is known with certainty. Do the sample data provide sufficient evidence to conclude that the mean size of California homes built exceeds the national average? Test using $\alpha = .01$.
   b. Suppose the actual mean size of new California homes was 2,330 square feet. What is the power of the test in part **a** to detect this 100-square-foot difference?
   c. If the California mean were actually 2,280 square feet, what is the power of the test in part **a** to detect this 50-square-foot difference?

6.87 **Manufacturers that practice sole sourcing.** If a manufacturer (the vendee) buys all items of a particular type from a particular vendor, the manufacturer is practicing *sole sourcing* (Schonberger and Knod, *Operations Management,* 2001). As part of a sole-sourcing arrangement, a vendor agrees to periodically supply its vendee with sample data from its production process. The vendee uses the data to investigate whether the mean length of rods produced by the vendor's production process is truly 5.0 millimeters (mm) or more, as claimed by the vendor and desired by the vendee.
   a. If the production process has a standard deviation of .01 mm, the vendor supplies $n = 100$ items to the vendee, and the vendee uses $\alpha = .05$ in testing $H_0: \mu = 5.0$ mm against $H_a: \mu < 5.0$ mm, what is the probability that the vendee's test will fail to reject the null hypothesis when in fact $\mu = 4.9975$ mm? What is the name given to this type of error?

b. Refer to part **a.** What is the probability that the vendee's test will reject the null hypothesis when in fact $\mu = 5.0$? What is the name given to this type of error?

c. What is the power of the test to detect a departure of .0025 mm below the specified mean rod length of 5.0 mm?

6.88 **Fuel economy of the Honda Civic.** According to the Environmental Protection Agency (EPA) *Fuel Economy Guide*, the 2009 Honda Civic automobile obtains a mean of 36 miles per gallon (mpg) on the highway. Suppose Honda claims that the EPA has underestimated the Civic's mileage. To support its assertion, the company selects $n = 50$ model 2009 Civic cars and records the mileage obtained for each car over a driving course similar to the one used by the EPA. The following data resulted: $\bar{x} = 38.3$ mpg, $s = 6.4$ mpg.

a. If Honda wishes to show that the mean mpg for 2009 Civic autos is greater than 36 mpg, what should the alternative hypothesis be? The null hypothesis?

b. Do the data provide sufficient evidence to support the auto manufacturer's claim? Test using $\alpha = .05$. List any assumptions you make in conducting the test.

c. Calculate the power of the test for the mean values of 36.5, 37.0, 37.5, 38.0, and 38.5, assuming $s = 6.4$ is a good estimate of σ.

d. Plot the power of the test on the vertical axis against the mean on the horizontal axis. Draw a curve through the points.

e. Use the power curve of part **d** to estimate the power for the mean value $\mu = 37.75$. Calculate the power for this value of μ and compare it to your approximation.

f. Use the power curve to approximate the power of the test when $\mu = 41$. If the true value of the mean mpg for this model is really 41 what (approximately) are the chances that the test will fail to reject the null hypothesis that the mean is 36?

6.89 **Solder-joint inspections.** Refer to Exercise 6.32 (p. 336), in which the performance of a particular type of laser-based inspection equipment was investigated. Assume that the standard deviation of the number of solder joints inspected on each run is 1.2. If $\alpha = .05$ is used in conducting the hypothesis test of interest using a sample of 48 circuit boards, and if the true mean number of solder joints that can be inspected is really equal to 9.5, what is the probability that the test will result in a Type II error?

6.8 Test of Hypothesis about a Population Variance

Although many practical problems involve inferences about a population mean (or proportion), it is sometimes of interest to make an inference about a population variance, σ^2. To illustrate, a quality control supervisor in a cannery knows that the exact amount each can contains will vary because there are certain uncontrollable factors that affect the amount of fill. The mean fill per can is important, but equally important is the variation of fill. If σ^2, the variance of the fill, is large, some cans will contain too little and others too much. Suppose regulatory agencies specify that the standard deviation of the amount of fill should be less than .1 ounce. To determine whether the process is meeting this specification, the supervisor randomly selects 10 cans and weighs the contents of each. The results are given in Table 6.6.

Table 6.6	Fill Weights (in Ounces) of 10 Cans								
16.00	16.06	15.95	16.04	16.10	16.05	16.02	16.03	15.99	16.02

Data Set: FILLAMOUNTS

Do these data provide sufficient evidence to indicate that the variability is as small as desired? To answer this question, we need a procedure for testing a hypothesis about σ^2.

Intuitively, it seems that we should compare the sample variance σ^2 to the hypothesized value of σ^2 (or s to σ) in order to make a decision about the population's variability. The quantity

$$\frac{(n-1)s^2}{\sigma^2}$$

has been shown to have a sampling distribution called a **chi-square** (χ^2) **distribution** when the population from which the sample is taken is *normally distributed*. Several chi-square distributions are shown in Figure 6.24.

$f(\chi^2)$

df = 1
df = 4
df = 6

0 2 4 6 8 10 12 14 16 χ^2

Figure 6.24
Several χ^2 probability distributions

FRIEDRICH R. HELMERT
(1843–1917)

Helmert Transformations

German Friedrich Helmert studied engineering sciences and mathematics at Dresden University, where he earned his PhD, then accepted a position as a professor of geodesy—the scientific study of the earth's size and shape—at the technical school in Aachen. Helmert's mathematical solutions to geodesy problems led him to several statistics-related discoveries. His greatest statistical contribution occurred in 1876, when he was the first to prove that the sampling distribution of the sample variance, s^2, is a chi-square distribution. Helmert used a series of mathematical transformations to obtain the distribution of s^2—transformations that have since been named "Helmert transformations" in his honor. Later in life, Helmert was appointed professor of advanced geodesy at the prestigious University of Berlin and director of the Prussian Geodesic Institute. ■

The upper-tail areas for this distribution have been tabulated and are given in Table VI in Appendix B, a portion of which is reproduced in Table 6.7. The table gives the values of χ^2, denoted as χ^2_α, that locate an area of α in the upper tail of the chi-square distribution; that is, $P(\chi^2 > \chi^2_\alpha) = \alpha$. In this case, as with the t-statistic, the shape of the chi-square distribution depends on the degrees of freedom associated with s^2, namely $(n - 1)$. Thus, for $n = 10$ and an upper-tail value $\alpha = .05$, you will have $n - 1 = 9$ df and $\chi^2_{.05} = 16.9190$ (highlighted in Table 6.7). To further illustrate the use of Table VI, we return to the can-filling example.

| Table 6.7 | **Reproduction of Part of Table VI in Appendix B: Critical Values of Chi Square** |

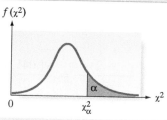

Degrees of Freedom	$\chi^2_{.100}$	$\chi^2_{.050}$	$\chi^2_{.025}$	$\chi^2_{.010}$	$\chi^2_{.005}$
1	2.70554	3.84146	5.02389	6.63490	7.87944
2	4.60517	5.99147	7.37776	9.21034	10.5966
3	6.25139	7.81473	9.34840	11.3449	12.8381
4	7.77944	9.48773	11.1433	13.2767	14.8602
5	9.23635	11.0705	12.8325	15.0863	16.7496
6	10.6446	12.5916	14.4494	16.8119	18.5476
7	12.0170	14.0671	16.0128	18.4753	20.2777
8	13.3616	15.5073	17.5346	20.0902	21.9550
9	14.6837	16.9190	19.0228	21.6660	23.5893
10	15.9871	18.3070	20.4831	23.2093	25.1882
11	17.2750	19.6751	21.9200	24.7250	25.7569
12	18.5494	21.0261	23.3367	26.2170	28.2995
13	19.8119	22.3621	24.7356	27.6883	29.8194
14	21.0642	23.6848	26.1190	29.1413	31.3193
15	22.3072	24.9958	27.4884	30.5779	32.8013
16	23.5418	26.2862	28.8454	31.9999	34.2672
17	24.7690	27.5871	30.1910	33.4087	35.7185
18	25.9894	28.8693	31.5264	34.8053	37.1564
19	27.2036	30.1435	32.8523	36.1908	38.5822

Example 6.12

Conducting a Test for the Variance, σ^2, of Fill Weights

Problem Refer to the fill weights for the sample of ten 16-ounce cans in Table 6.6. Do the data provide sufficient evidence to indicate that the true standard deviation σ of the fill measurements of all 16-ounce cans is less than .1 ounce?

Solution Here, we want to test whether $\sigma < .1$. Because the null and alternative hypotheses must be stated in terms of σ^2 rather than σ, we want to test the null hypothesis that $\sigma^2 = (.1)^2 = .01$ against the alternative that $\sigma^2 < .01$. Therefore, the elements of the test are

H_0: $\sigma^2 = .01$ (Fill variance equals .01—i.e., process specifications are not met.)

H_a: $\sigma^2 < .01$ (Fill variance is less than .01—i.e., process specifications are met.)

Test statistic: $\chi^2 = \dfrac{(n-1)s^2}{\sigma^2}$

Assumption: The distribution of the amounts of fill is approximately normal.

Rejection region: The smaller the value of s^2 we observe, the stronger the evidence in favor of H_a. Thus, we reject H_0 for "small values" of the test statistic. With $\alpha = .05$ and 9 df, the χ^2 value for rejection is found in Table VI and pictured in Figure 6.25. We will reject H_0 if $\chi^2 < 3.32511$.

(Remember that the area given in Table VI is the area to the *right* of the numerical value in the table. Thus, to determine the lower-tail value, which has $\alpha = .05$ to its *left*, we used the $\chi^2_{.95}$ column in Table VI.)

An Excel/DDXL analysis of the data in Table 6.6 is displayed in Figure 6.26. The value of s (highlighted) on the printout is $s = .0412$. Substituting into the formula for the test statistic, we have

$$\chi^2 = \frac{(n-1)s^2}{\sigma^2} = \frac{9(.0412)^2}{.01} = 1.53$$

Figure 6.25
Rejection region for Example 6.12

Because the test statistic falls into the rejection region, we reject H_0 in favor of H_a— that is, the supervisor can conclude that the variance σ^2 of the population of all amounts of fill is less than .01 ($\sigma < .1$) with probability of a Type I error equal to $\alpha = .05$. If this procedure is repeatedly used, it will incorrectly reject H_0 only 5% of the time. Thus, the quality control supervisor is confident in the decision that the cannery is operating within the desired limits of variability.

Look Back Note that both the test statistic (rounded) and the lower-tailed p-value of the test (.003) are highlighted at the bottom of the printout, Figure 6.26. Because $\alpha = .05$ exceeds the p-value, our decision to reject H_0 is confirmed.

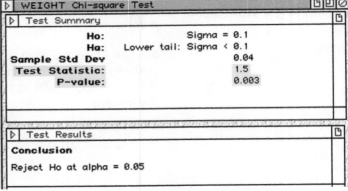

Figure 6.26
Excel/DDXL analysis of fill weights, Example 6.12

Now Work Exercise 6.98

One-tailed and two-tailed tests of hypothesis for σ^2 are given in the following box.*

Test of a Hypothesis about σ^2

One-Tailed Test	Two-Tailed Test

$H_0: \sigma^2 = \sigma_0^2$

$H_a: \sigma^2 < \sigma_0^2$ (or $H_a: \sigma^2 > \sigma_0^2$)

Test statistic: $\chi^2 = \dfrac{(n-1)s^2}{\sigma_0^2}$

Rejection region: $\chi^2 < \chi_{(1-\alpha)}^2$
(or $\chi^2 > \chi_\alpha^2$ when $H_a: \sigma^2 > \sigma_0^2$)

$H_0: \sigma^2 = \sigma_0^2$

$H_a: \sigma^2 \neq \sigma_0^2$

Test statistic: $\chi^2 = \dfrac{(n-1)s^2}{\sigma_0^2}$

Rejection region: $\chi^2 < \chi_{(1-\alpha/2)}^2$ or
$\chi^2 > \chi_{(\alpha/2)}^2$

where σ_0^2 is the hypothesized variance and the distribution of χ^2 is based on $(n-1)$ degrees of freedom.

Conditions Required for a Valid Hypothesis Test for s^2

1. A random sample is selected from the target population.

2. The population from which the sample is selected has a distribution that is approximately normal.

⚠️ **CAUTION** The procedure for conducting a hypothesis test for σ^2 in the above examples requires an assumption regardless of whether the sample size n is large or small. We must assume that the population from which the sample is selected has an approximate normal distribution. Unlike small sample tests for μ based on the t-statistic, *slight to moderate departures from normality will render the chi-square test invalid.* ▲

Exercises 6.90–6.101

Learning the Mechanics

6.90 Let χ_0^2 be a particular value of χ^2. Find the value of χ_0^2 such that
  a. $P(\chi^2 > \chi_0^2) = .10$ for $n = 12$
  b. $P(\chi^2 > \chi_0^2) = .05$ for $n = 9$
  c. $P(\chi^2 > \chi_0^2) = .025$ for $n = 5$

6.91 A random sample of n observations is selected from a normal population to test the null hypothesis that $\sigma^2 = 25$. Specify the rejection region for each of the following combinations of H_a, α, and n:
  a. $H_a: \sigma^2 \neq 25$; $\alpha = .05$; $n = 16$
  b. $H_a: \sigma^2 > 25$; $\alpha = .01$; $n = 23$
  c. $H_a: \sigma^2 > 25$; $\alpha = .10$; $n = 15$
  d. $H_a: \sigma^2 < 25$; $\alpha = .01$; $n = 13$
  e. $H_a: \sigma^2 \neq 25$; $\alpha = .10$; $n = 7$
  f. $H_a: \sigma^2 < 25$; $\alpha = .05$; $n = 25$

6.92 A random sample of seven measurements gave $\bar{x} = 9.4$ and $s^2 = 4.84$.
  a. What assumptions must you make concerning the population in order to test a hypothesis about σ^2?
  b. Suppose the assumptions in part **a** are satisfied. Test the null hypothesis, $\sigma^2 = 1$, against the alternative hypothesis, $\sigma^2 > 1$. Use $\alpha = .05$.
  c. Test the null hypothesis that $\sigma^2 = 1$ against the alternative hypothesis that $\sigma^2 \neq 1$. Use $\alpha = .05$.

6.93 Refer to Exercise 6.92. Suppose we had $n = 100$, $\bar{x} = 9.4$, and $s^2 = 4.84$.
  a. Test the null hypothesis, $H_0: \sigma^2 = 1$, against the alternative hypothesis, $H_a: \sigma^2 > 1$.
  b. Compare your test result with that of Exercise 6.92.

6.94 A random sample of $n = 7$ observations from a normal population produced the following measurements: 4, 0, 6,

---

*A confidence interval for σ^2 can also be formed using the chi-square distribution with $(n-1)$ degrees of freedom. A $(1-a)$ 100% confidence interval is

$$\frac{(n-1)s^2}{\chi_{a/2}^2} < \sigma^2 < \frac{(n-1)s^2}{\chi_{(1-a/2)}^2}$$

3, 3, 5, 9. Do the data provide sufficient evidence to indicate that $\sigma^2 < 1$? Test using $\alpha = .05$.

Applying the Concepts—Basic

6.95 **Latex allergy in health care workers.** Refer to the *Current Allergy & Clinical Immunology* (Mar. 2004) study of $n = 46$ hospital employees who were diagnosed with a latex allergy from exposure to the powder on latex gloves, Exercise 6.23 (p. 334). Recall that the number of latex gloves used per week by the sampled workers is summarized as follows: $\bar{x} = 19.3$ and $s = 11.9$. Let σ^2 represent the variance in the number of latex gloves used per week by all hospital employees. Consider testing $H_0: \sigma^2 = 100$ against $H_a: \sigma^2 \neq 100$.

a. Give the rejection region for the test at a significance level of $\alpha = .01$.

b. Calculate the value of the test statistic.

c. Use the results, parts **a** and **b**, to make the appropriate conclusion.

6.96 **A new dental bonding agent.** Refer to the *Trends in Biomaterials & Artificial Organs* (Jan. 2003) study of a new dental bonding adhesive (called *Smartbond*), Exercise 6.54 (p. 347). Recall that tests on a sample of 10 extracted teeth bonded with the new adhesive resulted in a mean breaking strength (after 24 hours) of $\bar{x} = 5.07$ Mpa and a standard deviation of $s = .46$ Mpa. The manufacturer must demonstrate that the breaking strength variance of the new adhesive is less than the variance of the standard composite adhesive, $\sigma^2 = .25$.

a. Set up the null and alternative hypotheses for the test.

b. Find the rejection region for the test using $\alpha = .01$.

c. Compute the test statistic.

d. Give the appropriate conclusion for the test.

e. What conditions are required for the test results to be valid?

6.97 **Golf tees produced from an injection mold.** Refer to Exercise 6.27 (p. 335) and the weights of tees produced by an injection mold process. If operating correctly, the process will produce tees with a weight variance of .000004 (ounces)^2. If the weight variance differs from .000004, the injection molder is out of control.

a. Set up the null and alternative hypotheses for testing whether the injection mold process is out of control.

b. Use the data saved in the **TEES** file to conduct the test, part **a**. Use $\alpha = .01$.

c. What conditions are required for inferences derived from the test to be valid? Are they reasonably satisfied?

Applying the Concepts—Intermediate

6.98 **Identifying type of land cover.** Refer to the *Geographical Analysis* (Oct. 2006) study of a new method for analyzing remote sensing data from satellite pixels, Exercise 6.25 (p. 335). Recall that the method uses a numerical measure of the distribution of gaps or hole sizes in the pixel, called lacunarity. Summary statistics for the lacunarity measurements in a sample of 100 grassland pixels are $\bar{x} = 225$ and $s = 20$. As stated in Exercise 6.25, it is known that the mean lacunarity measurement for all grassland pixels is 220. The method will be effective in identifying land cover if the standard deviation of the measurements is 10% (or less) of the true mean, i.e., if the standard deviation is less than 22.

a. Give the null and alternative hypotheses for a test to determine if, in fact, the standard deviation of all grassland pixels is less than 22.

b. A Minitab analysis of the data is shown at the bottom of the page. Locate and interpret the *p*-value of the test. Use $\alpha = .10$.

6.99 **Do ball bearings conform to specifications?** It is essential in the manufacture of machinery to use parts that conform to specifications. In the past, diameters of the ball bearings produced by a certain manufacturer had a variance of .00156. To cut costs, the manufacturer instituted a less expensive production method. The variance of the diameters of 100 randomly sampled bearings produced by the new process was .00211. Do the data provide sufficient evidence to indicate that diameters of ball-bearings produced by the new process are more variable than those produced by the old process?

6.100 **Cooling method for gas turbines.** Refer to the *Journal of Engineering for Gas Turbines and Power* (Jan. 2005) study of the performance of augmented gas turbine engines, Exercise 6.28 (p. 335). Recall that performance for each in a sample of 67 gas turbines was measured by heat rate

Minitab output for Exercise 6.98

Test for One Standard Deviation

```
Method
Null hypothesis            Sigma = 22
Alternative hypothesis     Sigma = < 22

The standard method is only for the normal distribution.

Statistics
N    StDev   Variance
100  20.0        400


Tests
Method     Chi-Square  DF  P-Value
Standard        81.82  99    0.105
```

(kilojoules per kilowatt per hour). The data are saved in the **GASTURBINE** file. Suppose that standard gas turbines have heat rates with a standard deviation of 1,500 kJ/kWh. Is there sufficient evidence to indicate that the heat rates of the augmented gas turbine engine are more variable than the heat rates of the standard gas turbine engine? Test using $\alpha = .05$.

Applying the Concepts—Advanced

6.101 Why do small firms export? Refer to the *Journal of Small Business Management* (Vol. 40, 2002) study of what motivates small firms to export, Exercise 6.33 (p. 336). Recall that in a survey of 137 exporting firms, each CEO was asked to respond to the statement "Management believes that the firm can achieve economies of scale by exporting" on a scale of 1 (strongly disagree) to 5 (strongly agree). Summary statistics for the $n = 137$ scale scores were reported as $\bar{x} = 3.85$ and $s = 1.5$.

a. Explain why the researcher will be unable to conclude that the true mean scale score exceeds 3.5 (as in Exercise 6.33) if the standard deviation of the scale scores is too large.

b. Give the largest value of the true standard deviation, σ, for which you will reject the null hypothesis $H_0: \mu = 3.5$ in favor of the alternative hypothesis $H_a: \mu > 3.5$ using $\alpha = .01$.

c. Based on the study results, is there evidence (at $\alpha = .01$) to indicate that σ is smaller than the value you determined in part **b**?

CHAPTER NOTES

Key Terms

Alternative (research)
   hypothesis 320, 321
Chi-square
   distribution 364
Hypothesis 320
Level of significance 325
Null distribution 357
Null hypothesis 320, 321
Observed significance level
   (*p*-value) 336

One-tailed (one-sided)
   test 325, 326
Power of the test 359
Rejection region 322
Test statistic 321
Two-tailed (two-sided)
   test 326
Type I error 322
Type II error 323
Upper-tailed test 326

Key Symbols

μ	Population mean
p	Population proportion, $P(\text{Success})$, in binomial trial
σ^2	Population variance
$\bar{x}$	Sample mean (estimator of μ)
$\hat{p}$	Sample proportion (estimator of p)
s^2	Sample variance (estimator of σ^2)
H_0	Null hypothesis
H_a	Alternative hypothesis
α	Probability of a Type I error
β	Probability of a Type II error
χ^2	Chi-square (sampling distribution of s^2 for normal data)

Key Ideas

Key Words for Identifying the Target Parameter

μ —Mean, Average
p —Proportion, Fraction, Percentage, Rate, Probability
σ^2 —Variance, Variability, Spread

Elements of a Hypothesis Test

1. *Null hypothesis* (H_0)
2. *Alternative hypothesis* (H_a)
3. *Test statistic* $(z, t, \text{ or } \chi^2)$
4. *Significance level* (α)
5. *p-value*
6. *Conclusion*

Errors in Hypothesis Testing

Type I Error = Reject H_0 when H_0 is true
                 (occurs with probabilitys α)
Type II Error = Accept H_0 when H_0 is false
                  (occurs with probability β)
Power of a Test = $P(\text{Reject } H_0 \text{ when } H_0 \text{ is false})$
                  $= 1 - \beta$

Forms of Alternative Hypothesis

Lower-tailed: $H_a: \mu < 50$
Upper-tailed: $H_a: \mu > 50$
Two-tailed: $H_a: \mu \neq 50$

Using *p*-values to Decide

1. Choose significance level (α)
2. Obtain *p*-value of the test
3. If $\alpha > p\text{-value}$, reject H_0

Guide to Selecting a One-Sample Hypothesis Test

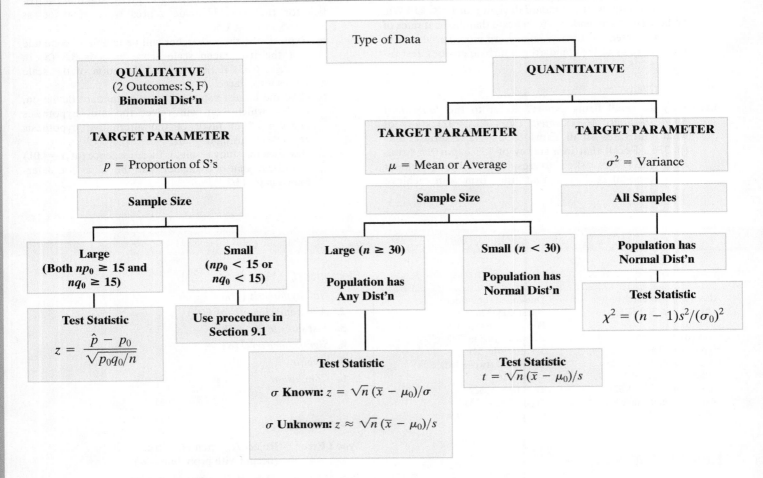

Supplementary Exercises 6.102–6.135

Note: List the assumptions necessary for the valid implementation of the statistical procedures you use in solving all these exercises.

Learning the Mechanics

6.102 Specify the differences between a large-sample and small-sample test of hypothesis about a population mean μ. Focus on the assumptions and test statistics.

6.103 *Complete the following statement:* The smaller the *p*-value associated with a test of hypothesis, the stronger the support for the _____ hypothesis. Explain your answer.

6.104 Which of the elements of a test of hypothesis can and should be specified *prior* to analyzing the data that are to be used to conduct the test?

6.105 If you select a very small value for α when conducting a hypothesis test, will β tend to be big or small? Explain.

6.106 If the rejection of the null hypothesis of a particular test would cause your firm to go out of business, would you want α to be small or large? Explain.

6.107 A random sample of 20 observations selected from a normal population produced $\bar{x} = 72.6$ and $s^2 = 19.4$.
 a. Test $H_0: \mu = 80$ against $H_a: \mu < 80$. Use $\alpha = .05$.
 b. Test $H_0: \mu = 80$ against $H_a: \mu \neq 80$. Use $\alpha = .01$.

6.108 A random sample of 175 measurements possessed a mean $\bar{x} = 8.2$ and a standard deviation $s = .79$.
 a. Test $H_0: \mu = 8.3$ against $H_a: \mu \neq 8.3$. Use $\alpha = .05$.
 b. Test $H_0: \mu = 8.4$ against $H_a: \mu \neq 8.4$. Use $\alpha = .05$.
 c. Test $H_0: \sigma = 1$ against $H_a: \sigma \neq 1$. Use $\alpha = .05$.
 d. Find the power of the test, part **a**, if $\mu_a = 8.5$.

6.109 A random sample of $n = 200$ observations from a binomial population yields $\hat{p} = .29$.
 a. Test $H_0: p = .35$ against $H_a: p < .35$. Use $\alpha = .05$.
 b. Test $H_0: p = .35$ against $H_a: p \neq .35$. Use $\alpha = .05$.

6.110 A *t*-test is conducted for the null hypothesis $H_0: \mu = 10$ versus the alternative $H_a: \mu > 10$ for a random sample of $n = 17$ observations. The test results are $t = 1.174$, *p*-value $= .1288$.
 a. Interpret the *p*-value.
 b. What assumptions are necessary for the validity of this test?
 c. Calculate and interpret the *p*-value assuming the alternative hypothesis was instead $H_a: \mu \neq 10$.

6.111 A random sample of 41 observations from a normal population possessed a mean $\bar{x} = 88$ and a standard deviation $s = 6.9$.
 a. Test $H_0: \sigma^2 = 30$ against $H_a: \sigma^2 > 30$. Use $\alpha = .05$.
 b. Test $H_0: \sigma^2 = 30$ against $H_a: \sigma^2 \neq 30$. Use $\alpha = .05$.

Applying the Concepts—Basic

6.112 Semester hours taken by CPA candidates. Refer to the *Journal of Accounting and Public Policy* (Spring 2002) study of $n = 100,000$ first-time candidates for the CPA exam, Exercise 5.92 (p. 310). The number of semester hours of college credit taken by the sampled candidates is summarized as follows: $\bar{x} = 141.31$ hours and $s = 17.77$ hours. Let μ represent the mean number of semester hours taken by all first-time candidates for the CPA exam. Consider testing $H_0: \mu = 140$ against $H_a: \mu > 140$.

a. Give the rejection region for the test at a significance level of $\alpha = .01$.

b. Calculate the value of the test statistic.

c. Use the results, parts **a** and **b**, to make the appropriate conclusion.

6.113 Unauthorized computer use. Refer to the Computer Security Institute (CSI) survey of computer crime, Exercise 2.146 (p. 106). Recall that in 1999, 62% of businesses suffered unauthorized use of computer systems. In a survey taken 7 years later, 320 of a sample of 616 businesses reported unauthorized use of computer systems. (*Computer Security Issues & Trends*, Spring 2006). Let p represent the true proportion of businesses that reported unauthorized use of computer systems in 2006.

a. Calculate a point estimate for p.

b. Set up the null and alternative hypothesis to test whether the value of p has changed since 1999.

c. Calculate the test statistic for the test, part **b**.

d. Find the rejection region for the test if $\alpha = .05$.

e. Use the results, parts **c** and **d**, to make the appropriate conclusion.

f. Find the p-value of the test and confirm that the conclusion based on the p-value agrees with the conclusion in part **e**.

6.114 Quality of cable TV news. In a survey of 500 television viewers with access to cable TV, each was asked whether they agreed with the statement, "Overall, I find the quality of news on cable networks (such as CNN, FOXNews, CNBC, and MSNBC) to be better than news on the ABC, CBS, and NBC networks." A total of 248 viewers agreed with the statement (*Cabletelevision Advertising Bureau*, May 2002). [*Note:* The survey respondents were contacted via e-mail on the Internet.]

a. Identify the population parameter of interest in the survey.

b. Give a point estimate of the population parameter.

c. Set up H_0 and H_a for testing whether the true percentage of TV viewers who find cable news to be better quality than network news differs from 50%.

d. Conduct the test, part **c**, using $\alpha = .10$ Make the appropriate conclusion in the words of the problem.

e. What conditions are required for the inference, part **d**, to be valid? Do they appear to be satisfied?

6.115 Beta-value of a stock. The "beta coefficient" of a stock is a measure of the stock's volatility (or risk) relative to the market as a whole. Stocks with beta coefficients greater than 1 generally bear greater risk (more volatility) than the market, whereas stocks with beta coefficients less than 1 are less risky (less volatile) than the overall market (Alexander, Sharpe, and Bailey, *Fundamentals of Investments*, 2000). A random sample of 15 high-technology stocks was selected at the end of 2009, and the mean and standard deviation of the beta coefficients were calculated: $\bar{x} = 1.23$, $s = .37$.

a. Set up the appropriate null and alternative hypotheses to test whether the average high-technology stock is riskier than the market as a whole.

b. Establish the appropriate test statistic and rejection region for the test. Use $\alpha = .10$.

c. What assumptions are necessary to ensure the validity of the test?

d. Calculate the test statistic and state your conclusion.

e. What is the approximate p-value associated with this test? Interpret it.

f. Conduct a test to determine if the variance of the stock beta values differs from .15. Use $\alpha = .05$.

6.116 A camera that detects liars. According to *New Scientist* (Jan. 2, 2002), a new thermal imaging camera that detects small temperature changes is now being used as a polygraph device. The U.S. Department of Defense Polygraph Institute (DDPI) claims the camera can correctly detect liars 75% of the time by monitoring the temperatures of their faces.

a. Give the null hypothesis for testing the claim made by the DDPI.

b. What is a Type I error for this problem? A Type II error?

6.117 Pouring temperature of an iron automotive casting. The Cleveland Casting Plant produces iron automotive castings for Ford Motor Company (*Quality Engineering*, Vol. 7, 1995). The pouring temperatures (in degrees Fahrenheit) for a sample of 10 crankshafts produced at the plant are listed on the next page. These data are saved in the **IRONTEMP** file. When the process is stable, the target pouring temperature of the molton iron is 2,550 degrees. Conduct a test to determine whether the true mean pouring temperature differs from the target setting. Test using $\alpha = .01$. Use the SPSS printout below to carry out the test.

SPSS Output for Exercise 6.117

One-Sample Test

				Test Value = 2550		
					95% Confidence Interval of the Difference	
	t	df	Sig. (2-tailed)	Mean Difference	Lower	Upper
POURTEMP	1.210	9	.257	8.70	-7.57	24.97

Data for Exercise 6.117

2,543	2,541	2,544	2,620	2,560	2,559	2,562
2,553	2,552	2,553				

Source: Price, B., and Barth, B. "A structural model relating process inputs and final product characteristics," *Quality Engineering,* Vol. 7, No. 4, 1995, p. 696 (Table 2). Reprinted by permission of the publisher (Taylor & Francis Group, www.informaworld.com).

Applying the Concepts—Intermediate

6.118 **Consumers' use of discount coupons.** In 1894, druggist Asa Candler began distributing handwritten tickets to his customers for free glasses of Coca-Cola at his soda fountain. That was the genesis of the discount coupon. In 1975, it was estimated that 65% of U.S. consumers regularly used discount coupons when shopping. In a more recent consumer survey, 72% said they regularly redeem coupons (Prospectiv 2008 Consumer Coupon Poll). Assume the recent survey consisted of a random sample of 1,000 shoppers.
   a. Does the survey provide sufficient evidence that the percentage of shoppers using cents-off coupons exceeds 65%? Test using $\alpha = .05$.
   b. Is the sample size large enough to use the inferential procedures presented in this section? Explain.
   c. Find the observed significance level for the test you conducted in part **a** and interpret its value.

6.119 **Errors in medical tests.** Medical tests have been developed to detect many serious diseases. A medical test is designed to minimize the probability that it will produce a "false positive" or a "false negative." A *false positive* refers to a positive test result for an individual who does not have the disease, whereas a false negative is a negative test result for an individual who does have the disease.
   a. If we treat a medical test for a disease as a statistical test of hypothesis, what are the null and alternative hypotheses for the medical test?
   b. What are the Type I and Type II errors for the test? Relate each to false positives and false negatives.
   c. Which of the errors has graver consequences? Considering this error, is it more important to minimize α or β? Explain.

6.120 **Drivers' use of the Lincoln Tunnel.** The Lincoln Tunnel (under the Hudson River) connects suburban New Jersey to midtown Manhattan. On Mondays at 8:30 A.M., the mean number of cars waiting in line to pay the Lincoln Tunnel toll is 1,220. Because of the substantial wait during rush hour, the Port Authority of New York and New Jersey is considering raising the amount of the toll between 7:30 and 8:30 A.M. to encourage more drivers to use the tunnel at an earlier or later time. Suppose the Port Authority experiments with peak-hour pricing for 6 months, increasing the toll from $4 to $7 during the rush hour peak. On 10 different workdays at 8:30 A.M. aerial photographs of the tunnel queues are taken and the number of vehicles counted. The results (saved in the **TUNNEL** file) follow:

1,260	1,052	1,201	942	1,062	999	931	849	867	735

Analyze the data for the purpose of determining whether peak-hour pricing succeeded in reducing the average number of vehicles attempting to use the Lincoln Tunnel during the peak rush hour.

6.121 **Point spreads of NFL games.** Refer to the *Chance* (Fall 1998) study of point-spread errors in NFL games,

Exercise 6.29 (p. 335). Recall that the difference between the actual game outcome and the point spread established by oddsmakers—the point-spread error—was calculated for 240 NFL games. The results are summarized as follows: $\bar{x} = -1.6$, $s = 13.3$. Suppose the researcher wants to know whether the true standard deviation of the point-spread errors exceeds 15. Conduct the analysis using $\alpha = .10$.

6.122 **Improving the productivity of chickens.** Refer to the *Applied Animal Behaviour Science* (Oct. 2000) study of the color of string preferred by pecking domestic chickens, Exercise 5.100 (p. 311). Recall that $n = 72$ chickens were exposed to blue string and the number of pecks each chicken took at the string over a specified time interval had a mean of $\bar{x} = 1.13$ pecks and a standard deviation of $s = 2.21$ pecks. Also recall that previous research has shown that $\mu = 7.5$ pecks if chickens are exposed to white string.
   a. Conduct a test (at $\alpha = .01$) to determine if the true mean number of pecks at blue string is less than $\mu = 7.5$ pecks.
   b. In Exercise 5.100, you used a 99% confidence interval as evidence that chickens are more apt to peck at white string than blue string. Do the test results, part **a,** support this conclusion? Explain.

6.123 **Are manufacturers satisfied with trade promotions?** Sales promotions that are used by manufacturers to entice retailers to carry, feature, or push the manufacturer's products are called *trade promotions*. A survey of 132 manufacturers conducted by Nielsen, found that 36% of the manufacturers were satisfied with their spending for trade promotions (*Survey of Trade Promotion Practices,* 2004). Is this sufficient evidence to reject a previous claim by the American Marketing Association that no more than half of all manufacturers are dissatisfied with their trade promotion spending?
   a. Conduct the appropriate hypothesis test at $\alpha = .02$. Begin your analysis by determining whether the sample size is large enough to apply the testing methodology presented in this chapter.
   b. Report the observed significance level of the test and interpret its meaning in the context of the problem.
   c. Calculate β, the probability of a Type II error, if in fact 55% of all manufacturers are dissatisfied with their trade promotion spending.

6.124 **Arresting shoplifters.** Shoplifting in the United States costs retailers about $35 million a day. Despite the seriousness of the problem, the National Association of Shoplifting Prevention (NASP) claims that only 50% of all shoplifting are turned over to police (www.shopliftingprevention.org, 2009). A random sample of 40 U.S. retailers were questioned concerning the disposition of the most recent shoplifter they apprehended. A total of 24 were turned over to police. Do these data provide sufficient evidence to contradict the NASP?
   a. Conduct a hypothesis test to answer the question of interest. Use $\alpha = .05$.
   b. Is the sample size large enough to use the inferential procedure of part **a**?
   c. Find the observed significance level of the hypothesis test in part **a.** Interpret the value.
   d. For what values of α would the observed significance level be sufficient to reject the null hypothesis of the test you conducted in part **b**?

6.125 Arresting shoplifters (cont'd). Refer to Exercise 6.124.
   a. Describe a Type II error in terms of this application.
   b. Calculate the probability β of a Type II error for this test assuming that the true fraction of shoplifters turned over to the police is $p = .55$.
   c. Suppose the number of retailers sampled is increased from 40 to 100. How does this affect the probability of a Type II error for $p = .55$?

6.126 Frequency marketing programs by restaurants. To instill customer loyalty, airlines, hotels, rental car companies, and credit card companies (among others) have initiated *frequency marketing programs* that reward their regular customers. More than 80 million people are members of the frequent flier programs of the airline industry (www.frequentflier.com). A large fast-food restaurant chain wished to explore the profitability of such a program. They randomly selected 12 of their 1,200 restaurants nationwide and instituted a frequency program that rewarded customers with a $5.00 gift certificate after every 10 meals purchased at full price. They ran the trial program for 3 months. The restaurants not in the sample had an average increase in profits of $1,047.34 over the previous 3 months, whereas the restaurants in the sample had the following changes in profit. These data are saved in the **PROFIT** file.

$2,232.90	$ 545.47	$3,440.70	$1,809.10
$6,552.70	$4,798.70	$2,965.00	$2,610.70
$3,381.30	$1,591.40	$2,376.20	−$2,191.00

Note that the last number is negative, representing a decrease in profits.
   a. Specify the appropriate null and alternative hypotheses for determining whether the mean profit change for restaurants with frequency programs is significantly greater (in a statistical sense) than $1,047.34.
   b. Conduct the test of part **b** using $\alpha = .05$. Does it appear that the frequency program would be profitable for the company if adopted nationwide?

6.127 EPA limits on vinyl chloride. The EPA sets an airborne limit of 5 parts per million (ppm) on vinyl chloride, a colorless gas used to make plastics, adhesives, and other chemicals. It is both a carcinogen and a mutagen (New Jersey Department of Health, *Hazardous Substance Fact Sheet*, 2005). A major plastics manufacturer, attempting to control the amount of vinyl chloride its workers are exposed to, has given instructions to halt production if the mean amount of vinyl chloride in the air exceeds 3.0 ppm. A random sample of 50 air specimens produced the following statistics: $\bar{x} = 3.1$ ppm, $s = .5$ ppm.
   a. Do these statistics provide sufficient evidence to halt the production process? Use $\alpha = .01$.
   b. If you were the plant manager, would you want to use a large or a small value for α for the test in part **a**? Explain.
   c. Find the *p*-value for the test and interpret its value.

6.128 EPA limits vinyl chloride (cont'd). Refer to Exercise 6.127.
   a. In the context of the problem, define a Type II error.
   b. Calculate β for the test described in part **a** of Exercise 6.127, assuming that the true mean is $\mu = 3.1$ ppm.
   c. What is the power of the test to detect a departure from the manufacturer's 3.0 ppm limit when the mean is 3.1 ppm?

   d. Repeat parts **b** and **c** assuming that the true mean is 3.2 ppm. What happens to the power of the test as the plant's mean vinyl chloride level departs further from the limit?

6.129 EPA limits on vinyl chloride (cont'd). Refer to Exercises 6.127 and 6.128.
   a. Suppose an α value of .05 is used to conduct the test. Does this change favor halting production? Explain.
   b. Determine the value of β and the power for the test when $\alpha = .05$ and $\mu = 3.1$.
   c. What happens to the power of the test when α is increased?

6.130 Evaluating a measuring instrument. One way of evaluating a measuring instrument is to repeatedly measure the same item and compare the average of these measurements to the item's known measured value. The difference is used to assess the instrument's accuracy (American Society for Quality). To evaluate a particular Metlar scale, an item whose weight is known to be 16.01 ounces is weighed five times by the same operator. The measurements (in ounces) are saved in the **METLAR** file and follow:

15.99	16.00	15.97	16.01	15.96

   a. In a statistical sense, does the average measurement differ from 16.01? Conduct the appropriate hypothesis test at $\alpha = .05$. What does your analysis suggest about the accuracy of the instrument?
   b. List any assumptions you make in conducting the hypothesis test, part **a**.
   c. Evaluate the instrument's precision by testing whether the standard deviation of the weight measurements is greater than .01. Use $\alpha = .05$.

6.131 Testing the validity of a TV advertisement. The manufacturer of an over-the-counter analgesic claims that its product brings pain relief to headache sufferers in less than 3.5 minutes, on average. In order to be able to make this claim in its television advertisements, the manufacturer was required by a particular television network to present statistical evidence in support of the claim. The manufacturer reported that for a random sample of 50 headache sufferers, the mean time to relief was 3.3 minutes and the standard deviation was 1.1 minutes.
   a. Do these data support the manufacturer's claim? Test using $\alpha = .05$.
   b. Report the *p*-value of the test.
   c. In general, do large *p*-values or small *p*-values support the manufacturer's claim? Explain.

Applying the Concepts—Advanced

6.132 NCAA "March Madness." For three weeks each March, the NCAA holds its annual men's basketball championship tournament. The 64 best college basketball teams in the nation play a single-elimination tournament—a total of 63 games—to determine the NCAA champion. Tournament followers, from hardcore gamblers to the casual fan who enters the office betting pool, have a strong interest in handicapping the games. To provide insight into this phenomenon, statisticians Hal Stern and Barbara Mock analyzed data from 13 previous NCAA tournaments and published their results in *Chance* (Winter 1998). The results of first-round games are summarized in the next table.

Summary of First-Round NCAA Tournament Games, 1985–1997

Matchup (Seeds)	Number of Games	Number Won by Favorite (Higher Seed)	Margin of Victory (Points) Mean	Margin of Victory (Points) Standard Deviation
1 vs 16	52	52	22.9	12.4
2 vs 15	52	49	17.2	11.4
3 vs 14	52	41	10.6	12.0
4 vs 13	52	42	10.0	12.5
5 vs 12	52	37	5.3	10.4
6 vs 11	52	36	4.3	10.7
7 vs 10	52	35	3.2	10.5
8 vs 9	52	22	−2.1	11.0

Source: Stern, H. S., and Mock, B. "College basketball upsets: Will a 16-seed ever beat a 1-seed?" *Chance*, Vol. 11, No. 1, Winter 1998, p. 29 (Table 3). Reprinted with permission from *Chance*. © 1998 by the American Statistical Association. All rights reserved.

a. A common perception among fans, media, and gamblers is that the higher seeded team has a better than 50-50 chance of winning a first-round game. Is there evidence to support this perception? Conduct the appropriate test for each matchup. What trends do you observe?

b. Is there evidence to support the claim that a 1-, 2-, 3-, or 4-seeded team will win by an average of more than 10 points in first-round games? Conduct the appropriate test for each matchup.

c. Is there evidence to support the claim that a 5-, 6-, 7-, or 8-seeded team will win by an average of less than 5 points in first-round games? Conduct the appropriate test for each matchup.

d. For each matchup, test the null hypothesis that the standard deviation of the victory margin is 11 points.

e. The researchers also calculated the difference between the game outcome (victory margin, in points) and point spread established by Las Vegas oddsmakers for a sample of 360 recent NCAA tournament games. The mean difference is .7, and the standard deviation of the difference is 11.3. If the true mean difference is 0, then the point spread can be considered a good predictor of the game outcome. Use this sample information to test the hypothesis that the point spread, on average, is a good predictor of the victory margin in NCAA tournament games.

6.133 Factors that inhibit learning in marketing. What factors inhibit the learning process in the classroom? To answer this question, researchers at Murray State University surveyed 40 students from a senior-level marketing class (*Marketing Education Review*, Fall 1994). Each student was given a list of factors and asked to rate the extent to which each factor inhibited the learning process in courses offered in their department. A 7-point rating scale was used, where 1 = "not at all" and 7 = "to a great extent." The factor with the highest rating was instructor related: "Professors who place too much emphasis on a single right answer rather than overall thinking and creative ideas." Summary statistics for the student ratings of this factor are $\bar{x} = 4.70$, $s = 1.62$.

a. Conduct a test to determine if the true mean rating for this instructor-related factor exceeds 4. Use $\alpha = .05$. Interpret the test results.

b. Examine the results of the study from a practical view, then discuss why "statistically significant" does not always imply "practically significant."

c. Because the variable of interest, rating, is measured on a 7-point scale, it is unlikely that the population of ratings will be normally distributed. Consequently, some analysts may perceive the test, part **a**, to be invalid and search for alternative methods of analysis. Defend or refute this argument.

6.134 Testing the placebo effect. *The placebo effect* describes the phenomenon of improvement in the condition of a patient taking a placebo—a pill that looks and tastes real but contains no medically active chemicals. Physicians at a clinic in La Jolla, California, gave what they thought were drugs to 7,000 asthma, ulcer, and herpes patients. Although the doctors later learned that the drugs were really placebos, 70% of the patients reported an improved condition (*Forbes*, May 22, 1995). Use this information to test (at $\alpha = .05$) the placebo effect at the clinic. Assume that if the placebo is ineffective, the probability of a patient's condition improving is .5.

Critical Thinking Challenge

6.135 The hot tamale caper. "Hot tamales" are chewy, cinnamon-flavored candies. A bulk vending machine is known to dispense, on average, 15 hot tamales per bag with a standard deviation of 3 per bag. *Chance* (Fall 2000) published an article on a classroom project in which students were required to purchase bags of hot tamales from the machine and count the number of candies per bag. One student group claimed they purchased five bags that had the following candy counts: 25, 23, 21, 21, and 20. These data are saved in the **TAMALES** file. There was some question as to whether the students had fabricated the data. Use a hypothesis test to gain insight into whether or not the data collected by the students are fabricated. Use a level of significance that gives the benefit of the doubt to the students.

References

Snedecor, G. W., and Cochran, W. G. *Statistical Methods,* 7th ed. Ames: Iowa State University Press, 1980.

Wackerly, D., Mendenhall, W., and Scheaffer, R. *Mathematical Statistics with Applications,* 7th ed. Belmont, CA: Thomson, Brooks/Cole, 2008.

USING TECHNOLOGY

SPSS: Tests of Hypotheses

Note: SPSS cannot currently conduct a test for a population variance.

Testing μ

Step 1 Access the SPSS spreadsheet file that contains the sample data.

Step 2 Click on the "Analyze" button on the SPSS menu bar and then click on "Compare Means" and "One-Sample T Test," as shown in Figure 6.S.1.

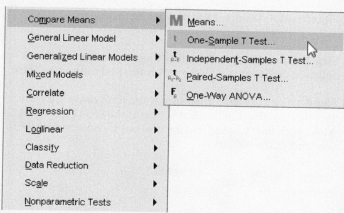

Figure 6.S.1 SPSS menu options for a test on a mean

Step 3 On the resulting dialog box (shown in Figure 6.S.2), specify the quantitative variable of interest in the "Test Variable(s)" box and the value of μ_0 for the null hypothesis in the "Test Value" box.

Figure 6.S.2 SPSS 1-sample t test for mean dialog box

Step 4 Click "OK." SPSS will automatically conduct a two-tailed test of hypothesis.

Important Note: The SPSS one-sample t-procedure uses the t-statistic to conduct the test of hypothesis. When the sample size n is small, this is the appropriate method. When the sample size n is large, the t-value will be approximately equal to the large-sample z-value and the resulting test will still be valid.

Testing p

Step 1 Access the SPSS spreadsheet file that contains the sample data.

Step 2 Click on the "Analyze" button on the SPSS menu bar and then click on "Nonparametric Tests" (see Figure 6.S.1).

Step 3 Select "Binomial" from the next menu.

Step 4 On the resulting dialog box (shown in Figure 6.S.3), specify the binomial variable of interest in the "Test Variable List" box and the value of p_0 for the null hypothesis in the "Test Proportion" box.

Figure 6.S.3 SPSS binomial test for proportion dialog box

Step 5 Click "OK" to generate the two-tailed test of hypothesis.

Important: SPSS requires the binomial variable to be entered as a quantitative variable. Typically, this is accomplished by entering two numerical values (e.g., 0 and 1) for the two outcomes of the variable. If the data have been entered in this fashion, select the "Get from data" option in the "Define Dichotomy" area of the dialog box.

You can also create the two outcome values for a quantitative variable by selecting the "Cut point" option in the "Define Dichotomy" area and specifying a numerical value. All values of the variables less than or equal to the cut point value are assigned to one group (success), and all other values are assigned to the other group (failure).

Minitab: Tests of Hypotheses

Testing μ

Step 1 Access the Minitab data worksheet that contains the sample data.

Step 2 Click on the "Stat" button on the Minitab menu bar and then click on "Basic Statistics" and "1-Sample t," as shown in Figure 6.M.1.

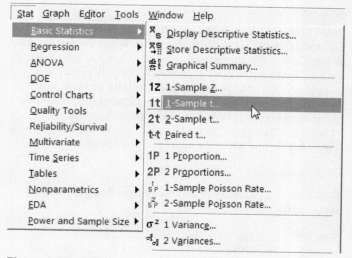

Figure 6.M.1 Minitab menu options for a test on a mean

Step 3 On the resulting dialog box (shown in Figure 6.M.2), click on "Samples in Columns" and then specify the quantitative variable of interest in the open box.

Figure 6.M.2 Minitab 1-sample t test for mean dialog box

Step 4 Check "Perform hypothesis test" and then specify the value of μ_0 for the null hypothesis in the "Hypothesized mean" box.

Step 5 Click on the "Options" button at the bottom of the dialog box and specify the form of the alternative hypothesis, as shown in Figure 6.M.3.

Figure 6.M.3 Minitab 1-sample t test options

Step 6 Click "OK" to return to the "1-Sample t" dialog box and then click "OK" again to produce the hypothesis test.

Note: If you want to produce a test for the mean from summary information (e.g., the sample mean, sample standard deviation, and sample size), click on "Summarized data" in the "1-Sample t" dialog box, enter the values of the summary statistics and μ_0, and then click "OK."

Important: The Minitab one-sample t-procedure uses the t-statistic to generate the hypothesis test. When the sample size n is small, this is the appropriate method. When the sample size n is large, the t-value will be approximately equal to the large-sample z-value, and the resulting test will still be valid. If you have a large sample and you know the value of the population standard deviation σ (which is rarely the case), select "1-sample Z" from the "Basic Statistics" menu options (see Figure 6.M.1) and make the appropriate selections.

Testing p

Step 1 Access the Minitab data worksheet that contains the sample data.

Step 2 Click on the "Stat" button on the Minitab menu bar and then click on "Basic Statistics" and "1 Proportion" (see Figure 6.M.1).

Step 3 On the resulting dialog box (shown in Figure 6.M.4), click on "Samples in Columns," and then specify the qualitative variable of interest in the open box.

Figure 6.M.4 Minitab 1 proportion test dialog box

Step 4 Check "Perform hypothesis test" and then specify the null hypothesis value p_0 in the "Hypothesized proportion" box.

Step 5 Click "Options," then specify the form of the alternative hypothesis in the resulting dialog box, as shown in Figure 6.M.5. Also, check the "Use test and interval based on normal distribution" box at the bottom.

Figure 6.M.5 Minitab 1 proportion test options

Step 6 Click "OK" to return to the "1-Proportion" dialog box and then click "OK" again to produce the test results.

Note: If you want to produce a confidence interval for a proportion from summary information (e.g., the number of successes and the sample size), click on "Summarized data" in the "1 Proportion" dialog box (see Figure 6.M.4). Enter the value for the number of trials (i.e., the sample size) and the number of events (i.e., the number of successes), and then click "OK."

Testing σ^2

Step 1 Access the Minitab data worksheet that contains the sample data set.

Step 2 Click on the "Stat" button on the Minitab menu bar and and then click on "Basic Statistics" and "1 Variance" (see Figure 6.M.1).

Step 3 Once the resulting dialog box appears (see Figure 6.M.6), click on "Samples in Columns" and then specify the quantitative variable of interest in the open box.

Step 4 Check "Perform hypothesis test" and specify the null hypothesis value of the standard deviation σ_0 in the open box.

Figure 6.M.6 Minitab 1 variance test dialog box

Step 5 Click on the "Options" button at the bottom of the dialog box and specify the form of the alternative hypothesis (similar to Figure 6.M.3).

Step 6 Click "OK" twice to produce the hypothesis test.

Note: If you want to produce a test for the variance from summary information (e.g., the sample standard deviation and sample size), click on "Summarized data" in the "1 Variance" dialog box (Figure 6.M.6) and enter the values of the summary statistics.

Excel/DDXL: Tests of Hypotheses

Testing μ

Step 1 Highlight (select) the data column you want to analyze on the Excel spreadsheet.

Step 2 Click on "Add-Ins" in the main Excel menu bar and select "DDXL." On the resulting menu, select "Hypothesis Tests," as shown in Figure 6.E.1.

Figure 6.E.1 Excel/DDXL menu options for hypothesis tests

Step 3 In the resulting window, select "1 Var t Test" in the Function Type box, as shown in Figure 6.E.2.

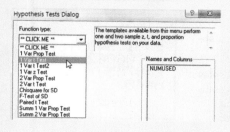

Figure 6.E.2 DDXL hypothesis tests dialog box

Step 4 Move the variable of interest into the "Quantitative Variable" box and then click "OK," as shown in Figure 6.E.3.

Figure 6.E.3 DDXL menu selections for test on a mean

Step 5 In the resulting window, specify the hypothesized value of μ, α, and the form of the alternative hypothesis and then click "Compute," as shown in Figure 6.E.4. The test results will appear.

Figure 6.E.4 DDXL t test on a mean setup options

Testing p

Step 1 Highlight (select) the data column you want to analyze on the Excel spreadsheet.

Step 2 Click on "Add-Ins" in the main Excel menu bar and select "DDXL." On the resulting menu, select "Hypothesis Tests," as shown in Figure 6.E.1.

Step 3 In the resulting window, select "1 Var Prop Test" in the Function Type box (see Figure 6.E.2).

Step 4 Move the variable of interest into the "Proportions Variable" box and then click "OK," as shown in Figure 6.E.5.

Figure 6.E.5 DDXL menu selections for test of a proportion

Step 5 In the resulting window, specify the hypothesized value of p, α, and the form of the alternative hypothesis and then click "Compute" as shown in Figure 6.E.6. The test results will appear.

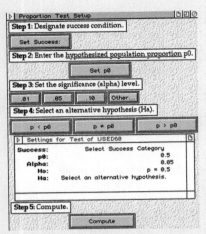

Figure 6.E.6 DDXL test on a proportion setup options

Testing σ^2

Step 1 Highlight (select) the data column you want to analyze on the Excel spreadsheet.

Step 2 Click on "Add-Ins" in the main Excel menu bar and select "DDXL." In the resulting window, select "Hypothesis Tests," as shown in Figure 6.E.1.

Step 3 In the resulting window, select "Chisquare for SD" in the Function Type box (see Figure 6.E.2).

Step 4 Move the variable of interest into the "Quantitative Variable" box and then click "OK," as shown in Figure 6.E.7.

Figure 6.E.7 DDXL menu selections for test of a variance

Step 5 In the resulting window, specify the hypothesized value of σ, α, and the form of the alternative hypothesis and then click "Compute" as shown in Figure 6.E.8. The test results will appear.

Figure 6.E.8 DDXL test on a variance setup options

TI-84 Graphing Calculator: Tests of Hypotheses

Note: The TI-84 graphing calculator cannot currently conduct a test for a population variance.

Hypothesis Test for a Population Mean (Large Sample Case)

Step 1 *Enter the Data (Skip to Step 2 if you have summary statistics, not raw data)*

- Press **STAT** and select **1:Edit**

Note: If the list already contains data, clear the old data. Use the up **ARROW** to highlight "L1."

- Press **CLEAR ENTER**
- Use the **ARROW** and **ENTER** keys to enter the data set into **L1**

Step 2 *Access the Statistical Tests Menu*

- Press **STAT**
- Arrow right to **TESTS**
- Press **ENTER** to select either **Z-Test** (if large sample and σ known) or **T-Test** (if σ unknown)

Step 3 *Choose "Data" or "Stats." ("Data" is selected when you have entered the raw data into a List. "Stats" is selected when you are given only the mean, standard deviation, and sample size.)*

- Press **ENTER**

If you selected "Data," enter the values for the hypothesis test where μ_0 = the value for μ in the null hypothesis, σ = assumed value of the population standard deviation.

- Set **List** to **L1**
- Set **Freq** to **1**
- Use the **ARROW** to highlight the appropriate alternative hypothesis
- Press **ENTER**
- Arrow down to "**Calculate**"
- Press **ENTER**

If you selected "Stats," enter the values for the hypothesis test where μ_0 = the value for μ in the null hypothesis, σ = assumed value of the population standard deviation.

- Enter the sample mean, sample standard deviation, and sample size
- Use the **ARROW** to highlight the appropriate alternative hypothesis
- Press **ENTER**
- Arrow down to "**Calculate**"
- Press **ENTER**

The chosen test will be displayed as well as the z (or t) test statistic, the p-value, the sample mean, and the sample size.

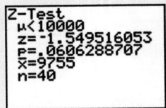

Testing *p*

Step 1 *Enter the Data (Skip to Step 2 if you have summary statistics, not raw data)*

- Press **STAT** and select **1:Edit**

Note: If the list already contains data, clear the old data. Use the up **ARROW** to highlight "**L1.**"

- Press **CLEAR ENTER**
- Use the **ARROW** and **ENTER** keys to enter the data set into **L1**

Step 2 *Access the Statistical Tests Menu*

- Press **STAT**
- Arrow right to **TESTS**
- Press **ENTER** after selecting **1-Prop Z Test**

Step 3 *Enter the hypothesized proportion p_0, the number of success x, and the sample size n*

- Use the **ARROW** to highlight the appropriate alternative hypothesis
- Press **ENTER**
- Arrow down to "**Calculate**"
- Press **ENTER**

The chosen test will be displayed as well as the *z*-test statistic and the *p*-value.

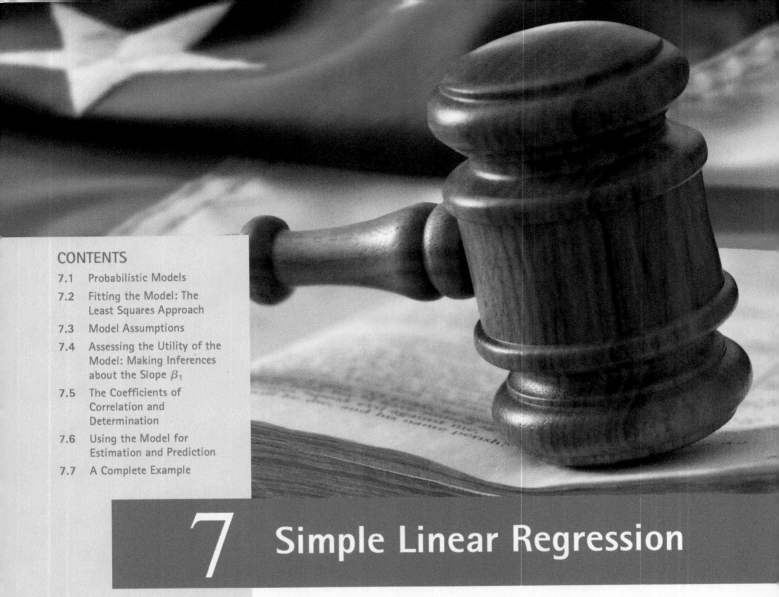

CONTENTS

7 Simple Linear Regression

Where We've Been

- Presented methods for estimating and testing population parameters (e.g., the mean, proportion, and variance) for a single sample

- Extended these methods to allow for a comparison of population parameters for multiple samples

Where We're Going

- Introduce the straight-line (*simple linear regression*) model as a means of relating one quantitative variable to another quantitative variable

- Introduce the *correlation coefficient* as a means of relating one quantitative variable to another quantitative variable

- Assess how well the simple linear regression model fits the sample data

- Employ the simple linear regression model for predicting the value of one variable from a specified value of another variable

Statistics IN Action   Legal Advertising—Does It Pay?

According to the American Bar Association, there are over 1 million lawyers competing for your business. To gain a competitive edge, these lawyers aggressively advertise their services. The advertising of legal services has long been a controversial subject, with many believing that it constitutes an unethical (and in some cases even illegal) practice. Nonetheless, legal advertisements appear in nearly all media, ranging from the covers of telephone directories to infomercials on television, as well as a significant presence on the Internet. In fact, Erickson Marketing, Inc., reports that "attorneys are the #1 category of advertising in the Yellow Pages."

For this *Statistics in Action*, we present an actual recent case involving two former law partners. One partner (A) sued the other (B) over who should pay what share of the expenses of their former partnership. Partner A handled personal injury (PI) cases, while partner B handled only worker's compensation (WC) cases. The firm's advertising was focused on personal injury only, but partner A claimed that the ads resulted in the firm getting more WC cases for partner B, and therefore partner B should share the advertising expenses.   *(continued)*

Statistics in Action
(continued)

Table SIA7.1 shows the firm's new PI and WC cases each month over a 42-month period for this partnership. Also shown is the total expenditure on advertising each month and over the previous six months. Do these data provide support for the hypothesis that increased advertising expenditures are associated with more PI cases? With more WC cases?

If advertising expenditures have a statistically significant association with the number of cases, does this necessarily mean that there is a causal relationship, that is, that spending more on advertising causes an increase in the number of cases? Based

Table SIA 7.1	Legal Advertising Data			
Month	Advertising Expenditure ($)	New PI Cases	New WC Cases	6 Months Cumulative Adv. Exp. ($)
1	9,221.55	7	26	n/a
2	6,684.00	9	33	n/a
3	200.00	12	18	n/a
4	14,546.75	27	15	n/a
5	5,170.14	9	19	n/a
6	5,810.30	13	26	n/a
7	5,816.20	11	24	41,632.74
8	8,236.38	7	22	38,227.39
9	−2,089.55	13	12	39,779.77
10	29,282.24	7	15	37,490.22
11	9,193.58	9	21	52,225.71
12	9,499.18	8	24	56,249.15
13	11,128.76	18	25	59,938.03
14	9,057.64	9	19	65,250.59
15	13,604.54	25	12	66,071.85
16	14,411.76	26	33	81,765.94
17	13,724.28	27	32	66,895.46
18	13,419.42	12	21	71,426.16
19	17,372.33	14	18	75,346.40
20	6,296.35	5	25	81,589.97
21	13,191.59	22	12	78,828.68
22	26,798.80	15	7	78,415.73
23	18,610.95	12	22	90,802.77
24	829.53	18	27	95,689.44
25	16,976.53	20	25	83,099.55
26	14,076.98	38	26	82,703.75
27	24,791.75	13	28	90,484.38
28	9,691.25	18	31	102,084.54
29	28,948.25	21	40	84,976.99
30	21,373.52	7	39	95,314.29
31	9,675.25	16	41	115,858.28
32	33,213.55	12	48	108,557.00
33	19,859.85	15	28	127,693.57
34	10,475.25	18	29	122,761.67
35	24,790.84	30	20	123,545.67
36	36,660.94	12	27	119,388.26
37	8,812.50	30	26	134,675.68
38	41,817.75	20	45	133,812.93
39	27,399.33	19	30	142,417.13
40	25,723.10	29	33	149,956.61
41	16,312.10	58	24	165,204.46
42	26,332.78	42	40	156,725.72
43	60,207.58	24	36	146,397.56
44	42,485.39	47	29	197,792.64
45	35,601.92	24	17	198,460.28
46	72,071.50	14	13	206,662.87
47	12,797.11	31	15	253,011.27
48	12,310.50	26	16	249,496.28

Source: Info Tech, Inc., Gainesville, Florida.

Data Set: LEGALADV

on these data, should partner A or partner B bear the brunt of the advertising expenditures?

The data for the case are saved in the **LEGALADV** file. In the *Statistics in Action Revisited* sections of this chapter, we examine the relationship between monthly advertising expenditure and the number of new legal cases in an attempt to answer these questions.

Data Set: LEGALADV

Statistics IN Action Revisited

- Estimating a Straight-Line Regression Model (p. 391)
- Assessing How Well a Straight-Line Regression Model Fits Data (p. 406)
- Using the Coefficient of Correlation and the Coefficient of Determination (p. 416)
- Prediction Using the Straight-Line Model (p. 425)

In Chapters 5–6, we described methods for making inferences about population means. The mean of a population was treated as a *constant,* and we showed how to use sample data to estimate or to test hypotheses about this constant mean. In many applications, the mean of a population is not viewed as a constant but rather as a variable. For example, the mean sale price of residences sold this year in a large city might be treated as a variable that depends on the square feet of living space in the residence. For example, the relationship might be

$$\text{Mean sale price} = \$30{,}000 + \$60 \text{ (square feet)}$$

This formula implies that the mean sale price of 1,000-square-foot homes is $90,000, the mean sale price of 2,000-square-foot homes is $150,000, and the mean sale price of 3,000-square-foot homes is $210,000.

In this chapter, we discuss situations in which the mean of the population is treated as a variable, dependent on the value of another variable. The dependence of residential sale price on the square feet of living space is one illustration. Other examples include the dependence of mean sales revenue of a firm on advertising expenditure, the dependence of mean starting salary of a college graduate on the student's GPA, and the dependence of mean monthly production of automobiles on the total number of sales in the previous month.

We begin our discussion with the simplest of all models relating a population mean to another variable—*the straight-line model.* We show how to use the sample data to estimate the straight-line relationship between the mean value of one variable, *y,* as it relates to a second variable, *x.* The methodology of estimating and using a straight-line relationship is referred to as *simple linear regression analysis.*

7.1 Probabilistic Models

An important consideration in merchandising a product is the amount of money spent on advertising. Suppose you want to model the monthly sales revenue of an appliance store as a function of the monthly advertising expenditure. The first question to be answered is this: "Do you think an exact relationship exists between these two variables?" That is, do you think it is possible to state the exact monthly sales revenue if the amount spent on advertising is known? We think you will agree with us that this is *not* possible for several reasons. Sales depend on many variables other than advertising expenditure—for example, time of year, the state of the general economy, inventory, and price structure. Even if many variables are included in a model, it is still unlikely that we would be able to predict the monthly sales *exactly.* There will almost certainly be some variation in monthly sales due strictly to *random phenomena* that cannot be modeled or explained.

If we were to construct a model that hypothesized an exact relationship between variables, it would be called a **deterministic model.** For example, if we believe that *y,* the monthly sales revenue, will be exactly 15 times *x,* the monthly advertising expenditure, we write

$$y = 15x$$

This represents a *deterministic relationship* between the variables y and x. It implies that y can always be determined exactly when the value of x is known. *There is no allowance for error in this prediction.*

If, on the other hand, we believe there will be unexplained variation in monthly sales—perhaps caused by important but unincluded variables or by random phenomena—we discard the deterministic model and use a model that accounts for this **random error.** This **probabilistic model** includes both a deterministic component and a random error component. For example, if we hypothesize that the sales y are related to advertising expenditure x by

$$y = 15x + \text{Random error}$$

we are hypothesizing a *probabilistic relationship* between y and x. Note that the deterministic component of this probabilistic model is $15x$.

Figure 7.1a shows the possible values of y and x for five different months, when the model is deterministic. All the pairs of (x, y) data points must fall exactly on the line because a deterministic model leaves no room for error.

Figure 7.1b shows a possible set of points for the same values of x when we are using a probabilistic model. Note that the deterministic part of the model (the straight line itself) is the same. Now, however, the inclusion of a random error component allows the monthly sales to vary from this line. Because we know that the sales revenue does vary randomly for a given value of x, the probabilistic model provides a more realistic model for y than does the deterministic model.

General Form of Probabilistic Models

$$y = \text{Deterministic component} + \text{Random error}$$

where y is the variable of interest. We always assume that the mean value of the random error equals 0. This is equivalent to assuming that the mean value of y, $E(y)$, equals the deterministic component of the model; that is,

$$E(y) = \text{Deterministic component}$$

In this chapter, we present the simplest of probabilistic models—the **straight-line model**—which derives its name from the fact that the deterministic portion of the model graphs as a straight line. Fitting this model to a set of data is an example of **regression analysis,** or **regression modeling.** The elements of the straight-line model are summarized in the next box.

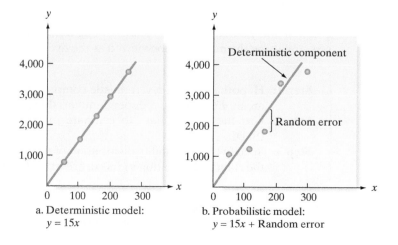

Figure 7.1

Possible sales revenues, y, for five different months, x

a. Deterministic model: $y = 15x$

b. Probabilistic model: $y = 15x + \text{Random error}$

FRANCIS GALTON (1822–1911)

The Law of Universal Regression

Francis Galton was the youngest of seven children born to a middle-class English family of Quaker faith. A cousin of Charles Darwin, Galton attended Trinity College (Cambridge, England) to study medicine. Due to the death of his father, Galton was unable to obtain his degree. His competence in both medicine and mathematics, however, led Galton to pursue a career as a scientist. Galton made major contributions to the fields of genetics, psychology, meteorology, and anthropology. Some consider Galton to be the first social scientist for his applications of the novel statistical concepts of the time—in particular, regression and correlation. While studying natural inheritance in 1886, Galton collected data on the heights of parents and adult children. He noticed the tendency for tall (or short) parents to have tall (or short) children, but the children were not as tall (or short), on average, as their parents. Galton called this phenomenon the "law of universal regression," for the average heights of adult children tended to "regress" to the mean of the population. Galton, with the help of his friend and disciple, Karl Pearson, applied the straight-line model to the height data, and the term *regression* model was coined. ∎

A First-Order (Straight-Line) Probabilistic Model

$$y = \beta_0 + \beta_1 x + \varepsilon$$

where

$y = $ **Dependent** *or* **response variable** (variable to be modeled)

$x = $ **Independent** *or* **predictor variable** (variable used as a predictor of y)*

$E(y) = \beta_0 + \beta_1 x = $ Deterministic component

ε (epsilon) $ = $ Random error component

β_0 (beta zero) $ = $ **y-intercept of the line,** that is, the point at which the line *intercepts or cuts through the y-axis* (see Figure 7.2)

β_1 (beta one) $ = $ **Slope of the line,** that is, the change (amount of increase or decrease) in the deterministic component of y for every 1-unit increase in x

[*Note:* A *positive* slope implies that $E(y)$ *increases* by the amount b_1 for each unit increase in x (see Figure 7.2). A *negative* slope implies that $E(y)$ *decreases* by the amount β_1.]

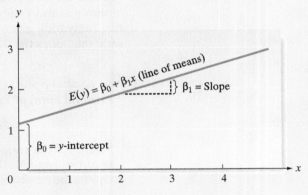

Figure 7.2
The straight-line model

In the probabilistic model, the deterministic component is referred to as the **line of means** because the mean of y, $E(y)$, is equal to the straight-line component of the model—that is,

$$E(y) = \beta_0 + \beta_1 x$$

Note that the Greek symbols β_0 and β_1, respectively, represent the y-intercept and slope of the model. They are population parameters that will be known only if we have access to the entire population of (x, y) measurements. Together with a specific value of the independent variable x, they determine the mean value of y, which is a specific point on the line of means (Figure 7.2).

The values of β_0 and β_1 will be unknown in almost all practical applications of regression analysis. The process of developing a model, estimating the unknown parameters, and using the model can be viewed as the five-step procedure shown in the next box.

Step 1: Hypothesize the deterministic component of the model that relates the mean, $E(y)$, to the independent variable x (Section 7.1).

Step 2: Use the sample data to estimate unknown parameters in the model (Section 7.2).

Step 3: Specify the probability distribution of the random error term and estimate the standard deviation of this distribution (Section 7.3).

*The word *independent* should not be interpreted in a probabilistic sense, as defined in Chapter 3. The phrase *independent variable* is used in regression analysis to refer to a predictor variable for the response y.

Step 4: Statistically evaluate the usefulness of the model (Sections 7.4 and 7.5).

Step 5: When satisfied that the model is useful, use it for prediction, estimation, and other purposes (Section 7.6).

Exercises 7.1–7.9

Learning the Mechanics

7.1 In each case, graph the line that passes through the given points.
   a. $(1, 1)$ and $(5, 5)$ **b.** $(0, 3)$ and $(3, 0)$
   c. $(-1, 1)$ and $(4, 2)$ **d.** $(-6, -3)$ and $(2, 6)$

7.2 Give the slope and y-intercept for each of the lines graphed in Exercise 7.1.

7.3 The equation for a straight line (deterministic model) is

$$y = \beta_0 + \beta_1 x$$

If the line passes through the point $(-2, 4)$, then $x = -2$, $y = 4$ must satisfy the equation; that is,

$$4 = \beta_0 + \beta_1(-2)$$

Similarly, if the line passes through the point $(4, 6)$, then $x = 4$, $y = 6$ must satisfy the equation; that is,

$$6 = \beta_0 + \beta_1(4)$$

Use these two equations to solve for β_0 and β_1; then find the equation of the line that passes through the points $(-2, 4)$ and $(4, 6)$.

7.4 Refer to Exercise 7.3. Find the equations of the lines that pass through the points listed in Exercise 7.1.

7.5 Plot the following lines:
   a. $y = 4 + x$ **b.** $y = 5 - 2x$
   c. $y = -4 + 3x$ **d.** $y = -2x$
   e. $y = x$ **f.** $y = .50 + 1.5x$

7.6 Give the slope and y-intercept for each of the lines graphed in Exercise 7.5.

7.7 Why do we generally prefer a probabilistic model to a deterministic model? Give examples for when the two types of models might be appropriate.

7.8 What is the line of means?

7.9 If a straight-line probabilistic relationship relates the mean $E(y)$ to an independent variable x, does it imply that every value of the variable y will always fall exactly on the line of means? Why or why not?

7.2 Fitting the Model: The Least Squares Approach

After the straight-line model has been hypothesized to relate the mean $E(y)$ to the independent variable x, the next step is to collect data and to estimate the (unknown) population parameters, the y-intercept β_0 and the slope β_1.

To begin with a simple example, suppose an appliance store conducts a 5-month experiment to determine the effect of advertising on sales revenue. The results are shown in Table 7.1. (The number of measurements and the measurements themselves are unrealistically simple to avoid arithmetic confusion in this introductory example.) This set of data will be used to demonstrate the five-step procedure of regression modeling given in Section 7.1. In this section, we hypothesize the deterministic component of the model and estimate its unknown parameters (steps 1 and 2). The model assumptions and the random error component (step 3) are the subjects of Section 7.3, whereas Sections 7.4 and 7.5 assess the utility of the model (step 4). Finally, we use the model for prediction and estimation (step 5) in Section 7.6.

Table 7.1	**Advertising-Sales Data**	
Month	Advertising Expenditure, x ($100s)	Sales Revenue, y ($1,000s)
1	1	1
2	2	1
3	3	2
4	4	2
5	5	4

Data Set: ADSALES

Step 1: *Hypothesize the deterministic component of the probabilistic model.* As stated before, we will consider only straight-line models in this chapter. Thus, the complete model to relate mean sales revenue $E(y)$ to advertising expenditure x is given by

$$E(y) = \beta_0 + \beta_1 x$$

Step 2: *Use sample data to estimate unknown parameters in the model.* This step is the subject of this section—namely, how can we best use the information in the sample of five observations in Table 7.1 to estimate the unknown y-intercept β_0 and slope β_1?

To determine whether a linear relationship between y and x is plausible, it is helpful to plot the sample data in a **scattergram** (or **scatterplot**). Recall (Section 2.9) that a scattergram locates each of the five data points on a graph, as shown in Figure 7.3. Note that the scattergram suggests a general tendency for y to increase as x increases. If you place a ruler on the scattergram, you will see that a line may be drawn through three of the five points, as shown in Figure 7.4. To obtain the equation of this visually fitted line, note that the line intersects the y-axis at $y = -1$, so the y-intercept is -1. Also, y increases exactly 1 unit for every 1-unit increase in x, indicating that the slope is $+1$. Therefore, the equation is

Figure 7.3

Scattergram for data in Table 7.1

$$\tilde{y} = -1 + 1(x) = -1 + x$$

where $\tilde{y}$ is used to denote the predicted y from the visual model.

One way to decide quantitatively how well a straight line fits a set of data is to note the extent to which the data points deviate from the line. For example, to evaluate the model in Figure 7.4, we calculate the magnitude of the *deviations* (i.e., the differences between the observed and the predicted values of y). These deviations, or **errors of prediction,** are the vertical distances between observed and predicted values (see Figure 7.4). The observed and predicted values of y, their differences, and their squared differences are shown in Table 7.2. Note that the *sum of errors* equals 0 and the *sum of squares of the errors* (SSE), which gives greater emphasis to large deviations of the points from the line, is equal to 2.

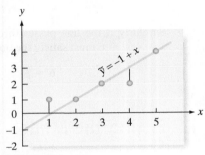

Figure 7.4

Visual straight line fitted to the data in Figure 7.3

You can see by shifting the ruler around the graph that it is possible to find many lines for which the sum of errors is equal to 0, but it can be shown that there is one (and only one) line for which the SSE is a *minimum*. This line is called the **least squares line,** the **regression line,** or the **least squares prediction equation.** The methodology used to obtain this line is called the **method of least squares.**

Table 7.2	Comparing Observed and Predicted Values for the Visual Model			
x	y	$\tilde{y} = -1 + x$	$(y - \tilde{y})$	$(y - \tilde{y})^2$
1	1	0	$(1 - 0) = 1$	1
2	1	1	$(1 - 1) = 0$	0
3	2	2	$(2 - 2) = 0$	0
4	2	3	$(2 - 3) = -1$	1
5	4	4	$(4 - 4) = 0$	0
			Sum of errors $= 0$	Sum of squared errors (SSE) $= 2$

To find the least squares prediction equation for a set of data, assume that we have a sample of n data points consisting of pairs of values of x and y, say (x_1, y_1), $(x_2, y_2), \ldots, (x_n, y_n)$. For example, the $n = 5$ data points shown in Table 7.2 are $(1, 1)$, $(2, 1)$, $(3, 2)$, $(4, 2)$, and $(5, 4)$. The fitted line, which we will calculate based on the five data points, is written as

$$\hat{y} = \hat{\beta}_0 + \hat{\beta}_1 x$$

The "hats" indicate that the symbols below them are estimates: $\hat{y}$ (y-hat) is an estimator of the mean value of y, $E(y)$, and a predictor of some future value of y; and $\hat{\beta}_0$ and $\hat{\beta}_1$ are estimators of β_0 and β_1, respectively.

For a given data point, say the point (x_i, y_i), the observed value of y is y_i, and the predicted value of y would be obtained by substituting x_i into the prediction equation:

$$\hat{y}_i = \hat{\beta}_0 + \hat{\beta}_1 x_i$$

And the deviation of the ith value of y from its predicted value is

$$(y_i - \hat{y}_i) = [y_i - (\hat{\beta}_0 + \hat{\beta}_1 x_i)]$$

Then the sum of squares of the deviations of the y-values about their predicted values for all the n points is

$$\text{SSE} = \sum [y_i - (\hat{\beta}_0 + \hat{\beta}_1 x_i)]^2$$

The quantities $\hat{\beta}_0$ and $\hat{\beta}_1$ that make the SSE a minimum are called the **least squares estimates** of the population parameters β_0 and β_1, and the prediction equation $\hat{y} = \hat{\beta}_0 + \hat{\beta}_1 x$ is called the *least squares line*.

The **least squares line** $\hat{y} = \hat{\beta}_0 + \hat{\beta}_1 x$ is one that has the following two properties:

1. The sum of the errors equals 0, i.e., mean error = 0.
2. The sum of squared errors (SSE) is smaller than for any other straight-line model, i.e., the error variance is minimum.

The values of $\hat{\beta}_0$ and $\hat{\beta}_1$ that minimize the SSE are (proof omitted) given by the formulas in the box.*

Formulas for the Least Squares Estimates

$$\text{Slope: } \hat{\beta}_1 = \frac{\text{SS}_{xy}}{\text{SS}_{xx}}$$

$$y\text{-intercept: } \hat{\beta}_0 = \bar{y} - \hat{\beta}_1 \bar{x}$$

$$\text{where** } \text{SS}_{xy} = \sum(x_i - \bar{x})(y_i - \bar{y})$$

$$\text{SS}_{xx} = \sum(x_i - \bar{x})^2$$

$$n = \text{Sample size}$$

---

*Students who are familiar with calculus should note that the values of β_0 and β_1 that minimize SSE $= \sum(y_i - \hat{y}_i)^2$ are obtained by setting the two partial derivatives $\partial\text{SSE}/\partial\beta_0$ and $\partial\text{SSE}/\partial\beta_1$ equal to 0. The solutions to these two equations yield the formulas shown in the box. Furthermore, we denote the *sample* solutions to the equations by $\hat{\beta}_0$ and $\hat{\beta}_1$, where the "hat" denotes that these are sample estimates of the true population intercept β_0 and true population slope β_1.

**Alternatively, you can use the following "shortcut" formulas:

$$\text{SS}_{xy} = \sum x_i y_i - \frac{(\sum x_i)(\sum y_j)}{n}$$

$$\text{SS}_{xx} = \sum x_i^2 - \frac{(\sum x_i)^2}{n}$$

Example 7.1

Applying the Method of Least Squares to the Advertising–Sales Data

Problem Refer to the advertising monthly-sales data presented in Table 7.1. Consider the straight-line model, $E(y) = \beta_0 + \beta_1 x$, where y = sales revenue (thousands of dollars) and x = advertising expenditure (hundreds of dollars).

a. Use the method of least squares to estimate the values of β_0 and β_1.

b. Predict the sales revenue when advertising expenditure is $200 (i.e., when $x = 2$).

c. Find SSE for the analysis.

d. Give practical interpretations to β_0 and β_1.

Solution

a. We used Excel to make the preliminary computations for finding the least squares line. The Excel spreadsheet is shown in Figure 7.5. Using the values on the spreadsheet, we find

$$\bar{x} = \frac{\Sigma x}{5} = \frac{15}{5} = 3$$

$$\bar{y} = \frac{\Sigma y}{5} = \frac{10}{5} = 2$$

$$SS_{xy} = \Sigma(x - \bar{x})(y - \bar{y}) = \Sigma(x - 3)(y - 2) = 7$$

$$SS_{xx} = \Sigma(x - \bar{x})^2 = \Sigma(x - 3)^2 = 10$$

Then the slope of the least squares line is

$$\hat{\beta}_1 = \frac{SS_{xy}}{SS_{xx}} = \frac{7}{10} = .7$$

and the y-intercept is

$$\hat{\beta}_0 = \bar{y} - \hat{\beta}_1 \bar{x} = 2 - (.7)(3) = 2 - 2.1 = -.1$$

The least squares line is thus

$$\hat{y} = \hat{\beta}_0 + \hat{\beta}_1 x = -.1 + .7x$$

The graph of this line is shown in Figure 7.6.

b. The predicted value of y for a given value of x can be obtained by substituting into the formula for the least squares line. Substituting $x = 2$ into the least squares equation yields

$$\hat{y} = -.1 + .7x = -.1 + .7(2) = 1.3$$

Thus, when advertising expenditure is $200, we predict monthly sales revenue to be $1,300. We show how to find a prediction interval for y in Section 7.6.

	A	B	C	D	E	F	G	H
1		AdvExp (X)	SalesRev (Y)	(X - 3)	(Y - 2)	(X-3)(Y-2)	(X-3)(X-3)	(Y-2)(Y-2)
2			1	1	-2	-1	2	4	1
3			2	1	-1	-1	1	1	1
4			3	2	0	0	0	0	0
5			4	2	1	0	0	1	0
6			5	4	2	2	4	4	4
7									
8	Totals		15	10	0	0	7	10	6
9	Mean		3	2					

Figure 7.5

Excel spreadsheet showing calculations for advertising-sales example

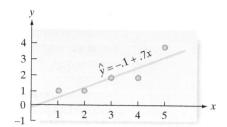

Figure 7.6
The line $\hat{y} = -.1 + .7x$ fitted to the data

c. The observed and predicted values of y, the deviations of the y values about their pre-dicted values, and the squares of these deviations are shown in the Excel spreadsheet, Figure 7.7. Note that SSE = 1.10, and (as we would expect) this is less than the SSE = 2.0 obtained in Table 7.2 for the visually fitted line.

	A	B	C	D	E	F
1	AdvExp (X)	SalesRev (Y)	Predicted Y=-.1+.7X	(Y-Yhat)	(Y-Yhat)(Y-Yhat)	
2	1	1	0.6	0.4	0.16	
3	2	1	1.3	-0.3	0.09	
4	3	2	2	0	0	
5	4	2	2.7	-0.7	0.49	
6	5	4	3.4	0.6	0.36	
7						
8			Sum	0	1.1	
9						
10						

Figure 7.7
Excel spreadsheet comparing observed and predicted values for advertising-sales example

Model Summary

Model	R	R Square	Adjusted R Square	Std. Error of the Estimate
1	.904[a]	.817	.756	.606

a. Predictors: (Constant), ADVEXP_X

ANOVA[b]

Model		Sum of Squares	df	Mean Square	F	Sig.
1	Regression	4.900	1	4.900	13.364	.035[a]
	Residual	1.100	3	.367		
	Total	6.000	4			

a. Predictors: (Constant), ADVEXP_X

b. Dependent Variable: SALES_Y

Coefficients[a]

Model		Unstandardized Coefficients		Standardized Coefficients	t	Sig.
		B	Std. Error	Beta		
1	(Constant)	-.100	.635		-.157	.885
	ADVEXP_X	.700	.191	.904	3.656	.035

a. Dependent Variable: SALES_Y

Figure 7.8a
SPSS printout for the advertising-sales regression

d. The estimated y-intercept, $\hat{\beta}_0 = -.1$, appears to imply that the estimated mean sales revenue is equal to $-.1$, or $-\$100$, when the advertising expenditure, x, is equal to \$0. Because negative sales revenues are not possible, this seems to make the model nonsensical. However, *the model parameters should be interpreted only within the sampled range of the independent variable*—in this case, for advertising expenditures between \$100 and \$500. Thus, the y-intercept—which is, by definition, at $x = 0$ (\$0 advertising expenditure)—is not within the range of the sampled values of x and is not subject to meaningful interpretation.

The slope of the least squares line, $\hat{\beta}_1 = .7$, implies that for every unit increase of x, the mean value of y is estimated to increase by .7 unit. In terms of this example, for every \$100 increase in advertising, the mean sales revenue is estimated to increase by \$700 *over the sampled range of advertising expenditures from \$100 to \$500.* Thus, the model does not imply that increasing the advertising expenditures from \$500 to \$1,000 will result in an increase in mean sales of \$3,500, because the range of x in the sample does not extend to \$1,000 ($x = 10$). Be careful to interpret the estimated parameters only within the sampled range of x.

Look Back The calculations required to obtain $\hat{\beta}_0$, $\hat{\beta}_1$, and SSE in simple linear regression, although straightforward, can become rather tedious. Even with the use of an Excel spreadsheet, the process is laborious, especially when the sample size is large. Fortunately, a statistical software package can significantly reduce the labor involved in regression calculations. The SPSS, Minitab, and Excel/DDXL outputs for the simple linear regression of the data in Table 7.1 are displayed in Figures 7.8a–c. The values of $\hat{\beta}_0$

Figure 7.8b

Minitab printout for the advertising-sales regression

Regression Analysis: SALES_Y versus ADVEXP_X

The regression equation is
SALES_Y = - 0.100 + 0.700 ADVEXP_X

Predictor	Coef	SE Coef	T	P
Constant	-0.1000	0.6351	-0.16	0.885
ADVEXP_X	0.7000	0.1915	3.66	0.035

S = 0.605530   R-Sq = 81.7%   R-Sq(adj) = 75.6%

Analysis of Variance

Source	DF	SS	MS	F	P
Regression	1	4.9000	4.9000	13.36	0.035
Residual Error	3	1.1000	0.3667		
Total	4	6.0000			

Figure 7.8c

Excel/DDXL printout for the advertising-sales regression

Regression: AdvExp (X) by SalesRev (Y)

Dependent variable is: SalesRev (Y)
No Selector
R squared = 81.7%   R squared (adjusted) = 75.6%
s = 0.6055   with   5 - 2 = 3   degrees of freedom

Source	Sum of Squares	df	Mean Square	F-ratio
Regression	4.9	1	4.9	13.4
Residual	1.1	3	0.366667	

Variable	Coefficient	s.e. of Coeff	t-ratio	prob
Constant	-0.1	0.6351	-0.157	0.8849
AdvExp (X)	0.7	0.1915	3.66	0.0354

and $\hat{\beta}_1$ are highlighted on the printouts. These values, $\hat{\beta}_0 = -.1$ and $\hat{\beta}_1 = .7$, agree exactly with our calculated values. The value of SSE = 1.10 is also highlighted on the printouts.

Now Work Exercise 7.16

Interpreting the Estimates of β_0 and β_1 in Simple Linear Regression

y-intercept: $\hat{\beta}_0$ represents the predicted value of y when $x = 0$ (*Caution:* This value will not be meaningful if the value $x = 0$ is nonsensical or outside the range of the sample data.)

slope: $\hat{\beta}_1$ represents the increase (or decrease) in y for every 1-unit increase in x (*Caution:* This interpretation is valid only for x-values within the range of the sample data.)

Even when the interpretations of the estimated parameters in a simple linear regression are meaningful, we need to remember that they are only estimates based on the sample. As such, their values will typically change in repeated sampling. How much confidence do we have that the estimated slope, $\hat{\beta}_1$ accurately approximates the true slope, β_1? This requires statistical inference, in the form of confidence intervals and tests of hypotheses, which we address in Section 7.4.

To summarize, we defined the best-fitting straight line to be the one that minimizes the sum of squared errors around the line, and we called it the *least squares line*. We should interpret the least squares line only within the sampled range of the independent variable. In subsequent sections, we show how to make statistical inferences about the model.

Statistics IN Action | Revisited | Estimating a Straight-Line Regression Model

We return to the legal advertising case involving two former law partners (p. 380). Recall that partner A (who handled PI cases) sued partner B (who handled WC cases) over who should pay what share of the advertising expenses of their former partnership. Monthly data were collected on the number of new PI cases, number of new WC cases, and the total amount spent (in thousands of dollars) on advertising over the previous six months. These data (shown in Table SIA7.1, p. 381) are saved in the **LEGALADV** file. Do these data provide support for the hypothesis that increased advertising expenditures are associated with more PI cases? Define y as the number of new PI cases per month and x as the cumulative 6-month advertising expenditures (in thousands of dollars). One way to investigate the link between these two variables is to fit the straight-line model, $E(y) = \beta_0 + \beta_1 x$, to the data in Table SIA7.1.

A Minitab scatterplot of the data and a simple linear regression printout are shown in Figure SIA7.1. Note that the least squares line is also displayed on the scatterplot. You can see that the line has a positive slope and, although there is some variation of the data points around the line, it appears that advertising expenditure (x) is fairly strongly related to the number of new PI cases (y). The estimated slope of the line (highlighted on Figure SIA7.1) is $\hat{\beta}_1 = .113$. Thus, we estimate a .113 increase in the number of new PI cases for every $1,000 increase in cumulative advertising expenditures.

Does such a relationship also exist between number of new WC cases and advertising expenditure? Now let y = number of new WC cases per month and x = cumulative 6-month advertising expenditures. A Minitab scatterplot and simple linear regression analysis for these two variables are shown in Figure SIA7.2. Compared to the previous scatterplot, the slope of the least squares line shown in Figure SIA7.2 is much flatter, and the variation of the data points around the line is much larger. Consequently, it does not appear that number of new WC cases is very strongly related to advertising expenditure. In fact, the estimated slope (highlighted in Figure SIA7.2) implies that a $1,000 increase in cumulative advertising expenditures will lead to only a $\hat{\beta}_1 = .0098$ increase in the number of new WC cases per month.

Based on these descriptive statistics (scatterplots and least squares lines), it appears that partner A's argument that partner B should share the advertising expenses is weak, at best. In the *Statistics in Action Revisited* sections that follow, we will provide a measure of reliability to this inference and investigate the legal advertising data further.

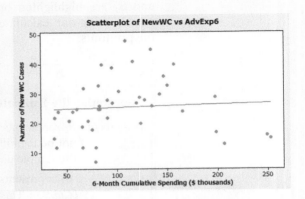

Regression Analysis: NewPI versus AdvExp6

```
The regression equation is
NewPI = 7.77 + 0.113 AdvExp6

Predictor      Coef   SE Coef      T      P
Constant      7.767    3.385    2.29  0.027
AdvExp6     0.11289  0.02793    4.04  0.000

S = 9.67521   R-Sq = 29.0%   R-Sq(adj) = 27.2%

Analysis of Variance

Source           DF       SS      MS      F      P
Regression        1   1529.5  1529.5  16.34  0.000
Residual Error    40   3744.4    93.6
Total             41   5273.9
```

Figure SIA7.1

Minitab analysis of new PI cases vs. 6-month cumulative advertising expenditure

Regression Analysis: NewWC versus AdvExp6

```
The regression equation is
NewWC = 24.6 + 0.0098 AdvExp6

Predictor      Coef   SE Coef      T      P
Constant     24.574    3.367    7.30  0.000
AdvExp6     0.00982  0.02778    0.35  0.725

S = 9.62296   R-Sq = 0.3%   R-Sq(adj) = 0.0%

Analysis of Variance

Source           DF       SS      MS      F      P
Regression        1    11.58   11.58   0.13  0.725
Residual Error    40  3704.06   92.60
Total             41  3715.64
```

Figure SIA7.2

Minitab analysis of new WC cases vs. 6-month cumulative advertising expenditure

---

Activity 7.1   *Keep the Change:* Least Squares Models

In this activity, you will once again use data collected in Activity 1.1 *Keep the Change: Collecting Data* (p. 16). For each student in your class, collect the sum of the data set *Purchase Totals,* the sum of the data set *Amounts Transferred,* and the number of purchases (the number of data items in the set *Purchase Totals*).

1. For each student in your class, form an ordered pair

   (Sum of Purchase Totals, Sum of Amounts Transferred)

   Use these ordered pairs to create a scattergram. Then use the ordered pairs to find the values of $\hat{\beta}_0$ and $\hat{\beta}_1$ in the least squares line for the data.

2. Suppose that three customers have made only one debit-card purchase each, as shown in the following table.

Customer	Purchases	Actual Amount Transferred	Estimated Amount Transferred	Difference
A	$3.49			
B	$30.49			
C	$300.49			

Complete the table by first finding the actual amount that will be transferred for each customer. Then use the least squares line $y = \hat{\beta}_0 + \hat{\beta}_1 x$ from Exercise 1 to estimate the amount transferred. Finally, calculate the difference between the actual and estimated amounts for each customer.

3. Based on your results in Exercise 2, comment on the usefulness of using your model from Exercise 1 to estimate the transferred amounts. Do you believe that the least squares model is an appropriate model in this situation? Explain.

4. For each student in your class, form an ordered pair

   (Number of Purchases, Sum of Amounts Transferred)

   Use these ordered pairs to create a scattergram. Then use the ordered pairs to find the values of $\hat{\beta}_0$ and $\hat{\beta}_1$ in the least squares line for the data. Create your own hypothetical data as in Exercise 2 to test your model. Do you believe that this model is more or less useful than the model in Exercise 1? Explain.

Exercises 7.10–7.24

Learning the Mechanics

7.10 The following table is similar to Table 7.3. It is used for making the preliminary computations for finding the least squares line for the given pairs of x and y values.

	x_i	y_i	x_i^2	$x_i y_i$
	7	2		
	4	4		
	6	2		
	2	5		
	1	7		
	1	6		
	3	5		
Totals	$\Sigma x_i =$	$\Sigma y_i =$	$\Sigma x_i^2 =$	$\Sigma x_i y_i =$

a. Complete the table.   **b.** Find SS_{xy}.
c. Find SS_{xx}.   **d.** Find $\hat{\beta}_1$.
e. Find $\bar{x}$ and $\bar{y}$.   **f.** Find $\hat{\beta}_0$.
g. Find the least squares line.

7.11 Refer to Exercise 7.7. After the least squares line has been obtained, the table below (which is similar to Table 7.4) can be used for (1) comparing the observed and the predicted values of y and (2) computing SSE.

x	y	$\hat{y}$	$(y - \hat{y})$	$(y - \hat{y})^2$
7	2			
4	4			
6	2			
2	5			
1	7			
1	6			
3	5			
			$\Sigma(y - \hat{y}) =$	$SSE = \Sigma(y - \hat{y})^2 =$

a. Complete the table.
b. Plot the least squares line on a scattergram of the data. Plot the following line on the same graph: $\hat{y} = 14 - 2.5x$.
c. Show that SSE is larger for the line in part **b** than it is for the least squares line.

7.12 Construct a scattergram for the data in the following table.

x	.5	1	1.5
y	2	1	3

a. Plot the following two lines on your scattergram:

$$y = 3 - x \quad \text{and} \quad y = 1 + x$$

b. Which of these lines would you choose to characterize the relationship between x and y? Explain.
c. Show that the SSE for both of these lines equals 0.
d. Which of these lines has the smaller SSE?
e. Find the least squares line for the data and compare it to the two lines described in part **a**.

7.13 Consider the following pairs of measurements (saved in the **LM10_13** file):

x	8	5	4	6	2	5	3
y	1	3	6	3	7	2	5

a. Construct a scattergram for these data.
b. What does the scattergram suggest about the relationship between x and y?
c. Find the least squares estimates of β_0 and β_1.
d. Plot the least squares line on your scattergram. Does the line appear to fit the data well? Explain.

● **Applet Exercise 7.1**

Use the applet *Regression by Eye* to explore the relationship between the pattern of data in a scattergram and the corresponding least squares model.

a. Run the applet several times. For each time, attempt to move the green line into a position that appears to minimize the vertical distances of the points from the line. Then click *Show regression line* to see the actual regression line. How close is your line to the actual line? Click *New data* to reset the applet.
b. Click the trash can to clear the graph. Use the mouse to place five points on the scattergram that are approximately in a straight line. Then move the green line to approximate the regression line. Click *Show regression line* to see the actual regression line. How close were you this time?
c. Continue to clear the graph and plot sets of five points with different patterns among the points. Use the green line to approximate the regression line. How close do you come to the actual regression line each time?
d. Based on your experiences with the applet, explain why we need to use more reliable methods of finding the regression line than just "eyeing" it.

Applying the Concepts—Basic

7.14 **In business, do nice guys finish first or last?** In baseball, there is an old saying that "nice guys finish last." Is this true in the business world? Researchers at Harvard University attempted to answer this question and reported their results in *Nature* (March 20, 2008). In the study, Boston-area college students repeatedly played a version of the game "prisoner's dilemma," where competitors choose cooperation, defection, or costly punishment. (Cooperation meant paying 1 unit for the opponent to receive 2 units, defection meant gaining 1 unit at a cost of 1 unit for the opponent, and punishment meant paying 1 unit for the opponent to lose 4 units.) At the conclusion of the games, the researchers recorded the average payoff and the number of times cooperation, defection, and punishment were used for each player. The scattergrams on the next page plot average payoff (y) against level of cooperation use, defection use, and punishment use, respectively.

a. Consider cooperation use (x) as a predictor of average payoff (y). Based on the scattergram, is there evidence of a linear trend?
b. Consider defection use (x) as a predictor of average payoff (y). Based on the scattergram, is there evidence of a linear trend?

c. Consider punishment use (x) as a predictor of average payoff (y). Based on the scattergram, is there evidence of a linear trend?

d. Refer to part **c.** Is the slope of the line relating punishment use (x) to average payoff (y) positive or negative?

e. The researchers concluded that "winners don't punish." Do you agree? Explain.

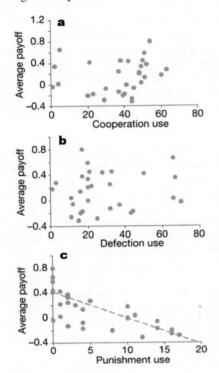

7.15 **State SAT scores.** Refer to the data on average state SAT scores for 2000 and 2007, Exercise 2.29 (p. 52). The first five observations and last two observations in the **SATSCORES** file are reproduced in the next table. In Exercise 2.120 (p. 93), you examined the relationship between the 2000 SAT scores and the 2007 SAT scores with a scatterplot.

State	2000	2007
Alabama	1114	1119
Alaska	1034	1036
Arizona	1044	1044
Arkansas	1117	1144
California	1015	1015
⋮	⋮	⋮
Wisconsin	1181	1185
Wyoming	1090	1136

Source: "College-Bound Seniors 2008." Copyright © 2008 the College Board. www.collegeboard.com. Reproduced with permission.

a. Write the equation of a straight-line model relating 2007 SAT scores (y) to 2000 SAT scores (x).

b. An SPSS simple linear regression printout for the data is shown at the bottom of the page. Find the least squares prediction equation.

c. Give a practical interpretation of the y-intercept of the least squares line. If a practical interpretation is not possible, explain why.

d. Give a practical interpretation of the slope of the least squares line. Over what range of x is the interpretation meaningful?

7.16 **Characteristics of diamonds sold at retail.** Refer to the *Journal of Statistics Education* data on 308 diamonds for sale on the open market, saved in the **DIAMONDS** file. In Exercise 2.121 (p. 93), you related the size of the diamond (number of carats) to the asking price (dollars) using a scatterplot.

a. Write the equation of a straight-line model relating asking price (y) to number of carats (x).

b. A Minitab simple linear regression printout for the data is shown on page 574. Find the equation of the least squares line.

c. Give a practical interpretation of the y-intercept of the least squares line. If a practical interpretation is not possible, explain why.

d. Give a practical interpretation of the slope of the least squares line. Over what range of x is the interpretation meaningful?

e. Use the least squares line to predict the asking price of a .52-carat diamond.

7.17 **Drug controlled-release rate study.** Researchers at Dow Chemical Co. investigated the effect of tablet surface area and volume on the rate at which a drug is released in a controlled-release dosage (*Drug Development and Industrial Pharmacy,* Vol. 28, 2002). Six similarly shaped tablets were prepared with different weights and thicknesses, and the ratio of surface area to volume was measured for each. Using a dissolution apparatus, each tablet was placed in 900 milliliters of deionized water, and the diffusional drug release

Drug Release Rate (% released/^{2} time)	Surface Area to Volume (mm^2/mm^3)
60	1.50
48	1.05
39	.90
33	.75
30	.60
29	.65

Source: Reynolds, T., Mitchell, S., and Balwinski, K. M. "Investigation of the effect of tablet surface area/volume on drug release from hydroxypropyl-methylcellulose controlled-release matrix tablets," *Drug Development and Industrial Pharmacy,* Vol. 28, No. 4, 2002, pp. 457–466 (Figure 3). Reprinted by permission of the publisher (Taylor & Francis Group, www.informaworld.com).

SPSS Output for Exercise 7.15

Coefficients[a]

Model		Unstandardized Coefficients B	Std. Error	Standardized Coefficients Beta	t	Sig.
1	(Constant)	-146.856	46.981		-3.126	.003
	SAT2000	1.144	.044	.966	26.007	.000

a. Dependent Variable: SAT2007

Minitab Output for Exercise 7.16

Regression Analysis: PRICE versus CARAT

```
The regression equation is
PRICE = - 2298 + 11599 CARAT


Predictor      Coef   SE Coef       T       P
Constant    -2298.4     158.5  -14.50   0.000
CARAT       11598.9     230.1   50.41   0.000


S = 1117.56    R-Sq = 89.3%    R-Sq(adj) = 89.2%


Analysis of Variance

Source           DF          SS          MS        F       P
Regression        1  3173248722  3173248722  2540.73   0.000
Residual Error  306   382178624     1248950
Total           307  3555427347
```

rate (percentage of drug released divided by the square root of time) was determined. The experimental data are listed in the table (p. 394) and saved in the **DOWDRUG** file.

a. Fit the simple linear model, $E(y) = \beta_0 + \beta_1 x$, where y = release rate and x = surface-area-to-volume ratio.

b. Interpret the estimates of β_0 and β_1.

c. Predict the drug release rate for a tablet that has a surface area/volume ratio of .50.

d. Comment on the reliability of the prediction in part **c.**

7.18 **Extending the life of an aluminum smelter pot.** An investigation of the properties of bricks used to line aluminum smelter pots was published in *The American Ceramic Society Bulletin* (Feb. 2005). Six different commercial bricks were evaluated. The life length of a smelter pot depends on the porosity of the brick lining (the less porosity, the longer the life); consequently, the researchers measured the apparent porosity of each brick specimen, as well as the mean pore diameter of each brick. The data are given in the accompanying table and saved in the **SMELTPOT** file.

Brick	Apparent Porosity (%)	Mean Pore Diameter (micrometers)
A	18.8	12.0
B	18.3	9.7
C	16.3	7.3
D	6.9	5.3
E	17.1	10.9
F	20.4	16.8

Source: Bonadia, P., et al. "Aluminosilicate refractories for aluminum cell linings," *The American Ceramic Society Bulletin*, Vol. 84, No. 2, Feb. 2005, pp. 26–31 (Table II). Reproduced with permission of American Ceramic Society, Inc. in the format Textbook and electronic usage via Copyright Clearance Center.

a. Find the least squares line relating porosity (y) to mean pore diameter (x).

b. Interpret the y-intercept of the line.

c. Interpret the slope of the line.

d. Predict the apparent porosity percentage for a brick with a mean pore diameter of 10 micrometers.

Applying the Concepts—Intermediate

7.19 **Ranking driving performance of professional golfers.** Refer to *The Sport Journal* (Winter 2007) study of a new method for ranking the total driving performance of golfers on the Professional Golf Association (PGA) tour, Exercise 2.50 (p. 63). Recall that the method computes a driving performance index based on a golfer's average driving distance (yards) and driving accuracy (percent of drives that land in the fairway). Data for the top 40 PGA golfers (as ranked by the new method) are saved in the **PGADRIVER** file. (The first five and last five observations are listed in the table.)

Rank	Player	Driving Distance (yards)	Driving Accuracy (%)	Driving Performance Index
1	Woods	316.1	54.6	3.58
2	Perry	304.7	63.4	3.48
3	Gutschewski	310.5	57.9	3.27
4	Wetterich	311.7	56.6	3.18
5	Hearn	295.2	68.5	2.82
⋮	⋮	⋮	⋮	⋮
36	Senden	291	66	1.31
37	Mickelson	300	58.7	1.30
38	Watney	298.9	59.4	1.26
39	Trahan	295.8	61.8	1.23
40	Pappas	309.4	50.6	1.17

Source: Wiseman, F., et al. "A new method for ranking total driving performance on the PGA Tour," *The Sport Journal*, Vol. 10, No. 1, Winter 2007 (Table 2).

a. Write the equation of a straight-line model relating driving accuracy (y) to driving distance (x).

b. Fit the model, part **a,** to the data using simple linear regression. Give the least squares prediction equation.

c. Interpret the estimated y-intercept of the line.

d. Interpret the estimated slope of the line.

e. In Exercise 2.126 (p. 95), you were informed that a professional golfer, practicing a new swing to increase his average driving distance, is concerned that his driving accuracy will be lower. Which of the two estimates, y-intercept or slope, will help you determine if the golfer's concern is a valid one? Explain.

7.20 **Sweetness of orange juice.** The quality of the orange juice produced by a manufacturer (e.g., Minute Maid, Tropicana) is constantly monitored. There are numerous sensory and chemical components that combine to make the best-tasting orange juice. For example, one manufacturer has developed a quantitative index of the "sweetness" of orange juice. (The higher the index, the sweeter the juice.) Is there a relationship between the sweetness index and a chemical measure such as the amount of water-soluble pectin (parts per million) in the orange juice? Data collected on these two variables for 24 production runs at a juice manufacturing plant are shown in the table and saved in the **OJUICE** file. Suppose a manufacturer wants to use simple linear regression to predict the sweetness (y) from the amount of pectin (x).

Run	Sweetness Index	Pectin (ppm)
1	5.2	220
2	5.5	227
3	6.0	259
4	5.9	210
5	5.8	224
6	6.0	215
7	5.8	231
8	5.6	268
9	5.6	239
10	5.9	212
11	5.4	410
12	5.6	256
13	5.8	306
14	5.5	259
15	5.3	284
16	5.3	383
17	5.7	271
18	5.5	264
19	5.7	227
20	5.3	263
21	5.9	232
22	5.8	220
23	5.8	246
24	5.9	241

Note: The data in the table are authentic. For confidentiality reasons, the manufacturer cannot be disclosed.

a. Find the least squares line for the data.
b. Interpret $\hat{\beta}_0$ and $\hat{\beta}_1$ in the words of the problem.
c. Predict the sweetness index if amount of pectin in the orange juice is 300 ppm. [*Note:* A measure of reliability of such a prediction is discussed in Section 7.6.]

7.21 **Most generous philanthropists.** Intel Corp. founder Gordon Moore donated over $7 million to environmental causes while Microsoft founder Bill Gates donated over $5 million to health, education, and libraries. These two entrepreneurs were the top two givers in *Business Week's* (Nov. 28, 2005) annual list of the 50 Most Generous Philanthropists. Data on total amount pledged and remaining net worth (in millions of dollars) for the 50 top givers are saved in the **TOP-GIVERS** file. (The data for the first 10 names on the list are given in the table at the bottom of the page.)

a. Propose a straight-line model relating amount pledged (y) to net worth (x).
b. Fit the model to the data in the **TOPGIVERS** file using the method of least squares.
c. Graph the least squares line on a scattergram of the data. Is there visual evidence of a linear relationship between the two variables? Is the relationship positive or negative?
d. Interpret the estimates of the y-intercept and slope in the words of the problem.

7.22 **FCAT scores and poverty.** In the state of Florida, elementary school performance is based on the average score obtained by students on a standardized exam, called the Florida Comprehensive Assessment Test (FCAT). An analysis of the link between FCAT scores and sociodemographic factors was published in the *Journal of Educational and Behavioral Statistics* (Spring 2004). Data on average math and reading FCAT scores of third-graders, as well as the percentage of students below the poverty level, for a sample of 22 Florida elementary schools are listed in the table on the next page.

a. Propose a straight-line model relating math score (y) to percentage (x) of students below the poverty level.
b. Fit the model to the data in the **FCAT** file using the method of least squares.
c. Graph the least squares line on a scattergram of the data. Is there visual evidence of a relationship between the two variables? Is the relationship positive or negative?
d. Interpret the estimates of the y-intercept and slope in the words of the problem.
e. Now consider a model relating reading score (y) to percentage (x) of students below the poverty level. Repeat parts **a–d** for this model.

Table for Exercise 7.21 (Selected data)

Donor	Company/Background	Pledged ($ millions)	Net Worth ($ millions)
Gordon Moore	Intel	7,046	4,600
Bill Gates	Microsoft	5,458	51,000
Warren Buffett	Berkshire Hathaway	2,622	40,000
George Soros	Investor	2,367	7,200
Eli Broad	SunAmerica	1,475	5,500
James Stowers	American Century	1,205	716
Walton Family	Wal-Mart	1,100	82,700
Alfred Mann	Medical devices	993	2,100
Michael Dell	Dell	933	18,000
George Kaiser	Oil and gas	617	4,500

Source: Business Week, Nov. 28, 2005, p. 61.

Elementary School	FCAT-Math	FCAT-Reading	% Below Poverty
1	166.4	165.0	91.7
2	159.6	157.2	90.2
3	159.1	164.4	86.0
4	155.5	162.4	83.9
5	164.3	162.5	80.4
6	169.8	164.9	76.5
7	155.7	162.0	76.0
8	165.2	165.0	75.8
9	175.4	173.7	75.6
10	178.1	171.0	75.0
11	167.1	169.4	74.7
12	177.0	172.9	63.2
13	174.2	172.7	52.9
14	175.6	174.9	48.5
15	170.8	174.8	39.1
16	175.1	170.1	38.4
17	182.8	181.4	34.3
18	180.3	180.6	30.3
19	178.8	178.0	30.3
20	181.4	175.9	29.6
21	182.8	181.6	26.5
22	186.1	183.8	13.8

Source: Tekwe, C.D., et al. "An empirical comparison of statistical models for value-added assessment of school performance," *Journal of Educational and Behavioral Statistics*, Vol. 29, No. 1, Spring 2004, pp. 11–36 (Table 2). © 2004. Reprinted by permission of SAGE Publications.

7.23 Survey of the top business schools. Each year, the *Wall Street Journal* and *Harris Interactive* track the opinions and experiences of college recruiters for large corporations and summarize the results in the Business School Survey. In 2005, the survey included rankings of 76 business schools. Survey data for the top 10 business schools are given in the table below. All the data are saved in the **BSCHOOL** file.

a. Select one of the variables as the dependent variable, y, and another as the independent variable, x. Use your knowledge of the subject area and common sense to help you select the variables.

b. Fit the simple linear model, $E(y) = \beta_0 + \beta_1 x$, to the data in the **BSCHOOL** file. Interpret the estimates of the slope and y-intercept.

Applying the Concepts—Advanced

7.24 Spreading rate of spilled liquid. Refer to the *Chemical Engineering Progress* (Jan. 2005) study of the rate at which a spilled volatile liquid will spread across a surface, Exercise 2.124 (p. 94). Recall that a DuPont Corp. engineer calculated the mass (in pounds) of a 50-gallon methanol spill after a period of time ranging from 0 to 60 minutes. Do the data in the table below (saved in the **LIQUIDSPILL** file) indicate that the mass of the spill tends to diminish as time increases? If so, how much will the mass diminish each minute?

Time (minutes)	Mass (pounds)	Time (minutes)	Mass (pounds)
0	6.64	22	1.86
1	6.34	24	1.60
2	6.04	26	1.37
4	5.47	28	1.17
6	4.94	30	0.98
8	4.44	35	0.60
10	3.98	40	0.34
12	3.55	45	0.17
14	3.15	50	0.06
16	2.79	55	0.02
18	2.45	60	0.00
20	2.14		

Source: Barry, J. "Estimating rates of spreading and evaporation of volatile liquids," *Chemical Engineering Progress*, Vol. 101, No. 1, Jan. 2005. Reproduced with permission. Copyright © 2005 AICHE.

School	Enrollment (# full-time students)	Annual Tuition ($)	Mean GMAT	% with Job Offer	Avg. Salary ($)
Dartmouth	503	38,400	704	—	119,800
Michigan	1,873	33,076	690	91	105,986
Carnegie Mellon	661	38,800	691	93	95,531
Northwestern	2,650	38,844	700	94	117,060
Yale	468	36,800	696	86	104,018
Pennsylvania	1,840	40,458	716	92	117,471
Cal., Berkeley	1,281	21,512	701	92	112,699
Columbia	1,796	38,290	709	95	126,319
North Carolina	855	16,375	652	86	92,565
Southern Cal.	1,588	37,558	685	82	88,839

Source: "Wall Street Journal's annual rankings of business schools," *The Wall Street Journal*, Sep. 21, 2005. Copyright 2005 by Dow Jones & Company, Inc. in the format Textbook via Copyright Clearance Center.

7.3 Model Assumptions

In Section 7.2, we assumed that the probabilistic model relating the firm's sales revenue y to the advertising dollars is

$$y = \beta_0 + \beta_1 x + \varepsilon$$

We also recall that the least squares estimate of the deterministic component of the model, $\beta_0 + \beta_1 x$, is

$$\hat{y} = \hat{\beta}_0 + \hat{\beta}_1 x = -.1 + .7x$$

Now we turn our attention to the random component **e** of the probabilistic model and its relation to the errors in estimating β_0 and β_1. We will use a probability distribution to characterize the behavior of ε. We will see how the probability distribution of **e** determines how well the model describes the relationship between the dependent variable y and the independent variable x.

Step 3 in a regression analysis requires us to specify the probability distribution of the random error **e**. We will make four basic assumptions about the general form of this probability distribution:

Assumption 1: The mean of the probability distribution of ε is 0—that is, the average of the values of **e** over an infinitely long series of experiments is 0 for each setting of the independent variable x. This assumption implies that the mean value of y, $E(y)$, for a given value of x is $E(y) = \beta_0 + \beta_1 x$.

Assumption 2: The variance of the probability distribution of ε is constant for all settings of the independent variable x. For our straight-line model, this assumption means that the variance of **e** is equal to a constant, say σ^2, for all values of x.

Assumption 3: The probability distribution of ε is normal.

Assumption 4: The values of ε associated with any two observed values of y are independent—that is, the value of ε associated with one value of y has no effect on the values of ε associated with other y values.

The implications of the first three assumptions can be seen in Figure 7.9, which shows distributions of errors for three values of x, namely, x_1, x_2, and x_3. Note that the relative frequency distributions of the errors are normal with a mean of 0 and a constant variance σ^2. (All the distributions shown have the same amount of spread or variability.) The straight line shown in Figure 7.9 is the line of means. It indicates the mean value of y for a given value of x. We denote this mean value as $E(y)$. Then, the line of means is given by the equation

$$E(y) = \beta_0 + \beta_1 x$$

These assumptions make it possible for us to develop measures of reliability for the least squares estimators and to develop hypothesis tests for examining the usefulness of the least squares line. We have various techniques for checking the validity of these assumptions, and we have remedies to apply when they appear to be invalid. Fortunately, the assumptions need not hold exactly in order for least squares estimators to be useful. The assumptions will be satisfied adequately for many applications encountered in practice.

It seems reasonable to assume that the greater the variability of the random error **e** (which is measured by its variance σ^2), the greater will be the errors in the estimation of the model parameters β_0 and β_1 and in the error of prediction when $\hat{y}$ is used to predict y for some value of x. Consequently, you should not be surprised, as we proceed through this chapter, to find that σ^2 appears in the formulas for all confidence intervals and test statistics that we will be using.

In most practical situations, σ^2 is unknown, and we must use our data to estimate its value. The best estimate of σ^2, denoted by s^2, is obtained by dividing the sum of squares of the deviations of the y values from the prediction line,

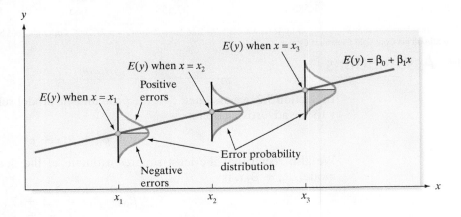

Figure 7.9
The probability distribution of ε

$$SSE = \sum (y_i - \hat{y}_i)^2$$

by the number of degrees of freedom associated with this quantity. We use 2 df to estimate the two parameters β_0 and β_1 in the straight-line model, leaving $(n - 2)$ df for the error variance estimation.

Estimation of σ^2 for a (First-Order) Straight-Line Model

$$s^2 = \frac{SSE}{\text{Degrees of freedom for error}} = \frac{SSE}{n - 2}$$

where $SSE = \sum (y_i - \hat{y}_i)^2 = SS_{yy} - \hat{\beta}_1 SS_{xy}$

$$SS^*_{yy} = \sum (y_i - \bar{y})^2$$

To estimate the standard deviation s of e, we calculate

$$s = \sqrt{s^2} = \sqrt{\frac{SSE}{n - 2}}$$

We will refer to s as the **estimated standard error of the regression model.**

⚠ **CAUTION** When performing these calculations, you may be tempted to round the calculated values of SS_{yy}, $\hat{\beta}_1$, and SS_{xy}. Be certain to carry at least six significant figures for each of these quantities to avoid substantial errors in calculation of the SSE. ▲

Example 7.2

Estimating σ for the Advertising–Sales Regression

Problem Refer to Example 7.1 and the simple linear regression of the advertising-sales data in Table 7.1.

a. Compute an estimate of σ.

b. Give a practical interpretation of the estimate.

Solution

a. We previously calculated SSE = 1.10 for the least squares line $\hat{y} = -.1 + .7x$. Recalling that there were $n = 5$ data points, we have $n - 2 = 5 - 2 = 3$ df for estimating σ^2. Thus,

$$s^2 = \frac{SSE}{n - 2} = \frac{1.10}{3} = .367$$

is the estimated variance, and

$$s = \sqrt{.367} = .61$$

is the standard error of the regression model.

b. You may be able to grasp s intuitively by recalling the interpretation of a standard deviation given in Chapter 2 and remembering that the least squares line estimates the mean value of y for a given value of x. Because s measures the spread of the distribution of y values about the least squares line, we should not be surprised to find that most of the observations lie within $2s$, or $2(.61) = 1.22$, of the least squares line. For this simple example (only five data points), all five sales revenue values fall within $2s$ (or \$1,220) of the least squares line. In section 7.6, we use s to evaluate the error of prediction when the least squares line is used to predict a value of y to be observed for a given value of x.

---

*Alternatively, you can use the following "shortcut" formula:

$$SS_{yy} = \sum y^2 - \frac{(\sum y)^2}{n}$$

Regression Analysis: SALES_Y versus ADVEXP_X

```
The regression equation is
SALES_Y = - 0.100 + 0.700 ADVEXP_X


Predictor      Coef  SE Coef       T      P
Constant    -0.1000   0.6351   -0.16  0.885
ADVEXP_X     0.7000   0.1915    3.66  0.035


S = 0.605530    R-Sq = 81.7%    R-Sq(adj) = 75.6%


Analysis of Variance

Source            DF       SS       MS      F      P
Regression         1   4.9000   4.9000  13.36  0.035
Residual Error     3   1.1000   0.3667
Total              4   6.0000
```

Figure 7.10
Minitab printout for the advertising-sales regression

Look Back The values of s^2 and s can also be obtained from a simple linear regression printout. The Minitab printout for the advertising-sales example is reproduced in Figure 7.10. The value of s^2 is highlighted at the bottom of the printout in the **MS** (Mean Square) column in the row labeled **Residual Error.** (In regression, the estimate of s^2 is called Mean Square for Error, or MSE.) The value, $s^2 = .3667$, agrees with the one calculated by hand. The value of s is also highlighted in Figure 7.10. This value, $s = .60553$, agrees (except for rounding) with our hand-calculated value.

Now Work Exercise 7.30

Interpretation of s, the Estimated Standard Deviation of E

We expect most ($\approx 95\%$) of the observed y values to lie within $2s$ of their respective least squares predicted values, $\hat{y}$.

Exercises 7.25–7.36

Learning the Mechanics

7.25 Visually compare the scattergrams shown below. If a least squares line were determined for each data set, which do you think would have the smallest variance, s^2? Explain.

7.26 Calculate SSE and s^2 for each of the following cases:
  a. $n = 20$, $SS_{yy} = 95$, $SS_{xy} = 50$, $\hat{\beta}_1 = .75$

  b. $n = 40$, $\sum y^2 = 860$, $\sum y = 50$, $SS_{xy} = 2{,}700$, $\hat{\beta}_1 = .2$
  c. $n = 10$, $\sum (y_i - \bar{y})^2 = 58$, $SS_{xy} = 91$, $SS_{xx} = 170$

7.27 Suppose you fit a least squares line to 26 data points and the calculated value of SSE is 8.34.
  a. Find s^2, the estimator of σ^2 (the variance of the random error term e).

Figure for Exercise 7.25

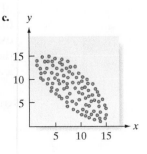

SPSS Output for Exercise 7.29

Model Summary

Mode l	R	R Square	Adjusted R Square	Std. Error of the Estimate
1	.966[a]	.932	.931	20.508

a. Predictors: (Constant), SAT2000

ANOVA[b]

Model		Sum of Squares	df	Mean Square	F	Sig.
1	Regression	284470.200	1	284470.200	676.377	.000[a]
	Residual	20608.388	49	420.579		
	Total	305078.588	50			

a. Predictors: (Constant), SAT2000

b. Dependent Variable: SAT2007

b. What is the largest deviation that you might expect between any one of the 26 points and the least squares line?

7.28 Refer to Exercise 7.10 (p. 393). Calculate SSE, s^2, and s for the least squares line. Use the value of s to determine where most of the errors of prediction lie.

Applying the Concepts—Basic

7.29 **State SAT scores.** Refer to the simple linear regression relating y = 2007 SAT scores to x = 2000 SAT scores, Exercise 7.15 (p. 394). The data are saved in the **SATSCORES** file. A portion of the SPSS printout of the analysis is shown above.

a. Locate the values of SSE, s^2, and s on the SPSS printout.

b. Give a practical interpretation of the value of s.

7.30 **Characteristics of diamonds sold at retail.** Refer to the simple linear regression relating y = asking price (dollars) to x = number of carats for diamonds sold on the open market, Exercise 7.16 (p. 394). The data are saved in the **DIAMONDS** file.

a. Locate the values of SSE, s^2, and s on the Minitab printout shown on p. 395.

b. Give a practical interpretation of the value of s.

7.31 **Drug controlled-release rate study.** Refer to simple linear regression relating the drug release rate (y) to surface area-to-volume ratio (x), Exercise 7.17 (p. 394): The data are saved in the **DOWDRUG** file.

a. Find the value of s for the straight-line model.

b. Give a practical interpretation of the value of s.

7.32 **Structurally deficient highway bridges.** Refer to Exercise 1.24 (p. 24) and the data on structurally deficient highway bridges compiled by the Federal Highway Administration (FHWA) into the National Bridge Inventory (NBI). For each state, the NBI lists the number of structurally deficient bridges and the total area (thousands of square feet) of the deficient bridges. The data for the 50 states (plus the District of Columbia and Puerto Rico) are saved in the **FHWABRIDGE** file. (The first five and last five observations are listed in the table on the next page.) For future planning and budgeting, the FHWA wants to estimate the total area of structurally deficient bridges in a state based on the number of deficient bridges.

a. Write the equation of a straight-line model relating total area (y) to number of structurally deficient bridges (x).

b. The model, part **a**, was fit to the data using Excel/DDXL, as shown below. Find the least squares prediction equation on the printout.

c. List the assumptions required for the regression analysis.

d. Locate the estimated standard error of the regression model, s, on the printout.

e. Use the value of s to find a range where most (about 95%) of the errors of prediction will fall.

Excel/DDXL Output for Exercise 7.32

▷	Regression: NumberSD by SDArea				

```
Dependent variable is:    SDArea
No Selector
R squared = 38.7%     R squared (adjusted) = 37.4%
s =  635.2  with  52 - 2 = 50  degrees of freedom

Source        Sum of Squares   df    Mean Square   F-ratio
Regression    12.7101e6         1    12.7101e6      31.5
Residual      20.1731e6        50       403462

Variable     Coefficient    s.e. of Coeff   t-ratio     prob
Constant     119.863        123              0.974       0.3346
NumberSD     0.345604         0.06158        5.61       ≤ 0.0001
```

Data for Exercise 7.32 (selected observations)

State	Number	Area (thousands of sq. ft.)
Alabama	1,899	432.7
Alaska	155	60.9
Arizona	181	110.5
Arkansas	997	347.3
California	3,140	5,177.9
⋮	⋮	⋮
Washington	400	502.0
West Virginia	1,058	331.5
Wisconsin	1,302	399.8
Wyoming	389	143.4
Puerto Rico	241	195.4

Applying the Concepts—Intermediate

7.33 **Sweetness of orange juice.** Refer to the study of the quality of orange juice produced at a juice manufacturing plant, Exercise 7.20 (p. 396). The data are saved in the **OJUICE** file. Recall that simple linear regression was used to predict the sweetness index (y) from the amount of pectin (x) in the orange juice.
   a. Find the values of SSE, s^2, and s for this regression.
   b. Explain why it is difficult to give a practical interpretation to s^2.
   c. Give a practical interpretation of the value of s.

7.34 **Are geography journals worth their cost?** Refer to the *Geoforum* (Vol. 37, 2006) study of whether the price of a geography journal is correlated with quality, Exercise 2.122 (p. 94). Several quantitative variables were recorded for each in a sample of 28 geography journals: cost of a 1-year subscription (dollars); Journal Impact Factor (JIF)—the average number of times articles from the journal have been cited; number of citations for the journal over the past five years; and, Relative Price Index (RPI). The data for the 28 journals are saved in the **GEOJRNL** file. (Selected observations are listed below.)

Journal	Cost ($)	JIF	Cites	RPI
J. Econ. Geogr.	468	3.139	207	1.16
Prog. Hum. Geog.	624	2.943	544	0.77
T. I. Brit. Geogr.	499	2.388	249	1.11
Econ. Geogr.	90	2.325	173	0.30
A. A. A. Geogr.	698	2.115	377	0.93
Geogr. Anal.	213	0.902	106	0.88
Geogr. J.	223	0.857	81	0.94
Appl. Geogr.	646	0.853	74	3.38

Source: Blomley, N. "Is this journal worth US$1118?" *Geoforum*, Vol. 37, 2006. Copyright © 2006 Elsevier Ltd. All rights reserved.

   a. Fit a straight-line model relating cost (y) to JIF (x). Find an estimate of σ, the standard deviation of the error term, and interpret its value.
   b. Fit a straight-line model relating cost (y) to number of citations (x). Find an estimate of σ, the standard deviation of the error term, and interpret its value.

   c. Fit a straight-line model relating cost (y) to RPI (x). Find an estimate of σ, the standard deviation of the error term, and interpret its value.
   d. Which predictor of cost—JIF, number of citations, or RPI—leads to a regression line with the smallest errors of prediction?

7.35 **FCAT scores and poverty.** Refer to the *Journal of Educational and Behavioral Statistics* (Spring 2004) study of scores on the Florida Comprehensive Assessment Test (FCAT), Exercise 7.22 (p. 396).
   a. Consider the simple linear regression relating math score (y) to percentage (x) of students below the poverty level. Find and interpret the value of s for this regression.
   b. Consider the simple linear regression relating reading score (y) to percentage (x) of students below the poverty level. Find and interpret the value of s for this regression.
   c. Which dependent variable, math score or reading score, can be more accurately predicted by percentage (x) of students below the poverty level? Explain.

Applying the Concepts—Advanced

7.36 **Life tests of cutting tools.** To improve the quality of the output of any production process, it is necessary first to understand the capabilities of the process (Gitlow, et al., *Quality Management: Tools and Methods for Improvement*, 1995). In a particular manufacturing process, the useful life of a cutting tool is related to the speed at which the tool is operated. The data in the table below (saved in the **CUTTOOLS** file) were derived from life tests for the two different brands of cutting tools currently used in the production process. For which brand would you feel more confident in using the least squares line to predict useful life for a given cutting speed? Explain.

Cutting Speed (meters per minute)	Useful Life (Hours)	
	Brand A	Brand B
30	4.5	6.0
30	3.5	6.5
30	5.2	5.0
40	5.2	6.0
40	4.0	4.5
40	2.5	5.0
50	4.4	4.5
50	2.8	4.0
50	1.0	3.7
60	4.0	3.8
60	2.0	3.0
60	1.1	2.4
70	1.1	1.5
70	.5	2.0
70	3.0	1.0

7.4 Assessing the Utility of the Model: Making Inferences about the Slope β_1

Now that we have specified the probability distribution of ε and found an estimate of the variance σ^2, we are ready to make statistical inferences about the model's usefulness for predicting the response y. This is step 4 in our regression modeling procedure.

Figure 7.11

Graph of the straight-line model when slope is zero, i.e., $y = \beta_0 + \varepsilon$

Refer again to the data of Table 7.1 and suppose the appliance store's sales revenue is *completely unrelated* to the advertising expenditure. What could be said about the values of β_0 and β_1 in the hypothesized probabilistic model

$$y = \beta_0 + \beta_1 x + \varepsilon$$

if x contributes no information for the prediction of y? The implication is that the mean of y—that is, the deterministic part of the model $E(y) = \beta_0 + \beta_1 x$—does not change as x changes. In the straight-line model, this means that the true slope, β_1, is equal to 0 (see Figure 7.11). Therefore, to test the null hypothesis that the linear model contributes no information for the prediction of y against the alternative hypothesis that the linear model is useful in predicting y, we test

$$H_0: \beta_1 = 0 \text{ against } H_a: \beta_1 \neq 0$$

If the data support the alternative hypothesis, we will conclude that x does contribute information for the prediction of y using the straight-line model (although the true relationship between $E[y]$ and x could be more complex than a straight line). Thus, in effect, this is a test of the usefulness of the hypothesized model.

The appropriate test statistic is found by considering the sampling distribution of $\hat{\beta}_1$, the least squares estimator of the slope β_1, as shown in the following box.

Sampling Distribution of $\hat{\beta}_1$

If we make the four assumptions about ε (see Section 7.3), the sampling distribution of the least squares estimator $\hat{\beta}_1$ of the slope will be normal with mean β_1 (the true slope) and standard deviation

$$\sigma_{\hat{\beta}_1} = \frac{\sigma}{\sqrt{SS_{xx}}} \quad \text{(see Figure 7.12)}$$

We estimate $\sigma_{\hat{\beta}_1}$ by $s_{\hat{\beta}_1} = \dfrac{s}{\sqrt{SS_{xx}}}$ and refer to this quantity as the **estimated standard error of the least squares slope $\hat{\beta}_1$.**

Figure 7.12

Sampling distribution of $\hat{\beta}_1$

Because σ is usually unknown, the appropriate test statistic is a t-statistic, formed as follows:

$$t = \frac{\hat{\beta}_1 - \text{Hypothesized value of } \beta_1}{s_{\hat{\beta}_1}} \qquad \text{where } s_{\hat{\beta}_1} = \frac{s}{\sqrt{SS_{xx}}}$$

Thus,

$$t = \frac{\hat{\beta}_1 - 0}{s/\sqrt{SS_{xx}}}$$

Note that we have substituted the estimator s for s and then formed the estimated standard error $s_{\hat{\beta}_1}$ by dividing s by $\sqrt{SS_{xx}}$. The number of degrees of freedom associated with this t-statistic is the same as the number of degrees of freedom associated with s. Recall that this number is $(n - 2)$ df when the hypothesized model is a straight line (see Section 7.3). The setup of our test of the usefulness of the straight-line model is summarized in the following boxes.

A Test of Model Utility: Simple Linear Regression

One-Tailed Test	Two-Tailed Test
H_0: $\beta_1 = 0$	H_0: $\beta_1 = 0$
H_a: $\beta_1 < 0$ (or H_a: $\beta_1 > 0$)	H_a: $\beta_1 \neq 0$

Test statistic: $t = \dfrac{\hat{\beta}_1}{s_{\hat{\beta}_1}} = \dfrac{\hat{\beta}_1}{s/\sqrt{SS_{xx}}}$

Rejection region: $t < -t_\alpha$

(or $t > t_\alpha$ when H_a: $\beta_1 > 0$)

Rejection region: $|t| > t_{\alpha/2}$

where t_a and $t_{\alpha/2}$ are based on $(n - 2)$ degrees of freedom

---

Conditions Required for a Valid Test: Simple Linear Regression

Refer to the four assumptions about **e** listed in Section 7.3.

Example 7.3

Testing the Regression Slope, β_1—Sales Revenue Model

Problem Refer to the simple linear regression analysis of the advertising-sales data, Examples 7.1 and 7.2. Conduct a test (at $\alpha = .05$) to determine if sales revenue (y) is linearly related to advertising expenditure (x).

Solution As stated previously, we want to test H_0: $\beta_1 = 0$ against H_a: $\beta_1 \neq 0$. For this example, $n = 5$. Thus t will be based on $n - 2 = 3$ df, and the rejection region (at $\alpha = .05$) will be

$$|t| > t_{.025} = 3.182$$

We previously calculated $\hat{\beta}_1 = .7$, $s = .61$, and $SS_{xx} = 10$. Thus, the test statistic is

$$t = \frac{\hat{\beta}_1}{s/\sqrt{SS_{xx}}} = \frac{.7}{.61/\sqrt{10}} = \frac{.7}{.19} = 3.7$$

Because this calculated t-value falls into the upper-tail rejection region (see Figure 7.13), we reject the null hypothesis and conclude that the slope β_1 is not 0. The sample

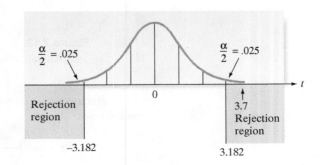

Figure 7.13

Rejection region and calculated t-value for testing H_0: $\beta_1 = 0$ versus H_a: $\beta_1 \neq 0$

Regression Analysis: SALES_Y versus ADVEXP_X

```
The regression equation is
SALES_Y = - 0.100 + 0.700 ADVEXP_X


Predictor       Coef    SE Coef       T      P
Constant      -0.1000    0.6351   -0.16  0.885
ADVEXP_X       0.7000    0.1915    3.66  0.035


S = 0.605530    R-Sq = 81.7%    R-Sq(adj) = 75.6%


Analysis of Variance

Source           DF       SS      MS       F      P
Regression        1   4.9000  4.9000   13.36  0.035
Residual Error    3   1.1000  0.3667
Total             4   6.0000
```

Figure 7.14

Minitab printout for the advertising-sales regression

evidence indicates that advertising expenditure x contributes information for the production of sales revenue y when a linear model is used.

[*Note:* We can reach the same conclusion by using the observed significance level (*p*-value) of the test from a computer printout. The Minitab printout for the advertising-sales example is reproduced in Figure 7.14. The test statistic and *two-tailed p*-value are highlighted on the printout. Because the *p*-value is smaller than $\alpha = .05$, we will reject H_0.]

Look Back What conclusion can be drawn if the calculated *t*-value does not fall in the rejection region or if the observed significance level of the test exceeds α? We know from previous discussions of the philosophy of hypothesis testing that such a *t*-value does *not* lead us to accept the null hypothesis—that is, we do not conclude that $\beta_1 = 0$. Additional data might indicate that β_1 differs from 0, or a more complex relationship may exist between x and y, requiring the fitting of a model other than the straight-line model.

Now Work Exercise 7.42

Interpreting *p*-Values for β Coefficients in Regression

Almost all statistical computer software packages report a *two-tailed p*-value for each of the β parameters in the regression model. For example, in simple linear regression, the *p*-value for the two-tailed test H_0: $\beta_1 = 0$ versus H_a: $\beta_1 \neq 0$ is given on the printout. If you want to conduct a *one-tailed* test of hypothesis, you will need to adjust the *p*-value reported on the printout as follows:

$$Upper\text{-}tailed\ test\ (H_a:\ b_1 > 0):\quad p\text{-value} = \begin{cases} p/2 & \text{if } t > 0 \\ 1 - p/2 & \text{if } t < 0 \end{cases}$$

$$Lower\text{-}tailed\ test\ (H_a:\ b_1 < 0):\quad p\text{-value} = \begin{cases} p/2 & \text{if } t < 0 \\ 1 - p/2 & \text{if } t > 0 \end{cases}$$

where p is the *p*-value reported on the printout and t is the value of the test statistic.

Another way to make inferences about the slope β_1 is to estimate it using a confidence interval. This interval is formed as shown in the next box.

> **A $100(1 - \alpha)$% Confidence Interval for the Simple Linear Regression Slope β_1**
>
> $$\hat{\beta}_1 \pm t_{\alpha/2}s_{\hat{\beta}_1}$$
>
> where the estimated standard error $\hat{\beta}_1$ is calculated by
>
> $$s_{\hat{\beta}_1} = \frac{s}{\sqrt{SS_{xx}}}$$
>
> and $t_{\alpha/2}$ is based on $(n - 2)$ degrees of freedom.

> **Conditions Required for a Valid Confidence Interval: Simple Linear Regression**
>
> Refer to the four assumptions about e listed in Section 7.3.

For the simple linear regression of sales revenue (Examples 7.1–7.3), $t_{a/2}$ is based on $(n - 2) = 3$ degrees of freedom, and, for $\alpha = .05, t_{.025} = 3.182$. Therefore, a 95% confidence interval for the slope β_1, the expected change in sales revenue for a \$100 increase in advertising expenditure, is

$$\hat{\beta}_1 \pm (t_{.025})s_{\hat{\beta}_1} = .7 \pm 3.182\left(\frac{s}{\sqrt{SS_{xx}}}\right) = .7 \pm 3.182\left(\frac{.61}{\sqrt{10}}\right) = .7 \pm .61$$

Thus, the interval estimate of the slope parameter β_1 is .09 to 1.31. [*Note:* This interval can also be obtained using statistical software and is highlighted on the SPSS printout, Figure 7.15.] In terms of this example, the implication is that we can be 95% confident that the *true* mean increase in monthly sales revenue per additional \$100 of advertising expenditure is between \$90 and \$1,310. This inference is meaningful only over the sampled range of x—that is, from \$100 to \$500 of advertising expenditures.

Because all the values in this interval are positive, it appears that β_1 is positive and that the mean of y, $E(y)$, increases as x increases. However, the rather large width of the confidence interval reflects the small number of data points (and, consequently, a lack of information) in the experiment. Particularly bothersome is the fact that the lower end of the confidence interval implies that we are not even recovering our additional expenditure because a \$100 increase in advertising may produce as little as a \$90 increase in mean sales. If we wish to tighten this interval, we need to increase the sample size.

Figure 7.15

SPSS printout with 95% confidence intervals for the advertising-sales regression βs

Coefficients^a

Model		Unstandardized Coefficients B	Unstandardized Coefficients Std. Error	Standardized Coefficients Beta	t	Sig.	95% Confidence Interval for B Lower Bound	95% Confidence Interval for B Upper Bound
1	(Constant)	-.100	.635		-.157	.885	-2.121	1.921
	ADVEXP_X	.700	.191	.904	3.656	.035	.091	1.309

a. Dependent Variable: SALES_Y

Statistics IN Action **Revisited** **Assessing How Well a Straight–Line Regression Model Fits Data**

In the previous *Statistics in Action Revisited,* we fit the straight-line model, $E(y) = \beta_0 + \beta_1 x$, where x = cumulative 6-month advertising expenditures and y represents either the number of new PI cases or the number of new WC cases per month. The SPSS regression printouts for the two analyses are shown in Figure SIA7.3. (The regression for y = number of new PI cases is shown at the top, and the regression for y = number of new WC cases is shown at the bottom of the printout.) The objective is to determine whether one or both of the dependent variables are statistically linearly related to cumulative 6-month advertising expenditures.

The two-tailed p-values for testing the null hypothesis, H_0: $\beta_1 = 0$ (highlighted on the printouts), are p-value ≈ 0 for number of new PI cases and p-value = .725 for number of new WC cases. For y = number of new PI cases, there is sufficient evidence to reject H_0 (at $\alpha = .01$) and conclude that number of new PI cases is linearly related to cumulative 6-month advertising expenditures. In contrast, for y = number of WC cases, there is insufficient evidence to

Coefficients[a]

Model		Unstandardized Coefficients		Standardized Coefficients	t	Sig.	95% Confidence Interval for B	
		B	Std. Error	Beta			Lower Bound	Upper Bound
1	(Constant)	7.767	3.385		2.295	.027	.926	14.609
	CUM. ADV (thous)	.113	.028	.539	4.042	.000	.056	.169

a. Dependent Variable: New PI Cases

Coefficients[a]

Model		Unstandardized Coefficients		Standardized Coefficients	t	Sig.	95% Confidence Interval for B	
		B	Std. Error	Beta			Lower Bound	Upper Bound
1	(Constant)	24.574	3.367		7.299	.000	17.770	31.379
	CUM. ADV (thous)	.010	.028	.056	.354	.725	-.046	.066

a. Dependent Variable: New WC Cases

Figure SIA7.3

SPSS simple linear regressions for legal advertising data

reject H_0 (at $\alpha = .01$); thus, there is no evidence of a linear relationship between the number of new WC cases and cumulative 6-month advertising expenditures.

We can gain further insight into this phenomenon by examining a 95% confidence interval for the slope, β_1. For y = number of new PI cases, the interval (highlighted on the SPSS printout) is (.056, .169). With 95% confidence, we can state that for every $1,000 increase in monthly advertising expenditures, the number of new PI cases each month will increase between .056 and .169. Now, a more realistic increase in cumulative 6-month advertising expenditures is, say, $20,000. Multiplying the endpoints of the interval by 20, we see that this increase in advertising

spending leads to an increase of anywhere between 1 and 3 new PI cases.

Now, for y = number of new WC cases, the 95% confidence interval for the slope (also highlighted on the SPSS printout) is (-.046, .066). Because the interval spans the value 0, we draw the same conclusion as we did with the hypothesis test—there is no statistical evidence of a linear relationship between the number of new WC cases and cumulative 6-month advertising expenditures.

Recall that partner A (who handled the PI cases) sued partner B (who handled the WC cases) for not paying a fair share of the advertising expenses. These results do not support partner A's argument because there is no evidence that partner B benefitted from advertising.

Exercises 7.37–7.52

Learning the Mechanics

7.37 Construct both a 95% and a 90% confidence interval for b_1 for each of the following cases:
  a. $\hat{\beta}_1 = 31$, $s = 3$, $SS_{xx} = 35$, $n = 10$
  b. $\hat{\beta}_1 = 64$, $SSE = 1,960$, $SS_{xx} = 30$, $n = 14$
  c. $\hat{\beta}_1 = -8.4$, $SSE = 146$, $SS_{xx} = 64$, $n = 20$

7.38 Consider the following pairs of observations:

x	1	4	3	2	5	6	0
y	1	3	3	1	4	7	2

  a. Construct a scattergram for the data.
  b. Use the method of least squares to fit a straight line to the seven data points in the table.
  c. Plot the least squares line on your scattergram of part **a.**
  d. Specify the null and alternative hypotheses you would use to test whether the data provide sufficient evidence to indicate that x contributes information for the (linear) prediction of y.

  e. What is the test statistic that should be used in conducting the hypothesis test of part **d**? Specify the degrees of freedom associated with the test statistic.
  f. Conduct the hypothesis test of part **d** using $\alpha = .05$.

7.39 Refer to Exercise 7.38. Construct an 80% and a 98% confidence interval for β_1.

7.40 Do the accompanying data provide sufficient evidence to conclude that a straight line is useful for characterizing the relationship between x and y?

x	4	2	4	3	2	4
y	1	6	5	3	2	4

Applying the Concepts—Basic

7.41 **State SAT Scores.** Refer to the SPSS simple linear regression relating y = average state SAT score in 2007 with x = average state SAT score in 2000, Exercise 7.15 (p. 394) and the data saved in the **SATSCORES** file.

a. Give the null and alternative hypotheses for determining whether a positive linear relationship exists between y and x.

b. Locate the p-value of the test on the SPSS printout. Interpret the result if $\alpha = .05$.

c. Find a 95% confidence interval for the slope, b_1. Interpret the result.

7.42 Characteristics of diamonds sold at retail. Refer to the Minitab simple linear regression analysis relating y = asking price (dollars) to x = number of carats for diamonds sold on the open market, Exercise 7.16 (p. 394). Recall that the data are saved in the **DIAMONDS** file.

a. Give the null and alternative hypotheses for determining whether a positive linear relationship exists between y and x.

b. Locate the p-value of the test on the Minitab printout. Interpret the result if $\alpha = .01$.

c. Find a 99% confidence interval for the slope, b_1. Interpret the result.

7.43 Drug controlled-release rate study. Refer to the simple linear regression analysis relating y = drug release rate to x = surface area-to-volume ratio, Exercise 7.17 (p. 394) and the data saved in the **DOWDRUG** file. Use the results of the regression to form a 90% confidence interval the slope, β_1. Interpret the result.

7.44 Sweetness of orange juice. Refer to the simple linear regression relating y = sweetness index of an orange juice sample with x = amount of water soluble pectin, Exercise 7.20 (p. 396) and the data saved in the **OJUICE** file. Use the results of the regression to form a 95% confidence interval the slope, β_1. Interpret the result.

Applying the Concepts—Intermediate

7.45 Ranking driving performance of professional golfers. Refer to *The Sport Journal* (Winter 2007) study of a new method for ranking the total driving performance of golfers on the PGA tour, Exercise 7.19 (p. 395). You fit a straight-line model relating driving accuracy (y) to driving distance (x) to the data saved in the **PGADRIVER** file.

a. Give the null and alternative hypotheses for testing whether driving accuracy (y) decreases linearly as driving distance (x) increases.

b. Find the test statistic and p-value of the test, part **a.**

c. Make the appropriate conclusion at $\alpha = .01$.

7.46 Are geography journals worth their cost? Refer to the *Geoforum* (Vol. 37, 2006) study of whether the price of a geography journal is correlated with quality, Exercise 7.34 (p. 402). The data are saved in the **GEO-JRNL** file.

a. In Exercise 7.34a, you fit a straight-line model relating cost (y) to JIF (x). Find and interpret a 95% confidence interval for the slope of the line.

b. In Exercise 7.34b, you fit a straight-line model relating cost (y) to number of citations (x). Find and interpret a 95% confidence interval for the slope of the line.

c. In Exercise 7.34c, you fit a straight-line model relating cost (y) to RPI (x). Find and interpret a 95% confidence interval for the slope of the line.

7.47 Survey of the top business schools. Refer to the *Wall Street Journal* (Sep. 25, 2005) Business School Survey, Exercise 7.23 (p. 397). If you pay more in tuition to go to a top business school, will it necessarily result in a higher probability of a job offer at graduation? Let y = percentage of graduates with job offers and x = tuition cost; then fit the simple linear model, $E(y) = \beta_0 + \beta_1 x$, to the data in the **BSCHOOL** file. Is there sufficient evidence (at $\alpha = .10$) of a positive linear relationship between y and x?

7.48 Spreading rate of spilled liquid. Refer to the *Chemical Engineering Progress* (Jan. 2005) study of the rate at which a spilled volatile liquid will spread across a surface, Exercise 7.24 (p. 397). For the data in the **LIQUIDSPILL** file, let y = mass of the spill and x = elapsed time of the spill.

a. Is there sufficient evidence (at $\alpha = .05$) to indicate that the mass of the spill tends to diminish linearly as time increases?

b. Give an interval estimate (with 95% confidence) of the decrease in spill mass for each minute of elapsed time.

7.49 Do New Jersey banks serve minority communities? Financial institutions have a legal and social responsibility to serve all communities. Do banks adequately serve both inner-city and suburban neighborhoods, both poor and wealthy communities? In New Jersey, banks have been charged with withdrawing from urban areas with a high percentage of minorities. To examine this charge, a regional New Jersey newspaper, the *Asbury Park Press,* compiled county by county data on the number (y) of people in each county per branch bank in the county and the percentage (x) of the population in each county that is minority. These data for each of New Jersey's 21 counties are provided in the table below and saved in the **NJBANKS** file.

County	Number of People per Bank Branch	Percentage of Minority Population
Atlantic	3,073	23.3
Bergen	2,095	13.0
Burlington	2,905	17.8
Camden	3,330	23.4
Cape May	1,321	7.3
Cumberland	2,557	26.5
Essex	3,474	48.8
Gloucester	3,068	10.7
Hudson	3,683	33.2
Hunterdon	1,998	3.7
Mercer	2,607	24.9
Middlesex	3,154	18.1
Monmouth	2,609	12.6
Morris	2,253	8.2
Ocean	2,317	4.7
Passaic	3,307	28.1
Salem	2,511	16.7
Somerset	2,333	12.0
Sussex	2,568	2.4
Union	3,048	25.6
Warren	2,349	2.8

Source: D'Ambrosio, P., and Chambers, S. "No checks and balances," *Asbury Park Press,* September 10, 1995.

a. Plot the data in a scattergram. What pattern, if any, does the plot reveal?

b. Consider the linear model $E(y) = b_0 + b_1 x$. If, in fact, the charge against the New Jersey banks is true, then an increase in the percentage of minorities (x) will lead to a decrease in the number of bank branches in a county and therefore will result in an increase in the number of people (y) per branch. Will the value of β_1 be positive or negative in this situation?

c. Do these data support or refute the charge made against the New Jersey banking community? Test using $\alpha = .01$.

7.50 **Evaluating managerial success.** H. Mintzberg's classic book *The Nature of Managerial Work* (1973) identified the roles found in all managerial jobs. An observational study of 19 managers from a medium-sized manufacturing plant extended Mintzberg's work by investigating which activities *successful* managers actually perform (*Journal of Applied Behavioral Science,* Aug. 1985). To measure success, the researchers devised an index based on the manager's length of time in the organization and his or her level within the firm; the higher the index, the more successful the manager. The next table presents data (saved in the **MANAGERS** file) that can be used to determine whether managerial

success is related to the extensiveness of a manager's network-building interactions with people outside the manager's work unit. Such interactions include phone and face-to-face meetings with customers and suppliers, attending outside meetings, and doing public relations work.

a. Construct a scattergram for the data.

b. Find the prediction equation for managerial success.

c. Find s for your prediction equation. Interpret the standard deviation s in the context of this problem.

d. Plot the least squares line on your scattergram of part **a.** Does it appear that the number of interactions with outsiders contributes information for the prediction of managerial success? Explain.

e. Conduct a formal statistical hypothesis test to answer the question posed in part **d.** Use $\alpha = .05$.

f. Construct a 95% confidence interval for β_1. Interpret the interval in the context of the problem.

Applying the Concepts—Advanced

7.51 **Does elevation impact hitting performance in baseball?** Refer to the *Chance* (Winter 2006) investigation of the effects of elevation on slugging percentage in Major League Baseball, Exercise 2.119 (p. 93). Recall that data were compiled on players' composite slugging percentage

Manager	Manager Success Index, y	Number of Interactions with Outsiders, x
1	40	12
2	73	71
3	95	70
4	60	81
5	81	43
6	27	50
7	53	42
8	66	18
9	25	35
10	63	82
11	70	20
12	47	81
13	80	40
14	51	33
15	32	45
16	50	10
17	52	65
18	30	20
19	42	21

City	Slug Pct.	Elevation
Anaheim	.480	160
Arlington	.605	616
Atlanta	.530	1,050
Baltimore	.505	130
Boston	.505	20
⋮	⋮	⋮
Denver	.625	5,277
⋮	⋮	⋮
Seattle	.550	350
San Francisco	.510	63
St. Louis	.570	465
Tampa	.500	10
Toronto	.535	566

Source: Schaffer, J., and Heiny, E. L. "The effects of elevation on slugging percentage in Major League Baseball," *Chance,* Vol. 19, No. 1, Winter 2006 (adapted from Figure 2, p. 30). Reprinted with permission from *Chance.* © 2006 by the American Statistical Association. All rights reserved.

Minitab Output for Exercise 7.51

Regression Analysis: SLUGPCT versus ELEVATION

```
The regression equation is
SLUGPCT = 0.515 + 0.000021 ELEVATION

Predictor        Coef      SE Coef      T       P
Constant      0.515140    0.007954   64.76   0.000
ELEVATION    0.00002074  0.00000719   2.89   0.008

S = 0.0369803    R-Sq = 23.6%    R-Sq(adj) = 20.7%

Analysis of Variance

Source          DF        SS          MS       F       P
Regression       1     0.011390    0.011390   8.33   0.008
Residual Error  27     0.036924    0.001368
Total           28     0.048314
```

at each of 29 cities for a recent season, as well as each city's elevation (feet above sea level). The data are saved in the **MLBPARKS** file. (Selected observations are shown in the table on page 588.) Consider a straight-line model relating slugging percentage (y) to elevation (x).

a. The model was fit to the data using Minitab, with the results shown in the printout on page 588. Locate the estimates of the model parameters on the printout.

b. Is there sufficient evidence (at $\alpha = .01$) of a positive linear relationship between elevation (x) and slugging percentage (y)? Use the p-value shown on the printout to make the inference.

c. Construct a scatterplot for the data and draw the least squares line on the graph. Locate the data point for Denver on the graph. What do you observe?

d. You learned in Exercise 2.119 that the Colorado Rockies, who play their home games in Coors Field, Denver, typically lead the league in team slugging percentage. Many baseball experts attribute this to the "thin air" of Denver—called the "mile-high" city due to its elevation. Remove the data point for Denver from the data set and refit the straight-line model to the remaining data. Repeat parts **a** and **b**. What conclusions can you draw about the "thin air" theory from this analysis?

7.52 Foreign investment risk. One of the most difficult tasks of developing and managing a global portfolio is assessing the risks of potential foreign investments. Duke University researcher C. R. Henry collaborated with two First Chicago Investment Management Company directors to examine the use of country credit ratings as a means of evaluating foreign investments (*Journal of Portfolio Management*, Winter 1995). To be effective, such a measure should help explain and predict the volatility of the foreign market in question. Data on annualized risk (y) and average credit rating (x) for 40 fictitious countries (based on the study results) are saved in the **GLOBRISKF** file. (The first and last five countries are shown in the table.)

Country	Annualized Risk (%)	Average Credit Rating
1	85.9	30.7
2	25.8	77.1
3	25.2	82.7
4	20.9	77.3
5	63.7	35.1
⋮	⋮	⋮
36	73.0	31.5
37	20.7	86.5
38	14.3	95.3
39	44.9	43.9
40	34.5	23.4

a. Do the data provide sufficient evidence to conclude that country credit risk (x) contributes information for the prediction of market volatility (y)?

b. Use a graph to visually locate any unusual data points (outliers).

c. Eliminate the outlier(s), part **b**, from the data set and rerun the simple linear regression analysis. Note any dramatic changes in the results.

7.5 The Coefficients of Correlation and Determination

In this section, we present two statistics that describe the adequacy of a model: the *coefficient of correlation* and the *coefficient of determination*.

Coefficient of Correlation

Recall (from Section 2.10) that a **bivariate relationship** describes a relationship between two variables, x and y. Scattergrams are used to graphically describe a bivariate relationship. In this section, we will discuss the concept of **correlation** and show how it can be used to measure the linear relationship between two variables x and y. A numerical descriptive measure of the linear association between x and y is provided by the *coefficient of correlation, r.*

The **coefficient of correlation,*** r, is a measure of the strength of the *linear* relationship between two variables x and y. It is computed (for a sample of n measurements on x and y) as follows:

$$r = \frac{SS_{xy}}{\sqrt{SS_{xx}SS_{yy}}}$$

where

$$SS_{xy} = \Sigma(x - \bar{x})(y - \bar{y})$$
$$SS_{xx} = \Sigma(x - \bar{x})^2$$
$$SS_{yy} = \Sigma(y - \bar{y})^2$$

*The value of r is often called the *Pearson correlation coefficient* to honor its developer, Karl Pearson. (See Biography p. 524.)

Note that the computational formula for the correlation coefficient r given in the definition involves the same quantities that were used in computing the least squares prediction equation. In fact, because the numerators of the expressions for $\hat{\beta}_1$ and r are identical, you can see that $r = 0$ when $\hat{\beta}_1 = 0$ (the case where x contributes no information for the prediction of y), and r is positive when the slope is positive and negative when the slope is negative. Unlike $\hat{\beta}_1$, the correlation coefficient r is *scaleless* and assumes a value between -1 and $+1$, regardless of the units of x and y.

A value of r near or equal to 0 implies little or no linear relationship between y and x. In contrast, the closer r comes to 1 or -1, the stronger the linear relationship between y and x. And if $r = 1$ or $r = -1$, all the sample points fall exactly on the least squares line. Positive values of r imply a positive linear relationship between y and x; that is, y increases as x increases. Negative values of r imply a negative linear relationship between y and x; that is, y decreases as x increases. Each of these situations is portrayed in Figure 7.16.

We demonstrate how to calculate the coefficient of correlation r using the data in Table 7.1 for the advertising-sales example. The quantities needed to calculate r are SS_{xy}, SS_{xx}, and SS_{yy}. The first two quantities have been calculated previously as $SS_{xy} = 7$ and $SS_{xx} = 10$. The calculation for $SS_{yy} = \Sigma(y - \bar{y})^2$ is shown on the last column of the Excel spreadsheet, Figure 7.5 (p. 388). The result is $SS_{yy} = 6$.

We now find the coefficient of correlation:

$$r = \frac{SS_{xy}}{\sqrt{SS_{xx}SS_{yy}}} = \frac{7}{\sqrt{(10)(6)}} = \frac{7}{\sqrt{60}} = .904$$

The fact that r is positive and near 1 in value indicates that the sales revenue y tends to increase as advertising expenditure x increases—*for this sample of five months.* This is the same conclusion we reached when we found the calculated value of the least squares slope to be positive.

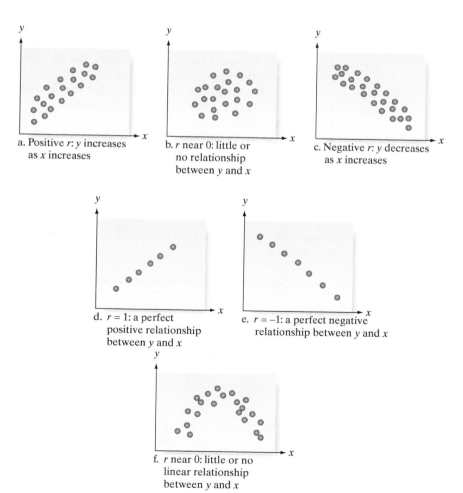

a. Positive r: y increases as x increases

b. r near 0: little or no relationship between y and x

c. Negative r: y decreases as x increases

d. $r = 1$: a perfect positive relationship between y and x

e. $r = -1$: a perfect negative relationship between y and x

f. r near 0: little or no linear relationship between y and x

Figure 7.16

Values of r and their implications

Example 7.4

Relating Crime Rate and Casino Employment Using the Correlation Coefficient

Problem Legalized gambling is available on several riverboat casinos operated by a city in Mississippi. The mayor of the city wants to know the correlation between the number of casino employees and the yearly crime rate. The records for the past 10 years are examined, and the results listed in Table 7.3 are obtained. Calculate the coefficient of correlation r for the data. Interpret the result.

Table 7.3	Data on Casino Employees and Crime Rate, Example 7.4	
Year	Number of Casino Employees, x (thousands)	Crime Rate, y (number of crimes per 1,000 population)
2000	15	1.35
2001	18	1.63
2002	24	2.33
2003	22	2.41
2004	25	2.63
2005	29	2.93
2006	30	3.41
2007	32	3.26
2008	35	3.63
2009	38	4.15

Data Set: CASINO

Solution Rather than use the computing formula given in the definition, we resort to using a statistical software package. The data of Table 7.3 were entered into a computer, and Minitab was used to compute r. The Minitab printout is shown in Figure 7.17.

The coefficient of correlation, highlighted at the top on the printout, is $r = .987$. Thus, the size of the casino workforce and crime rate in this city are very highly correlated—at least over the past 10 years. The implication is that a strong positive linear relationship exists between these variables (see the scatterplot at the bottom of Figure 7.17). We must be careful, however, not to jump to any unwarranted conclusions. For instance, the mayor may be tempted to conclude that hiring more casino workers next year will increase the crime rate—that is, that there is a *causal relationship* between the two variables. However, high correlation does not imply causality. The fact is, many things have probably contributed both to the increase in the casino workforce and to the increase in crime rate. The city's tourist trade has undoubtedly grown since riverboat casinos were legalized, and it is likely that the casinos have expanded both in services offered and in number. *We cannot infer a causal relationship on the basis of high*

Correlations: EMPLOYEES, CRIMERAT

Pearson correlation of EMPLOYEES and CRIMERAT = 0.987
P-Value = 0.000

Figure 7.17
Minitab correlation printout for Example 7.4

sample correlation. When a high correlation is observed in the sample data, the only safe conclusion is that a linear trend may exist between x *and* y.

Look Back Another variable, such as the increase in tourism, may be the underlying cause of the high correlation between x and y.

Now Work Exercise 7.66a,b

⚠ **CAUTION** When using the sample correlation coefficient, r, to infer the nature of the relationship between x and y, two caveats exist: (1) A *high correlation* does not necessarily imply that a causal relationship exists between x and y—only that a linear trend may exist; (2) a *low correlation* does not necessarily imply that x and y are unrelated—only that x and y are not strongly *linearly* related. ▲

Keep in mind that the correlation coefficient r measures the linear association between x values and y values in the sample, and a similar linear coefficient of correlation exists for the population from which the data points were selected. The **population correlation coefficient** is denoted by the symbol ρ (rho). As you might expect, ρ is estimated by the corresponding sample statistic, r. Or, instead of estimating ρ, we might want to test the null hypothesis $H_0: \rho = 0$ against $H_a: \rho \neq 0$—that is, we can test the hypothesis that x contributes no information for the prediction of y by using the straight-line model against the alternative that the two variables are at least linearly related.

However, we already performed this *identical* test in Section 7.4 when we tested $H_0: b_1 = 0$ against $H_a: b_1 \neq 0$—that is, the null hypothesis $H_0: \rho = 0$ is equivalent to the hypothesis $H_0: b_1 = 0$.* When we tested the null hypothesis $H_0: \beta_1 = 0$ in connection with the advertising-sales example, the data led to a rejection of the null hypothesis at the $\alpha = .05$ level. This rejection implies that the null hypothesis of a 0 correlation between the two variables (sales revenue and advertising expenditure) can also be rejected at the $\alpha = .05$ level. The only real difference between the least squares slope $\hat{\beta}_1$ and the coefficient of correlation r is the measurement scale. Therefore, the information they provide about the usefulness of the least squares model is to some extent redundant. Consequently, we will use the slope to make inferences about the existence of a positive or negative linear relationship between two variables.

For the sake of completeness, a summary of the test for linear correlation is provided in the following boxes.

A Test for Linear Correlation

One-Tailed Test	Two-Tailed Test
$H_0: \rho = 0$	$H_0: \rho = 0$
$H_a: \rho > 0$ (or $H_a: \rho < 0$)	$H_a: \rho \neq 0$

$$\text{Test statistic: } t = \frac{r\sqrt{n-2}}{\sqrt{1-r^2}} = \frac{\hat{\beta}_1}{s_{\hat{\beta}_1}}$$

Rejection region: $t > t_\alpha$ (or $t < -t_\alpha$)	*Rejection region:* $|t| > t_{\alpha/2}$

where the distribution of t depends an $(n - 2)$ df.

Condition Required for a Valid Test of Correlation

The sample of (x, y) values is randomly selected from a normal population.

---

*The two tests are equivalent in simple linear regression only.

Coefficient of Determination

Another way to measure the usefulness of the model is to measure the contribution of x in predicting y. To accomplish this, we calculate how much the errors of prediction of y were reduced by using the information provided by x. To illustrate, consider the sample shown in the scattergram of Figure 7.18a. If we assume that x contributes no information for the prediction of y, the best prediction for a value of y is the sample mean $\bar{y}$, which is shown as the horizontal line in Figure 7.18b. The vertical line segments in Figure 7.18b are the deviations of the points about the mean $\bar{y}$. Note that the sum of squares of deviations for the prediction equation $\hat{y} = \bar{y}$ is

$$SS_{yy} = \sum(y_i - \bar{y})^2$$

Now suppose you fit a least squares line to the same set of data and locate the deviations of the points about the line as shown in Figure 7.18c. Compare the deviations about the prediction lines in Figures 7.18b and 7.18c. You can see that

1. If x contributes little or no information for the prediction of y, the sums of squares of deviations for the two lines,

$$SS_{yy} = \sum(y_i - \bar{y})^2 \text{ and } SSE = \sum(y_i - \hat{y}_i)^2$$

will be nearly equal.

2. If x does contribute information for the prediction of y, the SSE will be smaller than SS_{yy}. In fact, if all the points fall on the least squares line, then SSE = 0.

Then the reduction in the sum of squares of deviations that can be attributed to x, expressed as a proportion of SS_{yy}, is

$$\frac{SS_{yy} - SSE}{SS_{yy}}$$

a. Scattergram of data

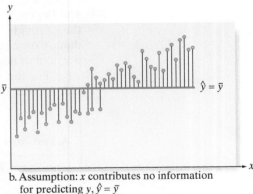

b. Assumption: x contributes no information for predicting y, $\hat{y} = \bar{y}$

c. Assumption: x contributes information for predicting y, $\hat{y} = \hat{\beta}_0 + \hat{\beta}_1 x$

Figure 7.18

A comparison of the sum of squares of deviations for two models

Note that SS_{yy} is the "total sample variation" of the observations around the mean $\bar{y}$ and that SSE is the remaining "unexplained sample variability" after fitting the line $\bar{y}$. Thus, the difference (SS_{yy} − SSE) is the "explained sample variability" attributable to the linear relationship with x. Then a verbal description of the proportion is

$$\frac{SS_{yy} - SSE}{SS_{yy}} = \frac{\text{Explained sample variability}}{\text{Total sample variablity}}$$

= Proportion of total sample variability explained by the linear relationship

In simple linear regression, it can be shown that this proportion—called the *coefficient of determination*—is equal to the square of the simple linear coefficient of correlation r.

Coefficient of Determination

$$r^2 = \frac{SS_{yy} - SSE}{SS_{yy}} = 1 - \frac{SSE}{SS_{yy}}$$

It represents the proportion of the total sample variability around $\bar{y}$ that is explained by the linear relationship between y and x. (In simple linear regression, it may also be computed as the square of the coefficient of correlation r.)

Note that r^2 is always between 0 and 1 because r is between −1 and +1. Thus, an r^2 of .60 means that the sum of squares of deviations of the y values about their predicted values has been reduced 60% by the use of the least squares equation $\hat{y}$, instead of $\bar{y}$, to predict y.

Example 7.5

Obtaining the Value of r^2 for the Sales Revenue Model

Problem Calculate the coefficient of determination for the advertising-sales example. The data are repeated in Table 7.4 for convenience. Interpret the result.

Solution From previous calculations,

$$SS_{yy} = 6 \quad \text{and} \quad SSE = \sum(y - \hat{y})^2 = 1.10$$

Then, from the definition, the coefficient of determination is given by

Table 7.4	**Advertising-Sales Data**
Advertising Expenditure, x ($100s)	Sales Revenue, y ($1,000s)
1	1
2	1
3	2
4	2
5	4

Data Set: ADSALES

$$r^2 = \frac{SS_{yy} - SSE}{SS_{yy}} - \frac{6.0 - 1.1}{6.0} = \frac{4.9}{6.0} = .82$$

Another way to compute r^2 is to recall (Section 7.6) that $r = .904$. Then we have $r^2 = (.904)^2 = .82$. A third way to obtain r^2 is from a computer printout. This value is highlighted on the SPSS printout reproduced in Figure 7.19. Our interpretation is as follows: We know that using advertising expenditure, x, to predict y with the least squares line

$$\hat{y} = -.1 + .7x$$

Model Summary

Model	R	R Square	Adjusted R Square	Std. Error of the Estimate
1	.904[a]	.817	.756	.606

a. Predictors: (Constant), ADVEXP_X

Figure 7.19
Portion of SPSS printout for advertising-sales regression

accounts for 82% of the total sum of squares of deviations of the five sample y values about their mean. Or, stated another way, 82% of the sample variation in sales revenue (y) can be "explained" by using advertising expenditure (x) in a straight-line model.

Now Work Exercise 7.62a

Practical Interpretation of the Coefficient of Determination, r^2

About $100(r^2)\%$ of the sample variation in y (measured by the total sum of squares of deviations of the sample y values about their mean $\bar{y}$) can be explained by (or attributed to) using x to predict y in the straight-line model.

Statistics IN Action **Revisited** | ## Using the Coefficient of Correlation and the Coefficient of Determination

In the previous *Statistics in Action Revisited* (p. 406), we discovered that cumulative 6-month advertising expenditures was a statistically useful linear predictor of number of new PI cases but not a useful linear predictor of number of new WC cases. Both the coefficients of correlation and determination (highlighted on the Minitab printouts in Figures SIA7.4 and Figures SIA7.5) also support this conclusion.

For y = number of new PI cases, the correlation coefficient value of $r = .539$ is statistically significantly different from 0 and indicates a moderate positive linear relationship between the variables. The coefficient of determination,

$r^2 = .29$, implies that almost 30% of the sample variation in number of new PI cases can be explained by using advertising expenditure (x) in the straight-line model. In contrast, for y = number of new WC cases, $r = .056$ is not statistically different from 0 and $r^2 = .003$ implies that only 0.3% of the sample variation in number of new WC cases can be explained by using advertising expenditure (x) in the straight-line model.

Regression Analysis: NewPI versus AdvExp6

```
The regression equation is
NewPI = 7.77 + 0.113 AdvExp6

Predictor       Coef    SE Coef       T       P
Constant       7.767      3.385    2.29   0.027
AdvExp6      0.11289    0.02793    4.04   0.000

S = 9.67521    R-Sq = 29.0%    R-Sq(adj) = 27.2%

Analysis of Variance

Source            DF       SS       MS       F       P
Regression         1   1529.5   1529.5   16.34   0.000
Residual Error    40   3744.4     93.6
Total             41   5273.9
```

Figure SIA7.4
Minitab printout with coefficients of correlation and determination for y = number of new PI cases

Correlations: NewPI, AdvExp6

```
Pearson correlation of NewPI and AdvExp6 = 0.539
P-Value = 0.000
```

Regression Analysis: NewWC versus AdvExp6

```
The regression equation is
NewWC = 24.6 + 0.0098 AdvExp6

Predictor      Coef    SE Coef      T       P
Constant     24.574     3.367    7.30   0.000
AdvExp6     0.00982    0.02778   0.35   0.725

S = 9.62296    R-Sq = 0.3%    R-Sq(adj) = 0.0%

Analysis of Variance

Source           DF       SS      MS      F       P
Regression        1    11.58   11.58   0.13   0.725
Residual Error   40  3704.06   92.60
Total            41  3715.64
```

Figure SIA7.5

Minitab printout with coefficients of correlation and determination for y = number of new WC cases

Correlations: NewWC, AdvExp6

```
Pearson correlation of NewWC and AdvExp6 = 0.056
P-Value = 0.725
```

Activity 7.2   *Keep the Change:* Correlation Coefficients

In this activity, you will use data collected in Activity 1.1, *Keep the Change: Collecting Data* (p. 16) and the results from Activity 7.1, *Keep the Change: Least Squares Models* on (p. 392) to study the strength of a linear relationship.

1. For each of the least squares models in Exercises 1 and 4 in Activity 7.1, calculate the corresponding correlation coefficient. Do these values support your conclusion about which model is more useful? Explain.

2. For each purchase in your original data set *Purchase Totals,* form the ordered pair

    (Purchase Total, Amount Transferred)

    Calculate the correlation coefficient and discuss the strength of the linear relationship between the two variables. Explain

why you might expect the slope of the corresponding least squares line to be close to zero. Find the least squares model and comment on its usefulness. Does the model produce estimated values that are meaningless for large purchase totals? Explain.

3. For each student in your class, form an ordered pair

    (Sum of Amounts Transferred, Bank Matching)

    Calculate the correlation coefficient. How strong is the linear relationship between the two variables? Find the least squares model. Is the slope $\hat{\beta}_1$ approximately 13 and the y-intercept $\hat{\beta}_0$ approximately 0? Explain why the line should have this slope and y-intercept. How good are the estimates given by the model in this situation?

Exercises 7.53–7.69

Learning the Mechanics

7.53 Describe the slope of the least squares line if
   a. $r = .7$ **b.** $r = -.7$
   c. $r = 0$ **d.** $r^2 = .64$

7.54 Explain what each of the following sample correlation coefficients tells you about the relationship between the x and y values in the sample:
   a. $r = 1$ **b.** $r = -1$ **c.** $r = 0$
   d. $r = -.90$ **e.** $r = .10$ **f.** $r = -.88$

7.55 Calculate r^2 for the least squares line in each of the following exercises. Interpret their values.
   a. Exercise 7.10   **b.** Exercise 7.13

7.56 Construct a scattergram for each data set. Then calculate r and r^2 for each data set. Interpret their values.

a.

x	-2	-1	0	1	2
y	-2	1	2	5	6

b.

x	-2	-1	0	1	2
y	6	5	3	2	0

c.

x	1	2	2	3	3	3	4
y	2	1	3	1	2	3	2

d.

x	0	1	3	5	6
y	0	1	2	1	0

Applet Exercise 7.2

Use the applet *Correlation by Eye* to explore the relationship between the pattern of data in a scattergram and the corresponding correlation coefficient.

a. Run the applet several times. Each time, guess the value of the correlation coefficient. Then click *Show r* to see the actual correlation coefficient. How close is your value to the actual value of *r*? Click *New data* to reset the applet.

b. Click the trash can to clear the graph. Use the mouse to place five points on the scattergram that are approximately in a straight line. Then guess the value of the correlation coefficient. Click *Show r* to see the actual correlation coefficient. How close were you this time?

c. Continue to clear the graph and plot sets of five points with different patterns among the points. Guess the value of *r*. How close do you come to the actual value of *r* each time?

d. Based on your experiences with the applet, explain why we need to use more reliable methods of finding the correlation coefficient than just "eyeing" it.

Applying the Concepts—Basic

7.57 RateMyProfessors.com. A popular Web site among college students is RateMyProfessors.com (RMP). Established over 10 years ago, RMP allows students to post quantitative ratings of their instructors. In *Practical Assessment, Research & Evaluation* (May 2007), University of Maine researchers investigated whether instructor ratings posted on RMP are correlated with the formal in-class student evaluations of teaching (SET) that all universities are required to administer at the end of the semester. Data collected for $n = 426$ University of Maine instructors yielded a correlation between RMP and SET ratings of .68.

a. Give the equation of a linear model relating SET rating (*y*) to RMP rating (*x*).

b. Give a practical interpretation of the value $r = .68$.

c. Is the estimated slope of the line, part **a,** positive or negative? Explain.

d. A test of the null hypothesis $H_0: \rho = 0$ yielded a *p*-value of .001. Interpret this result.

e. Compute the coefficient of determination, r^2, for the regression analysis. Interpret the result.

7.58 In business, do nice guys finish first or last? Refer to the *Nature* (March 20, 2008) study of the use of punishment in cooperation games, Exercise 7.14 (p. 393). Recall that college students repeatedly played a version of the game "prisoner's dilemma," and the researchers recorded the average payoff and the number of times cooperation, defection, and punishment were used for each player.

a. A test of no correlation between cooperation use (*x*) and average payoff (*y*) yielded a *p*-value of .33. Interpret this result.

b. A test of no correlation between defection use (*x*) and average payoff (*y*) yielded a *p*-value of .66. Interpret this result.

c. A test of no correlation between punishment use (*x*) and average payoff (*y*) yielded a *p*-value of .001. Interpret this result.

7.59 "Metaskills" and career management. In today's business environment, effective management of one's own career requires a skill set that includes adaptability, tolerance for ambiguity, self-awareness, and ability to identify change.

Management professors at Pace University (New York) used correlation coefficients to investigate the relationship between these "metaskills" and effective career management (*International Journal of Manpower,* Aug. 2000). Data were collected for 446 business graduates who had all completed a management metaskills course. Two of the many variables measured were self-knowledge skill level (*x*) and goal-setting ability (*y*). The correlation coefficient for these two variables was $r = .70$.

a. Give a practical interpretation of the value of *r*.

b. The *p*-value for a test of no correlation between the two variables was reported as *p*-value = .001. Interpret this result.

c. Find the coefficient of determination, r^2, and interpret the result.

7.60 Sports news on local TV broadcasts. *The Sports Journal* (Winter 2004) published the results of a study conducted to assess the factors that impact the time allotted to sports news on local television news broadcasts. Information on total time (in minutes) allotted to sports and audience ratings of the TV news broadcast (measured on a 100-point scale) was obtained from a national sample of 163 news directors. A correlation analysis on the data yielded $r = .43$.

a. Interpret the value of the correlation coefficient, *r*.

b. Find and interpret the value of the coefficient of determination, r^2.

7.61 Women in top management. An empirical analysis of women in upper management positions at U.S. firms was published in the *Journal of Organizational Culture, Communications and Conflict* (July 2007). Monthly data ($n = 252$ months) were collected for several variables, including the number of females in managerial positions, the number of females with a college degree, and the number of female high school graduates with no college degree. Similar data were collected for males.

a. The correlation coefficient relating number of females in managerial positions and number of females with a college degree was reported as $r = .983$. Interpret this result.

b. The correlation coefficient relating number of females in managerial positions and number of female high school graduates with no college degree was reported as $r = .074$. Interpret this result.

c. The correlation coefficient relating number of males in managerial positions and number of males with a college degree was reported as $r = .722$. Interpret this result.

d. The correlation coefficient relating number of males in managerial positions and number of male high school graduates with no college degree was reported as $r = .528$. Interpret this result.

Applying the Concepts—Intermediate

7.62 Characteristics of diamonds sold at retail. Refer to the Minitab simple linear regression analysis relating $y = $ asking price (dollars) to $x = $ number of carats for diamonds sold on the open market, Exercise 7.16 (p. 394) and the data saved in the **DIAMONDS** file.

a. Locate the coefficient of determination, r^2, on the Minitab printout and interpret the result.

b. Find the value of the coefficient of correlation, *r,* from the value of r^2 and the sign of the estimated slope. Interpret the result.

7.63 **Sweetness of orange juice.** Refer to the simple linear regression relating y = sweetness index of an orange juice sample with x = amount of water soluble pectin, Exercise 7.20 (p. 396) and the data saved in the **OJUICE** file. Find and interpret the coefficient of determination, r^2, and the coefficient of correlation, r.

7.64 **Performance ratings of government agencies.** The U.S. Office of Management and Budget (OMB) requires government agencies to produce annual performance and accounting reports (PARS) each year. Refer to *The Public Manager* (Summer 2008) listing of PARS evaluation scores for 24 government agencies, Exercise 2.123. (p. 94). Recall that evaluation scores ranged from 12 (lowest) to 60 (highest). The PARS evaluation scores for 2007 and 2008 are reproduced in the following table and saved in the **PARS** file.

a. Calculate and interpret the coefficient of correlation between the PARS scores in 2007 and 2008.

b. Is there sufficient evidence of a positive linear relationship between 2008 PARS score (y) and 2007 PARS score (x)? Test using $\alpha = .05$.

Agency	Score07	Score08
Transportation	55	53
Labor	53	51
Veterans	51	51
NRC	39	34
Commerce	37	36
HHS	37	35
DHS	37	30
Justice	35	37
Treasury	35	35
GSA	34	40
Agriculture	33	35
EPA	33	36
Social Security	33	33
USAID	32	42
Education	32	36
Interior	32	31
NASA	32	32
Energy	31	34
HUD	31	30
NSF	31	31
State	31	50
OPM	27	28
SBA	22	31
Defense	17	32

Source: Ellig, J., and Wray, H. "Measuring performance reporting quality," *The Public Manager*, Vol. 37, No. 2, Summer 2008 (p. 66). Copyright 2008 by *The Public Manager* in the format electronic usage via Copyright Clearance Center.

7.65 **Salary linked to height.** Are short people short-changed when it comes to salary? According to Business Professors T. A. Judge (University of Florida) and D. M. Cable (University of North Carolina), tall people tend to earn more money over their careers than short people (*Journal of Applied Psychology*, June 2004). Using data collected from participants in the National Longitudinal Surveys begun in 1979, the researchers computed the correlation between average earnings from 1985 to 2000 (in dollars) and height (in inches) for several occupations. The results are given in the table in the next column.

a. Interpret the value of r for people in sales occupations.

b. Compute r^2 for people in sales occupations. Interpret the result.

$$H_0 \qquad H_a$$

Occupation	Correlation, r	Sample Size, n
Sales	.41	117
Managers	.35	455
Blue Collar	.32	349
Service Workers	.31	265
Professional/Technical	.30	453
Clerical	.25	358
Crafts/Forepersons	.24	250

Source: Judge, T. A., and Cable, D. M. "The effect of physical height on workplace success and income: Preliminary test of a theoretical model," *Journal of Applied Psychology*, Vol. 89, No. 3, June 2004 (Table 5). Copyright © 2004 by the American Psychological Association. Reproduced with permission. The use of APA information does not imply endorsement by APA.

c. Give   and   for testing whether average earnings and height are positively correlated.

d. The test statistic for testing H_0 and H_a in part **c** is

$$t = \frac{r\sqrt{n-2}}{\sqrt{1-r^2}}$$

Compute this value for people in sales occupations.

e. Use the result, part **d**, to conduct the test at $\alpha = .01$. Give the appropriate conclusion.

f. Select another occupation and repeat parts **a–e**.

7.66 **The Forbes 400.** The Forbes 400 is an annual ranking of the 400 wealthiest people in the United States. The top 15 billionaires on this list for 2006 are described in the table at the top of the page 599 and saved in the **FORBES400** file.

[NW] **a.** Construct a scattergram for these data. What does the plot suggest about the relationship between age and net worth of billionaires?

[NW] **b.** Find the coefficient of correlation and explain what it tells you about the relationship between age and net worth.

c. If the correlation coefficient of part **b** had the opposite sign, how would that change your interpretation of the relationship between age and net worth?

d. Find the coefficient of determination for a straight-line model relating net worth (y) to age (x). Interpret the result in the words of the problem.

7.67 **Survey of the top business schools.** Refer to the *Wall Street Journal* (Sep. 25, 2005) Business School Survey, Exercise 7.23 (p. 397) and the data saved in the **BSCHOOL** file. Find and interpret r and r^2 for the simple linear regression relating y = percentage of graduates with job offers and x = tuition cost and then fit the simple linear model.

7.68 **Spreading rate of spilled liquid.** Refer to the *Chemical Engineering Progress* (Jan. 2005) study of the rate at which a spilled volatile liquid will spread across a surface, Exercise 7.24 (p. 397) and the data saved in the **LIQUIDSPILL** file. Find and interpret r and r^2 for the simple linear regression y = mass of the spill and x = elapsed time of the spill.

Applying the Concepts—Advanced

7.69 **Attitudes toward quality management.** Studies of Asian (particularly Japanese) and U.S. managers in the 1970s and 1980s found sharp differences of opinion and attitude toward quality management. Do these differences continue to exist? To find out, two California State University researchers (B. F. Yavas and T. M. Burrows) surveyed 100 U.S. and 96 Asian managers in the electronics manufacturing industry

Table for Exercise 7.66

Rank	Name	Net Worth ($ billions)	Age	Marital Status	Residence	Source of Wealth
1	Gates, Bill	53.0	50	married	Medina, WA	Microsoft
2	Buffett, Warren	46.0	76	widowed	Omaha, NE	Berkshire
3	Adelson, Sheldon	20.5	73	married	Las Vegas, NV	gambling
4	Ellison, Lawrence	19.5	62	married	Redwood, CA	Oracle
5	Allen, Paul	16.0	53	single	Seattle, WA	Microsoft
6	Walton, Jim	15.7	58	married	Bentonville, AR	Wal-Mart
7	Walton, Christy	15.6	51	widowed	Jackson, WY	Wal-Mart
8	Walton, S. Robson	15.6	62	married	Bentonville, AR	Wal-Mart
9	Dell, Michael	15.5	41	married	Austin, TX	Dell Computer
10	Walton, Alice	15.5	57	divorced	Fort Worth, TX	Wal-Mart
11	Walton, Helen	15.3	86	widowed	Bentonville, AR	Wal-Mart
12	Brin, Sheldon	14.1	23	single	Palo Alto, CA	Google
13	Page, Larry	14.0	33	single	San Francisco, CA	Google
14	Taylor, Jack	13.9	84	married	St. Louis, MO	Enterprise Rent-A-Car
15	Ballmer, Steve	13.6	50	married	Bellevue, WA	Microsoft

Source: "400 wealthiest people in the United States. The top 15 billionaires," *Forbes* 400, Sept. 21, 2006. Reprinted by permission of Forbes.com. © 2009 Forbes LLC.

(*Quality Management Journal,* Fall 1994). The table (saved in the **QLAGREE** file) gives the percentages of U.S. and Asian managers who agree with each of 13 randomly selected statements regarding quality. (For example, one statement is "Quality is a problem in my company." Another is "Improving quality is expensive.")

a. Find the coefficient of correlation r for these data.
b. Interpret r in the context of the problem.
c. Refer to part **b.** Using the coefficient of correlation r to make inferences about the difference in attitudes between U.S. and Asian managers regarding quality can be misleading. The value of r measures the strength of the linear relationship between two variables; it does not account for a difference between the means of the variables. To illustrate this, examine the hypothetical data in the following table (saved in the **QLAGREE2** file). Show that $r \approx 1$, but the Asian percentage is approximately 30 points higher for each quality statement. Would you conclude that the attitudes of U.S. and Asian managers are similar?

Statement	Percentage of Managers Who Agree	
	U.S.	Asian
1	36	38
2	31	42
3	28	43
4	27	48
5	78	58
6	74	49
7	43	46
8	50	56
9	31	65
10	66	58
11	18	21
12	61	69
13	53	45

Source: Yavas, B. F., and Burrows, T. M. "A comparative study of attitudes of U.S. and Asian managers toward product quality," *Quality Management Journal,* Vol. 2, No.1, September 1994, p. 49 (Table 5). Reprinted with permission from *Quality Management Journal.* © 1994 American Society for Quality. No further distribution allowed without permission.

Quality Statement	Hypothetical Percentage of Managers Who Agree	
	U.S.	Asian
1	20	50
2	30	65
3	40	70
4	50	80
5	55	90

7.6 Using the Model for Estimation and Prediction

If we are satisfied that a useful model has been found to describe the relationship between x and y, we are ready for step 5 in our regression modeling procedure: using the model for estimation and prediction.

The most common uses of a probabilistic model for making inferences can be divided into two categories. The first is using the model to estimate the mean value of y, $E(y)$, *for a specific value of* x. For our advertising-sales example, we may want to estimate the mean sales revenue for *all* months during which $400 ($x = 4$) is expended on advertising.

The second use of the model entails predicting a new individual y *value for a given* x. That is, if we decide to expend $400 in advertising next month, we may want to predict the firm's sales revenue for that month.

In the first case, we are attempting to estimate the mean value of y for a very large number of experiments at the given x value. In the second case, we are trying to predict the outcome of a single experiment at the given x value. Which of these model uses—estimating the mean value of y or predicting an individual new value of y (for the same value of x)—can be accomplished with the greater accuracy?

Before answering this question, we first consider the problem of choosing an estimator (or predictor) of the mean (or a new individual) y value. We will use the least squares prediction equation

$$\hat{y} = \hat{\beta}_0 + \hat{\beta}_1 x$$

both to estimate the mean value of y and to predict a specific new value of y for a given value of x. For our example, we found

$$\hat{y} = -.1 + .7x$$

so that the estimated mean sales revenue for all months when $x = 4$ (advertising is \$400) is

$$\hat{y} = -.1 + .7(4) = 2.7$$

or \$2,700. (Recall that the units of y are thousands of dollars.) The same value is used to predict a new y value when $x = 4$—that is, both the estimated mean and the predicted value of y are $\hat{y} = 2.7$ when $x = 4$, as shown in Figure 7.20.

The difference between these two model uses lies in the relative accuracy of the estimate and the prediction. These accuracies are best measured by using the sampling errors of the least squares line when it is used as an estimator and as a predictor, respectively. These errors are reflected in the standard deviations given in the next box.

Figure 7.20

Estimated mean value and predicted individual value of sales revenue y for $x = 4$

Sampling Errors for the Estimator of the Mean of y and the Predictor of an Individual New Value of y

1. The *standard deviation* of the sampling distribution of the estimator $\hat{y}$ of the *mean value of y* at a specific value of x, say x_p, is

$$\sigma_{\hat{y}} = \sigma\sqrt{\frac{1}{n} + \frac{(x_p - \bar{x})^2}{SS_{xx}}}$$

where σ is the standard deviation of the random error ε. We refer to $\sigma_{\hat{y}}$ as the **standard error of $\hat{y}$.**

2. The *standard deviation* of the prediction error for the predictor $\hat{y}$ of an individual *new y value* at a specific value of x is

$$\sigma_{(y-\hat{y})} = \sigma\sqrt{1 + \frac{1}{n} + \frac{(x_p - \bar{x})^2}{SS_{xx}}}$$

where σ is the standard deviation of the random error ε. We refer to $\sigma_{(y-\hat{y})}$ as the **standard error of the prediction.**

The true value of σ is rarely known, so we estimate σ by s and calculate the estimation and prediction intervals as shown in the next two boxes.

A 100(1 − α)% Confidence Interval for the Mean Value of y at x = x_p

$$\hat{y} \pm t_{\alpha/2} \text{ (Estimated standard error of } \hat{y})$$

or

$$\hat{y} \pm t_{\alpha/2}s\sqrt{\frac{1}{n} + \frac{(x_p - \bar{x})^2}{SS_{xx}}}$$

where $t_{\alpha/2}$ is based on $(n - 2)$ degrees of freedom.

A 100(1 − α)% Prediction Interval* for an Individual New Value of y at x = x_p

$$\hat{y} \pm t_{\alpha/2} \text{ (Estimated standard error of prediction)}$$

or

$$\hat{y} \pm t_{\alpha/2}s\sqrt{1 + \frac{1}{n} + \frac{(x_p - \bar{x})^2}{SS_{xx}}}$$

where $t_{\alpha/2}$ is based on $(n - 2)$ degrees of freedom.

Example 7.6

Estimating the Mean of y—Sales Revenue Model

Problem Refer to the sales-appraisal simple linear regression in previous examples. Find a 95% confidence interval for the mean monthly sales when the appliance store spends $400 on advertising.

Solution For a $400 advertising expenditure, $x = 4$, and the confidence interval for the mean value of y is

$$\hat{y} \pm t_{\alpha/2}s\sqrt{\frac{1}{n} + \frac{(x_p - \bar{x})^2}{SS_{xx}}} = \hat{y} \pm t_{.025}s\sqrt{\frac{1}{5} + \frac{(4 - \bar{x})^2}{SS_{xx}}}$$

where $t_{.025}$ is based on $n - 2 = 5 - 2 = 3$ degrees of freedom. Recall that $\hat{y} = 2.7$, $s = .61, \bar{x} = 3$, and $SS_{xx} = 10$. From Table V in Appendix B, $t_{.025} = 3.182$. Thus, we have

$$2.7 \pm (3.182)(.61)\sqrt{\frac{1}{5} + \frac{(4 - 3)^2}{10}} = 2.7 \pm (3.182)(.61)(.55)$$

$$= 2.7 \pm (3.182)(.34)$$

$$= 2.7 \pm 1.1 = (1.6, 3.8)$$

Therefore, when the store spends $400 a month on advertising, we are 95% confident that the mean sales revenue is between $1,600 and $3,800.

Look Back Note that we used a small amount of data (small in size) for purposes of illustration in fitting the least squares line. The interval would probably be narrower if more information had been obtained from a larger sample.

Now Work Exercise 7.70a–d

Example 7.7

Predicting an Individual value of y—Sales Revenue Model

Problem Refer, again, to the sales-appraisal regression. Predict the monthly sales for next month if $400 is spent on advertising. Use a 95% prediction interval.

---

*The term *prediction interval* is used when the interval formed is intended to enclose the value of a random variable. The term *confidence interval* is reserved for the estimation of population parameters (such as the mean).

Solution To predict the sales for a particular month for which $x_p = 4$, we calculate the 95% prediction interval as

$$\hat{y} \pm t_{\alpha/2}s\sqrt{1 + \frac{1}{n} + \frac{(x_p - \bar{x})^2}{SS_{xx}}} = 2.7 \pm (3.182)(.61)\sqrt{1 + \frac{1}{5} + \frac{(4 - 3)^2}{10}}$$

$$= 2.7 \pm (3.182)(.61)(1.14)$$

$$= 2.7 \pm (3.182)(.70)$$

$$= 2.7 \pm 2.2 = (.5, 4.9)$$

Therefore, we predict with 95% confidence that the sales revenue next month (a month in which we spend $400 in advertising) will fall in the interval from $500 to $4,900.

Look Back Like the confidence interval for the mean value of y, the prediction interval for y is quite large. This is because we have chosen a simple example (only five data points) to fit the least squares line. The width of the prediction interval could be reduced by using a larger number of data points.

Now Work Exercise 7.70e

Both the confidence interval for $E(y)$ and prediction interval for y can be obtained using a statistical software package. Figure 7.21 is a Minitab printout showing the confidence interval and prediction interval for the data in the advertising-sales example. The 95% confidence interval for $E(y)$ when $x = 4$, highlighted under "95% CI" in Figure 7.21, is (1.645, 3.755). The 95% prediction interval for y when $x = 4$, highlighted in Figure 7.21 under "95% PI," is (.503, 4.897). Both intervals agree with the ones computed in Examples 7.6–7.7.

Note that the prediction interval for an individual new value of y is *always* wider than the corresponding confidence interval for the mean value of y. To see this, consider the following. The error in estimating the mean value of y, $E(y)$, for a given value of x, say x_p, is the distance between the least squares line and the true line of means, $E(y) = \beta_0 + \beta_1 x$. This error, $[\hat{y} - E(y)]$, is shown in Figure 7.22. In contrast, *the*

```
Predicted Values for New Observations

New
Obs    Fit    SE Fit      95% CI           95% PI
  1  2.700    0.332   (1.645, 3.755)   (0.503, 4.897)


Values of Predictors for New Observations

New
Obs   ADVEXP_X
  1      4.00
```

Figure 7.21

Minitab printout giving 95% confidence interval for $E(y)$ and 95% prediction interval for y

Figure 7.22

Error of estimating the mean value of y for a given value of x

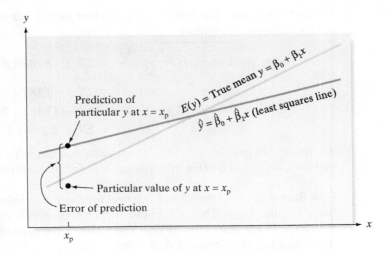

Figure 7.23

Error of predicting a future value of y for a given value of x

error $(y_p - \hat{y})$ *in predicting some future value of* y *is the sum of two errors*—the error of estimating the mean of y, $E(y)$, plus the random error that is a component of the value of y to be predicted (see Figure 7.23). Consequently, the error of predicting a particular value of y will be larger than the error of estimating the mean value of y for a particular value of x. Note from their formulas that both the error of estimation and the error of prediction take their smallest values when $x_p = \bar{x}$. The farther x_p lies from $\bar{x}$, the larger will be the errors of estimation and prediction. You can see why this is true by noting the deviations for different values of x_p between the line of means $E(y) = \beta_0 + \beta_1 x$ and the predicted line of means $\hat{y} = \hat{\beta}_0 + \hat{\beta}_1 x$ shown in Figure 7.23. The deviation is larger at the extremes of the interval where the largest and smallest values of x in the data set occur.

Both the confidence intervals for mean values and the prediction intervals for new values are depicted over the entire range of the regression line in Figure 7.24. You can see that the confidence interval is always narrower than the prediction interval, and they are both narrowest at the mean $\bar{x}$, increasing steadily as the distance $|x - \bar{x}|$ increases. In fact, when x is selected far enough away from $\bar{x}$ so that it falls outside the range of the sample data, it is dangerous to make any inferences about $E(y)$ or y.

⚠ **CAUTION** Using the least squares prediction equation to estimate the mean value of y or to predict a particular value of y for values of x that fall *outside the range* of the values of x contained in your sample data may lead to errors of estimation or prediction that are much larger than expected. Although the least squares model may provide a very good fit to the data over the range of x values contained in the sample, it could give a poor representation of the true model for values of x outside this region. ▲

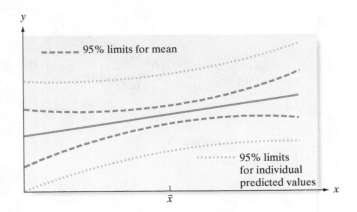

Figure 7.24

Confidence intervals for mean values and prediction intervals for new values

The confidence interval width grows smaller as n is increased; thus, in theory, you can obtain as precise an estimate of the mean value of y as desired (at any given x) by selecting a large enough sample. The prediction interval for a new value of y also grows smaller as n increases, but there is a lower limit on its width. If you examine the formula for the prediction interval, you will see that the interval can get no smaller than $\hat{y} \pm z_{\alpha/2}\sigma$.* Thus, the only way to obtain more accurate predictions for new values of y is to reduce the standard deviation of the regression model, σ. This can be accomplished only by improving the model, either by using a curvilinear (rather than linear) relationship with x or by adding new independent variables to the model, or both.

Statistics IN Action **Revisited**   ## Prediction Using the Straight-Line Model

In the two previous *Statistics in Action Revisited* sections, we demonstrated that x = cumulative 6-month advertising expenditures is a useful linear predictor of y = the number of new PI cases. The Minitab printout shown in Figure SIA7.6 gives a 95% prediction interval for the number of new PI cases in a month where cumulative spending on advertising over the past 6 months is x = $150,000. The highlighted interval is (4.78, 44.62). Thus, we can be 95% confident that for a given month with a 6-month cumulative advertising expenditure of $150,000, the law firm will add between 5 and 44 new PI cases that month.

The 95% confidence interval for the mean of y (also highlighted on the printout) is (20.89, 28.51). This indicates that for all months with cumulative spending on advertising of x = $150,000, the average number of new PI cases each

month will range between 21 and 28 cases. Of course, if these projections are to be useful for future planning, other economic factors that may affect the firm's business must be similar to those during the period over which the sample data were generated.

```
Predicted Values for New Observations

New
Obs    Fit   SE Fit       95% CI            95% PI
  1   24.70    1.89   (20.89, 28.51)   (4.78, 44.62)


Values of Predictors for New Observations

New
Obs   AdvExp6
  1      150
```

Figure SIA7.6

Minitab prediction interval for legal advertising straight-line model

---

Exercises 7.70–7.82

Learning the Mechanics

7.70 Consider the following pairs of measurements saved in the **LM10_70** file:

x	−2	0	2	4	6	8	10
y	0	3	2	3	8	10	11

a. Construct a scattergram for these data.
b. Find the least squares line and plot it on your scattergram.
c. Find s^2 and s.
d. Find a 90% confidence interval for the mean value of y when x = 3. Plot the upper and lower bounds of the confidence interval on your scattergram.

---

*The result follows from the facts that, for large n, $t_{\alpha/2} \approx z_{\alpha/2}$, $s \approx \sigma$, and the last two terms under the radical in the standard error of the predictor are approximately 0.

e. Find a 90% prediction interval for a new value of y when $x = 3$. Plot the upper and lower bounds of the prediction interval on your scattergram.

f. Compare the widths of the intervals you constructed in parts **d** and **e**. Which is wider and why?

7.71 Consider the pairs of measurements shown in the table and saved in the **LM10_71** file. For these data, $SS_{xx} = 38.9000$, $SS_{yy} = 33.600$, $SS_{xy} = 32.8$, and $\hat{y} = -.414 + .843x$.

x	4	6	0	5	2	3	2	6	2	1
y	3	5	-1	4	3	2	0	4	1	1

a. Construct a scattergram for these data.

b. Plot the least squares line on your scattergram.

c. Use a 95% confidence interval to estimate the mean value of y when $x_p = 6$. Plot the upper and lower bounds of the interval on your scattergram.

d. Repeat part **c** for $x_p = 3.2$ and $x_p = 0$.

e. Compare the widths of the three confidence intervals you constructed in parts **c** and **d** and explain why they differ.

7.72 Refer to Exercise 7.71.

a. Using no information about x, estimate and calculate a 95% confidence interval for the mean value of y. [*Hint:* Use the one-sample t methodology of Section 5.4.]

b. Plot the estimated mean value and the confidence interval as horizontal lines on your scattergram.

c. Compare the confidence intervals you calculated in parts **c** and **d** of Exercise 7.71 with the one you calculated in part **a** of this exercise. Does x appear to contribute information about the mean value of y?

d. Check the answer you gave in part **c** with a statistical test of the null hypothesis $H_0: \beta_1 = 0$ against $H_a: \beta_1 \neq 0$. Use $a = .05$.

7.73 In fitting a least squares line to $n = 10$ data points, the following quantities were computed:

$$SS_{xx} = 32 \quad \bar{x} = 3 \quad SS_{yy} = 26 \quad \bar{y} = 4 \quad SS_{xy} = 28$$

a. Find the least squares line.

b. Graph the least squares line.

c. Calculate SSE.

d. Calculate s^2.

e. Find a 95% confidence interval for the mean value of y when $x_p = 2.5$.

f. Find a 95% prediction interval for y when $x_p = 4$.

Applying the Concepts—Basic

7.74 **In business, do nice guys finish first or last?** Refer to the *Nature* (March 20, 2008) study of the use of punishment in cooperation games, Exercise 7.14 (p. 393). Recall that simple linear regression was used to model a player's average payoff (y) as a straight-line function of the number of times punishment was used (x) by the player.

a. If the researchers want to predict average payoff for a single player who used punishment 10 times, how should they proceed?

b. If the researchers want to predict the mean of the average payoffs for all players who used punishment 10 times, how should they proceed?

7.75 **Characteristics of diamonds sold at retail.** Refer to the Minitab simple linear regression analysis relating $y = $ asking price (dollars) to $x = $ number of carats for diamonds sold on the open market, Exercise 7.16 (p. 394) and the data saved in the **DIAMONDS** file. The portion of the Minitab printout giving a 95% confidence interval for $E(y)$ and a 95% prediction interval for y when $x = .52$ is shown below.

a. Locate and interpret the 95% confidence interval for $E(y)$.

b. Locate and interpret the 95% prediction interval for y.

7.76 **Drug controlled-release rate study.** Refer to the *Drug Development and Industrial Pharmacy* (Vol. 28, 2002) drug controlled-release rate study, Exercise 7.17 (p. 394) and the data saved in the **DOWDRUG** file. Recall that data for six drug tablets were used to fit the simple linear model, $E(y) = b_0 + b_1x$, where $y = $ drug release rate and $x = $ surface-area-to-volume ratio. An Excel/DDXL

Minitab output for Exercise 7.75

```
Predicted Values for New Observations

New
Obs     Fit    SE Fit        95% CI              95% PI
  1  3733.1    68.6   (3598.1, 3868.1)   (1529.8, 5936.3)


Values of Predictors for New Observations

New
Obs   CARAT
  1   0.520
```

Excel/DDXL Output for Exercise 7.76

▷ | 90% Conditional Mean Confidence Intervals and Prediction Intervals

RelRate	SA-Vol	Predicted Value	Lower Cond. Mean Limit	Upper Cond. Mean Limit	Lower Prediction Limit	Upper Prediction Limit
60	1.5	61.08377	57.25719	64.910349	55.33401	66.83353
48	1.05	44.921466	42.98937	46.853562	40.215085	49.627847
39	0.9	39.534031	37.781376	41.286687	34.898427	44.169636
33	0.75	34.146597	32.172187	36.121007	29.422687	38.870507
30	0.6	28.759162	25.266678	31.251646	23.79635	33.721975
29	0.65	30.554974	28.258066	32.851881	25.687447	35.4225

SPSS Output for Exercise 7.77

	run	sweet	pectin	lower90m	upper90m
1	1	5.2	220	5.64898	5.83848
2	2	5.5	227	5.63898	5.81613
3	3	6.0	259	5.57819	5.72904
4	4	5.9	210	5.66194	5.87173
5	5	5.8	224	5.64337	5.82560
6	6	6.0	215	5.65564	5.85493
7	7	5.8	231	5.63284	5.80379
8	8	5.6	268	5.55553	5.71011
9	9	5.6	239	5.61947	5.78019
10	10	5.9	212	5.65946	5.86497
11	11	5.4	410	5.05526	5.55416
12	12	5.6	256	5.58517	5.73592

printout giving a 90% prediction interval for each of the $n = 6$ observations in the sample is shown at the bottom of page 605. Select an observation and give a practical interpretation for this prediction interval.

7.77 Sweetness of orange juice. Refer to the simple linear regression of sweetness index y and amount of pectin x for $n = 24$ orange juice samples, Exercise 7.20 (p. 396) and the data saved in the **OJUICE** file. A 90% confidence interval for the mean sweetness index, $E(y)$, for each of the first 12 runs is shown on the SPSS spreadsheet above. Select an observation and interpret this interval.

Applying the Concepts—Intermediate

7.78 Ranking driving performance of professional golfers. Refer to *The Sport Journal* (Winter 2007) study of a new method for ranking the total driving performance of golfers on the PGA tour, Exercise 7.19 (p. 395). You fit a straight-line model relating driving accuracy (y) to driving distance (x) to the data saved in the **PGADRIVER** file. Of interest is predicting y and estimating $E(y)$ when $x = 300$ yards.
  a. Find and interpret a 95% prediction interval for y.
  b. Find and interpret a 95% confidence interval for $E(y)$.
  c. If you are interested in knowing the average driving accuracy of all PGA golfers who have a driving distance of 300 yards, which of the intervals is relevant? Explain.

7.79 Spreading rate of spilled liquid. Refer to the *Chemical Engineering Progress* (Jan. 2005) study of the rate at which a spilled volatile liquid will spread across a surface, Exercise 7.24 (p. 397) and the data saved in the **LIQUIDSPILL** file. Recall that simple linear regression was used to model y = mass of the spill as a function of x = elapsed time of the spill.
  a. Find a 99% confidence interval for the mean mass of all spills with an elapsed time of 15 minutes. Interpret the result.
  b. Find a 99% prediction interval for the mass of a single spill with an elapsed time of 15 minutes. Interpret the result.
  c. Compare the intervals, parts **a** and **b**. Which interval is wider? Will this always be the case? Explain.

7.80 Forecasting managerial needs. Managers are an important part of any organization's resource base. Accordingly, the organization should be just as concerned about forecasting its future managerial needs as it is with forecasting its needs for, say, the natural resources used in its production process (Northcraft and Neale, *Organizational Behavior: A Management Challenge*, 2001). A common forecasting procedure is to model the relationship between sales and the number of managers needed because the demand for managers is the result of the increases and decreases in the demand for products and services that a firm offers its customers. To develop this relationship, the data shown in the table below (saved in the **MANAGERS2** file) are collected from a firm's records.

$a = .05.$

Units Sold, x	Managers, y	Units Sold, x	Managers, y
5	10	30	22
4	11	31	25
8	10	36	30
7	10	38	30
9	9	40	31
15	10	41	31
20	11	51	32
21	17	40	30
25	19	48	32
24	21	47	32

  a. Test the usefulness of the model. Use   State your conclusion in the context of the problem.
  b. The company projects that it will sell 39 units next month. Use the least squares model to construct a 90% prediction interval for the number of managers needed next month.
  c. Interpret the interval in part **b**. Use the interval to determine the reliability of the firm's projection.

7.81 Predicting quit rates in manufacturing. The reasons given by workers for quitting their jobs generally fall into one of two categories: (1) worker quits to seek or take a different job, or (2) worker quits to withdraw from the labor force. Economic theory suggests that wages and quit rates are related. The table on the next page lists quit rates (quits per 100 employees) and the average hourly wage in a sample of 15 manufacturing industries. The data are saved in the **QUITTERS** file. Consider the simple linear regression of quit rate y on average wage x.

Industry	Quit Rate, y	Average Wage, x
1	1.4	$ 8.20
2	.7	10.35
3	2.6	6.18
4	3.4	5.37
5	1.7	9.94
6	1.7	9.11
7	1.0	10.59
8	.5	13.29
9	2.0	7.99
10	3.8	5.54
11	2.3	7.50
12	1.9	6.43
13	1.4	8.83
14	1.8	10.93
15	2.0	8.80

a. Do the data present sufficient evidence to conclude that average hourly wage rate contributes useful information for the prediction of quit rates? What does your model suggest about the relationship between quit rates and wages?

b. Find a 95% prediction interval for the quit rate in an industry with an average hourly wage of $9.00. Interpret the result.

c. Find a 95% confidence interval for the mean quit rate for industries with an average hourly wage of $9.00. Interpret this result.

Applying the Concepts—Advanced

7.82 Life tests of cutting tools. Refer to the data saved in the **CUTTOOLS** file, Exercise 7.36 (p. 402).

a. Use a 90% confidence interval to estimate the mean useful life of a brand A cutting tool when the cutting speed is 45 meters per minute. Repeat for brand B. Compare the widths of the two intervals and comment on the reasons for any difference.

b. Use a 90% prediction interval to predict the useful life of a brand A cutting tool when the cutting speed is 45 meters per minute. Repeat for brand B. Compare the widths of the two intervals to each other and to the two intervals you calculated in part **a.** Comment on the reasons for any differences.

c. Note that the estimation and prediction you performed in parts **a** and **b** were for a value of x that was not included in the original sample—that is, the value x = 45 was not part of the sample. However, the value is within the range of x values in the sample, so the regression model spans the x value for which the estimation and prediction were made. In such situations, estimation and prediction represent *interpolations.* Suppose you were asked to predict the useful life of a brand A cutting tool for a cutting speed of x = 100 meters per minute. Because the given value of x is outside the range of the sample x values, the prediction is an example of *extrapolation.* Predict the useful life of a brand A cutting tool that is operated at 100 meters per minute and construct a 95% prediction interval for the actual useful life of the tool. What additional assumption do you have to make in order to ensure the validity of an extrapolation?

7.7 A Complete Example

In the preceding sections, we have presented the basic elements necessary to fit and use a straight-line regression model. In this section, we will assemble these elements by applying them in an example with the aid of a computer.

Suppose a fire insurance company wants to relate the amount of fire damage in major residential fires to the distance between the burning house and the nearest fire station. The study is to be conducted in a large suburb of a major city; a sample of 15 recent fires in this suburb is selected. The amount of damage, y, and the distance between the fire and the nearest fire station, x, are recorded for each fire. The results are shown in Table 7.5 and saved in the **FIREDAM** file.

Step 1: First, we hypothesize a model to relate fire damage, y, to the distance from the nearest fire station, x. We hypothesize a straight-line probabilistic model:

$$y = \beta_0 + \beta_1 x + \varepsilon$$

Step 2: Next, we open the **FIREDAM** file and use a statistical software package to estimate the unknown parameters in the deterministic component of the hypothesized model. The Excel printout for the simple linear regression analysis is shown in Figure 7.25. The least squares estimates of the slope β_1 and intercept β_0, highlighted on the printout, are

$$\hat{\beta}_1 = 4.919331$$
$$\hat{\beta}_0 = 10.277929$$

Table 7.5	Fire Damage Data
Distance from Fire Station, x (miles)	Fire Damage, y (thousands of dollars)
3.4	26.2
1.8	17.8
4.6	31.3
2.3	23.1
3.1	27.5
5.5	36.0
.7	14.1
3.0	22.3
2.6	19.6
4.3	31.3
2.1	24.0
1.1	17.3
6.1	43.2
4.8	36.4
3.8	26.1

Data Set: FIREDAM

Regression Analysis

Regression Statistics	
Multiple R	0.960977715
R Square	0.923478169
Adjusted R Square	0.917591874
Standard Error	2.316346184
Observations	15

ANOVA

	df	SS	MS	F	Significance F
Regression	1	841.766358	841.766358	156.8861596	1.2478E-08
Residual	13	69.75097535	5.365459643		
Total	14	911.5173333			

	Coefficients	Standard Error	t Stat	P-value	Lower 95%	Upper 95%
Intercept	10.27792855	1.420277811	7.236562082	6.58556E-06	7.209605476	13.34625162
DISTANCE	4.919330727	0.392747749	12.52542054	1.2478E-08	4.070850963	5.767810491

Figure 7.25

Excel printout for fire damage regression analysis

and the least squares equation is (rounded)

$$\hat{y} = 10.278 + 4.919x$$

This prediction equation is graphed in the Minitab scatterplot, Figure 7.26.

The least squares estimate of the slope, $\hat{\beta}_1 = 4.919$, implies that the estimated mean damage increases by \$4,919 for each additional mile from the fire station. This interpretation is valid over the range of x, or from .7 to 6.1 miles from the station. The estimated y-intercept, $\hat{\beta}_0 = 10.278$, has the interpretation that a fire

Figure 7.26

Minitab scatterplot with least squares line for fire damage regression analysis

0 miles from the fire station has an estimated mean damage of $10,278. Although this would seem to apply to the fire station itself, remember that the y-intercept is meaningfully interpretable only if $x = 0$ is within the sampled range of the independent variable. Because $x = 0$ is outside the range ·in this case, $\hat{\beta}_0$ has no practical interpretation.

Step 3: Now we specify the probability distribution of the random error component ε. The assumptions about the distribution are identical to those listed in Section 7.3. Although we know that these assumptions are not completely satisfied (they rarely are for practical problems), we are willing to assume they are approximately satisfied for this example. The estimate of the standard deviation σ of ε, highlighted on the Excel printout (Figure 7.25) is

$$s = 2.31635$$

This implies that most of the observed fire damage (y) values will fall within approximately $2s = 4.64$ thousand dollars of their respective predicted values when using the least squares line. [*Note:* A more precise prediction interval for y is given in Step 5.]

Step 4: We can now check the usefulness of the hypothesized model—that is, whether x really contributes information for the prediction of y using the straight-line model. First, test the null hypothesis that the slope β_1 is 0—that is, that there is no linear relationship between fire damage and the distance from the nearest fire station, against the alternative hypothesis that fire damage increases as the distance increases. We test

$$H_0: \beta_1 = 0$$
$$H_a: \beta_1 > 0$$

The two-tailed observed significance level for testing $H_a: \beta_1 \neq 0$, highlighted on the printout, is approximately 0. When we divide this value in half, the p-value for our one-tailed test is also approximately 0. This small p-value leaves little doubt that mean fire damage and distance between the fire and station are at least linearly related, with mean fire damage increasing as the distance increases.

We gain additional information about the relationship by forming a 95% confidence interval for the slope β_1. The lower and upper endpoints of this interval are highlighted on the Excel printout shown in Figure 7.25.

This yields the interval (4.070, 5.768). We estimate (with 95% confidence) that the interval from $4,070 to $5,768 encloses the mean increase (β_1) in fire damage per additional mile distance from the fire station.

Another measure of the utility of the model is the coefficient of determination, r^2. The value (highlighted on Figure 7.25) is $r^2 = .9235$, which implies that about 92% of the sample variation in fire damage (y) is explained by the distance (x) between the fire and the fire station.

The coefficient of correlation, r, that measures the strength of the linear relationship between y and x is not shown on the Excel printout and must be calculated. Using the facts that $r = \sqrt{r^2}$ in simple linear regression and that r and $\hat{\beta}_1$ have the same sign, we find

$$r = +\sqrt{r^2} = \sqrt{.9235} = .96$$

The high correlation confirms our conclusion that β_1 is greater than 0; it appears that fire damage and distance from the fire station are positively correlated. All signs point to a strong linear relationship between y and x.

Step 5: We are now prepared to use the least squares model. Suppose the insurance company wants to predict the fire damage if a major residential fire were to occur 3.5 miles from the nearest fire station. A 95% confidence interval for $E(y)$ and

Predicted Values for New Observations

```
New
Obs    Fit    SE Fit      95% CI              95% PI
 1   27.496   0.604   (26.190, 28.801)   (22.324, 32.667)
```

Values of Predictors for New Observations

```
New
Obs  DISTANCE
 1      3.50
```

Figure 7.27
Minitab confidence and prediction interval for fire damage regression

prediction interval for y when $x = 3.5$ are shown on the Minitab printout, Figure 7.27. The predicted value (highlighted on the printout) is $\hat{y} = 27.496$, while the 95% prediction interval (also highlighted) is (22.3239, 32.6672). Therefore, with 95% confidence we predict fire damage in a major residential fire 3.5 miles from the nearest station to be between \$22,324 and \$32,667.

⚠ CAUTION We would not use this prediction model to make predictions for homes less than .7 mile or more than 6.1 miles from the nearest fire station. A look at the data in Table 7.7 reveals that all the x values fall between .7 and 6.1. It is dangerous to use the model to make predictions outside the region in which the sample data fall. A straight line might not provide a good model for the relationship between the mean value of y and the value of x when stretched over a wider range of x values. ▲

Exercise 7.83

Applying the Concepts—Intermediate

7.83 An MBA's work-life balance. The importance of having employees with a healthy work-life balance has been recognized by U.S. companies for decades. Many business schools offer courses that assist MBA students with developing good work-life balance habits, and most large companies have developed work-life balance programs for their employees. In April 2005, the Graduate Management Admission Council (GMAC) conducted a survey of over 2,000 MBA alumni to explore the work-life balance issue. (For example, one question asked alumni to state their level of agreement with the statement "My personal and work demands are overwhelming.") Based on these responses, the GMAC determined a work-life balance scale score for each MBA alumni. Scores ranged from 0 to 100, with lower scores indicating a higher imbalance between work and life. Many other variables, including average number of hours worked per week, were also measured. The data for the work-life balance study are saved in the **GMAC** file. (The first 15 observations are listed in the accompanying table.) Let x = average number of hours worked per week and y = work-life balance scale score for each MBA alumnus. Investigate the link between these two variables by conducting a complete simple linear regression analysis of the data. Summarize your findings in a professional report.

Data for Exercise 7.83 (selected observations)

WLB Score	Hours
75.22	50
64.98	45
49.62	50
44.51	55
70.10	50
54.74	60
55.98	55
21.24	60
59.86	50
70.10	50
29.00	70
64.98	45
36.75	40
35.45	40
45.75	50

Source: "Work-life balance: An MBA alumni report," *Graduate Management Admission Council (GMAC) Research Report* (Oct. 13, 2005). Reproduced with the permission of the Graduate Management Admission Council®.

CHAPTER NOTES

Key Terms

Key Symbols/Notation

y	Dependent variable (variable to be predicted)
x	Independent variable (variable used to predict y)
$E(y)$	Expected value (mean) of y
β_0	y-intercept of true line
β_1	slope of true line
$\hat{\beta}_0$	Least squares estimate of y-intercept
$\hat{\beta}_1$	Least squares estimate of slope
ε	Random error
$\hat{y}$	Predicted value of y for a given x-value
$(y - \hat{y})$	Estimated error of prediction
SSE	Sum of squared errors of prediction
r	Coefficient of correlation
r^2	Coefficient of determination
x_p	Value of x used to predict y

$$r^2 = \frac{SS_{yy} - SSE}{SS_{yy}} \qquad \text{Coefficient of determination}$$

$$\hat{y} \pm t_{\alpha/2}s\sqrt{\frac{1}{n} + \frac{(x_p - \bar{x})^2}{SS_{xx}}} \quad 100\%(1-\alpha) \text{ confidence interval for } E(y) \text{ when } x = x_p$$

$$\hat{y} \pm t_{\alpha/2}s\sqrt{1 + \frac{1}{n} + \frac{(x_p - \bar{x})^2}{SS_{xx}}} \quad 100\%(1-\alpha) \text{ prediction interval for } y \text{ when } x = x_p$$

Key Ideas

Simple Linear Regression Variables

y = **Dependent** variable (quantitative)
x = **Independent** variable (quantitative)

Method of Least Squares Properties

1. average error of prediction = 0
2. sum of squared errors is minimum

Practical Interpretation of y-Intercept

Predicted y-value when $x = 0$

(no practical interpretation if $x = 0$ is either nonsensical or outside range of sample data)

Practical Interpretation of Slope

Increase (or decrease) in y for every 1-unit increase in x

First-Order (Straight-Line) Model

$$E(y) = \beta_0 + \beta_1 x$$

where $E(y)$ = mean of y

    β_0 = **y-intercept** of line (point where line intercepts y-axis)
    β_1 = **slope** of line (change in y for every 1-unit change in x)

Coefficient of Correlation, r

1. ranges between -1 and $+1$
2. measures strength of *linear relationship* between y and x

Coefficient of Determination, r^2

1. ranges between 0 and 1
2. measures proportion of sample variation in y "explained" by the model

Practical Interpretation of Model Standard Deviation, s

Ninety-five percent of y-values fall within 2s of their respected predicted values

Width of *confidence interval for $E(y)$* will always be **narrower** than width of prediction interval for y

Guide to Simple Linear Regression

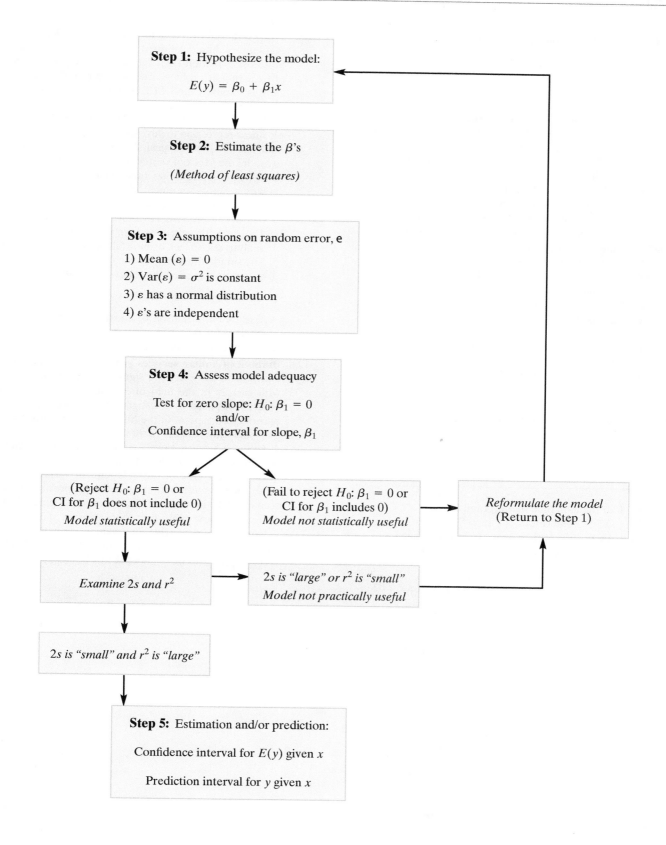

Step 1: Hypothesize the model:

$$E(y) = \beta_0 + \beta_1 x$$

Step 2: Estimate the β's

(Method of least squares)

Step 3: Assumptions on random error, **e**

1) Mean $(\varepsilon) = 0$
2) Var$(\varepsilon) = \sigma^2$ is constant
3) ε has a normal distribution
4) ε's are independent

Step 4: Assess model adequacy

Test for zero slope: H_0: $\beta_1 = 0$
and/or
Confidence interval for slope, β_1

(Reject H_0: $\beta_1 = 0$ or
CI for β_1 does not include 0)
Model statistically useful

(Fail to reject H_0: $\beta_1 = 0$ or
CI for β_1 includes 0)
Model not statistically useful

Reformulate the model
(Return to Step 1)

Examine 2s and r^2

2s is "large" or r^2 is "small"
Model not practically useful

2s is "small" and r^2 is "large"

Step 5: Estimation and/or prediction:

Confidence interval for $E(y)$ given x

Prediction interval for y given x

Supplementary Exercises 7.84–7.102

Learning the Mechanics

7.84 Consider the following sample data:

y	5	1	3
x	5	1	3

  a. Construct a scattergram for the data.

  b. It is possible to find many lines for which $\Sigma(y - \hat{y}) = 0$. For this reason, the criterion $\Sigma(y - \hat{y}) = 0$ is not used for identifying the "best-fitting" straight line. Find two lines that have $\Sigma(y - \hat{y}) = 0$.

  c. Find the least squares line.

  d. Compare the value of SSE for the least squares line to that of the two lines you found in part **b.** What principle of least squares is demonstrated by this comparison?

7.85 In fitting a least squares line to $n = 15$ data points, the following quantities were computed: $SS_{xx} = 55$, $SS_{yy} = 198$, $SS_{xy} = -88$, $\bar{x} = 1.3$, and $\bar{y} = 35$.

  a. Find the least squares line.

  b. Graph the least squares line.

  c. Calculate SSE.

  d. Calculate s^2.

  e. Find a 90% confidence interval for β_1. Interpret this estimate.

  f. Find a 90% confidence interval for the mean value of y when $x = 15$.

  g. Find a 90% prediction interval for y when $x = 15$.

7.86 Consider the following 10 data points, saved in the **LM10_86** file:

x	3	5	6	4	3	7	6	5	4	7
y	4	3	2	1	2	3	3	5	4	2

  a. Plot the data on a scattergram.

  b. Calculate the values of r and r^2.

  c. Is there sufficient evidence to indicate that x and y are linearly correlated? Test at the $\alpha = .10$ level of significance.

Applying the Concepts—Basic

7.87 **Predicting water erosion of soils.** The U.S. Department of Agriculture has developed and adopted the Universal Soil Loss Equation (USLE) for predicting water erosion of soils. In geographical areas where runoff from melting snow is common, the USLE requires an accurate estimate of snowmelt runoff erosion. An article in the *Journal of Soil and Water Conservation* (Mar.–Apr. 1995) used simple linear regression to develop a snowmelt erosion index. Data for 54 climatological stations in Canada were used to model the McCool winter-adjusted rainfall erosivity index, y, as a straight-line function of the once-in-5-year snowmelt runoff amount, x (measured in millimeters).

  a. The data points are plotted in the scattergram shown below. Is there visual evidence of a linear trend?

  b. The data for seven stations were removed from the analysis due to lack of snowfall during the study period. The simple linear regression on the remaining $n = 47$ data points yielded the following results:

$$\hat{y} = -6.72 + 1.39x; \; s_{\hat{\beta}_1} = .06$$

Use this information to construct a 90% confidence interval for β_1.

  c. Interpret the interval, part **b.**

7.88 **Burnout of human services professionals.** Emotional exhaustion, or *burnout,* is a significant problem for people with careers in the field of human services. Regression analysis was used to investigate the relationship between burnout and aspects of the human services professional's job and job-related behavior (*Journal of Applied Behavioral Science,* Vol. 22, 1986). Emotional exhaustion was measured with the Maslach Burnout Inventory, a questionnaire. One of the independent variables considered, called *concentration,* was the proportion of social contacts with individuals who belong to a person's work group. The next table lists the values of the emotional exhaustion index (higher values indicate greater exhaustion) and concentration for a sample of 25 human services professionals who work in a large public hospital.

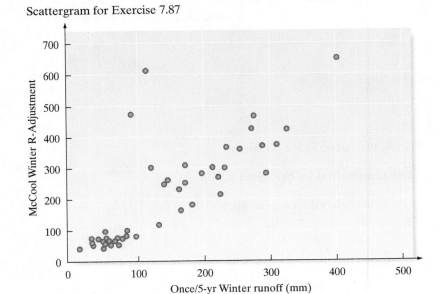

Scattergram for Exercise 7.87

These data are saved in the **BURNOUT** file. A Minitab printout of the simple linear regression is provided below.

a. Construct a scattergram for the data. Do the variables x and y appear to be related?

b. Find the correlation coefficient for the data and interpret its value. Does your conclusion mean that concentration causes emotional exhaustion? Explain.

Exhaustion Index, y	Concentration, x	Exhaustion Index, y	Concentration, x
100	20%	493	86%
525	60	892	83
300	38	527	79
980	88	600	75
310	79	855	81
900	87	709	75
410	68	791	77
296	12	718	77
120	35	684	77
501	70	141	17
920	80	400	85
810	92	970	96
506	77		

c. Test the usefulness of the straight-line relationship with concentration for predicting burnout. Use $\alpha = .05$.

d. Find the coefficient of determination for the model and interpret it.

e. Find a 95% confidence interval for the slope β_1. Interpret the result.

Minitab output for Exercise 7.88

```
The regression equation is
EXHAUST = - 29 + 8.87 CONCEN


Predictor   Coef   SE Coef    T      P
Constant   -29.5   106.7   -0.28  0.785
CONCEN     8.865   1.471    6.03  0.000


S = 174.207   R-Sq = 61.2%   R-Sq(adj) = 59.5%


Analysis of Variance

Source          DF      SS        MS      F      P
Regression       1   1102408  1102408  36.33  0.000
Residual Error  23    698009    30348
Total           24   1800417


Predicted Values for New Observations

New
Obs    Fit   SE Fit      95% CI             95% PI
 1   679.7    38.7   (599.7, 759.8)   (310.6, 1048.9)


Values of Predictors for New Observations

New
Obs   CONCEN
 1     80.0
```

f. Use a 95% confidence interval to estimate the mean exhaustion level for all professionals who have 80% of their social contacts within their work groups. Interpret the interval.

7.89 Retaliation against company "whistle-blowers." Individuals who report perceived wrongdoing of a corporation or public agency are known as *whistle-blowers*. Two researchers developed an index to measure the extent of retaliation against a whistle-blower (*Journal of Applied Psychology,* 1986). The index was based on the number of forms of reprisal actually experienced, the number of forms of reprisal threatened, and the number of people within the organization (e.g., coworkers or immediate supervisor) who retaliated against them. The table below lists the retaliation index (higher numbers indicate more extensive retaliation) and salary for a sample of 15 whistle-blowers from federal agencies. The data are saved in the **RETAL** file.

Retaliation Index	Salary	Retaliation Index	Salary
301	$62,000	535	$19,800
550	36,500	455	44,000
755	21,600	615	46,600
327	24,000	700	15,100
500	30,100	650	70,000
377	35,000	630	21,000
290	47,500	360	16,900
452	54,000		

Source: Data adapted from Near, J. P., and Miceli, M. P. "Retaliation against whistle blowers: Predictors and effects," *Journal of Applied Psychology,* Vol. 71, No. 1, 1986, pp. 137–145.

a. Construct a scattergram for the data. Does it appear that the extent of retaliation increases, decreases, or stays the same with an increase in salary? Explain.

b. Use the method of least squares to fit a straight line to the data.

c. Graph the least squares line on your scattergram. Does the least squares line support your answer to the question in part **a**? Explain.

d. Interpret the y-intercept, $\hat{\beta}_0$, of the least squares line in terms of this application. Is the interpretation meaningful?

e. Interpret the slope, $\hat{\beta}_1$, of the least squares line in terms of this application. Over what range of x is this interpretation meaningful?

f. Test the adequacy of the model using $\alpha = .05$.

7.90 Buying income of households. *Sales and Marketing Management* determined the "effective buying income" (EBI) of the average household in a state. Can the EBI be used to predict retail sales per household in the store-group category "eating and drinking places"?

a. Use the data for 13 states given in the table on the next page (and saved in the **EBI** file) to find the least squares line relating retail sales per household (y) to average household EBI (x).

b. Plot the least squares line, as well as the actual data points, on a scattergram.

c. Based on the graph, part **b,** give your opinion regarding the predictive ability of the least squares line.

d. Find a 95% confidence interval for the slope of the line.

e. Use the results, part **d,** to assess the adequacy of the straight-line model.

State	Average Household Buying Income ($)	Retail Sales: Eating and Drinking Places ($ per household)
Connecticut	60,998	2,553.8
New Jersey	63,853	2,154.8
Michigan	46,915	2,523.3
Minnesota	44,717	2,278.6
Florida	42,442	2,475.8
South Carolina	37,848	2,358.4
Mississippi	34,490	1,538.4
Oklahoma	34,830	2,063.1
Texas	44,729	2,363.5
Colorado	44,571	3,214.9
Utah	43,421	2,653.8
California	50,713	2,215.0
Oregon	40,597	2,144.0

Source: Table adapted from "The survey of buying power," *Sales and Marketing Management*, 1995.

7.91 Foreign vs. U.S. stock rates of return. If the economies of the world were tightly interconnected, the stock markets of different countries would move together. If they did, there would be no reason for investors to diversify their stock portfolios with stocks from a variety of countries (Sharpe, Alexander, and Bailey, *Investments,* 1999). The table below lists the correlations of returns on stocks in each of six countries with the returns of U.S. stocks.

Country	Correlation between Foreign and U.S. Stocks
Australia	.48
Canada	.74
France	.50
Germany	.43
Japan	.41
United Kingdom	.58

Source: Sharpe, W. F., Alexander, G. J., and Bailey, Jeffery V. *Investments.* Upper Saddle River, N.J.: Prentice Hall, 1999, p. 887.

a. Interpret the Australia/U.S. correlation. What does it suggest about the linear relationship between the stocks of the two countries?

b. Sketch a scattergram that is roughly consistent with the magnitude of the France/U.S. correlation.

c. Why must we be careful not to conclude from the information in the table that the country that is most tightly integrated with the United States is Canada?

7.92 Snow geese feeding trial. Researchers at the University of Toronto conducted a series of experiments to investigate whether a commercially sold pet food could serve as a substitute diet for baby snow geese (*Journal of Applied Ecology,* Vol. 32, 1995). Goslings were deprived of food until their guts were empty and then were allowed to feed for 6 hours on a diet of plants or Purina Duck Chow. For each feeding trial, the change in the weight of the gosling after 2.5 hours was recorded as a percentage of initial weight. Two other variables recorded were digestion efficiency (measured as a percentage) and amount of acid-detergent fiber in the digestive tract (also measured as a percentage). The data for 42 feeding trials are saved in the **SNOWGEESE** file. (The first and last five observations are shown in the table at the bottom of the page.)

a. The researchers were interested in the correlation between weight change (*y*) and digestion efficiency (*x*). Plot the data for these two variables in a scattergram. Do you observe a trend?

b. Find the coefficient of correlation relating weight change *y* to digestion efficiency *x*. Interpret this value.

c. Conduct a test (at $\alpha = .01$) to determine whether weight change *y* is correlated with digestion efficiency *x*.

d. Repeat parts **b** and **c** but exclude the data for trials that used duck chow from the analysis. What do you conclude?

e. The researchers were also interested in the correlation between digestion efficiency (*y*) and acid-detergent fiber (*x*). Repeat parts **a–d** for these two variables.

7.93 Evaluating managerial success. Refer to Exercise 7.50 (p. 409), in which managerial success, *y,* was modeled as a function of the number of contacts a manager makes with people outside his or her work unit, *x*, during a specific period of time. The data are saved in the **MANAGERS** file.

a. A particular manager was observed for 2 weeks, as in the *Journal of Applied Behavioral Science* study. She made 55 contacts with people outside her work unit. Predict the value of the manager's success index. Use a 90% prediction interval.

Table for Exercise 7.92

Feeding Trial	Diet	Weight Change (%)	Digestion Efficiency (%)	Acid-Detergent Fiber (%)
1	Plants	−6	0	28.5
2	Plants	−5	2.5	27.5
3	Plants	−4.5	5	27.5
4	Plants	0	0	32.5
5	Plants	2	0	32
⋮	⋮	⋮	⋮	⋮
38	Duck Chow	9	59	8.5
39	Duck Chow	12	52.5	8
40	Duck Chow	8.5	75	6
41	Duck Chow	10.5	72.5	6.5
42	Duck Chow	14	69	7

Source: Gadallah, F. L., and Jefferies, R. L. "Forage quality in brood rearing areas of the lesser snow goose and the growth of captive goslings," *Journal of Applied Biology,* Vol. 32, No. 2, 1995, pp. 281–282 (adapted from Figures 2 and 3). Reprinted with permission of John Wiley & Sons, Inc.

b. A second manager was observed for 2 weeks. This manager made 110 contacts with people outside his work unit. Why should caution be exercised in using the least squares model developed from the given data set to construct a prediction interval for this manager's success index?

c. In the context of this problem, determine the value of x for which the associated prediction interval for y is the narrowest.

Applying the Concepts—Intermediate

7.94 Hospital charges vs. length of stay. *Statistical Bulletin* (Oct.–Dec. 1999) reported the average hospital charge and the average length of hospital stay for patients undergoing radical prostatectomies in a sample of 12 states. The data are listed in the accompanying table and saved in the **HOSPITAL** file.

State	Average Hospital Charge ($)	Average Length of Stay (days)
Massachusetts	11,680	3.64
New Jersey	11,630	4.20
Pennsylvania	9,850	3.84
Minnesota	9,950	3.11
Indiana	8,490	3.86
Michigan	9,020	3.54
Florida	13,820	4.08
Georgia	8,440	3.57
Tennessee	8,790	3.80
Texas	10,400	3.52
Arizona	12,860	3.77
California	16,740	3.78

Source: Statistical Bulletin, Vol. 80, No. 4, Oct.–Dec. 1999, p. 13.

a. Plot the data on a scattergram.

b. Use the method of least squares to model the relationship between average hospital charge (y) and length of hospital stay (x).

c. Conduct a test of model adequacy using $\alpha = .10$.

d. Find the estimated standard error of the regression model.

e. What fraction of the states in the sample have average hospital charges within $\pm 2s$ of the least squares line?

f. Find and interpret the values of r and r^2 for the data.

7.95 Collecting Beanie Babies. Refer to Exercise 2.144 (p. 105) and the data on 50 Beanie Babies collector's items

Name	Age (months) as of Sept. 1998	Value ($)
1. Ally the Alligator	52	55.00
2. Batty the Bat	12	12.00
3. Bongo the Brown Monkey	28	40.00
4. Blackie the Bear	52	10.00
5. Bucky the Beaver	40	45.00
⋮	⋮	⋮
46. Stripes the Tiger (Gold/Black)	40	400.00
47. Teddy the 1997 Holiday Bear	12	50.00
48. Tuffy the Terrier	17	7.00
49. Tracker the Basset Hound	5	15.00
50. Zip the Black Cat	28	40.00

Source: Beanie World Magazine, Sept. 1998.

published in *Beanie World Magazine.* Can age (in months as of Sept. 1998) of a Beanie Baby be used to accurately predict its market value? Answer this question by conducting a complete simple linear regression analysis on the data saved in the **BEANIE** file. (The first and last five observations are shown in the table.)

7.96 Monetary values of NFL teams. Refer to the *Forbes* magazine (Sep. 11, 2008) report on the financial standings of each team in the National Football League (NFL), Exercise 2.24 (p. 49). The table listing the current value (without deduction for debt, except stadium debt) and operating income for each team is reproduced below. These data are saved in the **NFLTEAMVALUES** file.

Rank	Team	Current Value ($ mil)	Operating Income ($ mil)
1	Dallas Cowboys	1,612	30.6
2	Washington Redskins	1,538	58.1
3	New England Patriots	1,324	39.2
4	New York Giants	1,178	41.2
5	New York Jets	1,170	25.9
6	Houston Texans	1,125	43.9
7	Philadelphia Eagles	1,116	33.5
8	Indianapolis Colts	1,076	16.1
9	Chicago Bears	1,064	33.7
10	Baltimore Ravens	1,062	23
11	Denver Broncos	1,061	18.8
12	Tampa Bay Buccaneers	1,053	39.3
13	Miami Dolphins	1,044	36.1
14	Carolina Panthers	1,040	22.3
15	Cleveland Browns	1,035	19.3
16	Green Bay Packers	1,023	21.9
17	Kansas City Chiefs	1,016	11.9
18	Pittsburgh Steelers	1,015	14.4
19	Seattle Seahawks	1,010	8.9
20	Tennessee Titans	994	24.5
21	Cincinnati Bengals	941	22
22	New Orleans Saints	937	21.5
23	St. Louis Rams	929	26.4
24	Detroit Lions	917	−3.1
25	Arizona Cardinals	914	19.7
26	San Diego Chargers	888	19
27	Buffalo Bills	885	12.4
28	Jacksonville Jaguars	876	27.6
29	Atlanta Falcons	872	30.9
30	San Francisco 49ers	865	4.1
31	Oakland Raiders	861	27
32	Minnesota Vikings	839	18.9

Source: "NFL value," *Forbes,* September 11, 2008. First 32 observations—financial standings of the NFL. Reprinted by permission of Forbes.com. © 2009 Forbes LLC.

a. Propose a straight-line model relating an NFL team's current value (y) to its operating income (x).

b. Fit the model to the data using the method of least squares.

c. Interpret the least squares estimates of the slope and y-intercept in the words of the problem.

d. Statistically assess the adequacy of the model. Do you recommend using it to predict an NFL team's value?

7.97 Evaluating a truck weigh-in-motion program. The Minnesota Department of Transportation installed a state-of-the-art weigh-in-motion scale in the concrete surface of the eastbound lanes of Interstate 494 in Bloomington,

Minnesota. After installation, a study was undertaken to determine whether the scale's readings correspond with the static weights of the vehicles being monitored. (Studies of this type are known as *calibration studies*.) After some preliminary comparisons using a two-axle, six-tire truck carrying different loads (see the table below saved in the **TRUCKWTS** file), calibration adjustments were made in the software of the weigh-in-motion system, and the scales were reevaluated.

Trial Number	Static Weight of Truck, x (thousand pounds)	Weigh-in-Motion Reading Prior to Calibration Adjustment, y_1 (thousand pounds)	Weigh-in-Motion Reading After Calibration Adjustment, y_2 (thousand pounds)
1	27.9	26.0	27.8
2	29.1	29.9	29.1
3	38.0	39.5	37.8
4	27.0	25.1	27.1
5	30.3	31.6	30.6
6	34.5	36.2	34.3
7	27.8	25.1	26.9
8	29.6	31.0	29.6
9	33.1	35.6	33.0
10	35.5	40.2	35.0

Source: Adapted from data in Wright, J. L., Owen, F., and Pena, D. "Status of MN/DOT's weigh-in-motion program," St. Paul: Minnesota Department of Transportation, January 1983.

a. Construct two scattergrams, one of y_1 versus x and the other of y_2 versus x.

b. Use the scattergrams of part **a** to evaluate the performance of the weigh-in-motion scale both before and after the calibration adjustment.

c. Calculate the correlation coefficient for both sets of data and interpret their values. Explain how these correlation coefficients can be used to evaluate the weigh-in-motion scale.

d. Suppose the sample correlation coefficient for y_2 and x was 1. Could this happen if the static weights and the weigh-in-motion readings disagreed? Explain.

7.98 Energy efficiency of buildings. Firms planning to build new plants or make additions to existing facilities have become very conscious of the energy efficiency of proposed new structures and are interested in the relation between yearly energy consumption and the number of square feet of building shell. The accompanying table (saved in the **BTU** file) lists the energy consumption in British thermal units (a BTU is the amount of heat required to raise 1 pound of water 1°F) for 22 buildings that were all subjected to the same climatic conditions. Consider a straight-line model relating BTU consumption, y, to building shell area, x.

a. Find the least squares estimates of the intercept β_0 and the slope β_1.

b. Investigate the usefulness of the model you developed in part **a**. Is yearly energy consumption positively linearly related to the shell area of the building? Test using $\alpha = .10$.

c. Find the observed significance level of the test of part **b**. Interpret its value.

d. Find the coefficient of determination r^2 and interpret its value.

e. A company wishes to build a new warehouse that will contain 8,000 square feet of shell area. Find the predicted value of energy consumption and associated 95% prediction interval. Comment on the usefulness of this interval.

f. The application of the model you developed in part **a** to the warehouse problem of part **e** is appropriate only if certain assumptions can be made about the new warehouse. What are these assumptions?

BTU/Year (thousands)	Shell Area (square feet)
3,870,000	30,001
1,371,000	13,530
2,422,000	26,060
672,200	6,355
233,100	4,576
218,900	24,680
354,000	2,621
3,135,000	23,350
1,470,000	18,770
1,408,000	12,220
2,201,000	25,490
2,680,000	23,680
337,500	5,650
567,500	8,001
555,300	6,147
239,400	2,660
2,629,000	19,240
1,102,000	10,700
423,500	9,125
423,500	6,510
1,691,000	13,530
1,870,000	18,860

7.99 Top Florida law firms. Refer to *Florida Trend Magazine's* (April 2002) data on law firms with headquarters in the state of Florida, Exercise 2.145 (p. 105). Data on the number of lawyers and number of law offices, saved in the **FLALAW** file, are reproduced in the table on the next page. Suppose you want to predict the number of law offices (y) based on the number of lawyers (x) at the firm.

a. Use the method of least squares (and computer software) to find the best-fitting line to the data.

b. Evaluate the line by conducting a complete simple linear regression analysis.

c. A firm with 300 lawyers is planning on building its headquarters in Florida. How many law offices should the firm expect to build?

Applying the Concepts—Advanced

7.100 Regression through the origin. Sometimes it is known from theoretical considerations that the straight-line relationship between two variables, x and y, passes through the origin of the xy-plane. Consider the relationship between the total weight of a shipment of 50-pound bags of flour, y, and the number of bags in the shipment, x. Because a shipment containing $x = 0$ bags (i.e., no shipment at all) has a total weight of $y = 0$, a straight-line model of the relationship between x and y should pass through the point $x = 0$, $y = 0$. In such a case, you could

Table for Exercise 7.99

Rank	Firm	Headquarters	Number of Lawyers	Number of Offices
1	Holland & Knight	Tallahassee	529	11
2	Akerman Senterfit	Orlando	355	9
3	Greenberg Traurig	Miami	301	6
4	Carlton Fields	Tampa	207	6
5	Ruden McClosky Smit	Ft. Lauderdale	175	9
6	Fowler White Boggs	Tampa	175	7
7	Foley & Lardner	Orlando	159	5
8	GrayHarris	Orlando	158	6
9	Broad and Cassel	Orlando	150	7
10	Shutts & Bowen	Miami	144	5
11	Steel Hector & Davis	Miami	141	5
12	Gunster Yoakley	W. Palm Beach	140	6
13	Adorno & Zeder	Miami	105	4
14	Becker & Poliakoff	Ft. Lauderdale	100	12
15	Lowndes Drosdick	Orlando	100	1
16	Conroy Simberg Ganon	Hollywood	91	6
17	Stearns Weaver	Miami	85	3
18	Wicker Smith O'Hara	Miami	85	6
19	Rogers Towers Bailey	Jacksonville	80	2
20	Butler Burnette	Tampa	77	3
21	Bilzin Sumberg Dunn	Miami	70	1
22	Morgan Colling	Orlando	70	4
23	White & Case	Miami	70	1
24	Fowler White Burnett	Miami	64	4
25	Rissman Weisberg	Orlando	63	3
26	Rumberger Kirk	Orlando	63	4

Source: Florida Trend Magazine, April 2002, p. 105.

assume $\beta_0 = 0$ and characterize the relationship between x and y with the following model:

$$y = \beta_1 x + \varepsilon$$

The least squares estimate of β_1 for this model is

$$\hat{\beta}_1 = \frac{\sum x_i y_i}{\sum x_i^2}$$

From the records of past flour shipments, 15 shipments were randomly chosen, and the data shown in the table below were recorded. These data are saved in the **FLOUR2** file.

Weight of Shipment	Number of 50-Pound Bags in Shipment
5,050	100
10,249	205
20,000	450
7,420	150
24,685	500
10,206	200
7,325	150
4,958	100
7,162	150
24,000	500
4,900	100
14,501	300
28,000	600
17,002	400
16,100	400

a. Find the least squares line for the given data under the assumption that $\beta_0 = 0$. Plot the least squares line on a scattergram of the data.

b. Find the least squares line for the given data using the model

$$y = \beta_0 + \beta_1 x + \varepsilon$$

(i.e., do not restrict β_0 to equal 0). Plot this line on the same scatterplot you constructed in part **a**.

c. Refer to part **b**. Why might $\hat{\beta}_0$ be different from 0 even though the true value of β_0 is known to be 0?

d. The estimated standard error of $\hat{\beta}_0$ is equal to

$$s\sqrt{\frac{1}{n} + \frac{\bar{x}^2}{SS_{xx}}}$$

Use the t-statistic

$$t = \frac{\hat{\beta}_0 - 0}{s\sqrt{(1/n) + (\bar{x}^2/SS_{xx})}}$$

to test the null hypothesis $H_0: \beta_0 = 0$ against the alternative $H_a: \beta_0 \neq 0$. Use $\alpha = .10$. Should you include β_0 in your model?

Critical Thinking Challenges

7.101 Comparing cost functions. Managers are interested in modeling past cost behavior in order to make more accurate predictions of future costs. Models of past cost behavior are called *cost functions*. Factors that influence costs are called *cost drivers* (Horngren, Foster, and Datar, *Cost Accounting*, 1994). The cost data shown on the next page (and saved in the **RUG** file) are from a rug manufacturer.

Indirect manufacturing labor costs consist of machine maintenance costs and setup labor costs. Machine-hours and direct manufacturing labor-hours are cost drivers. Your task is to estimate and compare two alternative cost functions for indirect manufacturing labor costs. In the first, machine-hours is the independent variable; in the second, direct manufacturing labor-hours is the independent variable. Prepare a report that compares the two cost functions and recommends which should be used to explain and predict indirect manufacturing labor costs. Be sure to justify your choice.

Week	Indirect Manufacturing Labor Costs	Machine-Hours	Direct Manufacturing Labor-Hours
1	$1,190	68	30
2	1,211	88	35
3	1,004	62	36
4	917	72	20
5	770	60	47
6	1,456	96	45
7	1,180	78	44
8	710	46	38
9	1,316	82	70
10	1,032	94	30
11	752	68	29
12	963	48	38

Source: Data and exercise adapted from Horngren, C. T., Foster, G., and Datar, S. M. *Cost Accounting.* Englewood Cliffs, N.J.: Prentice Hall, 1994.

7.102 Spall damage in bricks. A recent civil suit revolved around a 5-building brick apartment complex located in the Bronx, New York, which began to suffer *spalling* damage (i.e., a separation of some portion of the face of a brick from its body). The owner of the complex alleged that the bricks were defectively manufactured. The brick manufacturer countered that poor design and shoddy management led to the damage. To settle the suit, an estimate of the rate of damage per 1,000 bricks, called the *spall rate,* was required (*Chance,* Summer 1994). The owner estimated the spall rate using several *scaffold-drop* surveys. (With this method, an engineer lowers a scaffold down at selected places on building walls and counts the number of visible spalls for every 1,000 bricks in the observation area.) The brick manufacturer conducted its own survey by dividing the walls of the complex into 83 wall segments and taking a photograph of each wall segment. (The number of spalled bricks that could be made out from each photo was recorded, and the sum over all 83 wall segments was used as an estimate of total spall damage.) In this court case, the jury was faced with the following dilemma: The scaffold-drop survey provided the most accurate estimate of spall rates in a given wall segment. Unfortunately, the drop areas were not selected at random from the entire complex; rather, drops were made at areas with high spall concentrations, leading to an overestimate of the total damage. On the other hand, the photo survey was complete in that all 83 wall segments in the complex were checked for spall damage. But the spall rate estimated by the photos, at least in areas of high spall concentration, was biased low (spalling damage cannot always be seen from a photo), leading to an underestimate of the total damage.

Drop Location	Drop Spall Rate (per 1,000 bricks)	Photo Spall Rate (per 1,000 bricks)
1	0	0
2	5.1	0
3	6.6	0
4	1.1	.8
5	1.8	1.0
6	3.9	1.0
7	11.5	1.9
8	22.1	7.7
9	39.3	14.9
10	39.9	13.9
11	43.0	11.8

Source: Fairley, W. B., et al. "Bricks, buildings, and the Bronx: Estimating masonry deterioration," *Chance,* Vol. 7. No. 3, Summer 1994, p. 36 (Figure 3). Reprinted with permission from *Chance.* © 1994 by the American Statistical Association. All rights reserved. [*Note:* The data points are estimated from the points shown on a scatterplot.]

The data in the table are the spall rates obtained using the two methods at 11 drop locations. Use the data (saved in the **BRICKS** file), as did expert statisticians who testified in the case, to help the jury estimate the true spall rate at a given wall segment. Then explain how this information, coupled with the data (not given here) on all 83 wall segments, can provide a reasonable estimate of the total spall damage (i.e., total number of damaged bricks).

References

Chatterjee, S., and Price, B. *Regression Analysis by Example,* 2nd ed. New York: Wiley, 1991.

Draper, N., and Smith, H. *Applied Regression Analysis,* 3rd ed. New York: Wiley, 1987.

Gitlow, H., Oppenheim, A., and Oppenheim, R. *Quality Management: Tools and Methods for Improvement,* 2nd ed. Burr Ridge, Ill.: Irwin, 1995.

Graybill, F. *Theory and Application of the Linear Model.* North Scituate, Mass.: Duxbury, 1976.

Kleinbaum, D., and Kupper, L. *Applied Regression Analysis and Other Multivariable Methods,* 2nd ed. North Scituate, Mass.: Duxbury, 1997.

Mendenhall, W. *Introduction to Linear Models and the Design and Analysis of Experiments.* Belmont, CA.: Wadsworth, 1968.

Mendenhall, W., and Sincich, T. A. *Second Course in Statistics: Regression Analysis,* 6th ed. Upper Saddle River, N.J.: Prentice Hall, 2003.

Montgomery, D., Peck, E., and Vining, G. *Introduction to Linear Regression Analysis,* 3rd ed. New York: Wiley, 2001.

Mosteller, F., and Tukey, J. W. *Data Analysis and Regression: A Second Course in Statistics.* Reading, Mass.: Addison-Wesley, 1977.

Neter, J., Kutner, M., Nachtsheim, C., and Wasserman, W. *Applied Linear Statistical Models,* 4th ed. Hornewood, Ill.: Richard Irwin, 1996.

Rousseeuw, P. J., and Leroy, A. M. *Robust Regression and Outlier Detection.* New York: Wiley, 1987.

Weisburg, S. *Applied Linear Regression,* 2nd ed. New York: Wiley, 1985.

USING TECHNOLOGY

SPSS: Simple Linear Regression

Regression Analysis

Step 1 Access the SPSS spreadsheet file that contains the two quantitative variables (dependent and independent variables).

Step 2 Click on the "Analyze" button on the SPSS menu bar and then click on "Regression" and "Linear," as shown in Figure 7.S.1.

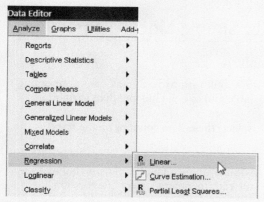

Figure 7.S.1 SPSS menu options for regression

Step 3 On the resulting dialog box (see Figure 7.S.2), specify the dependent variable in the "Dependent" box and the independent variable in the "Independent(s)" box. Be sure to select "Enter" in the "Method" box.

Figure 7.S.2 SPSS linear regression dialog box

Step 4 To produce confidence intervals for the model parameters, click the "Statistics" button and check the appropriate menu items in the resulting menu list.

Step 5 To obtain prediction intervals for *y* and confidence intervals for $E(y)$, click the "Save" button and check the appropriate items in the resulting menu list, as shown in Figure 7.S.3. (The prediction intervals will be added as new columns to the SPSS data spreadsheet.)

Step 6 To return to the main Regression dialog box from any of these optional screens, click "Continue." Click "OK" on the Regression dialog box to view the linear regression results.

Figure 7.S.3 SPSS linear regression save dialog box

Correlation Analysis

Step 1 Click on the "Analyze" button on the main menu bar and then click on "Correlate" (see Figure 7.S.1).

Step 2 Click on "Bivariate." The resulting dialog box appears in Figure 7.S.4.

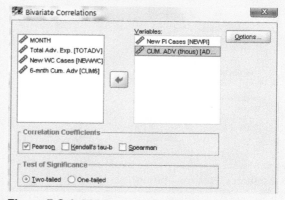

Figure 7.S.4 SPSS correlation dialog box

Step 3 Enter the variables of interest in the "Variables" box and check the "Pearson" option.

Step 4 Click "OK" to obtain a printout of the correlation.

Minitab: Simple Linear Regression

Regression Analysis

Step 1 Access the Minitab worksheet file that contains the two quantitative variables (dependent and independent variables).

Step 2 Click on the "Stat" button on the Minitab menu bar and then click on "Regression" and "Regression" again, as shown in Figure 7.M.1.

Figure 7.M.1 Minitab menu options for regression

Step 3 On the resulting dialog box (see Figure 7.M.2), specify the dependent variable in the "Response" box and the independent variable in the "Predictors" box.

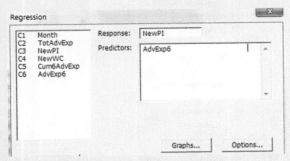

Figure 7.M.2 Minitab regression dialog box

Step 4 To produce prediction intervals for *y* and confidence intervals for $E(y)$, click the "Options" button. The resulting dialog box is shown in Figure 7.M.3.

Figure 7.M.3 Minitab regression options

Step 5 Check "Confidence limits" and/or "Prediction limits," specify the "Confidence level," and enter the value of *x* in the "Prediction intervals for new observations" box.

Step 6 Click "OK" to return to the main Regression dialog box and then click "OK" again to produce the Minitab simple linear regression printout.

Correlation Analysis

Step 1 Click on the "Stat" button on the Minitab main menu bar, then click on "Basic Statistics," and then click on "Correlation," as shown in Figure 7.M.4.

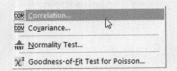

Figure 7.M.4 Minitab menu options for correlation

Step 2 On the resulting dialog box (see Figure 7.M.5), enter the two variables of interest in the "Variables" box.

Figure 7.M.5 Minitab correlation dialog box

Step 3 Click "OK" to obtain a printout of the correlation.

Excel/DDXL: Simple Linear Regression

Regression Analysis

Step 1 Create a workbook with two columns, one representing the dependent variable and one the independent variable.

Step 2 Highlight (select) these data columns on the Excel spreadsheet.

Step 3 Click on "Add-Ins" in the main Excel menu bar and select "DDXL." On the resulting menu, select "Regression," as shown in Figure 7.E.1.

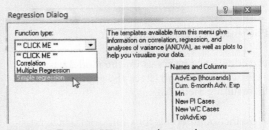

Figure 7.E.1 Excel/DDXL menu options for regression

Step 4 On the resulting menu, select "Simple Regression" in the Function Type box, as shown in Figure 7.E.2.

Figure 7.E.2 DDXL regression options

Step 5 Move the column with the values of the dependent variable into the "Response Variable" box and the column with the values of the independent variable into the "Explanatory Variable" box, as shown in Figure 7.E.3.

Step 6 Click "OK" to generate the simple linear regression printout.

Figure 7.E.3 DDXL regression dialog box

Figure 7.E.5 DDXL correlation dialog box

Step 7 Under the regression results are more options. One option is "95% Confidence and Prediction Intervals." (See Figure 7.E.4.) Selecting this option will generate a confidence interval for $E(y)$ and a prediction interval for y for each observation in the workbook.

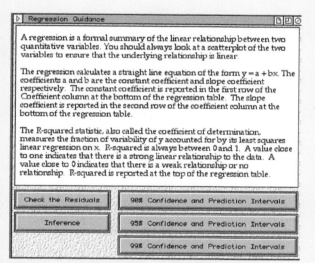

Figure 7.E.4 DDXL menu options for prediction intervals

Correlation Analysis

Step 1 Create a workbook with two columns, one representing the dependent variable and one the independent variable.

Step 2 Highlight (select) these data columns on the Excel spreadsheet.

Step 3 Click on "Add-Ins" in the main Excel menu bar and select "DDXL." On the resulting menu, select "Regression," as shown in Figure 7.E.1.

Step 4 On the resulting menu, select "Correlation" in the Function Type box (see Figure 7.E.2).

Step 5 Move the column with the values of the independent variable into the "x-Axis Quantitative Variable" box and the column with the values of the dependent variable into the "y-Axis Quantitative Variable" box, as shown in Figure 7.E.5.

Step 6 Click "OK" to generate the correlation printout.

TI-84 Graphing Calculator: Simple Linear Regression

Finding the Least Squares Regression Equation

Step 1 *Enter the data*
- Press **STAT** and select **1:Edit**

Note: If a list already contains data, clear the old data.
- Use the up arrow to highlight the list name, "**L1**" or "**L2**"
- Press **CLEAR ENTER**
- Enter your x-data in **L1** and your y-data in **L2**

Step 2 *Find the equation*
- Press **STAT** and highlight **CALC**
- Press **4** for **LinReg(ax + b)**
- Press **ENTER**
- The screen will show the values for a and b in the equation $y = ax + b$.

Finding r and r^2

Use this procedure if r and r^2 do not already appear on the LinReg screen from part I:

Step 1 *Turn the diagnostics feature on*
- Press **2nd 0** for **CATALOG**
- Press the **ALPHA** key and x^{-1} for **D**
- Press the down **ARROW** until **DiagnosticsOn** is highlighted
- Press **ENTER** twice

Step 2 *Find the regression equation as shown in part I above*

The values for r and r^2 will appear on the screen as well.

Graphing the Least Squares Line with the Scatterplot

Step 1 *Enter the data as shown in part I above*

Step 2 *Set up the data plot*

- Press **Y=** and **CLEAR** all functions from the Y registers
- Press **2ndY=** for **STAT PLOT**
- Press **1** for **Plot1**
- Set the cursor so that **ON** is flashing and press **ENTER**
- For **Type,** use the **AR-ROW** and **ENTER** keys to highlight and select the scatterplot (first icon in the first row)
- For **Xlist,** choose the column containing the *x*-data
- For **Ylist,** choose the column containing the *y*-data

Step 3 *Find the regression equation and store the equation in Y1*

- Press **STAT** and highlight **CALC**
- Press **4** for **LinReg(ax + b)** (*Note:* Don't press **ENTER** here because you want to store the regression equation in Y1.)
- Press **VARS**
- Use the right arrow to highlight **Y-VARS**
- Press **ENTER** to select **1:Function**
- Press **ENTER** to select **1:Y1**
- Press **ENTER**

Step 4 *View the scatterplot and regression line*

- Press **ZOOM** and then press **9** to select **9:ZoomStat**

You should see the data graphed along with the regression line.

Appendix A: Basic Counting Rules

Sample points associated with many experiments have identical characteristics. If you can develop a counting rule to count the number of sample points, it can be used to aid in the solution of many probability problems. For example, many experiments involve sampling n elements from a population of N. Then, as explained in Section 3.1, we can use the formula

$$\binom{N}{n} = \frac{N!}{n!(N-n)!}$$

to find the number of different samples of n elements that could be selected from the total of N elements. This gives the number of sample points for the experiment.

Here, we give you a few useful counting rules. You should learn the characteristics of the situation to which each rule applies. Then, when working a probability problem, carefully examine the experiment to see whether you can use one of the rules.

Learning how to decide whether a particular counting rule applies to an experiment takes patience and practice. If you want to develop this skill, try to use the rules to solve some of the exercises in Chapter 3. Proofs of the rules below can be found in the text by W. Feller listed in the references to Chapter 3.

> **Multiplicative Rule**
>
> You have k sets of different elements, n_1 in the first set, n_2 in the second set,..., and n_k in the kth set. Suppose you want to form a sample of k elements by *taking one element from each of the* k *sets*. The number of different samples that can be formed is the product
>
> $$n_1 \cdot n_2 \cdot n_3 \cdot \cdots \cdot n_k$$

Example A.1

Applying the Multiplicative Rule

Problem A product can be shipped by four airlines, and each airline can ship via three different routes. How many distinct ways exist to ship the product?

Solution A method of shipment corresponds to a pairing of one airline and one route. Therefore, $k = 2$, the number of airlines is $n_1 = 4$, the number of routes is $n_2 = 3$, and the number of ways to ship the product is

$$n_1 \cdot n_2 = (4)(3) = 12$$

Look Back How the multiplicative rule works can be seen by using a tree diagram, introduced in Section 3.6. The airline choice is shown by three branching lines in Figure A.1.

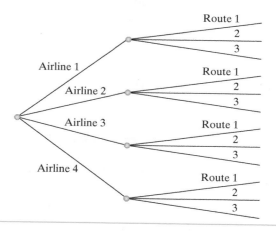

Figure A.1 Tree diagram for airline example

Example A.2

Applying the Multiplicative Rule

Problem You have 20 candidates for three different executive positions, E_1, E_2, and E_3. How many different ways could you fill the positions?

Solution For this example, there are $k = 3$ sets of elements:

Set 1: The candidates available to fill position E_1

Set 2: The candidates remaining (after filling E_1) that are available to fill E_2

Set 3: The candidates remaining (after filling E_1 and E_2) that are available to fill E_3

The numbers of elements in the sets are $n_1 = 20$, $n_2 = 19$, and $n_3 = 18$. Thus, the number of different ways to fill the three positions is

$$n_1 \cdot n_2 \cdot n_3 = (20)(19)(18) = 6,480$$

Partitions Rule

You have a *single* set of N distinctly different elements, and you want to partition it into k sets, the first set containing n_1 elements, the second containing n_2 elements, ..., and the kth containing n_k elements. The number of different partitions is

$$\frac{N!}{n_1! n_2! \cdot \cdots \cdot n_k!} \text{ where } n_1 + n_2 + n_3 + \cdots + n_k = N$$

Example A.3

Applying the Partitions Rule

Problem You have 12 construction workers available for 3 job sites. Suppose you want to assign 3 workers to job 1, 4 to job 2, and 5 to job 3. How many different ways could you make this assignment?

Solution For this example, $k = 3$ (corresponding to the $k = 3$ job sites), $N = 12$, and $n_1 = 3$, $n_2 = 4$, $n_3 = 5$. Then the number of different ways to assign the workers to the job sites is

$$\frac{N!}{n_1! n_2! n_3!} = \frac{12!}{3!4!5!} = \frac{12 \cdot 11 \cdot 10 \cdot \cdots \cdot 3 \cdot 2 \cdot 1}{(3 \cdot 2 \cdot 1)(4 \cdot 3 \cdot 2 \cdot 1)(5 \cdot 4 \cdot 3 \cdot 2 \cdot 1)} = 27,720$$

Combinations Rule

The combinations rule given in Chapter 3 is a special case ($k = 2$) of the partitions rule—that is, sampling is equivalent to partitioning a set of N elements into $k = 2$ groups: elements that appear in the sample and those that do not. Let $n_1 = n$, the number of elements in the sample, and $n_2 = N - n$, the number of elements remaining. Then the number of different samples of n elements that can be selected from N is

$$\frac{N!}{n_1! n_2!} = \frac{N!}{n!(N - n)!} = \binom{N}{n}$$

This formula was given in Section 3.1.

Example A.4

Applying the Combinations Rule

Problem How many samples of 4 firefighters can be selected from a group of 10?

Solution We have $N = 10$ and $n = 4$; then

$$\binom{N}{n} = \binom{10}{4} = \frac{10!}{4!6!} = \frac{10 \cdot 9 \cdot 8 \cdot \cdots \cdot 3 \cdot 2 \cdot 1}{(4 \cdot 3 \cdot 2 \cdot 1)(6 \cdot 5 \cdot \cdots \cdot 2 \cdot 1)} = 210$$

Appendix B: Tables

Table I Random Numbers

Row / Column	1	2	3	4	5	6	7	8	9	10	11	12	13	14
1	10480	15011	01536	02011	81647	91646	69179	14194	62590	36207	20969	99570	91291	90700
2	22368	46573	25595	85393	30995	89198	27982	53402	93965	34095	52666	19174	39615	99505
3	24130	48360	22527	97265	76393	64809	15179	24830	49340	32081	30680	19655	63348	58629
4	42167	93093	06243	61680	07856	16376	39440	53537	71341	57004	00849	74917	97758	16379
5	37570	39975	81837	16656	06121	91782	60468	81305	49684	60672	14110	06927	01263	54613
6	77921	06907	11008	42751	27756	53498	18602	70659	90655	15053	21916	81825	44394	42880
7	99562	72905	56420	69994	98872	31016	71194	18738	44013	48840	63213	21069	10634	12952
8	96301	91977	05463	07972	18876	20922	94595	56869	69014	60045	18425	84903	42508	32307
9	89579	14342	63661	10281	17453	18103	57740	84378	25331	12566	58678	44947	05585	56941
10	85475	36857	53342	53988	53060	59533	38867	62300	08158	17983	16439	11458	18593	64952
11	28918	69578	88231	33276	70997	79936	56865	05859	90106	31595	01547	85590	91610	78188
12	63553	40961	48235	03427	49626	69445	18663	72695	52180	20847	12234	90511	33703	90322
13	09429	93969	52636	92737	88974	33488	36320	17617	30015	08272	84115	27156	30613	74952
14	10365	61129	87529	85689	48237	52267	67689	93394	01511	26358	85104	20285	29975	89868
15	07119	97336	71048	08178	77233	13916	47564	81056	97735	85977	29372	74461	28551	90707
16	51085	12765	51821	51259	77452	16308	60756	92144	49442	53900	70960	63990	75601	40719
17	02368	21382	52404	60268	89368	19885	55322	44819	01188	65255	64835	44919	05944	55157
18	01011	54092	33362	94904	31273	04146	18594	29852	71585	85030	51132	01915	92747	64951
19	52162	53916	46369	58586	23216	14513	83149	98736	23495	64350	94738	17752	35156	35749
20	07056	97628	33787	09998	42698	06691	76988	13602	51851	46104	88916	19509	25625	58104
21	48663	91245	85828	14346	09172	30168	90229	04734	59193	22178	30421	61666	99904	32812
22	54164	58492	22421	74103	47070	25306	76468	26384	58151	06646	21524	15227	96909	44592
23	32639	32363	05597	24200	13363	38005	94342	28728	35806	06912	17012	64161	18296	22851
24	29334	27001	87637	87308	58731	00256	45834	15398	46557	41135	10367	07684	36188	18510
25	02488	33062	28834	07351	19731	92420	60952	61280	50001	67658	32586	86679	50720	94953
26	81525	72295	04839	96423	24878	82651	66566	14778	76797	14780	13300	87074	79666	95725
27	29676	20591	68086	26432	46901	20849	89768	81536	86645	12659	92259	57102	80428	25280
28	00742	57392	39064	66432	84673	40027	32832	61362	98947	96067	64760	64584	96096	98253
29	05366	04213	25669	26422	44407	44048	37937	63904	45766	66134	75470	66520	34693	90449
30	91921	26418	64117	94305	26766	25940	39972	22209	71500	64568	91402	42416	07844	69618
31	00582	04711	87917	77341	42206	35126	74087	99547	81817	42607	43808	76655	62028	76630
32	00725	69884	62797	56170	86324	88072	76222	36086	84637	93161	76038	65855	77919	88006
33	69011	65795	95876	55293	18988	27354	26575	08625	40801	59920	29841	80150	12777	48501
34	25976	57948	29888	88604	67917	48708	18912	82271	65424	69774	33611	54262	85963	03547
35	09763	83473	73577	12908	30883	18317	28290	35797	05998	41688	34952	37888	38917	88050
36	91576	42595	27958	30134	04024	86385	29880	99730	55536	84855	29080	09250	79656	73211
37	17955	56349	90999	49127	20044	59931	06115	20542	18059	02008	73708	83517	36103	42791
38	46503	18584	18845	49618	02304	51038	20655	58727	28168	15475	56942	53389	20562	87338
39	92157	89634	94824	78171	84610	82834	09922	25417	44137	48413	25555	21246	35509	20468
40	14577	62765	35605	81263	39667	47358	56873	56307	61607	49518	89656	20103	77490	18062
41	98427	07523	33362	64270	01638	92477	66969	98420	04880	45585	46565	04102	46880	45709

(continued)

Table I (continued)

Row	1	2	3	4	5	6	7	8	9	10	11	12	13	14
42	34914	63976	88720	82765	34476	17032	87589	40836	32427	70002	70663	88863	77775	69348
43	70060	28277	39475	46473	23219	53416	94970	25832	69975	94884	19661	72828	00102	66794
44	53976	54914	06990	67245	68350	82948	11398	42878	80287	88267	47363	46634	06541	97809
45	76072	29515	40980	07391	58745	25774	22987	80059	39911	96189	41151	14222	60697	59583
46	90725	52210	83974	29992	65831	38857	50490	83765	55657	14361	31720	57375	56228	41546
47	64364	67412	33339	31926	14883	24413	59744	92351	97473	89286	35931	04110	23726	51900
48	08962	00358	31662	25388	61642	34072	81249	35648	56891	69352	48373	45578	78547	81788
49	95012	68379	93526	70765	10592	04542	76463	54328	02349	17247	28865	14777	62730	92277
50	15664	10493	20492	38391	91132	21999	59516	81652	27195	48223	46751	22923	32261	85653
51	16408	81899	04153	53381	79401	21438	83035	92350	36693	31238	59649	91754	72772	02338
52	18629	81953	05520	91962	04739	13092	97662	24822	94730	06496	35090	04822	86774	98289
53	73115	35101	47498	87637	99016	71060	88824	71013	18735	20286	23153	72924	35165	43040
54	57491	16703	23167	49323	45021	33132	12544	41035	80780	45393	44812	12512	98931	91202
55	30405	83946	23792	14422	15059	45799	22716	19792	09983	74353	68668	30429	70735	25499
56	16631	35006	85900	98275	32388	52390	16815	69290	82732	38480	73817	32523	41961	44437
57	96773	20206	42559	78985	05300	22164	24369	54224	35083	19687	11052	91491	60383	19746
58	38935	64202	14349	82674	66523	44133	00697	35552	35970	19124	63318	29686	03387	59846
59	31624	76384	17403	53363	44167	64486	64758	75366	76554	31601	12614	33072	60332	92325
60	78919	19474	23632	27889	47914	02584	37680	20801	72152	39339	34806	08930	85001	87820
61	03931	33309	57047	74211	63445	17361	62825	39908	05607	91284	68833	25570	38818	46920
62	74426	33278	43972	10110	89917	15665	52872	73823	73144	88662	88970	74492	51805	99378
63	09066	00903	20795	95452	92648	45454	09552	88815	16553	51125	79375	97596	16296	66092
64	42238	12426	87025	14267	20979	04508	64535	31355	86064	29472	47689	05974	52468	16834
65	16153	08002	26504	41744	81959	65642	74240	56302	00033	67107	77510	70625	28725	34191
66	21457	40742	29820	96783	29400	21840	15035	34537	33310	06116	95240	15957	16572	06004
67	21581	57802	02050	89728	17937	37621	47075	42080	97403	48626	68995	43805	33386	21597
68	55612	78095	83197	33732	05810	24813	86902	60397	16489	03264	88525	42786	05269	92532
69	44657	66999	99324	51281	84463	60563	79312	93454	68876	25471	93911	25650	12682	73572
70	91340	84979	46949	81973	37949	61023	43997	15263	80644	43942	89203	71795	99533	50501
71	91227	21199	31935	27022	84067	05462	35216	14486	29891	68607	41867	14951	91696	85065
72	50001	38140	66321	19924	72163	09538	12151	06878	91903	18749	34405	56087	82790	70925
73	65390	05224	72958	28609	81406	39147	25549	48542	42627	45233	57202	94617	23772	07896
74	27504	96131	83944	41575	10573	08619	64482	73923	36152	05184	94142	25299	84387	34925
75	37169	94851	39117	89632	00959	16487	65536	49071	39782	17095	02330	74301	00275	48280
76	11508	70225	51111	38351	19444	66499	71945	05422	13442	78675	84081	66938	93654	59894
77	37449	30362	06694	54690	04052	53115	62757	95348	78662	11163	81651	50245	34971	52924
78	46515	70331	85922	38329	57015	15765	97161	17869	45349	61796	66345	81073	49106	79860
79	30986	81223	42416	58353	21532	30502	32305	86482	05174	07901	54339	58861	74818	46942
80	63798	64995	46583	09785	44160	78128	83991	42865	92520	83531	80377	35909	81250	54238
81	82486	84846	99254	67632	43218	50076	21361	64816	51202	88124	41870	52689	51275	83556
82	21885	32906	92431	09060	64297	51674	64126	62570	26123	05155	59194	52799	28225	85762

(continued)

Table I (continued)

Row \ Column	1	2	3	4	5	6	7	8	9	10	11	12	13	14
83	60336	98782	07408	53458	13564	59089	26445	29789	85205	41001	12535	12133	14645	23541
84	43937	46891	24010	25560	86355	33941	25786	54990	71899	15475	95434	98227	21824	19585
85	97656	63175	89303	16275	07100	92063	21942	18611	47348	20203	18534	03862	78095	50136
86	03299	01221	05418	38982	55758	92237	26759	86367	21216	98442	08303	56613	91511	75928
87	79626	06486	03574	17668	07785	76020	79924	25651	83325	88428	85076	72811	22717	50585
88	85636	68335	47539	03129	65651	11977	02510	26113	99447	68645	34327	15152	55230	93448
89	18039	14367	64337	06177	12143	46609	32989	74014	64708	00533	35398	58408	13261	47908
90	08362	15656	60627	36478	65648	16764	53412	09013	07832	41574	17639	82163	60859	75567
91	79556	29068	04142	16268	15387	12856	66227	38358	22478	73373	88732	09443	82558	05250
92	92608	82674	27072	32534	17075	27698	98204	63863	11951	34648	88022	56148	34925	57031
93	23982	25835	40055	67006	12293	02753	14827	23235	35071	99704	37543	11601	35503	85171
94	09915	96306	05908	97901	28395	14186	00821	80703	70426	75647	76310	88717	37890	40129
95	59037	33300	26695	62247	69927	76123	50842	43834	86654	70959	79725	93872	28117	19233
96	42488	78077	69882	61657	34136	79180	97526	43092	04098	73571	80799	76536	71255	64239
97	46764	86273	63003	93017	31204	36692	40202	35275	57306	55543	53203	18098	47625	88684
98	03237	45430	55417	63282	90816	17349	88298	90183	36600	78406	06216	95787	42579	90730
99	86591	81482	52667	61582	14972	90053	89534	76036	49199	43716	97548	04379	46370	28672
100	38534	01715	94964	87288	65680	43772	39560	12918	86537	62738	19636	51132	25739	56947

Source: Abridged from W. H. Beyer (ed.), *CRC Standard Mathematical Tables* 24th edition (Cleveland: The Chemical Rubber Company), 1976. Reproduced by permission of the publisher.

Table II Binomial Probabilities

Tabulated values are $\sum_{x=0}^{k} p(x)$. (Computations are rounded at the third decimal place.)

a. n = 5

k \ p	.01	.05	.10	.20	.30	.40	.50	.60	.70	.80	.90	.95	.99
0	.951	.774	.590	.328	.168	.078	.031	.010	.002	.000	.000	.000	.000
1	.999	.977	.919	.737	.528	.337	.188	.087	.031	.007	.000	.000	.000
2	1.000	.999	.991	.942	.837	.683	.500	.317	.163	.058	.009	.001	.000
3	1.000	1.000	1.000	.993	.969	.913	.812	.663	.472	.263	.081	.023	.001
4	1.000	1.000	1.000	1.000	.998	.990	.969	.922	.832	.672	.410	.226	.049

b. n = 6

k \ p	.01	.05	.10	.20	.30	.40	.50	.60	.70	.80	.90	.95	.99
0	.941	.735	.531	.262	.118	.047	.016	.004	.001	.000	.000	.000	.000
1	.999	.967	.886	.655	.420	.233	.109	.041	.011	.002	.000	.000	.000
2	1.000	.998	.984	.901	.744	.544	.344	.179	.070	.017	.001	.000	.000
3	1.000	1.000	.999	.983	.930	.821	.656	.456	.256	.099	.016	.002	.000
4	1.000	1.000	1.000	.998	.989	.959	.891	.767	.580	.345	.114	.033	.001
5	1.000	1.000	1.000	1.000	.999	.996	.984	.953	.882	.738	.469	.265	.059

c. n = 7

k \ p	.01	.05	.10	.20	.30	.40	.50	.60	.70	.80	.90	.95	.99
0	.932	.698	.478	.210	.082	.028	.008	.002	.000	.000	.000	.000	.000
1	.998	.956	.850	.577	.329	.159	.063	.019	.004	.000	.000	.000	.000
2	1.000	.996	.974	.852	.647	.420	.227	.096	.029	.005	.000	.000	.000
3	1.000	1.000	.997	.967	.874	.710	.500	.290	.126	.033	.003	.000	.000
4	1.000	1.000	1.000	.995	.971	.904	.773	.580	.353	.148	.026	.004	.000
5	1.000	1.000	1.000	1.000	.996	.981	.937	.841	.671	.423	.150	.044	.002
6	1.000	1.000	1.000	1.000	1.000	.998	.992	.972	.918	.790	.522	.302	.068

d. n = 8

k \ p	.01	.05	.10	.20	.30	.40	.50	.60	.70	.80	.90	.95	.99
0	.923	.663	.430	.168	.058	.017	.004	.001	.000	.000	.000	.000	.000
1	.997	.943	.813	.503	.255	.106	.035	.009	.001	.000	.000	.000	.000
2	1.000	.994	.962	.797	.552	.315	.145	.050	.011	.001	.000	.000	.000
3	1.000	1.000	.995	.944	.806	.594	.363	.174	.058	.010	.000	.000	.000
4	1.000	1.000	1.000	.990	.942	.826	.637	.406	.194	.056	.005	.000	.000
5	1.000	1.000	1.000	.999	.989	.950	.855	.685	.448	.203	.038	.006	.000
6	1.000	1.000	1.000	1.000	.999	.991	.965	.894	.745	.497	.187	.057	.003
7	1.000	1.000	1.000	1.000	1.000	.999	.996	.983	.942	.832	.570	.337	.077

(continued)

Table II	(continued)

e. n = 9

k \ p	.01	.05	.10	.20	.30	.40	.50	.60	.70	.80	.90	.95	.99
0	.914	.630	.387	.134	.040	.010	.002	.000	.000	.000	.000	.000	.000
1	.997	.929	.775	.436	.196	.071	.020	.004	.000	.000	.000	.000	.000
2	1.000	.992	.947	.738	.463	.232	.090	.025	.004	.000	.000	.000	.000
3	1.000	.999	.992	.914	.730	.483	.254	.099	.025	.003	.000	.000	.000
4	1.000	1.000	.999	.980	.901	.733	.500	.267	.099	.020	.001	.000	.000
5	1.000	1.000	1.000	.997	.975	.901	.746	.517	.270	.086	.008	.001	.000
6	1.000	1.000	1.000	1.000	.996	.975	.910	.768	.537	.262	.053	.008	.000
7	1.000	1.000	1.000	1.000	1.000	.996	.980	.929	.804	.564	.225	.071	.003
8	1.000	1.000	1.000	1.000	1.000	1.000	.998	.990	.960	.866	.613	.370	.086

f. n = 10

k \ p	.01	.05	.10	.20	.30	.40	.50	.60	.70	.80	.90	.95	.99
0	.904	.599	.349	.107	.028	.006	.001	.000	.000	.000	.000	.000	.000
1	.996	.914	.736	.376	.149	.046	.011	.002	.000	.000	.000	.000	.000
2	1.000	.988	.930	.678	.383	.167	.055	.012	.002	.000	.000	.000	.000
3	1.000	.999	.987	.879	.650	.382	.172	.055	.011	.001	.000	.000	.000
4	1.000	1.000	.998	.967	.850	.633	.377	.166	.047	.006	.000	.000	.000
5	1.000	1.000	1.000	.994	.953	.834	.623	.367	.150	.033	.002	.000	.000
6	1.000	1.000	1.000	.999	.989	.945	.828	.618	.350	.121	.013	.001	.000
7	1.000	1.000	1.000	1.000	.998	.988	.945	.833	.617	.322	.070	.012	.000
8	1.000	1.000	1.000	1.000	1.000	.998	.989	.954	.851	.624	.264	.086	.004
9	1.000	1.000	1.000	1.000	1.000	1.000	.999	.994	.972	.893	.651	.401	.096

g. n = 15

k \ p	.01	.05	.10	.20	.30	.40	.50	.60	.70	.80	.90	.95	.99
0	.860	.463	.206	.035	.005	.000	.000	.000	.000	.000	.000	.000	.000
1	.990	.829	.549	.167	.035	.005	.000	.000	.000	.000	.000	.000	.000
2	1.000	.964	.816	.398	.127	.027	.004	.000	.000	.000	.000	.000	.000
3	1.000	.995	.944	.648	.297	.091	.018	.002	.000	.000	.000	.000	.000
4	1.000	.999	.987	.838	.515	.217	.059	.009	.001	.000	.000	.000	.000
5	1.000	1.000	.998	.939	.722	.403	.151	.034	.004	.000	.000	.000	.000
6	1.000	1.000	1.000	.982	.869	.610	.304	.095	.015	.001	.000	.000	.000
7	1.000	1.000	1.000	.996	.950	.787	.500	.213	.050	.004	.000	.000	.000
8	1.000	1.000	1.000	.999	.985	.905	.696	.390	.131	.018	.000	.000	.000
9	1.000	1.000	1.000	1.000	.996	.966	.849	.597	.278	.061	.002	.000	.000
10	1.000	1.000	1.000	1.000	.999	.991	.941	.783	.485	.164	.013	.001	.000
11	1.000	1.000	1.000	1.000	1.000	.998	.982	.909	.703	.352	.056	.005	.000
12	1.000	1.000	1.000	1.000	1.000	1.000	.996	.973	.873	.602	.184	.036	.000
13	1.000	1.000	1.000	1.000	1.000	1.000	1.000	.995	.965	.833	.451	.171	.010
14	1.000	1.000	1.000	1.000	1.000	1.000	1.000	1.000	.995	.965	.794	.537	.140

(continued)

Table II   *(continued)*

h. $n = 20$

k \ p	.01	.05	.10	.20	.30	.40	.50	.60	.70	.80	.90	.95	.99
0	.818	.358	.122	.012	.001	.000	.000	.000	.000	.000	.000	.000	.000
1	.983	.736	.392	.069	.008	.001	.000	.000	.000	.000	.000	.000	.000
2	.999	.925	.677	.206	.035	.004	.000	.000	.000	.000	.000	.000	.000
3	1.000	.984	.867	.411	.107	.016	.001	.000	.000	.000	.000	.000	.000
4	1.000	.997	.957	.630	.238	.051	.006	.000	.000	.000	.000	.000	.000
5	1.000	1.000	.989	.804	.416	.126	.021	.002	.000	.000	.000	.000	.000
6	1.000	1.000	.998	.913	.608	.250	.058	.006	.000	.000	.000	.000	.000
7	1.000	1.000	1.000	.968	.772	.416	.132	.021	.001	.000	.000	.000	.000
8	1.000	1.000	1.000	.990	.887	.596	.252	.057	.005	.000	.000	.000	.000
9	1.000	1.000	1.000	.997	.952	.755	.412	.128	.017	.001	.000	.000	.000
10	1.000	1.000	1.000	.999	.983	.872	.588	.245	.048	.003	.000	.000	.000
11	1.000	1.000	1.000	1.000	.995	.943	.748	.404	.113	.010	.000	.000	.000
12	1.000	1.000	1.000	1.000	.999	.979	.868	.584	.228	.032	.000	.000	.000
13	1.000	1.000	1.000	1.000	1.000	.994	.942	.750	.392	.087	.002	.000	.000
14	1.000	1.000	1.000	1.000	1.000	.998	.979	.874	.584	.196	.011	.000	.000
15	1.000	1.000	1.000	1.000	1.000	1.000	.994	.949	.762	.370	.043	.003	.000
16	1.000	1.000	1.000	1.000	1.000	1.000	.999	.984	.893	.589	.133	.016	.000
17	1.000	1.000	1.000	1.000	1.000	1.000	1.000	.996	.965	.794	.323	.075	.001
18	1.000	1.000	1.000	1.000	1.000	1.000	1.000	.999	.992	.931	.608	.264	.017
19	1.000	1.000	1.000	1.000	1.000	1.000	1.000	1.000	.999	.988	.878	.642	.182

i. $n = 25$

k \ p	.01	.05	.10	.20	.30	.40	.50	.60	.70	.80	.90	.95	.99
0	.778	.277	.072	.004	.000	.000	.000	.000	.000	.000	.000	.000	.000
1	.974	.642	.271	.027	.002	.000	.000	.000	.000	.000	.000	.000	.000
2	.998	.873	.537	.098	.009	.000	.000	.000	.000	.000	.000	.000	.000
3	1.000	.966	.764	.234	.033	.002	.000	.000	.000	.000	.000	.000	.000
4	1.000	.993	.902	.421	.090	.009	.000	.000	.000	.000	.000	.000	.000
5	1.000	.999	.967	.617	.193	.029	.002	.000	.000	.000	.000	.000	.000
6	1.000	1.000	.991	.780	.341	.074	.007	.000	.000	.000	.000	.000	.000
7	1.000	1.000	.998	.891	.512	.154	.022	.001	.000	.000	.000	.000	.000
8	1.000	1.000	1.000	.953	.677	.274	.054	.004	.000	.000	.000	.000	.000
9	1.000	1.000	1.000	.983	.811	.425	.115	.013	.000	.000	.000	.000	.000
10	1.000	1.000	1.000	.994	.902	.586	.212	.034	.002	.000	.000	.000	.000
11	1.000	1.000	1.000	.998	.956	.732	.345	.078	.006	.000	.000	.000	.000
12	1.000	1.000	1.000	1.000	.983	.846	.500	.154	.017	.000	.000	.000	.000
13	1.000	1.000	1.000	1.000	.994	.922	.655	.268	.044	.002	.000	.000	.000
14	1.000	1.000	1.000	1.000	.998	.966	.788	.414	.098	.006	.000	.000	.000
15	1.000	1.000	1.000	1.000	1.000	.987	.885	.575	.189	.017	.000	.000	.000
16	1.000	1.000	1.000	1.000	1.000	.996	.946	.726	.323	.047	.000	.000	.000
17	1.000	1.000	1.000	1.000	1.000	.999	.978	.846	.488	.109	.002	.000	.000
18	1.000	1.000	1.000	1.000	1.000	1.000	.993	.926	.659	.220	.009	.000	.000
19	1.000	1.000	1.000	1.000	1.000	1.000	.998	.971	.807	.383	.033	.001	.000
20	1.000	1.000	1.000	1.000	1.000	1.000	1.000	.991	.910	.579	.098	.007	.000
21	1.000	1.000	1.000	1.000	1.000	1.000	1.000	.998	.967	.766	.236	.034	.000
22	1.000	1.000	1.000	1.000	1.000	1.000	1.000	1.000	.991	.902	.463	.127	.002
23	1.000	1.000	1.000	1.000	1.000	1.000	1.000	1.000	.998	.973	.729	.358	.026
24	1.000	1.000	1.000	1.000	1.000	1.000	1.000	1.000	1.000	.996	.928	.723	.222

Table III	**Poisson Probabilities**

Tabulated values are $\sum_{x=0}^{k} p(x)$. *(Computations are rounded at the third decimal place.)*

λ \ k	0	1	2	3	4	5	6	7	8	9
.02	.980	1.000								
.04	.961	.999	1.000							
.06	.942	.998	1.000							
.08	.923	.997	1.000							
.10	.905	.995	1.000							
.15	.861	.990	.999	1.000						
.20	.819	.982	.999	1.000						
.25	.779	.974	.998	1.000						
.30	.741	.963	.996	1.000						
.35	.705	.951	.994	1.000						
.40	.670	.938	.992	.999	1.000					
.45	.638	.925	.989	.999	1.000					
.50	.607	.910	.986	.998	1.000					
.55	.577	.894	.982	.998	1.000					
.60	.549	.878	.977	.997	1.000					
.65	.522	.861	.972	.996	.999	1.000				
.70	.497	.844	.966	.994	.999	1.000				
.75	.472	.827	.959	.993	.999	1.000				
.80	.449	.809	.953	.991	.999	1.000				
.85	.427	.791	.945	.989	.998	1.000				
.90	.407	.772	.937	.987	.998	1.000				
.95	.387	.754	.929	.981	.997	1.000				
1.00	.368	.736	.920	.981	.996	.999	1.000			
1.1	.333	.699	.900	.974	.995	.999	1.000			
1.2	.301	.663	.879	.966	.992	.998	1.000			
1.3	.273	.627	.857	.957	.989	.998	1.000			
1.4	.247	.592	.833	.946	.986	.997	.999	1.000		
1.5	.223	.558	.809	.934	.981	.996	.999	1.000		
1.6	.202	.525	.783	.921	.976	.994	.999	1.000		
1.7	.183	.493	.757	.907	.970	.992	.998	1.000		
1.8	.165	.463	.731	.891	.964	.990	.997	.999	1.000	
1.9	.150	.434	.704	.875	.956	.987	.997	.999	1.000	
2.0	.135	.406	.677	.857	.947	.983	.995	.999	1.000	
2.2	.111	.355	.623	.819	.928	.975	.993	.998	1.000	
2.4	.091	.308	.570	.779	.904	.964	.988	.997	.999	1.000
2.6	.074	.267	.518	.736	.877	.951	.983	.995	.999	1.000
2.8	.061	.231	.469	.692	.848	.935	.976	.992	.998	.999
3.0	.050	.199	.423	.647	.815	.916	.966	.988	.996	.999
3.2	.041	.171	.380	.603	.781	.895	.955	.983	.994	.998
3.4	.033	.147	.340	.558	.744	.871	.942	.977	.992	.997
3.6	.027	.126	.303	.515	.706	.844	.927	.969	.988	.996
3.8	.022	.107	.269	.473	.668	.816	.909	.960	.984	.994

(continued)

Table III	(continued)								
λ \ k	0	1	2	3	4	5	6	7	8	9
4.0	.018	.092	.238	.433	.629	.785	.889	.949	.979	.992
4.2	.015	.078	.210	.395	.590	.753	.867	.936	.972	.989
4.4	.012	.066	.185	.359	.551	.720	.844	.921	.964	.985
4.6	.010	.056	.163	.326	.513	.686	.818	.905	.955	.980
4.8	.008	.048	.143	.294	.476	.651	.791	.887	.944	.975
5.0	.007	.040	.125	.265	.440	.616	.762	.867	.932	.968
5.2	.006	.034	.109	.238	.406	.581	.732	.845	.918	.960
5.4	.005	.029	.095	.213	.373	.546	.702	.822	.903	.951
5.6	.004	.024	.082	.191	.342	.512	.670	.797	.886	.941
5.8	.003	.021	.072	.170	.313	.478	.638	.771	.867	.929
6.0	.002	.017	.062	.151	.285	.446	.606	.744	.847	.916

λ	10	11	12	13	14	15	16
2.8	1.000						
3.0	1.000						
3.2	1.000						
3.4	.999	1.000					
3.6	.999	1.000					
3.8	.998	.999	1.000				
4.0	.997	.999	1.000				
4.2	.996	.999	1.000				
4.4	.994	.998	.999	1.000			
4.6	.992	.997	.999	1.000			
4.8	.990	.996	.999	1.000			
5.0	.986	.995	.998	.999	1.000		
5.2	.982	.993	.997	.999	1.000		
5.4	.977	.990	.996	.999	1.000		
5.6	.972	.988	.995	.998	.999	1.000	
5.8	.965	.984	.993	.997	.999	1.000	
6.0	.957	.980	.991	.996	.999	.999	1.000

λ	0	1	2	3	4	5	6	7	8	9
6.2	.002	.015	.054	.134	.259	.414	.574	.716	.826	.902
6.4	.002	.012	.046	.119	.235	.384	.542	.687	.803	.886
6.6	.001	.010	.040	.105	.213	.355	.511	.658	.780	.869
6.8	.001	.009	.034	.093	.192	.327	.480	.628	.755	.850
7.0	.001	.007	.030	.082	.173	.301	.450	.599	.729	.830
7.2	.001	.006	.025	.072	.156	.276	.420	.569	.703	.810
7.4	.001	.005	.022	.063	.140	.253	.392	.539	.676	.788
7.6	.001	.004	.019	.055	.125	.231	.365	.510	.648	.765
7.8	.000	.004	.016	.048	.112	.210	.338	.481	.620	.741
8.0	.000	.003	.014	.042	.100	.191	.313	.453	.593	.717
8.5	.000	.002	.009	.030	.074	.150	.256	.386	.523	.653
9.0	.000	.001	.006	.021	.055	.116	.207	.324	.456	.587
9.5	.000	.001	.004	.015	.040	.089	.165	.269	.392	.522
10.0	.000	.000	.003	.010	.029	.067	.130	.220	.333	.458

λ	10	11	12	13	14	15	16	17	18	19
6.2	.949	.975	.989	.995	.998	.999	1.000			
6.4	.939	.969	.986	.994	.997	.999	1.000			
6.6	.927	.963	.982	.992	.997	.999	.999	1.000		
6.8	.915	.955	.978	.990	.996	.998	.999	1.000		
7.0	.901	.947	.973	.987	.994	.998	.999	1.000		
7.2	.887	.937	.967	.984	.993	.997	.999	.999	1.000	
7.4	.871	.926	.961	.980	.991	.996	.998	.999	1.000	
7.6	.854	.915	.954	.976	.989	.995	.998	.999	1.000	
7.8	.835	.902	.945	.971	.986	.993	.997	.999	1.000	

(continued)

Table III (continued)

λ \ k	10	11	12	13	14	15	16	17	18	19
8.0	.816	.888	.936	.966	.983	.992	.996	.998	.999	1.000
8.5	.763	.849	.909	.949	.973	.986	.993	.997	.999	.999
9.0	.706	.803	.876	.926	.959	.978	.989	.995	.998	.999
9.5	.645	.752	.836	.898	.940	.967	.982	.991	.996	.998
10.0	.583	.697	.792	.864	.917	.951	.973	.986	.993	.997

λ	20	21	22
8.5	1.000		
9.0	1.000		
9.5	.999	1.000	
10.0	.998	.999	1.000

λ	0	1	2	3	4	5	6	7	8	9
10.5	.000	.000	.002	.007	.021	.050	.102	.179	.279	.397
11.0	.000	.000	.001	.005	.015	.038	.079	.143	.232	.341
11.5	.000	.000	.001	.003	.011	.028	.060	.114	.191	.289
12.0	.000	.000	.001	.002	.008	.020	.046	.090	.155	.242
12.5	.000	.000	.000	.002	.005	.015	.035	.070	.125	.201
13.0	.000	.000	.000	.001	.004	.011	.026	.054	.100	.166
13.5	.000	.000	.000	.001	.003	.008	.019	.041	.079	.135
14.0	.000	.000	.000	.000	.002	.006	.014	.032	.062	.109
14.5	.000	.000	.000	.000	.001	.004	.010	.024	.048	.088
15.0	.000	.000	.000	.000	.001	.003	.008	.018	.037	.070

λ	10	11	12	13	14	15	16	17	18	19
10.5	.521	.639	.742	.825	.888	.932	.960	.978	.988	.994
11.0	.460	.579	.689	.781	.854	.907	.944	.968	.982	.991
11.5	.402	.520	.633	.733	.815	.878	.924	.954	.974	.986
12.0	.347	.462	.576	.682	.772	.844	.899	.937	.963	.979
12.5	.297	.406	.519	.628	.725	.806	.869	.916	.948	.969
13.0	.252	.353	.463	.573	.675	.764	.835	.890	.930	.957
13.5	.211	.304	.409	.518	.623	.718	.798	.861	.908	.942
14.0	.176	.260	.358	.464	.570	.669	.756	.827	.883	.923
14.5	.145	.220	.311	.413	.518	.619	.711	.790	.853	.901
15.0	.118	.185	.268	.363	.466	.568	.664	.749	.819	.875

λ	20	21	22	23	24	25	26	27	28	29
10.5	.997	.999	.999	1.000						
11.0	.995	.998	.999	1.000						
11.5	.992	.996	.998	.999	1.000					
12.0	.988	.994	.987	.999	.999	1.000				
12.5	.983	.991	.995	.998	.999	.999	1.000			
13.0	.975	.986	.992	.996	.998	.999	1.000			
13.5	.965	.980	.989	.994	.997	.998	.999	1.000		
14.0	.952	.971	.983	.991	.995	.997	.999	.999	1.000	
14.5	.936	.960	.976	.986	.992	.996	.998	.999	.999	1.000
15.0	.917	.947	.967	.981	.989	.994	.997	.998	.999	1.000

(continued)

Table III (continued)

λ \ k	4	5	6	7	8	9	10	11	12	13
16	.000	.001	.004	.010	.022	.043	.077	.127	.193	.275
17	.000	.001	.002	.005	.013	.026	.049	.085	.135	.201
18	.000	.000	.001	.003	.007	.015	.030	.055	.092	.143
19	.000	.000	.001	.002	.004	.009	.018	.035	.061	.098
20	.000	.000	.000	.001	.002	.005	.011	.021	.039	.066
21	.000	.000	.000	.000	.001	.003	.006	.013	.025	.043
22	.000	.000	.000	.000	.001	.002	.004	.008	.015	.028
23	.000	.000	.000	.000	.000	.001	.002	.004	.009	.017
24	.000	.000	.000	.000	.000	.000	.001	.003	.005	.011
25	.000	.000	.000	.000	.000	.000	.001	.001	.003	.006

λ \ k	14	15	16	17	18	19	20	21	22	23
16	.368	.467	.566	.659	.742	.812	.868	.911	.942	.963
17	.281	.371	.468	.564	.655	.736	.805	.861	.905	.937
18	.208	.287	.375	.469	.562	.651	.731	.799	.855	.899
19	.150	.215	.292	.378	.469	.561	.647	.725	.793	.849
20	.105	.157	.221	.297	.381	.470	.559	.644	.721	.787
21	.072	.111	.163	.227	.302	.384	.471	.558	.640	.716
22	.048	.077	.117	.169	.232	.306	.387	.472	.556	.637
23	.031	.052	.082	.123	.175	.238	.310	.389	.472	.555
24	.020	.034	.056	.087	.128	.180	.243	.314	.392	.473
25	.012	.022	.038	.060	.092	.134	.185	.247	.318	.394

λ \ k	24	25	26	27	28	29	30	31	32	33
16	.978	.987	.993	.996	.998	.999	.999	1.000		
17	.959	.975	.985	.991	.995	.997	.999	.999	1.000	
18	.932	.955	.972	.983	.990	.994	.997	.998	.999	1.000
19	.893	.927	.951	.969	.980	.988	.993	.996	.998	.999
20	.843	.888	.922	.948	.966	.978	.987	.992	.995	.997
21	.782	.838	.883	.917	.944	.963	.976	.985	.991	.994
22	.712	.777	.832	.877	.913	.940	.959	.973	.983	.989
23	.635	.708	.772	.827	.873	.908	.936	.956	.971	.981
24	.554	.632	.704	.768	.823	.868	.904	.932	.953	.969
25	.473	.553	.629	.700	.763	.818	.863	.900	.929	.950

λ \ k	34	35	36	37	38	39	40	41	42	43
19	.999	1.000								
20	.999	.999	1.000							
21	.997	.998	.999	.999	1.000					
22	.994	.996	.998	.999	.999	1.000				
23	.988	.993	.996	.997	.999	.999	1.000			
24	.979	.987	.992	.995	.997	.998	.999	.999	1.000	
25	.966	.978	.985	.991	.991	.997	.998	.999	.999	1.000

458   APPENDIX B: Tables

Table IV   Normal Curve Areas

z	.00	.01	.02	.03	.04	.05	.06	.07	.08	.09
.0	.0000	.0040	.0080	.0120	.0160	.0199	.0239	.0279	.0319	.0359
.1	.0398	.0438	.0478	.0517	.0557	.0596	.0636	.0675	.0714	.0753
.2	.0793	.0832	.0871	.0910	.0948	.0987	.1026	.1064	.1103	.1141
.3	.1179	.1217	.1255	.1293	.1331	.1368	.1406	.1443	.1480	.1517
.4	.1554	.1591	.1628	.1664	.1700	.1736	.1772	.1808	.1844	.1879
.5	.1915	.1950	.1985	.2019	.2054	.2088	.2123	.2157	.2190	.2224
.6	.2257	.2291	.2324	.2357	.2389	.2422	.2454	.2486	.2517	.2549
.7	.2580	.2611	.2642	.2673	.2704	.2734	.2764	.2794	.2823	.2852
.8	.2881	.2910	.2939	.2967	.2995	.3023	.3051	.3078	.3106	.3133
.9	.3159	.3186	.3212	.3238	.3264	.3289	.3315	.3340	.3365	.3389
1.0	.3413	.3438	.3461	.3485	.3508	.3531	.3554	.3577	.3599	.3621
1.1	.3643	.3665	.3686	.3708	.3729	.3749	.3770	.3790	.3810	.3830
1.2	.3849	.3869	.3888	.3907	.3925	.3944	.3962	.3980	.3997	.4015
1.3	.4032	.4049	.4066	.4082	.4099	.4115	.4131	.4147	.4162	.4177
1.4	.4192	.4207	.4222	.4236	.4251	.4265	.4279	.4292	.4306	.4319
1.5	.4332	.4345	.4357	.4370	.4382	.4394	.4406	.4418	.4429	.4441
1.6	.4452	.4463	.4474	.4484	.4495	.4505	.4515	.4525	.4535	.4545
1.7	.4554	.4564	.4573	.4582	.4591	.4599	.4608	.4616	.4625	.4633
1.8	.4641	.4649	.4656	.4664	.4671	.4678	.4686	.4693	.4699	.4706
1.9	.4713	.4719	.4726	.4732	.4738	.4744	.4750	.4756	.4761	.4767
2.0	.4772	.4778	.4783	.4788	.4793	.4798	.4803	.4808	.4812	.4817
2.1	.4821	.4826	.4830	.4834	.4838	.4842	.4846	.4850	.4854	.4857
2.2	.4861	.4864	.4868	.4871	.4875	.4878	.4881	.4884	.4887	.4890
2.3	.4893	.4896	.4898	.4901	.4904	.4906	.4909	.4911	.4913	.4916
2.4	.4918	.4920	.4922	.4925	.4927	.4929	.4931	.4932	.4934	.4936
2.5	.4938	.4940	.4941	.4943	.4945	.4946	.4948	.4949	.4951	.4952
2.6	.4953	.4955	.4956	.4957	.4959	.4960	.4961	.4962	.4963	.4964
2.7	.4965	.4966	.4967	.4968	.4969	.4970	.4971	.4972	.4973	.4974
2.8	.4974	.4975	.4976	.4977	.4977	.4978	.4979	.4979	.4980	.4981
2.9	.4981	.4982	.4982	.4983	.4984	.4984	.4985	.4985	.4986	.4986
3.0	.4987	.4987	.4987	.4988	.4988	.4989	.4989	.4989	.4990	.4990
3.1	.49903	.49906	.49910	.49913	.49916	.49918	.49921	.49924	.49926	.48829
3.2	.49931	.49934	.49936	.49938	.49940	.49942	.49944	.49946	.49948	.49950
3.3	.49952	.49953	.49955	.49957	.49958	.49960	.49961	.49962	.49964	.49965
3.4	.49966	.49968	.49969	.49970	.49971	.49972	.49973	.49974	.49975	.49976
3.5	.49977	.49978	.49978	.49979	.49980	.49981	.49981	.49982	.49983	.49983
3.6	.49984	.49985	.49985	.49986	.49986	.49987	.49987	.49988	.49988	.49989
3.7	.49989	.49990	.49990	.49990	.49991	.49991	.49992	.49992	.49992	.49992
3.8	.49993	.49993	.49993	.49994	.49994	.49994	.49994	.49995	.49995	.49995
3.9	.49995	.49995	.49996	.49996	.49996	.49996	.49996	.49996	.49997	.49997

Source: Abridged from Table I of A. Hald. *Statistical Tables and Formulas* (New York: Wiley), 1952. Reproduced by permission of A. Hald.

Table V   Critical Values of *t*

$f(t)$

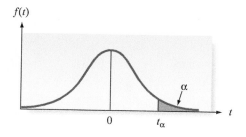

0   t_α t

Degrees of Freedom	$t_{.100}$	$t_{.050}$	$t_{.025}$	$t_{.010}$	$t_{.005}$	$t_{.001}$	$t_{.0005}$
1	3.078	6.314	12.706	31.821	63.657	318.31	636.62
2	1.886	2.920	4.303	6.965	9.925	22.326	31.598
3	1.638	2.353	3.182	4.541	5.841	10.213	12.924
4	1.533	2.132	2.776	3.747	4.604	7.173	8.610
5	1.476	2.015	2.571	3.365	4.032	5.893	6.869
6	1.440	1.943	2.447	3.143	3.707	5.208	5.959
7	1.415	1.895	2.365	2.998	3.499	4.785	5.408
8	1.397	1.860	2.306	2.896	3.355	4.501	5.041
9	1.383	1.833	2.262	2.821	3.250	4.297	4.781
10	1.372	1.812	2.228	2.764	3.169	4.144	4.587
11	1.363	1.796	2.201	2.718	3.106	4.025	4.437
12	1.356	1.782	2.179	2.681	3.055	3.930	4.318
13	1.350	1.771	2.160	2.650	3.012	3.852	4.221
14	1.345	1.761	2.145	2.624	2.977	3.787	4.140
15	1.341	1.753	2.131	2.602	2.947	3.733	4.073
16	1.337	1.746	2.120	2.583	2.921	3.686	4.015
17	1.333	1.740	2.110	2.567	2.898	3.646	3.965
18	1.330	1.734	2.101	2.552	2.878	3.610	3.922
19	1.328	1.729	2.093	2.539	2.861	3.579	3.883
20	1.325	1.725	2.086	2.528	2.845	3.552	3.850
21	1.323	1.721	2.080	2.518	2.831	3.527	3.819
22	1.321	1.717	2.074	2.508	2.819	3.505	3.792
23	1.319	1.714	2.069	2.500	2.807	3.485	3.767
24	1.318	1.711	2.064	2.492	2.797	3.467	3.745
25	1.316	1.708	2.060	2.485	2.787	3.450	3.725
26	1.315	1.706	2.056	2.479	2.779	3.435	3.707
27	1.314	1.703	2.052	2.473	2.771	3.421	3.690
28	1.313	1.701	2.048	2.467	2.763	3.408	3.674
29	1.311	1.699	2.045	2.462	2.756	3.396	3.659
30	1.310	1.697	2.042	2.457	2.750	3.385	3.646
40	1.303	1.684	2.021	2.423	2.704	3.307	3.551
60	1.296	1.671	2.000	2.390	2.660	3.232	3.460
120	1.289	1.658	1.980	2.358	2.617	3.160	3.373
∞	1.282	1.645	1.960	2.326	2.576	3.090	3.291

Source: This table is reproduced with the kind permission of the Trustees of Biometrika from E. S. Pearson and H. O. Hartley (eds.). *The Biometrika Tables for Statisticians,* Vol. 1, 3rd ed., Biometrika, 1966.

Table VI   **Critical Values of χ^2**

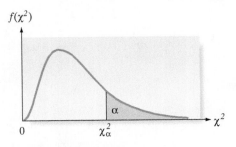

$f(\chi^2)$

Degrees of Freedom	$\chi^2_{.995}$	$\chi^2_{.990}$	$\chi^2_{.975}$	$\chi^2_{.950}$	$\chi^2_{.900}$
1	.0000393	.0001571	.0009821	.0039321	.0157908
2	.0100251	.0201007	.0506356	.102587	.210720
3	.0717212	.114832	.215795	.351846	.584375
4	.206990	.297110	.484419	.710721	1.063623
5	.411740	.554300	.831211	1.145476	1.61031
6	.675727	.872085	1.237347	1.63539	2.20413
7	.989265	1.239043	1.68987	2.16735	2.83311
8	1.344419	1.646482	2.17973	2.73264	3.48954
9	1.734926	2.087912	2.70039	3.32511	4.16816
10	2.15585	2.55821	3.24697	3.94030	4.86518
11	2.60321	3.05347	3.81575	4.57481	5.57779
12	3.07382	3.57056	4.40379	5.22603	6.30380
13	3.56503	4.10691	5.00874	5.89186	7.04150
14	4.07468	4.66043	5.62872	6.57063	7.78953
15	4.60094	5.22935	6.26214	7.26094	8.54675
16	5.14224	5.81221	6.90766	7.96164	9.31223
17	5.69724	6.40776	7.56418	8.67176	10.0852
18	6.26481	7.01491	8.23075	9.39046	10.8649
19	6.84398	7.63273	8.90655	10.1170	11.6509
20	7.43386	8.26040	9.59083	10.8508	12.4426
21	8.03366	8.89720	10.28293	11.5913	13.2396
22	8.64272	9.54249	10.9823	12.3380	14.0415
23	9.26042	10.19567	11.6885	13.0905	14.8479
24	9.88623	10.8564	12.4011	13.8484	15.6587
25	10.5197	11.5240	13.1197	14.6114	16.4734
26	11.1603	12.1981	13.8439	15.3791	17.2919
27	11.8076	12.8786	14.5733	16.1513	18.1138
28	12.4613	13.5648	15.3079	16.9279	18.9392
29	13.1211	14.2565	16.0471	17.7083	19.7677
30	13.7867	14.9535	16.7908	18.4926	20.5992
40	20.7065	22.1643	24.4331	26.5093	29.0505
50	27.9907	29.7067	32.3574	34.7642	37.6886
60	35.5346	37.4848	40.4817	43.1879	46.4589
70	43.2752	45.4418	48.7576	51.7393	55.3290
80	51.1720	53.5400	57.1532	60.3915	64.2778
90	59.1963	61.7541	65.6466	69.1260	73.2912
100	67.3276	70.0648	74.2219	77.9295	82.3581

(continued)

Table VI	(continued)				
Degrees of Freedom	$\chi^2_{.100}$	$\chi^2_{.050}$	$\chi^2_{.025}$	$\chi^2_{.010}$	$\chi^2_{.005}$
1	2.70554	3.84146	5.02389	6.63490	7.87944
2	4.60517	5.99147	7.37776	9.21034	10.5966
3	6.25139	7.81473	9.34840	11.3449	12.8381
4	7.77944	9.48773	11.1433	13.2767	14.8602
5	9.23635	11.0705	12.8325	15.0863	16.7496
6	10.6446	12.5916	14.4494	16.8119	18.5476
7	12.0170	14.0671	16.0128	18.4753	20.2777
8	13.3616	15.5073	17.5346	20.0902	21.9550
9	14.6837	16.9190	19.0228	21.6660	23.5893
10	15.9871	18.3070	20.4831	23.2093	25.1882
11	17.2750	19.6751	21.9200	24.7250	26.7569
12	18.5494	21.0261	23.3367	26.2170	28.2995
13	19.8119	22.3621	24.7356	27.6883	29.8194
14	21.0642	23.6848	26.1190	29.1413	31.3193
15	22.3072	24.9958	27.4884	30.5779	32.8013
16	23.5418	26.2962	28.8454	31.9999	34.2672
17	24.7690	27.5871	30.1910	33.4087	35.7185
18	25.9894	28.8693	31.5264	34.8053	37.1564
19	27.2036	30.1435	32.8523	36.1908	38.5822
20	28.4120	31.4104	34.1696	37.5662	39.9968
21	29.6151	32.6705	35.4789	38.9321	41.4010
22	30.8133	33.9244	36.7807	40.2894	42.7956
23	32.0069	35.1725	38.0757	41.6384	44.1813
24	33.1963	36.4151	39.3641	42.9798	45.5585
25	34.3816	37.6525	40.6465	44.3141	46.9278
26	35.5631	38.8852	41.9232	45.6417	48.2899
27	36.7412	40.1133	43.1944	46.9630	49.6449
28	37.9159	41.3372	44.4607	48.2782	50.9933
29	39.0875	42.5569	45.7222	49.5879	52.3356
30	40.2560	43.7729	46.9792	50.8922	53.6720
40	51.8050	55.7585	59.3417	63.6907	66.7659
50	63.1671	67.5048	71.4202	76.1539	79.4900
60	74.3970	79.0819	83.2976	88.3794	91.9517
70	85.5271	90.5312	95.0231	100.425	104.215
80	96.5782	101.879	106.629	112.329	116.321
90	107.565	113.145	118.136	124.116	128.299
100	118.498	124.342	129.561	135.807	140.169

Table VII   Percentage Points of the *F*-Distribution, $\alpha = .10$

$f(F)$

$\alpha = .10$

$F_{.10}$

0

F

		Numerator Degrees of Freedom							
v_1									
v_2	1	2	3	4	5	6	7	8	9
1	39.86	49.50	53.59	55.83	57.24	58.20	58.91	59.44	59.86
2	8.53	9.00	9.16	9.24	9.29	9.33	9.35	9.37	9.38
3	5.54	5.46	5.39	5.34	5.31	5.28	5.27	5.25	5.24
4	4.54	4.32	4.19	4.11	4.05	4.01	3.98	3.95	3.94
5	4.06	3.78	3.62	3.52	3.45	3.40	3.37	3.34	3.32
6	3.78	3.46	3.29	3.18	3.11	3.05	3.01	2.98	2.96
7	3.59	3.26	3.07	2.96	2.88	2.83	2.78	2.75	2.72
8	3.46	3.11	2.92	2.81	2.73	2.67	2.62	2.59	2.56
9	3.36	3.01	2.81	2.69	2.61	2.55	2.51	2.47	2.44
10	3.29	2.92	2.73	2.61	2.52	2.46	2.41	2.38	2.35
11	3.23	2.86	2.66	2.54	2.45	2.39	2.34	2.30	2.27
12	3.18	2.81	2.61	2.48	2.39	2.33	2.28	2.24	2.21
13	3.14	2.76	2.56	2.43	2.35	2.28	2.23	2.20	2.16
14	3.10	2.73	2.52	2.39	2.31	2.24	2.19	2.15	2.12
15	3.07	2.70	2.49	2.36	2.27	2.21	2.16	2.12	2.09
16	3.05	2.67	2.46	2.33	2.24	2.18	2.13	2.09	2.06
17	3.03	2.64	2.44	2.31	2.22	2.15	2.10	2.06	2.03
18	3.01	2.62	2.42	2.29	2.20	2.13	2.08	2.04	2.00
19	2.99	2.61	2.40	2.27	2.18	2.11	2.06	2.02	1.98
20	2.97	2.59	2.38	2.25	2.16	2.09	2.04	2.00	1.96
21	2.96	2.57	2.36	2.23	2.14	2.08	2.02	1.98	1.95
22	2.95	2.56	2.35	2.22	2.13	2.06	2.01	1.97	1.93
23	2.94	2.55	2.34	2.21	2.11	2.05	1.99	1.95	1.92
24	2.93	2.54	2.33	2.19	2.10	2.04	1.98	1.94	1.91
25	2.92	2.53	2.32	2.18	2.09	2.02	1.97	1.93	1.89
26	2.91	2.52	2.31	2.17	2.08	2.01	1.96	1.92	1.88
27	2.90	2.51	2.30	2.17	2.07	2.00	1.95	1.91	1.87
28	2.89	2.50	2.29	2.16	2.06	2.00	1.94	1.90	1.87
29	2.89	2.50	2.28	2.15	2.06	1.99	1.93	1.89	1.86
30	2.88	2.49	2.28	2.14	2.05	1.98	1.93	1.88	1.85
40	2.84	2.44	2.23	2.09	2.00	1.93	1.87	1.83	1.79
60	2.79	2.39	2.18	2.04	1.95	1.87	1.82	1.77	1.74
120	2.75	2.35	2.13	1.99	1.90	1.82	1.77	1.72	1.68
∞	2.71	2.30	2.08	1.94	1.85	1.77	1.72	1.67	1.63

(continued)

Table VII	(continued)								
ν_1	Numerator Degrees of Freedom								
ν_2	10	12	15	20	24	30	40	60	120	∞

ν_2	10	12	15	20	24	30	40	60	120	∞
1	60.19	60.71	61.22	61.74	62.00	62.26	62.53	62.79	63.06	63.33
2	9.39	9.41	9.42	9.44	9.45	9.46	9.47	9.47	9.48	9.49
3	5.23	5.22	5.20	5.18	5.18	5.17	5.16	5.15	5.14	5.13
4	3.92	3.90	3.87	3.84	3.83	3.82	3.80	3.79	3.78	3.76
5	3.30	3.27	3.24	3.21	3.19	3.17	3.16	3.14	3.12	3.10
6	2.94	2.90	2.87	2.84	2.82	2.80	2.78	2.76	2.74	2.72
7	2.70	2.67	2.63	2.59	2.58	2.56	2.54	2.51	2.49	2.47
8	2.54	2.50	2.46	2.42	2.40	2.38	2.36	2.34	2.32	2.29
9	2.42	2.38	2.34	2.30	2.28	2.25	2.23	2.21	2.18	2.16
10	2.32	2.28	2.24	2.20	2.18	2.16	2.13	2.11	2.08	2.06
11	2.25	2.21	2.17	2.12	2.10	2.08	2.05	2.03	2.00	1.97
12	2.19	2.15	2.10	2.06	2.04	2.01	1.99	1.96	1.93	1.90
13	2.14	2.10	2.05	2.01	1.98	1.96	1.93	1.90	1.88	1.85
14	2.10	2.05	2.01	1.96	1.94	1.91	1.89	1.86	1.83	1.80
15	2.06	2.02	1.97	1.92	1.90	1.87	1.85	1.82	1.79	1.76
16	2.03	1.99	1.94	1.89	1.87	1.84	1.81	1.78	1.75	1.72
17	2.00	1.96	1.91	1.86	1.84	1.81	1.78	1.75	1.72	1.69
18	1.98	1.93	1.89	1.84	1.81	1.78	1.75	1.72	1.69	1.66
19	1.96	1.91	1.86	1.81	1.79	1.76	1.73	1.70	1.67	1.63
20	1.94	1.89	1.84	1.79	1.77	1.74	1.71	1.68	1.64	1.61
21	1.92	1.87	1.83	1.78	1.75	1.72	1.69	1.66	1.62	1.59
22	1.90	1.86	1.81	1.76	1.73	1.70	1.67	1.64	1.60	1.57
23	1.89	1.84	1.80	1.74	1.72	1.69	1.66	1.62	1.59	1.55
24	1.88	1.83	1.78	1.73	1.70	1.67	1.64	1.61	1.57	1.53
25	1.87	1.82	1.77	1.72	1.69	1.66	1.63	1.59	1.56	1.52
26	1.86	1.81	1.76	1.71	1.68	1.65	1.61	1.58	1.54	1.50
27	1.85	1.80	1.75	1.70	1.67	1.64	1.60	1.57	1.53	1.49
28	1.84	1.79	1.74	1.69	1.66	1.63	1.59	1.56	1.52	1.48
29	1.83	1.78	1.73	1.68	1.65	1.62	1.58	1.55	1.51	1.47
30	1.82	1.77	1.72	1.67	1.64	1.61	1.57	1.54	1.50	1.46
40	1.76	1.71	1.66	1.61	1.57	1.54	1.51	1.47	1.42	1.38
60	1.71	1.66	1.60	1.54	1.51	1.48	1.44	1.40	1.35	1.29
120	1.65	1.60	1.55	1.48	1.45	1.41	1.37	1.32	1.26	1.19
∞	1.60	1.55	1.49	1.42	1.38	1.34	1.30	1.24	1.17	1.00

Denominator Degrees of Freedom

Table VIII   Percentage Points of the *F*-Distribution, $\alpha = .05$

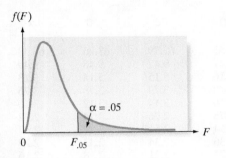

$f(F)$

$\alpha = .05$

0 $F_{.05}$ F

ν_1	Numerator Degrees of Freedom								
ν_2	1	2	3	4	5	6	7	8	9
1	161.4	199.5	215.7	224.6	230.2	234.0	236.8	238.9	240.5
2	18.51	19.00	19.16	19.25	19.30	19.33	19.35	19.37	19.38
3	10.13	9.55	9.28	9.12	9.01	8.94	8.89	8.85	8.81
4	7.71	6.94	6.59	6.39	6.26	6.16	6.09	6.04	6.00
5	6.61	5.79	5.41	5.19	5.05	4.95	4.88	4.82	4.77
6	5.99	5.14	4.76	4.53	4.39	4.28	4.21	4.15	4.10
7	5.59	4.74	4.35	4.12	3.97	3.87	3.79	3.73	3.68
8	5.32	4.46	4.07	3.84	3.69	3.58	3.50	3.44	3.39
9	5.12	4.26	3.86	3.63	3.48	3.37	3.29	3.23	3.18
10	4.96	4.10	3.71	3.48	3.33	3.22	3.14	3.07	3.02
11	4.84	3.98	3.59	3.36	3.20	3.09	3.01	2.95	2.90
12	4.75	3.89	3.49	3.26	3.11	3.00	2.91	2.85	2.80
13	4.67	3.81	3.41	3.18	3.03	2.92	2.83	2.77	2.71
14	4.60	3.74	3.34	3.11	2.96	2.85	2.76	2.70	2.65
15	4.54	3.68	3.29	3.06	2.90	2.79	2.71	2.64	2.59
16	4.49	3.63	3.24	3.01	2.85	2.74	2.66	2.59	2.54
17	4.45	3.59	3.20	2.96	2.81	2.70	2.61	2.55	2.49
18	4.41	3.55	3.16	2.93	2.77	2.66	2.58	2.51	2.46
19	4.38	3.52	3.13	2.90	2.74	2.63	2.54	2.48	2.42
20	4.35	3.49	3.10	2.87	2.71	2.60	2.51	2.45	2.39
21	4.32	3.47	3.07	2.84	2.68	2.57	2.49	2.42	2.37
22	4.30	3.44	3.05	2.82	2.66	2.55	2.46	2.40	2.34
23	4.28	3.42	3.03	2.80	2.64	2.53	2.44	2.37	2.32
24	4.26	3.40	3.01	2.78	2.62	2.51	2.42	2.36	2.30
25	4.24	3.39	2.99	2.76	2.60	2.49	2.40	2.34	2.28
26	4.23	3.37	2.98	2.74	2.59	2.47	2.39	2.32	2.77
27	4.21	3.35	2.96	2.73	2.57	2.46	2.37	2.31	2.25
28	4.20	3.34	2.95	2.71	2.56	2.45	2.36	2.29	2.24
29	4.18	3.33	2.93	2.70	2.55	2.43	2.35	2.28	2.22
30	4.17	3.32	2.92	2.69	2.53	2.42	2.33	2.27	2.21
40	4.08	3.23	2.84	2.61	2.45	2.34	2.25	2.18	2.12
60	4.00	3.15	2.76	2.53	2.37	2.25	2.17	2.10	2.04
120	3.92	3.07	2.68	2.45	2.29	2.17	2.09	2.02	1.96
∞	3.84	3.00	2.60	2.37	2.21	2.10	2.01	1.94	1.88

Denominator Degrees of Freedom

(continued)

Table VIII	(continued)									
ν_1	Numerator Degrees of Freedom									
ν_2	10	12	15	20	24	30	40	60	120	∞
1	241.9	243.9	245.9	248.0	249.1	250.1	251.1	252.2	253.3	254.3
2	19.40	19.41	19.43	19.45	19.45	19.46	19.47	19.48	19.49	19.50
3	8.79	8.74	8.70	8.66	8.64	8.62	8.59	8.57	8.55	8.53
4	5.96	5.91	5.86	5.80	5.77	5.75	5.72	5.69	5.66	5.63
5	4.74	4.68	4.62	4.56	4.53	4.50	4.46	4.43	4.40	4.36
6	4.06	4.00	3.94	3.87	3.84	3.81	3.77	3.74	3.70	3.67
7	3.64	3.57	3.51	3.44	3.41	3.38	3.34	3.30	3.27	3.23
8	3.35	3.28	3.22	3.15	3.12	3.08	3.04	3.01	2.97	2.93
9	3.14	3.07	3.01	2.94	2.90	2.86	2.83	2.79	2.75	2.71
10	2.98	2.91	2.85	2.77	2.74	2.70	2.66	2.62	2.58	2.54
11	2.85	2.79	2.72	2.65	2.61	2.57	2.53	2.49	2.45	2.40
12	2.75	2.69	2.62	2.54	2.51	2.47	2.43	2.38	2.34	2.30
13	2.67	2.60	2.53	2.46	2.42	2.38	2.34	2.30	2.25	2.21
14	2.60	2.53	2.46	2.39	2.35	2.31	2.27	2.22	2.18	2.13
15	2.54	2.48	2.40	2.33	2.29	2.25	2.20	2.16	2.11	2.07
16	2.49	2.42	2.35	2.28	2.24	2.19	2.15	2.11	2.06	2.01
17	2.45	2.38	2.31	2.23	2.19	2.15	2.10	2.06	2.01	1.96
18	2.41	2.34	2.27	2.19	2.15	2.11	2.06	2.02	1.97	1.92
19	2.38	2.31	2.23	2.16	2.11	2.07	2.03	1.98	1.93	1.88
20	2.35	2.28	2.20	2.12	2.08	2.04	1.99	1.95	1.90	1.84
21	2.32	2.25	2.18	2.10	2.05	2.01	1.96	1.92	1.87	1.81
22	2.30	2.23	2.15	2.07	2.03	1.98	1.94	1.89	1.84	1.78
23	2.27	2.20	2.13	2.05	2.01	1.96	1.91	1.86	1.81	1.76
24	2.25	2.18	2.11	2.03	1.98	1.94	1.89	1.84	1.79	1.73
25	2.24	2.16	2.09	2.01	1.96	1.92	1.87	1.82	1.77	1.71
26	2.22	2.15	2.07	1.99	1.95	1.90	1.85	1.80	1.75	1.69
27	2.20	2.13	2.06	1.97	1.93	1.88	1.84	1.79	1.73	1.67
28	2.19	2.12	2.04	1.96	1.91	1.87	1.82	1.77	1.71	1.65
29	2.18	2.10	2.03	1.94	1.90	1.85	1.81	1.75	1.70	1.64
30	2.16	2.09	2.01	1.93	1.89	1.84	1.79	1.74	1.68	1.62
40	2.08	2.00	1.92	1.84	1.79	1.74	1.69	1.64	1.58	1.51
60	1.99	1.92	1.84	1.75	1.70	1.65	1.59	1.53	1.47	1.39
120	1.91	1.83	1.75	1.66	1.61	1.55	1.50	1.43	1.35	1.25
∞	1.83	1.75	1.67	1.57	1.52	1.46	1.39	1.32	1.22	1.00

Source: From Merrington, M., and Thompson, C. M. "Tables of percentage points of the inverted beta (*F*)-distribution," *Biometrika*, 1943, 33, 73–88. Reproduced by permission of the *Biometrika* Trustees.

Table IX   Percentage Points of the *F*-Distribution, $\alpha = .025$

$f(F)$

$\alpha = .025$

$F_{.025}$

0

ν_1	Numerator Degrees of Freedom								
ν_2	1	2	3	4	5	6	7	8	9
1	647.8	799.5	864.2	899.6	921.8	937.1	948.2	956.7	963.3
2	38.51	39.00	39.17	39.25	39.30	39.33	39.36	39.37	39.39
3	17.44	16.04	15.44	15.10	14.88	14.73	14.62	14.54	14.47
4	12.22	10.65	9.98	9.60	9.36	9.20	9.07	8.98	8.90
5	10.01	8.43	7.76	7.39	7.15	6.98	6.85	6.76	6.68
6	8.81	7.26	6.60	6.23	5.99	5.82	5.70	5.60	5.52
7	8.07	6.54	5.89	5.52	5.29	5.12	4.99	4.90	4.82
8	7.57	6.06	5.42	5.05	4.82	4.65	4.53	4.43	4.36
9	7.21	5.71	5.08	4.72	4.48	4.32	4.20	4.10	4.03
10	6.94	5.46	4.83	4.47	4.24	4.07	3.95	3.85	3.78
11	6.72	5.26	4.63	4.28	4.04	3.88	3.76	3.66	3.59
12	6.55	5.10	4.47	4.12	3.89	3.73	3.61	3.51	3.44
13	6.41	4.97	4.35	4.00	3.77	3.60	3.48	3.39	3.31
14	6.30	4.86	4.24	3.89	3.66	3.50	3.38	3.29	3.21
15	6.20	4.77	4.15	3.80	3.58	3.41	3.29	3.20	3.12
16	6.12	4.69	4.08	3.73	3.50	3.34	3.22	3.12	3.05
17	6.04	4.62	4.01	3.66	3.44	3.28	3.16	3.06	2.98
18	5.98	4.56	3.95	3.61	3.38	3.22	3.10	3.01	2.93
19	5.92	4.51	3.90	3.56	3.33	3.17	3.05	2.96	2.88
20	5.87	4.46	3.86	3.51	3.29	3.13	3.01	2.91	2.84
21	5.83	4.42	3.82	3.48	3.25	3.09	2.97	2.87	2.80
22	5.79	4.38	3.78	3.44	3.22	3.05	2.93	2.84	2.76
23	5.75	4.35	3.75	3.41	3.18	3.02	2.90	2.81	2.73
24	5.72	4.32	3.72	3.38	3.15	2.99	2.87	2.78	2.70
25	5.69	4.29	3.69	3.35	3.13	2.97	2.85	2.75	2.68
26	5.66	4.27	3.67	3.33	3.10	2.94	2.82	2.73	2.65
27	5.63	4.24	3.65	3.31	3.08	2.92	2.80	2.71	2.63
28	5.61	4.22	3.63	3.29	3.06	2.90	2.78	2.69	2.61
29	5.59	4.20	3.61	3.27	3.04	2.88	2.76	2.67	2.59
30	5.57	4.18	3.59	3.25	3.03	2.87	2.75	2.65	2.57
40	5.42	4.05	3.46	3.13	2.90	2.74	2.62	2.53	2.45
60	5.29	3.93	3.34	3.01	2.79	2.63	2.51	2.41	2.33
120	5.15	3.80	3.23	2.89	2.67	2.52	2.39	2.30	2.22
∞	5.02	3.69	3.12	2.79	2.57	2.41	2.29	2.19	2.11

Denominator Degrees of Freedom

(continued)

Table IX	(continued)									
ν_1	Numerator Degrees of Freedom									
ν_2	10	12	15	20	24	30	40	60	120	∞
1	968.6	976.7	984.9	993.1	997.2	1,001	1,006	1,010	1,014	1,018
2	39.40	39.41	39.43	39.45	39.46	39.46	39.47	39.48	39.49	39.50
3	14.42	14.34	14.25	14.17	14.12	14.08	14.04	13.99	13.95	13.90
4	8.84	8.75	8.66	8.56	8.51	8.46	8.41	8.36	8.31	8.26
5	6.62	6.52	6.43	6.33	6.28	6.23	6.18	6.12	6.07	6.02
6	5.46	5.37	5.27	5.17	5.12	5.07	5.01	4.96	4.90	4.85
7	4.76	4.67	4.57	4.47	4.42	4.36	4.31	4.25	4.20	4.14
8	4.30	4.20	4.10	4.00	3.95	3.89	3.84	3.78	3.73	3.67
9	3.96	3.87	3.77	3.67	3.61	3.56	3.51	3.45	3.39	3.33
10	3.72	3.62	3.52	3.42	3.37	3.31	3.26	3.20	3.14	3.08
11	3.53	3.43	3.33	3.23	3.17	3.12	3.06	3.00	2.94	2.88
12	3.37	3.28	3.18	3.07	3.02	2.96	2.91	2.85	2.79	2.72
13	3.25	3.15	3.05	2.95	2.89	2.84	2.78	2.72	2.66	2.60
14	3.15	3.05	2.95	2.84	2.79	2.73	2.67	2.61	2.55	2.49
15	3.06	2.96	2.86	2.76	2.70	2.64	2.59	2.52	2.46	2.40
16	2.99	2.89	2.79	2.68	2.63	2.57	2.51	2.45	2.38	2.32
17	2.92	2.82	2.72	2.62	2.56	2.50	2.44	2.38	2.32	2.25
18	2.87	2.77	2.67	2.56	2.50	2.44	2.38	2.32	2.26	2.19
19	2.82	2.72	2.62	2.51	2.45	2.39	2.33	2.27	2.20	2.13
20	2.77	2.68	2.57	2.46	2.41	2.35	2.29	2.22	2.16	2.09
21	2.73	2.64	2.53	2.42	2.37	2.31	2.25	2.18	2.11	2.04
22	2.70	2.60	2.50	2.39	2.33	2.27	2.21	2.14	2.08	2.00
23	2.67	2.57	2.47	2.36	2.30	2.24	2.18	2.11	2.04	1.97
24	2.64	2.54	2.44	2.33	2.27	2.21	2.15	2.08	2.01	1.94
25	2.61	2.51	2.41	2.30	2.24	2.18	2.12	2.05	1.98	1.91
26	2.59	2.49	2.39	2.28	2.22	2.16	2.09	2.03	1.95	1.88
27	2.57	2.47	2.36	2.25	2.19	2.13	2.07	2.00	1.93	1.85
28	2.55	2.45	2.34	2.23	2.17	2.11	2.05	1.98	1.91	1.83
29	2.53	2.43	2.32	2.21	2.15	2.09	2.03	1.96	1.89	1.81
30	2.51	2.41	2.31	2.20	2.14	2.07	2.01	1.94	1.87	1.79
40	2.39	2.29	2.18	2.07	2.01	1.94	1.88	1.80	1.72	1.64
60	2.27	2.17	2.06	1.94	1.88	1.82	1.74	1.67	1.58	1.48
120	2.16	2.05	1.94	1.82	1.76	1.69	1.61	1.53	1.43	1.31
∞	2.05	1.94	1.83	1.71	1.64	1.57	1.48	1.39	1.27	1.00

Denominator Degrees of Freedom

Source: From Merrington, M., and Thompson, C. M. "Tables of percentage points of the inverted beta (*F*)-distribution," *Biometrika,* 1943, 33, 73–88. Reproduced by permission of the *Biometrika* Trustees.

Table X   Percentage Points of the *F*-Distribution, $\alpha = .01$

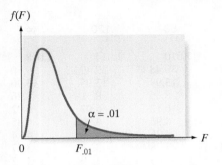

ν_1	Numerator Degrees of Freedom								
ν_2	1	2	3	4	5	6	7	8	9
1	4,052	4,999.5	5,403	5,625	5,764	5,859	5,928	5,982	6,022
2	98.50	99.00	99.17	99.25	99.30	99.33	99.36	99.37	99.39
3	34.12	30.82	29.46	28.71	28.24	27.91	27.67	27.49	27.35
4	21.20	18.00	16.69	15.98	15.52	15.21	14.98	14.80	14.66
5	16.26	13.27	12.06	11.39	10.97	10.67	10.46	10.29	10.16
6	13.75	10.92	9.78	9.15	8.75	8.47	8.26	8.10	7.98
7	12.25	9.55	8.45	7.85	7.46	7.19	6.99	6.84	6.72
8	11.26	8.65	7.59	7.01	6.63	6.37	6.18	6.03	5.91
9	10.56	8.02	6.99	6.42	6.06	5.80	5.61	5.47	5.35
10	10.04	7.56	6.55	5.99	5.64	5.39	5.20	5.06	4.94
11	9.65	7.21	6.22	5.67	5.32	5.07	4.89	4.74	4.63
12	9.33	6.93	5.95	5.41	5.06	4.82	4.64	4.50	4.39
13	9.07	6.70	5.74	5.21	4.86	4.62	4.44	4.30	4.19
14	8.86	6.51	5.56	5.04	4.69	4.46	4.28	4.14	4.03
15	8.68	6.36	5.42	4.89	4.56	4.32	4.14	4.00	3.89
16	8.53	6.23	5.29	4.77	4.44	4.20	4.03	3.89	3.78
17	8.40	6.11	5.18	4.67	4.34	4.10	3.93	3.79	3.68
18	8.29	6.01	5.09	4.58	4.25	4.01	3.84	3.71	3.60
19	8.18	5.93	5.01	4.50	4.17	3.94	3.77	3.63	3.52
20	8.10	5.85	4.94	4.43	4.10	3.87	3.70	3.56	3.46
21	8.02	5.78	4.87	4.37	4.04	3.81	3.64	3.51	3.40
22	7.95	5.72	4.82	4.31	3.99	3.76	3.59	3.45	3.35
23	7.88	5.66	4.76	4.26	3.94	3.71	3.54	3.41	3.30
24	7.82	5.61	4.72	4.22	3.90	3.67	3.50	3.36	3.26
25	7.77	5.57	4.68	4.18	3.85	3.63	3.46	3.32	3.22
26	7.72	5.53	4.64	4.14	3.82	3.59	3.42	3.29	3.18
27	7.68	5.49	4.60	4.11	3.78	3.56	3.39	3.26	3.15
28	7.64	5.45	4.57	4.07	3.75	3.53	3.36	3.23	3.12
29	7.60	5.42	4.54	4.04	3.73	3.50	3.33	3.20	3.09
30	7.56	5.39	4.51	4.02	3.70	3.47	3.30	3.17	3.07
40	7.31	5.18	4.31	3.83	3.51	3.29	3.12	2.99	2.89
60	7.08	4.98	4.13	3.65	3.34	3.12	2.95	2.82	2.72
120	6.85	4.79	3.95	3.48	3.17	2.96	2.79	2.66	2.56
∞	6.63	4.61	3.78	3.32	3.02	2.80	2.64	2.51	2.41

(continued)

Table X	**(continued)**								
ν_1	**Numerator Degrees of Freedom**								
ν_2	**10**	**12**	**15**	**20**	**24**	**30**	**40**	**60**	**120**	**∞**

ν_2	10	12	15	20	24	30	40	60	120	∞
1	6,056	6,106	6,157	6,209	6,235	6,261	6,287	6,313	6,339	6,366
2	99.40	99.42	99.43	99.45	99.46	99.47	99.47	99.48	99.49	99.50
3	27.23	27.05	26.87	26.69	26.60	26.50	26.41	26.32	26.22	26.13
4	14.55	14.37	14.20	14.02	13.93	13.84	13.75	13.65	13.56	13.46
5	10.05	9.89	9.72	9.55	9.47	9.38	9.29	9.20	9.11	9.02
6	7.87	7.72	7.56	7.40	7.31	7.23	7.14	7.06	6.97	6.88
7	6.62	6.47	6.31	6.16	6.07	5.99	5.91	5.82	5.74	5.65
8	5.81	5.67	5.52	5.36	5.28	5.20	5.12	5.03	4.95	4.86
9	5.26	5.11	4.96	4.81	4.73	4.65	4.57	4.48	4.40	4.31
10	4.85	4.71	4.56	4.41	4.33	4.25	4.17	4.08	4.00	3.91
11	4.54	4.40	4.25	4.10	4.02	3.94	3.86	3.78	3.69	3.60
12	4.30	4.16	4.01	3.86	3.78	3.70	3.62	3.54	3.45	3.36
13	4.10	3.96	3.82	3.66	3.59	3.51	3.43	3.34	3.25	3.17
14	3.94	3.80	3.66	3.51	3.43	3.35	3.27	3.18	3.09	3.00
15	3.80	3.67	3.52	3.37	3.29	3.21	3.13	3.05	2.96	2.87
16	3.69	3.55	3.41	3.26	3.18	3.10	3.02	2.93	2.84	2.75
17	3.59	3.46	3.31	3.16	3.08	3.00	2.92	2.83	2.75	2.65
18	3.51	3.37	3.23	3.08	3.00	2.92	2.84	2.75	2.66	2.57
19	3.43	3.30	3.15	3.00	2.92	2.84	2.76	2.67	2.58	2.49
20	3.37	3.23	3.09	2.94	2.86	2.78	2.69	2.61	2.52	2.42
21	3.31	3.17	3.03	2.88	2.80	2.72	2.64	2.55	2.46	2.36
22	3.26	3.12	2.98	2.83	2.75	2.67	2.58	2.50	2.40	2.31
23	3.21	3.07	2.93	2.78	2.70	2.62	2.54	2.45	2.35	2.26
24	3.17	3.03	2.89	2.74	2.66	2.58	2.49	2.40	2.31	2.21
25	3.13	2.99	2.85	2.70	2.62	2.54	2.45	2.36	2.27	2.17
26	3.09	2.96	2.81	2.66	2.58	2.50	2.42	2.33	2.23	2.13
27	3.06	2.93	2.78	2.63	2.55	2.47	2.38	2.29	2.20	2.10
28	3.03	2.90	2.75	2.60	2.52	2.44	2.35	2.26	2.17	2.06
29	3.00	2.87	2.73	2.57	2.49	2.41	2.33	2.23	2.14	2.03
30	2.98	2.84	2.70	2.55	2.47	2.39	2.30	2.21	2.11	2.01
40	2.80	2.66	2.52	2.37	2.29	2.20	2.11	2.02	1.92	1.80
60	2.63	2.50	2.35	2.20	2.12	2.03	1.94	1.84	1.73	1.60
120	2.47	2.34	2.19	2.03	1.95	1.86	1.76	1.66	1.53	1.38
∞	2.32	2.18	2.04	1.88	1.79	1.70	1.59	1.47	1.32	1.00

Denominator Degrees of Freedom

Table XI	Control Chart Constants				
Number of Observations in Subgroup, n	A_2	d_2	d_3	D_3	D_4
2	1.880	1.128	.853	.000	3.267
3	1.023	1.693	.888	.000	2.574
4	.729	2.059	.880	.000	2.282
5	.577	2.326	.864	.000	2.114
6	.483	2.534	.848	.000	2.004
7	.419	2.704	.833	.076	1.924
8	.373	2.847	.820	.136	1.864
9	.337	2.970	.808	.184	1.816
10	.308	3.078	.797	.223	1.777
11	.285	3.173	.787	.256	1.744
12	.266	3.258	.778	.283	1.717
13	.249	3.336	.770	.307	1.693
14	.235	3.407	.762	.328	1.672
15	.223	3.472	.755	.347	1.653
16	.212	3.532	.749	.363	1.637
17	.203	3.588	.743	.378	1.622
18	.194	3.640	.738	.391	1.608
19	.187	3.689	.733	.403	1.597
20	.180	3.735	.729	.415	1.585
21	.173	3.778	.724	.425	1.575
22	.167	3.819	.720	.434	1.566
23	.162	3.858	.716	.443	1.557
24	.157	3.895	.712	.451	1.548
25	.153	3.931	.709	.459	1.541

Source: ASTM Manual on the Presentation of Data and Control Chart Analysis, Philadelphia, PA: American Society for Testing Materials, pp. 134–136, 1976.

Table XII	Critical Values for the Durbin-Watson d Statistic, $\alpha = .05$									
	$k = 1$		$k = 2$		$k = 3$		$k = 4$		$k = 5$	
n	d_L	d_U	d_L	d_U	d_L	d_U	d_L	d_U	d_L	d_U
15	1.08	1.36	.95	1.54	.82	1.75	.69	1.97	.56	2.21
16	1.10	1.37	.98	1.54	.86	1.73	.74	1.93	.62	2.15
17	1.13	1.38	1.02	1.54	.90	1.71	.78	1.90	.67	2.10
18	1.16	1.39	1.05	1.53	.93	1.69	.92	1.87	.71	2.06
19	1.18	1.40	1.08	1.53	.97	1.68	.86	1.85	.75	2.02
20	1.20	1.41	1.10	1.54	1.00	1.68	.90	1.83	.79	1.99
21	1.22	1.42	1.13	1.54	1.03	1.67	.93	1.81	.83	1.96
22	1.24	1.43	1.15	1.54	1.05	1.66	.96	1.80	.96	1.94
23	1.26	1.44	1.17	1.54	1.08	1.66	.99	1.79	.90	1.92
24	1.27	1.45	1.19	1.55	1.10	1.66	1.01	1.78	.93	1.90
25	1.29	1.45	1.21	1.55	1.12	1.66	1.04	1.77	.95	1.89
26	1.30	1.46	1.22	1.55	1.14	1.65	1.06	1.76	.98	1.88
27	1.32	1.47	1.24	1.56	1.16	1.65	1.08	1.76	1.01	1.86
28	1.33	1.48	1.26	1.56	1.18	1.65	1.10	1.75	1.03	1.85
29	1.34	1.48	1.27	1.56	1.20	1.65	1.12	1.74	1.05	1.84
30	1.35	1.49	1.28	1.57	1.21	1.65	1.14	1.74	1.07	1.83
31	1.36	1.50	1.30	1.57	1.23	1.65	1.16	1.74	1.09	1.83
32	1.37	1.50	1.31	1.57	1.24	1.65	1.18	1.73	1.11	1.82
33	1.38	1.51	1.32	1.58	1.26	1.65	1.19	1.73	1.13	1.81
34	1.39	1.51	1.33	1.58	1.27	1.65	1.21	1.73	1.15	1.81
35	1.40	1.52	1.34	1.58	1.28	1.65	1.22	1.73	1.16	1.80
36	1.41	1.52	1.35	1.59	1.29	1.65	1.24	1.73	1.18	1.80
37	1.42	1.53	1.36	1.59	1.31	1.66	1.25	1.72	1.19	1.80
38	1.43	1.54	1.37	1.59	1.32	1.66	1.26	1.72	1.21	1.79
39	1.43	1.54	1.38	1.60	1.33	1.66	1.27	1.72	1.22	1.79
40	1.44	1.54	1.39	1.60	1.34	1.66	1.29	1.72	1.23	1.79
45	1.48	1.57	1.43	1.62	1.38	1.67	1.34	1.72	1.29	1.78
50	1.50	1.59	1.46	1.63	1.42	1.67	1.38	1.72	1.34	1.77
55	1.53	1.60	1.49	1.64	1.45	1.68	1.41	1.72	1.38	1.77
60	1.55	1.62	1.51	1.65	1.48	1.69	1.44	1.73	1.41	1.77
65	1.57	1.63	1.54	1.66	1.50	1.70	1.47	1.73	1.44	1.77
70	1.58	1.64	1.55	1.67	1.52	1.70	1.49	1.74	1.46	1.77
75	1.60	1.65	1.57	1.68	1.54	1.71	1.51	1.74	1.49	1.77
80	1.61	1.66	1.59	1.69	1.56	1.72	1.53	1.74	1.51	1.77
85	1.62	1.67	1.60	1.70	1.57	1.72	1.55	1.75	1.52	1.77
90	1.63	1.68	1.61	1.70	1.59	1.73	1.57	1.75	1.54	1.78
95	1.64	1.69	1.62	1.71	1.60	1.73	1.57	1.75	1.56	1.78
100	1.65	1.69	1.63	1.72	1.61	1.74	1.59	1.76	1.57	1.78

Source: From Durbin, J., and Watson, G. S. "Testing for serial correlation in least squares regression, II," *Biometrika*, 1951, 30, 159–178. Reproduced by permission of the *Biometrika* Trustees.

Table XIII   Critical Values for the Durbin-Watson _d_ Statistic, $\alpha = .01$

n	k = 1		k = 2		k = 3		k = 4		k = 5	
	d_L	d_U	d_L	d_U	d_L	d_U	d_L	d_U	d_L	d_U
15	.81	1.07	.70	1.25	.59	1.46	.49	1.70	.39	1.96
16	.84	1.09	.74	1.25	.63	1.44	.53	1.66	.44	1.90
17	.87	1.10	.77	1.25	.67	1.43	.57	1.3	.48	1.85
18	.90	1.12	.80	1.26	.71	1.42	.61	1.60	.52	1.80
19	.93	1.13	.83	1.26	.74	1.41	.65	1.58	.56	1.77
20	.95	1.15	.86	1.27	.77	1.41	.68	1.57	.60	1.74
21	.97	1.16	.89	1.27	.80	1.41	.72	1.55	.63	1.71
22	1.00	1.17	.91	1.28	.83	1.40	.75	1.54	.66	1.69
23	1.02	1.19	.94	1.29	.86	1.40	.77	1.53	.70	1.67
24	1.04	1.20	.96	1.30	.88	1.41	.80	1.53	.72	1.66
25	1.05	1.21	.98	1.30	.90	1.41	.83	1.52	.75	1.65
26	1.07	1.22	1.00	1.31	.93	1.41	.85	1.52	.78	1.64
27	1.09	1.23	1.02	1.32	.95	1.41	.88	1.51	.81	1.63
28	1.10	1.24	1.04	1.32	.97	1.41	.90	1.51	.83	1.62
29	1.12	1.25	1.05	1.33	.99	1.42	.92	1.51	.85	1.61
30	1.13	1.26	1.07	1.34	1.01	1.42	.94	1.51	.88	1.61
31	1.15	1.27	1.08	1.34	1.02	1.42	.96	1.51	.90	1.60
32	1.16	1.28	1.10	1.35	1.04	1.43	.98	1.51	.92	1.60
33	1.17	1.29	1.11	1.36	1.05	1.43	1.00	1.51	.94	1.59
34	1.18	1.30	1.13	1.36	1.07	1.43	1.01	1.51	.95	1.59
35	1.19	1.31	1.14	1.27	1.08	1.44	1.03	1.51	.97	1.59
36	1.21	1.32	1.15	1.38	1.10	1.44	1.04	1.51	.99	1.59
37	1.22	1.32	1.16	1.38	1.11	1.45	1.06	1.51	1.00	1.59
38	1.23	1.33	1.18	1.39	1.12	1.45	1.07	1.52	1.02	1.58
39	1.24	1.34	1.19	1.39	1.14	1.45	1.09	1.52	1.03	1.58
40	1.25	1.34	1.20	1.40	1.15	1.46	1.10	1.52	1.05	1.58
45	1.29	1.38	1.24	1.42	1.20	1.48	1.16	1.53	1.11	1.58
50	1.32	1.40	1.28	1.45	1.24	1.49	1.20	1.54	1.16	1.59
55	1.36	1.43	1.32	1.47	1.28	1.51	1.25	1.55	1.21	1.59
60	1.38	1.45	1.35	1.48	1.32	1.52	1.28	1.56	1.25	1.60
65	1.41	1.47	1.38	1.50	1.35	1.53	1.31	1.57	1.28	1.61
70	1.43	1.49	1.40	1.52	1.37	1.55	1.34	1.58	1.31	1.61
75	1.45	1.50	1.42	1.53	1.39	1.56	1.37	1.59	1.34	1.62
80	1.47	1.52	1.44	1.54	1.42	1.57	1.39	1.60	1.36	1.62
85	1.48	1.53	1.46	1.55	1.43	1.58	1.41	1.60	1.39	1.63
90	1.50	1.54	1.47	1.56	1.45	1.59	1.43	1.61	1.41	1.64
95	1.51	1.55	1.49	1.57	1.47	1.60	1.45	1.62	1.42	1.64
100	1.52	1.56	1.50	1.58	1.48	1.60	1.46	1.63	1.44	1.65

Source: From Durbin, J., and Watson, G. S. "Testing for serial correlation in least squares regression, II," _Biometrika,_ 1951, 30, 159–178. Reproduced by permission of the _Biometrika_ Trustees.

Table XIV   **Critical Values of T_L and T_U for the Wilcoxon Rank Sum Test: Independent Samples**

Test statistic is the rank sum associated with the smaller sample (if equal sample sizes, either rank sum can be used).

a. $\alpha = .025$ one-tailed; $\alpha = .05$ two-tailed

n_2 \ n_1	3 T_L	3 T_U	4 T_L	4 T_U	5 T_L	5 T_U	6 T_L	6 T_U	7 T_L	7 T_U	8 T_L	8 T_U	9 T_L	9 T_U	10 T_L	10 T_U
3	5	16	6	18	6	21	7	23	7	26	8	28	8	31	9	33
4	6	18	11	25	12	28	12	32	13	35	14	38	15	41	16	44
5	6	21	12	28	18	37	19	41	20	45	21	49	22	53	24	56
6	7	23	12	32	19	41	26	52	28	56	29	61	31	65	32	70
7	7	26	13	35	20	45	28	56	37	68	39	73	41	78	43	83
8	8	28	14	38	21	49	29	61	39	73	49	87	51	93	54	98
9	8	31	15	41	22	53	31	65	41	78	51	93	63	108	66	114
10	9	33	16	44	24	56	32	70	43	83	54	98	66	114	79	131

b. $\alpha = .05$ one-tailed; $\alpha = .10$ two-tailed

n_2 \ n_1	3 T_L	3 T_U	4 T_L	4 T_U	5 T_L	5 T_U	6 T_L	6 T_U	7 T_L	7 T_U	8 T_L	8 T_U	9 T_L	9 T_U	10 T_L	10 T_U
3	6	15	7	17	7	20	8	22	9	24	9	27	10	29	11	31
4	7	17	12	24	13	27	14	30	15	33	16	36	17	39	18	42
5	7	20	13	27	19	36	20	40	22	43	24	46	25	50	26	54
6	8	22	14	30	20	40	28	50	30	54	32	58	33	63	35	67
7	9	24	15	33	22	43	30	54	39	66	41	71	43	76	46	80
8	9	27	16	36	24	46	32	58	41	71	52	84	54	90	57	95
9	10	29	17	39	25	50	33	63	43	76	54	90	66	105	69	111
10	11	31	18	42	26	54	35	67	46	80	57	95	69	111	83	127

Source: From Wilcoxon, F., and Wilcox, R. A. "Some rapid approximate statistical procedures," 1964, 20–23. Courtesy of Lederle Laboratories Division of American Cyanamid Company, Madison, NJ.

Table XV	Critical Values of T_0 in the Wilcoxon Paired Difference Signed Rank Test					
One-Tailed	Two-Tailed	$n = 5$	$n = 6$	$n = 7$	$n = 8$	$n = 9$	$n = 10$
$\alpha = .05$	$\alpha = .10$	1	2	4	6	8	11
$\alpha = .025$	$\alpha = .05$		1	2	4	6	8
$\alpha = .01$	$\alpha = .02$			0	2	3	5
$\alpha = .005$	$\alpha = .01$				0	2	3
		$n = 11$	$n = 12$	$n = 13$	$n = 14$	$n = 15$	$n = 16$
$\alpha = .05$	$\alpha = .10$	14	17	21	26	30	36
$\alpha = .025$	$\alpha = .05$	11	14	17	21	25	30
$\alpha = .01$	$\alpha = .02$	7	10	13	16	20	24
$\alpha = .005$	$\alpha = .01$	5	7	10	13	16	19
		$n = 17$	$n = 18$	$n = 19$	$n = 20$	$n = 21$	$n = 22$
$\alpha = .05$	$\alpha = .10$	41	47	54	60	68	75
$\alpha = .025$	$\alpha = .05$	35	40	46	52	59	66
$\alpha = .01$	$\alpha = .02$	28	33	38	43	49	56
$\alpha = .005$	$\alpha = .01$	23	28	32	37	43	49
		$n = 23$	$n = 24$	$n = 25$	$n = 26$	$n = 27$	$n = 28$
$\alpha = .05$	$\alpha = .10$	83	92	101	110	120	130
$\alpha = .025$	$\alpha = .05$	73	81	90	98	107	117
$\alpha = .01$	$\alpha = .02$	62	69	77	85	93	102
$\alpha = .005$	$\alpha = .01$	55	61	68	76	84	92
		$n = 29$	$n = 30$	$n = 31$	$n = 32$	$n = 33$	$n = 34$
$\alpha = .05$	$\alpha = .10$	141	152	163	175	188	201
$\alpha = .025$	$\alpha = .05$	127	137	148	159	171	183
$\alpha = .01$	$\alpha = .02$	111	120	130	141	151	162
$\alpha = .005$	$\alpha = .01$	100	109	118	128	138	149
		$n = 35$	$n = 36$	$n = 37$	$n = 38$	$n = 39$	
$\alpha = .05$	$\alpha = .10$	214	228	242	256	271	
$\alpha = .025$	$\alpha = .05$	195	208	222	235	250	
$\alpha = .01$	$\alpha = .02$	174	186	198	211	224	
$\alpha = .005$	$\alpha = .01$	160	171	183	195	208	
		$n = 40$	$n = 41$	$n = 42$	$n = 43$	$n = 44$	$n = 45$
$\alpha = .05$	$\alpha = .10$	287	303	319	336	353	371
$\alpha = .025$	$\alpha = .05$	264	279	295	311	327	344
$\alpha = .01$	$\alpha = .02$	238	252	267	281	297	313
$\alpha = .005$	$\alpha = .01$	221	234	248	262	277	292
		$n = 46$	$n = 47$	$n = 48$	$n = 49$	$n = 50$	
$\alpha = .05$	$\alpha = .10$	389	408	427	446	466	
$\alpha = .025$	$\alpha = .05$	361	379	397	415	434	
$\alpha = .01$	$\alpha = .02$	329	345	362	380	398	
$\alpha = .005$	$\alpha = .01$	307	323	339	356	373	

Source: From Wilcoxon, F., and Wilcox, R. A. "Some rapid approximate statistical procedures," 1964, p. 28. Courtesy of Lederle Laboratories Division of American Cyanamid Company, Madison, NJ.

Table XVI — Critical Values of Spearman's Rank Correlation Coefficient

The values correspond to a one-tailed test of H_0: $p = 0$. The value should be doubled for two-tailed tests.

n	$\alpha = .05$	$\alpha = .025$	$\alpha = .01$	$\alpha = .005$	n	$\alpha = .05$	$\alpha = .025$	$\alpha = .01$	$\alpha = .005$
5	.900	—	—	—	18	.399	.476	.564	.625
6	.829	.886	.943	—	19	.388	.462	.549	.608
7	.714	.786	.893	—	20	.377	.450	.534	.591
8	.643	.738	.833	.881	21	.368	.438	.521	.576
9	.600	.683	.783	.833	22	.359	.428	.508	.562
10	.564	.648	.745	.794	23	.351	.418	.496	.549
11	.523	.623	.736	.818	24	.343	.409	.485	.537
12	.497	.591	.703	.780	25	.336	.400	.475	.526
13	.475	.566	.673	.745	26	.329	.392	.465	.515
14	.457	.545	.646	.716	27	.323	.385	.456	.505
15	.441	.525	.623	.689	28	.317	.377	.448	.496
16	.425	.507	.601	.666	29	.311	.370	.440	.487
17	.412	.490	.582	.645	30	.305	.364	.432	.478

Source: From Olds, E. G. "Distribution of sums of squares of rank differences for small samples," *Annals of Mathematical Statistics*, 1938, 9. Reproduced with the permission of the editor, *Annals of Mathematical Statistics*.

Table XVII Critical Values of the Studentized Range, $\alpha = .05$

ν \ k	2	3	4	5	6	7	8	9	10	11
1	17.97	26.98	32.82	37.08	40.41	43.12	45.40	47.36	49.07	50.59
2	6.08	8.33	9.80	10.88	11.74	12.44	13.03	13.54	13.99	14.39
3	4.50	5.91	6.82	7.50	8.04	8.48	8.85	9.18	9.46	9.72
4	3.93	5.04	5.76	6.29	6.71	7.05	7.35	7.60	7.83	8.03
5	3.64	4.60	5.22	5.67	6.03	6.33	6.58	6.80	6.99	7.17
6	3.46	4.34	4.90	5.30	5.63	5.90	6.12	6.32	6.49	6.65
7	3.34	4.16	4.68	5.06	5.36	5.61	5.82	6.00	6.16	6.30
8	3.26	4.04	4.53	4.89	5.17	5.40	5.60	5.77	5.92	6.05
9	3.20	3.95	4.41	4.76	5.02	5.24	5.43	5.59	5.74	5.87
10	3.15	3.88	4.33	4.65	4.91	5.12	5.30	5.46	5.60	5.72
11	3.11	3.82	4.26	4.57	4.82	5.03	5.20	5.35	5.49	5.61
12	3.08	3.77	4.20	4.51	4.75	4.95	5.12	5.27	5.39	5.51
13	3.06	3.73	4.15	4.45	4.69	4.88	5.05	5.19	5.32	5.43
14	3.03	3.70	4.11	4.41	4.64	4.83	4.99	5.13	5.25	5.36
15	3.01	3.67	4.08	4.37	4.60	4.78	4.94	5.08	5.20	5.31
16	3.00	3.65	4.05	4.33	4.56	4.74	4.90	5.03	5.15	5.26
17	2.98	3.63	4.02	4.30	4.52	4.70	4.86	4.99	5.11	5.21
18	2.97	3.61	4.00	4.28	4.49	4.67	4.82	4.96	5.07	5.17
19	2.96	3.59	3.98	4.25	4.47	4.65	4.79	4.92	5.04	5.14
20	2.95	3.58	3.96	4.23	4.45	4.62	4.77	4.90	5.01	5.11
24	2.92	3.53	3.90	4.17	4.37	4.54	4.68	4.81	4.92	5.01
30	2.89	3.49	3.85	4.10	4.30	4.46	4.60	4.72	4.82	4.92
40	2.86	3.44	3.79	4.04	4.23	4.39	4.52	4.63	4.73	4.82
60	2.83	3.40	3.74	3.98	4.16	4.31	4.44	4.55	4.65	4.73
120	2.80	3.36	3.68	3.92	4.10	4.24	4.36	4.47	4.56	4.64
∞	2.77	3.31	3.63	3.86	4.03	4.17	4.29	4.39	4.47	4.55

ν \ k	12	13	14	15	16	17	18	19	20
1	51.96	53.20	54.33	55.36	56.32	57.22	58.04	58.83	59.56
2	14.75	15.08	15.38	15.65	15.91	16.14	16.37	16.57	16.77
3	9.95	10.15	10.35	10.52	10.69	10.84	10.98	11.11	11.24
4	8.21	8.37	8.52	8.66	8.79	8.91	9.03	9.13	9.23
5	7.32	7.47	7.60	7.72	7.83	7.93	8.03	8.12	8.21
6	6.79	6.92	7.03	7.14	7.24	7.34	7.43	7.51	7.59
7	6.43	6.55	6.66	6.76	6.85	6.94	7.02	7.10	7.17
8	6.18	6.29	6.39	6.48	6.57	6.65	6.73	6.80	6.87
9	5.98	6.09	6.19	6.28	6.36	6.44	6.51	6.58	6.64
10	5.83	5.93	6.03	6.11	6.19	6.27	6.34	6.40	6.47
11	5.71	5.81	5.90	5.98	6.06	6.13	6.20	6.27	6.33
12	5.61	5.71	5.80	5.88	5.95	6.02	6.09	6.15	6.21
13	5.53	5.63	5.71	5.79	5.86	5.93	5.99	6.05	6.11
14	5.46	5.55	5.64	5.71	5.79	5.85	5.91	5.97	6.03
15	5.40	5.49	5.57	5.65	5.72	5.78	5.85	5.90	5.96
16	5.35	5.44	5.52	5.59	5.66	5.73	5.79	5.84	5.90
17	5.31	5.39	5.47	5.54	5.61	5.67	5.73	5.79	5.84
18	5.27	5.35	5.43	5.50	5.57	5.63	5.69	5.74	5.79
19	5.23	5.31	5.39	5.46	5.53	5.59	5.65	5.70	5.75
20	5.20	5.28	5.36	5.43	5.49	5.55	5.61	5.66	5.71
24	5.10	5.18	5.25	5.32	5.38	5.44	5.49	5.55	5.59
30	5.00	5.08	5.15	5.21	5.27	5.33	5.38	5.43	5.47
40	4.90	4.98	5.04	5.11	5.16	5.22	5.27	5.31	5.36
60	4.81	4.88	4.94	5.00	5.06	5.11	5.15	5.20	5.24
120	4.71	4.78	4.84	4.90	4.95	5.00	5.04	5.09	5.13
∞	4.62	4.68	4.74	4.80	4.85	4.89	4.93	4.97	5.01

Appendix C: Calculation Formulas for Analysis of Variance

C.1 Formulas for the Calculations in the Completely Randomized Design

$$CM = \text{Correction for mean}$$

$$= \frac{(\text{Total of all observations})^2}{\text{Total number of observations}} = \frac{\left(\sum_{i=1}^{n} y_i\right)^2}{n}$$

$$SS(\text{Total}) = \text{Total sum of squares}$$

$$= (\text{Sum of squares of all observations}) - CM = \sum_{i=1}^{n} y_i^2 - CM$$

$$SST = \text{Sum of squares for treatments}$$

$$= \left(\begin{array}{c}\text{Sum of squares of treatment totals with} \\ \text{each square divided by the number of} \\ \text{observations for that treatment}\end{array}\right) - CM$$

$$= \frac{T_1^2}{n_1} + \frac{T_2^2}{n_2} + \cdots + \frac{T_k^2}{n_k} - CM$$

$$SSE = \text{Sum of squares for error} = SS(\text{Total}) - SST$$

$$MST = \text{Mean square for treatments} = \frac{SST}{k-1}$$

$$MSE = \text{Mean square for error} = \frac{SSE}{n-k}$$

$$F = \text{Test statistic} = \frac{MST}{MSE}$$

where

$$n = \text{Total number of observations}$$
$$k = \text{Number of treatments}$$
$$T_i = \text{Total for treatment } i \ (i = 1, 2, \ldots, k)$$

C.2 Formulas for the Calculations in the Randomized Block Design

$$CM = \text{Correction for mean}$$

$$= \frac{(\text{Total of all observations})^2}{\text{Total number of observations}} = \frac{\left(\sum y_i\right)^2}{n}$$

$$\text{SS(Total)} = \text{Total sum of squares}$$

$$= (\text{Sum of squares of all observations}) - \text{CM} = \sum y_i^2 - \text{CM}$$

$$\text{SST} = \text{Sum of squares for treatments}$$

$$= \left(\begin{array}{c} \text{Sum of squares of treatment totals with} \\ \text{each square divided by } b, \text{ the number of} \\ \text{observations for that treatment} \end{array} \right) - \text{CM}$$

$$= \frac{T_1^2}{b} + \frac{T_2^2}{b} + \cdots + \frac{T_p^2}{b} - \text{CM}$$

$$\text{SST} = \text{Sum of squares for blocks}$$

$$= \left(\begin{array}{c} \text{Sum of squares of block totals with} \\ \text{each square divided by } k, \text{ the number} \\ \text{of observations in that block} \end{array} \right) - \text{CM}$$

$$= \frac{B_1^2}{k} + \frac{B_2^2}{k} + \cdots + \frac{B_b^2}{k} - \text{CM}$$

$$\text{SSE} = \text{Sum of squares for error} = \text{SS(Total)} - \text{SST} - \text{SSB}$$

$$\text{MST} = \text{Mean square for treatments} = \frac{\text{SST}}{k-1}$$

$$\text{MSB} = \text{Mean square for blocks} = \frac{\text{SSB}}{b-1}$$

$$\text{MSE} = \text{Mean square for error} = \frac{\text{SSE}}{n-k-b+1}$$

$$F = \text{Test statistic} = \frac{\text{MST}}{\text{MSE}}$$

where

$$n = \text{Total number of observations}$$
$$b = \text{Number of blocks}$$
$$k = \text{Number of treatments}$$
$$T_i = \text{Total for treatment } i \ (i = 1, 2, \ldots, k)$$
$$B_i = \text{Total for block } i \ (i = 1, 2, \ldots, b)$$

C.3 Formulas for the Calculations for a Two–Factor Factorial Experiment

$$\text{CM} = \text{Correction for mean}$$

$$= \frac{(\text{Total of all } n \text{ measurements})^2}{n} = \frac{\left(\sum\limits_{i=1}^{n} y_i \right)^2}{n}$$

$$\text{SS(Total)} = \text{Total sum of squares}$$

$$= (\text{Sum of squares of all } n \text{ measurements}) - \text{CM} = \sum\limits_{i=1}^{n} y_i^2 - \text{CM}$$

$$\text{SS}(A) = \text{Sum of squares for main effects, factor } A$$

$$= \left(\begin{array}{c} \text{Sum of squares of the totals } A_1, A_2, \ldots, A_a \\ \text{divided by the number of measurements} \\ \text{in a single total, namely } br \end{array} \right) - \text{CM}$$

$$= \frac{\sum_{i=1}^{a} A_i^2}{br} - \text{CM}$$

SS(B) = Sum of squares for main effects, factor B

$$= \left(\begin{array}{c} \text{Sum of squares of the totals } B_1, B_2, \ldots, B_b \\ \text{divided by the number of measurements} \\ \text{in a single total, namely } ar \end{array} \right) - \text{CM}$$

$$= \frac{\sum_{i=1}^{b} B_i^2}{ar} - \text{CM}$$

SS(AB) = Sum of squares for AB interaction

$$= \left(\begin{array}{c} \text{Sum of squares of the cell totals} \\ AB_{11}, AB_{12}, \ldots, AB_{ab} \text{ divided by} \\ \text{the number of measurements} \\ \text{in a single total, namely } r \end{array} \right) - \text{SS}(A) - \text{SS}(B) - \text{CM}$$

$$= \frac{\sum_{j=1}^{b} \sum_{i=1}^{a} AB_{ij}^2}{r} - \text{SS}(A) - \text{SS}(B) - \text{CM}$$

where

a = Number of levels of factor A

b = Number of levels of factor B

r = Number of replicates (observations per treatment)

A_i = Total for level i of factor A ($i = 1, 2, \ldots, a$)

B_j = Total for level j of factor B ($j = 1, 2, \ldots, b$)

AB_{ij} = Total for treatment (i, j), i.e., for ith level of factor A and jth level of factor B

C.4 Tukey's Multiple Comparisons Procedure (Equal Sample Sizes)

Step 1 Select the desired experimentwise error rate, α

Step 2 Calculate

$$\omega = q_\alpha(k, v) \frac{s}{\sqrt{n_t}}$$

where

k = Number of sample means (i.e., number of treatments)

$s = \sqrt{\text{MSE}}$

v = Number of degress of freedom associated with MSE

n_t = Number of observations in each of the k samples (i.e., number of observations per treatment)

$q_\alpha(k, v)$ = Critical value of the Studentized range (Table XVII in Appendix B)

Step 3 Calculate and rank the k sample means.

Step 4 Place a bar over those pairs of treatment means that differ by less than ω. A pair of treatments not connected by an overbar (i.e., differing by more than ω) implies a difference in the corresponding population means.

Note: The confidence level associated with all inferences drawn from the analysis is $(1 - \alpha)$.

C.5 Bonferroni Multiple Comparisons Procedure (Pairwise Comparisons)

Step 1 Calculate for each treatment pair (i, j)

$$B_{ij} = t_{\alpha/(2c)}s\sqrt{\frac{1}{n_i} + \frac{1}{n_j}}$$

where

k = Number of sample (treatment) means in the experiment

c = Number of pairwise comparisons
   [*Note:* If all pairwise comparisons are to be made, then
   $c = k(k - 1)/2$]

$s = \sqrt{MSE}$

v = Number of degrees of freedom associated with MSE

n_i = Number of observations in sample for treatment i

n_j = Number of observations in sample for treatment j

$t_{\alpha/(2c)}$ = Critical value of t distribution with v df and tail area $\alpha/(2c)$ (Table V in Appendix B)

Step 2 Rank the sample means and place a bar over any treatment pair (i, j) whose sample means differ by less than B_{ij}. Any pair of means not connected by an overbar implies a difference in the corresponding population means.

Note: The level of confidence associated with all inferences drawn from the analysis is at least $(1 - \alpha)$.

C.6 Scheffé's Multiple Comparisons Procedure (Pairwise Comparisons)

Step 1 Calculate Scheffé's critical difference for each pair of treatments (i, j):

$$S_{ij} = \sqrt{(k - 1)(F_\alpha)(MSE)\left(\frac{1}{n_1} + \frac{1}{n_j}\right)}$$

where

k = Number of sample (treatment) means

MSE = Mean squared error

n_i = Number of observations in sample for treatment i

n_j = Number of observations in sample for treatment j

F_α = Critical value of F distribution with $k - 1$ numerator df and v denominator df (Tables XII, XIII, IX, and X in Appendix B)

v = Number of degrees of freedom associated with MSE

Step 2 Rank the k sample means and place a bar over any treatment pair (i, j) that differs by less than S_{ij}. Any pair of sample means not connected by an overbar implies a difference in the corresponding population means.

Appendix D: Calculus and Probability

The theory of continuous random variables is based on Integral Calculus. In this appendix, we supply some details and ask you to work with what you studied in your Business Calculus II class. Continuous random variables are discussed, as are normal, uniform and binomial random variables.

1. Continuous Random Variables

1.1. Continuous Models. Consider a discrete random variable x with probability distribution given by the function $p(x)$ (as in section 4.4) with many possible values. For simplicity we shall assume here that the values are all nonnegative integers $x = 0, 1, 2, \cdots$. Consider the probability that x has a value in the interval $[a, b]$, i.e., $P(a \leq x \leq b) = p(a) + p(a + 1) + \cdots + p(b)$. This value is the sum of the areas of the rectangles having heights $p(x)$, bases of length 1 and with midpoints x, for $x = a$ to $x = b$. This is illustrated below for a random variable x such that $x = 0, 1, 2, \cdots, 16$ are the possible values.

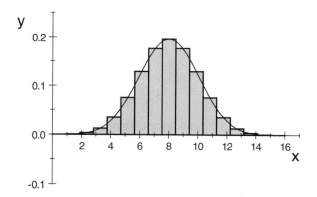

The areas of the bars must sum to $\sum p(x) = 1$. The probability $P(7 \leq x \leq 10) = p(7) + p(8) + p(9) + p(10)$ is the cumulative area of the bars as shown below.

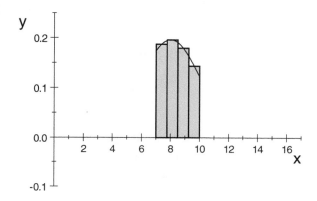

The probability distribution is approximated by drawing a curve (as shown) through the midpoint of the top of each rectangle and the probabilities are approximately the areas under the curve. Instead of the probability function $p(x)$ for a

481

countable list of values of x, we deal instead with the a function $f(x)$ and the curve $y = f(x)$. This motivates the idea of a continuous random variable given by areas under a curve as a model of a discrete random variable with "many" possible values, as discussed in the next subsection.

1.2. Continuous Random Variables. A continuous random variable (section 5.1) x is described by its *probability density function $f(x)$*, or **pdf** for short.

A probability density function is required to satisfy

(1) $f(x) \geq 0$ for all x, and
(2) $\int_{-\infty}^{\infty} f(x)dx = 1$

Indeed, any function $f(x)$ satisfying the properties is the probability density function for a random variable x.

The probability that x assumes a value in the interval $[a, b]$ is

$$P(a \leq x \leq b) = \int_{a}^{b} f(x)dx.$$

This entails the following two general facts:

- $P(x = a) = \int_{a}^{a} f(x)dx = 0$. So the probability of hitting a single value is zero.
- $P(a < x < b) = \int_{a}^{b} f(x)dx$. So it doesn't matter whether we use the closed interval $[a, b]$ or the open one (a, b). The endpoints don't contribute anything to the area.

These properties have no analogs in the discrete case.

1.3. Mean and Standard Deviation: The *mean* of a random variable x with probability density function $f(x)$ is defined to be

(D.1)
$$\mu = \int_{-\infty}^{\infty} xf(x)dx$$

The mean is also known as the *expected value of x*. The *variance* of x is defined to be the expected squared deviation from μ:

$$\sigma^2 = \int_{-\infty}^{\infty} (x-\mu)^2 f(x)dx$$

This quantity simplifies to

$$\sigma^2 = \int_{-\infty}^{\infty} x^2 f(x)dx - \mu^2$$

To use this **shortcut formula**, first compute the term $\int_{-\infty}^{\infty} x^2 f(x)dx$ (the expected value of x^2). Subtract μ^2 as a second step. To find the *standard deviation* take the square root of σ^2.

The shortcut formula is proved as in the discrete case (see Section 4.3, p. 191) as follows:

$$\sigma^2 = \int_{-\infty}^{\infty} (x - \mu)^2 \, f(x)dx$$

$$= \int_{-\infty}^{\infty} (x^2 - 2x\mu + \mu^2)f(x)dx$$

$$= \int_{-\infty}^{\infty} x^2 f(x)dx - \int_{-\infty}^{\infty} 2x\mu f(x)dx + \int_{-\infty}^{\infty} \mu^2 f(x)dx$$

$$= \int_{-\infty}^{\infty} x^2 f(x)dx - 2\mu \int_{-\infty}^{\infty} x f(x)dx + \mu^2 \int_{-\infty}^{\infty} f(x)dx$$

$$= \int_{-\infty}^{\infty} x^2 f(x)dx - 2\mu \cdot \mu + \mu^2 \cdot 1$$

$$= \int_{-\infty}^{\infty} x^2 f(x)dx - \mu^2$$

where we multiply out, move the constant μ outside, and use the definition of μ (D.1) and the property 2 in the definition of probability density function.

These expressions are the continuous analogs of the formulas $\mu = \sum x p(x)$ and $\sigma^2 = \sum (x-\mu)^2 p(x) = \sum x^2 p(x) - \mu^2$ for the discrete case where the density function $f(x)$ plays the role of the probability function $p(x)$ and the sum is replaced by an integral. Instead of weighting by $p(x)$, we weight by $f(x)$. It may help to think of the definite integrals informally as infinite sums where the infinitesimals $f(x)dx$ replace $p(x)$.

2. The Uniform Distribution

This is covered in section 5.2. Here the probability density function is given by

$$f(x) = \begin{cases} \frac{1}{d-c} & \text{if } c \leq x \leq d \\ 0 & \text{otherwise} \end{cases}$$

where $c < d$ are fixed endpoints. The random variable x is said to be *uniform on* $[c, d]$.

Probabilities are computed as integrals

$$P(a \leq x \leq b) = \int_a^b f(x)dx$$

$$= \int_a^b \frac{1}{d-c} dx$$

$$= \frac{1}{d-c} x \Big]_z^b = \frac{b-a}{d-c}$$

The case where the interval of definition is $[0, 1]$ is appealing because of its simplicity and because the random variable represents a random number chosen from the unit interval $[0, 1]$.

EXAMPLE 1. Compute $P(x > 0.5)$, the mean, and the standard deviation for a uniform random variable on the interval $[0, 1]$.

Example 1.

We have

$$f(x) = \begin{cases} 1 \ if \ 0 \leq x \leq 1 \\ 0 \ otherwise \end{cases}$$

and

$$P(x > .5) = \int_{.5}^{\infty} f(x)dx$$

$$= \int_{.5}^{1} 1 dx$$

$$= x\big|_{.5}^{1} = \frac{1}{2}$$

In addition

$$\mu = \int_{-\infty}^{\infty} xf(x)dx$$

$$= \int_{0}^{1} x dx$$

$$= \frac{x^2}{2}\bigg|_{0}^{1} = \frac{1}{2}$$

and

$$\int_{-\infty}^{\infty} x^2 f(x)dx$$

$$= \int_{0}^{1} x^2 1 dx$$

$$= \frac{x^3}{3}\bigg|_{0}^{1} = \frac{1}{3}$$

Hence $\sigma^2 = \int_{-\infty}^{\infty} x^2 f(x)dx - \mu^2 = \frac{1}{3} - \left(\frac{1}{2}\right)^2 = \frac{1}{12}$. *So the standard deviation is* $\sigma = \frac{1}{\sqrt{12}}$.

EXERCISE 1. Repeat this example for a uniform random variable on the interval $[0, 2]$. *I.e.* compute $P(x > 0.5)$, and show that $\mu = 1$ and $\sigma = \frac{2}{\sqrt{12}}$.

3. The Normal Distribution

A normal random variable is determined by its mean μ and standard deviation σ. The normal probability density function is

(D.2)
$$f(x) = \frac{1}{\sigma\sqrt{2\pi}} e^{-\frac{1}{2}\left(\frac{x-\mu}{\sigma}\right)^2}$$

When $\mu = 0$ and $\sigma = 1$, we have the standard normal random variable z, with standard normal probability density function

(D.3)
$$f(z) = \frac{1}{\sqrt{2\pi}} e^{-\frac{1}{2}z^2}$$

where we have changed variables from x to z, adhering to convention.

It can be checked using differentiation, that standard normal probability density function has a single maximum at $z = 0$, inflection points at $x = \pm 1$. It approaches zero as $x \rightarrow \pm\infty$ and thus has the x-axis as a horizontal asymptote. These properties will help in sketching normal curves and their verification would make a good Calculus I exercise.

Let x be a normal random variable with mean μ and standard deviation σ. The following transformation of x is known as *standardizing* the normal random variable x. To compute probabilities for x we proceed by computing areas as follows: First we integrate the probability density function D.2 for x over an interval $a \leq x \leq b$ to get the probability

$$P(a \leq x \leq b) = \int_a^b \frac{1}{\sigma\sqrt{2\pi}} e^{-\frac{1}{2}\left(\frac{x-\mu}{\sigma}\right)^2} dx$$

Now we perform the substitution $z = \frac{x-\mu}{\sigma} = \frac{1}{\sigma}x - \frac{\mu}{\sigma}$, $dz = \frac{1}{\sigma}dx$ (This is usually called a u-substitution, but we are using z instead of u.). Thus $dx = \sigma dz$ and we obtain

$$\int_a^b \frac{1}{\sigma\sqrt{2\pi}} e^{-\frac{1}{2}\left(\frac{x-\mu}{\sigma}\right)^2} dx = \int_{\frac{a-\mu}{\sigma}}^{\frac{b-\mu}{\sigma}} \frac{1}{\sigma\sqrt{2\pi}} e^{-\frac{1}{2}z^2} \cdot \sigma dz$$

$$= \int_{\frac{a-\mu}{\sigma}}^{\frac{b-\mu}{\sigma}} \frac{1}{\sqrt{2\pi}} e^{-\frac{1}{2}z^2} dz$$

$$= P\left(\frac{a-\mu}{\sigma} \leq z \leq \frac{b-\mu}{\sigma}\right)$$

The conclusion of this is that if we use the substitution $z = \frac{x-\mu}{\sigma}$ and change the endpoints a, b accordingly, then the integral becomes the integral of the standard normal density D.3 over the standardized endpoints $\frac{a-\mu}{\sigma} \leq z \leq \frac{b-\mu}{\sigma}$. It is not hard to see that the random variable

$$z = \frac{x-\mu}{\sigma}$$

has a standard normal distribution, and we obtain the

CONCLUSION 1 (standardizing normal probabilities). To compute probabilities for an arbitrary normal random variable, one can use the standard normal probability density function and standardized endpoints:

$$P(a \leq x \leq b) = P\left(\frac{a - \mu}{\sigma} \leq z \leq \frac{b - \mu}{\sigma}\right)$$

3.1. Computing standard normal curve areas by numerical integration (TI 83/84).

The standard normal probabilities can be computed the very old-fashioned way with tables, with a graphing calculator (as discussed in the section 5.3), or many programs and online apps. Unfortunately, it is impossible to compute it exactly via antidifferentiation in a closed form. But, a good method is to numerically approximate the definite integral. On the TI-83/84: Enter `Y1=(1/(2π)^0.5))e^((−).5x²)` or just `Y1=.3989e^((−).5x²)`. Of course one can use Y2, etc. and retain for future use. Note: use the unary $(-)$ in the bottom row of your calculator. To find $P(c \leq x \leq d)$ numerically:

(1) Hit the MATH key. This takes you to the MATH menu.

(2) Scroll down (or up) until the cursor is on `fnInt(` and hit ENTER or instead of scrolling around, you can just hit the number 9 since it is `9:fnInt(`.

(3) Type (Yl, x, c, d) where c, d are the numerical limits (endpoints).

(4) Hit ENTER

Example 2.

EXAMPLE 2. Compute the following probabilities for a normal random variable x

(1) $P(3 \leq x)$ if x is a standard normal random variable.

(2) $P(-8 \leq x \leq 8)$ if x is normally distributed with mean 0 and standard deviation 1.

(3) $P(-4 \leq x \leq 4)$ if x is normally distributed with mean 0 and standard deviation 2.

Solutions: $P(3 \leq z)$ is computed by entering `fnInt (Yl,x, 3,888)` with $Y1 = .3989e^{\wedge}(-.5x^2)$. The answer is 0.00135 (to 3 significant digits). Here we use 888 as a large value for the upper limit, though a smaller number such as 8, would work as well, as $z = 8$ represents a value 8 standard deviations above the mean, a very very big value. To be convinced of this, calculate $P(-8 \leq x \leq 8) = \int_{-8}^{8} \frac{1}{\sqrt{2\pi}} e^{-\frac{1}{2}z^2} dz = 1.000\ 000$.

$$P(-4 \leq x \leq 4) = P(-2 \leq z \leq 2) = \int_{-2}^{2} \frac{1}{\sqrt{2\pi}} e^{-\frac{1}{2}z^2} dz =$$

0.9545, the value approximated by the 95% in the Empirical rule (see p. 191 and note that the normal distribution is the ideal mound-shaped distribution).

3.2. Binomials and Normals.

We illustrate, in an example, the connection between the binomial random variable and the normal distribution. The actual random variable we showed in 1.1 is a binomial random variable with $n = 16$ and $p = .5$. Thus x is the number of heads in the flip of 16 fair coins. As in section 5.5, the values are approximated by using a normal distribution with mean $\mu = np = 8$ and $\sigma = \sqrt{16(.5)(.5)} = 2$. Here the fitted binomial curve we used seems to be quite close to the normal probability density function $f(x) = \frac{1}{4\sqrt{2\pi}} e^{-.5(\frac{x-8}{4})^2}$. The two curves are superimposed in the graph below with the normal in black and the binomial curve in red.

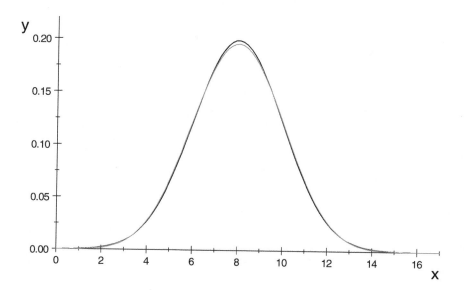

Since the interval $\mu \pm 3\sigma$ is $8 \pm 3(2)$ or $[2, 14]$ is within the interval $[0, 16]$, the rule of thumb in section 5.5 says that the approximation by the normal is good.

The black curve is the function $\binom{16}{x}\frac{1}{2^{16}}$, defined for any real number x, which defined using gamma functions. (This topic is outside of the scope of this text.)

Answers to Selected Exercises

Chapter 1

1.3 population; variables; summary tools; conclusions   **1.5** published source; designed experiment; survey; observationally   **1.13** qualitative; qualitative   **1.15 a.** all U.S. citizens **b.** president's job performance; qualitative **c.** 2000 polled individuals **d.** Estimate the proportion of all U.S. citizens who believe the president is doing a good job. **e.** survey **f.** not very likely   **1.17** I. qualitative II. quantitative III. qualitative IV. qualitative V. qualitative VI. quantitative   **1.19 a.** sample, if interested in CEOs of all U.S companies; population, if interested in only the 500 CEOs in the 2008 scoreboard **b.** (1) qualitative; (2) quantitative; (3) quantitative; (4) quantitative; (5) quantitative; (6) quantitative   **1.21 a.** all satellite radio subscribers **b.** satellite receiver in car status **c.** qualitative **d.** 501 satellite subscribers surveyed; yes **e.** estimate of proportion of all satellite subscribers that have a car receiver is $396/501 = .79$ **1.23 a.** quantitative **b.** quantitative **c.** qualitative **d.** quantitative **e.** qualitative **f.** quantitative **g.** qualitative   **1.25 b.** speed of the deliveries; accuracy of the invoices; quality of the packaging **c.** total numbers of questionnaires received   **1.27 a.** all accounting alumni of the large university **b.** quantitative: age, income, job satisfaction score, Machiavellian rating; qualitative: gender, education level **c.** 198 alumni who returned the questionnaire **d.** survey **e.** Machiavellian behavior is not required to achieve success in business **f.** Nonrespondents may be more Machiavellian in nature, biasing the results   **1.31 a.** all persons over 14 in U.S. **b.** employment status; qualitative **c.** inferential

Chapter 2

2.1 16; .18; .45; .15; .14   **2.3 a.** pie chart **b.** task category **c.** material handling (34%) **d.** 58,880 **e.** 52%   **2.5 a.** qualitative   **2.7 a.** all non-cash transactions made during the year **b.** 21.46 billion **c.** 50%   **2.9** companies and employees created 73% of blogs/forums   **2.11** Most often: F color (26.6%), clarity VS1 (26.3%); least often: D color (5.2%), IF clarity (14.3%)   **2.13 a.** response time **c.** 3,570 **d.** No   **2.15. d.** most aquifers are bedrock; most MTBE levels are below the limit; 80% of private wells and 60% of public wells are not contaminated   **2.17** 50, 75, 125, 100, 25, 50, 50, 25   **2.19 a.** frequency histogram **b.** 14 **c.** 49   **2.21 a.** approximately 30% **b.** approximately 80%   **2.23 b.** years 1996–2000 had the highest number of firms with at least one acquisition   **2.25 d.** HRD group   **2.27 c.** penalties for CAA tend to be smaller   **2.29 a.** 2007 SAT scores are shifted to the right of the scores from 2000 **c.** similar conclusion **d.** Colorado ($\approx$ 50 point improvement)   **2.31** "inside job" not likely because histogram appears similar to frequency distribution   **2.33 a.** 12 **b.** 40 **c.** 7 **d.** 21 **e.** 144   **2.35 a.** 11.2 **b.** 12 **c.** 30   **2.37 a.** $\bar{x} = 2.717, m = 2.65$ **2.41** mode $= 15; \bar{x} = 14.545; m = 15$ **2.43 a.** mean less than median **b.** mean greater than median **c.** equal   **2.45 a.** mean $= 653$; average amount of sparkling wine exported by the 30 countries is $653,000 **b.** median $= 231$; half the 30 export values are above $231,000 **c.** mean $= 481$; average change in amount exported by the 30 countries is 481% **d.** median $= 156$; half the 30 percentage changes are above 156%   **2.47 a.** 11 **b.** 9 **c.** 7 **d.** honey dosage leads to greatest improvement   **2.49 a.** $\bar{x} = .63$; average number of carats of 308 diamonds is .63 **b.** $m = .62$; 50% of the diamonds weigh less than .62 carat **c.** mode $= 1.0$; carat value of 1.0 occurred the most often **d.** mean or median   **2.51** data are probably not skewed but close to symmetric   **2.53** joint: $= 2.6545, m = 1.5$; no prefiling: $= 4.2364, m = 3.2$; prepack: $= 1.8185, m = 1.4$; three centers   **2.55 a.** median **b.** mean   **2.57 a.** R $= 4, s^2 = 2.3, s = 1.52$ **b.** R $= 6, s^2 = 3.619, s = 1.90$ **c.** R $= 10, s^2 = 7.111, s = 2.67$ **d.** R $= 4, s^2 = 1.395, s = 1.18$ **2.59 a.** $\bar{x} = 5.6, s^2 = 17.3, s = 4.1593$ **b.** $\bar{x} = 13.75$ feet, $s^2 = 152.25$ square feet, $s = 12.339$ feet **c.** $\bar{x} = -2.5, s^2 = 4.3, s = 2.0736$ **d.** $\bar{x} = .33$ ounce, $s^2 = .0587$ square ounce, $s = .2422$ ounce   **2.61** Data set 1: 0,1,2,3,4,5,6,7,8,9; data set 2: 0,0,1,1,2,2,3,3,9,9   **2.63 a.** R $= 3, s^2 = 1.3, s = 1.14$ **b.** R $= 3, s^2 = 1.3, s = 1.14$ **c.** R $= 3, s^2 = 1.3, s = 1.14$ **d.** no effect   **2.65 a.** R $= \$4,882$ thousand **b.** $s = \$1,113$ thousand **c.** 1,238,769   **2.67 a.** .92 **b.** .0768 **c.** .2772 **d.** standard deviation   **2.69 a.** R $= 10, s^2 = 7.10, s = 2.67$ **b.** R $= 8, s^2 = 4.67, s = 2.16$ **c.** R $= 8, s^2 = 4.50, s = 2.12$ **2.71 a.** dollars; quantitative **b.** at least $3/4$; at least $8/9$; nothing; nothing   **2.73** approx. 68%; approx. 95%; essentially all   **2.75** between R/6 $= 104.17$ and R/4 $= 156.25$; not feasible   **2.77 a.** (105.77, 176.85) **b.** at least $3/4$ **c.** nothing   **2.79 a.** at most 25% **b.** $\approx 2.5\%$ **2.81.** $\bar{x} = 234.74, s = 9.91$; (205.0, 264.5)   **2.83 a.** at least $8/9$ of the velocities fall within (906, 966) **b.** no   **2.85** do not buy   **2.87** 11:30 and 4:00   **2.89 a.** 25%, 75% **b.** 50%, 50% **c.** 80%, 20% **d.** 16%, 84%   **2.91 a.** $z = 2$ **b.** $z = -3$ **c.** $z = -2$ **d.** $z = 1.67$ **2.93** average score is 279; 10% of 8th graders score below 231; 25% score below 255; 75% score below 304; 90% score below 324   **2.95** half the graduates have starting salaries less than $41,100; half the graduates have mid-career salaries less than $71,100; 90% of the graduates have mid-career salaries less than $131,000   **2.97** no   **2.99 a.** 0 **b.** 21 **c.** $\bar{x} = 5.24, s = 7.24; z = 5.90$ **d.** yes   **2.101** not necessarily because the standard deviation will be large for right-skewed data   **2.103 a.** $z = .727$, no **b.** $z = -3.273$, yes **c.** $z = 1.364$, no **d.** $z = 3.727$, yes   **2.107 a.** 50% of expenditures are less than $6,232; 25% are less than $5,309; 75% are less than $7,216 **b.** $1,907 **c.** $.75 - .25 = .50$ **2.109. a.** $z = 1.05$, no **b.** greater than 194.6 or less than 88   **2.111 b.** Joint: 1.5; None firms: 3.2; Prepack: 1.4 **d.** no **e.** yes   **2.113 a.** 8 outliers: 56, 72, 74, 78, 83, 83, 84, and 84 **b.** 4 outliers: 56, 72, 74, and 78 **c.** no   **2.115 b.** customers 268, 269, and 264 **c.** 2.06, 2.13, and 3.14   **2.119** no   **2.121** increasing   **2.123 a.** yes **b.** USAID and State   **2.125** moderate positive trend; yes   **2.129 a.** $-1, 1, 2$ **b.** 0, 4, 6 **c.** 1, 3, 4 **d.** .1, .3, .4   **2.131 a.** 6, 27, 5.20 **b.** 6.25, 28.25, 5.32 **c.** 7, 37.67, 6.14 **d.** 3, 0, 0   **2.137 a.** .082, .173, .167, .174, .139, .098, .074, .046, .048; 16.7% of articles published were in the Buyer Behavior area **b.** lower percentage for Marketing Research   **2.139** 60% of cars have 4-star rating   **2.141 a.** body defect **b.** paint or dents   **2.143** $\bar{x} = 52.04; m = 56.7$; mode $= 56.7$ **2.145 a.** $\bar{x} = 144.5; m = 102.5$; mode $= 70$ **b.** $\bar{x} = 5.23; m = 5$; mode $= 6$ **c.** median **d.** mean **e.** increasing   **2.147 a.** grounding and fire **b.** $\bar{x} = 66.19, s = 56.05$; $(-101.96, 234.34)$ **2.149 c.** approved brands tend to have lower costs   **2.151 a.** no scale on vertical axis **b.** add vertical axis scale   **2.153 a.** skewed right **c.** $\approx .38$ **d.** no, $z = 3.333$ **2.155 a.** both height and width of bars change   **2.157** Laid off: $m = 40.5$; not laid off: $m = 40$; company probably not vulnerable   **2.159** yes; no observations recorded in interval just below interval centered at 1.000 cm

Chapter 3

3.1 a. .5 **b.** .3 **c.** .6   **3.3** $P(A) = .55, P(B) = .50, P(C) = .70$ **3.5 a.** 10 **b.** 20 **c.** 15,504   **3.7 a.** $(B_1, B_2), (B_1, R_1), (B_1, R_2), (B_1, R_3), (B_2, R_1),$ $(B_2, R_2), (B_2, R_3), (R_1, R_2), (R_1, R_3), (R_2, R_3)$ **b.** $P(E_i) = 1/10$ **c.** $P(A) = 1/10, P(B) = 3/5, P(C) = 3/10$ **3.9 a.** Brown, yellow, red, blue, orange, and green **b.** $P(Br) = 0.13, P(Y) = 0.14, P(R) = 0.13, P(Bl) = 0.24, P(O) = 0.2, P(G) = 0.16$ **c.** .13 **d.** .43 **e.** .76   **3.11** .0057   **3.13 a.** None, 1-2, 3-5, 6-9, 10 or more **b.** $P(none) = 0.25, P(1–2) = 0.31, P(3–5) = 0.25, P(6–9) = 0.05, P(10 \text{ or more}) = 0.14$ **c.** .44   **3.15 a.** $1/100 = .01$ **b.** .0095; yes   **3.17 a.** .325 **b.** .711   **3.19** 455   **3.21 a.** 6; $(G_1G_2G_3), (G_1G_2G_4), (G_1G_2G_5), (G_2G_3G_4), (G_2G_3G_5),$ $(G_2G_4G_5)$ **b.** .282, .065, .339, .032, .008, .274 **c.** .686   **3.23 a.** 1 to 2 **b.** 1/2 **c.** 2/5   **3.25 a.** 32 **b.** 1/32 **c.** 12 **d.** $12/32 = .375$ **e.** .5   **3.27 b.** $P(A) = 7/8,$ $P(B) = 1/2, P(A \cup B) = 7/8, P(A^c) = 1/8, P(A \cap B) = 1/2$ **d.** no   **3.29 a.** 3/4 **b.** 13/20 **c.** 1 **d.** 2/5 **e.** 1/4 **f.** 7/20 **g.** 1 **h.** 1/4   **3.31 a.** .65 **b.** .72 **c.** .25 **d.** .08 **e.** .35 **f.** .72 **g.** 0 **h.** A and C, B and C, C and D **3.33 a.** $A \cap B$ **b.** A^c **c.** $C \cup B$ **d.** $B^c \cap A^c$ **3.35 a.** .43 **b.** .84   **3.37 a.** AC, AW, AF, IC, IW, and IF **b.** .148, .066, .426, .176, .052, .132 **c.** .640 **d.** .118 **e.** .176 **f.** .786 **g.** .676   **3.39 a.** $P \cap S \cap A$ **b.** 1/5 **c.** $A \cup S$; 4/5 **d.** $P \cap S$; 3/10   **3.41 a.** .684 **b.** .124 **c.** no **d.** .316 **e.** .717 **f.** .091   **3.43 a.** $P(A) = .281, P(B) = .276, P(C) = .044, P(D) = .079, P(E) = .044$ **b.** 0 **c.** .557 **d.** 0 **e.** .325 **f.** A and B, A and C, A and D, A and E **3.45 a.** .09 **b.** .09 **c.** .84 **d.** no **e.** column events not mutually exclusive   **3.47 a.** .5 **b.** .25 **c.** no   **3.49 a.** .08 **b.** .4 **c.** .52   **3.51 a.** .8, .7, .6 **b.** .25, .375, .375 **d.** no   **3.53 a.** .37 **b.** .68 **c.** .15 **d.** .2206 **e.** 0 **f.** 0 **g.** no   **3.55 a.** A and C, B and C **b.** none **c.** .65, .90   **3.57** 3/5   **3.59 a.** .26 **b.** .013   **3.61 a.** .1875 **b.** .60   **3.63 a.** $P(R) = .68, P(A|R) = .07$ **b.** $P(A \cap R) = .048$ **3.65 a.** .222 **b.** .183   **3.67 a.** $P(A \mid I) = .9, P(B \mid I) = .95, P(A \mid I^c) = .2, P(B \mid I^c) = .1$ **b.** .855 **c.** .02 **d.** .995   **3.69 a.** .23 **b.** .729   **3.71.** .60   **3.73 a.** $(.5)^{10} = .000977$ **b.** .00195 **c.** .99805   **3.75** random samples are likely to be representative   **3.77 a.** 35,820,200 **b.** 1/35,820,200   **3.81 a.** .000186 **c.** no   **3.85 a.** .158 **b.** .074 **c.** .768   **3.87** .0063   **3.89 a.** .52, .39, .09 **b.** .516   **3.91** .6982   **3.93 a.** Supplier 4; $P(S_4 \mid D) = .7147$ **b.** Suppliers 4 or 6   **3.95 b.** .6   **3.97 a.** 0 **b.** no   **3.99** .5   **3.101 a.** 0, .2, .9, 1, .7, .3, .4, 0   **3.103 a.** 2,118,760   **3.105** .73   **3.107 a.** false **b.** true **c.** true **d.** false   **3.109 a.** $B \cap C$ **b.** A^c **c.** $C \cup B$ **d.** $A \cap C^c$ **3.111 b.** .95 **c.** .25 **d.** .5   **3.113. a.** .5 **b.** .034 **c.** .058   **3.115 a.** .00000625 **b.** .0135 **c.** doubt validity of the manufacturer's claim **d.** no   **3.117 a.** .006 **b.** .012 **c.** .018   **3.119 a.** .006 **b.** .0022 **c.** .4133 **d.** .3601 **e.** no   **3.121** .79   **3.123 a.** LLLL, LLLU, LLUL, LULL, ULLL, LLUU, LULU, LUUL, ULLU, ULUL, UULL, LUUU, ULUU, UULU, UUUL, UUUU **b.** 1/16 **c.** 5/16   **3.125 a.** .7127 **b.** .2873 **c.** .9639 **d.** .3078 **e.** .0361 **f.** 3   **3.127** .526   **3.129 a.** .0362 **b.** .0352   **3.131** Marilyn

Chapter 4

4.1 a. discrete **b.** continuous **c.** continuous **d.** discrete **e.** discrete   **4.3** discrete   **4.5** discrete   **4.11 a.** $p(x) = 1/6$ for all x values   **4.13 a.** .25 **b.** .40 **c.** .75   **4.15 a.** $p(0) = p(3) = 1/8, p(1) = p(2) = 3/8$ **b.** 1/2   **4.17 a.** $\mu = 0, \sigma^2 = 2.94, \sigma = 1.71$ **c.** .96   **4.19 a.** $p(1) = 0, p(2) = .0408, p(3) = .1735, p(4) = .6020, p(5) = .1837$ **b.** .1837 **c.** .0408 **d.** 3.93   **4.21 a.** yes **b.** .06 **c.** .28 **d.** .82   **4.23 b.** $p(0) = .1160, p(1) = .3124, p(2) = .3364, p(3) = .1811, p(4) = .0488, p(5) = .0053$ **c.** .0541   **4.25 a.** .23 **b.** .0809 **c.** .77   **4.27 a.** .508 **b.** .391 **c.** .094 **d.** .007   **4.29 b.** .85 **c.** .6, 0, 0, .7 **d.** a_1: 2.4; a_2: 1.5; $a_3 - a_5$: .90; a_6: 1.65 **e.** a_1: .86, (.68, 4.12); a_2: .67, (.16, 2.84); $a_3 - a_5$: .3, (.3, 1.5); a_6: .57, (.51, 2.79)   **4.31 a.** p($300,000) = .3, p($0) = .7 **b.** $90,000   **4.33 a.** $p(x) = .05$ for all x-values **b.** 52.5 **c.** $(-5.16, 110.16)$ **f.** 33.25, 38.3577 **g.** .525 **i.** .20 **j.** .65   **4.35** $.25   **4.37 a.** discrete **b.** binomial **d.** 3.5; 1.02   **4.39 a.** .4096 **b.** .3456 **c.** .027 **d.** .0081 **e.** .3456 **f.** .027   **4.41 a.** 12.5, 6.25, 2.5 **b.** 16, 12.8, 3.578 **c.** 60, 24, 4.899 **d.** 63, 6.3, 2.510 **e.** 48, 9.6, 3.098 **f.** 40, 38.4, 6.197   **4.43 b.** .20 **c.** 20   **4.45 a.** 54 **b.** .0806, .1056   **4.47 b.** $n = 20, p = .8.$ **c.** .174 **d.** .804 **e.** 16   **4.49 a.** .055 **b.** in 2020, more than 9% of Denver bridges will have a rating of 4 or below   **4.51 a.** .01; .09 **b.** .048; .001   **4.53 a.** $\mu = 560, \sigma = 12.96$ **b.** no, $z = -12.35$ **4.55 b.** $\mu = 2.4, \sigma = 1.47$ **c.** $p = .90, q = .10, n = 24, \mu = 21.60, \sigma = 1.47$ **4.57 a.** discrete **b.** Poisson **c.** $\mu = 3, \sigma = 1.73$ **4.59 a.** .3 **b.** .119 **c.** .167 **d.** .167   **4.61 a.** .920 **b.** .677 **c.** .423 **d.** decreases   **4.63 a.** hypergeometric **b.** binomial   **4.65 a.** .383 **b.** .0002   **4.67 a.** .0111 **b.** .05 **c.** $\mu = 4.5, \sigma = 2.12$ **4.69** .2693   **4.71 a.** .125 **b.** 5   **4.73** .25   **4.75 a.** ≈ 0 **b.** ≈ 0 **c.** yes   **4.77** No; probability of only 5 females selected is ≈ 0 **4.79 a.** .0721 **b.** .0594 **c.** .2434 **d.** .3457 **e.** .5 **f.** .9233   **4.81 a.** .6826 **b.** .9500 **c.** .90 **d.** .9544   **4.83 a.** 0 **b.** .8413 **c.** .8413 **d.** .1587   **4.85 a.** $-.81$ **b.** .55 **c.** 1.43 **d.** .21 **e.** -2.05 **f.** .50   **4.87 a.** -2.5 **b.** 0 **c.** $-.625$ **d.** -3.75 **e.** 1.25 **f.** -1.25 **4.89 a.** .3830 **b.** .3023 **c.** .1525 **d.** .7333 **e.** .1314 **f.** .9545   **4.91 a.** .1558 **b.** .2586 **c.** .0062 **d.** .9525   **4.93 a.** .2743 **b.** .008   **4.95 a.** .8413 **b.** .7528   **4.97 a.** 69.2 **b.** 42.2   **4.99 a.** 25.14% **b.** 90.375   **4.101 a.** .8106 **b.** .1894 **c.** $1,246,100   **4.103** 5.1   **4.105 a.** .68 **b.** .95 **c.** 1.00   **4.107** Plot c   **4.109 a.** 7; yes **b.** 6.444 **c.** IQR/s = 1.09   **4.111** no   **4.113** IQR/s = 1.3   **4.115** none   **4.117** $z = -.75$ for minimum value of 128   **4.119 a.** no **b.** yes **c.** no **d.** yes **e.** yes **f.** yes   **4.121 a.** .1788 **b.** .5236 **c.** .6950   **4.123** .0537   **4.125 a.** 280 **b.** ≈ 0 **4.127** .1762   **4.129** .2676; no   **4.131 a.** .4681 **b.** .0436 **c.** .9822   **4.133 a.** $f(x) = .04$ $(20 \le x \le 45)$, 0 otherwise **b.** 32.5, 7.22   **4.135 a.** $f(x) = 1/4$ $(3 \le x \le 7)$, 0 otherwise **b.** 5, 1.155 **c.** .578   **4.137 a.** .367879 **b.** .950213 **c.** .223130 **d.** .993262   **4.139 a.** 0 **b.** 1 **c.** 1   **4.141 a.** .133; .571 **b.** .267; 0   **4.143 a.** .449329 **b.** .864665   **4.145** yes   **4.147 a.** continuous **c.** 7, .2887, (6.422, 7.577) **d.** .5 **e.** 0 **f.** .75 **g.** .0002   **4.149 a.** 17 **b.** .5862   **4.151 a.** .753403 **b.** .667 **c.** .811   **4.153** .4444   **4.159** 2.7   **4.163** no   **4.165 a.** 100, 5 **b.** 100, 2 **c.** 100, 1 **d.** 100, 1.414 **e.** 100, .447 **f.** 100, .316   **4.167 a.** .0228 **b.** .0668 **c.** .0062 **d.** .8185 **e.** .0013   **4.169 a.** .8944 **b.** .0228 **c.** .1292 **d.** .9699   **4.171 a.** 141 **b.** 1.8 **c.** $\approx$ normal **d.** 0.56 **e.** .2877   **4.173** .0838   **4.175 a.** $\approx$ normal with $\mu_{\bar{x}} = .53$ and $\sigma_{\bar{x}} = .0273$ **b.** .0336 **c.** before: $p = .0139$; after: $p = .3557$; after   **4.177 a.** .0034 **b.** ≈ 0; true mean is larger than 6 ppb   **4.179 a.** $\approx$ normal **b.** .0091 **c.** .9544   **4.181** Handrubbing: $p = .2743$; handwashing: $p = .0047$; handrubbing   **4.183 a.** .2734 **b.** .4096 **c.** .3432   **4.185 a.** .192 **b.** .228 **c.** .772 **d.** .987 **e.** .960 **f.** 14, 4.2, 2.049 **g.** .975   **4.187 a.** Poisson **b.** binomial **c.** binomial   **4.189 a.** discrete **b.** continuous **c.** continuous **d.** continuous   **4.191 a.** .9821 **b.** .0179 **c.** .9505 **d.** .3243 **e.** .9107 **f.** .0764   **4.193 a.** exponential **b.** uniform **c.** normal   **4.195 a.** .6915 **b.** .1587 **c.** .1915 **d.** .3085 **e.** 0 **f.** 1   **4.197 a.** 47.68 **b.** 47.68 **c.** 30.13 **d.** 41.5 **e.** 30.13   **4.199 a.** .5 **b.** .0606 **c.** .0985 **d.** .8436   **4.203 b.** .2592 **c.** .0870 **d.** .6826 **e.** 3.00   **4.205 a.** .5, .289 **b.** .2 **c.** no, $p = .005$ **4.207 a.** 89.34, 1.31 **c.** .8461 **d.** .0367   **4.209 a.** .221199 **b.** .002394 **c.** .082085   **4.211 a.** .367869 **b.** .606531 **c.** .135335; .135335 **d.** .814046   **4.213 b.** 20, 4.47 **c.** no, $z = -3.58$ **d.** 0   **4.215** no   **4.217 a.** .8264 **b.** 17 times **c.** .6217 **d.** 0, -157 **4.219 a.** 1.25, 1.09; no **b.** .007 **c.** not applicable   **4.221 a.** $\mu = 113.24, \sigma = 4.19$ **b.** $z = 6.38$ **4.223** 292   **4.225** .9332   **4.227** $\bar{x} = 5.935$ minutes; $P(\bar{x} < 6 \mid \mu = 15) \approx 0$, therefore, appears drug is effective

Chapter 5

5.1 a. 1.645 **b.** 2.575 **c.** 1.96 **d.** 1.28   **5.3 a.** 28 ± .784 **b.** 102 ± .65 **c.** 15 ± .0588 **d.** 4.05 ± .163 **e.** no   **5.5 a.** 26.2 ± .96 **b.** In repeated sampling, 95% of all confidence intervals constructed will include μ. **c.** 26.2 ± 1.26 **d.** increases **e.** yes   **5.9** yes   **5.11** 6,563 ± 97.65   **5.13 a.** 4.25 ± 4.14 **b.** 99% confident that true mean number of blogs/forums falls between .11 and 8.39 **c.** no; apply the Central Limit Theorem   **5.15 a.** μ = mean salary of all 500 CEOs   **5.17 a.** 99.6 **b.** 99.6 ± 2.24 **c.** 95% confident that true Mach rating score of all purchasing managers is between 97.36 and 101.84. **d.** yes   **5.19** (12.43, 25.57); (2.05, 11.95); SAT–Math   **5.21 a.** $z_{.10}$ = 1.28, $t_{.10}$ = 1.533 **b.** $z_{.05}$ = 1.645, $t_{.05}$ = 2.132 **c.** $z_{.025}$ = 1.96, $t_{.025}$ = 2.776 **d.** $z_{.01}$ = 2.33, $t_{.01}$ = 3.747 **e.** $z_{.005}$ = 2.575, $t_{.005}$ = 4.604   **5.23 a.** 2.228 **b.** 2.228 **c.** −1.812 **d.** 1.725 **e.** 4.032   **5.25 a.** 5 ± 1.88 **b.** 5 ± 2.39 **c.** 5 ± 3.75 **d.** 5 ± .78, 5 ± .94, 5 ± 1.28; decreased width   **5.27** (71.67, 79.13)   **5.29 a.** (−320, 5,922) **b.** normally distributed   **5.31 a.** (303.4, 413.6) **c.** ≈ normal **d.** no   **5.33 a.** $\overline{x}$ = 1.857, s = 1.195 **c.** 1.857 ± .45 **d.** 90% confident that true mean number of suicide bombings/attacks per transgression against United States is between 1.407 and 2.307 **e.** .90   **5.35 a.** all 441 firms in *Forbes* Largest Private Companies list **b.** 4.61 ± 3.06 **d.** ≈ normal **e.** yes   **5.37 a.** yes **b.** no **c.** no **d.** no   **5.39 a.** yes **b.** .46 ± .065   **5.41 a.** all American adults **b.** 1,000 adults surveyed **c.** proportion of all American adults who think Starbucks coffee is overpriced **d.** .73 ± .028   **5.43 a.** .46 **b.** (.433, .487) **c.** 90% confident that true proportion of contractors with Web site falls between .433 and .487 **d.** 90% of all similarly constructed intervals contain the true proportion   **5.45 a.** .03 **b.** .03 ± .01   **5.47 a.** .42 **b.** .42 ± .015 **c.** yes   **5.49** .269 ± .014; 90% confident that true percentage of all firms with acquisitions is between 25.5% and 28.3%   **5.51 a.** .867 **b.** (.781, .953) **d.** not believable   **5.53 a.** true proportion of all fillets that are red snapper **c.** .27 ± .17 **d.** 95% confident that true proportion of all fillets that are red snapper is between .10 and .44   **5.55** .85 ± .002   **5.57 a.** 68 **b.** 31   **5.59** 34   **5.61 a.** 0.98, 0.784, 0.56, 0.392, 0.196   **5.63** 21   **5.65** 1,692   **5.67** 14,735   **5.69** 43; 171; 385   **5.71** no   **5.73 a.** .7746 **b.** .8944 **c.** .9487 **d.** .995   **5.75 a.** 1.00 **b.** .6124 **c.** 0 **d.** As n increases, standard error decreases.   **5.77** .42 ± .011   **5.79 a.** 36.03 ± 3.40 **b.** .7 ± .159   **5.81 a.** .56 ± .012 **c.** 95% confident that true proportion of active NFL players who select a professional coach as most influential is between .548 and .572   **5.83 a.** 156.46 **b.** 18.70 **c.** 156.46 ± 37.405 **d.** not reasonable   **5.85** No; .086 ± .041   **5.87 a.** −1.725 **b.** 3.250 **c.** 1.860 **d.** 2.898   **5.89 a.** 32.5 ± 5.15 **b.** 23,871   **5.91** (1) p = proportion with excellent health; (2), (3), and (4) μ = mean number of days health not good   **5.93 b.** .29 ± .028   **5.95** 97   **5.97** .694 ± .092   **5.99** .667 ± .065   **5.101 a.** 49.3 ± 8.6 **b.** 99% confident that mean amount removed from all soil specimens is between 40.70% and 57.90% **c.** normal distribution **d.** possible   **5.103 a.** 66.83 ± 6.17 **b.** 45.39 ± 4.14   **5.105** 154   **5.107 a.** .833 ± .149 **b.** no **c.** 1,337   **5.111** 818   **5.115 a.** yes **b.** missing measure of reliability **c.** 95% CI for μ: .932 ± .037

Chapter 6

6.1 null; alternative   **6.3** α **6.5** Reject H_0 when H_0 is true; accept H_0 when H_0 is true; Reject H_0 when H_0 is false; accept H_0 when H_0 is false   **6.7** no   **6.9 a.** H_0: p = .60 **b.** $|z| > 2.576$ **6.11** H_0: p = .045, H_a: $p < .045$ **6.13** H_0: μ = 863, H_a: $\mu < 863$ **6.15 a.** unsafe; safe **c.** α **6.17 c.** α **e.** decrease **f.** increase   **6.19 a.** $z > 2.14$ **b.** .0162   **6.21 a.** $z = -1.61$, reject H_0 **b.** $z = -1.61$, do not reject H_0 **6.23 a.** $z < -2.33$ **b.** $z = -.40$ **c.** do not reject H_0 **6.25** yes; $z = 2.50$, do not reject H_0: μ = 220   **6.27 a.** H_0: μ = .250, H_a: $\mu \neq .250$ **b.** yes, $z = 7.02$ **6.29** $z = -1.86$, do not reject H_0 **6.31 a.** no **b.** $z = .61$, do not reject H_0 **d.** no **e.** $z = -.83$, do not reject H_0 **6.33 a.** $z = 2.73$, reject H_0 **c.** no   **6.35 a.** do not reject H_0 **b.** reject H_0 **c.** reject H_0 **d.** do not reject H_0 **e.** do not reject H_0 **6.37** .0150   **6.39** .03   **6.41** .06   **6.43 a.** .057 **b.** do not reject H_0 **6.45 a.** .0693 **b.** do not reject H_0 **6.47 a.** $z = 26.15$, p-value ≈ 0, reject H_0 **b.** $z = -14.24$, p-value ≈ 0, reject H_0 **6.49 a.** small n, data normal **b.** mound-shaped and symmetric; t is flatter than z **6.51 a.** $|t| > 2.160$ **b.** $t > 2.500$ **c.** $t > 1.397$ **d.** $t < -2.718$ **e.** $|t| > 1.729$ **f.** $t < -2.353$ **6.53 a.** population is normally distributed **b.** reject H_0 at α = .05 **c.** .076   **6.55 a.** H_0: μ = 2, H_a: $\mu \neq 2$ **b.** $t = -1.02$ **c.** $|t| > 2.093$ **d.** do not reject H_0 **e.** .322   **6.57 a.** yes, p-value = .0229 **b.** 90% CI: (1.41, 2.31); evidence that $\mu \neq 2.5$ **c.** yes **d.** population is normal **e.** validity of inference is suspect   **6.59** yes, $t = -2.53$ **6.61** no, $t = 2.97$ **6.63** yes, using α = .10; Plant 1: p-value = .197; Plant 2: p-value = .094   **6.65 a.** −2.33 **c.** reject H_0 **d.** .0099   **6.67 a.** $z = 1.13$, do not reject H_0 **b.** .1292   **6.69 a.** .42 **b.** H_0: p = .3, H_a: $p > .3$ **c.** $z = 16.56$ **d.** $z > 2.33$ **e.** reject H_0 **f.** ≈ 0   **6.71** yes, $z = -3.54$ **6.73 a.** H_0: p = .5, H_a: $p < .5$ **b.** .231 **c.** do not reject H_0 **6.75 a.** no, $z = 1.49$ **b.** .0681   **6.77 a.** no, $z = 1.37$ **b.** yes, $z = -4.58$ **6.79** $z = 1.20$, do not reject H_0 **6.81 b.** 532.9 **d.** .1949 **e.** .8051   **6.83 c.** .1469 **d.** .8531   **6.85 c.** .5359 **d.** .0409   **6.87 a.** .1949, Type II error **b.** .05, Type I error **c.** .8051   **6.89** .1075   **6.91 a.** $\chi^2 < 6.26214$ or $\chi^2 > 27.4884$ **b.** $\chi^2 > 40.2894$ **c.** $\chi^2 > 21.0642$ **d.** $\chi^2 < 3.57056$ **e.** $\chi^2 < 1.63539$ or $\chi^2 > 12.5916$ **f.** $\chi^2 < 13.8484$ **6.93 a.** $\chi^2 = 479.16$, reject H_0 **6.95 a.** $\chi^2 < 24.3$ or $\chi^2 > 73.1$ **b.** $\chi^2 = 63.72$ **c.** do not reject H_0 **6.97 a.** H_0: σ^2 = .000004, H_a: $\sigma^2 \neq .000004$ **b.** $\chi^2 = 48.49$, do not reject H_0 **c.** tee weights ≈ normal   **6.99** at α = .05, yes; $\chi^2 = 133.90$ **6.101 b.** 1.76 **c.** yes; $\chi^2 = 99$ **6.103** alternative   **6.105** big   **6.107 a.** $t = -7.51$, reject H_0 **b.** $t = -7.51$, reject H_0 **6.109 a.** $z = -1.78$, reject H_0 **b.** $z = -1.78$, do not reject H_0 **6.111 a.** $\chi^2 = 63.48$, reject H_0 **b.** $\chi^2 = 63.48$, reject H_0 **6.113 a.** .52 **b.** H_0: p = .62, H_a: $p \neq .62$ **c.** $z = -5.16$ **d.** $|z| > 1.96$ **e.** reject H_0 **f.** ≈ 0   **6.115 a.** H_0: μ = 1, H_a: $\mu > 1$ **b.** reject H_0 if $t > 1.345$ **d.** $t = 2.41$ **e.** .01 < p-value < .025, reject H_0 **f.** $\chi^2 = 12.78$, do not reject H_0 **6.117** p-value = .257, do not reject H_0 **6.119 a.** H_0: No disease, H_a: Disease   **6.121** $\chi^2 = 187.9$, do not reject H_0 **6.123 a.** $z = -3.22$, do not reject H_0 **b.** p ≈ 1 **c.** .8159   **6.125 a.** concluding percentage of shoplifters turned over to police is 50% when, in fact, the percentage is higher than 50% **b.** .8461 **c.** decreases to .7389   **6.127 a.** no, $z = 1.41$ **b.** small **c.** .0793   **6.129 a.** no **b.** β = .5910, power = .4090 **c.** increases   **6.131 a.** $z = -1.29$, do not reject H_0 **b.** .0985 **c.** Small   **6.133 a.** $z = 2.73$, reject H_0 **6.135** $z = 7.83$, reject H_0

Chapter 7

7.3 β_1 = 1/3, β_0 = 14/3, y = 14/3 + 1/3x **7.9** no   **7.11 a.** $\Sigma(y - \hat{y})$ = 0.02, SSE = 1.2204 **c.** SSE = 108.00   **7.13 b.** negative linear relationship **c.** 8.54; −.994   **7.15 a.** $y = \beta_0 + \beta_1 x + \varepsilon$ **b.** $\hat{y} = -146.856 + 1.144x$ **c.** no practical interpretation **d.** for every 1-point increase in 2000 SAT score, estimate 2007 SAT score to increase 1.144 points   **7.17 a.** $\hat{y} = 7.21 + 35.92x$ **b.** y-intercept: no practical interpretation; slope: for each unit change in surface area to volume, estimate drug release rate to increase by 35.92 **c.** 25.17 **d.** not reliable; $x = 50$ is outside range   **7.19 a.** $E(y) = \beta_0 + \beta_1 x$ **b.** $\hat{y} = 250.14 - .629x$ **c.** no practical interpretation **d.** for every 1-yard increase in driving distance, driving accuracy to decrease .629% **e.** slope   **7.21 a.** $E(y) = \beta_0 + \beta_1 x$ **b.** $\hat{y} = 488.09 + 0.034x$ **d.** y-intercept: no practical interpretation; slope: for each additional \$1 million of net worth, estimate amount pledged to increase by \$.034 million   **7.25** Plot b   **7.27 a.** .3475 **b.** 1.179   **7.29 a.** SSE $= 20,608.39$, $s^2 = 420.58$, $s = 20.51$ **b.** about 95% of the observed SAT scores fall within 41 points of their least squares predicted values   **7.31 a.** $s = 2.01$ **b.** about 95% of the observed release rates fall within 4% of their least squares predicted values   **7.33 a.** SSE $= 1.017$, $s^2 = .0462$, $s = .215$ **c.** about 95% of the observed sweetness index values fall within .43 units of their least squares predicted values   **7.35 a.** $s = 5.37$; about 95% of the observed FCAT-Math scores fall within 10.74 points of their least squares predicted values **b.** $s = 3.42$; about 95% of the observed FCAT-Reading scores fall within 6.84 points of their least squares predicted values **c.** reading score   **7.37 a.** 95% CI: 31 ± 1.17; 90% CI: $31 \pm .94$ **b.** 95% CI: 64 ± 5.08; 90% CI: 64 ± 4.15 **c.** 95% CI: $-8.4 \pm .75$; 90% CI: $-8.4 \pm .62$ **7.39** 80% CI: $.82 \pm .33$; 98% CI: $.82 \pm .76$ **7.41 a.** $H_0: \beta_1 = 0$, $H_a: \beta_1 > 0$ **b.** reject H_0, p-value ≈ 0 **c.** (1.06, 1.23)   **7.43** (30.17, 41.67); 90% confident that for each additional unit increase in surface area to volume, the increase in the drug release rate is between 30.17 and 41.67   **7.45 a.** $H_0: \beta_1 = 0$, $H_a: \beta_1 < 0$ **b.** $t = -13.23$, p-value ≈ 0 **c.** reject H_0 **7.47** no, $t = .66$ **7.49 a.** increasing trend **b.** positive **c.** support; $t = 4.60$, reject H_0 **7.51 a.** $\hat{y} = .515 + .00002074x$ **b.** yes, p-value $= .008/2 = .004$ **c.** possible outlier **d.** do not reject H_0 **7.53 a.** positive **b.** negative **c.** 0 slope **d.** positive or negative   **7.55 a.** .9438 **b.** .8020   **7.57 a.** $E(y) = \beta_0 + \beta_1 x$ **b.** moderately strong positive linear relationship between RMP and SET ratings **c.** positive **d.** reject $H_0: p = 0$ **e.** .4624   **7.59 a.** moderately strong positive linear relationship between skill level and goal-setting ability **b.** reject H_0 at $\alpha = .01$ **c.** .49   **7.61 a.** strong positive linear relationship between number of females in managerial positions and number of females with college degree **b.** very weak positive linear relationship between number of females in managerial positions and number of female HS graduates with no college **c.** moderately strong positive linear relationship between number of males in managerial positions and number of males with college degree **d.** moderate positive linear relationship between number of males in managerial positions and number of male HS graduates with no college degree **7.63** $r^2 = .2286$; $r = -.478$ **7.65 a.** weak/moderate positive linear relationship between height and average earnings **b.** $r^2 = .168$; 16.8% of the total sample variation in average earnings is explained by the linear relationship with height **c.** $H_0: p = 0$, $H_a: p > 0$ **d.** $t = 4.82$ **e.** reject H_0 **7.67** $r = .243$, $r^2 = .059$ **7.69 a.** .57 **c.** no   **7.71 c.** 4.64 ± 1.12 **d.** $2.28 \pm .63$; $-.41 \pm 1.17$ **7.73 a.** $\hat{y} = 1.375 \pm .875x$ **c.** 1.5 **d.** .1875 **e.** (3.23, 3.89) **f.** (3.81, 5.94)   **7.75 a.** (3,598.1, 3,868.1); 95% confident that mean price of all diamonds with .52 carat falls between \$3,598 and \$3,868 **b.** (1,529.8, 5,936.3); 95% confident that price of a diamond with .52 carat falls between \$1,530 and \$5,936   **7.77** for run $= 1$: 90% confident that mean sweetness index of all runs with pectin value of 220 falls between 5.65 and 5.84   **7.79 a.** (2.955, 4.066); 99% confident that the mean mass of all spills with elapsed time of 15 minutes is between 2.995 and 4.066 **b.** (1.02, 6.00); 99% confident that the actual mass of a single spill with elapsed time of 15 minutes is between 1.02 and 6.0 **c.** prediction interval for y; yes   **7.81 a.** yes, $t = -5.91$; negative **b.** (.656, 2.829) **c.** (1.467, 2.018)   **7.83** $t = 12.56$; p-value $= 0$; reject H_0; $r^2 = .07$ **7.85 a.** $\hat{y} = 37.08 - 1.6x$ **c.** 57.2 **d.** 4.4 **e.** $-1.6 \pm .5$ **f.** 13.08 ± 6.93 **g.** 13.08 ± 7.86 **7.87 a.** yes **b.** $1.39 \pm .10$ **c.** 90% confident that for each 1 mm increase in Winter runoff, rainfall erosivity index increases between 1.29 and 1.49 **7.89 b.** $\hat{y} = 569.58 - .0019x$ **e.** range of x: \$15,100 to \$70,000 **f.** $t = -.62$; do not reject H_0 **7.91 a.** moderate positive linear relationship between rates of returns for the two countries   **7.93 a.** 57.14 ± 34.82 **b.** 110 is outside range of x **c.** $\bar{x} = 44$ **7.95** $\hat{y} = -92.46 + 8.347x$, $t = 3.25$, reject H_0 **7.97 c.** $r_1 = .965$, $r_2 = .996$ **d.** yes   **7.99 a.** $\hat{y} = 2.7803 + 0.01696x$ **b.** $t = 4.02$, reject H_0; $r^2 = .402$ **c.** 8   **7.101** machine-hours: $t = 3.30$, $p = .008$, reject H_0, $r^2 = .521$; labor-hours: $t = 1.43$, $p = .183$, do not reject H_0, $r^2 = .170$

Index

Photo Credits

Normal Curve Areas

0   z

z	.00	.01	.02	.03	.04	.05	.06	.07	.08	.09
.0	.0000	.0040	.0080	.0120	.0160	.0199	.0239	.0279	.0319	.0359
.1	.0398	.0438	.0478	.0517	.0557	.0596	.0636	.0675	.0714	.0753
.2	.0793	.0832	.0871	.0910	.0948	.0987	.1026	.1064	.1103	.1141
.3	.1179	.1217	.1255	.1293	.1331	.1368	.1406	.1443	.1480	.1517
.4	.1554	.1591	.1628	.1664	.1700	.1736	.1772	.1808	.1844	.1879
.5	.1915	.1950	.1985	.2019	.2054	.2088	.2123	.2157	.2190	.2224
.6	.2257	.2291	.2324	.2357	.2389	.2422	.2454	.2486	.2517	.2549
.7	.2580	.2611	.2642	.2673	.2704	.2734	.2764	.2794	.2823	.2852
.8	.2881	.2910	.2939	.2967	.2995	.3023	.3051	.3078	.3106	.3133
.9	.3159	.3186	.3212	.3238	.3264	.3289	.3315	.3340	.3365	.3389
1.0	.3413	.3438	.3461	.3485	.3508	.3531	.3554	.3577	.3599	.3621
1.1	.3643	.3665	.3686	.3708	.3729	.3749	.3770	.3790	.3810	.3830
1.2	.3849	.3869	.3888	.3907	.3925	.3944	.3962	.3980	.3997	.4015
1.3	.4032	.4049	.4066	.4082	.4099	.4115	.4131	.4147	.4162	.4177
1.4	.4192	.4207	.4222	.4236	.4251	.4265	.4279	.4292	.4306	.4319
1.5	.4332	.4345	.4357	.4370	.4382	.4394	.4406	.4418	.4429	.4441
1.6	.4452	.4463	.4474	.4484	.4495	.4505	.4515	.4525	.4535	.4545
1.7	.4554	.4564	.4573	.4582	.4591	.4599	.4608	.4616	.4625	.4633
1.8	.4641	.4649	.4656	.4664	.4671	.4678	.4686	.4693	.4699	.4706
1.9	.4713	.4719	.4726	.4732	.4738	.4744	.4750	.4756	.4761	.4767
2.0	.4772	.4778	.4783	.4788	.4793	.4798	.4803	.4808	.4812	.4817
2.1	.4821	.4826	.4830	.4834	.4838	.4842	.4846	.4850	.4854	.4857
2.2	.4861	.4864	.4868	.4871	.4875	.4878	.4881	.4884	.4887	.4890
2.3	.4893	.4896	.4898	.4901	.4904	.4906	.4909	.4911	.4913	.4916
2.4	.4918	.4920	.4922	.4925	.4927	.4929	.4931	.4932	.4934	.4936
2.5	.4938	.4940	.4941	.4943	.4945	.4946	.4948	.4949	.4951	.4952
2.6	.4953	.4955	.4956	.4957	.4959	.4960	.4961	.4962	.4963	.4964
2.7	.4965	.4966	.4967	.4968	.4969	.4970	.4971	.4972	.4973	.4974
2.8	.4974	.4975	.4976	.4977	.4977	.4978	.4979	.4979	.4980	.4981
2.9	.4981	.4982	.4982	.4983	.4984	.4984	.4985	.4985	.4986	.4986
3.0	.4987	.4987	.4987	.4988	.4988	.4989	.4989	.4989	.4990	.4990
3.1	.49903	.49906	.49910	.49913	.49916	.49918	.49921	.49924	.49926	.48829
3.2	.49931	.49934	.49936	.49938	.49940	.49942	.49944	.49946	.49948	.49950
3.3	.49952	.49953	.49955	.49957	.49958	.49960	.49961	.49962	.49964	.49965
3.4	.49966	.49968	.49969	.49970	.49971	.49972	.49973	.49974	.49975	.49976
3.5	.49977	.49978	.49978	.49979	.49980	.49981	.49981	.49982	.49983	.49983
3.6	.49984	.49985	.49985	.49986	.49986	.49987	.49987	.49988	.49988	.49989
3.7	.49989	.49990	.49990	.49990	.49991	.49991	.49992	.49992	.49992	.49992
3.8	.49993	.49993	.49993	.49994	.49994	.49994	.49994	.49995	.49995	.49995
3.9	.49995	.49995	.49996	.49996	.49996	.49996	.49996	.49996	.49997	.49997

Source: Abridged from Table I of A. Hald. *Statistical Tables and Formulas* (New York: Wiley), 1952. Reproduced by permission of A. Hald.

Critical Values of *t*

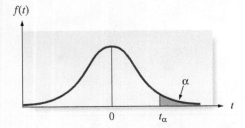

$f(t)$

Degrees of Freedom	$t_{.100}$	$t_{.050}$	$t_{.025}$	$t_{.010}$	$t_{.005}$	$t_{.001}$	$t_{.0005}$
1	3.078	6.314	12.706	31.821	63.657	318.31	636.62
2	1.886	2.920	4.303	6.965	9.925	22.326	31.598
3	1.638	2.353	3.182	4.541	5.841	10.213	12.924
4	1.533	2.132	2.776	3.747	4.604	7.173	8.610
5	1.476	2.015	2.571	3.365	4.032	5.893	6.869
6	1.440	1.943	2.447	3.143	3.707	5.208	5.959
7	1.415	1.895	2.365	2.998	3.499	4.785	5.408
8	1.397	1.860	2.306	2.896	3.355	4.501	5.041
9	1.383	1.833	2.262	2.821	3.250	4.297	4.781
10	1.372	1.812	2.228	2.764	3.169	4.144	4.587
11	1.363	1.796	2.201	2.718	3.106	4.025	4.437
12	1.356	1.782	2.179	2.681	3.055	3.930	4.318
13	1.350	1.771	2.160	2.650	3.012	3.852	4.221
14	1.345	1.761	2.145	2.624	2.977	3.787	4.140
15	1.341	1.753	2.131	2.602	2.947	3.733	4.073
16	1.337	1.746	2.120	2.583	2.921	3.686	4.015
17	1.333	1.740	2.110	2.567	2.898	3.646	3.965
18	1.330	1.734	2.101	2.552	2.878	3.610	3.922
19	1.328	1.729	2.093	2.539	2.861	3.579	3.883
20	1.325	1.725	2.086	2.528	2.845	3.552	3.850
21	1.323	1.721	2.080	2.518	2.831	3.527	3.819
22	1.321	1.717	2.074	2.508	2.819	3.505	3.792
23	1.319	1.714	2.069	2.500	2.807	3.485	3.767
24	1.318	1.711	2.064	2.492	2.797	3.467	3.745
25	1.316	1.708	2.060	2.485	2.787	3.450	3.725
26	1.315	1.706	2.056	2.479	2.779	3.435	3.707
27	1.314	1.703	2.052	2.473	2.771	3.421	3.690
28	1.313	1.701	2.048	2.467	2.763	3.408	3.674
29	1.311	1.699	2.045	2.462	2.756	3.396	3.659
30	1.310	1.697	2.042	2.457	2.750	3.385	3.646
40	1.303	1.684	2.021	2.423	2.704	3.307	3.551
60	1.296	1.671	2.000	2.390	2.660	3.232	3.460
120	1.289	1.658	1.980	2.358	2.617	3.160	3.373
∞	1.282	1.645	1.960	2.326	2.576	3.090	3.291

Source: This table is reproduced with the kind permission of the Trustees of Biometrika from E. S. Pearson and H. O. Hartley (eds.). *The Biometrika Tables for Statisticians,* Vol. 1, 3rd ed., Biometrika, 1966.

Selected Formulas

CHAPTER 2

Relative Frequency $= (\text{frequency})/n$

$$\bar{x} = \frac{\Sigma x}{n}$$

$$s^2 = \frac{\Sigma(x - \bar{x})^2}{n - 1} = \frac{\Sigma x^2 - \frac{(\Sigma x)^2}{n}}{n - 1}$$

$$s = \sqrt{s^2}$$

$$z = \frac{x - \mu}{\sigma} = \frac{x - \bar{x}}{s}$$

Chebyshev $= \text{At least} \left(1 - \frac{1}{k^2}\right)100\%$

$\text{IQR} = Q_U - Q_L$

CHAPTER 3

$$P(A^c) = 1 - P(A)$$

$$P(A \cup B) = P(A) + P(B) - P(A \cap B)$$

$$= P(A) + P(B) \text{ if } A \text{ and } B \text{ mutually exclusive}$$

$$P(A \cap B) = P(A|B) \cdot P(B) = P(B|A) \cdot P(A)$$

$$= P(A) \cdot P(B) \text{ if } A \text{ and } B \text{ independent}$$

$$P(A|B) = \frac{P(A \cap B)}{P(B)}$$

$$\binom{N}{n} = \frac{N!}{n!(N - n)!}$$

Bayes's: $P(S_i|A) =$

$$\frac{P(S_i)P(A|S_i)}{P(S_1)P(A|S_1) + P(S_2)P(A|S_2) + \cdots + P(S_k)P(A|S_k)}$$

CHAPTER 5

CI for μ: $\bar{x} \pm (z_{\alpha/2})\sigma/\sqrt{n}$ (large n)

$\bar{x} \pm (t_{\alpha/2})s/\sqrt{n}$ (small n, σ unknown)

CI for p: $\hat{p} \pm z_{\alpha/2}\sqrt{\frac{\hat{p}\hat{q}}{n}}$

Estimating μ: $n = (z_{\alpha/2})^2(\sigma^2)/(\text{SE})^2$

Estimating p: $n = (z_{\alpha/2})^2(pq)/(\text{SE})^2$

CHAPTER 4

Key Formulas

Random Variable	Prob. Dist'n	Mean	Variance
General Discrete:	Table, formula, or graph for $p(x)$	$\sum\limits_{\text{all } x} x \cdot p(x)$	$\sum\limits_{\text{all } x} (x - \mu)^2 \cdot p(x)$
Binomial:	$p(x) = \binom{n}{x}p^x q^{n-x}$ $x = 0, 1, 2, \ldots, n$	np	npq
Poisson:	$p(x) = \frac{\lambda^x e^{-\lambda}}{x!}$ $x = 0, 1, 2, \ldots$	λ	λ
Uniform:	$f(x) = 1/(d - c)$ $(c \leq x \leq d)$	$(c + d)/2$	$(d - c)^2/12$
Normal:	$f(x) = \frac{1}{\sigma\sqrt{2\pi}} e^{-\frac{1}{2}[(x-\mu)/\sigma]^2}$	μ	σ^2
Standard Normal:	$f(z) = \frac{1}{\sqrt{2\pi}} e^{-\frac{1}{2}(z)^2}$ $z = (x - \mu)/\sigma$	$\mu = 0$	$\sigma^2 = 1$
Sample Mean:(large n)	$f(\bar{x}) = \frac{1}{\sigma_{\bar{x}}\sqrt{2\pi}} e^{-\frac{1}{2}[(\bar{x}-\mu)/\sigma_{\bar{x}}]^2}$	$\mu_{\bar{x}} = \mu$	$\sigma_{\bar{x}^2} = \sigma^2/n$

CHAPTER 6

Test for μ: $z = \dfrac{\bar{x} - \mu}{\sigma/\sqrt{n}}$ (large n)

$t = \dfrac{\bar{x} - \mu}{s/\sqrt{n}}$ (small n, σ unknown)

Test for p: $z = \dfrac{\hat{p} - p_0}{\sqrt{p_0 q_0/n}}$

Test for σ^2: $\chi^2 = (n - 1)s^2/(\sigma_0)^2$

CHAPTER 7

CI for $\mu_1 - \mu_2$:

$\left. (\bar{x}_1 - \bar{x}_2) \pm z_{\alpha/2}\sqrt{\dfrac{\sigma_1^2}{n_1} + \dfrac{\sigma_2^2}{n_2}} \right\}$ (large n_1 and n_2)

Test for $\mu_1 - \mu_2$:

$\left. z = \dfrac{(\bar{x}_1 - \bar{x}_2) - (\mu_1 - \mu_2)}{\sqrt{\dfrac{\sigma_1^2}{n_1} + \dfrac{\sigma_2^2}{n_2}}} \right\}$ (large n_1 and n_2)

$s_p^2 = \dfrac{(n_1 - 1)s_1^2 + (n_2 - 1)s_2^2}{n_1 + n_2 - 2}$

CI for $\mu_1 - \mu_2$:

$\left. (\bar{x}_1 - \bar{x}_2) \pm t_{\alpha/2}\sqrt{s_p^2\left(\dfrac{1}{n_1} + \dfrac{1}{n_2}\right)} \right\}$ (small n_1 and/or n_2)

Test for $\mu_1 - \mu_2$:

$\left. t = \dfrac{(\bar{x}_1 - \bar{x}_2) - (\mu_1 - \mu_2)}{\sqrt{s_p^2\left(\dfrac{1}{n_1} + \dfrac{1}{n_2}\right)}} \right\}$ (small n_1 and/or n_2)

CI for μ_d: $\bar{x}_d \pm t_{\alpha/2}\dfrac{s_d}{\sqrt{n}}$

Test for μ_d: $t = \dfrac{\bar{x}_d - \mu_d}{s_d/\sqrt{n}}$

CI for $p_1 - p_2$: $(\hat{p}_1 - \hat{p}_2) \pm z_{\alpha/2}\sqrt{\dfrac{\hat{p}_1\hat{q}_1}{n_1} + \dfrac{\hat{p}_2\hat{q}_2}{n_2}}$

Test for $p_1 - p_2$: $z = \dfrac{(\hat{p}_1 - \hat{p}_2) - (p_1 - p_2)}{\sqrt{\hat{p}\hat{q}\left(\dfrac{1}{n_1} + \dfrac{1}{n_2}\right)}}$

$\hat{p} = \dfrac{x_1 + x_2}{n_1 + n_2}$

Test for (σ_1^2/σ_2^2): $F = (s_1^2/s_2^2)$

Estimating $\mu_1 - \mu_2$: $n_1 = n_2 = (z_{\alpha/2})^2(\sigma_1^2 + \sigma_2^2)/(\text{ME})^2$

Estimating $p_1 - p_2$: $n_1 = n_2 = (z_{\alpha/2})^2(p_1q_1 + p_2q_2)/(\text{ME})^2$

CHAPTER 8

ANOVA Test for completely randomized design:
$F = \text{MST/MSE}$

ANOVA Test for randomized block design:
$F = \text{MST/MSE}$

ANOVA Test for factorial design interaction:
$F = \text{MS(A} \times \text{B)/MSE}$

Pairwise comparisons: $c = k(k - 1)/2$

CHAPTER 9

Multinomial test: $\chi^2 = \sum \dfrac{(n_i - E_i)^2}{E_i}$

$E_i = n(p_{i0})$

Contingency table test: $\chi^2 = \sum \dfrac{(n_{ij} - E_{ij})^2}{E_{ij}}$

$E_{ij} = \dfrac{R_i C_j}{n}$

CHAPTER 10

$\text{SS}_{xx} = \sum x^2 - \dfrac{(\sum x)^2}{n}$

$\text{SS}_{yy} = \sum y^2 - \dfrac{(\sum y)^2}{n}$

$\text{SS}_{xy} = \sum xy - \dfrac{(\sum x)(\sum y)}{n}$

$\hat{y} = \hat{\beta}_0 + \hat{\beta}_1 x$

$\hat{\beta}_1 = \dfrac{\text{SS}_{xy}}{\text{SS}_{xx}}$

$\hat{\beta}_0 = \bar{y} - \hat{\beta}_1\bar{x}$

$r = \dfrac{\text{SS}_{xy}}{\sqrt{\text{SS}_{xx}}\sqrt{\text{SS}_{yy}}}$

(Continued on previous page)